Stanley Gibb

CW00736182

Great Britain
CONCISE
Stamp Catalogue

2011 edition

STANLEY GIBBONS LTD
London and Ringwood

By Appointment to
Her Majesty The Queen
Stanley Gibbons Ltd., London
Philatelists

Published by *Stanley Gibbons Publications*
Editorial, Sales Offices and Distribution Centre:
7 Parkside, Christchurch Road, Ringwood,
Hants BH24 3SH

First Edition — May 1986
Second Edition — May 1987
Third Edition — May 1988
Fourth Edition — May 1989
Fifth Edition — May 1990
Sixth Edition — May 1991
Seventh Edition — May 1992
Eighth Edition — April 1993
Ninth Edition — April 1994
Tenth Edition — April 1995
11th Edition — April 1996
12th Edition — April 1997
13th Edition — April 1998
14th Edition — April 1999
15th Edition — May 2000
16th Edition — April 2001
17th Edition — April 2002
18th Edition — April 2003
19th Edition — April 2004
20th Edition — May 2005
21st Edition — April 2006
22nd Edition — April 2007
23rd Edition — April 2008
24th Edition — April 2009
24th Edition — reprinted June 2009
25th Edition — May 2010
26th Edition — April 2011

© Stanley Gibbons Ltd. 2011

ISBN 13: 978-0-85259-808-5
ISBN 10: 0-85259-808-4
Item No. R2887-11

Printed by Burlington

Stanley Gibbons Holdings Plc.
Stanley Gibbons Ltd,
Stanley Gibbons Auctions
399 Strand, London WC2R 0LX

Auction Room and Specialist Departments.
Open Monday–Friday, 9.30 a.m. to 5.00 p.m.
Shop: Open Monday–Friday 9 a.m. to 5.30 p.m.
and Saturday 9.30 a.m. to 5.30 p.m.
Telephone: 020 7836 8444, Fax: 020 7836 7342,
E-mail: *enquiries@stanleygibbons.co.uk* and
Internet: *www.stanleygibbons.com* for all departments.

Stanley Gibbons Publications
Gibbons Stamp Monthly
7 Parkside, Christchurch Road, Ringwood
Hants BH24 3SH
Telephone: 01425 472363
(24 hour answerphone service),
Fax: 01425 470247 and E-mail: *info@stanleygibbons.co.uk*
Publications Mail Order, Freephone 0800 611622.
Monday–Friday 8.30 a.m. to 5.00 p.m.

Fraser's
399 Strand, London WC2R 0LX
Open Monday–Friday 9.00 a.m. to 5.30 p.m.
and Saturday 10.00 a.m. to 4.00 p.m.
Telephone: 020 7836 8444,
Fax: 020 7836 7342,
E-mail: *info@frasersautographs.co.uk*
and Internet: *www.frasersautographs.com*

Contents

Andrew Vaughan
Philatelics Limited

Preface

The past few years have seen some significant developments in the technology of stamp production and distribution. Such changes present problems for catalogue editors, since the features of these innovations seldom conform to the long-established criteria which determine if and how a particular item should be listed.

Assuming that the basic criterion that a stamp should be "Freely available at face value" has been met, this depends very much on collector interest. Inevitably, when a new development takes place, some collectors will embrace it with enthusiasm, seeking to acquire every possible permutation of stamp involved, while others will turn their back on it and concentrate their attentions on the stamps of an earlier period. In between will be the vast majority, who will prefer to build up a representative collection of current issues, without seeking out every slight change and variation.

Every catalogue must tread a fine line between listing in too much or too little detail; it is up to the individual collector to decide what is appropriate to be included in their albums. The catalogue can only provide guidance along one of the many possible paths of philately.

Two such developments are of particular reference to this, the 26th, edition of the Stanley Gibbons *Great Britain Concise Catalogue*; the "Security" Machins and Royal Mail Faststamps.

The former section has been completely rewritten in a form which should make it easier for future issues to be added to the listings, while "source codes" which identify whether a particular stamp has come from a business sheet or a booklet of twelve, etc, are listed for the first time and stamps with and without date codes are also included. We are particularly grateful to John Deering, the well-known specialist Machin dealer and *Gibbons Stamp Monthly* correspondent for his help and advice in the compilation of the listing, which we hope will meet the needs of the many collectors of this series.

Royal Mail "Faststamps", or "Post and Go" stamps have presented a further dilemma, since each new design has, to date, been available in five different "values" and, at the time of going to press, there have already been 13 different designs, with more on the way.

It has been decided to list each design or group of designs as a separate set of five values since this is the way in which the majority seem to prefer to collect them. More detailed listings may be provided in future editions of the *Great Britain Specialised Catalogue*. Once again, we thank John Deering for his advice, here.

However, it should not be thought that the only significant developments in this edition concern current issues. A straightforward listing of the 'Parliamentary envelopes', introduced for the use of Members of Parliament in January 1840, is provided for the first time and the listing of Queen Victoria Telegraph Stamps, which were added to this catalogue last year, has been moved to the end of the Queen Victoria stamp section for this edition.

Further plate flaws have been added, this time to the popular King George VI "Arms" stamps, where the most prominent varieties from volume 2 of the *Specialised Catalogue* are now illustrated in colour.

Following representations from a number of collectors and dealers, most notably Geoff Mitchell and Rowan Baker, the issue numbers for Royal Mail PHQ cards are now included for the first time and thanks go to Mr. Mitchell for his help in providing the details of these.

The new Machin section, which was created last year, is now easier to find, and notes have been added, within the main listings to identify where stamps have been moved to this part of the catalogue.

PRICES

Each year, all the prices in this catalogue are carefully checked and amended where necessary, to ensure that it presents an accurate reflection of the current market for British stamps. It is interesting to note that, while prices in some sections of that market seem to rise consistently, year after year, others are rather less predictable, reflecting the ebbs and flows of current collector demand.

Dare we say that this is another good reason why one should always have the latest edition of this catalogue to refer to.

In Queen Victoria there are increases in all sections; line-engraved, embossed, surface-printed and officials, with the price for a fine used Penny Black now up to £300, while an unused one with inverted watermark jumps from £35,000 to £45,000! Telegraph stamps, now included in the Queen Victoria section, have also been repriced, in some cases quite significantly.

Unmounted mint stamps of King Edward VII see some increases, while the famous 2d "Tyrian plum" now hits £100,000. In King George V it is the increasingly popular watermark varieties which see the really big increases, with the Multiple Cypher inverted watermark pair rising from £21,000 to £28,000. Listed varieties and "Specimen" overprints are up in King George VI, while in Queen Elizabeth it is once again the varieties and errors which make the largest increases. Here we note that the 3d. Post Office Tower with "Tower omitted" is up from £4750 to £5500 and, in the decimal issues, the 13p Rose, missing value, jumps up from £85,000 to £95,000. Many imperforate pairs are also well up in the decimal period, with the 15½p and 19½p from the 1982 Christmas set in this form both up from £4000 to £6000.

There are significant increases also for several modern issues, particularly those available only from booklets, while the prices for all booklets have been extensively reviewed, with a number of notable increases being recorded.

As always, a number of other changes and amendments have been made throughout the catalogue and we would like to thank collectors, auction houses and members of the philatelic trade for their assistance in keeping the Great Britain Concise Catalogue up to date.

We would also like to express our appreciation to all our colleagues who have contributed to this latest edition, particularly Lesley Brine, who lists all the new issues, Vicky Anscombe, who has once again had to look after the design and layout within a very tight time-frame, Michelle Briggs who has checked the proofs and, of course, Colin Avery and his team for reviewing the prices. Our thanks to them all.

HUGH JEFFERIES
VINCE CORDELL
April 2011

Features of this Catalogue

The Concise Catalogue, now in its 26th year of publication, has established itself as an essential guide for the "one-country" collector of Great Britain. The popularity of Great Britain stamps continues to grow — the Concise Catalogue supplies the information to enhance your collection.

+ All issues from the Penny Black of 1840 to 22 March 2011 including Regional, Postage Due, Official and Postal Fiscal stamps.
+ All different stamp designs are illustrated.
+ Every basic stamp listed, including those with different watermarks or perforations and those showing graphite lines or phosphor bands.
+ Unmounted mint and mounted mint prices quoted for 1887 "Jubilee" series and all King Edward VII and King George V issues.
+ Missing colours, missing embossing, watermark errors, imperforate errors and phosphor omitted varieties from those stamps normally issued with phosphor bands.
+ Gutter Pairs and "Traffic light" Gutter Pairs listed in mint sets.
+ First Day Covers for Special Issues from 1924 and for King Edward VIII and King George VI definitives. For the present reign the coverage also extends to Prestige Booklet panes and Regionals. All British Post Office special First Day of Issue postmarks are illustrated and priced on cover.
+ Post Office Picture Cards (PHQ cards) are priced as sets, both mint and used with First Day of Issue postmarks.
+ Presentation, Collector and Gift Packs, including the scarce versions with foreign inscriptions.
+ Quick-reference diagrams for listed Machin decimal booklet panes.
+ Design Index for Commemorative and Special Stamps after the Philatelic Information Section.
+ Machin and commemorative underprints given separate catalogue numbers.
+ Post Office Yearbooks.
+ Royal Mail Postage Labels priced in mint or used sets and on British Post Office First Day Covers.
+ Royal Mail "Fast Stamps" given full listing in separate section
+ Notes on Postage Due bisects based on research by Mr. P. Frost.
+ Wartime issues for the Channel Islands.
+ Separate section for Post Office Stamp Booklets with dated editions of King George VI and Queen Elizabeth listed separately.
+ Post Office Label Sheets, popularly known as 'Generic Smilers'.
+ Specimen overprints up to 1952.
+ Helpful introductory section providing definitions and guidance for the collector and including all watermark illustrations shown together to assist identification.
+ Addresses for specialist philatelic societies covering Great Britain stamps.
+ Post Office Telegraph Stamps
+ Recently discovered errors and new items listed: 97e, 476a, 476b, 476c, 478a, 478b, 478c, 571d, 572c, 590a, 1027a, 1063a, 1244a, 1293b, 2055a, 2210b, 2213a, 2214a, 2242ab, **MS**2613a, X1012Eay, X1022Ey, 1514aEy, 1664b, 1667Ey, Y1743saEy, 2039ab, 2040ab, 2295a, 2295Ey, 2654Ey, 2655Ey, EN7a, D38wi.

We would like to thank all those who have assisted in the compilation of this catalogue. Special thanks for amendments to this edition are due to Messrs C. Adams, D. Aggersberg, R. Baker, I. Billings, R.C.W. Brookes, A. Claridge, A. Crook, P. Dauwalder, J. Deering, N. Kennedy, A. Lajer, G. Mitchell, A. Myer, R. Oliver, P. Ramsay, N. Robertson, P. Sanderson, D. Smythe, F. Spencer and J. Temayne.

STANLEY GIBBONS PUBLICATIONS
OVERSEAS REPRESENTATION

Stanley Gibbons Publications are available overseas from the following distributors.

Australia *Renniks Publications PTY LTD*
Unit 3 37-39 Green Street,
Banksmeadow, NSW 2019, Australia
Tel: +612 9695 7055
Website: www.renniks.com

Belgium *N.V. deZittere (D.Z.T.)/ Davo*
Heuvelstraat 106, 3390 Tielt
(Brabant), België
Tel: +32 16772673
E-mail: dzt@dezittere.be
Website: www.dezittere.be

Canada *Unitrade Associates*
99 Floral Parkway, Toronto,
Ontario, M6L 2C4, Canada
Tel: +1 416 242 5900
Website: www.unitradeassoc.com

Denmark *Samlerforum/Davo*
Ostergade 3, DK7470, Karup,
Denmark
Tel: +45 97102900
Website: www.samlerforum.dk

Finland *Davo C/o Kapylan*
Merkkiky Pohjolankatu 1,
00610 Helsinki, Finland
Tel: +358 9 792851
E-mail: jarnosoderstrom@
kapylanmerkki.fi

France *ARPHI/Davo*
Rue de Jouy 58, 78220 Viroflay,
France
Tel: +33 130242162
E-mail: info@arphi.net

Germany *Schaubek Verlag Leipzig*
Am Glaeschen 23, D- 04420
Markranstaedt, 04420
Germany
Tel: +49 34 205 67823
Website: www.schaubek.de

India *Trustin Philatelic*
B/4 Ahuja Palace Building,
96 Richmond Road, Bangalore,
560025
Tel: +918 0221 11555
E-mail: trustin@vsnl.net

Italy *Ernesto Marini S.R.L.*
V.Struppa, 300, Genova, 16165, Italy
Tel: +3901 0247-3530
Website: www.ernestomarini.it

Japan *Japan Philatelic*
Po Box 2, Suginami-Minami,
Tokyo 168-8081, Japan
Tel: +81 3330 41641
Website: www.yushu.co.jp

Netherlands *Uitgeverij Davo BV*
Po Box 411, Ak Deventer,
7400, Netherlands
Tel: +315 7050 2700
Website: www.davo.nl

New Zealand *House of Stamps*
Po Box 12, Paraparaumu,
New Zealand
Tel: +61 6364 8270
Website: www.houseofstamps.co.nz

New Zealand *Philatelic Distributors*
PO Box 863, 15 Mount Edgecumbe
Street, New Plymouth 4615,
New Zealand
Tel: +6 46 758 65 68
Website: www.stampcollecta.com

Norway *Davo Norge A/S*
P O Box 738, Ovre Vollgate 15,
Sentrum, N01 05, Oslo
Norway
Tel: +47 22428610
E-mail: glenn@wenca.no

Saudi Arabia *Arabian Stamp Centre*
P O Box 54645, Riyadh, 11524,
Saudi Arabia
Fax: +966 1 419 1379
Website: www.ArabianStamps.com

Singapore *C S Philatelic Agency*
Peninsula Shopping Centre #04-29,
3 Coleman Street
179804, Singapore
Tel: +65 6337-1859
Website: www.cs.com.sg

Sweden *Chr Winther Sorensen AB*
Box 43, S-310 20 Knaered, Sweden
Tel: +46 43050743
Website: www.ifsda.org/i/dealer.
php?mid=2100&asscd=SE

USA *Filatco*
Po Box 1461, Appleton,
WI 54912, USA
Tel: +1 920 735 0701
Website: www.filatco.com

USA *Regency Superior*
229 N. Euclid Avenue, St. Louis,
MO 63108
Tel: +1 314 361 5699
Website: www.RegencySuperior.
com

Great Britain Philatelic Societies

The Great Britain Philatelic Society.
Hon. Membership Secretary: Peter
Tanner, "High Standings", 13 Huberts
Close, Gerrards Cross, Bucks SL9 7EN.

The Modern British Philatelic Circle.
Hon. Membership Secretary: A. J.
Wilkins, 3 Buttermere Close, Brierley
Hill, West Midlands, DY5 3SD.

The Great Britain Collectors' Club.
Secretary: Mr L. Rosenblum, 103
East Camino Real PMB, Sunnydale
CA, USA

Prices

The prices quoted in this catalogue are the estimated selling prices of Stanley Gibbons Ltd at the time of publication. They are, *unless it is specifically stated otherwise*, for examples in fine condition for the issue concerned. Superb examples are worth more; those of a lower quality considerably less.

All prices are subject to change without prior notice and Stanley Gibbons Ltd may from time to time offer stamps below catalogue price. Individual low value stamps sold at 399, Strand are liable to an additional handling charge. Purchasers of new issues are asked to note that the prices charged for them contain an element for the service rendered and so may exceed the prices shown when the stamps are subsequently catalogued.

No guarantee is given to supply all stamps priced, since it is not possible to keep every catalogued item in stock.

Quotation of prices

The prices in the left-hand column are for unused stamps and those in the right-hand column are for used.

A dagger (†) denotes that the item listed does not exist in that condition and a blank, or dash, that it exists, or may exist, but no market price is known.

Prices are expressed in pounds and pence sterling. One pound comprises 100 pence (£1 = 100p).

The method of notation is as follows: pence in numerals (e.g. 5 denotes five pence); pounds and pence up to £100, in numerals (e.g. 4·25 denotes four pounds and twenty-five pence); prices above £100 expressed in whole pounds with the "£" sign shown.

Unused and Used stamps

The prices for unused stamps of Queen Victoria issued before 1887 are for lightly hinged examples. Unused stamps of the 1887 "Jubilee" issue and from the reigns of King Edward VII and King George V are priced in both unmounted and mounted condition. Unused prices for King Edward VIII to Queen Elizabeth II issues are for unmounted mint (though when not available, mounted mint stamps are often supplied at a lower price). Prices for used stamps are for postally used examples.

Prices quoted for bisects on cover or on large piece are for those dated during the period officially authorised.

Minimum price

The minimum price quoted is 10 pence. For individual stamps prices between 10 pence and 95 pence are provided as a guide for catalogue users. The lowest price charged for individual stamps or sets purchased from Stanley Gibbons Ltd is £1.

Set prices

Set prices are generally for one of each value, excluding shades and varieties, but including major colour changes. Where there are alternative shades, etc., the cheapest is usually included. The number of stamps in the set is always stated for clarity.

The mint and used prices for sets containing *se-tenant* pieces are based on the prices quoted for such combinations, and not on those for individual stamps.

Gutter Pairs

These, and traffic light gutter pairs, are priced as complete sets.

Used on Cover prices

To assist collectors, cover prices are quoted in a third column for postage and Official stamps issued in the reign of Queen Victoria and in boxed notes for the 1887 "Jubilee" issue and for King Edward VII and King George V stamps.

The cover should be of non-philatelic origin, bearing the correct postal rate for the period and distance involved and cancelled with the markings normal to the offices concerned. Purely philatelic items have a cover value only slightly greater than the catalogue value for the corresponding used stamps. This applies generally to those high-value stamps used philatelically rather than in the normal course of commerce.

Oversized covers, difficult to accommodate on an album page, should be reckoned as worth little more than the corresponding value of the used stamps. The condition of a cover affects its value. Except for "wreck covers", serious damage or soiling reduce the value where the postal markings and stamps are ordinary ones. Conversely, visual appeal adds to the value and this can include freshness of appearance, important addresses, old-fashioned but legible handwriting, historic town-names, etc. The prices quoted are a base on which further value would be added to take account of the cover's postal historical importance in demonstrating such things as unusual, scarce or emergency cancels, interesting routes, significant postal markings, combination usage, the development of postal rates, and so on.

However, it should also be noted that multiples of some stamps are frequently more commonly found on cover than single usages and in such cases the cover might be worth less than the price quoted.

First Day Cover prices

Prices are quoted for commemorative first day covers from 1924 British Empire Exhibition pair onwards. These prices are for special covers (from 1937) franked with complete sets and cancelled by ordinary operational postmarks to the end of 1962 or the various standard "First Day of Issue" markings from 1963.

Prices are provided for King Edward VIII and King George VI definitives on plain covers with operational postmarks of the first day of issue. For some values special covers also exist and these are worth more than the prices quoted.

The Philatelic Bureau and other special "First Day of Issue" postmarks provided by the Post Office since 1963 are listed under each issue. Prices quoted are for these postmarks used on illustrated covers (from 1964 those produced by the Post Office), franked with complete sets.

The British Post Office did not introduce special First Day of Issue postmarks for definitive issues until the first instalment of the Machin £sd series, issued 5 June 1967, although "First Day" treatment had been provided for some Regional stamps from 8 June 1964 onwards. Prices for the First Day Covers from 1952 to 1966, showing definitive stamps are for the stamps indicated, used on illustrated envelopes and postmarked with operational cancellations.

From 1967 onwards the prices quoted are for stamps as indicated, used on illustrated envelopes and postmarked with special First Day of Issue handstamps. Other definitives issued during this period were not accepted for "First Day" treatment by the British Post Office.

Guarantee
All stamps are guaranteed genuine originals in the following terms:

If not as described, and returned by the purchaser, we undertake to refund the price paid to us in the original transaction. If any stamp is certified as genuine by the Expert Committee of the Royal Philatelic Society, London, or by B.P.A. Expertising Ltd, the purchaser shall not be entitled to make any claim against us for any error, omission or mistake in such certificate.

Consumers' statutory rights are not affected by the above guarantee.

The recognised Expert Committees in this country are those of the Royal Philatelic Society, 41 Devonshire Place, London W1G 6JY, and B.P.A. Expertising Ltd, P.O. Box 137, Leatherhead, Surrey KT22 0RG. They do not undertake valuations under any circumstances and fees are payable for their services.

Contacting the Catalogue Editor
The Editor is always interested in hearing from people who have new information which will improve or correct the Catalogue. As a general rule he must see and examine the actual stamps before they can be considered for listing; photographs or photocopies are insufficent evidence.

Submissions should be made in writing to the Catalogue Editor, Stanley Gibbons Publications. The cost of return postage for items submitted is appreciated, and this should include the registration fee if required.

Where information is solicited purely for the benefit of the enquirer, the editor cannot undertake to reply if the answer is already contained in these published notes or if return postage is omitted. Written or email communications are greatly preferred to enquiries by telephone and the editor regrets that he or his staff cannot see personal callers without a prior appointment being made. Correspondence may be subject to delay during the production period of each new edition.

Please note that the following classes of material are outside the scope of this Catalogue:
(a) Non-postal revenue or fiscal stamps.
(b) Postage stamps used fiscally.
(c) Local carriage labels and private local issues.
(d) Punctured postage stamps (perfins).
(e) Telegraph stamps.
(f) Bogus or phantom stamps.
(g) Railway or airline letter fee stamps, bus or road transport company labels.
(h) Postal stationery cut-outs.
(i) All types of non-postal labels and souvenirs.
(j) Documentary labels for the postal service, e.g. registration, recorded delivery, airmail etiquettes, etc.
(k) Privately applied embellishments to official issues and privately commissioned items generally.
(l) Stamps for training postal staff.

> **We regret we do not give opinions as to the genuineness of stamps, nor do we identify stamps or number them by our Catalogue.**

General Abbreviations
Alph	Alphabet
Anniv	Anniversary
Brt	Bright (colour)
C,c	Chalky paper
C.	Overprinted in carmine
Des	Designer; designed
Dp	Deep (colour)
Eng	Engraver; engraved
Horiz	Horizontal; horizontally
Imp, Imperf	Imperforate
Inscr	Inscribed
L	Left
Litho	Lithographed
Lt	Light (colour)
mm	Millimetres
MS	Miniature sheet
O,o	Ordinary paper
Opt(d)	Overprint(ed)
P, Perf	Perforated
Photo	Photogravure
Pl	Plate
Pr	Pair
Ptd	Printed
Ptg	Printing
PVA	Polyvinyl alcohol (gum)
R	Right
R.	Row
Recess	Recess-printed
T	Type
Typo	Typographed
Un	Unused
Us	Used
Vert	Vertical; vertically
W or wmk	Watermark
Wmk s	Watermark sideways

(†) = Does not exist.

(—) (or blank price column) = Exists, or may exist, but no market price is known.

/ between colours means "on" and the colour following is that of the paper on which the stamp is printed.

Printers
B.W.	Bradbury Wilkinson & Co, Ltd.
Cartor	Cartor S.A., La Loupe, France
D.L.R.	De La Rue & Co, Ltd, London, and (from 1961) Bogota, Colombia. De La Rue Security Print (*formerly Harrison & Sons Ltd*) from 8 September 1997.
Enschedé	Joh. Enschedé en Zonen, Haarlem, Netherlands.
Harrison	Harrison & Sons, Ltd, High Wycombe.
J.W.	John Waddington Security Print, Ltd, Leeds.
P.B.	Perkins Bacon Ltd, London.
Questa	Questa Colour Security Printers, Ltd.
Waterlow	Waterlow & Sons, Ltd, London.
Walsall	Walsall Security Printers, Ltd.

Philatelic information

Catalogue Numbers

The catalogue number appears in the extreme left column. The boldface Type numbers in the next column are merely cross-reference to illustrations. Catalogue numbers in the *Gibbons Stamp Monthly* Supplements are provisional only and may need to be altered when the lists are consolidated.

Our Catalogue numbers are universally recognised in specifying stamps and as a hallmark of status.

Inverted and other watermark varieties incorporate "Wi", etc., within the number. Other items which appear in this Catalogue but not *Part 1 (British Commonwealth) Catalogue,* incorporate "Ea", etc.

Catalogue Illustrations

Stamps and first day postmarks are illustrated at three-quarters linear size. Stamps not illustrated are the same size and format as the value shown, unless otherwise indicated. Overprints, surcharges and watermarks are normally actual size. Illustrations of varieties are often enlarged to show the detail. Illustrations of miniature sheets are half linear size and their dimensions, in millimetres, are stated with the width given first.

Designers

Designers' names are quoted where known, though space precludes naming every individual concerned in the production of a set. In particular, photographers supplying material are usually named only when they also make an active contribution in the design stage; posed photographs of reigning monarchs are, however, an exception to this rule.

Printing Errors

Errors in printing are of major interest to this Catalogue. Authenticated items meriting consideration would include: background, centre or frame inverted or omitted; centre or subject transposed; error of colour; error or omission of value; double prints and impressions; printed both sides; and so on. Designs *tête-bêche*, whether intentionally or by accident, are listable. Colours only partially omitted are not listed. However, stamps with embossing, phosphor or both omitted and stamps printed on the gummed side are included.

Printing technology has radically improved over the years, during which time photogravure and lithography have become predominant. Varieties nowadays are more in the nature of flaws which are almost always outside the scope of this book.

In no catalogue, however, do we list such items as: dry prints, kiss prints, doctor-blade flaws, colour shifts or registration flaws (unless they lead to the complete omission of a colour from an individual stamp), lithographic ring flaws, and so on. Neither do we recognise fortuitous happenings like paper creases or confetti flaws.

Paper Types

All stamps listed are deemed to be on "ordinary" paper of the wove type and white in colour; only departures from this are normally mentioned.

A coloured paper is one that is coloured right through (front and back of the stamp). In the Catalogue the colour of the paper is given in *italics*, thus:
purple/*yellow* = purple design on yellow paper.
Papers have been made specially white in recent years by, for example, a very heavy coating of chalk. We do not classify shades of whiteness of paper as distinct varieties. The availability of many postage stamps for revenue purposes made necessary some safeguard against the illegitimate re-use of stamps with removable cancellations. This was at first secured by using fugitive inks and later by printing on chalky (chalk-surfaced) paper, both of which made it difficult to remove any form of obliteration without also damaging the stamp design. We have indicated the existence of the papers by the letters "**O**" (ordinary) and "**C**" (chalky) after the description of all stamps where the chalky paper may be found. Where no indication is given the paper is "ordinary".

Our chalky paper is specifically one which shows a black mark when touched with a silver wire. Stamps on chalk-surfaced paper can easily lose this coating through immersion in water.

Perforation Measurement

The gauge of a perforation is the number of holes in a length of 2 cm.

The Gibbons *Instanta* gauge is the standard for measuring perforations. The stamp is viewed against a dark background with the transparent gauge put on top of it. Though the gauge measures to decimal accuracy, perforations read from it are generally quoted in the Catalogue to the nearest half. For example:
Just over perf 12¾ to just under 13¼ .... = perf 13
Perf 13¼ exactly, rounded up .... = perf 13½
Just over perf 13¼ to just under 13¾ .... = perf 13½
Perf 13¾ exactly, rounded up .... = perf 14
However, where classification depends on it, actual quarter-perforations are quoted. Perforations are usually abbreviated (and spoken) as follows, though sometimes they may be spelt out for clarity.

P 14: perforated alike on all sides (read: "perf 14").

P 14 x 15: the first figure refers to top and bottom, the second to left and right sides (read: "perf 14 by 15"). This is a compound perforation.

Such headings as "P 13 x 14 (vert) and P 14 x 13 (horiz)" indicate which perforations apply to which stamp format— vertical or horizontal.

From 1992 onwards most definitive and greetings stamps from both sheets and booklets occur with a large elliptical (oval) hole inserted in each line of vertical perforations as a security measure. The £10 definitive, No. 1658, is unique in having two such holes in the horizontal perforations.

Elliptical Perforations

Perforation Errors

Authenticated errors, where a stamp normally perforated is accidentally issued imperforate, are listed provided no traces of perforations (blind holes or indentations) remain. They must be provided as pairs, both stamps wholly imperforate, and are only priced in that form.

Numerous part-perforated stamps have arisen from the introduction of the Jumelle Press. This has a rotary perforator with rows of pins on one drum engaging with holes on another. Engagement is only gradual when the perforating unit is started up or stopped, giving rise to perforations "fading out", a variety mentioned above as not listed.

Stamps from the Jumelle printings sometimes occur imperforate between stamp and sheet margin. Such errors are not listed in this catalogue, but are covered by the volumes of the *Great Britain Specialised Catalogue*.

Pairs described as "imperforate between" have the line of perforations between the two stamps omitted.

Imperf between (horiz pair): a horizontal pair of stamps with perfs all around the edges but none between the stamps.

Imperf between (vert pair): a vertical pair of stamps with perfs all around the edges but none between the stamps.

Imperf between (vertical pair)

Imperf horizontally (vertical pair)

Where several of the rows have escaped perforation the resulting varieties are listable. Thus:

Imperf vert (horiz pair): a horizontal pair of stamps perforated at top and bottom; all three vertical directions are imperf—the two outer edges and between the stamps.

Imperf horiz (vert pair): a vertical pair perforated at left and right edges; all three horizontal directions are imperf—the top, bottom and between the stamps.

Varieties of double, misplaced or partial perforation caused by error or machine malfunction are not listable, neither are freaks, such as perforations placed diagonally from paper folds, nor missing holes caused by broken pins.

Phosphor Issues

Machines which sort mail electronically have been introduced progressively and the British Post Office issued the first stamps specially marked for electronic sorting in 1957. This first issue had easily visible graphite lines printed on the back beneath the gum (see Nos. 561/6). They were issued in the Southampton area where the experiment was carried out.

The graphite lines were replaced by phosphor bands, activated by ultra-violet light. The bands are printed on the front of the stamps and show as a matt surface against the usual smooth or shiny appearance of the untreated surface of the paper. The bands show clearly in the top or bottom horizontal margins of the sheet.

The first phosphor issues appeared in 1959 (see Nos. 599/609) and these stamps also had graphite lines on the back. Further details will be found in the listings above No. 599 and 619. From 1962 onwards most commemoratives were issued in versions with or without bands. From 1967 all commemorative stamps had phosphor bands, but from 1972 they were replaced by "all-over" phosphor covering the entire area of the stamp.

After a considerable period of development a special paper was produced in which the phosphor had been incorporated into the coating. From 15 August 1979 to April 1996 phosphorised paper was accepted for use generally, replacing phosphor bands on most issues for all values except the second class letter rate. Phosphorised paper can only be identified by ultra-violet light. The Stanley Gibbons Uvitec Micro ultra-violet lamp is firmly recommended for use in identifying the phosphor stamps listed in this Catalogue. *Warning*. Never stare at the lighted lamp but follow the manufacturer's instructions. Phosphor bands were reintroduced for all issues from April 1996.

During the years 1967 to 1972, when all issues, except the high values, should have shown phosphor bands, a number of stamps appeared with them omitted in error. These varieties are listed in this Catalogue. Stamps with "all-over" phosphor omitted can only be detected by the use of an ultra-violet lamp and these varieties are listed in the Stanley Gibbons *Great Britain Specialised Catalogue*. Note that prices are for unmounted mint examples only. Varieties such as double bands, misplaced or printed on the back are not listed in this Catalogue.

Gum Description

All stamps listed are assumed to have gum of some kind and original gum (o.g.) means that which was present on the stamp as issued to the public. Deleterious climates and the presence of certain chemicals can cause gum to crack and, with early stamps, even make the paper deteriorate. Unscrupulous fakers are adept in removing it and regumming the stamp to meet the unreasoning demand often made for "full o.g." in cases where such a thing is virtually impossible.

The gum normally used on stamps has been gum arabic until the late 1960's when synthetic adhesives were introduced. Harrison and Sons Ltd for instance use

Multi-value Coil Strip

polyvinyl alcohol, known to philatelists as PVA (see note above SG723).

From 1993 many stamps have been issued with self-adhesive gum. Unused prices are for such stamps with backing paper attached, as issued. Initially such stamps were issued with a water-soluble layer of gum allowing used examples to be "soaked off", but with the 2008 Christmas issue, most self-adhesive stamps are issued without the water-soluble layer of gum, preventing their removal from paper without damage. Used stamps from this later period should be collected "on piece".

Colour Identification
The 200 colours most used for stamp identification are given in the Stanley Gibbons Stamp Colour Key. The Catalogue has used the Colour Key as a standard for describing new issues for some years. The names are also introduced as lists are rewritten, though exceptions are made for those early issues where traditional names have become universally established.

In compound colour names the second is the predominant one, thus:
orange-red = a red tending towards orange.
red-orange = an orange containing more red than usual.

When comparing actual stamps with colour samples in the Colour Key, view in a good north daylight (or its best substitute: fluorescent "colour-matching" light). Sunshine is not recommended. Choose a solid portion of the stamp design; if available, marginal markings such as solid bars of colour or colour check dots are helpful. Shading lines in the design can be misleading as they appear lighter than solid colour. Furthermore, the listings refer to colours as issued: they may deteriorate into something different through the passage of time.

Shades are particularly significant when they can be linked to specific printings. In general, shades need to be quite marked to fall within the scope of this Catalogue.

Modern colour printing by lithography is prone to marked differences of shade, even within a single run, and variations can occur within the same sheet. Such shades are not listed.

Errors of Colour
Major colour errors in stamps or overprints which qualify for listing are: wrong colours; albinos (colourless impressions), where these have Expert Committee certificates; colours completely omitted, but only on unused stamps (if found on used stamps the information is usually footnoted) and with good credentials, missing colours being frequently faked.

Colours only partially omitted are not recognised. Colour shifts, however spectacular, are not listed.

Booklet Stamps
Single stamps from booklets are listed if they are distinguishable in some way (such as watermark or phosphor bands) from similar sheet stamps.

Booklet panes are listed where they contain stamps of different denominations *se-tenant*, where stamp-size printed labels are included, or where such panes are otherwise identifiable. Booklet panes are placed in the listing under the lowest denomination present.

In the listing of complete booklets the numbers and prefix letters are the same as used in the Stanley Gibbons *Great Britain Specialised Catalogue*.

Coil Stamps
Stamps only issued in coil form are given full listing. If stamps are issued in both sheets and coils, the coil stamps are listed separately only where there is some feature (e.g.

Booklet Pane with Printed Labels

Se-tenant Pane of Four

watermark sideways or gum change) by which single stamps can be distinguished. Coil strips containing different values *se-tenant* are also listed.

Coil join pairs are generally too random and easily faked to permit listing; similarly ignored are coil stamps which have accidentally suffered an extra row of perforations from the claw mechanism in a malfunctioning vending machine.

Gutter pair

Gutter Pairs

In 1988 the recess-printed Castle high value definitives were issued in sheets containing four panes separated by a gutter margin. All modern Great Britain commemoratives and special stamps are produced in sheets containing two panes separated by a blank horizontal or vertical margin known as a gutter. This feature first made its appearance on some supplies of the 1972 Royal Silver Wedding 3p and marked the introduction of Harrison & Sons' new "Jumelle" stamp-printing press. There are advantages for both the printer and the Post Office in such a layout which has been used for most commemorative issues since 1974.

Traffic Light Gutter Pair

The term "gutter pair" is used for a pair of stamps separated by part of the blank gutter margin as illustrated below. Most printers include some form of colour check device on the sheet margins, in addition to the cylinder or plate numbers. Harrison & Sons use round "dabs", or spots of colour, resembling traffic lights. For the period from the 1972 Royal Silver Wedding until the end of 1979 these colour dabs appeared in the gutter margin. There was always one example to every double pane sheet of stamps. They can also be found in the high value Machin issue printed in photogravure. Gutter pairs showing these "traffic lights" are worth considerably more than the normal version.

From the 2004 Entente Cordiale set, Walsall reintroduced traffic lights in the gutters of certain sets. Where these extend over more than one section of gutter margin on any value, they are priced in blocks rather than pairs.

Miniature Sheets

A miniature sheet contains a single stamp or set with wide inscribed or decorated margins. The stamps often also exist in normal sheet format. This Catalogue lists, with **MS** prefix, complete miniature sheets which have been issued by the Post Office and which are valid for postal purposes.

Stamps from miniature sheets, not also available in normal sheet format, are not individually listed or priced in this catalogue.

Miniature Sheet containing a set of stamps

Se-tenant Combinations

Se-tenant means "joined together". Some sets include stamps of different design arranged *se-tenant* as blocks or strips and, in mint condition, these are usually collected unsevered as issued. The set prices quoted in this catalogue refer to the unsevered combination plus singles of any other values in the set.

13 August 1975 Public Railways Presentation Pack

Presentation and Souvenir Packs

Special Packs comprising slip-in cards with printed commemorative inscriptions and notes on the back and with protective covering, were introduced in 1964 for the Shakespeare issue. Definitive issues first appeared in Presentation Packs in 1960. Notes will be found in the listings to describe souvenir books issued on special occasions.

Issues of 1968–1969 (British Paintings to the Prince of Wales Investiture) were also issued in packs with text in German for sale through the Post Office's German Agency and these are also included.

Collectors packs, first called gift packs, containing commemoratives issued in the preceding twelve months, first appeared in 1967. These are listed and priced.

Type A. First day of Issue Slogan

Type B. Large Handstamp   **Type C.** Small Handstamp

Type D. Maltese Cross   **Type E**

Type F. £ Sign   **Type G.** Three Lions

Type H. Four Castles   **Type I.** Windsor Keep

Type J. Millennium (2000 issues are inscr "Beyond 2000")   **Type K.** Arms of Post Office

Illustrations shown at 66 percent.

Yearbooks

Special Post Office Yearbooks were first available in 1984. They contain all of the commemorative issues for one year in a hardbound book, illustrated in colour complete with slip case. These are listed and priced.

Commemorative First Day Covers

Until 1963 the Post Office did not provide any special first day of issue postmark facilities for collectors. Several philatelic organisations and stamp dealers did produce pictorial covers for the various commemorative issues and collectors serviced these to receive ordinary operational postmarks. Occasionally a special handstamp was produced which coincided with a new stamp issue, or relevant slogan postmarks, like the 1953 "Long Live the Queen" type, were in general use at the time.

On 21 March 1963 the Post Office installed special posting boxes at eleven main post offices so that collectors could obtain "uniformly high standard" impressions, from normal operational postmarks, for their first day covers. From 7 May 1963 special "First Day of Issue" slogans (Type A) were aplied to mail posted in these special boxes, whose number had, by then, risen to thirty. The Philatelic Bureau accepted orders by post for such covers from the issue of 16 May 1963 onwards.

The slogan type was replaced on 23 April 1964 by "First Day of Issue" handstamps (Type B). These were, initially, of considerable size, but were later replaced by smaller versions (Type C) which remained in use at nearly 200 principal offices until the Christmas issue of 2 November 1998. From 1970 the Bureau postmarks as Type C were inscribed "British Philatelic Bureau".

Since 1972 the Post Office has provided for virtually all issues an additional "alternative" pictorial "First Day of Issue" cancellation, at a location connected with the issue. Being available from the Bureau, these cancellations are illustrated and listed in this catalogue.

From 12 January 1999 (Millennium Inventors' Tale issue) the "alternative" pictorial postmark has been applied to all covers posted in special first day boxes throughout the country, replacing the local, non-pictorial, cancels. A bilingual version is used when the "alternative" office is in Wales. For collectors who prefer plain postmarks a non-pictorial version of the "alternative" postmark is available from Royal Mail Special Handstamp Centres.

"First Day of Issue" postmarks of standard or pictorial type have occasionally been provided on a "one-off" basis for places linked to particular stamp issues, eg Weymouth for the 1975 Sailing set. Such postmarks, which are not available from the Bureau, are footnoted only.

Royal Mail established Special Handstamp Centres in 1990 where all sponsored special handstamps and many "First Day of Issue" postmarks are now applied.

Pictorial local "First Day of Issue" postmarks were in use between 1988 and 1998 applied to covers posted in first day boxes and sent to main offices or Special Handstamp Centres. These included Birmingham (1993–98), Durham (1988–98), City of London (1989–98), London (1993–98), Newcastle upon Tyne (1992–94), and St Albans (1995–98). Different designs were used at the Glasgow Handstamp Centre for various places, 1993–98. As these postmarks were not available from the Bureau they are not included in this catalogue.

First day cover prices for modern issues are based on those with a Philatelic Bureau (later, "Tallents House" postmark.

Post Office Label Sheets

This catalogue lists complete "Generic Smilers" sheets in a section following the booklet listings. "Personalised" and "Corporate" sheets are not listed, neither are identifiable single stamps from label sheets.

No Value Indicated Stamps

From 22 August 1989 various definitive and special stamps appeared inscribed "2nd", "1st" or "E" instead of a face value. These were sold at the current minimum rates for these services which were as follows:

Inland Postage Rate	2nd Class	1st Class
5 September 1988	14p.	19p.
2 October 1989	15p.	20p.
17 September 1990	17p.	22p.
16 September 1991	18p.	24p.
1 November 1993	19p.	25p.
8 July 1996	20p.	26p.
26 April 1999	19p.	26p.
17 April 2000	19p.	27p.
8 May 2003	20p.	28p.
1 April 2004	21p.	28p.
7 April 2005	21p.	30p.
3 April 2006	23p.	32p.
2 April 2007	24p.	34p.
7 April 2008	27p.	36p.
6 April 2009	30p.	39p.
6 April 2010	32p.	41p.
4 April 2011	36p.	46p.

European Airmail Rate

26 April 1999	30p.
25 October 1999	34p.
27 April 2000	36p.
2 July 2001	37p.
27 March 2003	38p.
1 April 2004	40p.

From June 2004, European Airmail rate stamps reverted to showing a face value.

From 21 August 2006 "Large" letters were charged at a higher rate following the introduction of "Pricing in Proportion". Rates as follows:

Inland Postage Rate	2nd Class Large	1st Class Large
21 August 2006	37p.	44p.
2 April 2007	40p.	48p.
7 April 2008	42p.	52p.
6 April 2009	47p.	61p.
6 April 2010	51p.	66p.
4 April 2011	58p.	75p.

PHQ Cards

From 1973 the Post Office produced sets of picture cards to accompany commemorative issues which can be sent through the post as postcards. Each card shows an enlarged colour reproduction of one stamp, initially of a single value from one set and subsequently of all values.

PHQ Card cancelled on First Day of Issue

The Post Office gives each card a "PHQ" serial number, hence the term. The cards are usually on sale shortly before the date of issue of the stamps, but there is no officially designated "first day". Cards are priced in fine mint condition for complete sets as issued. Used prices are for cards franked with the stamp affixed, on the obverse, as illustrated; the stamp being cancelled with an official postmark for first day of issue or reverse.

Watermark Types

Stamps are on unwatermarked paper except where the heading to the set states otherwise.

AS DESCRIBED (Read through front of stamp)		AS SEEN DURING WATERMARK DETECTION (Stamp face down and back examined))
GvR	Normal	ЯvƆ
ЯʌƆ	Inverted	ƐʌЯ
ЯvƆ	Reversed	GvR
ƐʌЯ	Reversed and inverted	ЯʌƆ
GvR	Sideways	ƆvЯ
GvR	Sideways inverted	ЯvƆ

Watermarks are detected for Catalogue description by one of four methods: (1) holding stamps to the light; (2) laying stamps face down on a dark background; (3) by use of the Morley-Bright Detector, which works by revealing the thinning of the paper at the watermark; or (4) by the more complex electric watermark detectors such as the Stanley Gibbons Detectamark.

The diagram below shows how watermark position is described in the Catalogue. Watermarks are usually impressed so that they read normally when looked through from the printed side. However, since philatelists customarily detect watermarks by looking at the back of the stamp, the watermark diagram also makes clear what is actually seen. Note that "G v R" is only an example and illustrations of the different watermarks employed are shown in the listings. The illustrations are actual size and shown in normal positions (from the front of the stamps).

Watermark Errors and Varieties

Watermark errors are recognised as of major importance. They comprise stamps showing the wrong watermark devices or stamps printed on paper with the wrong watermark. Stamps printed on paper showing broken or deformed bits on the dandy roll, are not listable.

2 Small Crown **4** Large Crown **9** (Extends over three stamps) **13** V R

15 Small Garter **16** Medium Garter **17** Large Garter **20** Emblems **33** Spray of Rose **39** Maltese Cross

40 Large Anchor **47** Small Anchor **48** Orb **49** Imperial Crown **100** Simple Cypher **103** Multiple Cypher

110 Single Cypher **111** Block Cypher **117** PUC £1 **125** E 8 R **127**

133 **153** Tudor Crown **165** St. Edward's Crown **179** Multiple Crowns **F5** Double-lined Anchor **F6** Single-lined Anchor

General Types of watermark as seen through the front of the stamp

Underprints

From 1982 various values appeared with underprints, printed on the reverse, in blue, over the gum. These were usually from special stamp booklets, sold at a discount by the Post Office, but in 1985 surplus stocks of such underprinted paper were used for other purposes.

In this Catalogue stamps showing underprints are priced mint only. Used examples can be obtained, but care has to be taken in floating the stamps since the ink employed to print the device is solvent in water.

Underprint Types

1 Star with central dot   **2** Double-lined Star   **3** Double-lined "D"

4 Multiple double lined stars

5 Multiple double-lined "D"

(Types **4/5** are shown ¾ actual size)

Note: Types 4/5 are arranged in a random pattern so that the stamps from the same sheet or booklet pane will show the underprint in a slightly different position to the above. Stamps, when inspected, should be placed the correct way up, face down, when comparing with the illustrations.

Specimen Stamps

From 1847 stamps have been overprinted "SPECIMEN" for a variety of purposes, including the provision of samples to postmasters, as a security overprint on printers' or official reference copies and, from 1859, on examples of current British stamps sent to the International Bureau of the Univeral Postal Union for distribution to member nations.

Numerous styles were employed for these "Specimen" overprints, which are now listed in this catalogue up to the end of the reign of King George VI. The different types are illustrated here. Note that for ease of reference type numbers are the same as those given in the *Stanley Gibbons Great Britain Specialised Catalogue* and "missing" type numbers may have been used on stamps outside the scope of this catalogue or may refer to "Cancelled" overprints, which are, likewise, not listed here.

SPECIMEN
1

SPECIMEN
2

SPECIMEN
4

SPECIMEN
5

SPECIMEN
6

SPECIMEN
7

SPECIMEN
8

SPECIMEN
9

SPECIMEN
10

SPECIMEN
11

SPECIMEN
12

SPECIMEN
13

SPECIMEN
15

SPECIMEN
16

SPECIMEN
17

SPECIMEN
22

SPECIMEN
23

SPECIMEN
26

SPECIMEN
29

SPECIMEN
30

SPECIMEN
31

SPECIMEN
32

"Specimen" stamps are listed at the end of each reign and following the Departmental Official, Postage Due and Postal Fiscal sections with the Stanley Gibbons number of the unoverprinted stamps shown in brackets after the colour, followed by the plate number (where shown on the stamp) and the types of "Specimen" overprints found. The different types are not listed here and where more than one type was used the price given is for the cheapest version. Imperforate "Specimen" overprints are also not listed, unless the stamp was normally issued in that form.

More detailed listings will be found in Volumes 1 and 2 of the *Great Britain Specialised Catalogue*.

Guide to Entries

(A) Accession to the Throne

(B) Illustration – Generally all stamps are illustrated. To comply with Post Office regulations illustrations are reduced to 75%, with overprints shown actual size.

(C) Illustration or Type Number – These are bold figures found below each illustration. The type numbers are also given in bold in the second column of figures alongside the SG Catalogue number to indicate the design of each stamp.

(D) Date of Issue – When a set of definitive stamps have been issued over several years the Year Date given is for the earliest issue, commemorative sets are set in chronological order.

(E) Notes, other explanatory information – Covering paper, printers, watermarks etc.

(F) Perforations – The 'perforation' is the number of holes in a length of 2cm, as measured by the Stanley Gibbons *Instanta* gauge. From 1992 certain stamps occur with a large elliptical (oval) hole inserted in each line of vertical perforations. From 2009 certain stamps have U-shaped die-cut slits.

(G) Stanley Gibbons Catalogue Number – This is a unique number for each stamp to help the collector identify stamps, in the listing. The Stanley Gibbons numbering system is universally recognized as definitive, where insufficient numbers have been left to provide for additional stamps listings, some stamps will have a suffix letter after the catalogue number.

(H) Catalogue Value – Mint/Unused. Prices quoted for pre-1945 stamps are for lightly hinged examples. Prices quoted of unused King Edward VIII to Queen Elizabeth issues are for unmounted mint. Some sets are priced for unmouted mint and mounted mint, as well as used.

(I) Catalogue Value – Used. Prices generally refer to fine postally used examples.

Prices

Before February 1971 British currency was:

£1 = 20s One pound = twenty shillings *and*
1s = 12d One Shilling = 12 pence

Under decimalisation this became:

£1 = 100p One pound = one hundred (new) pence

Shown in Catalogue as	Explanation
10	10 pence
1.75	£1.75
15.00	£15
£150	£150
£2300	£2300

(J) Face Value – This refers to the value of the stamp and is sold at the Post Office when issued. Some modern stamps do not have their values in figures but instead shown as a letter.

(K) Watermarks – Stamps are on unwatermarked paper except where the heading to the set says otherwise. Please see pages xv and xvi for a detailed explanation of watermarks.

(L) Colour – All colours used in the printing process are detailed from the colour dabs in the sheet margin (working from top to bottom).

(M) Sets of Stamps – Two or more stamps with a common theme or subject.

(N) First Day Covers – Prices for first day covers are for complete sets used on plain covers or on special covers.

(O) Presentation Packs – Special packs consisting of the issue and slip-in cards with printed information inside a protective covering.

(P) PHQ Cards – Each card shows a large reproduction of a current British stamp.

(Q) Sets of Gutters – The term is used for a pair of stamps separated by part of the blank gutter margin or with Traffic Lights on the gutter margin.

(R) Footnote – Further information on background or key facts on issues.

(S) Other Types of Stamps – Postage Dues, Officials and Regional Issues

(T) Number Prefix – Stamps other than definitives and commemoratives have a prefix letter before the catalogue number.

(U) Date of issue detail – Information on day, month and year of issue with as much detail as is available.

A Accession to the Throne ──────

Queen Elizabeth II

6 February 1952

Further detailed information on the stamps of Queen Elizabeth II will be found in Volumes 3, 4 and 5 of the Stanley Gibbons *Great Britain Specialised Catalogue.*

B Illustration

C Illustration or Type Number ──────── 153 Tudor Crown   154

(Des Enid Marx (T **154**), M. Farrar-Bell (T **155/6**), G. Knipe (T **157**), Mary Adshead (T **158**), E. Dulac (T **159/60**). Portrait by Dorothy Wilding)

D Date of Issue ──────── 1952–54. W **153**. P 15×14. ●──────── **F** Perforations

515	**154**	½d. orange-red (31.8.53)	10	15
		Wi. Watermark inverted (3.54)	1·00	60
516		1d. ultramarine (31.8.53)	20	20
		a. Booklet pane. Three stamps plus three printed labels	35·00	
		Wi. Watermark inverted (3.54)	6·00	2·75
517		1½d. green (5.12.52)	10	20
		a. Watermark sideways (15.10.54)	50	70
		b. Imperf pane*		
		Wi. Watermark inverted (5.53)	1·00	70
518		2d. red-brown (31.8.53)	20	20
		a. Watermark sideways (8.10.54)	1·25	2·00
		Wi. Watermark inverted (3.54)	30·00	18·00
519	**155**	2½d. carmine-red (Type I) (5.12.52)	15	15
		a. Watermark sideways (15.11.54)	7·00	8·00
		b. Type II (booklets) (5.53)	1·25	1·25
		bWi. Watermark inverted (5.53)	60	75

H Catalogue Value – Unused

G Stanley Gibbons Catalogue Number ────

I Catalogue Value – Used

U Date of issue detail

J Face Value

E Notes, other explanatory information

See also Nos. 540/56, 561/6, 570/94 and 599/618a.
*BOOKLET ERRORS. This pane of 6 stamps is completely imperf (see No. 540a, etc).

First Day Covers

5.12.52	1½d., 2½d. (517, 519)		25·00
6.7.53	5d., 8d., 1s. (522, 525, 529)		50·00
31.8.53	½d., 1d., 2d. (515/16, 518)		50·00

U Date of issue detail ────────

(Des E. Fuller (2½d.), M. Goaman (4d.), E. Dulac (1s.3d.), M. Farrar-Bell (1s.6d.). Portrait (except 1s.3d.) by Dorothy Wilding)

1953 (3 June). *Coronation.* W **153**. P 15×14.

532	**161**	2½d. carmine-red	20	25
533	**162**	4d. ultramarine	1·10	1·90
534	**163**	1s.3d. deep yellow-green	5·00	3·00
535	**164**	1s.6d. deep grey-blue	10·00	4·75
		Set of 4	1·25	1·25
		Set of 4 Gutter Pairs	4·00	
		First Day Cover		3·00
		Presentation Pack (P.O. Pack No. 60)		
		P.H.Q. Card (No. 950)	£140	£150

K Watermark
L Colour

Q Sets of Gutters

M Sets ────────

N FDC for Complete Sets ────

O Presentation Packs

P PHQ Cards ────────

The 3½p. exists with ordinary PVA gum.
For a £1 value as Type **163** see Nos. **MS**2147 and 2380. ●──── **R** Footnote

POSTAGE DUE STAMPS ●──── **S** Other Types of Stamps

PERFORATIONS. All postage due stamps to No. D101 are perf 14×15.

D **1**   D **2**

(Des G. Eve. Typo Somerset House (early trial printings of ½d., 1d., 2d. and 5d.; all printings of 1s.) or Harrison (later printings of all values except 1s.))

1914 (20 Apr)–**22**. W **100** (*Simple Cypher*) (sideways).

			Unmtd mint	Mtd mint	Used
D1	D **1**	½d. emerald	1·50	50	25
		Wi. Watermark sideways-inverted	2·00	1·00	1·00
		Wj. Watermark sideways and reversed	18·00	12·00	15·00
		Wk. Watermark sideways-inverted and reversed			
		s. Optd "SPECIMEN"		45·00	

H Catalogue Value – Unused

T Number Prefix ────────

Commemorative Design Index

This index gives an easy reference to the inscriptions and designs of the Special Stamps 1953 to April 2000. Where a complete set shares an inscription or type of design, then only the catalogue number of the first stamp is given in addition to separate entries for stamps depicting popular thematic subjects. Paintings, inventions, etc., are indexed under the name of the artist or inventor, where this is shown on the stamp.

UNITED KINGDOM OF GREAT BRITAIN AND IRELAND

Queen Victoria
20 June 1837–22 January 1901

PARLIAMENTARY ENVELOPES. When the Uniform Penny Postage was introduced on 10 January 1840 the free franking privileges of Members of Parliament were abolished. During the same month, special envelopes were introduced for mail posted from the Houses of Parliament and these remained in use until the introduction of stamps and the Mulready stationery in May 1840. Envelopes are priced in used condition only.

Inscribed "Houses of Parliament" in black (16 Jan 1840)

PE1	1d. envelope	from	£18000
PE2	2d. envelope	from	£38000
PE2a	4d. envelope	from	

Inscribed "House of Lords" in vermilion (Jan 1840)

PE3	1d. envelope	from	£25000
PE4	2d. envelope		

Inscribed "House of Commons" in black (Jan 1840)

PE5	1d. envelope	from	£4000

MULREADY ENVELOPES AND LETTER SHEETS, so called from the name of the designer, William Mulready, were issued concurrently with the first British adhesive stamps.

1d. black	Envelopes:	£325 unused; £475 used.
	Letter Sheets:	£300 unused; £450 used.
2d. blue	Envelopes:	£400 unused; £1800 used.
	Letter Sheets:	£375 unused; £1800 used.

LINE-ENGRAVED ISSUES
GENERAL NOTES

Brief notes on some aspects of the line-engraved stamps follow, but for further information and a full specialist treatment of these issues collectors are recommended to consult Volume 1 of the Stanley Gibbons *Great Britain Specialised Catalogue*.

Alphabet I

Alphabet II

Alphabet III

Alphabet IV

Typical Corner Letters of the four Alphabets

Alphabets. Four different styles were used for the corner letters on stamps prior to the issue with letters in all four corners, these being known to collectors as:

Alphabet I. Used for all plates made from 1840 to the end of 1851. Letters small.

Alphabet II. Plates from 1852 to mid-1855. Letters larger, heavier and broader.

Alphabet III. Plates from mid-1855 to end of period. Letters tall and more slender.

Alphabet IV. 1861. 1d. Die II, Plates 50 and 51 only. Letters were hand-engraved instead of being punched on the plate. They are therefore inconsistent in shape and size but generally larger and outstanding.

While the general descriptions and the illustrations of typical letters given above may be of some assistance, only long experience and published aids can enable every stamp to be allocated to its particular Alphabet without hesitation, as certain letters in each are similar to those in one of the others.

Blued Paper. The blueing of the paper of the earlier issues is believed to be due to the presence of prussiate of potash in the printing ink, or in the paper, which, under certain conditions, tended to colour the paper when the sheets were damped for printing. An alternative term is bleuté paper.

Corner Letters. The corner letters on the early British stamps were intended as a safeguard against forgery, each stamp in the sheet having a different combination of letters. Taking the first 1d. stamp, printed in 20 horizontal rows of 12, as an example, the lettering is as follows:

Row 1.   A A, A B, A C, etc. to A L.

Row 2.   B A, B B, B C, etc. to B L.

and so on to

Row 20   T A, T B, T C, etc. to T L.

On the stamps with four corner letters, those in the upper corners are in the reverse positions to those in the lower corners. Thus in a sheet of 240 (12 × 20) the sequence is:

```
            A A   B A   C A        L A
  Row 1.                  etc. to
            A A   A B   A C        A L
            A B   B B   C B        L B
  Row 2.                  etc. to
            B A   B B   B C        B L
            and so on to
            A T   B T   C T        L T
  Row 20.                 etc. to
            T A   T B   T C        T L
```

Placing letters in all four corners was not only an added precaution against forgery but was meant to deter unmarked parts of used stamps being pieced together and passed off as an unused whole.

Dies. The first die of the 1d. was used for making the original die of the 2d., both the No Lines and White Lines issues. In 1855 the 1d. Die I was amended by retouching the head and deepening the lines on a transferred impression of the original. This later version, known to collectors as Die II, was used for making the dies for the 1d. and 2d. with letters in all four corners and also for the 1½d.

The two dies are illustrated above No. 17 in the catalogue.

Double letter   Guide line in corner

Guide line through value

Double Corner Letters. These are due to the workman placing his letter-punch in the wrong position at the first attempt, when lettering the plate, and then correcting the mistake; or to a slight shifting of the punch when struck. If a wrong letter was struck in the first instance, traces of a wrong letter may appear in a corner in addition to the correct one. A typical example is illustrated.

Guide Lines and Dots. When laying down the impressions of the design on the early plates, fine vertical and horizontal guide lines were marked on the plates to assist the operative. These were usually removed from the gutter margins, but could not be removed from the stamp impression without damage to the plate, so that in such cases they appear on the printed stamps, sometimes in the corners, sometimes through "POSTAGE" or the value. Typical examples are illustrated.

Guide dots or cuts were similarly made to indicate the spacing of the guide lines. These too sometimes appear on the stamps.

Ivory Head

"Ivory Head". The so-called "ivory head" variety is one in which the Queen's Head shows white on the back of the stamp. It arises from the comparative absence of ink in the head portion of the design, with consequent absence of blueing. (See "Blued Paper", on page 1).

Line-engraving. In this context "line-engraved" is synonymous with recess-printing, in which the engraver cuts recesses in a plate and printing (the coloured areas) is from these recesses. "Line-engraved" is the traditional philatelic description for these stamps; other equivalent terms found are "engraving in *taille-douce*" (French) or "in *intaglio*" (Italian).

Plates. Until the introduction of the stamps with letters in all four corners, the number of the plate was not indicated in the design of the stamp, but was printed on the sheet margin. By long study of identifiable blocks and the minor variation in the design, coupled with the position of the corner letters, philatelists are now able to allot many of these stamps to their respective plates. Specialist collectors often endeavour to obtain examples of a given stamp printed from its different plates and our catalogue accordingly reflects this depth of detail.

Maltese Cross   Type of Town postmark

Type of Penny Post cancellation

Example of 1844 type postmark

Postmarks. The so-called "Maltese Cross" design was the first employed for obliterating British postage stamps and was in use from 1840 to 1844. Being hand-cut, the obliterating stamps varied greatly in detail and some distinctive types can be allotted to particular towns or offices. Local types, such as those used at Manchester, Norwich, Leeds, etc., are keenly sought. A red ink was first employed, but was superseded by black, after some earlier experiments, In February 1841. Maltese Cross obliterations in other colours are rare.

Obliterations of this type, numbered 1 to 12 in the centre, were used at the London Chief Office in 1843 and 1844.

Some straight-line cancellations were in use in 1840 at the Penny Post receiving offices, normally applied on the envelope, the adhesives then being obliterated at the Head Office. They are nevertheless known, with or without Maltese Cross, on the early postage stamps.

In 1842 some offices in S.W. England used dated postmarks in place of the Maltese Cross, usually on the back of the letter since they were not originally intended as obliterators. These town postmarks have likewise been found on adhesives.

In 1844 the Maltese Cross design was superseded by numbered obliterators of varied type, one of which is illustrated. They are naturally comparatively scarce on the first 1d. and 2d. stamps.

Like the Maltese Cross they are found in various colours, some of which are rare.

Re-entry

"Union Jack" re-entry

Re-entries. Re-entries on the plate show as a doubling of part of the design of the stamp generally at top or bottom. Many re-entries are very slight while others are most marked. A typical one is illustrated.

The *"Union Jack"* re-entry, so-called owing to the effect of the re-entry on the appearance of the corner stars (see illustration) occurs on stamp L K of Plate 75 of the 1d. red, Die I.

T A (T L)   M A (M L)

Varieties of Large Crown Watermark

I   II

Two states of Large Crown Watermark

Watermarks. Two watermark varieties, as illustrated, consisting of crowns of entirely different shape, are found in sheets of the Large Crown paper and fall on stamps lettered M A and T A (or M L and T L when the paper is printed on the wrong side). Both varieties are found on the 1d. rose-red of 1857, while the M A (M L) variety comes also on some plates of the 1d. of 1864 (Nos. 43, 44) up to about Plate 96. On the 2d. the T A (T L) variety is known on plates 8 and 9, and the M A (M L) on later prints of plate 9. These varieties may exist inverted, or inverted reversed on stamps lettered A A and A L and H A and H L, and some are known.

In 1861 a minor alteration was made in the Large Crown watermark by the removal of the two vertical strokes, representing fleurs-de-lis, which projected upwards from the uppermost of the three horizontal curves at the base of the Crown. Hence two states are distinguishable, as illustrated.

CONDITION–IMPERFORATE
LINE-ENGRAVED ISSUES

The prices quoted for the 1840 and 1841 imperforate Line engraved issues are for "fine" examples. As condition is most important in assessing the value of a stamp, the following definitions will assist collectors in the evaluation of individual examples.

Four main factors are relevant when considering quality.

(a) Impression. This should be clean and the surface free of any rubbing or unnatural blurring which would detract from the appearance.

(b) Margins. This is perhaps the most difficult factor to evaluate. Stamps described as "fine", the standard adopted in this catalogue for pricing purposes, should have margins of the recognised width, defined as approximately one half of the distance between two adjoining unsevered stamps. Stamps described as "very fine" or "superb" should have margins which are proportionately larger than those of a "fine" stamp. Examples with close margins should not, generally, be classified as "fine".

(c) Cancellation. On a "fine" stamp this should be reasonably clear and not noticeably smudged. A stamp described as "superb" should have a neat cancellation, preferably centrally placed or to the right.

(d) Appearance. Stamps, at the prices quoted, should always be without any tears, creases, bends or thins and should not be toned on either the front or back. Stamps with such defects are worth only a proportion of the catalogue price.

Good

Fine

Very Fine

Superb

The actual size illustrations of 1840 1d. blacks show the various grades of quality. When comparing these illustrations it should be assumed that they are all from the same plate and that they are free of any hidden defects.

PRINTERS. Nos. 1/53a were recess-printed by Perkins, Bacon & Petch, known from 1852 as Perkins, Bacon & Co.

STAMPS ON COVER. Prices are quoted, for those Victorian and Edwardian issues usually found used on cover. In general these prices refer to single examples of the cheapest versions of each basic stamp with other shades, plates or varieties, together with unusual frankings and postmarks, being worth more. However multiples of some stamps may be more common than single usages and in this case the covers might be worth considerably less than the price quoted.

1   1a   **2** Small Crown

(Eng Charles and Frederick Heath)

1840 (6 May). Letters in lower corners. Wmk Small Crown, W **2**. Imperf.

			Un	Used	Used on cover
1	**1**	1d. intense black	£16000	£450	
2		1d. black	£10000	£300	£600
		Wi. Watermark inverted	£45000	£2000	
3		1d. grey-black (worn plate)	£14000	£425	
4	**1a**	2d. deep full blue	£40000	£1000	
5		2d. blue	£32000	£700	£2200
		Wi. Watermark inverted	£65000	£4500	
6		2d. pale blue	£40000	£900	

The 1d. stamp in black was printed from Plates 1 to 11. Plate 1 exists in two states (known to collectors as 1a and 1b), the latter being the result of extensive repairs.

Repairs were also made to plates 2, 5, 6, 8, 9, 10 and 11, and certain impressions exist in two or more states.

The so-called "Royal reprint" of the 1d. black was made in 1864, from Plate 66, Die II, on paper with Large Crown watermark, inverted. A printing was also made in carmine, on paper with the same watermark, normal.

For 1d. black with "VR" in upper corners see No. V1 under Official Stamps. The 2d. stamps were printed from Plates 1 and 2.

Plates of 1d. black

	Un	Used	Used on cover
1a	£14000	£350	£700
1b	£10000	£300	£600
2	£10000	£300	£600
3	£15000	£400	£725
4	£10000	£325	£650
5	£10000	£300	£650
6	£11000	£300	£650
7	£11000	£325	£700
8	£14000	£425	£800
9	£16000	£475	£950
10	£22000	£750	£3000
11	£18000	£4000	£15000

Varieties of 1d. black

		Un	Used
a.	On *bleuté* paper (Plates 1 to 8) ......from		£600
b.	Double letter in corner ......from	£10500	£325
bb.	Re-entry ......from	£11000	£350
bc.	"PB" re-entry (Plate 5, 3rd state)	—	£7000
c.	Guide line in corner	£10500	£325
cc.	Large letters in each corner (E J, I L, J C and P A) (Plate 1b) ......from	£10500	£450
d.	Guide line through value	£10500	£350
g.	Obliterated by Maltese Cross		
	In red	—	£350
	In black	—	£300
	In blue	—	£12000
	In magenta	—	£2500
	In yellow	—	
	In violet	—	£10000
h.	Obliterated by Maltese Cross with number in centre ......from	—	£17000
i.	Obliterated "Penny Post" in black (without Maltese Cross) ......from	—	£5000
j.	Obliterated by town postmark (without Maltese Cross)		
	In black ......from	—	£12000
	In yellow ......from	—	£50000
	In red ......from	—	£12500
k	Obliterated by 1844 type postmark in black ......from	—	£1500

OFFICIAL STAMP

In 1840 the 1d. black (Type **1**), with "V R" in the upper corners, was prepared for official use, but was never issued for postal purposes. Obliterated specimens are those which were used for experimental trials of obliterating inks, or those that passed through the post by oversight.

V **1**

1840. Prepared for use but not issued; "V" "R" in upper corners. Imperf.
V1   V **1**   1d. black £28000 £28000

Plates of 2d. blue

Plate		Un	Used	Used on cover
1	Shades from	£32000	£700	£2200
2	Shades from	£45000	£850	£2500

Varieties of 2d. blue

		Un	Used
a.	Double letter in corner	—	£750
aa.	Re-entry	—	£850
b.	Guide line in corner	—	£725
c.	Guide line through value	—	£725
e.	Obliterated by Maltese Cross		
	In red	—	£800
	In black	—	£700
	In blue	—	£12000
	In magenta	—	£8000
f.	Obliterated by Maltese Cross with number in centre ......from	—	£9500
g.	Obliterated "Penny Post" in black (without Maltese Cross) ......from	—	£6000
h.	Obliterated by town postmark (without Maltese Cross) in black ......from	—	£4500
i.	Obliterated by 1844 type postmark		
	In black ......from	—	£1700
	In blue ......from	—	£12000

Stanley Gibbons Luxury Hingeless Albums

Produced in conjunction with DAVO (Netherlands), the SG Luxury Hingeless Albums comprise dark blue padded leatherette, peg fitting binders, embossed with country crest, complete with matching slipcase. The SG Luxury Hingeless albums come with clear mounts and pages are updated annually with printed supplements.

Great Britain

Covering the stamps of Great Britain from 1840-2009, the Great Britain Luxury Hingeless album runs in line with the Stanley Gibbons Collect British Stamps catalogue. An index is provided at the front of each volume covering date of issue, brief description, SG number and the page number where the stamp can be found.

R5284	Great Britain Luxury Vol 1 Album (1840-1970)	£128.75
R5285	Great Britain Luxury Vol 2 Album (1970-1989)	£148.25
R5290	Great Britain Luxury Vol 3 Album (1990-1999)	£122.75
R5295	Great Britain Luxury Vol 4 Album (2000-2007)	£117.50
R5331	Great Britain Luxury Vol 5 Album (2008-2009)	£76.75
R5284(SO)	Great Britain Luxury Volume 1-5 Album Set	£505.75

Great Britain QEII

Covering the stamps of the reign of Queen Elizabeth II (1952-2009), the Stanley Gibbons Luxury Hingeless Great Britain QEII albums are designed to be used in conjunction with the Stanley Gibbons catalogue, Collect British Stamps. The GB QEII comes complete with an Index page as per the standard GB Luxury Hingeless.

R5546	Queen Elizabeth Luxury Vol 1 (1952-1989)	£139.95
R5581	Queen Elizabeth Luxury Vol 2 (1990-1999)	£127.75
R5583	Queen Elizabeth Luxury Vol 3 (2000-2007)	£139.95
R5618	Queen Elizabeth Luxury Vol 4 Album (2008-2009)	£76.75
R5546(SO)	Queen Elizabeth Luxury Vol 1-4 Album Set	£434.25
R5546(SC)	Queen Elizabeth SG Wide Slipcase Only	£13.25

Prices correct as of April 2011 and subject to change.

Our Luxury Hingeless range also includes albums for Jersey, Guernsey, Alderney, Isle of Man, Australia, Canada, New Zealand and Falkland Islands (including Dependencies).

For our full range of albums, visit www.stanleygibbons.com

Stanley Gibbons Publications
7 Parkside, Christchurch Road, Ringwood, Hampshire, BH24 3SH
Tel: +44 (0)1425 472 363 | Fax: +44 (0)1425 470 247
Email: orders@stanleygibbons.com
www.stanleygibbons.com

Est 1856
STANLEY GIBBONS

1841 (10 Feb). *Printed from "black" plates. Wmk* W **2**. *Paper more or less blued. Imperf.*

			Un	Used	Used on cover
7	**1**	1d. red-brown (*shades*)	£2700	£110	£225
		a. "PB" re-entry (Plate 5, 3rd state)	—	£2000	
		Wi. Watermark inverted (Plates 1b, 8 and 10) .... *from*	—	£2500	

The first printings of the 1d. in red-brown were made from Plates 1b, 2, 5 and 8 to 11 used for the 1d. black.

1d. red-brown from "black" plates

Plate	Un	Used	Used on cover
1b	£17500	£300	£550
2	£15000	£300	£550
5	£10000	£200	£350
8	£12000	£175	£250
9	£4750	£175	£250
10	£2700	£175	£250
11	£6500	£110	£225

1841 (late Feb). *Plate 12 onwards. Wmk* W **2**. *Paper more or less blued. Imperf.*

			Un	Used	Used on cover
8	**1**	1d. red-brown	£500	25·00	35·00
		s. Opt. "SPECIMEN" (1)	£3000		
		Wi. Watermark inverted	£3800	£350	
8a		1d. red-brown on very blue paper	£600	25·00	
9		1d. pale red-brown (worn plates)	£575	35·00	
10		1d. deep red-brown	£800	40·00	
11		1d. lake-red	£5000	£750	
12		1d. orange-brown	£1800	£225	

Error. No letter "A" in right lower corner (Stamp B (A), Plate 77)

			Un	Used	
12a	**1**	1d. red-brown	—	£24000	

The error "No letter A in right corner" was due to the omission to insert this letter on stamp B A of Plate 77. The error was discovered some months after the plate was registered and was then corrected.

There are innumerable variations in the colour shade of the 1d. "red" and those given in the above list represent colour groups each covering a wide range.

Varieties of 1d. red-brown, etc.

		Un	Used
b.	Major re-entry from	—	80·00
c.	Double letter in corner from	—	30·00
d.	Double Star (Plate 75) "Union Jack" re-entry	£27500	£2700
e.	Guide line in corner	—	25·00
f.	Guide line through value	—	25·00
g.	Thick outer frame to stamp	—	25·00
h.	Ivory head	£525	25·00
i.	Treasury roulette	£80000	£7000
j.	Left corner letter "S" inverted (Plates 78, 105, 107) .... *from*	—	£150
k.	P converted to R (Plates 30/1, 33, 83, 86) ...... *from*	—	75·00
l.	Obliterated by Maltese Cross		
	In red	—	£4500
	In black	—	50·00
	In blue	—	£550
m.	Obliterated by Maltese Cross with number in centre		
	No. 1	—	£140
	No. 2	—	£140
	No. 3	—	£175
	No. 4	—	£425
	No. 5	—	£140
	No. 6	—	£120
	No. 7	—	£120
	No. 8	—	£120
	No. 9	—	£140
	No. 10	—	£250
	No. 11	—	£250
	No. 12	—	£250
n.	Obliterated "Penny Post" in black (without Maltese Cross)	—	£900
o.	Obliterated by town postmark (without Maltese Cross)		
	In black .... *from*	—	£675
	In blue .... *from*	—	£2000
	In green .... *from*	—	£3500
	In yellow .... *from*	—	—
	In red .... *from*	—	£10000
p.	Obliterated by 1844 type postmark		
	In blue .... *from*	—	£180
	In red .... *from*	—	£7500
	In green .... *from*	—	£2500
	In violet .... *from*	—	£3500
	In black .... *from*	—	25·00
	In olive-yellow/brown .... *from*	—	£2000

Stamps with thick outer frame to the design are from plates on which the frame-lines have been straightened or recut, particularly Plates 76 and 90.

For "Union Jack" re-entry see General Notes to Line-engraved Issues. In "P converted to R" the corner letter "R" is formed from the "P", the distinctive long tail having been hand-cut.

KEY TO LINE-ENGRAVED ISSUES

S.G Nos.	Description	Date	Wmk	Perf	Die	Alphabet
	THE IMPERFORATE ISSUES					
1/3	1d. black	6.5.40	SC	Imp	I	I
4/6	2d. no lines	8.5.40	SC	Imp	I	I
	PAPER MORE OR LESS BLUED					
7	1d. red-brown	Feb 1841	SC	Imp	I	I
8/12	1d. red-brown	Feb 1841	SC	Imp	I	I
8/12	1d. red-brown	6.2.52	SC	Imp	I	II
13/15	2d. white lines	13.3.41	SC	Imp	I	I
	THE PERFORATED ISSUES					
	ONE PENNY VALUE					
16a	1d. red-brown	1848	SC	Roul	I	I
16b	1d. red-brown	1850	SC	16	I	I
16c	1d. red-brown	1853	SC	16	I	II
17/18	1d. red-brown	Feb 1854	SC	16	I	II
22	1d. red-brown	Jan 1855	SC	14	I	II
24/5	1d. red-brown	28.2.55	SC	14	II	II
21	1d. red-brown	1.3.55	SC	16	II	II
26	1d. red-brown	15.5.55	LC	16	II	II
29/33	1d. red-brown	Aug 1855	LC	14	II	III
	NEW COLOURS ON WHITE PAPER					
37/41	1d. rose-red	Nov 1856	LC	14	II	III
36	1d. rose-red	26.12.57	LC	16	II	III
42	1d. rose-red	1861	LC	14	II	IV
	TWO PENCE VALUE					
19, 20	2d. blue	1.3.54	SC	16	I	I
23	2d. blue	22.2.55	SC	14	I	I
23a	2d. blue	5.7.55	SC	14	I	II
20a	2d. blue	18.8.55	SC	16	I	II
27	2d. blue	20.7.55	LC	16	I	II
34	2d. blue	20.7.55	LC	14	I	II
35	2d. blue	2.7.57	LC	14	I	III
36a	2d. blue	1.2.58	LC	16	I	III
	LETTERS IN ALL FOUR CORNERS					
48/9	½d. rose-red	1.10.70	W9	14		—
43/4	1d. rose-red	1.4.64	LC	14		II
53a	1½d. rosy mauve	1860	LC	14		II
51/3	1½d. rose-red	1.10.70	LC	14		II
45	2d. blue	July 1858	LC	14		II
46/7	2d. thinner lines	7.7.69	LC	14		II

Watermarks: SC = Small Crown, T **2**. LC = Large Crown, T **4**.
Dies: See notes above No. 17 in the catalogue.
Alphabets: See General Notes to this section.

3 White lines added

1841 (13 Mar)−51. *White lines added. Wmk* W **2**. *Paper more or less blued. Imperf.*

			Un	Used	Used on cover
13	**3**	2d. pale blue	£5500	85·00	
14		2d. blue	£4500	75·00	£250
		s. Opt. "SPECIMEN" (1)	£5000		
		Wi. Watermark inverted	£20000	£650	
15		2d. deep full blue	£6500	85·00	
15aa		2d. violet-blue (1851)	£20000	£1300	

The 2d. stamp with white lines was printed from Plates 3 and 4.

No. 15aa came from Plate 4 and the quoted price is for examples on thicker, lavender tinted paper.

Plates of 2d. blue

Plate		Un	Used
3 shades.....from		£4500	85·00
4 shades.....from		£5250	75·00

Varieties of 2d. blue

		Un	Used
a.	Guide line in corner	—	90·00
b.	Guide line through value	£4750	90·00
bb.	Double letter in corner	—	95·00
be.	Re-entry	£6250	£160
c.	Ivory head	£5000	90·00
e.	Obliterated by Maltese Cross		
	In red	—	—
	In black	—	£225
	In blue.......................................	—	£4000
f.	Obliterated by Maltese Cross with number in centre		
	No. 1	—	£550
	No. 2	—	£550
	No. 3	—	£550
	No. 4	—	£550
	No. 5	—	£650
	No. 6	—	£550
	No. 7	—	£900
	No. 8	—	£700
	No. 9	—	£900
	No. 10	—	£1000
	No. 11	—	£650
	No. 12	—	£375
g.	Obliterated by town postmark (without Maltese Cross)		
	In black....................................from	—	£2200
	In blue ....from	—	£3500
h.	Obliterated by 1844 type postmark		
	In black ....from	—	75·00
	In blue ....from	—	£700
	In red ....from	—	£25000
	In green ....from	—	£4000

1841 (Apr). *Trial printing (unissued) on Dickinson silk-thread paper. No wmk. Imperf.*

16	**1**	1d. red-brown (Plate 11)............................		£6500

Eight sheets were printed on this paper, six being gummed, two ungummed, but we have only seen examples without gum.

1848. *Wmk W **2**. Rouletted approx 11½ by Henry Archer.*

16a	**1**	1d. red-brown (Plates 70, 71)		£25000

1850. *Wmk W **2**. P 16 by Henry Archer.*

			Un	Used	Used on cover
16b	**1**	1d. red-brown (Alph 1) (from Plates 90–101, 105, 107, 108, 116) from	£2800	£600	£1800
		bWi.Watermark inverted	—	£3750	

1853. *Wmk W **2**. Government Trial Perforation.*

16c	**1**	1d. red-brown (p 16) (Alph II) (on cover)		£18000

SEPARATION TRIALS. Although the various trials of machines for rouletting and perforating were unofficial, Archer had the consent of the authorities in making his experiments, and sheets so experimented upon were afterwards used by the Post Office.

As Archer ended his experiments in 1850 and plates with corner letters of Alphabet II did not come into issue until 1852, perforated stamps with corner letters of Alphabet I may safely be assumed to be Archer productions, if genuine.

The Government trial perforation is believed to have been done on Archer's machines after they had been purchased in 1853. As Alphabet II was by that time in use, the trials can be distinguished from the perforated stamps listed below by being dated prior to 24 February 1854, the date when the perforated stamps were officially issued.

Die I, Alphabet I, stamps from plates 74 and 113 perforated 14 have been recorded for many years, but it is now generally recognised that the type of comb machine used, producing one extension hole in the side margins, cannot be contemporary with other trials of this period.

Die I

Die II

4 Large Crown

Die I: The features of the portrait are lightly shaded and consequently lack emphasis.

Die II: (Die I retouched): The lines of the features have been deepened and appear stronger.

The eye is deeply shaded and made more lifelike. The nostril and lips are more clearly defined, the latter appearing much thicker. A strong downward stroke of colour marks the corner of the mouth. There is a deep indentation of colour between lower lip and chin. The band running from the back of the ear to the chignon has a bolder horizontal line below it than in Die I.

1854–57. *Paper more or less blued.*

*(a) Wmk Small Crown, W **2**. P 16.*

			Un	Used	Used on cover
17	**1**	1d. red-brown (Die I) (24.2.54)	£325	25·00	50·00
		a. Imperf three sides (horiz pair)	†	—	
		Wi. Watermark inverted	—	£190	
18		1d. yellow-brown (Die I)	£375	45·00	
19	**3**	2d. dp blue (Plate 4) (12.3.54)	£4000	90·00	£175
		a. Imperf three sides (horiz pair)	†	—	
		s. Opt. "SPECIMEN" (2)	£1700		
		Wi. Watermark inverted	—	£275	
20		2d. pale blue (Plate 4).....................	£4500	£100	
20a		2d. blue (Plate 5) (18.8.55)	£8000	£300	£450
		aWi. Watermark inverted	—	£700	
21	**1**	1d. red-brown (Die II) (22.2.55)	£400	60·00	£100
		a. Imperf (Plates 2, 14)			
		Wi. Watermark inverted..............	£950	£225	

*(b) Wmk Small Crown, W **2**. P 14.*

			Un	Used	Used on cover
22	**1**	1d. red-brown (Die I) (1.55)	£550	80·00	£140
		Wi. Watermark inverted	—	£275	
23	**3**	2d. blue (Plate 4) (22.2.55)	£9000	£200	£300
		s. Opt. "SPECIMEN" (2)	£1700		
		Wi. Watermark inverted	£10000	£500	
23a		2d. blue (Plate 5) (4.7.55)	£9500	£300	£425
		b. Imperf (Plate 5)		£600	
		aWi. Watermark inverted	—	£600	
24	**1**	1d. red-brown (Die II) (27.2.55)	£600	60·00	£100
		Wi. Watermark inverted	£2000	£300	
24a		1d. deep red-brown (very blue paper) (Die II)	£750	£100	
25		1d. orange-brown (Die II)	£1600	£150	

*(c) Wmk Large Crown, W **4**. P 16.*

			Un	Used	Used on cover
26	**1**	1d. red-brown (Die II) (15.5.55)	£2000	£110	£200
		a. Imperf (Plate 7)			
		Wi. Watermark inverted	—	£350	
27	**3**	2d. blue (Plate 5) (20.7.55)	£14000	£375	£475
		a. Imperf	—	£7000	
		Wi. Watermark inverted	—	£750	

*(d) Wmk Large Crown, W **4**. P 14.*

			Un	Used	Used on cover
29	**1**	1d. red-brown (Die II) (6.55)	£225	18·00	35·00
		a. Imperf (shades) (Plates 22, 24, 25, 32, 43)	£3800	£3000	
		s. Opt. "SPECIMEN" (2)	£550		
		Wi. Watermark inverted	£900	£120	
30		1d. brick-red (Die II)	£275	40·00	
31		1d. plum (Die II) (2.56)	£3500	£800	
32		1d. brown-rose (Die II).....................	£300	50·00	
33		1d. orange-brown (Die II) (3.57) ...	£600	55·00	
34	**3**	2d. blue (Plate 5) (20.7.55)	£2250	60·00	£150
		Wi. Watermark inverted	—	£250	
35		2d. blue (Plate 6) (2.7.57)...............	£2750	60·00	£150
		a. Imperf	—	£7000	
		b. Imperf horiz (vert pair)	†	—	
		Wi. Watermark inverted	—	£250	

*17/35a **For well-centred, lightly used +125%**

1856–58. *Wmk Large Crown, W **4**. Paper no longer blued.*

(a) P 16.

			Un	Used	Used on cover
36	**1**	1d. rose-red (Die II) (26.12.57)	£2400	65·00	£140
		Wi. Watermark inverted	—	£300	
36a	**3**	2d. blue (Plate 6) (1.2.58)	£12000	£325	£450
		aWi. Watermark inverted	—	£750	

(b) Die II. P 14.

			Un	Used	Used on cover
37	**1**	1d. red-brown (11.56)	£1500	£300	£800
38		1d. pale red (9.4.57)	90·00	30·00	
		a. Imperf	£4000	£3500	
		s. Opt. "SPECIMEN" (6, 7, 10)........	£180		
39		1d. pale rose (3.57)	90·00	30·00	
40		1d. rose-red (9.57)	45·00	10·00	20·00
		a. Imperf	£4000	£2800	
		b. Imperf vert (horiz pair)	†	—	
		Wi. Watermark inverted................	£120	60·00	
41		1d. deep rose-red (7.57)	£140	20·00	

1861. *Letters engraved on plate instead of punched (Alphabet IV).*

			Un	Used	Used on cover
42	**1**	1d. rose-red (Die II) (Plates 50 & 51)	£250	35·00	60·00
		a. Imperf	—	£5500	
		Wi. Watermark inverted	£650	£175	

*36/42a **For well-centred, lightly used +125%**

The original die (Die I) was used to provide roller dies for the laying down of all the line-engraved stamps from 1840 to 1855. In that year a new master die was laid down (by means of a Die I roller die) and the impression was retouched by hand engraving by William Humphrys. This retouched die, always known to philatelists as Die II, was from that time used for preparing all new roller dies.

One Penny. The numbering of the 1d. plates recommenced at 1 on the introduction of Die II. Plates 1 to 21 were Alphabet II from which a scarce plum shade exists. Corner letters of Alphabet III appear on Plate 22 and onwards. As an experiment, the corner letters were engraved by hand on Plates 50 and 51 in 1856, instead of being punched (Alphabet IV), but punching was again resorted to from Plate 52 onwards. Plates 50 and 51 were not put into use until 1861.

Two Pence. Unlike the 1d. the old sequence of plate numbers continued. Plates 3 and 4 of the 2d. had corner letters of Alphabet I, Plate 5 Alphabet II and Plate 6 Alphabet III. In Plate 6 the white lines are thinner than before.

In both values, varieties may be found as described in the preceding issues—ivory heads, inverted watermarks, re-entries, and double letters in corners.

The change of perforation from 16 to 14 was decided upon late in 1854 since the closer holes of the former gauge tended to cause the sheets of stamps to break up when handled, but for a time both gauges were in concurrent use. Owing to faulty alignment of the impressions on the plates and to shrinkage of the paper when dampened, badly perforated stamps are plentiful in the line-engraved issues.

| 5 | 6 | Showing position of the plate number on the 1d. and 2d. values. (Plate 170 shown) |

1858–79. *Letters in all four corners. Wmk Large Crown, W* **4**. *Die II* (1d. and 2d.). P 14.

			Un	Used*	Used on cover
43	**5**	1d. rose-red (1.4.64)	18·00	2·50	6·00
		s. Opt. "SPECIMEN" (1, 6, 8, 9)	£175		
44		1d. lake-red	18·00	2·50	
		a. Imperf..................from	£6000	£3000	
		Wi. Watermark inverted.........from	90·00	25·00	

*43/4a **For well-centred, lightly used** +125%

The following plate numbers are known imperf (No. 44a); 72, 79, 80, 81, 82, 83, 84, 85, 86, 87, 88, 90, 91, 92, 93, 96, 97, 98, 100, 101, 102, 103, 104, 105, 107, 108, 109, 112, 113, 114, 116, 117, 120, 121, 122, 136, 137, 142, 146, 148, 158, 162, 164, 166, 171, 174, 191 and 202.

The numbering of this series of 1d. red plates follows after that of the previous 1d. stamp, last printed from Plate 68.

Plates 69, 70, 75, 126 and 128 were prepared for this issue but rejected owing to defects, and stamps from these plates do not exist, so that specimens which appear to be from these plates (like many of those which optimistic collectors believe to be from Plate 77) bear other plate numbers. Owing to faulty engraving or printing it is not always easy to identify the plate number. Plate 77 was also rejected but some stamps printed from it were used. One specimen is in the Tapling Collection and six or seven others are known. Plates 226 to 228 were made but not used.

Specimens from most of the plates are known with inverted watermark. The variety of watermark described in the General Notes to this section occurs on stamp M A (or M L) on plates up to about 96 (Prices from £110 used).

Re-entries in this issue are few, the best being on stamps M K and T K of Plate 71 and on S L and T L, Plate 83.

Plate	Un	Used	Plate	Un	Used
71	45·00	3·50	88	£170	8·50
72	50·00	4·50	89	50·00	2·50
73	50·00	3·50	90	50·00	2·50
74	50·00	2·50	91	60·00	6·50
76	40·00	2·50	92	40·00	2·50
77	—		93	55·00	2·50
78	£110	2·50	94	50·00	5·50
79	38·00	2·50	95	45·00	2·50
80	55·00	2·50	96	50·00	2·50
81	55·00	2·75	97	45·00	4·00
82	£110	4·50	98	55·00	6·50
83	£140	8·00	99	60·00	5·50
84	70·00	2·75	100	65·00	2·75
85	50·00	3·75	101	65·00	10·00
86	60·00	4·50	102	50·00	2·50
87	38·00	2·50	103	55·00	4·00

Plate	Un	Used	Plate	Un	Used
104	80·00	5·50	166	50·00	6·50
105	£110	8·00	167	50·00	2·50
106	60·00	2·50	168	55·00	9·00
107	65·00	8·00	169	65·00	8·00
108	85·00	2·75	170	40·00	2·50
109	90·00	4·00	171	18·00	2·50
110	65·00	10·00	172	35·00	2·50
111	55·00	2·75	173	75·00	10·00
112	75·00	2·75	174	35·00	2·50
113	55·00	14·00	175	65·00	4·00
114	£290	14·00	176	65·00	2·75
115	£110	2·75	177	45·00	2·50
116	80·00	10·00	178	65·00	4·00
117	50·00	2·50	179	55·00	2·75
118	55·00	2·50	180	65·00	5·50
119	50·00	2·50	181	50·00	2·50
120	18·00	2·50	182	£100	5·50
121	45·00	10·00	183	60·00	3·50
122	18·00	2·50	184	35·00	2·75
123	45·00	2·50	185	55·00	3·50
124	32·00	2·50	186	70·00	2·75
125	45·00	2·50	187	55·00	2·50
127	60·00	2·75	188	75·00	11·00
129	45·00	9·00	189	75·00	7·50
130	60·00	2·75	190	55·00	6·50
131	70·00	18·00	191	35·00	8·00
132	£150	25·00	192	55·00	2·50
133	£125	10·00	193	35·00	2·50
134	18·00	2·50	194	55·00	9·00
135	£100	28·00	195	55·00	9·00
136	£100	22·00	196	55·00	5·50
137	32·00	2·75	197	60·00	10·00
138	22·00	2·50	198	45·00	6·50
139	65·00	18·00	199	60·00	6·50
140	22·00	2·50	200	65·00	2·50
141	£125	10·00	201	35·00	5·50
142	75·00	28·00	202	65·00	2·50
143	65·00	16·00	203	35·00	18·00
144	£100	22·00	204	60·00	2·75
145	35·00	2·75	205	60·00	3·50
146	45·00	6·50	206	60·00	10·00
147	55·00	3·50	207	65·00	10·00
148	45·00	3·50	208	60·00	18·00
149	45·00	6·50	209	55·00	10·00
150	18·00	2·50	210	70·00	13·00
151	65·00	10·00	211	75·00	22·00
152	65·00	6·00	212	65·00	12·00
153	£110	10·00	213	65·00	12·00
154	55·00	2·50	214	70·00	20·00
155	55·00	2·75	215	70·00	20·00
156	50·00	2·50	216	75·00	20·00
157	55·00	2·50	217	75·00	8·00
158	35·00	2·50	218	70·00	9·00
159	35·00	2·50	219	£100	75·00
160	35·00	2·50	220	45·00	8·00
161	65·00	8·00	221	75·00	18·00
162	55·00	8·00	222	85·00	45·00
163	55·00	3·50	223	£120	65·00
164	55·00	3·50	224	£150	55·00
165	50·00	2·50	225	£3000	£700

			Un	Used*	Used on cover
45	**6**	2d. blue (thick lines) (7.58)	£300	12·00	40·00
		a. Imperf (Plate 9)		£8500	
		s. Opt. "SPECIMEN" (1, 7)	£450		
		Wi. Watermark inverted	£1100	£180	
		Plate			
		7	£1400	50·00	
		8	£1300	35·00	
		9	£300	12·00	
		12	£2200	£120	
46		2d. blue (thin lines) (1.7.69)	£325	22·00	60·00
		s. Opt. "SPECIMEN" (pl. 14, 15)			
		(6, 8, 9, 10)	£200		
		Wi. Watermark inverted	£1800	£225	
47		2d. deep blue (thin lines)	£325	22·00	
		a. Imperf (Plate 13)	£8500		
		Plate			
		13	£325	22·00	
		14	£425	30·00	
		15	£400	30·00	

*45/7 **For well-centred, lightly used** +125%

Plates 10 and 11 of the 2d. were prepared but rejected. Plates 13 to 15 were laid down from a new roller impression on which the white lines were thinner.

There are some marked re-entries and repairs, particularly on Plates 7, 8, 9 and 12.

Stamps with inverted watermark may be found and also the T A (T L) and M A (M L) watermark varieties (see General Notes to this section).

Though the paper is normally white, some printings showed blueing and stamps showing the "ivory head" may therefore be found.

7

Showing the plate number (9)

9

1870 (1 Oct). *Wmk W* **9**, *extending over three stamps.* P 14.

			Un	Used*	Used on cover
48	7	½d. rose-red	90·00	18·00	60·00
49		½d. rose	90·00	18·00	
		a. Imperf (Plates 1, 4, 5, 6, 8, 14)			
		.................................from	£3700	£2500	
		s. Opt. "SPECIMEN" (various plates) (2, 8, 9, 10)	£175		
		Wi. Watermark inverted	—	£125	
		Wj. Watermark reversed	—	£125	
		Wk. Watermark inverted & reversed	£250	80·00	
		Plate			
		1	£275	75·00	
		3	£200	40·00	
		4	£130	30·00	
		5	90·00	18·00	
		6	£100	18·00	
		8	£500	£100	
		9	£5500	£700	
		10	£110	18·00	
		11	£100	18·00	
		12	£100	18·00	
		13	£100	18·00	
		14	£100	18·00	
		15	£150	40·00	
		19	£250	55·00	
		20	£300	75·00	

*48/9a **For well-centred, lightly used +200%**

The ½d. was printed in sheets of 480 (24 × 20) so that the check letters run from

A A   X T
to
A A   T X

Plates 2, 7, 16, 17 and 18 were not completed while Plates 21 and 22, though made, were not used.

Owing to the method of perforating, the outer side of stamps in either the A or X row (ie the left or right side of the sheet) is imperf.

Stamps may be found with watermark inverted or reversed, or without watermark, the latter due to misplacement of the paper when printing.

8

Position of plate number

1870 (1 Oct). *Wmk W* **4**. P 14.

			Un	Used*	Used on cover
51	8	1½d. rose-red	£400	60·00	£250
		s. Opt. "SPECIMEN" (pl. 1) (2, 6)	£400		
		sa. Opt. "SPECIMEN" (pl. 3) (8, 9, 10)	£225		
52		1½d. lake-red	£500	60·00	
		a. Imperf (Plates 1 & 3) ....from	£8500	†	
		Wi. Watermark inverted	—	£475	
		Plate			
		(1)	£600	80·00	
		3	£400	60·00	
		Error of lettering. OP–PC (Plate 1)			
53	8	1½d. rose-red	£22000	£1500	£6000

Prepared for use in 1860, but not issued; blued paper.

53a	8	1½d. rosy mauve (Plate 1)	£7000		
		b. Error of lettering, OP–PC for CP–PC	—	†	
		s. Opt. "SPECIMEN" (2, 6)	£2000		

*51/3 **For well-centred, lightly used +125%**

Owing to a proposed change in the postal rates, 1½d. stamps were first printed in 1860, in rosy mauve, No. 53a, but the change was not approved and the greater part of the stock was destroyed, although three or four postally used examples have been recorded.

In 1870 a 1½d. stamp was required and was issued in rose-red. Plate 1 did not have the plate number in the design of the stamps, but on stamps from Plate 3 the number will be found in the frame as shown above. Plate 2 was defective and was not used.

The error of lettering OP–PC on Plate 1 was apparently not noticed by the printer, and therefore not corrected.

EMBOSSED ISSUES

Volume 1 of the Stanley Gibbons Great Britain Specialised Catalogue gives further detailed information on the embossed issues.

PRICES. The prices quoted are for cut-square stamps with average to fine embossing. Stamps with exceptionally clear embossing are worth more.

10   **11**   **12**

13

Position of die number

(Primary die engraved at the Royal Mint by William Wyon. Stamps printed at Somerset House)

1847–54. *Imperf (For paper and wmk see footnote).*

			Un	Used	Used on cover
54	10	1s. pale green (11.9.47)	£17500	£850	£1100
		s. Opt. "SPECIMEN" (red opt)	£2600		
		sa. Opt. "SPECIMEN" (black opt) (1, 2)	£2400		
55		1s. green	£17500	£900	
56		1s. deep green	£20000	£900	
		Die 1 (1847)	£17500	£850	
		Die 2 (1854)	£20000	£950	
57	11	10d. brown (6.11.48)	£8000	£1200	£2200
		s. Opt. "SPECIMEN" (1, 2)	£2600		
		Die 1 (1848)	£8500	£1200	
		Die 2 (1850)	£8000	£1200	
		Die 3 (1853)	£8000	£1200	
		Die 4 (1854)	£8500	£1200	
58	12	6d. mauve (1.3.54)	£15000	£900	
		s. Opt. "SPECIMEN" (1, 2)	£3000		
59		6d. dull lilac	£15000	£900	£1400
60		6d. purple	£15000	£900	
		Wi. Watermark upright	—	£900	
		Wj. Watermark inverted	—	£900	
		Wk. Watermark inverted and reversed	£15000	£900	
61		6d. violet	£20000	£3500	

The 1s. and 10d. are on "Dickinson" paper with "silk" threads. The 6d. is on paper watermarked V R in single-lined letters, W 13, which may be found in four ways—upright, inverted, upright reversed, and inverted reversed.

The die numbers are indicated on the base of the bust. Only Die 1 (1 W W) of the 6d. was used for the adhesive stamps. The 10d. is from Die 1 (W.W.1 on stamps), and Dies 2 to 5 (2W.W., 3W.W., 4W.W. and 5W.W.) but the number and letters on stamps from Die 1 are seldom clear and many specimens are known without any trace of them. Because of this the stamp we previously listed as "No die number" has been deleted. That they are from Die 1 is proved by the existence of blocks showing stamps with and without the die number. The 1s. is from Dies 1 and 2 (W.W.1, W.W.2).

The normal arrangement of the "silk" threads in the paper was in pairs running down each vertical row of the sheets, the space between the threads of each pair being approximately 5 mm and between pairs of threads 20 mm. Varieties due to misplacement of the paper in printing show a single thread on the first stamp from the sheet margin and two threads 20 mm apart on the other stamps of the row. Faulty manufacture is the cause of stamps with a single thread in the middle.

Through bad spacing of the impressions, which were handstruck, all values may be found with two impressions more or less overlapping. Owing to the small margin allowed for variation of spacing, specimens with good margins on all sides are not common.

Double impressions are known of all values.

Later printings of the 6d. had the gum tinted green to enable the printer to distinguish the gummed side of the paper.

SURFACE-PRINTED ISSUES
GENERAL NOTES

Volume 1 of the Stanley Gibbons *Great Britain Specialised Catalogue* gives further detailed information on the surface-printed Issues.

"Abnormals". The majority of the great rarities in the surface printed group of issues are the so-called "abnormals", whose existence is due to the practice of printing six sheets from every plate as soon as made, one of which was kept for record purposes at Somerset House, while the others were perforated and usually issued. If such plates were not used for general production or if, before they came into full use, a change of watermark or colour took place, the six sheets originally printed would differ from the main issue in plate, colour or watermark and, if issued would be extremely rare.

The abnormal stamps of this class listed in this Catalogue and distinguished, where not priced, by an asterisk (*) are:

No.
78	3d. Plate 3 (with white dots)
152	4d. vermilion, Plate 16
153	4d. sage-green, Plate 17
109	6d. mauve, Plate 10
124/a	6d. pale chestnut & 6d. chestnut, Plate 12
145	6d. pale buff, Plate 13
88	9d. Plate 3 (hair lines)
98	9d. Plate 5 (see footnote to No. 98)
113	10d. Plate 2
91	1s. Plate 3 ("Plate 2")
148/50	1s. green, Plate 14
120	2s. blue, Plate 3

Those which may have been issued, but of which no specimens are known, are 2½d. wmk. Anchor, Plates 4 and 5; 3d. wmk Emblems, Plate 5; 3d. wmk Spray, Plate 21, 6d. grey, wmk Spray, Plate 18; 8d. orange, Plate 2; 1s. wmk Emblems, Plate 5; 5s. wmk Maltese Cross, Plate 4.

The 10d. Plate 1, wmk Emblems (No. 99), is sometimes reckoned among the abnormals, but was an error, due to the use of the wrong paper.

Corner Letters. With the exception of the 4d., 6d. and 1s. of 1855–57, the ½d., 1½d., 2d. and 5d. of 1880, the 1d. lilac of 1881 and the £5 (which had letters in lower corners only, and in the reverse order to the normal) all the surface-printed stamps issued prior to 1887 had letters in all four corners, as in the later line-engraved stamps. The arrangement is the same, the letters running in sequence right across and down the sheets, whether these were divided into panes or not. The corner letters existing naturally depend on the number of stamps in the sheet and their arrangement.

Imprimaturs and Imperforate Stamps. The Post Office retained in their records (now in the National Postal Museum) one imperforate sheet from each plate, known as the Imprimatur (or officially approved) sheet. Some stamps were removed from time to time for presentation purposes and have come on to the market, but these imperforates are not listed as they were not issued. Full details can be found in Volume 1 of the Great Britain Specialised Catalogue.

However, other imperforate stamps are known to have been issued and these are listed where it has been possible to prove that they do not come from the Imprimatur sheets. It is therefore advisable to purchase these only when accompanied by an Expert Committee certificate of genuineness.

Plate Numbers. All stamps from No. 75 to No. 163 bear in their designs either the plate number or, in one or two earlier instances, some other indication by which one plate can be distinguished from another. With the aid of these and of the corner letters it is thus possible to "reconstruct" a sheet of stamps from any plate of any issue or denomination.

Surface-printing. In this context the traditional designation "surface-printing" is synonymous with typo(graphy)—a philatelic term—or letterpress—the printers' term—as meaning printing from (the surface of) raised type. It is also called relief printing, as the image is in relief (in French, *en épargne*), unwanted parts of the design having been cut away. Duplicate impressions can be electrotyped or stereotyped from an original die, the resulting *clichés* being locked together to form the printing plate.

Wing Margins. As the vertical gutters (spaces) between the panes, into which sheets of stamps of most values were divided until the introduction of the Imperial Crown watermark, were perforated through the centre with a single row of holes, instead of each vertical row of stamps on the inner side of the panes having its own line of perforation as is now usual, a proportion of the stamps in each sheet have what is called a "wing margin" about 5 mm wide on one or other side.

The stamps with "wing margins" are the watermark Emblems and Spray of these series (3d, 6d, 9d, 10d, 1s and 2s) with letters D, E, H or I in S.E. corner, and the watermark Garter series (4d. and 8d.) with letters F or G in S.E. corner. Knowledge of this lettering will enable collectors to guard against stamps with wing margin cut down and re-perforated, but note that wing margin stamps of Nos. 62 to 73 are also to be found re-perforated.

PRINTERS. The issues of Queen Victoria, Nos. 62/214, were typo by Thomas De La Rue & Co.

PERFORATIONS. All the surface-printed issues of Queen Victoria are perf 14, with the exception of Nos. 126/9.

KEY TO SURFACE-PRINTED ISSUES 1855–83

S.G. Nos.	Description	Watermark	Date of Issue
		NO CORNER LETTERS	
62	4d. carmine	Small Garter	31.7.55
63/5	4d. carmine	Medium Garter	25.2.56
66/a	4d. carmine	Large Garter	Jan 1857
69/70	6d. lilac	Emblems	21.10.56
71/3	1s. green	Emblems	1.11.56
		SMALL WHITE CORNER LETTERS	
75/7	3d. carmine	Emblems	1.5.62
78	3d. carmine (dots)	Emblems	Aug 1862
79/82	4d. red	Large Garter	15.1.62
83/5	6d. lilac	Emblems	1.12.62
86/8	9d. bistre	Emblems	15.1.62
89/91	1s. green	Emblems	1.12.62
		LARGE WHITE CORNER LETTERS	
92	3d. rose	Emblems	1.3.65
102/3	3d. rose	Spray	July 1867
93/4	4d. vermilion	Large Garter	4.7.65
96/7	6d. lilac	Emblems	7.3.65
104/7	6d. lilac	Spray	21.6.67
108/9	6d. lilac	Spray	8.3.69
122/4	6d. chestnut	Spray	12.4.72
125	6d. grey	Spray	24.4.73
98	9d. straw	Emblems	30.10.65
110/11	9d. straw	Spray	3.10.67
99	10d. brown	Emblems	11.11.67
112/14	10d. brown	Spray	1.7.67
101	1s. green	Emblems	19.1.65
115/17	1s. green	Spray	13.7.67
118/20b	2s. blue	Spray	1.7.67
121	2s. brown	Spray	27·2.80
126/7	5s. rose	Cross	1.7.67
128	10s. grey	Cross	26.9.78
129	£1 brown-lilac	Cross	26.9.78
130, 134	5s. rose	Anchor	25.11.82
131, 135	10s. grey-green	Anchor	Feb 1883
132, 136	£1 brown-lilac	Anchor	Dec 1882
133, 137	£5 orange	Anchor	21.3.82
		LARGE COLOURED CORNER LETTERS	
138/9	2½d. rosy mauve	Anchor	1.7.75
141	2½d. rosy mauve	Orb	1.5.76
142	2½d. blue	Orb	5-2.80
157	2½d. blue	Crown	23.3.81
143/4	3d. rose	Spray	5.7.73
158	3d. rose	Crown	Jan 1881
159	3d. on 3d. lilac	Crown	1.1.83
152	4d. vermilion	Large Garter	1.3.76
153	4d. sage-green	Large Garter	12.3.77
154	4d. brown	Large Garter	15.8.80
160	4d. brown	Crown	9.12.80
145	6d. buff	Spray	15.3.73
146/7	6d. grey	Spray	20.3.74
161	6d. grey	Crown	1.1.81
162	6d. on 6d. lilac	Crown	1.1.83
156a	8d. purple-brown	Large Garter	July 1876
156	8d. orange	Large Garter	11.9.76
148/50	1s. green	Spray	1.9.73
151	1s. brown	Spray	14.10.80
163	1s. brown	Crown	24.5.81

Watermarks:		
	Anchor	W **40, 47**
	Cross	W **39**
	Crown	W **49**
	Emblems	W **20**
	Large Garter	W **17**
	Medium Garter	W **16**
	Orb	W **48**
	Small Garter	W **15**
	Spray	W **33**

14

15 Small Garter

16 Medium Garter   **17** Large Garter

1855–57. *No corner letters.*

(a) Wmk Small Garter, W **15**. *Highly glazed, deeply blued paper*
(31 July 1855)

			Un	Used*	Used on cover
62	**14**	4d. carmine (*shades*)	£7250	£375	£650
		a. Paper slightly blued	£7500	£375	
		b. White paper	—	£875	
		s. Opt. "SPECIMEN" (2, 3)	£900		
		Wi. Watermark inverted	—	£1000	

(b) Wmk Medium Garter, W **16**.

(i) Thick, blued highly glazed paper (25 February 1856).

63	**14**	4d. carmine (*shades*)	£9000	£475	£700
		a. White paper	£9000		
		s. Opt. "SPECIMEN" (2)	£800		
		Wi. Watermark inverted	—	£1100	

(ii) Ordinary thin white paper (September 1856).

64	**14**	4d. pale carmine	£8250	£400	£600
		a. Stamp printed double	†	—	
		s. Opt. "SPECIMEN" (2)	£800		
		Wi. Watermark inverted	—	£1100	

(iii) Ordinary white paper, specially prepared ink (1 November 1856).

65	**14**	4d. rose or deep rose	£8250	£425	£600
		s. Opt. "SPECIMEN" (4)	£1600		
		Wi Watermark inverted	—	†	—

(c) Wmk Large Garter, W **17**. *Ordinary white paper (January 1857).*

66	**14**	4d. rose-carmine	£1750	£120	£190
		a. Rose	£1350	£120	
		aWi. Watermark inverted	£3500	£300	
		aWj. Watermark inverted and reversed			
		b. Thick glazed paper	£4250	£300	
		bWi. Watermark inverted			
		s. Opt. "SPECIMEN" (2, 7)	£375		

*62/6b **For well-centred, lightly used +125%**

18   **19**

20 Emblems wmk (normal)   **20a** Watermark error, three roses and shamrock   **20b** Watermark error, three roses and thistle

(d) Wmk Emblems, W **20**.

			Un	Used*	Used on cover
69	**18**	6d. deep lilac (21.10.56)	£1500	£125	
		s. Opt. "SPECIMEN" (2, 4, 7, 8)	£500		
70		6d. pale lilac	£1100	£100	£190
		a. Azure paper	£6750	£775	
		b. Thick paper	£3000	£300	
		c. Error. Watermark W **20a**			
		Wi. Watermark inverted	—	£275	
		Wj. Watermark reversed			
		Wk. Watermark inverted and reversed			
71	**19**	1s. deep green (1.11.56)	£4750	£425	
		s. Opt. "SPECIMEN" (2, 4, 7)	£800		
72		1s. green	£2500	£260	£350
73		1s. pale green	£2500	£260	
		a. Azure paper	—	£1800	

		b. Thick paper	—	£300	
		c. Imperf	—	†	—
		Wi. Watermark inverted	—	£500	
		Wj. Watermark reversed	—	£1100	
		Wk. Watermark inverted and reversed			

*69/73b **For well-centred, lightly used +125%**

21   **22**

23   **24**   **25** Plate 2

A. White dots added   B. Hair lines

1862–64. *A small uncoloured letter in each corner, the 4d. wmk Large Garter, W* **17**, *the others Emblems, W* **20**.

			Un	Used*	Used on cover
75	**21**	3d. deep carmine-rose (Plate 2) (1.5.62)	£4000	£425	
		s. Opt. "SPECIMEN" (2, 5, 6, 8)	£400		
76		3d. bright carmine-rose	£2000	£250	£450
		a. Error. Watermark W **20b** (stamp TF)		£8000	
		Wi. Watermark inverted	—	£750	
77		3d. pale carmine-rose	£2000	£250	
		b. Thick paper	£2800	£350	
		Wj. Watermark reversed			
78		3d. rose (with white dots, Type A, Plate 3) (8.62)	£40000	£11000	
		a. Imperf (Plate 3)	£5500		
		s. Opt. "SPECIMEN" (2)	£1500		
79	**22**	4d. brt red (Plate 3) (15.1.62)	£1800	£120	
		s. Opt. "SPECIMEN" (2, 5, 6, 8)	£350		
80		4d. pale red	£1500	£100	£225
		Wi. Watermark inverted	—	£250	
81		4d. brt red (Hair lines, Type B, Plate 3) (16.10.63)	£2000	£130	
		s. Opt. "SPECIMEN" (2)	£400		
82		4d. pale red (Hair lines, Type B, Plate 4)	£1800	£100	£225
		a. Imperf (Plate 4)	£3500		
		Wi. Watermark inverted	—	£275	
83	**23**	6d. dp lilac (Plate 3) (1.12.62)	£2100	£120	
		s. Opt. "SPECIMEN" (2, 5, 8)	£450		
84		6d. lilac	£1700	£100	£185
		a. Azure paper	—	£1300	
		b. Thick paper	—	£275	
		c. Error. Shamrock missing from wmk (stamp TF)			
		d. Error. Watermark W **20b** (stamp TF)	—	£7500	
		e. Hyphen omitted (KA)*			
		s. Opt. "SPECIMEN" (2, 5, 8)	£500		
		Wi. Watermark inverted	£6500	£325	
		Wj. Watermark reversed			
		Wk. Watermark inverted and reversed			
85		6d. lilac (Hair lines, Plate 4) (20.4.64)	£2400	£200	£300
		a. Imperf (watermark inverted)	£4000		
		Eb. Imperf and watermark upright	£4500		
		c. Thick paper	£3000	£240	
		d. Error. Watermark W **20b** (stamp TF)	£500		
		s. Opt. "SPECIMEN" (2)	£500		
		Wi. Watermark inverted	£6500	£375	
		Wj. Watermark reversed			
		Wk. Watermark inverted and reversed			
86	**24**	9d. bistre (Plate 2) (15.1.62)	£4750	£500	£875
		s. Opt. "SPECIMEN" (2, 6)	£600		

STANLEY GIBBONS
GREAT BRITAIN SPECIALIST DEPARTMENT

We invite collectors and specialists to have access to one of the finest selections of GB stock in the world by registering to receive our renowned free monthly colour brochure of between 500-550 specialist items from across the whole GB collecting spectrum, from pre-stamp postal history through to modern QE II errors.

Please contact Mark Facey on 020 7557 4424 or Michael Barrell on 020 7557 4448 or email mfacey@stanleygibbons.co.uk or mbarrell@stanleygibbons.co.uk to register.

Stanley Gibbons Limited, 399 Strand, London WC2R 0LX
Tel: 020 7836 8444   Fax: 020 7836 7342
To view all our stock 24 hours a day visit www.stanleygibbons.com

	Wi. Watermark inverted	£8750	£600
	Wj. Watermark reversed	—	£700
	Wk. Watermark inverted and reversed	£3500	£375
87	9d. straw	£3500	£375
	a. On azure paper		
	b. Thick paper	£5000	£450
	c. Error. Watermark W **20b** (stamp TF)	†	—
88	9d. bistre (Hair lines, Plate 3) (5.62)	£28000	£10000
89 **25**	1s. dp green (Plate No. 1 Plate 2) (1.12.62)	£3800	£375
90	1s. green (Plate No. 1 Plate 2)	£2500	£225	£350
	a. "K" in lower left corner in white circle (stamp KD)	£15000	£1700
	ab. "K" normal (stamp KD)	—	£2000
	b. On azure paper		
	c. Error. Watermark W **20b** (stamp TF)	—	£300
	d. Thick paper	—	£300
	da. Thick paper, "K" in circle as No. 90a	—	£3000
	s. Opt. "SPECIMEN" (2, 5, 8)	£450	
	Wi. Watermark inverted	—	£325
	Wj. Watermark reversed		
	Wk. Watermark inverted and reversed	—	£325
91	1s. deep green (Plate No. 2 = Plate 3)	£32000	
	a. Imperf	£5750	
	s. Opt. "SPECIMEN" (2)	£3500	
	aWi. Watermark inverted	£5750	

*75/91 For well-centred, lightly used +125%

The 3d. as Type **21**, but with network background in the spandrels, was never issued. Opt. "SPECIMEN" price £800.

The plates of this issue may be distinguished as follows:

3d.	Plate 2	No white dots.
	Plate 3	White dots as illustration A.
4d.	Plate 3	No hair lines. Roman I next to lower corner letters.
	Plate 4	Hair lines in corners. (Illustration B.). Roman II.
6d.	Plate 3	No hair lines.
	Plate 4	Hair lines in corners.
9d.	Plate 2	No hair lines.
	Plate 3	Hair lines in corners. Beware of faked lines.
1s.	Plate 2	Numbered 1 on stamps
	Plate 3	Numbered 2 on stamps & with hair lines.

*One used example on piece has been recorded, cancelled by a Glasgow Duplex postmark dated 06.1.1863.

The 9d. on azure paper (No. 87a) is very rare, only one confirmed example being known.

The variety "K" in circle, No. 90a, is believed to be due to a damaged letter having been cut out and replaced. It is probable that the punch was driven in too deeply, causing the flange to penetrate the surface, producing an indentation showing as an uncoloured circle.

The watermark variety "three roses and a shamrock" illustrated in W **20a** was evidently due to the substitution of an extra rose for the thistle in a faulty watermark bit. It is found on stamp TA of Plate 4 of the 3d., Plates 1 (No. 70c), 3, 5 and 6 of the 6d., Plate 4 of the 9d. and Plate 4 of the 1s.

Similar problems occurred on stamp TF of the 6d. and 9d. Here the shamrock emblem became detached and a used example of the 6d. (No. 84) is known showing it omitted. It was replaced by a third rose (W **20b**) and this variety exists on the 6d. (Nos. 84/5 and 97) and 9d. (Nos. 87 and 98).

1865–67. *Large uncoloured corner letters. Wmk Large Garter (4d.); others Emblems.*

			Un	Used*	Used on cover
92	**26**	3d. rose (Plate 4) (1.3.65)	£1900	£200	£350
		a. Error. Watermark W **20a**	£4250	£900	
		b. Thick paper	£3000	£200	
		s. Opt. "SPECIMEN" (2)	£3750		
		Wi. Watermark inverted	—	£375	
		Wj. Watermark reversed			
		Wk. Watermark inverted and reversed			
93	**27**	4d. dull vermilion (4.7.65)	£525	85·00	
		s. Opt. "SPECIMEN" (pl. 14) (8)	£300		
94		4d. vermilion	£450	60·00	£125
		a. Imperf (Plates 11, 12)	£5000		
		Wi. Watermark inverted	£475	60·00	
		Plate			
		7 (1865)	£600	£110	
		8 (1866)	£500	65·00	
		9 (1867)	£500	65·00	
		10 (1868)	£700	£140	
		11 (1869)	£500	65·00	
		12 (1870)	£475	60·00	
		13 (1872)	£550	60·00	
		14 (1873)	£600	90·00	
96	**28**	6d. dp lilac (with hyphen)(7.3.65)	£1500	£175	
		s. Opt. "SPECIMEN" (pl. 5) (2)	£4000		
97		6d. lilac (with hyphen)	£900	£100	£175
		a. Thick paper	£1000	£110	
		b. Stamp doubly printed (Plate 6)	—	£12000	
		c. Error. Watermark W **20a** (Pl 5, 6) ... *from*	—	£1500	
		d. Error. Watermark W **20b** (Plate 5)			
		e. Imperf (Plate 5)			
		Wi. Watermark inverted	—	£180	
		Wj. Watermark reversed			
		Wk. Watermark inverted and reversed	†	—	
		Plate			
		5 (1865)	£900	£100	
		6 (1867)	£3000	£180	
98	**29**	9d. straw (Plate 4) (25.10.65)	£4250	£550	£1000
		a. Thick paper	£5000	£700	
		b. Error. Watermark W **20a**	—	£2500	
		c. Error. Watermark W **20b** (stamp TF)			
		s. Opt. "SPECIMEN" (2)	£800		
		Wi. Watermark inverted	—	£1400	
99	**30**	10d. red-brown (Plate 1) (11.11.67)	*	£45000	
101	**31**	1s. green (Plate 4) (19.1.65)	£2500	£225	£350
		a. Error. Watermark W **20a**	—	£1500	
		ab. Error. Watermark W **20b**			
		b. Thick paper	£2800	£300	
		c. Imperf between (vert pair)	—	£15000	
		s. Opt. "SPECIMEN" (2)	£500		
		Wi. Watermark inverted	—	£600	
		Wj. Imperf watermark inverted			

*92/101c For well-centred, lightly used +100%

From mid-1866 to about the end of 1871 4d. stamps of this issue appeared generally with watermark inverted.

Unused examples of No. 98 from Plate 5 exist, but this was never put to press and all evidence points to such stamps originating from a portion of the Imprimatur sheet which was perforated by De La Rue in 1887 for insertion in albums to be presented to members of the Stamp Committee (*Price £18000 un*).

The 10d. stamps, No. 99, were printed in error on paper watermarked "Emblems" instead of on "Spray of Rose".

26   **27**

28 (with hyphen)   **28a** (without hyphen)

32   **33** Spray of Rose

34

29   **30**   **31**

1867–80. *Wmk Spray of Rose.* W **33**.

			Un	Used*	Used on cover
102	**26**	3d. deep rose (12.7.67)	£800	90·00	
103		3d. rose	£450	60·00	£110
		a. Imperf (Plates 5, 6) ... *from*	£5000		
		s. Opt. "SPECIMEN" (pl. 5) (8)	£225		
		sa. Opt. "SPECIMEN" (pl. 6) (2, 8)	£250		
		sb. Opt. "SPECIMEN" (pl. 7) (2, 6)	£250		
		sc. Opt. "SPECIMEN" (pl. 8) (8)	£250		

			Un	Used*	Used on cover
		sd. Opt. "SPECIMEN" (pl. 10) (2, 8, 9)	£220		
		Wi. Watermark inverted	£2000	£200	
		Plate			
		4 (1867)	£1500	£250	
		5 (1868)	£450	60·00	
		6 (1870)	£475	60·00	
		7 (1871)	£550	65·00	
		8 (1872)	£525	60·00	
		9 (1872)	£525	65·00	
		10 (1873)	£775	£140	
104	28	6d. lilac (with hyphen) (Plate 6) (21.6.67)	£1500	90·00	£175
		a. Imperf		£5000	
		Wi. Watermark inverted	—	£250	
105		6d. dp lilac (with hyphen) (Plate 6)	£1500	90·00	
106		6d. purple (with hyphen) (Plate 6)	£1500	£125	
107		6d. brt violet (with hyphen) (Plate 6) (22.7.68)	£1500	£100	
108	28a	6d. dull violet (without hyphen) (Plate 8) (8.3.69)	£650	90·00	
		s. Opt. "SPECIMEN" (pl. 8) (1, 8)	£300		
		Wi. Watermark inverted	—	£250	
109		6d. mauve (without hyphen)	£550	90·00	£130
		a. Imperf (Plate Nos. 8 & 9)	£10000	£4500	
		s. Opt. "SPECIMEN" (pl. 9) (6, 8)	£300		
		Wi. Watermark inverted	—	£225	
		Plate			
		8 (1869, mauve)	£600	£125	
		9 (1870, mauve)	£550	85·00	
		10 (1869, mauve)	*	£30000	
110	29	9d. straw (Plate No. 4)(3.10.67)	£2000	£275	£425
		s. Opt. "SPECIMEN" (2, 8, 9, 10, 11)	£375		
		Wi. Watermark inverted	—	£600	
111		9d. pale straw (Plate No. 4)	£1900	£250	
		a. Imperf (Plate 4)	£10000		
112	30	10d. red-brown (1.7.67)	£2800	£325	£700
		s. Opt. "SPECIMEN" (2, 5, 6, 8, 9, 10, 11)	£400		
		Wi. Watermark inverted	—	£700	
113		10d. pale red-brown	£2800	£350	
114		10d. deep red-brown	£4000	£525	
		a. Imperf (Plate 1)	£10000		
		Plate			
		1 (1867)	£2800	£325	
		2 (1867)	£45000	£14000	
115	31	1s. deep green (13.7.67)	£1100	65·00	
117		1s. green	£650	40·00	85·00
		a. Imperf between (horiz pair) (Pl 7)			
		b. Imperf (Plate 4)	£8000	£5000	
		s. Opt. "SPECIMEN" (pl. 4) (1, 8, 9)	£300		
		sa. Opt. "SPECIMEN" (pl. 5) (2, 6, 8, 9)	£325		
		sb. Opt. "SPECIMEN" (pl. 6) (8, 9)	£325		
		sc. Opt. "SPECIMEN" (pl. 7) (9)	£325		
		Wi. Watermark inverted	£1700	£150	
		Plate			
		4 (1867)	£1200	70·00	
		5 (1871)	£650	40·00	
		6 (1871)	£1000	40·00	
		7 (1873)	£1200	70·00	
118	32	2s. dull blue (1.7.67)	£3250	£185	£700
		s. Opt. "SPECIMEN" (2, 5, 8, 9, 10, 11)	£450		
		Wi. Watermark inverted	—	£750	
119		2s. deep blue	£3750	£185	
		a. Imperf (Plate 1)	£15000		
120		2s. pale blue	£3750	£225	
		aa. Imperf (Plate 1)	£15000		
120a		2s. cobalt	£20000	£2500	
120b		2s. milky blue	£18000	£1700	
		Plate			
		1 (1867)	£3250	£185	
		3 (1868)	*	£12000	
121		2s. brown (Plate No. 1) (27.2.80)	£22000	£3500	
		a. Imperf	£25000		
		b. No watermark	†	—	
		s. Opt. "SPECIMEN" (9)	£3000		
		Wi. Watermark inverted	—	£4700	

*102/21 **For well-centred, lightly used +75%**

Examples of the 1s. from Plates 5 and 6 without watermark are postal forgeries used at the Stock Exchange Post Office in the early 1870s. (*Prices from £800*)

1872–73. Uncoloured letters in corners. *Wmk Spray, W* **33**.

			Un	Used*	Used on cover
122	34	6d. deep chestnut (Plate 11) (12.4.72)	£1100	£120	
		s. Opt. "SPECIMEN" (2, 6, 8)	£275		

			Un	Used*	Used on cover
122a		6d. chestnut (Plate 11) (22.5.72)	£675	55·00	£120
		Wi. Watermark inverted	—	£250	
122b		6d. pale chestnut (Plate 11) (1872)	£575	55·00	
123		6d. pale buff (19.10.72)	£800	£110	£250
		Wi. Watermark inverted	—	£300	
		Plate			
		11 (1872, pale buff)	£800	£110	
		12 (1872, pale buff)	£3000	£300	
124		6d. chestnut (Plate 12) (1872)	*	£3500	
124a		6d. pale chestnut (Plate 12) (1872)	*	£3250	
125		6d. grey (Plate No. 12) (24.4.73)	£1600	£240	£250
		a. Imperf	£10000		
		s. Opt. "SPECIMEN" (6, 8, 9)	£325		
		Wi. Watermark inverted	£4500	£550	

*122/5 **For well-centred, lightly used +50%**

35

36

37

38

39 Maltese Cross

40 Large Anchor

1867–83. Uncoloured letters in corners.

(a) Wmk Maltese Cross, W **39**. *P* 15½ × 15.

			Un	Used*
126	35	5s. rose (1.7.67)	£8250	£600
		s. Opt. "SPECIMEN" (2, 6)	£850	
127		5s. pale rose	£8250	£600
		a. Imperf (Plate 1)	£15000	
		s. Opt. "SPECIMEN" (pl. 2) (8, 9)	£1200	
		Plate		
		1 (1867)	£8250	£600
		2 (1874)	* £12500	£1200
128	36	10s. greenish grey (Plate 1) (26.9.78)	£50000	£2800
		s. Opt. "SPECIMEN" (8, 9)	£3800	
129	37	£1 brown-lilac (Plate 1) (26.9.78)	£80000	£4000
		s. Opt. "SPECIMEN" (9)	£5800	

(b) Wmk Large Anchor, W **40**. *P* 14.

(i) Blued paper

			Un	Used*
130	35	5s. rose (Plate 4) (25.11.82)	£35000	£4000
		s. Opt. "SPECIMEN" (9)	£4250	
		Wi. Watermark inverted	—	£15000
131	36	10s. grey-green (Plate 1) (2.83)	£125000	£4800
		s. Opt. "SPECIMEN" (9)	£8000	
132	37	£1 brown-lilac (Plate 1) (12.82)	£140000	£9000
		s. Opt. "SPECIMEN" (9)	£12000	

Stanley Gibbons
Great Britain Mail Order

Stanley Gibbons Mail Order Department provide the perfect support for those starting or furthering their collection, particularly for more modern issues. We produce regular brochures listing our available Great Britain, Channel Islands and Isle of Man material, as well as mailings for many Commonwealth countries.

Our friendly, personal service is built on the traditions of Stanley Gibbons and we are keen to help you fill your supplement pages. If you're looking for particular stamps, send your wants list to Mrs. Lesley Mourne at the address below or telephone us to discuss your needs.

Contact us today for any of the following:

- Mint and used Great Britain stamps
- Presentation Packs
- First Day Covers
- Regional Issues
- Postage Dues
- Booklets
- Smilers Sheets
- Channel Islands and Isle of Man issues
- Commonwealth stamps

For your free copy of the latest Great Britain Mail Order List call us on 020 7557 4460

Did you know...
we also offer a mail order service for Commonwealth material.
Contact us on the details below for further information.

Est 1856
STANLEY GIBBONS

Stanley Gibbons Mail Order
399 Strand, London, WC2R 0LX
Tel: +44 (0)20 7557 4460 | Fax: +44 (0)20 7557 4499
Email: lmourne@stanleygibbons.co.uk
www.stanleygibbons.com

133	**38**	£5 orange (Plate 1) (21.3.82)	£65000	£13000
		s. Opt. "SPECIMEN" (9, 11)	£3400	

(ii) White paper.

134	**35**	5s. rose (Plate 4)	£30000	£3250
135	**36**	10s. greenish grey (Plate 1)	£140000	£4000
136	**37**	£1 brown-lilac (Plate 1)	£170000	£8000
		s. Opt. "SPECIMEN" (6, 9)	£11000	
137	**38**	£5 orange (Plate 1)	£12500	£4500
		s. Opt. "SPECIMEN" (9, 11, 16)	£4000	

*126/37 **For well-centred, lightly used +75%**

41   **42**   **43**

44   **45**   **46**

47 Small Anchor   **48** Orb

1873–80. *Large coloured letters in the corners.*

*(a) Wmk Small Anchor, W **47**.*

			Un	Used*	Used on cover
138	**41**	2½d. rosy mauve (*blued paper*) (1.7.75)	£750	£140	
		a. Imperf			
		s. Opt. "SPECIMEN" (pl. 1) (8)	£200		
		Wi. Watermark inverted	£2500	£300	
		Plate			
		1 (*blued paper*) (1875)	£750	£140	
		2 (*blued paper*) (1875)	£7500	£1500	
		3 (*blued paper*) (1875)	—	£5000	
139		2½d. rosy mauve (*white paper*)	£525	90·00	£160
		Wi. Watermark inverted	£2250	£200	
		Plate			
		1 (*white paper*) (1875)	£525	90·00	
		2 (*white paper*) (1875)	£525	90·00	
		3 (*white paper*) (1875)	£800	£130	

Error of Lettering L H—F L for L H—H L (*Plate* 2).

140	**41**	2½d. rosy mauve	£22000	£2250	

*(b) Wmk Orb, W **48**.*

141	**41**	2½d. rosy mauve (1.5.76)	£425	55·00	£100
		s. Opt. "SPECIMEN" (pl. 3) (10)	—		
		sa. Opt. "SPECIMEN" (pl. 5) (9)	£180		
		sb. Opt. "SPECIMEN" (pl. 6) (8, 9)	£180		
		sc. Opt. "SPECIMEN" (pl. 7) (9)	£180		
		sd. Opt. "SPECIMEN" (pl. 10) (9)	£180		
		se. Opt. "SPECIMEN" (pl. 16) (9)	£180		
		Wi. Watermark inverted	£1500	£125	
		Plate			
		3 (1876)	£1100	£125	
		4 (1876)	£425	55·00	
		5 (1876)	£425	55·00	
		6 (1876)	£425	55·00	
		7 (1877)	£425	55·00	
		8 (1877)	£425	55·00	
		9 (1877)	£425	55·00	
		10 (1878)	£475	70·00	
		11 (1878)	£425	55·00	
		12 (1878)	£425	55·00	
		13 (1878)	£425	55·00	
		14 (1879)	£425	55·00	
		15 (1879)	£425	55·00	
		16 (1879)	£425	55·00	
		17 (1880)	£1400	£275	
142	**41**	2½d. blue (5.2.80)	£475	45·00	80·00

		s. Opt. "SPECIMEN" (pl. 17) (9)	£140	
		Wi. Watermark inverted	£1750	£200
		Plate		
		17 (1880)	£475	60·00
		18 (1880)	£475	45·00
		19 (1880)	£475	45·00
		20 (1880)	£475	45·00

*(c) Wmk Spray, W **33**.*

143	**42**	3d. rose (5.7.73)	£350	50·00	70·00
		s. Opt. "SPECIMEN" (pl. 14) (2)	£250		
		sa. Opt. "SPECIMEN" (pl. 17) (8, 9)	£220		
		sb. Opt. "SPECIMEN" (pl. 18) (8, 9, 10)	£220		
		sc. Opt. "SPECIMEN" (pl. 19) (9, 10)	£220		
		Wi. Watermark inverted	£1500	£250	
144		3d. pale rose	£400	50·00	
		Plate			
		11 (1873)	£350	50·00	
		12 (1873)	£400	50·00	
		14 (1874)	£425	50·00	
		15 (1874)	£350	50·00	
		16 (1875)	£350	50·00	
		17 (1875)	£400	50·00	
		18 (1875)	£400	50·00	
		19 (1875)	£350	50·00	
		20 (1879)	£650	£110	
145	**43**	6d. pale buff (Plate 13) (15.3.73)	*	£20000	
146		6d. deep grey (20.3.74)	£600	£100	£140
		s. Opt. "SPECIMEN" (pl. 14) (8, 10)	£275		
		sa. Opt. "SPECIMEN" (pl. 15) (8, 9)	£275		
		sb. Opt. "SPECIMEN" (pl. 16) (9)	£275		
147		6d. grey	£400	70·00	
		Wi. Watermark inverted	£1500	£225	
		13 (1874)	£400	70·00	
		14 (1875)	£400	70·00	
		15 (1876)	£400	70·00	
		16 (1878)	£400	70·00	
		17 (1880)	£750	£150	
148	**44**	1s. deep green (1.9.73)	£900	£160	
150		1s. green	£500	£120	£190
		s. Opt. "SPECIMEN" (pl. 11) (8)	£275		
		sa. Opt. "SPECIMEN" (pl. 12) (8, 9, 10)	£275		
		sb. Opt. "SPECIMEN" (pl. 13) (9)	£275		
		Wi. Watermark inverted	£2000	£225	
		Plate			
		8 (1873)	£650	£140	
		9 (1874)	£650	£140	
		10 (1874)	£600	£160	
		11 (1875)	£600	£140	
		12 (1875)	£500	£120	
		13 (1876)	£500	£120	
		14 (—)*	*	£35000	
151		1s. orange-brown (Plate 13) (14.10.80)	£4000	£600	£1800
		s. Opt. "SPECIMEN" (9)	£475		
		Wi. Watermark inverted	£10000	£1300	

*(d) Wmk Large Garter, W **17**.*

152	**45**	4d. vermilion (1.3.76)	£2400	£450	£900
		s. Opt. "SPECIMEN" (pl. 15) (9)	£350		
		Wi. Watermark inverted	—	£850	
		Plate			
		15 (1876)	£2400	£450	
		16 (1877)	*	£30000	
153		4d. sage-green (12.3.77)	£1000	£275	£500
		s. Opt. "SPECIMEN" (pl. 15) (9)	£300		
		sa. Opt. "SPECIMEN" (pl. 16) (9)	£300		
		Wi. Watermark inverted	—	£500	
		Plate			
		15 (1877)	£1100	£300	
		16 (1877)	£1000	£275	
		17 (1877)	*	£17500	
154		4d. grey-brown (Plate 17) (15.8.80)	£2400	£500	£1600
		a. Imperf	£12000		
		s. Opt. "SPECIMEN" (9)	£300		
		Wi. Watermark inverted	—	£950	
156	**46**	8d. orange (Plate 1) (11.9.76)	£1500	£325	£550
		s. Opt. "SPECIMEN" (8, 9)	£300		
		Wi. Watermark inverted	—	£700	

*138/56 **For well-centred, lightly used +100%**

1876 (July). *Prepared for use but not issued.*

156a	**46**	8d. purple-brown (Plate 1)	£8500	
		s. Opt. "SPECIMEN" (8, 9)	£4750	

KEY TO SURFACE-PRINTED ISSUES
1880–1900

S.G. Nos.	Description	Date of Issue
164/5	½d. green	14.10.80
187	½d. slate-blue	1.4.84
197/e	½d. vermilion	1.1.87
213	½d. blue-green	17.4.1900
166	1d. Venetian red	1.1.80
170/1	1d. lilac, Die I	12.7.81
172/4	1d. lilac, Die II	12.12.81
167	1½d. Venetian red	14.10.80
188	1½d. lilac	1.4.84
198	1½d. purple and green	1.1.87
168/a	2d. rose	8.12.80
189	2d. lilac	1.4.84
199/200	2d. green and red	1.1.87
190	2½d. lilac	1.4.84
201	2½d. purple on blue paper	1.1.87
191	3d. lilac	1.4.84
202/4	3d. purple on yellow paper	1.1.87
192	4d. dull green	1.4.84
205/a	4d. green and brown	1.1.87
206	4½d. green and carmine	15.9.92
169	5d. indigo	15.3.81
193	5d. dull green	1.4.84
207	5d. purple and blue, Die I	1.1.87
207a	5d. purple and blue, Die II	1888
194	6d. dull green	1.4.84
208/a	6d. purple on rose-red paper	1.1.87
195	9d. dull green	1.8.83
209	9d. purple and blue	1.1.87
210/b	10d. purple and carmine	24.2.90
196	1s. dull green	1.4.84
211	1s. green	1.1.87
214	1s. green and carmine	11.7.1900
175	2s.6d. lilac on blued paper	2.7.83
178/9	2s.6d. lilac	1884
176	5s. rose on blued paper	1.4.84
180/1	5s. rose	1884
177/a	10s. ultramarine on blued paper	1.4.84
182/3a	10s. ultramarine	1884
185	£1 brown-lilac, wmk Crowns	1.4.84
186	£1 brown-lilac, wmk Orbs	6.1.88
212	£1 green	28.1.91

Note that the £5 value used with the above series is listed as Nos. 133 and 137.

49 Imperial Crown   **(50)**

1880–83. *Wmk Imperial Crown,* W **49**.

			Un	Used*	Used on cover
157	**41**	2½d. blue (23.3.81)	£350	30·00	45·00
		s. Opt. "SPECIMEN" (pl. 23) (9)	£160		
		Wi. Watermark inverted	—	£350	
		Plate			
		21 (1881)	£400	40·00	
		22 (1881)	£350	40·00	
		23 (1881)	£350	30·00	
158	**42**	3d. rose (3.81)	£400	85·00	£140
		s. Opt. "SPECIMEN" (pl. 21) (9)	£220		
		Wi. Watermark inverted	—	£400	
		Plate			
		20 (1881)	£775	£150	
		21 (1881)	£400	85·00	
159	**50**	3d. on 3d lilac (C.) (Plate 21) (1.1.83)	£500	£140	£350
		s. Opt. "SPECIMEN" (9)	£275		
		Wi. Watermark inverted			
160	**45**	4d. grey-brown (8.12.80)	£350	65·00	£140
		s. Opt. "SPECIMEN" (pl. 17) (9)	£220		
		sa. Opt. "SPECIMEN" (pl. 18) (9)	£240		
		Wi. Watermark inverted	—	£650	
		Plate			
		17 (1880)	£350	65·00	
		18 (1882)	£350	65·00	
161	**43**	6d. grey (1.1.81)	£350	70·00	£120
		s. Opt. "SPECIMEN" (pl. 18) (9)	£250		
		Wi. Watermark inverted	—	£600	

		Plate			
		17 (1881)	£400	70·00	
		18 (1882)	£350	70·00	
162	**50**	6d. on 6d. lilac (C.) (Plate 18) (1.1.83)	£550	£140	£350
		a. Slanting dots (various) *..from*	£1800	£375	
		b. Opt double	—	£10000	
		s. Opt. "SPECIMEN" (9)	£275		
		Wi. Watermark inverted	£2700	£700	
163	**44**	1s. orange-brown (24.5.81)	£550	£150	£450
		s. Opt. "SPECIMEN" (pl. 13) (9)	£275		
		sa. Opt. "SPECIMEN" (pl. 14) (9)	£275		
		Wi. Watermark inverted	£2750	£850	
		Plate			
		13 (1881)	£700	£150	
		14 (1881)	£550	£150	

157/63 **For well-centred, lightly used +75%*
The 1s. plate 14 (line perf 14) exists in purple but was not issued in this shade (*Price £15000 unused*). Examples were included in a few of the Souvenir Albums prepared for members of the "Stamp Committee of 1884".

52   **53**

54   **55**   **56**

1880–81. Wmk Imperial Crown, W **49**.

164	**52**	½d. deep green (14.10.80)	45·00	12·00	22·00
		a. Imperf	£4000		
		b. No watermark	£7750		
		s. Opt. "SPECIMEN" (9)	55·00		
		Wi. Watermark inverted	—	£550	
165		½d. pale green	45·00	18·00	
166	**53**	1d. Venetian red (1.1.80)	22·00	12·00	25·00
		a. Imperf	£4000		
		s. Opt. "SPECIMEN" (9)	90·00		
		Wi. Watermark inverted	—	£275	
167	**54**	1½d. Venetian red (14.10.80)	£200	45·00	£130
		s. Opt. "SPECIMEN" (9)	70·00		
		Wi. Watermark inverted	†		
168	**55**	2d. pale rose (8.12.80)	£275	90·00	£225
		s. Opt. "SPECIMEN" (9)	95·00		
		Wi. Watermark inverted	£2200	£700	
168a		2d. deep rose	£300	90·00	
169	**56**	5d. indigo (15.3.81)	£675	£110	£225
		a. Imperf	£6500	£4000	
		s. Opt. "SPECIMEN" (9, 12, 13) .	£140		
		Wi. Watermark inverted	—	£4500	

164/9 **For well-centred, lightly used +75%*
Two used examples of the 1d. value have been reported on the Orb (fiscal) watermark.

57   Die I   Die II

1881. Wmk Imperial Crown, W **49**.

		(a) 14 dots in each corner, Die I (12 July).			
170	**57**	1d. lilac	£200	30·00	50·00
		s. Opt. "SPECIMEN" (9)	60·00		
		Wi. Watermark inverted	—	£550	
171		1d. pale lilac	£200	30·00	
		(b) 16 dots in each corner, Die II (13 December).			
172	**57**	1d. lilac	2·50	2·00	3·00
		s. Opt. "SPECIMEN" (9, 12)	50·00		
		Wi. Watermark inverted	40·00	25·00	
172a		1d. bluish lilac	£475	£150	
173		1d. deep purple	2·50	2·00	
		a. Printed both sides	£800	†	
		b. Frame broken at bottom	£850	£300	
		c. Printed on gummed side	£800	†	
		d. Imperf three sides (pair)	£7500	†	

			e. Printed both sides but impression on back inverted	£850	†

e. Printed both sides but
impression on back
inverted...................... £850 †
f. No watermark.................. £7500 †
g. Blued paper................. £4500
174 1d. mauve.................... 2·50 1·50
a. Imperf (pair)............... £6000
*170/4 **For well-centred, lightly used +50%**
1d. stamps with the words "PEARS SOAP" printed on the back in orange, blue or mauve *price from £550, unused.*
The variety "frame broken at bottom" (No. 173b) shows a white space just inside the bottom frame-line from between the "N" and "E" of "ONE" to below the first "N" of "PENNY", breaking the pearls and cutting into the lower part of the oval below "PEN".

58   59

60

1883–84. *Coloured letters in the corners.* Wmk Large Anchor, W **40.**
(a) Blued paper.

			Un	Used*
175	58	2s.6d. lilac (2.7.83)...................	£6000	£1300
		s. Opt. "SPECIMEN" (9, 11, 12, 13)........	£500	
176	59	5s. rose (1.4.84)....................	£18000	£3750
		s. Opt. "SPECIMEN" (9, 11)...........	£1400	
177	60	10s. ultramarine (1.4.84)...........	£38000	£8000
		s. Opt. "SPECIMEN" (9).............	£2500	
177a		10s. cobalt (5.84).................	£60000	£13000
		s. Opt. "SPECIMEN" (9).............	£3800	

(b) White paper.

178	58	2s.6d. lilac...................	£500	£140
179		2s.6d. deep lilac.................	£700	£200
		a. On blued paper.................	£8500	£3500
		Wi. Watermark inverted...........	—	£7000
180	59	5s. rose...................	£950	£200
		Wi. Watermark inverted...........	†	£9000
181		5s. crimson.................	£850	£200
		s. Opt. "SPECIMEN" (9, 11, 12, 13).....	£375	
182	60	10s. cobalt.................	£37000	£7500
		s. Opt. "SPECIMEN" (9)...........	£2700	
183		10s. ultramarine.............	£2000	£475
		s. Opt. "SPECIMEN" (9, 11, 13).....	£400	
183a		10s. pale ultramarine............	£2250	£475

*175/83a **For well-centred, lightly used +50%**
For No. 180 perf 12 see second note below No. 196.

61

Broken frames, Plate 2

1884 (1 Apr). Wmk Three Imperial Crowns, W **49.**

185	61	£1 brown-lilac...................	£32000	£2750
		a. Frame broken................	£50000	£4000
		s. Opt. "SPECIMEN" (9, 11, 12).......	£2600	
		Wi. Watermark inverted............	—	£35000

1888 (Feb). Watermark Three Orbs, W **48.**

186	61	£1 brown-lilac................	£65000	£4000
		a. Frame broken............	£125000	£6500
		s. Opt. "SPECIMEN" (11).........		£6500

*185/6a **For well-centred, lightly used +50%**
The broken-frame varieties, Nos. 185a and 186a, are on Plate 2 stamps JC and TA, as illustrated. See also No. 212a.

62   63   64

65   66

1883 (1 Aug). (9d.) or **1884** (1 Apr) (others). Wmk Imperial Crown, W **49** (sideways on horiz designs).

187	52	½d. slate-blue................	25·00	8·00	15·00
		a. Imperf..................	£3500		
		s. Opt. "SPECIMEN" (9).........	45·00		
		Wi. Watermark inverted.........	—	£250	
188	62	1½d. lilac.................	£110	38·00	£100
		a. Imperf.................	£3500		
		s. Opt. "SPECIMEN" (9)........	75·00		
		Wi. Watermark inverted........	—	£200	
189	63	2d. lilac................	£175	70·00	£125
		a. Imperf..............	£4000		
		s. Opt. "SPECIMEN" (9).......	75·00		
		Wi. Watermark sideways inverted.......	£75·00		
190	64	2½d. lilac.............	75·00	15·00	25·00
		a. Imperf.............	£4000		
		s. Opt. "SPECIMEN" (9).......	75·00		
		Wi. Watermark sideways inverted.......	£400		
191	65	3d. lilac.............	£225	90·00	£150
		a. Imperf.............	£4000		
		s. Opt. "SPECIMEN" (9).......	75·00		
		Wi. Watermark inverted.........	†	£850	
192	66	4d. dull green.........	£450	£185	£275
		a. Imperf.............	£4500		
		s. Opt. "SPECIMEN" (9).......	£160		
193	62	5d. dull green.........	£450	£185	£275
		a. Imperf.............	£5000		
		s. Opt. "SPECIMEN" (9).......	£160		
194	63	6d. dull green.........	£475	£200	£300
		a. Imperf.............	£5000		
		s. Opt. "SPECIMEN" (9).......	£190		
		Wi. Watermark sideways inverted.......	£750		
195	64	9d. dull green (1.8.83)......	£950	£400	£2000
		s. Opt. "SPECIMEN" (9).......	£350		
		Wi. Watermark sideways inverted.......	£1500	£650	
196	65	1s. dull green.........	£1100	£250	£475
		a. Imperf.............	£7500		
		s. Opt. "SPECIMEN" (9).......	£300		
		Wi. Watermark-inverted........			

*187/96 **For well-centred, lightly used +100%**
The above prices are for stamps in the true dull green colour. Stamps which have been soaked, causing the colour to run, are virtually worthless.
Stamps of the above set and No. 180 are also found perf 12; these are official perforations, but were never issued. A second variety of the 5d. is known with a line instead of a stop under the "d" in the value; this was never issued and is therefore only known unused (*Price* £30000).

71   72   73

74	75	76
77	78	79
80	81	82

Die I   Die II

Die I: Square dots to right of "d".
Die II: Thin vertical lines to right of "d".

1887 (1 Jan)–**92**. *"Jubilee" issue. New types. The bicoloured stamps have the value tablets, or the frames including the value tablets, in the second colour. Wmk Imperial Crown, W **49** (Three Crowns on £1).*

			Unmtd Mint	Mtd Mint	Used*
197	71	½d. vermilion	2·25	1·50	1·00
		a. Printed on gummed side...	£3750	£2500	
		b. Printed both sides			
		c. Doubly printed	—	£25000	
		d. Imperf	—	£3700	
		s. Opt. "SPECIMEN" (9, 10, 12)		32·00	
		Wi. Watermark inverted	65·00	40·00	40·00
197e		½d. orange-vermilion	2·25	1·50	1·00
198	72	1½d. dull purple & pale green	22·00	15·00	7·00
		a. Purple part of design double	—	—	£6500
		s. Opt. "SPECIMEN" (6, 9, 12)..		45·00	
		Wi. Watermark inverted	£1200	£750	£350
199	73	2d. green & scarlet	£475	£350	£225
200		2d. grey-green & carmine	40·00	28·00	12·00
		s. Opt. "SPECIMEN" (9, 10, 12)		50·00	
		Wi. Watermark inverted	£1300	£750	£375
201	74	2½d. purple/*blue*	35·00	22·00	3·00
		a. Printed on gummed side...	£10000	£7500	
		b. Imperf three sides	—	£7000	
		c. Imperf	—	£9000	
		Ed. Missing "d" in value	†	†	£6500
		s. Opt. "SPECIMEN" (6, 9, 12, 13)		60·00	
		Wi. Watermark inverted	£3000	£2200	£1000
202	75	3d. purple/*yellow*	35·00	22·00	3·25
		a. Imperf (wmk inverted)	—	£9500	
		s. Opt. "SPECIMEN" (6, 9, 12)..		45·00	
		Wi. Watermark inverted	—	—	£575
203		3d. deep purple/*yellow*	45·00	22·00	3·25
204		3d. purple/*orange* (1890)	£1250	£750	
205	76	4d. green & purple-brown	50·00	30·00	13·00
		aa. Imperf	—	£9500	
		s. Opt. "SPECIMEN" (6, 9, 10, 12)		45·00	
		Wi. Watermark inverted	£1200	£750	£450
205a		4d. green & dp brown	50·00	30·00	13·00
206	77	4½d. green & carmine (15.9.92) .	15·00	10·00	40·00
		s. Opt. "SPECIMEN" (9, 13)		£325	
		Wi. Watermark inverted			
206a		4½d. green & dp brt carmine	£800	£550	£450
207	78	5d. dull purple & blue (Die I)	£900	£600	£100
		s. Opt. "SPECIMEN" (9, 12)		90·00	
207a		5d. dull purple and blue (Die II) (1888)	50·00	35·00	11·00
		s. Opt. "SPECIMEN" (9, 12)		50·00	

208	79	6d. purple/*rose-red*	50·00	30·00	10·00
		s. Opt. "SPECIMEN" (9, 10, 12)		50·00	
		Wi. Watermark inverted	£8000	£6000	£1250
208a		6d. deep purple/*rose-red*	50·00	30·00	11·00
209	80	9d. dull purple & blue	90·00	60·00	40·00
		s. Opt. "SPECIMEN" (6, 9, 12)..		55·00	
		Wi. Watermark inverted	£8000	£6000	£2250
210	81	10d. dull purple and carmine (*shades*) (24.2.90)	70·00	45·00	38·00
		aa. Imperf	—	£15000	
		s. Opt. "SPECIMEN" (9, 13, 15)		80·00	
		Wi. Watermark inverted	£10000	£8000	£2750
210a		10d. dull purple and deep dull carmine	£600	£450	£225
210b		10d. dull purple & scarlet	£140	80·00	50·00
211	82	1s. dull green	£325	£200	60·00
		s. Opt. "SPECIMEN" (9, 10, 12)		55·00	
		Wi. Watermark inverted	£1800	£1100	£775
212	61	£1 green (28.1.91)	£6750	£3600	£750
		a. Frame broken	£15000	£8000	£1800
		s. Opt. "SPECIMEN" (9, 11, 13, 15, 16)		£950	
		Wi. Watermark inverted	—	£85000	£10000

*197/212a For well-centred, lightly used +50%
The broken-frame varieties, No. 212a, are on Plate 2 stamps JC or TA, as illustrated above No. 185.
½d. stamps with "PEARS SOAP" printed on the back in orange, blue or mauve, price from £525 each.
No used price is quoted for No. 204 as it is not possible to authenticate the paper colour on stamps in used condition.

1900. *Colours changed.* Wmk Imperial Crown, W **49**.

213	71	½d. blue-green (17.4)	2·25	1·75	2·00
		a. Printed on gummed side...	—	—	—
		b. Imperf	£8500	£6500	
		s. Opt. "SPECIMEN" (11, 15)		£550	
		Wi. Watermark inverted	65·00	40·00	40·00
214	82	1s. green & carmine (11.7)	85·00	50·00	£125
		s. Opt. "SPECIMEN" (15)		£800	
		Wi. Watermark inverted	£2250	£1500	£850
Set of 14			£800	£525	£325

*213/14 For well-centred, lightly used +50%
The ½d. No. 213, in bright blue, is a colour changeling caused by a constituent of the ink used for some months in 1900.

USED ON COVER PRICES					
No. 197	£6	No. 205	£35	No. 209	£200
No. 198	£22	No. 206	£75	No. 210	£225
No. 200	£24	No. 207	£175	No. 211	£125
No. 201	£6	No. 207a	£40	No. 213	£6
No. 202	£30	No. 208	£75	No. 214	£850

DEPARTMENTAL OFFICIALS

The following Official stamps were exclusively for the use of certain government departments. Until 1882 official mail used ordinary postage stamps purchased at post offices, the cash being refunded once a quarter. Later the government departments obtained Official stamps by requisition.

Official stamps were on sale to the public for a short time at Somerset House but they were not sold from post offices. The system of only supplying the Government departments with stamps was open to abuse so that all official stamps were withdrawn on 13 May 1904.

OVERPRINTS, PERFORATIONS, WATERMARKS. All official stamps were overprinted by Thomas De La Rue & Co. and are perf 14. Except for the 5s., and 10s. on Anchor, they are on Crown watermarked paper unless otherwise stated.

INLAND REVENUE

These stamps were used by revenue officials in the provinces, mail to and from Head Office passing without a stamp. The London Office used these stamps only for foreign mail.

I.R.   I. R.

OFFICIAL   OFFICIAL

(O **1**)   (O **2**)

Optd with Types O **1** (½d. to 1s.) or O **2** (others).

1882–1901. *Stamps of Queen Victoria.*

(a) Issues of 1880–81

			Un	*Used	Used on cover
O1		½d. dp green (1.11.82)	£110	40·00	80·00
		s. Opt. "SPECIMEN" (9)	£275		

O2	½d. pale green	70·00	28·00	
O3	1d. lilac (Die II) (1.10.82)	6·00	4·00	25·00
	a. Optd in blue-black	£200	75·00	
	b. "OFFICIAL" omitted	—	£8500	
	s. Opt. "SPECIMEN" (9, 15)	£160		
	Wi Watermark inverted	—	£1700	
O4	6d. grey (Plate 18) (3.11.82)	£450	£110	
	s. Opt. "SPECIMEN" (9, 15)	£275		

No. O3 with the lines of the overprint transposed is an essay.

(b) Issues of 1884–88

O5	½d. slate-blue (8.5.85)	70·00	24·00	£100
	s. Opt. "SPECIMEN" (9)	£275		
O6	2½d. lilac (12.3.85)	£400	£150	£1100
	s. Opt. "SPECIMEN" (9)	£275		
O7	1s. dull green (12.3.85)	£5500	£1500	
	s. Opt. "SPECIMEN" (9)	£1200		
O8	5s. rose (*blued paper*) (wmk Anchor) (12.3.85)	£17000	£6000	
	s. Opt. "SPECIMEN" (9, 11)	£2400		
O9	5s. rose (wmk Anchor) (3.90)	£7500	£2200	
	a. Raised stop after "R"	£7500	£2500	
	b. Optd in blue-black	£9000	£2500	
	s. Opt. "SPECIMEN" (9, 11, 13, 16)	£1400		
O9c	10s. cobalt (*blued paper*) (wmk Anchor) (12.3.85)	£35000	£8000	
	ca. Raised stop after "R"			
	cb. cobalt (white paper) (wmk Anchor)	£20000	£6500	
	cs. Opt. "SPECIMEN" (11)	£3750		
O9d	10s. ultramarine (*blued paper*) (wmk Anchor) (12.3.85)	£22000	£7000	
	ds. Opt. "SPECIMEN" (10)	£3250		
O10	10s. ultramarine (wmk Anchor) (3.90)	£10000	£3500	
	a. Raised stop after "R"	£11000	£4000	
	b. Optd in blue-black	£11000	£4000	
	s. Opt. "SPECIMEN" (9, 10, 11, 16)	£2200		
O11	£1 brown-lilac (wmk Crowns) (12.3.85)	£60000	£22000	
	a. Frame broken	£65000	—	
	b. Optd in blue-black	£160000		
	s. Opt. "SPECIMEN" (11)	£4750		
O12	£1 brown-lilac (wmk Orbs) (3.90)	£90000	£30000	
	a. Frame broken	£120000		
	s. Opt. "SPECIMEN" (9, 11)	£8500		

Nos. O3, O13, O15 and O16 may be found showing worn impressions of the overprints with thicker letters.

(c) Issues of 1887–92.

O13	½d. vermilion (15.5.88)	10·00	4·00	80·00
	a. Without "I.R."	£5500		
	b. Imperf	£4500		
	c. Opt double (imperf)	£6000		
	s. Opt. "SPECIMEN" (9, 15)	90·00		
O14	2½d. purple/*blue* (2.92)	£120	15·00	£325
	s. Opt. "SPECIMEN" (9, 13, 15)	90·00		
O15	1s. dull green (9.89)	£850	£250	£2800
	s. Opt. "SPECIMEN" (9, 15)	£220		
O16	£1 green (6.92)	£12000	£2250	
	a. No stop after "R"	—	£3500	
	b. Frame broken	£17500	£4500	
	s. Opt. "SPECIMEN" (9, 10, 15)	£2000		

(d) Issues of 1887 and 1900.

O17	½d. blue-green (4.01)	15·00	10·00	£250
	s. Opt. "SPECIMEN" (15)	£125		
O18	6d. purple/rose-red (1.7.01)	£325	90·00	
	s. Opt. "SPECIMEN" (15, 16)	£220		
O19	1s. green and carmine (12.01)	£3500	£1250	
	s. Opt. "SPECIMEN" (15)	£900		

*O1/19 For well-centred, lightly used +35%

OFFICE OF WORKS

These were issued to Head and Branch (local) offices in London and to Branch (local) offices at Birmingham, Bristol, Edinburgh, Glasgow, Leeds, Liverpool, Manchester and Southampton. The overprints on stamps of value 2d. and upwards were created later in 1902, the 2d. for registration fees and the rest for overseas mail.

O. W.

OFFICIAL
(O 3)

Optd with Type O 3

1896 (24 Mar)–**02**. Stamps of Queen Victoria.

		Un	*Used	Used on Cover
O31	½d. vermilion	£250	£110	£550

O32	½d. blue-green (2.02)	£350	£160	
	s. Opt. "SPECIMEN" (15)	£350		
O33	1d. lilac (Die II)	£400	£110	£600
	s. Opt. "SPECIMEN" (9, 15, 16)	£250		
O34	5d. dull purple & blue (II) (29.4.02)	£3000	£1000	
	s. Opt. "SPECIMEN" (16)	£850		
O35	10d. dull purple & carmine (28.5.02)	£5000	£1500	
	s. Opt. "SPECIMEN" (16)	£1800		

ARMY

Letters to and from the War Office in London passed without postage. The overprinted stamps were distributed to District and Station Paymasters nationwide, including Cox and Co., the Army Agents, who were paymasters to the Household Division.

ARMY

ARMY

OFFICIAL
(O 4)

OFFICIAL
(O 5)

1896 (1 Sept)–**01**. Stamps of Queen Victoria optd with Type O **4** (½d., 1d.) or O **5** (2½d., 6d.).

		Un	*Used	Used on cover
O41	½d. vermilion	5·00	2·50	45·00
	a. "OFFICIAl" (R.13/7)	£225	£100	
	b. Lines of opt transposed	£4000		
	s. Opt. "SPECIMEN" (9)	£180		
	Wi. Watermark inverted	£550	£225	
O42	½d. blue-green (6.00)	5·00	10·00	
	s. Opt. "SPECIMEN" (15)	£250		
	Wi. Watermark inverted	£950	£600	
O43	1d. lilac (Die II)	5·00	4·00	70·00
	a. "OFFICIAl" (R.13/7)	£180	£110	
	s. Opt. "SPECIMEN" (9)	£180		
O44	2½d. purple/*blue*	35·00	25·00	£500
	s. Opt. "SPECIMEN" (9)	£180		
O45	6d. purple/rose-red (20.9.01)	80·00	45·00	£1200
	s. Opt. "SPECIMEN" (15)	£325		

Nos. O41a and O43a occur in sheets overprinted by Forme 1.

GOVERNMENT PARCELS

These stamps were issued to all departments, including Head Office, for use on parcels weighing over 3 lb. Below this weight government parcels were sent by letter post to avoid the 55% of the postage paid from accruing to the railway companies, as laid down by parcel-post regulations. Most government parcels stamps suffered heavy postmarks in use.

GOVᵀ PARCEL8
(O 7)

Optd as Type O 7

1883 (1 Aug)–**86**. Stamps of Queen Victoria.

O61	1½d. lilac (1.5.86)	£325	70·00
	a. No dot under "T"	£650	£120
	b. Dot to left of "T"	£650	£120
	s. Opt. "SPECIMEN" (9)	£175	
O62	6d. dull green (1.5.86)	£2500	£1000
	s. Opt. "SPECIMEN" (9)	£250	
O63	9d. dull green	£2000	£800
	s. Opt. "SPECIMEN" (9)	£250	
O64	1s. orange-brown (watermark Crown, Pl 13)	£1300	£225
	a. No dot under "T"	£2000	£350
	b. Dot to left of "T"	£2000	£350
	s. Opt. "SPECIMEN" (9)	£275	
O64c	1s. orange-brown (Pl 14)	£2750	£400
	ca. No dot under "T"	£3250	£600
	cb. Dot to left of "T"		

1887–90. Stamps of Queen Victoria.

O65	1½d. dull purple & pale green (29.10.87)	£110	15·00
	a. No dot under "T"	£200	40·00
	b. Dot to right of "T"	£200	40·00
	c. Dot to left of "T"	£200	40·00
	s. Opt. "SPECIMEN" (9, 10, 13, 15)	£250	
O66	6d. purple/rose-red (19.12.87)	£200	50·00
	a. No dot under "T"	£300	75·00
	b. Dot to right of "T"	£350	95·00
	c. Dot to left of "T"	£350	95·00
	s. Opt. "SPECIMEN" (9, 13, 15)	£250	

O67	9d. dull purple & blue (21.8.88)		£300	75·00
	a. Optd in blue-black		£250	
	s. Opt "SPECIMEN" (9. 10. 13. 15)		£250	
	Wi. Watermark inverted			
O68	1s. dull green (25.3.90)		£550	£225
	a. No dot under "T"		£900	—
	b. Dot to right of "T"		£900	£350
	c. Dot to left of "T"		£950	£350
	d. Optd in blue-black			
	s. Opt. "SPECIMEN" (9, 13, 15)		£250	

1891–1900. *Stamps of Queen Victoria.*

O69	1d. lilac (Die II) (18.6.97)		75·00	18·00
	a. No dot under "T"		£120	45·00
	b. Dot to left of "T"		£120	45·00
	c. Opt inverted		£6500	£2800
	d. Ditto. Dot to left of "T"		£7500	£3200
	s. Opt. "SPECIMEN" (15)		£350	
	Wi. Watermark inverted		—	£375
O70	2d. grey-green & carmine (24.10.91)		£175	30·00
	a. No dot under "T"		£300	65·00
	b. Dot to left of "T"		£300	65·00
	s. Opt. "SPECIMEN" (9, 11, 13, 15)		£250	
O71	4½d. green & carmine (29.9.92)		£275	£200
	b. Dot to right of "T"			
	s. Opt. "SPECIMEN" (9, 13, 15)		£250	
	Wi. Watermark inverted		—	£7500
O72	1s. green & carmine (11.00)		£500	£200
	a. Opt inverted			† £13000
	s. Opt. "SPECIMEN" (9)		£300	

*O61/72 **For well-centred lightly used** +100%

BOARD OF EDUCATION

BOARD

OF

EDUCATION

(O **8**)
*Optd with Type O **8***

1902 (19 Feb). *Stamps of Queen Victoria.*

O81	5d. dull purple & blue (II)		£3700	£850
	s. Opt. "SPECIMEN" (15)		£950	
O82	1s. green & carmine		£9500	£4500
	s. Opt. "SPECIMEN" (15)		£2500	

POST OFFICE TELEGRAPH STAMPS

The telegraph system in the United Kingdom was originally operated by private companies, some of which issued their own stamps.

The Post Office took over the service in 1870, producing telegraph forms with impressed 1s. stationery dies and blank forms to which postage stamps were applied.

To assist in the separate accounting of revenues from the postal and telegraph services, special Post Office Telegraph stamps were issued from 1 February 1876 and from 1 May of that year the use of postage stamps to pre-pay telegraph services was prohibited.

Telegraph stamps were in use for little over five years, when it was decided to withdraw them and postage stamps were, once again, used for telegraph services.

PLATE NUMBERS Like the postage stamps of the period, all telegraph stamps showed their plate number within the design. These are listed under their respective values.

WATERMARKS To differentiate them from postage stamps, all telegraph stamps were in horizontal format and the watermarks appear sideways. Apart from the Shamrock watermark, WW**12**, all were as used for postage stamps of the period. For the purposes of this listing, watermark sideways refers to the top of the watermark device pointing to the right of the stamp *as viewed from the gummed side of the stamp*; watermark sideways inverted refers to the top of the device pointing to the left.

T **1**   T **2**   T **3**

T **4**   T **5**   T **6**

T **7**   T **8**

T **9**

T **10**

T **11**

T **12**

1876 (1 February). *Wmks as listed.* P 15×15½ (5s. T **11**, 10s., £5), P 14 (others).

T1	T **1**	½d. orange (W12) (Plate 5) (1.4.80)	15·00	25·00
		a. Imperf. (vert. pair)	£1800	
		s. Optd "SPECIMEN" (9)	45·00	
T2	T **2**	1d. red-brown (W12)	15·00	12·00
		Wi. Watermark inverted	£175	£125
		s. Optd "SPECIMEN" (9, 10)	45·00	
		Plate 1	15·00	15·00
		2	20·00	12·00
		3	20·00	15·00
T3	T **3**	3d. carmine (W33 sideways)	60·00	30·00
		Wi. Watermark sideways inverted	£225	£200
		s. Optd "SPECIMEN" (9, 10)	55·00	
		Plate 1	60·00	40·00
		2	60·00	30·00
		3	75·00	50·00
T4		3d. carmine (W49 sideways inverted) (8.8.81?)	£100	70·00
		Plate 3	£100	70·00
		4 (watermark sideways)	£325	£150
		5. (watermark sideways) (plate 1)	£325	£150
T5	T **4**	4d. sage-green (W17 sideways inverted) (Plate 1) (1.3.77)	£100	75·00
		a. Imperf (vert. pair)		
		wi. Watermark sideways	—	—
		s. Optd "SPECIMEN" (9,11)	55·00	
T6	T **5**	6d. grey (W33 sideways) (1.3.77)	70·00	35·00
		s. Optd "SPECIMEN" (9,11)	55·00	
		Plate 1	70·00	35·00
		2	£200	£100
T7		6d. grey (W49 sideways inverted) (1.81)	£140	80·00
		a. Imperf (vert. pair)		
T8	T **6**	1s. deep green (W33 sideways)	55·00	25·00
		Wi. Watermark sideways inverted	£350	
		Plate s. Optd "SPECIMEN" (9,10)	80·00	

	1		£110	35·00
	2		65·00	35·00
	3		65·00	35·00
	4		£140	30·00
	5		55·00	25·00
	6		55·00	25·00
	7		£250	30·00
	8		£110	30·00
	9		£110	30·00
	10		£140	40·00
T9		1s. brown-orange (W33 sideways) (10.80)	£140	80·00
	s.	Optd "SPECIMEN" (9)	85·00	
	Plate 10		£140	80·00
	12		£175	£100
T10		1s. brown-orange (W49 sideways) (2.81?)	£175	£100
	a.	Imperf (vert. pair)		
	Wi.	Watermark sideways inverted	£150	£100
	s.	Optd "SPECIMEN" (12)	£225	
	Plate 11		£175	£100
	12		£175	£100
T11	T 7	3s. slate-blue (W33 sideways) (Plate 1) (1.3.77)	90·00	35·00
	Wi.	Watermark sideways inverted	—	£350
	s.	Optd "SPECIMEN" (8, 9, 11)	95·00	
T12		3s. slate-blue (W49 sideways inverted) (Plate 1) (8.81)	£6000	£2800
T13	T 8	5s. rose (W39) (P15×15½)	£850	£100
	s.	Optd "SPECIMEN" (8, 9, 10)	£170	
	Plate 1		£850	£100
	2		£1600	£275
T14		5s. rose (W39) (P. 14) (Plate 2) (1880)	£6500	£400
T15		5s. rose (W40) (P. 14) (Plate 3) (5.81)	£6500	£800
	s.	Optd "SPECIMEN" (9, 12)	£750	
T16	T 9	10s. grey-green (W39) (Plate 1) (13.77)	£1200	£300
	s.	Optd "SPECIMEN" (8, 9, 11)	£300	
T17	T 10	£1 brown-lilac (W12 sideways ×3) (Plate 1) (1.3.77)	£6500	£700
	s.	Optd "SPECIMEN" (8, 9, 11)	£750	
T18	T 11	£5 orange (W12 sideways inverted ×3), (Plate 1) (1.3.77)	£16000	£2500
	s.	Optd "SPECIMEN" (8, 9, 11)	£2200	

King Edward VII

22 January 1901 – 6 May 1910

PRINTINGS. Distinguishing De La Rue printings from the provisional printings of the same values made by Harrison & Sons Ltd. or at Somerset House may prove difficult in some cases. For very full guidance Volume 2 of the Stanley Gibbons *Great Britain Specialised Catalogue* should prove helpful.

Note that stamps perforated 15×14 must be Harrison; the 2½d., 3d. and 4d. in this perforation are useful reference material, their shades and appearance in most cases matching the Harrison perf 14 printings.

Except for the 6d. value, all stamps on chalk-surfaced paper were printed by De La Rue.

Of the stamps on ordinary paper, the De La Rue impressions are usually clearer and of a higher finish than those of the other printers. The shades are markedly different except in some printings of the 4d., 6d. and 7d. and in the 5s., 10s. and £1.

Used stamps in good, clean, unrubbed condition and with dated postmarks can form the basis of a useful reference collection, the dates often assisting in the assignment to the printers.

PRICES. For Nos. 215/456a prices are quoted for unmounted mint, mounted mint and used stamps.

USED STAMPS. For well-centred, lightly used examples of King Edward VII stamps, add the following percentages to the used prices quoted below:

De La Rue printings (Nos. 215/66)—3d. values + 35%, 4d. orange + 100%, 6d. + 75%, 7d. and 1s. + 25%, all other values + 50%. *Harrison printings* (Nos. 267/86)—all values and perforations + 75%. *Somerset House printings* (Nos. 287/320)—1s. values + 25%, all other values + 50%.

83   84   85

86   87   88

89   90   91

92   93

94   95   96

97

(Des E. Fuchs)

1902 (1 Jan)–**10**. *Printed by De La Rue & Co.* Wmk Imperial Crown W **49** (½d. to 1s. Three Crowns on £1); Large Anchor, W **40** (2s.6d. to 10s.). Ordinary paper. P 14.

			Unmtd mint	Mtd mint	Used
215	83	½d. dull blue-green (1.1.02)	2·75	2·00	1·50
		s. Opt. "SPECIMEN" (15)		£300	
		Wi. Watermark inverted	£3750	£2750	£2000
216		½d. blue-green	2·75	2·00	1·50
217		½d. pale yellowish green (26.11.04)	2·75	2·00	1·50
218		½d. yellowish green	2·75	2·00	1·50
		a. Booklet pane. Five stamps plus St. Andrew's Cross label (6.06)	£850	£500	
		b. Doubly printed (bottom row on one pane) (Control H9)	£35000	£25000	
		s. Opt. "SPECIMEN" (17, 22)		£250	
		Wi. Watermark inverted	22·00	12·00	9·00
219		1d. scarlet (1.1.02)	2·75	2·00	1·50
		s. Opt. "SPECIMEN" (15, 16, 17, 22)		£250	
220		1d. brt scarlet	2·75	2·00	1·50
		a. Imperf (pair)	£30000	£28000	
		Wi. Watermark inverted	8·00	4·00	3·00
221	84	1½d. dull purple and green (21.3.02)	75·00	45·00	20·00
		s. Opt. "SPECIMEN" (15)		£250	
222		1½d. slate-purple & green	90·00	45·00	20·00
		Wi. Watermark inverted	—	—	£800
223		1½d. pale dull purple and green (*chalk-surfaced paper*) (7.05)	70·00	40·00	20·00
		s. Opt. "SPECIMEN" (17)		£650	
224		1½d. slate-purple & bluish green (*chalk-surfaced paper*)	70·00	40·00	18·00
225	85	2d. yellowish green and carmine-red (25.3.02)	95·00	45·00	20·00
		s. Opt. "SPECIMEN" (16)		£500	
		Wi. Watermark inverted	£24000		
226		2d. grey-green and carmine-red (1904)	£100	55·00	30·00
227		2d. pale grey-green and carmine-red (*chalk-surfaced paper*) (4.06)	75·00	40·00	28·00
		s. Opt. "SPECIMEN" (17)		£650	
		Wi. Watermark inverted			
228		2d. pale grey-green and scarlet (*chalk-surfaced paper*) (1909)	75·00	40·00	28·00
229		2d. dull blue-green and carmine (*chalk-surfaced paper*) (1907)	£180	90·00	50·00
230	86	2½d. ultramarine (1.1.02)	32·00	20·00	10·00
		s. Opt. "SPECIMEN" (15, 17)		£100	

231		2½d. pale ultramarine	32·00	20·00	10·00
		Wi. Watermark inverted	—	—	£3000
232	**87**	3d. dull purple/*orange-yellow* (20.3.02)	75·00	40·00	15·00
		s. Opt. "SPECIMEN" (15)		£300	
		Wi. Watermark inverted			
		a. Chalk-surfaced paper (3.06)	£400	£200	75·00
232b		3d. dp purple/*orange-yellow*	75·00	40·00	15·00
232c		3d. pale reddish purple/ *orange-yellow (chalk- surfaced paper)* (3.06)	£400	£200	70·00
		cs. Opt. "SPECIMEN" (17)		£650	
233		3d. dull reddish purple/ *yellow (lemon back) (chalk- surfaced paper)*	£400	£200	80·00
233b		3d. pale purple/*lemon (chalk- surfaced paper)*	80·00	40·00	18·00
234		3d. purple/*lemon (chalk- surfaced paper)*	80·00	40·00	18·00
235	**88**	4d. green and grey-brown (27.3.02)	£120	50·00	30·00
		s. Opt. "SPECIMEN" (16)		£400	
		Wi. Watermark inverted			
236		4d. green & chocolate-brown	£120	50·00	30·00
		a. Chalk-surfaced paper (1.06)	70·00	40·00	18·00
		Wi. watermark inverted			£8500
238		4d. deep green and chocolate- brown *(chalk-surfaced paper)* (1.06)	70·00	40·00	18·00
239		4d. brown-orange (1.11.09)	£350	£180	£140
		s. Opt. "SPECIMEN" (17)		£600	
240		4d. pale orange (12.09)	45·00	20·00	15·00
241		4d. orange-red (12.09)	45·00	20·00	15·00
242	**89**	5d. dull purple and ultramarine (14.5.02)	£135	60·00	20·00
		aas. Opt. "SPECIMEN" (16)		£300	
		a. Chalk-surfaced paper (5.06)	£110	50·00	20·00
244		5d. slate-purple and ultramarine *(chalk-surfaced paper)* (5.06)	£100	50·00	20·00
		as. Opt. "SPECIMEN" (17)		£650	
		Wi. Watermark inverted	£6800	£4250	
245	**83**	6d. pale dull purple (1.1.02)	75·00	40·00	20·00
		aas. Opt. "SPECIMEN" (15)		£350	
		a. Chalk-surfaced paper (1.06)	75·00	40·00	20·00
246		6d. slate-purple	75·00	40·00	20·00
248		6d. dull purple *(chalk-surfaced paper)* (1.06)	75·00	40·00	20·00
		s. Opt. "SPECIMEN" (17)		£650	
		Wi. Watermark inverted	—	—	£3000
249	**90**	7d. grey-black (4.5.10)	22·00	12·00	20·00
		s. Opt. "SPECIMEN" (17)		£650	
249a		7d. dp grey-black	£160	£110	£100
250	**91**	9d. dull purple and ultramarine (7.4.02)	£210	£100	60·00
		aas. Opt. "SPECIMEN" (16)		£350	
		a. Chalk-surfaced paper (6.05)	£240	£100	60·00
		aWi. Watermark inverted	—	—	£3000
251		9d. slate-purple & ultramarine	£210	£100	60·00
		a. Chalk-surfaced paper (6.05)	£210	£100	60·00
		as. Opt. "SPECIMEN" (17)		£650	
254	**92**	10d. dull purple and carmine (3.7.02)	£250	£100	60·00
		aas. Opt. "SPECIMEN" (16)		£450	
		a. No cross on crown	£750	£400	£250
		b. Chalk-surfaced paper (9.06)	£250	90·00	60·00
255		10d. slate-purple and carmine *(chalk-surfaced paper)* (9.06)	£250	90·00	60·00
		a. No cross on crown	£700	£425	£275
		as. Opt. "SPECIMEN" (17)		£650	
256		10d. dull purple and scarlet *(chalk-surfaced paper)* (9.10)	£240	95·00	60·00
		a. No cross on crown	£700	£425	£250
257	**93**	1s. dull green and carmine (24.3.02)	£190	80·00	35·00
		aas. Opt. "SPECIMEN" (16)		£325	
		a. Chalk-surfaced paper (9.05)	£190	80·00	35·00
		as. Opt. "SPECIMEN" (17)		£650	
259		1s. dull green & scarlet *(chalk- surfaced paper)* (9.10)	£195	80·00	50·00
260	**94**	2s.6d. lilac (5.4.02)	£500	£225	£140
		s. Opt. "SPECIMEN" (15, 16)		£350	
		Wi. Watermark inverted	£6000	£4250	£3000
261		2s.6d. pale dull purple *(chalk- surfaced paper)* (7.10.05)	£650	£275	£150
		s. Opt. "SPECIMEN" (17)		—	
		Wi. Watermark inverted	£9500	£6000	£3500
262		2s.6d. dull purple *(chalk-surfaced paper)*	£550	£250	£150
263	**95**	5s. brt carmine (5.4.02)	£800	£350	£200
		s. Opt. "SPECIMEN" (16, 17)		£350	
		Wi. Watermark inverted	—	£60000	£5000

264		5s. dp brt carmine	£850	£350	£200
265	**96**	10s. ultramarine (5.4.02)	£2000	£850	£475
		s. Opt. "SPECIMEN" (16, 17)		£450	
		Wi. Watermark inverted	—	—	£40000
266	**97**	£1 dull blue-green (16.6.02)	£3500	£2000	£750
		s. Opt. "SPECIMEN" (16, 17)		£1250	
		Wi. Watermark inverted	—	£75000	£20000

USED ON COVER PRICES					
No. 215	£2.50	No. 217	£2.50	No. 219	£2.50
No. 222	£30	No. 225	£32	No. 230	£22
No. 232	£30	No. 236a	£40	No. 240	£35
No. 242	£50	No. 245	£50	No. 249	£195
No. 250	£200	No. 254	£225	No. 257	£150
No. 260	£700	No. 263	£950		

97a

1910 (May). *Prepared for use, by De La Rue but not issued.* Wmk Imperial Crown, W **49**. P 14.

266a	**97**	2d. Tyrian plum		—	£100000
		s. Opt. "SPECIMEN" (17)		£55000	

One example of this stamp is known used, but it was never issued to the public.

1911. *Printed by Harrison & Sons. Ordinary paper.* Wmk Imperial Crown W **49**.

(a) P 14.

267	**83**	½d. dull yellow-green (3.5.11)	3·75	2·75	1·50
		s. Opt. "SPECIMEN" (22)		£300	
		Wi. Watermark inverted	45·00	15·00	15·00
268		½d. dull green	4·25	3·00	1·50
269		½d. deep dull green	17·00	11·00	6·00
270		½d. pale bluish green	75·00	40·00	40·00
		a. Booklet pane. Five stamps plus St. Andrew's Cross label	£1200	£750	
		b. Watermark sideways	†	†	£28000
		c. Imperf (pair)	—	£35000	†
271		½d. brt green (fine impression) (6.11)	£425	£275	£170
272		1d. rose-red (3.5.11)	15·00	8·00	12·00
		aas. Opt. "SPECIMEN" (22)		£300	
		Wi. Watermark inverted	35·00	20·00	30·00
		a. No wmk (brick-red)	65·00	50·00	90·00
273		1d. deep rose-red	15·00	8·00	12·00
274		1d. rose-carmine	85·00	55·00	30·00
275		1d. aniline pink (5.11)	£1200	£650	£350
275a		1d. aniline rose	£275	£180	£140
276	**86**	2½d. brt blue (10.7.11)	£160	65·00	35·00
		Wi. Watermark inverted	£1900	£1000	
277	**87**	3d. purple/*lemon* (12.9.11)	£200	90·00	£225
		s. Opt. "SPECIMEN" (22)		£240	
277a		3d. grey/*lemon*	£7000	£4500	
278	**88**	4d. brt orange (12.7.11)	£220	£100	50·00
		s. Opt. "SPECIMEN" (22)		£240	

(b) P 15×14.

279	**83**	½d. dull green (30.10.11)	65·00	40·00	45·00
279a		½d. deep dull green	75·00	40·00	45·00
280		1d. rose-red (4.10.11)	80·00	45·00	25·00
281		1d. rose-carmine	35·00	15·00	15·00
282		1d. pale rose-carmine	40·00	22·00	15·00
283	**86**	2½d. brt blue (14.10.11)	50·00	22·00	15·00
		s. Opt. "SPECIMEN" (22)		—	
284		2½d. dull blue	50·00	22·00	15·00
		Wi. Watermark inverted	—	—	£650
285	**87**	3d. purple/*lemon* (22.9.11)	70·00	45·00	15·00
285a		3d. grey/*lemon*	£4250	£3250	
286	**88**	4d. brt orange (11.11.11)	60·00	30·00	15·00
Set of 5			£250	£130	90·00

USED ON COVER PRICES					
No. 267	£4	No. 272	£18	No. 276	£50
No. 277	£550	No. 278	£175	No. 279	£100
No. 281	£30	No. 283	£35	No. 285	£40
No. 286	£65				

1911–13. *Printed at Somerset House. Ordinary paper.* Wmk as 1902–10. P 14.

287	**84**	1½d. reddish purple and bright green (13.7.11)	90·00	45·00	35·00
288		1½d. dull purple and green	60·00	30·00	28·00

289		1½d. slate-purple and green (9.12)	65·00	30·00	28·00
290	85	2d. dp dull green and red (8.8.11)	60·00	28·00	20·00
		s. Opt. "SPECIMEN" (22)		£275	
291		2d. dp dull green & carmine	60·00	28·00	20·00
292		2d. grey-green and bright carmine (carmine shows clearly on back) (11.3.12)...	55·00	28·00	25·00
293	89	5d. dull reddish purple and bright blue (7.8.11)	60·00	30·00	20·00
		s. Opt. "SPECIMEN" (2)		—	
294		5d. deep dull reddish purple and bright blue	55·00	30·00	20·00
295	83	6d. royal purple (31.10.11)	£110	50·00	85·00
296		6d. bright magenta (chalk-surfaced paper) (31.10.11)..	£17000	£12000	
		s. Opt. "SPECIMEN" (2)		£5500	
297		6d. dull purple	60·00	30·00	20·00
		s. Opt. "SPECIMEN" (2)		£320	
298		6d. reddish purple (11.11)	60·00	30·00	25·00
		a. No cross on crown (various shades)	£1500	£950	
299		6d. very deep reddish purple (11.11)	£120	55·00	40·00
300		6d. dark purple (3.12)	60·00	30·00	20·00
301		6d. dull purple "Dickinson" coated paper* (3.13)	£425	£250	£180
303		6d. deep plum (chalk-surfaced paper) (7.13)	60·00	30·00	70·00
		a. No cross on crown	£1850	£1200	
305	90	7d. slate-grey (1.8.12)	25·00	15·00	22·00
		s. Opt. "SPECIMEN" (26)		£320	
306	91	9d. reddish purple and light blue (24.7.11)	£180	80·00	75·00
		s. Opt. "SPECIMEN" (22)		£375	
306a		9d. dp dull reddish purple and dp brt blue (9.11)	£180	80·00	75·00
307		9d. dull reddish purple and blue (10.11)	£125	60·00	60·00
307a		9d. dp plum & blue (7.13)	£120	60·00	60·00
308		9d. slate-purple and cobalt-blue (3.12)	£300	£140	£110
309	92	10d. dull purple and scarlet (9.10.11)	£175	80·00	75·00
		s. Opt. "SPECIMEN" (22)		£320	
310		10d. dull reddish purple and aniline pink	£500	£275	£225
311		10d. dull reddish purple and carmine (5.12)	£140	80·00	60·00
		a. No cross on crown	£2750	£1750	
312	93	1s. dark green and scarlet (13.7.11)	£240	£120	60·00
		s. Opt. "SPECIMEN" (22, 23, 26)		£320	
313		1s. deep green and scarlet (9.10.11)	£175	80·00	40·00
		Wi. Wmk inverted	£225	£120	†
314		1s. green & carmine (15.4.12) .	£135	55·00	35·00
315	94	2s.6d. dull greyish purple (15.9.11)	£1500	£850	£450
		s. Opt. "SPECIMEN" (22)		£350	
316		2s.6d. dull reddish purple	£600	£275	£180
		Wi. Watermark inverted	†	†	—
317		2s.6d. dark purple	£650	£300	£190
318	95	5s. carmine (29.2.12)	£850	£400	£200
		s. Opt. "SPECIMEN" (26)		—	
319	96	10s. blue (14.1.12)	£2100	£1000	£600
320	97	£1 deep green (3.9.11)	£3000	£2000	£750
		s. Opt. "SPECIMEN" (22)		£2000	

*No. 301 was on an experimental coated paper which does not respond to the silver test.

USED ON COVER PRICES

No. 288	£50	No. 290	£50	No. 293	£65
No. 297	£85	No. 305	£195	No. 307	£190
No. 311	£225	No. 314	£160	No. 316	£950
No. 318	£950				

DEPARTMENTAL OFFICIALS

INLAND REVENUE

These stamps were used by revenue officials in the provinces, mail to and from Head Office passing without a stamp. The London Office used these stamps only for foreign mail.

1902–04. *Stamps of King Edward VII optd with type O1 or O2. Ordinary paper.*

			Un	Used	Used on cover
O20		½d. blue-green (4.2.02)	30·00	3·25	£120

		s. Opt. "SPECIMEN" (15)	£350		
O21		1d. scarlet (4.2.02)	20·00	2·25	80·00
		s. Opt. "SPECIMEN" (15)	£350		
O22		2½d. ultramarine (19.2.02)	£900	£250	
		s. Opt. "SPECIMEN" (15, 16)	£475		
O23		6d. pale dull purple (14.3.04)	£375000	£170000	
		s. Opt. "SPECIMEN" (16)	£40000		
O24		1s. dull green & carmine (29.4.02)	£3500	£700	
		s. Opt. "SPECIMEN" (16)	£1000		
O25		5s. brt carmine (29.4.02)	£30000	£9000	
		a. Raised stop after "R"	£35000	£10000	
		s. Opt. "SPECIMEN" (16)	£7000		
O26		10s. ultramarine (29.4.02)	£95000	£40000	
		a. Raised stop after "R"	£120000	£45000	
		s. Opt. "SPECIMEN" (16)	£19000		
O27		£1 blue-green (29.4.02)	£60000	£24000	
		s. Opt. "SPECIMEN" (16)	£13500		

OFFICE OF WORKS

These were issued to Head and Branch (local) offices in London and to Branch (local) offices at Birmingham, Bristol, Edinburgh, Glasgow, Leeds, Liverpool, Manchester and Southampton. The overprints on stamps of value 2d. and upwards were created later in 1902, the 2d. for registration fees and the rest for overseas mail.

1902 (11 Feb)–03. *Stamps of King Edward VII optd with type O3. Ordinary paper.*

O36		½d. blue-green (2.02)	£550	£160	£1750
		s. Opt. "SPECIMEN" (15)	£350		
O37		1d. scarlet	£550	£160	£400
		s. Opt. "SPECIMEN" (15)	£350		
O38		2d. yellowish green & carmine-red (27.4.02)	£1900	£400	£3000
		s. Opt. "SPECIMEN" (16)	£700		
O39		2½d. ultramarine (29.4.02)	£3250	£600	£4000
		s. Opt. "SPECIMEN" (16)	£800		
O40		10d. dull purple & carmine (28.5.03) .	£35000	£6750	
		s. Opt. "SPECIMEN" (16)	£7250		

*O31/40 **For well-centred, lightly used** +25%

ARMY

ARMY

OFFICIAL

(O 6)

1902–03. *Stamps of King Edward VII optd with Type O 4 (Nos. O48/50) or Type O 6 (O52). Ordinary paper.*

O48		½d. blue-green (11.2.02)	5·50	2·25	£100
		s. Opt. "SPECIMEN" (15)	£300		
O49		1d. scarlet (11.2.02)	5·50	2·25	£100
		a. "ARMY" omitted	†	—	
		s. Opt. "SPECIMEN" (15)	£300		
O50		6d. pale dull purple (23.8.02)	£160	75·00	
		s. Opt. "SPECIMEN" (16)	£375		
O52		6d. pale dull purple (12.03)	£3000	£1500	

GOVERNMENT PARCELS

1902. *Stamps of King Edward VII optd with type O7. Ordinary paper.*

O74		1d. scarlet (30.10.02)	32·00	13·00	
		s. Opt. "SPECIMEN" (16)	£250		
O75		2d. yellowish green & carmine-red (29.4.02)	£150	38·00	
		s. Opt. "SPECIMEN" (16)	£250		
O76		6d. pale dull purple (19.2.02)	£250	38·00	
		a. Opt double, one albino	£25000		
		s. Opt. "SPECIMEN" (16)	£250		
O77		9d. dull purple & ultramarine (28.8.02)	£600	£160	
		s. Opt. "SPECIMEN" (16)	£425		
O78		1s. dull green & carmine (17.12.02)	£1300	£275	
		s. Opt. "SPECIMEN" (16)	£475		

The "no dot under T" variety occured on R.12/3 and 20/2. The "dot to left of T" comes four times in the sheet on R.2/7, 6/7, 7/9 and 12/9. The best example of the "dot to right of T" is on R.20/1. All three varieties were corrected around 1897.

BOARD OF EDUCATION

1902 (19 Feb)–04. *Stamps of King Edward VII optd with type O8. Ordinary paper.*

			Un	*Used	Used on cover
O83		½d. blue-green	£160	38·00	£375
		s. Opt. "SPECIMEN" (15)	£300		

O84	1d. scarlet	£160	38·00	£400
	s. Opt. "SPECIMEN" (15)	£300		
O85	2½d. ultramarine	£4500	£400	
	s. Opt. "SPECIMEN" (15)	£950		
O86	5d. dull purple & ultramarine			
	(6.2.04)	£27000	£9500	
	s. Opt. "SPECIMEN" (16)	£5000		
O87	1s. dull green & carmine (23.12.02)	£140000		
	s. Opt. "SPECIMEN" (16)	£28000		

ROYAL HOUSEHOLD

R.H.

OFFICIAL
(O **9**)

1902. *Stamps of King Edward VII optd with Type O **9**. Ordinary paper.*

		Un	*Used	Used on cover
O91	½d. blue-green (29.4.02)	£375	£200	£1100
	s. Opt. "SPECIMEN" (16)	£650		
O92	1d. scarlet (19.2.02)	£325	£175	£1000
	s. Opt. "SPECIMEN" (15)	£650		

ADMIRALTY

ADMIRALTY   ADMIRALTY

OFFICIAL   OFFICIAL
(O **10**)   (O **11**)
                      (with different "M")

1903 (1 Apr). *Stamps of King Edward VII optd with Type O **10**. Ordinary paper.*

		Un	*Used	Used on cover
O101	½d. blue-green	27·00	13·00	
	s. Opt. "SPECIMEN" (16)	£325		
O102	1d. scarlet	16·00	6·50	£300
	s. Opt. "SPECIMEN" (16)	£325		
O103	1½d. dull purple & green	£300	£140	
	s. Opt. "SPECIMEN" (16)	£425		
O104	2d. yellowish green & carmine red	£325	£150	
	s. Opt. "SPECIMEN" (16)	£425		
O105	2½d. ultramarine	£450	£140	
	s. Opt. "SPECIMEN" (16)	£425		
O106	3d. purple/*yellow*	£400	£150	
	s. Opt. "SPECIMEN" (16)	£425		

1903–04. *Stamps of King Edward VII optd with Type O **11**. Ordinary paper.*

		Un	*Used	cover
O107	½d. blue-green (9.03)	55·00	22·00	£500
	s. Opt. "SPECIMEN" (16)	£325		
O108	1d. scarlet (12.03)	55·00	22·00	£140
	s. Opt. "SPECIMEN" (16)	£325		
O109	1½d. dull purple & green (2.04)	£1100	£600	
O110	2d. yellowish green & carmine red			
	(3.04)	£2600	£800	
	s. Opt. "SPECIMEN" (16)	£500		
O111	2½d. ultramarine (3.04)	£2750	£850	
O112	3d. dull purple/*orange-yellow*			
	(12.03)	£2400	£350	
	s. Opt. "SPECIMEN" (16)	£500		

Stamps of various issues perforated with a Crown and initials ("H.M.O.W.", "O.W.", "B.T." or "S.O.") or with initials only ("H.M.S.O." or "D.S.I.R.") have also been used for official purposes, but these are outside the scope of this catalogue.

King George V
6 May 1910 – 20 January 1936

Further detailed information on the issues of King George V will be found in Volume 2 of the Stanley Gibbons *Great Britain Specialised Catalogue*.

PRINTERS. Types **98** to **102** were typographed by Harrison & Sons Ltd, with the exception of certain preliminary printings made at Somerset House and distinguishable by the controls "A.11", "B.11" or "B.12" (the Harrison printings do not have a full stop after the letter). The booklet stamps, Nos. 334/7, and 344/5 were printed by Harrison only.

WATERMARK VARIETIES. Many British stamps to 1967 exist without watermark owing to misplacement of the paper, and with either inverted, reversed, or inverted and reversed watermarks. A proportion of the low-value stamps issued in booklets have the watermark inverted in the normal course of printing.

Low values with *watermark sideways* are normally from stamp rolls used on machines with sideways delivery or, from June 1940, certain booklets.

STAMPS WITHOUT WATERMARK. Stamps found without watermark, due to misplacement of the sheet in relation to the dandy roll, are not listed here but will be found in the *Great Britain Specialised Catalogue*.

The 1½d. and 5d. 1912–22, and ½d., 2d. and 2½d., 1924–26, listed here, are from whole sheets completely without watermark.

98	**99**	**100** Simple Cypher

For type difference with T **101/2** see notes below the latter.

Die A	Die B

Dies of Halfpenny

Die A. The three upper scales on the body of the right hand dolphin form a triangle; the centre jewel of the cross inside the crown is suggested by a comma.

Die B. The three upper scales are incomplete; the centre jewel is suggested by a crescent.

Die A	Die B

Dies of One Penny

Die A. The second line of shading on the ribbon to the right of the crown extends right across the wreath; the line nearest to the crown on the right hand ribbon shows as a short line at the bottom of the ribbon.

Die B. The second line of shading is broken in the middle; the first line is little more than a dot.

(Des Bertram Mackennal and G. W. Eve. Head from photograph by W. and D. Downey. Die eng J. A. C. Harrison)

1911–12. Wmk Imperial Crown, W **49**. P 15×14.

321	**98**	½d. pale green (Die A) (22.6.11)	10·00	5·00	4·00
322		½d. green (Die A) (22.6.11)	8·00	4·00	4·00

		a. Error. Perf 14 (8.11)	—	£18000	£1000
		s. Opt. "SPECIMEN" (22)		£800	
		Wi. Watermark inverted	£20000	—	£2000
323		½d. bluish green (Die A)	£400	£300	£180
324		½d. yellow-green (Die B)	18·00	12·00	1·50
		s. Opt. "SPECIMEN" (22)		£350	
325		½d. bright green (Die B)	13·00	8·00	1·50
		a. Watermark sideways	—	—	£5500
		Wi. Watermark inverted	35·00	20·00	7·50
326		½d. bluish green (Die B)	£260	£160	£100
327	**99**	1d. carmine-red (Die A) (22.6.11)	10·00	4·50	2·50
		c. Watermark sideways	†	†	£15000
		s. Opt. "SPECIMEN" (22)		£550	
		Wi. Watermark inverted	£2200	£1500	£1250
328		1d. pale carmine (Die A) (22.6.11)	25·00	14·00	3·00
		a. No cross on crown	£1250	£850	£500
329		1d. carmine (Die B)	15·00	10·00	3·00
		s. Opt. "SPECIMEN" (22)		£550	
		Wi. Watermark inverted	35·00	20·00	7·50
330		1d. pale carmine (Die B)	15·00	10·00	4·00
		a. No cross on crown	£1100	£800	£500
331		1d. rose-pink (Die B)	£225	£125	45·00
332		1d. scarlet (Die B) (6.12)	75·00	45·00	18·00
		s. Opt. "SPECIMEN" (22)		£750	
		Wi. Watermark inverted	75·00	45·00	18·00
333		1d. aniline scarlet (Die B)	£350	£225	£110

For note on the aniline scarlet No. 333 see below No. 343.

1912 (28 Sept). *Booklet stamps*. Wmk Royal Cypher ("Simple"), W **100**. P 15×14.

334	**98**	½d. pale green (Die B)	90·00	45·00	40·00
335		½d. green (Die B)	90·00	45·00	40·00
		s. Opt. "SPECIMEN" (22, 26)		£300	
		Wi. Watermark inverted	90·00	45·00	40·00
		Wj. Watermark reversed	£900	£625	£400
		Wk. Watermark inverted and reversed	£900	£625	£400
336	**99**	1d. scarlet (Die B)	40·00	30·00	30·00
		s. Opt. "SPECIMEN" (22, 26)		£325	
		Wi. Watermark inverted	40·00	30·00	30·00
		Wj. Watermark reversed	£1200	£850	
		Wk. Watermark inverted and reversed	—	—	£200
337		1d. bright scarlet (Die B)	40·00	30·00	30·00

101	**102**	**103** Multiple Cypher

Type differences

½d. In T **98** the ornament above "P" of "HALFPENNY" has two thin lines of colour and the beard is undefined. In T **101** the ornament has one thick line and the beard is well defined.

1d. In T **99** the body of the lion is unshaded and in T **102** it is shaded.

1912 (1 Jan). Wmk Imperial Crown, W **49**. P 15×14.

338	**101**	½d. deep green	28·00	15·00	8·00
339		½d. green	15·00	8·00	4·00
		s. Opt. "SPECIMEN" (26)		£325	
340		½d. yellow-green	15·00	8·00	4·00
		a. No cross on crown	£190	£100	55·00
		Wi. Watermark inverted	£1200	£850	£450
341	**102**	1d. bright scarlet	10·00	5·00	2·00
		a. No cross on crown	£150	80·00	55·00
		b. Printed double, one albino	£275	£180	
		Wi. Watermark inverted	£600	£400	£350

Selling your stamp collection?

Warwick and Warwick have an expanding requirement for world collections, single country collections, single items, covers, proof material and specialised collections, with G.B. material being particularly in demand. Our customer base is increasing dramatically and we need an ever-larger supply of quality material to keep pace with demand. The market has never been stronger and if you are considering the sale of your collection, now is the time to act.

FREE VALUATIONS
We will provide a free, professional valuation of your collection, without obligation on your part to proceed. Either we will make you a fair, binding private treaty offer, or we will recommend inclusion of your property in our next public auction.

FREE TRANSPORTATION
We can arrange insured transportation of your collection to our Warwick offices completely free of charge. If you decline our offer, we ask you to cover the return carriage costs only.

FREE VISITS
Visits by our valuers are possible anywhere in the country or abroad, usually within 48 hours, in order to value larger collections. Please phone for details.

VALUATION DAYS
We are staging a series of valuation days across the country. Please visit our website or telephone for further details.

EXCELLENT PRICES
Because of the strength of our customer base we are in a position to offer prices that we feel sure will exceed your expectations.

ACT NOW
Telephone or email Ian Hunter today with details of your property.

Get the experts on your side!

Warwick & Warwick

AUCTIONEERS AND VALUERS
www.warwickandwarwick.com

Warwick & Warwick Ltd.
Chalon House, Scar Bank, Millers Road
Warwick CV34 5DB England
Tel: (01926) 499031 · Fax: (01926) 491906
Email: ian.hunter@warwickandwarwick.com

342		1d. scarlet	10·00	5·00	2·00
343		1d. aniline scarlet*	£275	£175	£100
		a. No cross on crown	£2000	£1400	

*Our prices for the aniline scarlet 1d. stamps, Nos. 333 and 343, are for the specimens in which the colour is suffused on the surface of the stamp and shows through clearly on the back. Specimens without these characteristics but which show "aniline" reactions under the quartz lamp are relatively common.

1912 (Aug). Wmk Royal Cypher ("Simple"), W **100**. P 15×14.

344	**101**	½d. green	14·00	7·00	3·00
		a. No cross on crown	£300	£200	£125
		s. Opt. "SPECIMEN" (26)		£550	
		Wi. Watermark inverted	£550	£350	£225
		Wj. Watermark reversed	£550	£350	£225
		Wk. Watermark inverted and reversed	15·00	8·00	4·50
345	**102**	1d. scarlet	15·00	8·00	4·50
		a. No cross on crown	£175	£100	50·00
		Wi. Watermark inverted	28·00	18·00	25·00
		Wj. Watermark reversed	£110	75·00	75·00
		Wk. Watermark inverted and reversed	20·00	12·00	20·00

1912 (Sept). Wmk Royal Cypher ("Multiple"), W **103**. P 15×14.

346	**101**	½d. green (Oct)	20·00	12·00	8·00
		a. No cross on crown	£280	£175	£125
		b. Imperf	£250	£175	
		c. Watermark sideways	†	†	£4000
		d. Printed on gummed side	—	—	†
		Wi. Watermark inverted	20·00	12·00	20·00
		Wj. Watermark reversed	22·00	15·00	20·00
		Wk. Watermark inverted and reversed	50·00	35·00	35·00
347		½d. yellow-green	20·00	15·00	8·00
348		½d. pale green	25·00	15·00	8·00
349	**102**	1d. bright scarlet	25·00	18·00	10·00
350		1d. scarlet	25·00	18·00	10·00
		a. No cross on crown	£225	£150	60·00
		b. Imperf	£225	£150	
		c. Watermark sideways	£275	£175	£200
		d. Watermark sideways. No cross on crown	£1200	£750	
		Wi. Watermark inverted	35·00	22·00	28·00
		Wj. Watermark reversed	35·00	22·00	28·00
		Wk. Watermark inverted and reversed	£1600	£1000	£650

104

105

106

107

108

No. 357a

No. 357ab

No. 357ac

Die I

Die II

Two Dies of the 2d.

Die I.—Inner frame-line at top and sides close to solid of background. Four complete lines of shading between top of head and oval frame-line. These four lines do not extend to the oval itself. White line round "TWOPENCE" thin.

Die II.—Inner frame-line further from solid of background. Three lines between top of head and extending to the oval. White line round "TWOPENCE" thicker.

(Des Bertram Mackennal (heads) and G. W. Eve (frames). Coinage head (½, 1½, 2, 3 and 4d.); large medal head (1d., 2½d.); intermediate medal head (5d. to 1s.); small medal head used for fiscal stamps. Dies eng J. A. C. Harrison) (Typo by Harrison & Sons Ltd., except the 6d. printed by the Stamping Department of the Board of Inland Revenue, Somerset House. The latter also made printings of the following which can only be distinguished by the controls: ½d. B.13; 1½d. A.12; 2d. C.13; 2½d. A.12; 3d. A12, B.13, C.13; 4d. B.13; 5d. B.13; 7d. C.13; 8d. C.13; 9d. agate B.13; 10d. C.13; 1s. C.13)

1912–24. Wmk Royal Cypher ("Simple"), W **100**. Chalk-surfaced paper (6d.). P 15×14.

351	**105**	½d. green (16.1.13)	3·00	1·00	1·00
		a. Partial double print (half of bottom row) (Control G15)	—	£25000	
		b. Gummed both sides	£25000	—	—
		s. Opt. "SPECIMEN" (23, 26)		£150	
		Wi. Watermark inverted	4·00	3·00	1·50
		Wj. Watermark reversed	25·00	15·00	12·00
		Wk. Watermark inverted and reversed	6·00	4·00	3·50
352		½d. bright green	3·00	1·00	1·00
353		½d. deep green	10·00	5·00	2·00
354		½d. yellow-green	10·00	6·00	3·00
355		½d. very yellow (Cyprus) green (1914)	£12000	£8000	†
356		½d. blue-green	60·00	40·00	25·00
357	**104**	1d. bright scarlet (8.10.12)	3·00	1·00	1·00
		a. "Q" for "O" (R. 1/4) (Control E14)	£240	£175	£175
		ab. "Q" for "O" (R. 4/11) (Control T22)	£450	£350	£190
		ac. Reversed "Q" for "O" (R. 15/9) (Control T22)	£400	£300	£240
		ad. Inverted "Q" for "O" (R. 20/3)	£500	£375	£240
		b. Tête-bêche (pair)	—	£75000	†
		s. Opt. "SPECIMEN" (23, 26)		£200	
		Wi. Watermark inverted	4·00	2·00	1·00
		Wj. Watermark reversed	45·00	30·00	25·00
		Wk. Watermark inverted and reversed	6·00	3·00	2·50
358		1d. vermilion	9·00	5·00	2·50
359		1d. pale rose-red	30·00	20·00	5·00
360		1d. carmine-red	20·00	11·00	5·00
361		1d. scarlet-vermilion	£180	£125	50·00
		a. Printed on back	£450	£300	†
362	**105**	1½d. red-brown (15.10.12)	6·00	4·00	1·50
		a. "PENCF" (R. 15/12)	£400	£300	£250
		b. Booklet pane. Four stamps plus two printed labels (2.24)	£800	£600	
		s. Opt. "SPECIMEN" (23, 26)		£125	
		Wi. Watermark inverted	9·00	5·00	2·00
		Wj. Watermark reversed	60·00	45·00	35·00
		Wk. Watermark inverted and reversed	15·00	8·00	6·00
363		1½d. chocolate-brown	20·00	11·00	2·00
		a. No watermark	£325	£225	£225
364		1½d. chestnut	9·00	5·00	1·00
		a. "PENCF" (R. 15/12)	£175	£125	£110
365		1½d. yellow-brown	30·00	20·00	16·00
366	**106**	2d. orange-yellow (Die I) (20.8.12)	14·00	8·00	3·00
367		2d. reddish orange (Die I) (11.13)	10·00	6·00	3·00
368		2d. orange (Die I)	8·00	4·00	3·00
		s. Opt. "SPECIMEN" (26)		£250	
		Wi. Watermark inverted	22·00	12·00	10·00
		Wj. Watermark reversed	25·00	15·00	12·00
		Wk. Watermark inverted and reversed	18·00	8·00	8·00
369		2d. brt orange (Die I)	8·00	5·00	3·00

370		2d. orange (Die II) (9.21)	8·00	5·00	3·50
		s. Opt. "SPECIMEN" (15, 23)....		£750	
		Wi. Watermark inverted..........	50·00	35·00	35·00
		Wk. Watermark inverted and reversed	£160	£110	£100
371	**104**	2½d. cobalt-blue (18.10.12)	22·00	12·00	4·00
371a		2½d. bright blue (1914)	22·00	12·00	4·00
372		2½d. blue	22·00	12·00	4·00
		s. Opt. "SPECIMEN" (15, 23, 26)		£120	
		Wi. Watermark inverted...........	£120	85·00	75·00
		Wj. Watermark reversed	45·00	28·00	25·00
		Wk. Watermark inverted and reversed	45·00	28·00	25·00
373		2½d. indigo-blue* (1920)	£5000	£3500	£2500
373a		2½d. dull Prussian blue* (12.20)	£1700	£1000	£800
374	**106**	3d. dull reddish violet (9.10.12)	22·00	12·00	3·00
375		3d. violet	15·00	8·00	3·00
		s. Opt. "SPECIMEN" (15, 23, 26)		£250	
		Wi. Watermark inverted...........	£160	95·00	£110
		Wj. Watermark reversed	£400	£225	£225
		Wk. Watermark inverted and reversed	40·00	30·00	30·00
376		3d. bluish violet (11.13)	15·00	9·00	3·00
377		3d. pale violet	17·00	10·00	3·00
378		4d. dp grey-green (15.1.13)	75·00	45·00	25·00
379		4d. grey-green	25·00	15·00	2·00
		s. Opt. "SPECIMEN" (15, 23, 26)		£125	
		Wi. Watermark inverted...........	50·00	30·00	30·00
		Wj. Watermark reversed	£300	£175	£175
		Wk. Watermark inverted and reversed	85·00	50·00	50·00
380		4d. pale grey-green.....................	40·00	25·00	5·00
381	**107**	5d. brown (30.6.13)	25·00	15·00	5·00
		s. Opt. "SPECIMEN" (15, 23, 26)		£250	
		Wi. Watermark inverted...........	£950	£550	£550
		Wj. Watermark reversed	†	†	—
		Wk. Watermark inverted and reversed	£450	£350	£350
382		5d. yellow-brown.......................	25·00	15·00	5·00
		a. No watermark	£1800	£1100	
383		5d. bistre-brown	£250	£140	65·00
384		6d. dull purple (1.8.13)	45·00	25·00	10·00
		s. Opt. "SPECIMEN" (15, 23, 26)		£200	
385		6d. reddish purple (8.13)	30·00	15·00	7·00
		a. Perf 14 (9.20)	£150	90·00	£110
		Wi. Watermark inverted............	85·00	50·00	50·00
		Wj. Watermark reversed	£4500	£3500	
		Wk. Watermark inverted and reversed	85·00	50·00	50·00
386		6d. deep reddish purple............	75·00	40·00	5·00
387		7d. olive (1.8.13)	35·00	20·00	10·00
		s. Opt. "SPECIMEN" (26)...........		£200	
		Wi. Watermark inverted............	80·00	50·00	50·00
		Wj. Watermark reversed	†	†	—
		Wk. Watermark inverted and reversed	£4750	£4000	
388		7d. bronze-green (1915)	£120	70·00	25·00
389		7d. sage-green (1917)	£120	70·00	18·00
390		8d. black/*yellow* (1.8.13)	55·00	32·00	11·00
		s. Opt. "SPECIMEN" (26)...........		£250	
		Wi. Watermark inverted............	£190	£110	£110
		Wj. Watermark reversed	£275	£180	£180
		Wk. Watermark inverted and reversed	£5750	£4500	
391		8d. black/yellow-buff (granite) (5.17)	60·00	40·00	15·00
392	**108**	9d. agate (30.6.13)	30·00	15·00	6·00
		a. Printed double, one albino		£400	
		s. Opt. "SPECIMEN" (26)...........		£400	
		Wi. Watermark inverted............	£200	£125	£125
		Wk. Watermark inverted and reversed	£200	£125	£125
393		9d. deep agate	45·00	25·00	6·00
393a		9d. olive-green (9.22)	£225	£110	30·00
		as. Opt. "SPECIMEN" (15, 23)....		£700	
		aWi. Watermark inverted..........	£1200	£800	£750
		aWk. Watermark inverted and reversed	£1200	£800	£750
393b		9d. pale olive-green....................	£250	£120	40·00
394		10d. turquoise-blue (1.8.13)	40·00	22·00	20·00
		s. Opt. "SPECIMEN" (15, 23, 26)		£400	
		Wi. Watermark inverted............	£3750	£2500	£1500
		Wk. Watermark inverted and reversed	£475	£325	£275
394a		10d. deep turquoise-blue	£150	90·00	30·00
395		1s. bistre (1.8.13)........................	35·00	20·00	4·00

		s. Opt. "SPECIMEN" (15, 23, 26, 31)		£350	
		Wi. Watermark inverted............	£325	£250	£200
		Wk. Watermark inverted and reversed	£110	65·00	65·00
396		1s. bistre-brown	55·00	35·00	12·00
Set of 15			£475	£250	95·00

Imperf stamps of this issue exist but may be war-time colour trials.

†The impression of No. 361a is set sideways and is very pale. Nos. 362a and 364a occur on Plates 12 and 29 and are known from Controls L18, M18, M19, O19 and Q21. The flaws were corrected by 1921.

*No. 373 comes from Control O20 and also exists on toned paper.

No. 373a comes from Control R21 and also exists on toned paper, but both are unlike the rare Prussian blue shade of the 1935 2½d. Jubilee issue.

Examples of the 2d., T **106** which were in the hands of philatelists, are known bisected in Guernsey from 27 December 1940 to February 1941.

See also Nos. 418/29.

1913 (Aug). *Wmk Royal Cypher ("Multiple"), W* **103**. P 15×14.

397	**105**	½d. bright green	£250	£150	£180
		a. Watermark sideways	†		† £18000
		Wi. Watermark inverted............	£1200	£900	
398	**104**	1d. dull scarlet............................	£350	£225	£225
		Wi. Watermark inverted............	£1600	£1100	

Both these stamps were originally issued in rolls only. Subsequently sheets were found, so that horizontal pairs and blocks are known but are of considerable rarity.

109

A

110 Single Cypher

Major Re-entries on 2s.6d.

No. 400a

Nos. 406/7a

No. 415b

No. 417a

(Des Bertram Mackennal. Dies eng J. A. C. Harrison. Recess)

High values, so-called "Sea Horses" design: T 109. Background around portrait consists of horizontal lines, Type A. Wmk Single Cypher, W 110.
P 11×12.

1913 (30 June). *Printed by Waterlow Bros & Layton.*

399	**109**	2s.6d. deep sepia-brown	£750	£280	£180
		s. Opt. "SPECIMEN" (23, 26)....		£600	
400		2s.6d. sepia-brown	£550	£225	£140
		a. Re-entry (Plate 3, R. 2/1).......	£2500	£1500	£700
401		5s. rose-carmine	£1200	£500	£300
		s. Opt. "SPECIMEN" (26)..........		£750	
402		10s. indigo-blue (1 Aug).............	£2000	£950	£450
		s. Opt. "SPECIMEN" (23, 26, 29)...................................		£1100	
403		£1 green (1 Aug)	£4800	£3000	£1250
		s. Opt. "SPECIMEN" (23, 26)...		£2700	
404		£1 dull blue-green (1 Aug)......	£4800	£3000	£1500

*399/404 **For well-centred, lightly used +35%**

1915 (Sept–Dec). *Printed by De la Rue & Co.*

405	**109**	2s.6d. deep yellow-brown (Oct)...	£650	£300	£225
		Wi. Watermark inverted.............	£2400	£1200	
406		2s.6d. yellow-brown (inc. worn plates)...............................	£500	£250	£200
		a. Re-entry (Plate 3, R. 2/1).......	£2800	£1800	£850
		s. Opt. "SPECIMEN" (23)..........		£1200	
		Wi. Watermark inverted.............	£1800	£950	£950
		Wj. Watermark reversed	£1800	£950	£950
		Wk. Watermark inverted and reversed	£4500	£3500	
407		2s.6d. grey brown (inc. worn plates)...............................	£650	£350	£280
		a. Re-entry (Plate 3, R. 2/1).......	£2800	£1800	£850
		Wi. Watermark inverted.............	£1800	£950	£950
		Wj. Watermark reversed	£1800	£950	£950
408		2s.6d. sepia (seal-brown)..............	£500	£250	£225
		Wi. Watermark inverted.............	£1800	£950	£950
		Wj. Watermark reversed	£1800	£950	£950
409		5s. bright carmine.......................	£1000	£425	£350
		s. Opt. "SPECIMEN" (23)..........		£1000	
		Wi. Watermark inverted.............	£6800	£4200	
		Wj. Watermark reversed	£6250	£4000	
		Wk. Watermark inverted and reversed	—	£14000	†
410		5s. pale carmine (worn plate)...	£1200	£600	£450
411		10s. deep blue (Dec)....................	£5500	£3000	£950
		s. Opt. "SPECIMEN" (26)..........	£2400		
412		10s. blue......................................	£3500	£2500	£800
		Wi. Watermark inverted and reversed	—	—	†
413		10s. pale blue..............................	£3800	£2800	£800

*405/13 **For well-centred, lightly used +45%**

No. 406/7 were produced from the original Waterlow plates as were all De La Rue 5s and 10s printings. Examples of No. 406/7, 410 and 411 occur showing degrees of plate wear.

1918 (Dec)–**19**. *Printed by Bradbury, Wilkinson & Co, Ltd.*

413a	**109**	2s.6d. olive-brown	£325	£150	90·00
		as. Opt. "SPECIMEN" (15, 23, 26, 31, 32)		£900	
414		2s.6d. chocolate-brown.................	£280	£125	70·00
415		2s.6d. reddish brown	£280	£125	70·00
415a		2s.6d. pale brown.......................	£300	£140	70·00
		b. Major re-entry (Plate 3/5L, R. 1/2)....................................	£1500	£800	£450
416		5s. rose-red (1.19).......................	£450	£280	£120
		s. Opt. "SPECIMEN" (15, 23, 26, 31, 32)		£1100	
417		10s. dull grey-blue (1.19)	£800	£375	£160
		a. Re-entry (Plate 1/3L, R. 1/1)	£2250	£1500	£950
		s. Opt. "SPECIMEN" (15, 23, 26, 31, 32)		£1200	
Set of 4 (inc. no. 403)			£5800	£2700	£1400

*413a/17 **For well-centred, lightly used +35%**

DISTINGUISHING PRINTINGS. Note that the £1 value was only printed by Waterlow.

Waterlow and De La Rue stamps measure exactly 22.1 mm vertically. In the De La Rue printings the gum is usually patchy and yellowish, and the colour of the stamp, particularly in the 5s., tends to show through the back. The holes of the perforation are smaller than those of the other two printers, but there is a thick perforation tooth at the top of each vertical side.

In the Bradbury Wilkinson printings the height of the stamp is 22.6 – 23.1 mm due to the use of curved plates. On most of the 22.6 mm high stamps a minute coloured guide dot appears in the margin just above the middle of the upper frame-line.

For (1934) re-engraved Waterlow printings see Nos. 450/2.

> Note: All illustrations of re-entries on Nos. 399-417 are copyright GB Philatelic Publications Ltd and Bryan Kearsley and are reproduced with their permission.

UNITED KINGDOM OF GREAT BRITAIN AND NORTHERN IRELAND

111 Block Cypher

111a

The watermark Type **111a**, as compared with Type **111**, differs as follows: Closer spacing of horizontal rows (12½ mm instead of 14½ mm). Letters shorter and rounder. Watermark thicker. The dandy roll to produce watermark Type **111a** was provided by Somerset House in connection with experiments in paper composition undertaken during 1924–25. These resulted in a change from rag only paper to that made from a mixture including esparto and sulphite.

(Typo by Waterlow & Sons, Ltd (all values except 6d.) and later, 1934–35, by Harrison & Sons, Ltd (all values). Until 1934 the 6d. was printed at Somerset House where a printing of the 1½d. was also made in 1926 (identifiable only by control E.26). Printings by Harrisons in 1934–35 can be identified, when in mint condition, by the fact that the gum shows a streaky appearance vertically, the Waterlow gum being uniformly applied, but Harrisons also used up the balance of the Waterlow "smooth gum" paper)

1924 (Feb)–**26**. *Wmk Block Cypher, W 111.* P 15×14.

418	**105**	½d. green.....................................	2·00	1·00	1·00
		a. Watermark sideways (5.24).....	18·00	9·00	3·25
		aWi. Watermark sideways inverted..............................	£600	£450	
		b. Doubly printed.....................	£15000	£10000	†
		c. No watermark........................	£6000	—	—
		s. Opt. "SPECIMEN" (15, 23, 30, 32)		90·00	
		Wi. Watermark inverted.............	7·00	3·50	1·00
419	**104**	1d. scarlet....................................	2·00	1·00	1·00
		a. Watermark sideways.............	40·00	20·00	15·00
		b. Experimental paper, W **111a** (10.24).........................	40·00	22·00	
		c. Partial double print, one inverted..............................	—	£18000	
		d. Inverted "Q" for "O" (R. 20/3)	£850	£500	
		s. Opt. "SPECIMEN" (15, 23, 30, 32)		90·00	
		Wi. Watermark inverted..............	7·00	4·00	1·50

420	**105**	1½d. red-brown	2·00	1·00	1·00
		a. *Tête-bêche* (pair)	£750	£500	£800
		b. Watermark sideways (8.24)	20·00	10·00	3·50
		bWi. Watermark sideways			
		inverted..................................	—	£900	
		c. Printed on the gummed			
		side	£1000	£650	
		d. Booklet pane. Four stamps			
		plus two printed labels			
		(3.24)	£300	£225	
		e. Ditto. Watermark sideways	£12000	£8000	
		f. Experimental paper, W			
		111a (10.24)	£140	90·00	80·00
		g. Double impression..............	—	£18000	†
		s. Opt. "SPECIMEN" (15, 23,			
		30, 32)		90·00	
		Wi. Watermark inverted.............	3·50	2·00	1·00
421	**106**	2d. orange (Die II) (7.24)	4·00	2·50	2·50
		a. No watermark........................	£2250	£950	
		b. Watermark sideways (7.26)	£190	£100	£100
		c. Partial double print..............	—	£30000	†
		s. Opt. "SPECIMEN" (23, 32)....		£100	
		Wi. Watermark inverted.............	60·00	40·00	40·00
422	**104**	2½d. blue (10.10.24)	10·00	5·00	3·00
		a. No watermark........................	£3500	£1800	
		b. Watermark sideways	†	†	£15000
		s. Opt. "SPECIMEN" (23, 32)....		£500	
		Wi. Watermark inverted.............	£125	70·00	50·00
423	**106**	3d. violet (10.10.24)....................	20·00	10·00	2·50
		s. Opt. "SPECIMEN" (23, 32)....		£700	
		Wi. Watermark inverted.............	£125	70·00	50·00
424		4d. grey-green (10.10.24)..........	28·00	12·00	2·50
		a. Printed on the gummed			
		side	£5500	£3500	†
		s. Opt. "SPECIMEN" (23, 32)....		£600	
		Wi. Watermark inverted.............	£200	£110	75·00
425	**107**	5d. brown (17.10.24)	40·00	20·00	3·00
		s. Opt. "SPECIMEN" (23, 26,			
		32)		£125	
		Wi. Watermark inverted.............	£150	£100	85·00
426		6d. reddish purple (*chalk-*			
		surfaced paper) (9.24)	20·00	12·00	2·50
		Wi. Watermark inverted.............	90·00	60·00	40·00
		Wk. Watermark inverted and			
		reversed	£600	£400	£300
426*a*		6d. purple (6.26)	6·00	3·00	1·50
		as. Opt. "SPECIMEN" (23, 26,			
		32)	£400		
		aWi. Watermark inverted.............	£125	75·00	60·00
427	**108**	9d. olive-green (11.11.24).........	40·00	12·00	3·50
		s. Opt. "SPECIMEN" (23, 26,			
		32)		£125	
		Wi. Watermark inverted.............	£125	80·00	70·00
428		10d. turquoise-blue (28.11.24)..	85·00	40·00	40·00
		s. Opt. "SPECIMEN" (23, 32)....		£700	
		Wi. Watermark inverted.............	£3750	£2400	£1800
429		1s. bistre-brown (10.24)............	50·00	22·00	3·00
		s. Opt. "SPECIMEN" (23, 32)....		£500	
		Wi. Watermark inverted.............	£600	£375	£350
Set of 12..			£250	£110	60·00

There are numerous shades in this issue.

The 6d. on chalk-surfaced and ordinary papers was printed by both Somerset House and Harrisons. The Harrison printings have streaky gum, differ slightly in shade, and that on chalk-surfaced paper is printed in a highly fugitive ink. The prices quoted are for the commonest (Harrison) printing in each case.

112

(Des H. Nelson. Eng J. A. C. Harrison. Recess Waterlow)

1924–25. *British Empire Exhibition*. W **111**. P 14.

(a) Dated "1924" (23.4.24).

430	**112**	1d. scarlet	12·00	10·00	11·00
		s. Opt. "SPECIMEN" (15, 23,			
		30)...		£900	
431		1½d. brown	20·00	15·00	15·00
		s. Opt. "SPECIMEN" (15, 23,			
		30)...		£900	
Set of 2			30·00	25·00	26·00
First Day Cover......................................					£450

(b) Dated "1925" (9.5.25).

432	**112**	1d. scarlet	25·00	15·00	30·00
		s. Opt. "SPECIMEN" (30)...........		£800	

433		1½d. brown	60·00	40·00	70·00
		s. Opt. "SPECIMEN" (30)..........		£800	
Set of 2			80·00	55·00	£100
First Day Cover......................................					£1700

113   **114**   **115**

116 St. George and the Dragon

117

(Des J. Farleigh (T **113** and **115**), E. Linzell (T **114**) and H. Nelson (T **116**). Eng C. G. Lewis (T **113**), T. E. Storey (T **115**), both at the Royal Mint; J. A. C. Harrison, of Waterlow (T **114** & **116**). Typo by Waterlow from plates made at the Royal Mint, except T **116**, recess by Bradbury, Wilkinson from die and plate of their own manufacture)

1929 (10 May). *Ninth U.P.U. Congress, London.*

(a) W **111**. P 15×14.

434	**113**	½d. green...	3·00	2·25	2·25
		a. Watermark sideways	80·00	40·00	40·00
		Wi. Watermark inverted.............	35·00	15·00	12·00
435	**114**	1d. scarlet	3·00	2·25	2·25
		a. Watermark sideways	£140	75·00	75·00
		Wi. Watermark inverted.............	35·00	15·00	12·00
436		1½d. purple-brown.........................	3·00	2·25	1·75
		a. Watermark sideways	90·00	40·00	40·00
		b. Booklet pane. Four stamps			
		plus two printed labels.......	£425	£375	
		Wi. Watermark inverted.............	15·00	5·00	6·00
437	**115**	2½d. blue	20·00	10·00	10·00
		s. Opt. "SPECIMEN" (32)...........		£2500	
		Wi. Watermark inverted.............	£3750	£2400	£1100

(b) W **117**. P 12.

438	**116**	£1 black	£1100	£750	£550
		s. Opt. "SPECIMEN" (32, red			
		opt)		£3000	
Set of 4 (to 2½d.)			28·00	15·00	14·50
First Day Cover (4 vals.)					£600
First Day Cover (5 vals.)					£12000

PRINTERS. All subsequent issues to No. 2025 were printed in photogravure by Harrison & Sons Ltd *except where otherwise stated.*

118   **119**   **120**

| 121 | 122 |

| B | 123 |

(Eng. J.A.C. Harrison. Recess Waterlow)

1934–36. W **111**. P 15×14.

439	118	½d. green (17.11.34)	1·00	50	50
		a. Watermark sideways	17·00	10·00	3·50
		aWi. Watermark sideways inverted	£600	£450	£150
		b. Imperf three sides	£6500	£4500	
		s. Opt. "SPECIMEN" (23, 32)		£500	
		Wi. Watermark inverted	22·00	11·00	1·50
440	119	1d. scarlet (24.9.34)	1·00	50	50
		a. Imperf (pair)	£6500	£4500	
		b. Printed on gummed side	£900	£650	
		c. Watermark sideways (30.4.35)	35·00	20·00	8·00
		cWi. Watermark sideways inverted	£175	£100	—
		d. Double impression	†	†	£20000
		e. Imperf between (pair)	£9000	£6000	
		f. Imperf (three sides) (pair)	£8000	£5000	
		s. Opt. "SPECIMEN" (23, 32)		£600	
		Wi. Watermark inverted	20·00	9·00	3·00
441	118	1½d. red-brown (20.8.34)	1·00	50	50
		a. Imperf (pair)	£1600	£1100	
		b. Imperf (three sides) (lower stamp in vert pair)	£5000	£3500	
		c. Imperf between (horiz pair)			
		d. Watermark sideways	15·00	10·00	4·00
		dWi. Watermark sideways inverted			
		e. Booklet pane. Four stamps plus two printed labels (1.35)	£275	£190	
		s. Opt. "SPECIMEN" (23, 32)		£600	
		Wi. Watermark inverted	8·00	4·00	1·00
442	120	2d. orange (19.1.35)	1·50	75	75
		a. Imperf (pair)	£6500	£4750	
		b. Watermark sideways (30.4.35)	£225	£125	90·00
		s. Opt. "SPECIMEN" (30, 32)		—	
443	119	2½d. bright blue (18.3.35)	2·50	1·50	1·25
		s. Opt. "SPECIMEN" (23)		£650	
444	120	3d. reddish violet (18.3.35)	3·00	1·50	1·25
		s. Opt. "SPECIMEN" (23, 30)		£600	
		Wi. Watermark inverted	—	—	£9000
445		4d. dp grey-green (2.12.35)	4·00	2·00	1·25
		s. Opt. "SPECIMEN" (23, 30)		£650	
		Wi. Watermark inverted	†	†	£9000
446	121	5d. yellow-brown (17.2.36)	13·00	6·50	2·75
		s. Opt. "SPECIMEN" (23)		£650	
447	122	9d. dp olive-green (2.12.35)	20·00	12·00	2·25
		s. Opt. "SPECIMEN" (23)		£650	
448		10d. turquoise-blue (24.2.36)	30·00	15·00	10·00
		s. Opt. "SPECIMEN" (23, 32)		£650	
449		1s. bistre-brown (24.2.36)	40·00	15·00	1·25
		a. Double impression	—	—	†
		s. Opt. "SPECIMEN" (23, 32)		£125	
Set of 11			95·00	50·00	20·00

Owing to the need for wider space for the perforations the size of the designs of the ½d. and 2d. were once, and the 1d. and 1½d. twice reduced from that of the first printings.

The format description, size in millimetres and S.G. catalogue number are given but further details will be found in the *Great Britain Specialised Catalogue*, Volume 2.

(Eng. J.A.C. Harrison. Recess Waterlow)

1934 (16 Oct). *T* **109** (re-engraved). *Background around portrait consists of horizontal and diagonal lines, Type B.* W **110**. P 11×12.

450	109	2s.6d. chocolate-brown	£150	80·00	40·00
		s. Opt. "SPECIMEN" (23, 30)		£3250	
451		5s. bright rose-red	£400	£175	85·00
		s. Opt. "SPECIMEN" (23, 30)		£3250	
452		10s. indigo	£500	£350	80·00
		s. Opt. "SPECIMEN" (23, 30)		£3250	
Set of 3			£1000	£575	£190

There are numerous other minor differences in the design of this issue.

(Des B. Freedman)

1935 (7 May). *Silver Jubilee*. W **111**. P 15×14.

453	123	½d. green	1·00	1·00	1·00
		s. Opt. "SPECIMEN" (23)		£1200	
		Wi. Watermark inverted	15·00	8·00	3·00
454		1d. scarlet	2·00	1·50	2·00
		s. Opt. "SPECIMEN" (23)		£1200	
		Wi. Watermark inverted	15·00	8·00	4·00
455		1½d. red-brown	1·25	1·00	1·00
		s. Opt. "SPECIMEN" (23)		£1200	
		Wi. Watermark inverted	5·00	3·00	1·50
456		2½d. blue	8·00	5·00	6·50
		s. Opt. "SPECIMEN" (23)		£1500	
456a		2½d. Prussian blue	£16000	£11000	£13000
Set of 4			11·00	7·50	9·50
First Day Cover					£600

The 1d., 1½d. and 2½d. values differ from T **123** in the emblem in the panel at right.

Four sheets of No. 456a, printed in the wrong shade, were issued in error by the Post Office Stores Department on 25 June 1935. It is known that three from the sheets were sold from the sub-office at 134 Fore Street, Upper Edmonton, London, between that date and 4 July.

Description	Size	S.G. Nos.	Date of Issue
½d. intermediate format	18.4×22.2	—	19.11.34
½d. small format	17.9×21.7	439	14.2.35
1d. large format	18.7×22.5	—	24.9.34
1d. intermediate format	18.4×22.2	—	1934
1d. small format	17.9×21.7	440	8.2.35
1½d. large format	18.7×22.5	—	20.8.34
1½d. intermediate format	18.4×22.2	—	1934
1½d. small format	17.9×21.7	441	7.2.35
2d. intermediate format	18.4×22.2	—	21.1.35
2d. small format	18.15×21.7	442	1935

There are also numerous minor variations, due to the photographic element in the process.

Examples of 2d., T **120**, which were in the hands of philatelists are known bisected in Guernsey from 27 December 1940 to February 1941.

King Edward VIII

20 January – 10 December 1936

Further detailed information on the stamps of King Edward VIII will be found in Volume 2 of the Stanley Gibbons *Great Britain Specialised Catalogue*.

> **PRICES.** From S.G. 457 prices quoted in the first column are for stamps in unmounted mint condition.

124   **125**

(Des H. Brown, adapted Harrison using a photo by Hugh Cecil)

1936. W **125**. P 15×14.

457	**124**	½d. green (1.9.36)	30	30
		a. Double impression		
		s. Opt. "SPECIMEN" (30, 32)	£750	
		Wi. Watermark inverted	10·00	5·00
458		1d. scarlet (14.9.36)	60	50
		s. Opt. "SPECIMEN" (30, 32)	£750	
		Wi. Watermark inverted	9·00	5·00
459		1½d. red-brown (1.9.36)	30	30
		a. Booklet pane. Four stamps plus two printed labels (10.36)	85·00	
		b. Imperf (pair)	£32000	
		s. Opt. "SPECIMEN" (30, 32)	£750	
		Wi. Watermark inverted	1·00	1·00
460		2½d. bright blue (1.9.36)	30	85
		s. Opt. "SPECIMEN" (30)	£750	
Set of 4			1·25	1·75

First Day Covers

1.9.36	½d., 1½d., 2½d. (457, 459/60)		£150
14.9.36	1d. (458)		£180

King George VI

11 December 1936 – 6 February 1952

Further detailed information on the stamps of King George VI will be found in Volume 2 of the Stanley Gibbons *Great Britain Specialised Catalogue*.

126 King George VI and Queen Elizabeth

127

Colon flaw (Cyl. 7 No dot, R. 10/1, later corrected)

(Des E. Dulac)

1937 (13 May). *Coronation*. W **127**. P 15×14.

461	126	1½d. maroon	30	30
		a. Colon flaw	20·00	
		s. Opt. "SPECIMEN" (32)	£600	
First Day Cover				35·00

128

129

130

King George VI and National Emblems

(Des T **128/9**, E. Dulac (head) and E. Gill (frames). T **130**, E. Dulac (whole stamp))

1937–47. W **127**. P 15×14.

462	128	½d. green (10.5.37)	30	25
		a. Watermark sideways (1.38)	50	50
		ab. Booklet pane of 4 (6.40)	85·00	
		s. Opt "SPECIMEN" (32)		
		Wi. Watermark inverted	10·00	60
463		1d. scarlet (10.5.37)	30	25
		a. Watermark sideways (2.38)	20·00	9·00
		ab. Booklet pane of 4 (6.40)	£100	
		s. Opt "SPECIMEN" (32)		
		Wi. Watermark inverted	38·00	3·00
464		1½d. red-brown (30.7.37)	30	25
		a. Watermark sideways (2.38)	1·00	1·25
		b. Booklet pane. Four stamps plus two printed labels (8.37)	£120	
		c. Imperf three sides (pair)	£5000	
		s. Opt "SPECIMEN" (26)		
		Wi. Watermark inverted	15·00	1·25
465		2d. orange (31.1.38)	1·20	50
		a. Watermark sideways (2.38)	75·00	40·00
		b. Bisected (on cover)	†	50·00
		s. Opt. "SPECIMEN" (26)	£325	
		Wi. Watermark inverted	60·00	22·00
466		2½d. ultramarine (10.5.37)	40	25
		a. Watermark sideways (6.40)	75·00	35·00
		b. *Tête-bêche* (horiz pair)	£22000	
		Wi. Watermark inverted	55·00	22·00
467		3d. violet (31.1.38)	5·00	1·00
		s. Opt. "SPECIMEN" (26, 30)	£300	
468	129	4d. grey-green (21.11.38)	60	75

		a. Imperf (pair)	£7000	
		b. Imperf three sides (horiz pair)	£7500	
		s. Opt. "SPECIMEN" (23)	£200	
469		5d. brown (21.11.38)	3·50	85
		a. Imperf (pair)	£7000	
		b. Imperf three sides (horiz pair)	£7500	
		s. Opt. "SPECIMEN" (23)	£250	
470		6d. purple (30.1.39)	1·50	60
		s. Opt. "SPECIMEN" (23)		
471	130	7d. emerald-green (27.2.39)	5·00	60
		a. Imperf three sides (horiz pair)	£7500	
		s. Opt. "SPECIMEN" (23)	£250	
472		8d. bright carmine (27.2.39)	7·50	80
		s. Opt. "SPECIMEN" (23)	£250	
473		9d. deep olive-green (1.5.39)	6·50	80
		s. Opt. "SPECIMEN" (23)	£250	
474		10d. turquoise-blue (1.5.39)	7·00	80
		aa. Imperf (pair)		
		aas. Opt. "SPECIMEN" (23)	£250	
474a		11d. plum (29.12.47)	3·00	2·75
		as. Opt. "SPECIMEN" (30)	£275	
475		1s. bistre-brown (1.5.39)	9·00	75
		s. Opt. "SPECIMEN" (23, 33)	£160	
Set of 15			45·00	10·00

For later printings of the lower values in apparently lighter shades and different colours, see Nos. 485/90 and 503/8.

No. 465b was authorised for use in Guernsey from 27 December 1940 until February 1941.

Nos. 468b and 469b are perforated at foot only and each occurs in the same sheet as Nos. 468a and 469a.

No. 471a is also perforated at foot only, but occurs on the top row of a sheet.

First Day Covers

10.5.37	½d., 1d., 2½d. (462/3, 466)	45·00
30.7.37	1½d. (464)	45·00
31.1.38	2d., 3d. (465/467)	£100
21.11.38	4d., 5d. (468/9)	65·00
30.1.39	6d. (470)	60·00
27.2.39	7d., 8d. (471/2)	85·00
1.5.39	9d., 10d., 1s. (473/4, 475)	£500
29.12.47	11d. (474a)	55·00

131

132

133

Mark in shield (R. 1/7)

Gashed diadem (R. 2/7)

Gashed crown (R. 5/5)   Broken stem (R. 1/4)

Blot on scroll
(R. 2/5)
Scratch on scroll (R. 4/6)

(Des E. Dulac (T **131**) and Hon. G. R. Bellew (T **132**). Eng J. A. C. Harrison. Recess Waterlow)

1939–48. W **133**. P 14.

476	**131**	2s.6d. brown (4.9.39)	95·00	8·00
		a. Mark in shield	£125	40·00
		b. Gashed diadem	£125	40·00
		c. Gashed crown	£125	40·00
		s. Opt. "SPECIMEN" (23)	£275	
476a		2s.6d. yellow-green (9.3.42)	15·00	1·50
		s. Opt. "SPECIMEN" (23)	£275	
477		5s. red (21.8.39)	20·00	2·00
		s. Opt. "SPECIMEN" (23)	£275	
478	**132**	10s. dark blue (30.10.39)	£260	22·00
		a. Broken stem	£275	40·00
		b. Blot on scroll	£275	40·00
		c. Scratch on scroll	£275	40·00
		s. Opt. "SPECIMEN" (23)	£475	
478a		10s. ultramarine (30.11.42)	45·00	5·00
		s. Opt. "SPECIMEN" (30)	£400	
478b		£1 brown (1.10.48)	25·00	26·00
		s. Opt. "SPECIMEN" (30)	—	
Set of 6			£425	60·00

First Day Covers

21.8.39	5s. (477)	£800
4.9.39	2s.6d. brown (476)	£1800
30.10.39	10s. dark blue (478)	£3250
9.3.42	2s.6d. yellow-green (476a)	£1750
30.11.42	10s. ultramarine (478a)	£3750
1.10.48	£1 (478b)	£325

134 Queen Victoria and King George VI

(Des H. L. Palmer)

1940 (6 May). *Centenary of First Adhesive Postage Stamps.* W **127**. P 14½×14.

479	**134**	½d. green	30	75
		s. Opt. "SPECIMEN" (23, 30)	—	
480		1d. scarlet	1·00	75
		s. Opt. "SPECIMEN" (23, 30)	—	
481		1½d. red-brown	50	1·50
		s. Opt. "SPECIMEN" (23, 30)	—	
482		2d. orange	1·00	75
		a. Bisected (on cover)	†	40·00
		s. Opt. "SPECIMEN" (23, 30)	—	
483		2½d. ultramarine	2·25	50
		s. Opt. "SPECIMEN" (23, 30)	—	
484		3d. violet	3·00	3·50
		s. Opt. "SPECIMEN" (23, 30)	—	
Set of 6			8·75	5·25
First Day Cover				55·00

No. 482a was authorised for use on Guernsey from 27 December 1940 until February 1941.

1941–42. *Head as Nos. 462/7, but with lighter background to provide a more economic use of the printing ink.* W **127**. P 15×14.

485	**128**	½d. pale green (1.9.41)	30	30
		a. Tête-bêche (horiz pair)	£16000	
		b. Imperf (pair)	£7500	
		s. Opt. "SPECIMEN" (23)	—	
		Wi. Watermark inverted	4·00	50
486		1d. pale scarlet (11.8.41)	30	30
		a. Watermark sideways (10.42)	5·00	4·50
		b. Imperf (pair)	£7000	
		c. Imperf three sides (horiz pair)	£7500	
		s. Opt. "SPECIMEN" (23)	—	
487		1½d. pale red-brown (28.9.42)	60	80
		s. Opt. "SPECIMEN" (23)	—	
488		2d. pale orange (6.10.41)	50	50
		a. Watermark sideways (6.42)	28·00	19·00
		b. Tête-bêche (horiz pair)	£16000	
		c. Imperf (pair)	£6500	
		d. Imperf pane*	£18000	
		s. Opt. "SPECIMEN" (23)	—	
		Wi. Watermark inverted	4·00	1·00
489		2½d. light ultramarine (21.7.41)	30	30
		a. Watermark sideways (8.42)	15·00	12·00
		b. Tête-bêche (horiz pair)	£16000	
		c. Imperf (pair)	£4250	
		d. Imperf pane*	£12000	
		e. Imperf three sides (horiz pair)	£6500	
		s. Opt. "SPECIMEN" (23)	—	
		Wi. Watermark inverted	1·50	1·00
490		3d. pale violet (3.11.41)	2·50	1·00
		s. Opt. "SPECIMEN" (32)	—	
Set of 6			3·50	2·75

First Day Covers

21.7.41	2½d. (489)	45·00
11.8.41	1d. (486)	22·00
1.9.41	½d. (485)	22·00
6.10.41	2d. (488)	60·00
3.11.41	3d. (490)	£110
28.9.42	1½d. (487)	55·00

135   **136**

Extra porthole aft (Cyl. 11 No dot, R. 16/1)   Extra porthole fore (Cyl. 8 Dot, R. 5/6)   Seven berries (Cyl. 4 No dot, R. 12/5)

(Des H. L. Palmer (T **135**) and R. Stone (T **136**))

1946 (11 June). *Victory.* W **127**. P 15×14.

491	**135**	2½d. ultramarine	20	20
		a. Extra porthole aft	65·00	
		b. Extra porthole fore	90·00	
		s. Opt. "SPECIMEN" (30)	—	
492	**136**	3d. violet	20	50
		a. Seven berries	30·00	
		s. Opt. "SPECIMEN" (30)	—	
Set of 2			40	50
First Day Cover				65·00

137   **138** King George VI and Queen Elizabeth

(Des G. Knipe and Joan Hassall from photographs by Dorothy Wilding)

1948 (26 Apr). *Royal Silver Wedding.* W **127**. P 15×14 (2½d.) or 14×15 (£1).

493	**137**	2½d. ultramarine	35	20
		s. Opt. "SPECIMEN" (30)	—	
494	**138**	£1 blue	40·00	40·00
		s. Opt. "SPECIMEN" (30)	—	
Set of 2			40·00	40·00
First Day Cover				£425

1948 (10 May). Stamps of 1d. and 2½d. showing seaweed-gathering were on sale at eight Head Post Offices in Great Britain, but were primarily for use in the Channel Islands and are listed there (see Nos. C1/2, after Royal Mail Postage Labels).

139 Globe and Laurel Wreath   **140** "Speed"

141 Olympic Symbol   **142** Winged Victory

White blob on Lands   Spot below "9" (Cyl. 3 No dot R. 8/4)
End (Cyl. 3 No dot R. 7/3)

Crown flaw (Cyl. 1 No dot,
R. 20/2, later retouched)

(Des P. Metcalfe (T **139**), A. Games (T **140**), S. D. Scott (T **141**) and E. Dulac (T **142**))

1948 (29 July). Olympic Games. W **127**. P 15×14.

495	**139**	2½d. ultramarine	35	10
		s. Opt. "SPECIMEN" (30)	£175	
496	**140**	3d. violet	35	50
		a. Crown flaw	45·00	
		s. Opt. "SPECIMEN" (30)	£175	
497	**141**	6d. bright purple	2·50	75
		s. Opt. "SPECIMEN" (30)	£175	
498	**142**	1s. brown	3·75	2·00
		a. White blob on Lands End	65·00	
		b. Spot below "9"	65·00	
		s. Opt. "SPECIMEN" (30)	£175	
Set of 4			6·00	3·00
First Day Cover				45·00

143 Two Hemispheres   **144** UPU Monument, Berne

145 Goddess Concordia, Globe   **146** Posthorn and Globe
and Points of Compass

Retouched background to "1/-"
(R. 8/5)

Lake in Asia (Cyl. 3 Dot,   Lake in India (Cyl. 2 No dot,
R. 14/1)   R. 8/2)

(Des Mary Adshead (T **143**), P. Metcalfe (T **144**), H. Fleury (T **145**) and Hon. G. R. Bellew (T **146**))

1949 (10 Oct). 75th Anniv of Universal Postal Union. W **127**. P 15×14.

499	**143**	2½d. ultramarine	25	10
		a. Lake in Asia	70·00	
		b. Lake in India	55·00	
		s. Opt. "SPECIMEN" (31)	—	
500	**144**	3d. violet	25	50
		s. Opt. "SPECIMEN" (31)	—	
501	**145**	6d. bright purple	50	75
		s. Opt. "SPECIMEN" (31)	—	
502	**146**	1s. brown	1·00	1·25
		a. Retouched background to "1/-"	60·00	
		s. Opt. "SPECIMEN" (31)	—	
Set of 4			1·50	2·50
First Day Cover				80·00

1950–52. 4d. as No. 468 and others as Nos. 485/9, but colours changed. W **127**. P 15×14.

503	**128**	½d. pale orange (3.5.51)	30	30
		a. Imperf (pair)	£5250	
		b. Tête-bêche (horiz pair)	£16000	
		c. Imperf pane*	£15000	
		Wi. Watermark inverted	50	50
504		1d. light ultramarine (3.5.51)	30	30
		a. Watermark sideways (5.51)	1·10	1·25
		b. Imperf (pair)	£4250	
		c. Imperf three sides (horiz pair)	£5500	
		d. Booklet pane. Three stamps plus three printed labels (3.52)	30·00	
		e. Ditto. Partial tête-bêche pane	£6500	
		Wi. Watermark inverted	4·50	2·50
505		1½d. pale green (3.5.51)	65	60
		a. Watermark sideways (9.51)	3·25	5·00
		Wi. Watermark inverted	6·00	1·00
506		2d. pale red-brown (3.5.51)	75	40
		a. Watermark sideways (5.51)	1·75	2·00
		b. Tête-bêche (horiz pair)	£16000	
		c. Imperf three sides (horiz pair)	£7000	
		Wi. Watermark inverted	6·00	6·50
507		2½d. pale scarlet (3.5.51)	60	40
		a. Watermark sideways (5.51)	1·75	1·75
		b. Tête-bêche (horiz pair)		
		Wi. Watermark inverted	2·00	1·25
508	**129**	4d. light ultramarine (2.10.50)	2·00	1·75
		a. Double impression	†	£7000
Set of 6			4·00	3·25

*BOOKLET ERRORS. Those listed as "imperf panes" show one row of perforations either at the top or at the bottom of the pane of 6.

No. 504c is perforated at foot only and occurs in the same sheet as No. 504b.

No. 506c is also perforated at foot only.

First Day Covers

2.10.50	4d. (508)		£120
3.5.51	½d., 1d., 1½d., 2d., 2½d. (503/7)		55·00

147 H.M.S. Victory   **148** White Cliffs of Dover

149 St. George and the Dragon   **150** Royal Coat of Arms

(Des Mary Adshead (T **147/8**), P. Metcalfe (T **149/50**). Recess
Waterlow)

1951 (3 May). W **133**. P 11×12.

509	**147**	2s.6d. yellow-green	7·50	1·00
		s. Opt. "SPECIMEN" (30)	£800	
510	**148**	5s. red	35·00	1·00
		s. Opt. "SPECIMEN" (30)	£800	
511	**149**	10s. ultramarine	15·00	7·50
		s. Opt. "SPECIMEN" (30)	£800	
512	**150**	£1 brown	45·00	18·00
		s. Opt. "SPECIMEN" (30)	£800	
Set of 4			£100	25·00
First Day Cover				£950

151 "Commerce and Prosperity"   **152** Festival Symbol

(Des E. Dulac (T **151**), A. Games (T **152**))

1951 (3 May). *Festival of Britain*. W **127**. P 15×14.

513	**151**	2½d. scarlet	20	15
514	**152**	4d. ultramarine	30	35
Set of 2			40	40
First Day Cover				38·00

Queen Elizabeth II

6 February 1952

Further detailed information on the stamps of Queen Elizabeth II will be found in Volumes 3, 4 and 5 of the Stanley Gibbons *Great Britain Specialised Catalogue*.

153 Tudor Crown	**154**

155	**156**	**157**

158	**159**	**160**

Queen Elizabeth II and National Emblems

I	II

Two types of the 2½d.

Type I:— In the frontal cross of the diadem, the top line is only half the width of the cross.

Type II:— The top line extends to the full width of the cross and there are signs of strengthening in other parts of the diadem.

(Des Enid Marx (T **154**), M. Farrar-Bell (T **155/6**), G. Knipe (T **157**), Mary Adshead (T **158**), E. Dulac (T **159/60**). Portrait by Dorothy Wilding)

1952–54. W **153.** P 15×14.

515	**154**	½d. orange-red (31.8.53)	10	15
		Wi. Watermark inverted (3.54)	1·00	60
516		1d. ultramarine (31.8.53)	20	20
		a. Booklet pane. Three stamps plus three printed labels	35·00	
		Wi. Watermark inverted (3.54)	6·00	2·75
517		1½d. green (5.12.52)	10	20
		a. Watermark sideways (15.10.54)	50	70
		b. Imperf pane*		
		Wi. Watermark inverted (5.53)	1·00	70
518		2d. red-brown (31.8.53)	20	20
		a. Watermark sideways (8.10.54)	1·25	2·00
		Wi. Watermark inverted (3.54)	30·00	18·00
519	**155**	2½d. carmine-red (Type I) (5.12.52)	15	15
		a. Watermark sideways (15.11.54)	7·00	8·00
		b. Type II (booklets) (5.53)	1·25	1·25
		bWi. Watermark inverted (5.53)	60	75
520		3d. deep lilac (18.1.54)	1·50	90
521	**156**	4d. ultramarine (2.11.53)	3·25	1·25
522	**157**	5d. brown (6.7.53)	75	3·50
523		6d. reddish purple (18.1.54)	4·00	1·00
		a. Imperf three sides (pair)	£3000	

524		7d. bright green (18.1.54)	9·50	5·50
525	**158**	8d. magenta (6.7.53)	75	85
526		9d. bronze-green (8.2.54)	23·00	4·75
527		10d. Prussian blue (8.2.54)	18·00	4·75
528		11d. brown-purple (8.2.54)	35·00	15·00
529	**159**	1s. bistre-brown (6.7.53)	80	50
530	**160**	1s.3d. green (2.11.53)	4·50	3·25
531		1s.6d. grey-blue (2.11.53)	14·00	3·75
Set of 17			£100	40·00

See also Nos. 540/56, 561/6, 570/94 and 599/618a.

*BOOKLET ERRORS. This pane of 6 stamps is completely imperf (see No. 540a, etc).

Stamps with *sideways watermark* come from left-side delivery coils and stamps with *inverted watermark* are from booklets.

For stamps as Types **154/5** and **157/60** with face values in decimal currency see Nos. 2031/3, 2258/9, **MS**2326. and **MS**2367

First Day Covers

5.12.52	1½d., 2½d. (517, 519)	25·00
6.7.53	5d., 8d., 1s. (522, 525, 529)	50·00
31.8.53	½d., 1d., 2d. (515/16, 518)	50·00
2.11.53	4d., 1s.3d., 1s.6d. (521, 530/1)	£170
18.1.54	3d., 6d., 7d. (520, 523/4)	£110
8.2.54	9d., 10d., 11d. (526/8)	£225

161	**162**

163	**164**

(Des E. Fuller (2½d.), M. Goaman (4d.), E. Dulac (1s.3d.), M. Farrar-Bell (1s.6d.). Portrait (except 1s.3d.) by Dorothy Wilding)

1953 (3 June). *Coronation.* W **153.** P 15×14.

532	**161**	2½d. carmine-red	20	25
533	**162**	4d. ultramarine	1·10	1·90
534	**163**	1s.3d. deep yellow-green	5·00	3·00
535	**164**	1s.6d. deep grey-blue	10·00	4·75
Set of 4			16·00	9·00
First Day Cover				75·00

For a £1 value as Type **163** see Nos. **MS**2147 and 2380.

165 St. Edward's Crown

166 Carrickfergus Castle	**167** Caernarvon Castle

168 Edinburgh Castle

169 Windsor Castle

(Des L. Lamb. Portrait by Dorothy Wilding. Recess Waterlow (until 31.12.57) and De La Rue (subsequently))

1955–58. W **165**. P 11×12.

536	**166**	2s.6d. black-brown (23.9.55)	13·00	2·00
		a. De La Rue printing (17.7.58)	30·00	2·50
		Wi. Watermark inverted	†	£3000
537	**167**	5s. rose-carmine (23.9.55)	35·00	4·00
		a. De La Rue printing (30.4.58)	65·00	10·00
538	**168**	10s. ultramarine (1.9.55)	85·00	14·00
		a. De La Rue printing. Dull ultramarine (25.4.58)	£225	22·00
539	**169**	£1 black (1.9.55)	£130	35·00
		a. De La Rue printing (28.4.58)	£350	65·00
Set of 4 (Nos. 536/9)			£225	50·00
Set of 4 (Nos. 536a/9a)			£600	90·00
First Day Cover (538/9)				£850
First Day Cover (536/7)				£650

See also Nos. 595/8a & 759/62.

On 1 January 1958, the contract for printing the high values, T **166** to **169**, was transferred to De La Rue & Co, Ltd. The work of the two printers is very similar, but the following notes will be helpful to those attempting to identify Waterlow and De La Rue stamps of the W **165** issue.

The De La Rue sheets are printed in pairs and have a -| or |-shaped guide-mark at the centre of one side-margin, opposite the middle row of perforations, indicating left and right-hand sheets respectively.

The Waterlow sheets have a small circle (sometimes crossed) instead of a "|-" and this is present in both side-margins opposite the 6th row of stamps, though one is sometimes trimmed off. Short dashes are also present in the perforation gutter between the marginal stamps marking the middle of the four sides and a cross is at the centre of the sheet. The four corners of the sheet have two lines forming a right-angle as trimming marks, but some are usually trimmed off. All these gutter marks and sheet trimming marks are absent in the De La Rue printings. De La Rue used the Waterlow die and no alterations were made to it, so that no difference exists in the design or its size, but the making of new plates at first resulted in slight but measurable variations in the width of the gutters between stamps, particularly the horizontal, as follows:

	Waterlow	De La Rue
Horiz gutters, mm	3.8 to 4.0	3.4 to 3.8

Later D.L.R. plates were however less distinguishable in this respect.

For a short time in 1959 the D.L.R. 2s.6d. appeared with one dot in the bottom margin below the first stamp. It is possible to sort singles with reasonable certainty by general characteristics. The individual lines of the D.L.R. impression are cleaner and devoid of the whiskers of colour of Waterlow's, and the whole impression lighter and clearer.

Owing to the closer setting of the horizontal rows the strokes of the perforating comb are closer; this results in the topmost tooth on each side of De La Rue stamps being narrower than the corresponding teeth in Waterlow's which were more than normally broad.

Shades also help. The 2s.6d. D.L.R. is a warmer, more chocolate shade than the blackish brown of Waterlow; the 5s. a lighter red with less carmine than Waterlow's; the 10s. more blue and less ultramarine; the £1 less intense black.

The paper of D.L.R. printings is uniformly white, identical with that of Waterlow printings from February 1957 onwards, but earlier Waterlow printings are on paper which is creamy by comparison.

In this and later issues the dates of issue given for changes of watermark or paper are those on which supplies were first sent by the Supplies Department to Postmasters.

A used example of No. 538a has been reported with watermark inverted.

1955–58. W **165**. P 15×14.

540	**154**	½d. orange-red (booklets 8.55, sheets 12.12.55)	15	15
		a. Part perf pane*	£4750	
		Wi. Watermark inverted (9.55)	20	30
541		1d. ultramarine (19.9.55)	30	15
		a. Booklet pane. Three stamps plus three printed labels	16·00	
		b. *Tête-bêche* (horiz pair)		
		Wi. Watermark inverted (9.55)	65	60
542		1½d. green (booklet 8.55, sheets 11.10.55)	25	30
		a. Watermark sideways (7.3.56)	35	70
		b. *Tête-bêche* (horiz pair)	£3750	
		Wi. Watermark inverted (8.55)	60	60
543		2d. red-brown (6.9.55)	25	35
		aa. Imperf between (vert pair)	£4250	
		a. Watermark sideways (31.7.56)	55	70
		ab. Imperf between (horiz pair)	£4250	
		Wi. Watermark inverted (9.55)	11·00	9·00
543b		2d. light red-brown (17.10.56)	20	20

		ba. *Tête-bêche* (horiz pair)	£3200	
		bb. Imperf pane*	£5250	
		bc. Part perf pane*	£5250	
		hWi. Watermark inverted (1.57)	9·00	7·00
		d. Watermark sideways (5.3.57)	8·00	7·00
544	**155**	2½d. carmine-red (Type I) (28.9.55)	20	25
		a. Watermark sideways (Type I) (23.3.56)	1·50	1·75
		b. Type II (booklets 9.55, sheets 1957)	45	45
		ba. *Tête-bêche* (horiz pair)	£3200	
		bb. Imperf pane*	£5000	
		bc. Part perf pane*	£4250	
		bWi. Watermark inverted (9.55)	25	70
545		3d. deep lilac (17.7.56)	25	25
		aa. *Tête-bêche* (horiz pair)	£3000	
		a. Imperf three stamps (pair)	£2500	
		b. Watermark sideways (22.11.57)	18·00	17·00
		Wi. Watermark inverted (1.10.57)	1·00	1·00
546	**156**	4d. ultramarine (14.11.55)	1·25	45
547	**157**	5d. brown (21.9.55)	6·00	6·00
548		6d. reddish purple (20.12.55)	4·50	1·25
		aa. Imperf three sides (pair)	£4700	
		a. *Deep claret* (8.5.58)	4·50	1·40
		ab. Imperf three sides (pair)	£4700	
549		7d. bright green (23.4.56)	50·00	10·00
550	**158**	8d. magenta (21.12.55)	7·00	1·25
551		9d. bronze-green (15.12.55)	20·00	2·75
552		10d. Prussian blue (22.9.55)	20·00	2·75
553		11d. brown-purple (28.10.55)	50	1·10
554	**159**	1s. bistre-brown (3.11.55)	22·00	65
555		1s.3d. green (27.3.56)	30·00	1·60
556	**160**	1s.6d. grey-blue (27.3.56)	23·00	1·60
Set of 18			£160	27·00

The dates given for Nos. 540/556 are those on which they were first issued by the Supplies Dept to postmasters.

In December 1956 a completely imperforate sheet of No. 543b was noticed by clerks in a Kent post office, one of whom purchased it against P.O. regulations. In view of this irregularity we do not consider it properly issued.

Types of 2½d. In this issue, in 1957, Type II formerly only found in stamps from booklets, began to replace Type I on sheet stamps.

*BOOKLET ERRORS. Those listed as "imperf panes" show one row of perforations either at top or bottom of the booklet pane; those as "part perf panes" have one row of 3 stamps imperf on three sides.

For Nos. 542 and 553 in Presentation Pack, see after No. 586.

170 Scout Badge and "Rolling Hitch"

171 "Scouts coming to Britain"

172 Globe within a Compass

(Des Mary Adshead (2½d.), P. Keely (4d.), W. H. Brown (1s.3d.))

1957 (1 Aug). *World Scout Jubilee Jamboree*. W **165**. P 15×14.

557	**170**	2½d. carmine-red	50	50
558	**171**	4d. ultramarine	75	1·50
559	**172**	1s.3d. green	4·50	4·50
Set of 3			5·00	5·75
First Day Cover				25·00

173

½d. to 1½d., 2½d., 3d. 2d. Graphite-line arrangements (Stamps viewed from back)

(Adapted F. Langfield)

1957 (12 Sept). *46th Inter-Parliamentary Union Conference*. W **165**. P 15×14.

560	**173**	4d. ultramarine	1·00	1·00
First Day Cover				£140

GRAPHITE-LINED ISSUES. These were used in connection with automatic sorting machinery, first introduced experimentally at Southampton. The graphite lines were printed in black on the back, beneath the gum; two lines per stamp, except for the 2d. In November 1959 phosphor bands were introduced (see notes after No. 598).

1957 (19 Nov). *Graphite-lined issue. Two graphite lines on the back, except 2d. value, which has one line.* W **165**. P 15×14.

561	**154**	½d. orange-red	25	25
562		1d. ultramarine	40	40
563		1½d. green	1·20	1·40
		a. Both lines at left	£1500	£600
564		2d. light red-brown	1·60	2·25
		a. Line at left	£675	£250
565	**155**	2½d. carmine-red (Type II)	8·50	7·00
566		3d. deep lilac	80	50
Set of 6			12·00	10·50
First Day Cover				85·00

No. 564a results from a misplacement of the line and horizontal pairs exist showing one stamp without line. No. 563a results from a similar misplacement. See also Nos. 587/94.

176 Welsh Dragon

177 Flag and Games Emblem

178 Welsh Dragon

(Des R. Stone (3d.), W. H. Brown (6d.), P. Keely (1s.3d.))

1958 (18 July). *Sixth British Empire and Commonwealth Games, Cardiff.* W **165**. P 15×14.

567	**176**	3d. deep lilac	20	20
568	**177**	6d. reddish purple	40	45
569	**178**	1s.3d. green	2·25	2·40
Set of 3			2·50	2·75
First Day Cover				85·00

179 Multiple Crowns

1958–65. W **179**. P 15×14.

570	**154**	½d. orange-red (25.11.58)	10	10
		a. Watermark sideways (26.5.61)	30	40
		c. Part perf pane*	£3500	
		Wi. Watermark inverted (11.58)	40	40
		k. Chalk-surfaced paper (15.7.63)	2·50	2·75
		kWi. Watermark inverted	2·75	3·00
		l. Booklet pane. No. 570a×4	7·50	
		m. Booklet pane. No. 570k×3 *se-tenant* with 574k	9·00	
		n. Booklet pane. No. 570a×2 *se-tenant* with 574l×2 (1.7.64)	2·25	
571		1d. ultramarine (booklets 11.58, sheets 24.3.59)	10	10
		aa. Imperf (vert pair from coil)		
		a. Watermark sideways (26.5.61)	1·50	1·25
		b. Part perf pane*	£4250	
		c. Imperf pane	£5500	
		d. Tête-bêche (horiz pair)		
		Wi. Watermark inverted (11.58)	25	20
		l. Booklet pane. No. 571a×4	10·00	
		m. Booklet pane. No. 571a×2 *se-tenant* with 575a×2 (1d. values at left) (16.8.65)	10·00	
		ma. Ditto. 1d. values at right	11·00	
572		1½d. green (booklets 12.58, sheets 30.8.60)	10	15
		a. Imperf three sides (horiz strip of 3).	£7500	
		b. Watermark sideways (26.5.61)	9·00	7·00

		c. Tête-bêche (horiz pair)		
		Wi. Watermark inverted (12.58)	1·50	80
		l. Booklet pane. No. 572b×4	35·00	
573		2d. light red-brown (4.12.58)	10	10
		a. Watermark sideways (3.4.59)	50	1·00
		Wi. Watermark inverted (10.4.61)	£140	70·00
574	**155**	2½d. carmine-red (Type II) (booklets 11.58, sheets 15.9.59)	10	20
		a. Imperf strip of 3		
		b. *Tête-bêche* (horiz pair)	£5500	
		c. Imperf pane*	£4000	
		Wi. Watermark inverted (Type II) (11.58)	4·50	3·00
		d. Watermark sideways (Type I) (10.11.60)	25	40
		da. Imperf strip of 6		
		e. Type I (wmk upright) (4.10.61)	70	70
		k. Chalk-surfaced paper (Type II) (15.7.63)	50	80
		kWi. Do. Watermark inverted (15.7.63)	75	1·25
		l. Watermark sideways (Type II) (1.7.64)	70	1·25
575		3d. deep lilac (booklets 11.58, sheets 8.12.58)	10	20
		a. Watermark sideways (24.10.58)	25	35
		b. Imperf pane*	£3750	
		c. Part perf pane*	£3500	
		d. Phantom "R" (Cyl 41 no dot)	£350	
		Eda. Do. First retouch	25·00	
		Edb. Do. Second retouch	25·00	
		e. Phantom "R" (Cyl 37 no dot)	50·00	
		Eea. Do. Retouch	15·00	
		Wi. Watermark inverted (11.58)	25	40
		l. Booklet pane. No. 575a×4 (26.5.61)	3·25	
576	**156**	4d. ultramarine (29.10.58)	45	35
		a. *Deep ultramarine*†† (28.4.65)	15	15
		ab. Watermark sideways (31.5.65)	70	55
		ac. Imperf pane*	£4750	
		ad. Part perf pane*	£4000	
		ae. Double impression	£3000	
		al. Booklet pane. No. 576ab×4 (16.8.65)	3·25	
		aWi. Watermark inverted (21.6.65)	60	50
577		4½d. chestnut (9.2.59)	10	25
		Ea. Phantom frame	7·50	
578	**157**	5d. brown (10.11.58)	30	40
579		6d. deep claret (23.12.58)	30	25
		a. Imperf three sides (pair)	£3000	
		b. Imperf (pair)	£3500	
580		7d. brt green (26.11.58)	50	45
581	**158**	8d. magenta (24.2.60)	60	40
582		9d. bronze-green (24.3.59)	60	40
583		10d. Prussian blue (18.11.58)	1·00	50
584	**159**	1s. bistre-brown (30.10.58)	45	30
585		1s.3d. green (17.6.59)	45	30
586	**160**	1s.6d. grey-blue (16.12.58)	4·00	40
Set of 17	(one of each value)		8·00	4·25
First Day Cover (577)				£250
*Presentation Pack***			£275	

*BOOKLET ERROR. See note after No. 556.
**This was issued in 1960 and comprises Nos. 542, 553, 570/1 and 573/86. It exists in two forms: (a) inscribed "10s6d" for sale in the U.K.; and (b) inscribed "$1.80" for sale in the U.S.A.
††This "shade" was brought about by making more deeply etched cylinders, resulting in apparent depth of colour in parts of the design. There is no difference in the colour of the ink.

Sideways watermark. The 2d., 2½d., 3d. and 4d. come from coils and the ½d., 1d., 1½d., 2½d., 3d. and 4d. come from booklets. In coil stamps the sideways watermark shows the top of the watermark to the left *as seen from the front of the stamp*. In the *booklet* stamps it comes equally to the left or right.

Nos. 570k and 574k only come from 2s. "Holiday Resort" experimental undated booklets issued in 1963, in which one page contained 1 × 2½d. *se-tenant* with 3×½d. (See No. 570l).

No. 574l comes from coils, and the "Holiday Resort" experimental booklets dated "1964" comprising four panes each containing two of these 2½d. stamps *se-tenant* vertically with two ½d. No. 570a. (See No. 570m).

2½d. imperf. No. 574a comes from a booklet with watermark upright. No. 574da is from a coil with sideways watermark.

No. 574e comes from sheets bearing cylinder number 42 and is also known on vertical delivery coils.

In 1964 No. 575 was printed from cylinder number 70 no dot and dot on an experimental paper which is distinguishable by an additional watermark letter "T" lying on its side, which occurs about four times in the sheet, usually in the side margins, 48,000 sheets were issued.

No. 575 is known imperforate and *tête-bêche*. These came from booklet sheets which were not issued (*price £25 per pair*).

For a full range of Stanley Gibbons catalogues, please visit **www.stanleygibbons.com**

Phantom "R" varieties

179a Nos. 575d and 615a (Cyl 41 no dot)　　**179b** No. 575Eda

179c No. 575e (Cyl 37 no dot)

179d Phantom Frame variety Nos. 577Ea and 616Eba

3d. An incomplete marginal rule revealed an "R" on cyls 37 and 41 no dot below R. 20/12. It is more noticeable on cyl 41 because of the wider marginal rule. The "R" on cyl 41 was twice retouched, the first being as illustrated here (No. 575Eda) and traces of the "R" can still be seen in the second retouch.

No. 575d is best collected in a block of 4 or 6 with full margins in order to be sure that it is not 615a with phosphor lines removed.

The retouch on cyl 37 is not easily identified: there is no trace of the "R" but the general appearance of that part of the marginal rule is uneven.

4½d. An incomplete marginal rule revealed a right-angled shaped frame-line on cyl 8 no dot below R. 20/12. It occurs on ordinary and phosphor.

WHITER PAPER. On 18 May 1962 the Post Office announced that a whiter paper was being used for the current issue (including Nos. 595/8). This is beyond the scope of this catalogue, but the whiter papers are listed in Vol. 3 of the Stanley Gibbons *Great Britain Specialised Catalogue.*

1958 (24 Nov)–**61**. *Graphite-lined issue. Two graphite lines on the back, except 2d. value, which has one line.* W **179**. P 15×14.

587	**154**	½d. orange-red (15.6.59)	9·00	9·00
		Wi. Watermark inverted (4.8.59)	3·25	4·00
588		1d. ultramarine (18.12.58)	2·00	1·50
		a. Misplaced graphite lines (7.61)*	80	1·25
		b. Three graphite lines	20·00	18·00
		Wi. Watermark inverted (4.8.59)	1·50	2·00
589		1½d. green (4.8.59)	90·00	80·00
		Wi. Watermark inverted (4.8.59)	75·00	60·00
590		2d. light red-brown (24.11.58)	9·00	3·50
		a. One line at left	£950	
591	**155**	2½d. carmine-red (Type II) (9.6.59)	10·00	10·00
		Wi. Watermark inverted (21.8.59)	65·00	50·00
592		3d. deep lilac (24.11.58)	50	65
		a. Misplaced graphite lines (5.61)*	£480	£380
		b. One graphite line	£700	£300
		c. Three graphite lines	32·00	22·00
		Wi. Watermark inverted (4.8.59)	45	75
593	**156**	4d. ultramarine (29.4.59)	5·50	5·00
		a. Misplaced graphite lines (1961)*	£2200	
594		4½d. chestnut (3.6.59)	6·50	5·00
Set of 8 (cheapest)			£110	70·00

Nos. 587/9 were only issued in booklets or coils (587/8).

*No. 588a (in coils), and Nos. 592a/c and 593a (all in sheets) result from the use of a residual stock of graphite-lined paper. As the use of graphite lines had ceased, the register of the lines in relation to the stamps was of no importance and numerous misplacements occurred - two lines close together, one line only, etc. No. 588a refers to two lines at left or right; No. 592a refers to stamps with two lines only at left and both clear of the perforations No. 592b refers to stamps with a single line and Nos. 588b, 592c and 593a to stamps with two lines at left (with left line down perforations) and traces of a third line down the opposite perforations.

No. 592 Wi was included in 4s.6d. booklets, L15 and L16, dated April and June 1959. These represent productions dates not issue dates.

(Recess D.L.R. (until 31.12.62), then B.W.)

1959–68. W **179**. P 11×12.

595	**166**	2s.6d. black-brown (22.7.59)	10·00	75
		Wi. Watermark inverted	—	£2200
		a. B.W. printing (1.7.63)	35	40
		aWi. Watermark inverted	£2750	£250
		k. Chalk-surfaced paper (30.5.68)	50	1·50
596	**167**	5s. scarlet-vermilion (15.6.59)	45·00	2·00
		Wi. Watermark inverted	£7500	£525
		a. B.W. ptg. *Red* (shades) (3.9.63)	1·20	50
		ab. Printed on the gummed side	£1500	
		aWi. Watermark inverted	£375	£200
597	**168**	10s. blue (21.7.59)	55·00	5·00
		a. B.W. ptg. *Bright ultramarine* (16.10.63)	4·50	4·50
		aWi. Watermark inverted	—	£2200
598	**169**	£1 black (23.6.59)	£120	12·00
		Wi. Watermark inverted	—	£2500
		a. B.W. printing (14.11.63)	13·00	8·00
		aWi. Watermark inverted	£12000	£3500
Set of 4 (Nos. 595/8)			£195	17·00
Set of 4 (Nos. 595a/8a)			15·00	11·00
Presentation Pack (1960)*			£1250	

The B.W. printings have a marginal Plate Number. They are generally more deeply engraved than the D.L.R. showing more of the Diadem detail and heavier lines on Her Majesty's face. The vertical perf is 11.9 to 12 against D.L.R. 11.8.

*This exists in three forms: (a) inscribed "$6.50" for sale in the U.S.A.; (b) without price for sale in the U.K.; (c) inscribed "£1 18s" for sale in the U.K. See also Nos. 759/62.

PHOSPHOR BAND ISSUES. These are printed on the front and are wider than graphite lines. They are not easy to see but show as broad vertical bands at certain angles to the light.

Values representing the rate for printed papers (and when this was abolished in 1968 for second issue class mail) have one band and others two, three or four bands as stated, according to the size and format.

In the small size stamps the bands are on each side with the single band at left (*except where otherwise stated*). In the large size commemorative stamps the single band may be at left, centre or right, varying in different designs. The bands are vertical on both horizontal and vertical designs *except where otherwise stated.*

The phosphor was originally applied typographically but later usually by photogravure and sometimes using flexography, a typographical process using rubber cylinders.

Three different types of phosphor have been used, distinguishable by the colour emitted under an ultra-violet lamp, the first being green, then blue and now violet. Different sized bands are also known. All these are fully listed in Vol. 3 of the Stanley Gibbons *Great Britain Specialised Catalogue.*

Varieties. Misplaced and missing phosphor bands are known but such varieties are beyond the scope of this Catalogue.

1959 (18 Nov). *Phosphor-Graphite issue. Two phosphor bands on front and two graphite lines on back, except 2d. value, which has one band on front and one line on back.* (a) W **165**. P 15×14.

599	**154**	½d. orange-red	4·00	3·75
600		1d. ultramarine	11·00	11·00
601		1½d. green	4·00	4·00

(b) W **179**.

605	**154**	2d. light red-brown (1 band)	5·00	4·25
		a. Error. W **165**	£180	£150
606	**155**	2½d. carmine-red (Type II)	22·00	18·00
607		3d. deep lilac	10·00	8·00
608	**156**	4d. ultramarine	20·00	16·00
609		4½d. chestnut	30·00	20·00
Set of 8			85·00	70·00
Presentation Pack			£300	

Examples of the 2½d., No. 606, exist showing watermark W **165** in error. It is believed that phosphor-graphite stamps of this value with this watermark were not used by the public for postal purposes.

The Presentation Pack was issued in 1960 and comprises two each of Nos. 599/609. It exists in two forms: (a) inscribed "3s 8d" for sale in the U.K. and (b) inscribed "50c" for sale in the U.S.A.

1960 (22 June)–**67**. *Phosphor issue. Two phosphor bands on front, except where otherwise stated.* W **179**. P 15×14.

610	**154**	½d. orange-red	10	15
		a. Watermark sideways (14.7.61)	10·00	10·00
		Wi. Watermark inverted (14.8.60)	90	90
		l. Booklet pane. No. 610Ua×4	40·00	
611		1d. ultramarine	10	10
		a. Watermark sideways (14.7.61)	90	90

	Wi.	Watermark inverted (14.8.60)	25	30
	I.	Booklet pane. No. 611a×4	9·00	
	m.	Booklet pane. No. 611a×2 *se-tenant* with 615d×2† (16.8.65)	15·00	
	ma.	Booklet pane. No. 611a×2 *se-tenant* with 615dEa×2 (16.8.65)......................	15·00	
	n.	Booklet pane. No. 611a×2 *se-tenant* with 615b×2†† (11.67)........................	8·00	
612		1½d. green..	15	15
	a.	Watermark sideways (14.7.61)	10·00	10·00
	Wi.	Watermark inverted (14.8.60)	12·00	9·50
	I.	Booklet pane. No. 612a×4	42·00	
613		2d. light red-brown (1 band)	16·00	18·00
613a		2d. light red-brown (2 bands) (4.10.61)	10	15
	aa.	Imperf three sides*** (pair)................	£4500	
	ab.	Watermark sideways (6.4.67)..............	30	60
614	**155**	2½d. carmine-red (Type II) (2 bands)*	40	30
	Wi.	Watermark inverted (14.8.60)	£170	£140
614a		2½d. carmine-red (Type II) (1 band) (4.10.61)	60	75
	aWi.	Watermark inverted (3.62)	40·00	38·00
614b		2½d. carmine-red (Type I) (1 band) (4.10.61)	45·00	40·00
615		3d. deep lilac (2 bands).............................	60	55
	a.	Phantom "R" (Cyl 41 no dot)..............	40·00	
	Wi.	Watermark inverted (14.8.60)	50	90
	b.	Watermark sideways (14.7.61)	1·75	1·75
	I.	Booklet pane. No. 615b×4..................	20·00	
615c		3d. deep lilac (1 band at right) (29.4.65)	60	55
	cEa.	Band at left......................................	60	70
	cWi.	Watermark inverted (band at right) (2.67)	8·00	7·00
	cWia.	Watermark inverted (band at left) (2.67)	65·00	60·00
	d.	Watermark sideways (band at right) (16.8.65)	5·50	5·00
	dEa.	Watermark sideways (band at left) .	5·50	5·00
	e.	One centre band (8.12.66)................	40	45
	eWi.	Watermark inverted (8.67)	3·00	3·50
	ea.	Wmk sideways (19.6.67)...................	70	50
616	**156**	4d. ultramarine..	3·50	3·50
	a.	*Deep ultramarine* (28.4.65)	25	25
	aa.	Part perf pane...................................	£4750	
	ab.	Wmk sideways	35	50
	aWi.	Watermark inverted (21.6.65)	40	40
	al.	Booklet pane. No. 616ab×4	2·50	
616b		4½d. chestnut (13.9.61)............................	25	30
	Eba.	Phantom frame	15·00	
616c	**157**	5d. brown (9.6.67)....................................	25	35
617		6d. purple..	30	30
617a		7d. bright green (15.2.67)	55	50
617b	**158**	8d. magenta (28.6.67)	40	45
617c		9d. bronze-green (29.12.66)	60	55
617d		10d. Prussian blue (30.12.66)	70	60
617e	**159**	1s. bistre-brown (28.6.67)	40	35
618		1s.3d. green...	1·90	2·50
618a	**160**	1s.6d. grey-blue (12.12.66)	2·00	2·00
Set of 17 (one of each value)			7·50	8·00

The automatic facing equipment was brought into use on 6 July 1960 but the phosphor stamps may have been released a few days earlier.

The stamps with watermark sideways are from booklets except Nos. 613ab and 615ea which are from coils. No. 616ab comes from both booklets and coils.

No. 615a. See footnote after No. 586.

*No. 614 with two bands on the creamy paper was originally from cylinder 50 dot and no dot. When the change in postal rates took place in 1965 it was reissued from cylinder 57 dot and no dot on the whiter paper. Some of these latter were also released in error in districts of S.E. London in September 1964. The shade of the reissue is slightly more carmine.

***This comes from the bottom row of a sheet which is imperf at bottom and both sides.

†Booklet pane No. 611m shows the 1d. stamps at left and No. 611ma the 1d. stamps at right.

††Booklet pane No. 611n comes from 2s. booklets of January and March 1968. The two bands on the 3d. stamp were intentional because of the technical difficulties in producing one band and two band stamps *se-tenant*.

The Phosphor-Graphite stamps had the phosphor applied by typography but the Phosphor issue can be divided into those with the phosphor applied typographically and others where it was applied by photogravure. Moreover the photogravure form can be further divided into those which phosphoresce green and others which phosphoresce blue under ultra-violet light. From 1965 violet phosphorescence was introduced in place of the blue. All these are fully listed in Vol. 3 of the Stanley Gibbons *Great Britain Specialised Catalogue*.

Unlike previous one-banded phosphor stamps, No. 615c has a broad band extending over two stamps so that alternate stamps have the band at left or right (same prices either way). No. 615cWi comes from the 10s phosphor booklet of February 1967 and No. 615eWi comes from the 10s. phosphor booklets of August 1967 and February 1968.

Nos. 615a (Phantom "R") and 615Eba (Phantom frame), see illustrations following No. 586.

180 Postboy of 1660   **181** Posthorn of 1660

Broken mane (Cyl. 1 No dot, R. 17/2)

(Des R. Stone (3d.), Faith Jaques (1s.3d.))

1960 (7 July). *Tercentenary of Establishment of General Letter Office.* W **179** (sideways on 1s.3d.). P 15×14 (3d.) or 14×15 (1s.3d.).

619	**180**	3d. deep lilac	50	50
		a. Broken mane.............................	35·00	
620	**181**	1s.3d. green.................................	3·75	4·25
Set of 2			3·75	4·25
First Day Cover				65·00

182 Conference Emblem

(Des R. Stone (emblem, P. Rahikainen))

1960 (19 Sept). *First Anniversary of European Postal and Telecommunications Conference. Chalk-surfaced paper.* W **179**. P 15×14.

621	**182**	6d. bronze-green and purple	2·00	50
622		1s.6d. brown and blue............................	9·50	5·00
Set of 2			11·00	5·50
First Day Cover				65·00

SCREENS. Up to this point all photogravure stamps were printed in a 200 screen (200 dots per linear inch), but all later commemorative stamps are a finer 250 screen. Exceptionally No. 622 has a 200 screen for the portrait and a 250 screen for the background.

184 "Growth of Savings"

183 Thrift Plant   **185** Thrift Plant

(Des P. Gauld (2½d.), M. Goaman (others))

1961 (28 Aug). *Centenary of Post Office Savings Bank. Chalk-surfaced paper.* W **179** (*sideways on* 2½d.) P 14×15 (2½d.) or 15×14 (others)

A. "Timson" Machine

623A	**183**	2½d. black and red	25	25
		a. Black omitted	£25000	
624A	**184**	3d. orange-brown and violet	20	20
		a. Orange-brown omitted	£550	
		Eb. Perf through side sheet margin	35·00	38·00
625A	**185**	1s.6d. red and blue	2·50	2·25
Set of 3			2·75	2·50
First Day Cover				75·00

B. "Thrissell" Machine

623B	**183**	2½d. black and red	2·25	2·25
624B	**184**	3d. orange-brown and violet	40	40
		a. Orange-brown omitted	£1500	

2½d. TIMSON. Cyls 1E-1F. Deeply shaded portrait (brownish black).

2½d. THRISSELL. Cyls 1D-1B or 1D (dot)-1B (dot). Lighter portrait (grey-black).

3d. TIMSON. Cyls 3D-3E. Clear, well-defined portrait with deep shadows and bright highlights.

3d. THRISSELL. Cyls 3C-3B or 3C (dot)-3B (dot). Dull portrait, lacking in contrast.

Sheet marginal examples *without* single extension perf hole on the short side of the stamp are always "Timson", as are those with large punch-hole *not* coincident with printed three-sided box guide mark.

The 3d. "Timson" perforated completely through the right hand side margin comes from a relatively small part of the printing perforated on a sheet-fed machine.

Normally the "Timsons" were perforated in the reel, with three large punch-holes in both long margins and the perforations completely through both short margins. Only one punch-hole coincides with the guide-mark.

The "Thrissells" have one large punch-hole in one long margin, coinciding with guide-mark and one short margin imperf (except sometimes for encroachments).

186 C.E.P.T. Emblem   **187** Doves and Emblem

188 Doves and Emblem

(Des M. Goaman (doves T. Kurpershoek))

1961 (18 Sept). *European Postal and Telecommunications (C.E.P.T.) Conference, Torquay. Chalk-surfaced paper.* W **179**. P 15×14.

626	**186**	2d. orange, pink and brown	15	10
		a. Orange omitted	£18000	
		b. Pink omitted		
627	**187**	4d. buff, mauve and ultramarine	15	15
628	**188**	10d. turquoise, pale green and Prussian blue	15	50
		a. Pale green omitted	£22500	
		b. Turquoise omitted	£7000	
Set of 3			40	60
First Day Cover				6·00

189 Hammer Beam Roof, Westminster Hall   **190** Palace of Westminster

(Des Faith Jaques)

1961 (25 Sept). *Seventh Commonwealth Parliamentary Conference. Chalk-surfaced paper.* W **179** (*sideways on* 1s.3d.) P 15×14 (6d.) or 14×15 (1s.3d.).

629	**189**	6d. purple and gold	25	25
		a. Gold omitted	£2400	

630	**190**	1s.3d. green and blue	2·50	2·75
		a. Blue (Queen's head) omitted	£35000	
		b. Green omitted		
Set of 2			2·75	3·00
First Day Cover				30·00

191 "Units of Productivity"   **192** "National Productivity"

193 "Unified Productivity"

Lake in Scotland (Cyls. 2A-2B Dot, R. 1/3)   Kent omitted (Cyls. 2C-2B No. Dot, R. 18/2)

(Des D. Gentleman)

1962 (14 Nov). *National Productivity Year. Chalk-surfaced paper.* W **179** (*inverted on* 2½d. *and* 3d.). P 15×14.

631	**191**	2½d. myrtle-green and carmine-red (*shades*)	20	20
		Ea. Blackish olive and carmine-red	25	15
		p. One phosphor band. *Blackish olive and carmine-red*	60	50
632	**192**	3d. light blue and violet (*shades*)	50	25
		a. Light blue (Queen's head) omitted	£5000	
		b. Lake in Scotland	25·00	
		c. Kent omitted	30·00	
		p. Three phosphor bands	1·50	80
633	**193**	1s.3d. carmine, light blue and deep green	1·50	1·75
		a. Light blue (Queen's head) omitted	£15000	
		p. Three phosphor bands	35·00	22·00
Set of 3 (Ordinary)			2·00	1·90
Set of 3 (Phosphor)			30·00	22·00
First Day Cover (Ordinary)				55·00
First Day Cover (Phosphor)				£150

194 Campaign Emblem and Family   **195** Children of Three Races

(Des M. Goaman)

1963 (21 Mar). *Freedom from Hunger. Chalk-surfaced paper.* W **179** (*inverted*). P 15×14.

634	**194**	2½d. crimson and pink	25	10
		p. One phosphor band	3·00	1·25
635	**195**	1s.3d. bistre-brown and yellow	1·90	1·90
		p. Three phosphor bands	30·00	23·00
Set of 2 (Ordinary)			2·00	2·00
Set of 2 (Phosphor)			30·00	24·00
First Day Cover (Ordinary)				35·00
First Day Cover (Phosphor)				52·00

196 "Paris Conference"

(Des R. Stone)

1963 (7 May). *Paris Postal Conference Centenary. Chalk-surfaced paper.*
W **179** (inverted). P 15×14.

636	**196**	6d. green and mauve	50	50
		a. Green omitted	£5500	
		p. Three phosphor bands	6·00	7·00
First Day Cover (Ordinary)				16·00
First Day Cover (Phosphor)				37·00

197 Posy of Flowers

198 Woodland Life

"Caterpillar" flaw (Cyl. 3B Dot, R. 3/2)

(Des S. Scott (3d.), M. Goaman (4½d.))

1963 (16 May). *National Nature Week. Chalk-surfaced paper.*
P 15×14.

637	**197**	3d. yellow, green, brown and black	15	15
		a. "Caterpillar" flaw	30·00	
		p. Three phosphor bands	60	60
		pa. "Caterpillar" flaw	30·00	
638	**198**	4½d. black, blue, yellow, magenta and brown-red	35	35
		p. Three phosphor bands	3·00	3·00
Set of 2 (Ordinary)			50	50
Set of 2 (Phosphor)			3·50	3·50
First Day Cover (Ordinary)				22·00
First Day Cover (Phosphor)				40·00

Special First Day of Issue Postmark

	Ordinary	Phosphor
London E.C. (Type A)	24·00	30·00

This postmark was used on First Day Covers serviced by the Philatelic Bureau.

199 Rescue at Sea

200 19th-century Lifeboat

201 Lifeboatmen

(Des D. Gentleman)

1963 (31 May). *Ninth International Lifeboat Conference, Edinburgh. Chalk-surfaced paper.* W **179**. P 15×14.

639	**199**	2½d. blue, black and red	25	25
		p. One phosphor band	50	60
640	**200**	4d. red, yellow, brown, black and blue	50	50
		p. Three phosphor bands	50	60
641	**201**	1s.6d. sepia, yellow and grey-blue	3·00	3·25
		p. Three phosphor bands	48·00	28·00
Set of 3 (Ordinary)			3·25	3·50
Set of 3 (Phosphor)			48·00	28·00
First Day Cover (Ordinary)				35·00
First Day Cover (Phosphor)				55·00

Special First Day of Issue Postmark

	Ordinary	Phosphor
London	65·00	80·00

This postmark was used on First Day Covers serviced by the Philatelic Bureau.

202 Red Cross   **203**

204

(Des H. Bartram)

1963 (15 Aug). *Red Cross Centenary Congress. Chalk-surfaced paper.* W **179**. P 15×14.

642	**202**	3d. red and deep lilac	25	25
		a. Red omitted	£15000	
		p. Three phosphor bands	1·10	1·00
		pa. Red omitted	£35000	
643	**203**	1s.3d. red, blue and grey	3·00	3·00
		p. Three phosphor bands	35·00	27·00
644	**204**	1s.6d. red, blue and bistre	3·00	3·00
		p. Three phosphor bands	35·00	27·00
Set of 3 (Ordinary)			5·00	5·75
Set of 3 (Phosphor)			65·00	55·00
First Day Cover (Ordinary)				40·00
First Day Cover (Phosphor)				90·00

Special First Day of Issue Postmark

 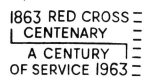

	Ordinary	Phosphor
London E.C	75·00	£100

This postmark was used on First Day Covers serviced by the Philatelic Bureau.

205 Commonwealth Cable

(Des P. Gauld)

1963 (3 Dec). *Opening of COMPAC (Trans-Pacific Telephone Cable). Chalk-surfaced paper.* W **179**. P 15×14.

645	**205**	1s.6d. blue and black	2·75	2·50
		a. Black omitted	£7500	
		p. Three phosphor bands	16·00	15·50
First Day Cover (Ordinary)				28·00
First Day Cover (Phosphor)				40·00

Special First Day of Issue Postmark

	Ordinary	Phosphor
Philatelic Bureau, London E.C.1 (Type A)	45·00	50·00

PRESENTATION PACKS. Special Packs comprising slip-in cards with printed commemorative inscriptions and descriptive notes on the back and with protective covering, were introduced in 1964 with the Shakespeare issue. These are listed and priced. Issues of 1968-69 (British Paintings to the Prince of Wales Investiture) were also issued in packs with text in German for sale through the Post Office's German Agency and these are also quoted. Subsequently, however, the packs sold in Germany were identical with the normal English version with the addition of a separate printed insert card with German text. These, as also English packs with Japanese and Dutch printed cards for sale in Japan and the Netherlands respectively, are listed in Vols. 3 and 5 of the Stanley Gibbons *Great Britain Specialised Catalogue.*

206 Puck and Bottom (*A Midsummer Night's Dream*) **207** Feste (*Twelfth Night*)

208 Balcony Scene (*Romeo and Juliet*) **209** "Eve of Agincourt" (*Henry V*)

210 Hamlet contemplating Yorick's Skull (*Hamlet*) and Queen Elizabeth II

(Des D. Gentleman. Photo Harrison & Sons (3d., 6d., 1s.3d., 1s.6d.). Des C. and R. Ironside. Recess B.W. (2s.6d.))

1964 (23 Apr). *Shakespeare Festival. Chalk-surfaced paper.* W **179**. P 11×12 (2s.6d.) or 15×14 (others).

646	**206**	3d. yellow-bistre, black and deep violet-blue (*shades*)	15	15
		p. Three phosphor bands	25	30
647	**207**	6d. yellow, orange, black and yellow-olive (*shades*)	30	30
		p. Three phosphor bands	75	1·00
648	**208**	1s.3d. cerise, blue-green, black and sepia (*shades*)	75	1·00
		Wi. Watermark inverted	£800	
		p. Three phosphor bands	4·00	6·50
		pWi. Watermark inverted	£325	
649	**209**	1s.6d. violet, turquoise, black and blue (*shades*)	1·00	85
		Wi. Watermark inverted		£1300
		p. Three phosphor bands	8·00	8·00
650	**210**	2s.6d. deep slate-purple (*shades*)	2·75	2·75
		Wi. Watermark inverted	£550	
Set of 5 (Ordinary)			4·50	4·50
Set of 4 (Phosphor)			12·00	14·00
First Day Cover (Ordinary)				12·00
First Day Cover (Phosphor)				17·00
Presentation Pack (Ordinary)			22·00	

The 3d. is known with yellow-bistre missing in the top two-thirds of the figures of Puck and Bottom. This occurred in the top row only of a sheet.

Special First Day of Issue Postmark

	Ordinary	Phosphor
Stratford-upon-Avon. Warwicks	15·00	22·00

This postmark was used on First Day Covers serviced by the Philatelic Bureau, as well as on covers posted at Stratford P.O.

211 Flats near Richmond Park ("Urban Development") **212** Shipbuilding Yards, Belfast ("Industrial Activity")

213 Beddgelert Forest Park, Snowdonia ("Forestry") **214** Nuclear Reactor, Dounreay ("Technological Development")

Short line under 2½d. (Cyl. 3D, various positions)

(Des D. Bailey)

1964 (1 July). *20th International Geographical Congress, London. Chalk-surfaced paper.* W **179**. P 15×14.

651	**211**	2½d. black, olive-yellow, olive-grey and turquoise-blue	10	10
		a. Short line under 2½d.	10·00	
		p. One phosphor band	40	50
652	**212**	4d. orange-brown, red-brown, rose, black and violet	30	30
		a. Violet (face value) omitted	£300	
		c. Violet and red-brown (dock walls) omitted	£550	
		d. Red brown (dock walls) omitted	£850	
		Wi. Watermark inverted	£850	
		p. Three phosphor bands	1·25	1·25
653	**213**	8d. yellow-brown, emerald, green and black	75	85
		a. Green (lawn) omitted	£20000	
		Wi. Watermark inverted	£1700	
		p. Three phosphor bands	2·50	2·75
654	**214**	1s.6d. yellow-brown, pale pink, black and brown	3·50	3·50
		Wi. Watermark inverted	45·00	
		p. Three phosphor bands	28·00	22·00
Set of 4 (Ordinary)			4·50	4·50
Set of 4 (Phosphor)			30·00	24·00
First Day Cover (Ordinary)				22·00
First Day Cover (Phosphor)				40·00
Presentation Pack (Ordinary)			£160	

A used example of the 4d. is known with the red-brown omitted.

Special First Day of Issue Postmark

	Ordinary	Phosphor
G.P.O. Philatelic Bureau, London E.C.1 (Type B)	25·00	35·00

215 Spring Gentian **216** Dog Rose

217 Honeysuckle **218** Fringed Water Lily

Broken petal (Cyl. 3A Dot, R. 1/2)	Line through "INTER" (Cyl. 2A No dot, R. 1/1)

(Des M. and Sylvia Goaman)

1964 (5 Aug). *Tenth International Botanical Congress, Edinburgh. Chalk-surfaced paper.* W **179**. P 15×14.

655	**215**	3d. violet, blue and sage-green	25	25
		a. Blue omitted	£20000	
		b. Sage-green omitted	£23000	
		c. Broken petal	30·00	
		p. Three phosphor bands	40	40
		pc. Broken petal	30·00	
656	**216**	6d. apple-green, rose, scarlet and green	50	50
		p. Three phosphor bands	2·50	2·75
657	**217**	9d. lemon, green, lake and rose-red	1·75	2·25
		a. Green (leaves) omitted	£22000	
		Wi. Watermark inverted	50·00	
		p. Three phosphor bands	4·50	4·00
		pb. Line through "INTER"	30·00	
658	**218**	1s.3d. yellow, emerald, reddish violet and grey-green	2·50	2·50
		a. Yellow (flowers) omitted	£45000	
		Wi. Watermark inverted	£2000	
		p. Three phosphor bands	25·00	20·00
Set of 4 (Ordinary)			4·50	4·50
Set of 4 (Phosphor)			30·00	24·00
First Day Cover (Ordinary)				30·00
First Day Cover (Phosphor)				40·00
Presentation Pack (Ordinary)			£160	

Unissued Goaman designs of the 3d and 9d values on perforated and gummed paper are known.

Special First Day of Issue Postmark

	Ordinary	Phosphor
G.P.O. Philatelic Bureau, London E.C.1 (Type B)	28·00	45·00

219 Forth Road Bridge	**220** Forth Road and Railway Bridges

(Des A. Restall)

1964 (4 Sept). *Opening of Forth Road Bridge. Chalk-surfaced paper.* W **179**. P 15×14.

659	**219**	3d. black, blue and reddish violet	10	10
		p. Three phosphor bands	1·00	1·50
660	**220**	6d. blackish lilac, light blue and carmine-red	40	40
		a. Light blue omitted	£6250	
		Wi. Watermark inverted	5·00	
		p. Three phosphor bands	4·50	4·75
		pWi. Watermark inverted	£800	
Set of 2 (Ordinary)			50	50
Set of 2 (Phosphor)			5·00	5·75
First Day Cover (Ordinary)				7·00
First Day Cover (Phosphor)				18·00
Presentation Pack (Ordinary)			£400	

Special First Day of Issue Postmarks

	Ordinary	Phosphor
G.P.O. Philatelic Bureau, London E.C.1 (Type B)	20·00	28·00
North Queensferry, Fife	40·00	£130
South Queensferry, West Lothian	32·00	95·00

The Queensferry postmarks were applied to First Day Covers sent to a temporary Philatelic Bureau at Edinburgh

221 Sir Winston Churchill

(Des D. Gentleman and Rosalind Dease, from photograph by Karsh)

1965 (8 July). *Churchill Commemoration. Chalk-surfaced paper.* W **179**. P 15×14.

I. "REMBRANDT" Machine

661	**221**	4d. black and olive-brown	10	10
		Wi. Watermark inverted	3·00	
		p. Three phosphor bands	25	25

II. "TIMSON" Machine

661*a*	**221**	4d. black and olive-brown	35	35

III. "L. & M. 4" Machine

662	–	1s.3d. black and grey	30	40
		Wi. Watermark inverted	£100	
		p. Three phosphor bands	2·50	3·00
Set of 2 (Ordinary)			40	50
Set of 2 (Phosphor)			2·75	3·25
First Day Cover (Ordinary)				7·00
First Day Cover (Phosphor)				9·00
Presentation Pack (Ordinary)			70·00	

The 1s.3d. shows a closer view of Churchill's head.

Two examples of the 4d. value exist with the Queen's head omitted, one due to something adhering to the cylinder and the other due to a paper fold. The stamp also exists with Churchill's head omitted, also due to a paper fold.

4d. REMBRANDT, Cyls 1A-1B dot and no dot. Lack of shading detail on Churchill's portrait. Queen's portrait appears dull and coarse. This is a rotary machine which is sheet-fed.

4d. TIMSON, Cyls 5A-6B no dot. More detail on Churchill's portrait –furrow on forehead, his left eyebrow fully drawn and more shading on cheek. Queen's portrait lighter and sharper. This is a reel-fed two-colour 12-in. wide rotary machine and the differences in impressions are due to the greater pressure applied by this machine.

1s.3d. Cyls 1A-1B no dot. The "Linotype and Machinery No. 4" machine is an ordinary sheet-fed rotary press machine. Besides being used for printing the 1s.3d. stamps it was also employed for overprinting the phosphor bands on both values.

Special First Day of Issue Postmark

	Ordinary	Phosphor
G.P.O. Philatelic Bureau, London E.C.1 (Type B)	8·00	12·00

A First Day of Issue handstamp was provided at Bladon, Oxford, for this issue.

222 Simon de Montfort's Seal

223 Parliament Buildings (after engraving by Hollar, 1647)

(Des S. Black (6d.), R. Guyatt (2s.6d.))

1965 (19 July). *700th Anniversary of Simon de Montfort's Parliament. Chalk-surfaced paper.* W **179**. P 15×14.

663	**222**	6d. olive-green	20	20
		p. Three phosphor bands	60	1·00
664	**223**	2s.6d. black, grey and pale drab	80	1·50
		Wi. Watermark inverted	40·00	
Set of 2 (Ordinary)			1·00	1·25
First Day Cover (Ordinary)				15·00
First Day Cover (Phosphor)				26·00
Presentation Pack (Ordinary)			75·00	

Special First Day of Issue Postmark

Ordinary

G.P.O. Philatelic Bureau, London E.C.1 (Type B) .... 15·00

A First Day of Issue handstamp was provided at Evesham, Worcs, for this issue.

224 Bandsmen and Banner   **225** Three Salvationists

(Des M. Farrar-Bell (3d.), G. Trenaman (1s.6d.))

1965 (9 Aug). *Salvation Army Centenary. Chalk-surfaced paper.* W **179**. P 15×14.

665	**224**	3d. indigo, grey-blue, cerise, yellow and brown..............	25	25
		p. One phosphor band..................	25	40
666	**225**	1s.6d. red, blue, yellow and brown..............	1·00	1·50
		p. Three phosphor bands..............	2·50	2·75
Set of 2 (*Ordinary*)			1·00	1·50
Set of 2 (*Phosphor*)			2·50	3·00
First Day Cover (*Ordinary*)				23·00
First Day Cover (*Phosphor*)				33·00

The Philatelic Bureau did not provide First Day Cover services for Nos. 665/70.

226 Lister's Carbolic Spray   **227** Lister and Chemical Symbols

(Des P. Gauld (4d.), F. Ariss (1s.))

1965 (1 Sept). *Centenary of Joseph Lister's Discovery of Antiseptic Surgery. Chalk-surfaced paper.* W **179**. P 15×14.

667	**226**	4d. indigo, brown-red and grey-black...	25	15
		a. Brown-red (tube) omitted..................	£550	
		b. Indigo omitted	£6500	
		p. Three phosphor bands.....................	25	25
		pa. Brown-red (tube) omitted..............	£7000	
668	**227**	1s. black, purple and new blue..............	1·00	1·10
		Wi. Watermark inverted.....................	£600	
		p. Three phosphor bands.....................	2·00	2·50
		pWi. Watermark inverted.....................	£500	
Set of 2 (*Ordinary*)			1·00	1·25
Set of 2 (*Phosphor*)			2·25	2·50
First Day Cover (*Ordinary*)				12·00
First Day Cover (*Phosphor*)				15·00

228 Trinidad Carnival Dancers   **229** Canadian Folk-dancers

(Des D. Gentleman and Rosalind Dease)

1965 (1 Sept). *Commonwealth Arts Festival. Chalk-surfaced paper.* W **179**. P 15×14.

669	**228**	6d. black and orange.....................	20	20
		p. Three phosphor bands.....................	30	50
670	**229**	1s.6d. black and light reddish violet	80	1·10
		p. Three phosphor bands.....................	2·50	3·50
Set of 2 (*Ordinary*)			1·00	1·25
Set of 2 (*Phosphor*)			2·75	3·50
First Day Cover (*Ordinary*)				16·50
First Day Cover (*Phosphor*)				22·00

230 Flight of Supermarine Spitfires   **231** Pilot in Hawker Hurricane Mk I

232 Wing-tips of Supermarine Spitfire and Messerschmitt Bf 109   **233** Supermarine Spitfires attacking Heinkel He-111H Bomber

234 Supermarine Spitfire attacking Junkers Ju 87B "Stuka" Dive-bomber   **235** Hawker Hurricanes Mk I over Wreck of Dornier Do-17Z Bomber

236 Anti-aircraft Artillery in Action   **237** Air-battle over St. Paul's Cathedral

(Des D. Gentleman and Rosalind Dease (4d.×6 and 1s.3d.), A. Restall (9d.))

1965 (13 Sept). *25th Anniv of Battle of Britain. Chalk-surfaced paper.* W **179**. P 15×14.

671	**230**	4d. yellow-olive and black.......................	25	25
		a. Block of 6. Nos. 671/6........................	8·00	8·00
		p. Three phosphor bands........................	50	50
		pa. Block of 6. Nos. 671p/6p.....................	10·00	12·00
672	**231**	4d. yellow-olive, olive-grey and black...	25	25
		p. Three phosphor bands........................	50	50
673	**232**	4d. red, new blue, yellow-olive, olive-grey and black	25	25
		p. Three phosphor bands........................	50	50
674	**233**	4d. olive-grey, yellow-olive and black...	25	25
		p. Three phosphor bands........................	50	50
675	**234**	4d. olive-grey, yellow-olive and black...	25	25
		p. Three phosphor bands........................	50	50
676	**235**	4d. olive-grey, yellow-olive, new blue and black	25	25
		a. New blue omitted	†	£6500
		p. Three phosphor bands........................	50	50
677	**236**	9d. bluish violet, orange and slate purple	1·75	1·75
		Wi. Watermark inverted........................	85·00	
		p. Three phosphor bands........................	1·75	2·50
678	**237**	1s.3d. lt grey, dp grey, black, lt blue and bright blue	1·75	1·75
		Wi. Watermark inverted........................	£175	
		p. Three phosphor bands........................	1·75	2·50
		pWi. Watermark inverted........................	5·00	
Set of 8 (*Ordinary*)			8·00	8·00
Set of 8 (*Phosphor*)			10·00	12·00
First Day Cover (*Ordinary*)				25·00
First Day Cover (*Phosphor*)				28·00
Presentation Pack (*Ordinary*)			70·00	

Nos. 671/6 were issued together *se-tenant* in blocks of 6 (3×2) within the sheet. No. 676a is only known commercially used on cover from Truro.

Special First Day of Issue Postmark

Ordinary Phosphor

G.P.O. Philatelic Bureau, London E.C.1 (Type C) .... 25·00   28·00

238 Tower and Georgian Buildings   **239** Tower and "Nash" Terrace, Regent's Park

(Des C. Abbott)

1965 (8 Oct). *Opening of Post Office Tower. Chalk-surfaced paper.*
W **179** (*sideways on* 3d.). P 14×15 (3d.) or 15×14 (1s.3d.).

679	**238**	3d.	olive-yellow, new blue and bronze-green	10	15
		a.	Olive-yellow (Tower) omitted	£5500	£2000
		p.	One phosphor band at right	15	15
		pEa.	Band at left	15	15
		pEb.	Horiz pair. Nos. 679p/pEa	30	50
680	**239**	1s.3d.	bronze-green, yellow-green and blue	30	45
		Wi.	Watermark inverted	60·00	
		p.	Three phosphor bands	30	50
		pWi.	Watermark inverted	60·00	
Set of 2 (Ordinary)				40	60
Set of 2 (Phosphor)				45	65
First Day Cover (Ordinary)					6·50
First Day Cover (Phosphor)					7·00
Presentation Pack (Ordinary)				6·50	
Presentation Pack (Phosphor)				6·50	

The one phosphor band on No. 679p was produced by printing broad phosphor bands across alternate vertical perforations. Individual stamps show the band at right or left.

Special First Day of Issue Postmark

	Ordinary	*Phosphor*
G.P.O. Philatelic Bureau, London E.C.1 (Type C)	10·00	12·00

The Philatelic Bureau did not provide First Day Cover services for Nos. 681/4.

240 U.N. Emblem   **241** I.C.Y. Emblem

Broken circle (Cyl. 1A Dot, R. 11/4)   Lake in Russia (Cyl. 1A Dot, R. 19/3)

(Des J. Matthews)

1965 (25 Oct). *20th Anniv of U.N.O. and International Co-operation Year. Chalk-surfaced paper.* W **179**. P 15×14.

681	**240**	3d.	black, yellow-orange and light blue	25	20
		a.	Broken circle	30·00	
		b.	Lake in Russia	30·00	
		p.	One phosphor band	25	30
		pa.	Broken circle	30·00	
		pb.	Lake in Russia	30·00	
682	**241**	1s.6d.	black, brt purple and light blue	1·00	80
		Wi.	Watermark inverted		£2000
		p.	Three phosphor bands	2·75	3·00
Set of 2 (Ordinary)				1·00	1·00
Set of 2 (Phosphor)				2·50	3·25
First Day Cover (Ordinary)					12·00
First Day Cover (Phosphor)					14·00

242 Telecommunications Network   **243** Radio Waves and Switchboard

(Des A. Restall)

1965 (15 Nov). *I.T.U. Centenary. Chalk-surfaced paper.* W **179**. P 15×14.

683	**242**	9d.	red, ultramarine, deep slate, violet, black and pink	50	40
		Wi.	Watermark inverted	25·00	
		p.	Three phosphor bands	1·00	75
		pWi.	Watermark inverted	90·00	
684	**243**	1s.6d.	red, greenish blue, indigo, black and light pink	1·50	1·25

a. Light pink omitted	£4200	
Wi. Watermark inverted	£300	
p. Three phosphor bands	4·25	5·25
Set of 2 (Ordinary)	1·50	1·60
Set of 2 (Phosphor)	4·25	6·00
First Day Cover (Ordinary)		17·00
First Day Cover (Phosphor)		20·00

Originally scheduled for issue on 17 May 1965, supplies from the Philatelic Bureau were sent in error to reach a dealer on that date and another dealer received his supply on 27 May.

244 Robert Burns (after Skirving chalk drawing)   **245** Robert Burns (after Nasmyth portrait)

(Des G. Huntly)

1966 (25 Jan). *Burns Commemoration. Chalk-surfaced paper.* W **179**. P 15×14.

685	**244**	4d.	black, dp violet-blue and new blue	15	15
		p.	Three phosphor bands	25	50
686	**245**	1s.3d.	black, slate-blue and yellow-orange	40	70
		p.	Three phosphor bands	2·25	2·25
Set of 2 (Ordinary)				55	85
Set of 2 (Phosphor)				2·50	2·25
First Day Cover (Ordinary)					4·00
First Day Cover (Phosphor)					6·00
Presentation Pack (Ordinary)				60·00	

Special First Day of Issue Postmarks
(35 mm diameter)

	Ordinary	*Phosphor*
Alloway, Ayrshire	12·00	12·00
Ayr	12·00	12·00
Dumfries	18·00	18·00
Edinburgh	18·00	18·00
Glasgow	18·00	18·00
Kilmarnock, Ayrshire	18·00	18·00

A special Philatelic Bureau was set up in Edinburgh to deal with First Day Covers of this issue. The Bureau serviced covers to receive the above postmarks, and other versions were applied locally. The locally applied handstamps were 38-39mm in diameter, the Bureau postmarks, applied by machine, 35mm. The Ayr, Edinburgh, Glasgow and Kilmarnock postmarks are similar in design to that for Alloway. Similar handstamps were also provided at Greenock and Mauchline, but the Bureau did not provide a service for these.

246 Westminster Abbey   **247** Fan Vaulting, Henry VII Chapel

(Des Sheila Robinson. Photo Harrison (3d.). Des and eng Bradbury, Wilkinson. Recess (2s.6d.))

1966 (28 Feb). *900th Anniversary of Westminster Abbey. Chalk-surfaced paper (3d.).* W **179**. P 15×14 (3d.) or 11×12 (2s.6d.).

687	**246**	3d.	black, red-brown and new blue	15	20
		p.	One phosphor band	20	25
688	**247**	2s.6d.	black	55	80
Set of 2				70	1·00
First Day Cover (Ordinary)					6·00
First Day Cover (Phosphor)					14·00
Presentation Pack (Ordinary)				55·00	

Special First Day of Issue Postmark

	Ordinary
G.P.O. Philatelic Bureau, London E.C.1 (Type B)	10·00

The Bureau did not provide a First Day Cover service for the 3d. phosphor stamp.

248 View near Hassocks, Sussex

249 Antrim, Northern Ireland

250 Harlech Castle, Wales

251 Cairngorm Mountains Scotland

"AN" for "AND" (Cyl. 1A No dot, R. 10/3)

(Des L. Rosoman. Queen's portrait, adapted by D. Gentleman from coinage)

1966 (2 May). *Landscapes. Chalk-surfaced paper.* W **179**. P 15×14.

689	**248**	4d. black, yellow-green and new blue..	10	15
		p. Three phosphor bands	10	15
690	**249**	6d. black, emerald and new blue	15	20
		a. "AN" for "AND"	35·00	
		Wi. Watermark inverted	6·00	
		p. Three phosphor bands	15	20
		pa. "AN" for "AND"	25·00	
		pWi. Watermark inverted	£140	
691	**250**	1s.3d. black, greenish yellow and greenish blue	25	35
		p. Three phosphor bands	25	35
692	**251**	1s.6d. black, orange and Prussian blue	40	35
		Wi. Watermark inverted	18·00	
		p. Three phosphor bands	40	40
Set of 4 (*Ordinary*)			80	95
Set of 4 (*Phosphor*)			80	1·00
First Day Cover (*Ordinary*)			7·00	
First Day Cover (*Phosphor*)			8·50	

A block of four of No. 689 is known with the top right stamp showing the face value and the bottom right the Queen's head and the face value both omitted due to a paper fold.....................PRICE £10000

Special First Day of Issue Postmark

252 Players with Ball

253 Goalmouth Mêlée

254 Goalkeeper saving Goal

(Des D. Gentleman (4d.), W. Kempster (6d.), D. Caplan (1s.3d.). Queen's portrait adapted by D. Gentleman from coinage)

1966 (1 June). *World Cup Football Championship. Chalk-surfaced paper.* W **179** (*sideways* on 4d.). P 14×15 (4d.) or 15×14 (others).

693	**252**	4d. red, reddish purple, bright blue, flesh and black	10	25
		p. Two phosphor bands	10	25
694	**253**	6d. black, sepia, red, apple-green and blue	15	25
		a. Black omitted	£200	
		b. Apple-green omitted	£5500	
		c. Red omitted	£11000	
		Wi. Watermark inverted	5·00	
		p. Three phosphor bands	15	25
		pa. Black omitted	£2600	
695	**254**	1s.3d. black, blue, yellow, red and light yellow-olive	50	1·00
		a. Blue omitted	£325	
		Wi. Watermark inverted	£140	
		p. Three phosphor bands	50	1·00
		pWi. Watermark inverted	2·00	
Set of 3 (*Ordinary*)			70	1·00
Set of 3 (*Phosphor*)			50	1·00
First Day Cover (*Ordinary*)			20·00	
First Day Cover (*Phosphor*)			22·00	
Presentation Pack (*Ordinary*)			15·00	

Special First Day of Issue Postmark

255 Black-headed Gull **256** Blue Tit

257 European Robin **258** Blackbird

(Des J. Norris Wood)

1966 (8 Aug). *British Birds. Chalk-surfaced paper.* W **179**. P 15×14.

696	**255**	4d. grey, black, red, emerald-green, brt blue, greenish yellow and bistre	20	20
		Wi. Watermark inverted	4·00	
		a. Block of 4. Nos. 696/9	1·00	2·00
		ab. Black (value), etc. omitted* (*block of four*)	£18000	
		c. Black only omitted*		
		aWi. Watermark inverted (*block of four*)..	18·00	
		p. Three phosphor bands	20	20
		pWi. Watermark inverted	20·00	
		pa. Block of 4. Nos. 696p/9p	75	2·00
		paWi. Watermark inverted (*block of four*)..	80·00	
697	**256**	4d. black, greenish yellow, grey, emerald-green, brt blue and bistre	20	20
		Wi. Watermark inverted	4·00	
		p. Three phosphor bands	20	20
		pWi. Watermark inverted	20·00	
698	**257**	4d. red, greenish yellow, black, grey, bistre, reddish brown and emerald-green	20	20
		a. Black only omitted		
		Wi. Watermark inverted	4·00	
		p. Three phosphor bands	20	20
		pWi. Watermark inverted	20·00	
699	**258**	4d. black, reddish brown, greenish yellow, grey and bistre**	20	20
		Wi. Watermark inverted	4·00	
		p. Three phosphor bands	20	20
		pWi. Watermark inverted	20·00	
Set of 4 (*Ordinary*)			1·00	2·00
Set of 4 (*Phosphor*)			75	2·00
First Day Cover (*Ordinary*)			8·00	
First Day Cover (*Phosphor*)			8·00	
Presentation Pack (*Ordinary*)			11·00	

Nos. 696/9 were issued together *se-tenant* in blocks of four within the sheet.

*In No. 696ab the blue, bistre and reddish brown are also omitted but in No. 696ac only the black is omitted.

**In No. 699 the black was printed over the bistre. Other colours omitted, and the stamps affected:

d.	Greenish yellow (Nos. 696/9) .	£1100
pd.	Greenish yellow (Nos. 696p/9p)	£2000
e.	Red (Nos. 696 and 698)	£1100
f.	Emerald-green (Nos. 696/8)	£200
pf.	Emerald-green (Nos. 696p/8p)	£200
g.	Bright blue (Nos. 696/7)	£700
pg.	Bright blue (Nos. 696p and 697p)	£6000
h.	Bistre (Nos. 696/9)	£200
ph.	Bistre (Nos. 696p/9p)	£2750
j.	Reddish brown (Nos. 698/9)	£125
pj.	Reddish brown (Nos. 698p and 699p)	£175

The prices quoted are for each stamp.

Special First Day of Issue Postmark

	Ordinary	*Phosphor*
G.P.O. Philatelic Bureau, London E.C.1 (Type C)	22·00	22·00

259 Cup Winners

1966 (18 Aug). *England's World Cup Football Victory. Chalk-surfaced paper.* W **179** (*sideways*). P 14×15.

700	**259**	4d. red, reddish purple, bright blue, flesh and black	30	30
		First Day Cover		13·00

These stamps were only put on sale at post offices in England, the Channel Islands and the Isle of Man, and at the Philatelic Bureau in London and also, on 22 August, in Edinburgh on the occasion of the opening of the Edinburgh Festival as well as at Army post offices at home and abroad.

The Philatelic Bureau did not service First Day Covers for this stamp, but a First Day of Issue handstamp was provided inscribed "Harrow & Wembley" to replace the "Wembley, Middx", postmark of the initial issue.

260 Jodrell Bank Radio Telescope

261 British Motor-cars

262 "SRN 6" Hovercraft

263 Windscale Reactor

(Des D. and A. Gillespie (4d., 6d.), A. Restall (others))

1966 (19 Sept). *British Technology. Chalk-surfaced paper.* W **179**. P 15×14.

701	**260**	4d. black and lemon	15	10
		p. Three phosphor bands	10	10
702	**261**	6d. red, dp blue and orange	25	20
		a. Red (Mini-cars) omitted	£19000	
		b. Deep blue (Jaguar & inscr) omitted	£16000	
		p. Three phosphor bands	15	25
703	**262**	1s.3d. black, orange-red, slate and light greenish blue	50	40
		p. Three phosphor bands	35	40
704	**263**	1s.6d. black, yellow-green, bronze-green, lilac and deep blue	50	60
		p. Three phosphor bands	50	60
Set of 4 (Ordinary)			1·00	1·10
Set of 4 (Phosphor)			1·00	1·10
First Day Cover (Ordinary)				5·00
First Day Cover (Phosphor)				5·00
Presentation Pack (Ordinary)			12·00	

Special First Day of Issue Postmark

	Ordinary	*Phosphor*
G.P.O. Philatelic Bureau, Edinburgh 1 (Type C)	10·00	10·00

264   **265**

266   **267**

268   **269**

All the above show battle scenes and they were issued together *se-tenant* in horizontal strips of six within the sheet.

270 Norman Ship

271 Norman Horsemen attacking Harold's Troops

HARRISON AND SONS LTD
Club flaw (Cyl. 1A No dot, R. 7/2)

(All the above are scenes from the Bayeux Tapestry)

(Des D. Gentleman. Photo. Queen's head die-stamped (6d., 1s.3d.))

1966 (14 Oct). *900th Anniv of Battle of Hastings. Chalk-surfaced paper.* W **179** (*sideways on* 1s.3d.). P 15×14.

705	**264**	4d. black, olive-green, bistre, deep blue, orange, magenta, green, blue and grey	10	10
		a. Strip of 6. Nos. 705/10	1·90	2·25
		ab. Imperforate strip of six	£3500	
		aWi. Strip of 6. Watermark inverted	45·00	
		Wi. Watermark inverted	7·00	
		p. Three phosphor bands	10	10
		pa. Strip of 6. Nos. 705p/10p	1·90	2·25
		pWi. Watermark inverted	3·00	
		paWi. Strip of 6. Watermark inverted	20·00	
706	**265**	4d. black, olive-green, bistre, deep blue, orange, magenta, green, blue and grey	10	10

		Wi. Watermark inverted		7·00	
		p. Three phosphor bands		10	10
		pWi. Watermark inverted		2·00	
707	266	4d. black, olive-green, bistre, deep blue, orange, magenta, green, blue and grey		10	10
		Wi. Watermark inverted		7·00	
		p. Three phosphor bands		10	10
		pWi. Watermark inverted		3·00	
708	267	4d. black, olive-green, bistre, deep blue, magenta, green, blue and grey		10	10
		Wi. Watermark inverted		7·00	
		p. Three phosphor bands		10	10
		pWi. Watermark inverted		3·00	
709	268	4d. black, olive-green, bistre, deep blue, orange, magenta, green, blue and grey		10	10
		Wi. Watermark inverted		7·00	
		p. Three phosphor bands		10	10
		pWi. Watermark inverted		3·00	
710	269	4d. black, olive-green, bistre, deep blue, orange, magenta, green, blue and grey		10	10
		Wi. Watermark inverted		7·00	
		p. Three phosphor bands		10	25
		pWi. Watermark inverted		3·00	
711	270	6d. black, olive-green, violet, blue, green and gold		10	10
		Wi. Watermark inverted		42·00	
		p. Three phosphor bands		10	10
		pWi. Watermark inverted		55·00	
712	271	1s.3d. black, lilac, bronze-green, rosine, bistre-brown and gold		20	75
		a. Lilac omitted		£5000	
		b. Club flaw		25·00	
		Wi. Watermark sideways inverted (top of crown pointing to right)*		35·00	
		p. Four phosphor bands		20	75
		pa. Lilac omitted		£1250	
		pb. Club flaw		25·00	
		pWi. Watermark sideways inverted (top of crown pointing to right)*		35·00	

Set of 8 (Ordinary)	2·00	2·25
Set of 8 (Phosphor)	2·00	2·25
First Day Cover (Ordinary)		8·00
First Day Cover (Phosphor)		9·00
Presentation Pack (Ordinary)	9·00	

*The normal sideways watermark shows the tops of the Crowns pointing to the left, as seen from the *back of the stamp.*

Other colours omitted in the 4d. values and the stamps affected:

b. Olive-green (Nos. 705/10)	65·00
pb. Olive-green (Nos. 705p/10p)	65·00
c. Bistre (Nos. 705/10)	65·00
pc. Bistre (Nos. 705p/10p)	65·00
d. Deep blue (Nos. 705/10)	75·00
pd. Deep blue (Nos. 705p/10p)	75·00
e. Orange (Nos. 705/7 and 709/10)	65·00
pe. Orange (Nos. 705p/7p and 709p/10p)	65·00
f. Magenta (Nos. 705/10)	65·00
pf. Magenta (Nos. 705p/10p)	65·00
g. Green (Nos. 705/10)	65·00
pg. Green (Nos. 705p/10p)	65·00
h. Blue (Nos. 705/10)	65·00
ph. Blue (Nos. 705p/10p)	65·00
j. Grey (Nos. 705/10)	65·00
pj. Grey (Nos. 705p/10p)	65·00
pk. Magenta and green (Nos. 705p/10p)	75·00

The prices quoted are for each stamp.

Nos. 705 and 709, with grey and blue omitted, have been seen commercially used, posted from Middleton-in-Teesdale.

The 6d. phosphor is known in a yellowish gold as well as the reddish gold as used in the 1s.3d.

Three examples of No. 712 in a right-hand top corner block of 10 (2×5) are known with the Queen's head omitted as a result of a double paper fold prior to die-stamping. The perforation is normal. Of the other seven stamps, four have the Queen's head misplaced and three are normal.

MISSING GOLD HEADS. The 6d. and 1s.3d. were also issued with the die-stamped gold head omitted but as there can also be removed by chemical means we are not prepared to list them unless a way is found of distinguishing the genuine stamps from the fakes which will satisfy the Expert Committees.

The same remarks apply to Nos. 713/14.

Special First Day of Issue Postmark

	Ordinary	Phosphor
G.P.O. Philatelic Bureau, Edinburgh 1 (Type C)	10·00	12·00

A First Day of Issue handstamp was provided at Battle, Sussex, for this issue.

272 King of the Orient   **273** Snowman

Missing "T" (Cyl. 1E No dot, R. 6/2)

(Des Tasveer Shemza (3d.), J. Berry (1s.6d.) (winners of children's design competition). Photo, Queen's head die-stamped)

1966 (1 Dec). *Christmas. Chalk-surfaced paper.* W **179** (*sideways on* 3d.). P 14×15.

713	272	3d. black, blue, green, yellow, red and gold		10	25
		a. Queen's head double*		£6000	†
		ab. Queen's head double, one albino		£650	
		b. Green omitted			
		c. Missing "T"		20·00	
		p. One phosphor band at right		10	25
		pEa. Band at left		10	25
		pEb. Horiz pair. Nos. 713p/pEa		20	60
		pc. Missing "T"		20·00	
714	273	1s.6d. blue, red, pink, black and gold		30	50
		a. Pink (hat) omitted		£3800	
		Wi. Watermark inverted		15·00	
		p. Two phosphor bands		30	50
		pWi. Watermark inverted		50·00	

Set of 2 (Ordinary)	40	40
Set of 2 (Phosphor)	40	45
First Day Cover (Ordinary)		2·50
First Day Cover (Phosphor)		2·00
Presentation Pack (Ordinary)	12·00	

No. 713a refers to stamps showing two impressions, one directly below the other, both with embossing. Examples showing two partial strikes on opposite sides of the stamp, caused by a colour shift are common.

The single phosphor band on No. 713p was produced by printing broad phosphor bands across alternate perforations. Individual* show the band at right or left.

Special First Day of Issue Postmarks

	Ordinary	Phosphor
G.P.O. Philatelic Bureau, Edinburgh 1 (Type C)	7·00	7·00
Bethlehem, Llandeilo, Carms (Type C)	8·00	8·00

274 Sea Freight   **275** Air Freight

Broken strut (Cyl. 2J No dot, R. 13/6)

(Des C. Abbott)

1967 (20 Feb). *European Free Trade Association (EFTA). Chalk-surfaced paper.* W **179**. P 15×14.

715	**274**	9d. deep blue, red, lilac, green, brown, new blue, yellow and black	25	20
		a. Black (Queen's head, etc.), brown, new blue and yellow omitted	£1250	
		b. Lilac omitted	£135	
		c. Green omitted	£135	
		d. Brown (rail trucks) omitted	95·00	
		e. New blue omitted	£135	
		f. Yellow omitted	£135	
		Wi. Watermark inverted	95·00	
		p. Three phosphor bands	25	20
		pb. Lilac omitted	£225	
		pc. Green omitted	£135	
		pd. Brown omitted	95·00	
		pe. New blue omitted	£135	
		pf. Yellow omitted	£180	
		pWi. Watermark inverted	95·00	
716	**275**	1s.6d. violet, red, deep blue, brown, green, blue-grey, new blue, yellow and black	50	45
		a. Red omitted	£550	
		b. Deep blue omitted	£135	
		c. Brown omitted	£135	
		d. Blue-grey omitted	£135	
		f. Yellow omitted	£135	
		g. Green omitted	£135	
		h. Broken strut	25·00	
		Wi. Watermark inverted	30·00	
		p. Three phosphor bands	25	40
		pa. Red omitted	£550	
		pb. Deep blue omitted	£550	
		pc. Brown omitted	95·00	
		pd. Blue-grey omitted	£135	
		pf. New blue omitted	£135	
		ph. Broken strut	25·00	
		pWi. Watermark inverted	30·00	

Set of 2 (Ordinary)	50	65
Set of 2 (Phosphor)	50	60
First Day Cover (Ordinary)		3·00
First Day Cover (Phosphor)		3·00
Presentation Pack (Ordinary)	3·50	

Special First Day of Issue Postmark

	Ordinary	Phosphor
G.P.O. Philatelic Bureau, Edinburgh 1 (Type C)	6·00	6·00

276 Hawthorn and Bramble

277 Larger Bindweed and Viper's Bugloss

278 Ox-eye Daisy, Coltsfoot and Buttercup

279 Bluebell, Red Campion and Wood Anemone

T **276/9** were issued together *se-tenant* in blocks of four within the sheet.

280 Dog Violet

281 Primroses

(Des Rev. W. Keble Martin (T **276/9**), Mary Grierson (others))

1967 (24 Apr). *British Wild Flowers. Chalk-surfaced paper.* W **179**. P 15×14.

717	**276**	4d. grey, lemon, myrtle-green, red, agate and slate-purple	20	20
		a. Block of 4. Nos. 717/20	80	2·25

		aWi. Block of 4. Watermark inverted	9·00	
		b. Grey double*	£5000	
		c. Red omitted	£5500	
		f. Slate-purple omitted	2·00	
		Wi. Watermark inverted	2·00	
		p. Three phosphor bands	10	15
		pa. Block of 4. Nos. 717p/20p	50	2·00
		paWi. Block of 4. Watermark inverted	9·00	
		pd. Agate omitted	£4500	
		pf. Slate-purple omitted	£525	
		pWi. Watermark inverted	2·00	
718	**277**	4d. grey, lemon, myrtle-green, red, agate and violet	20	20
		b. Grey double*		
		Wi. Watermark inverted	2·00	
		p. Three phosphor bands	10	15
		pd. Agate omitted	£4500	
		pe. Violet omitted		
		pWi. Watermark inverted	2·00	
719	**278**	4d. grey, lemon, myrtle-green, red and agate	20	20
		b. Grey double*		
		Wi. Watermark inverted	2·00	
		p. Three phosphor bands	10	15
		pd. Agate omitted	£4500	
		pWi. Watermark inverted	2·00	
720	**279**	4d. grey, lemon, myrtle-green, reddish purple, agate and violet	20	20
		b. Grey double*		
		c. Reddish purple omitted	£2000	
		d. Value omitted†	£10000	
		Wi. Watermark inverted	2·00	
		p. Three phosphor bands	10	15
		pd. Agate omitted	£4500	
		pe. Violet omitted		
		pWi. Watermark inverted	2·00	
721	**280**	9d. lavender-grey, green, reddish violet and orange-yellow	20	25
		Wi. Watermark inverted	1·25	
		p. Three phosphor bands	15	25
722	**281**	1s.9d. lavender-grey, green, greenish yellow and orange	25	35
		p. Three phosphor bands	20	30

Set of 6 (Ordinary)	1·00	2·25
Set of 6 (Phosphor)	75	2·00
First Day Cover (Ordinary)		5·00
First Day Cover (Phosphor)		5·00
Presentation Pack (Ordinary)	6·00	
Presentation Pack (Phosphor)	6·00	

*The double impression of the grey printing affects the Queen's head, value and inscription.

†No. 720d was caused by something obscuring the face value on R14/6 during the printing of one sheet.

Special First Day of Issue Postmark

	Ordinary	Phosphor
G.P.O. Philatelic Bureau, Edinburgh 1 (Type C)	8·00	10·00

PHOSPHOR BANDS. Issues from No. 723 are normally with phosphor bands only, except for the high values but most stamps have appeared with the phosphor bands omitted in error. Such varieties are listed under "Ey" numbers and are priced unused only. See also further notes after 1971–95 Decimal Machin issue.

PHOSPHORISED PAPER. Following the adoption of phosphor bands the Post Office started a series of experiments involving the addition of the phosphor to the paper coating before the stamps were printed. No. 743c was the first of these experiments to be issued for normal postal use. See also notes after 1971–96 Decimal Machin issue.

PVA GUM. Polyvinyl alcohol was introduced by Harrisons in place of gum arabic in 1968. As it is almost invisible a small amount of pale yellowish colouring was introduced to make it possible to check that the stamps had been gummed. Although this can be distinguished from gum arabic in unused stamps there is, of course, no means of detecting it in used examples. Where the two forms of gum exist on the same stamps, the PVA type are listed under "Ev" numbers, except in the case of the 1d. and 4d. (vermilion), both one centre band, which later appeared with gum arabic and these have "Eg" numbers and are priced unused only. All stamps printed from No. 763 onwards were issued with PVA gum only *except where otherwise stated*.

It should be further noted that gum arabic is shiny in appearance, and that, normally, PVA gum has a matt appearance. However, depending upon the qualities of the paper ingredients and the resultant absorption of the gum, occasionally, PVA gum has a shiny appearance. In such cases, especially in stamps from booklets, it is sometimes impossible to be absolutely sure which gum has been used except by testing the stamps chemically which destroys them. Therefore, whilst all gum arabic is shiny it does not follow that all shiny gum is gum arabic.

282	**282a**

Two types of the 2d.

I. Value spaced away from left side of stamp (cylinders 1 no dot and dot).

II. Value close to left side from new multipositive used for cylinders 5 no dot and dot onwards. The portrait appears in the centre, thus conforming to the other values.

Three types of the Machin head, known as Head A, B or C, are distinguished by specialists. These are illustrated in Vol. 3 of the *Great Britain Specialised Catalogue*.

(Des after plaster cast by Arnold Machin)

1967 (5 June)–**70**. *Chalk-surfaced paper. Two phosphor bands except where otherwise stated. PVA gum except Nos. 725m, 728, 729, 731, 731Ea, 740, 742/Ea, 743/a and 744/Ea. No wmk. P 15×14.*

723	**282**	½d. orange-brown (5.2.68)	10	20
		Ey. Phosphor omitted	30·00	
724		1d. light olive (*shades*) (2 bands)		
		(5.2.68)	10	10
		a. Imperf (coil strip)†	£2200	
		b. Part perf pane*	£5000	
		c. Imperf pane*		
		d. Uncoated paper (1970)**	90·00	
		Ey. Phosphor omitted	1·00	
		l. Booklet pane. No. 724×2 *se-tenant* with 730×2 (6.4.68)	3·00	
		lEy. Booklet pane. Phosphor omitted	75·00	
		m. Booklet pane. No. 724×4 *se-tenant* with 734×2 (6.1.69)	3·50	
		mEy. Booklet pane. Phosphor omitted	£160	
		n. Booklet pane. No. 724×6, 734×3, 734Eb×3 & 735×3 *se-tenant* (1.12.69)	8·50	
		na. Booklet pane. Uncoated paper**	£900	
		nEy. Booklet pane. Phosphor omitted	£150	
725		1d. yellowish olive (1 centre band) (16.9.68)	30	35
		Eg. Gum arabic (27.8.69)	30	
		l. Booklet pane. No. 725×4 *se-tenant* with 732×2	4·00	
		lEy. Booklet pane. Phosphor omitted	30·00	
		m. Coil strip. No. 728×2 *se-tenant* with 729, 725Eg & 733Eg (27.8.69)	1·25	
726		2d. lake-brown (Type I) (2 bands) (5.2.68)	10	15
		Ey. Phosphor omitted	30·00	
727		2d. lake-brown (Type II) (2 bands) (1969)	15	20
		Ey. Phosphor omitted	1·00	
728		2d. lake-brown (Type II) (1 centre band) (27.8.69)	70	90
729		3d. violet (*shades*) (1 centre band) (8.8.67)	15	10
		a. Imperf (vert pair)	£850	
		Ey. Phosphor omitted	1·25	
		Ev. PVA gum (*shades*) (12.3.68)	15	
		Evy. Phosphor omitted	2·00	
730		3d. violet (2 bands) (6.4.68)	30	35
		a. Uncoated paper**	£2200	
731		4d. deep sepia (*shades*) (2 bands)	10	10
		Ey. Phosphor omitted	1·00	
		Ea. Deep olive-brown	10	15
		Eay. Phosphor omitted	2·00	
		b. Part perf pane*	£3500	
		Ev. PVA gum (*shades*) (22.1.68)	10	
		Evy. Phosphor omitted	2·00	
732		4d. deep olive-brown (*shades*) (1 centre band) (16.9.68)	10	10
		a. Part perf pane*	£3500	
		l. Booklet pane. Two stamps plus two printed labels	1·00	
		lEy. Booklet pane. Phosphor omitted	60·00	
733		4d. bright vermilion (1 centre band) (6.1.69)	10	10
		a. Tête-bêche (horiz pair)	£3800	
		b. Uncoated paper**	6·00	
		Ey. Phosphor omitted	1·25	
		Eg. Gum arabic (27.8.69)	10	
		Egy. Phosphor omitted	£1650	

		l. Booklet pane. Two stamps plus two printed labels (3.3.69)	1·00	
		lEy. Booklet pane. Phosphor omitted	70·00	
734		4d. bright vermilion (1 band at left) (6.1.69)	1·50	1·90
		a. Uncoated paper**	£275	
		Eb. One band at right (1.12.69)	1·75	2·50
		Eba. Ditto. Uncoated paper**	£275	
735		5d. royal blue (*shades*) (1.7.68)	10	10
		a. Imperf pane*	£2750	
		b. Part perf pane*	£1800	
		c. Imperf (pair)††	£250	
		d. Uncoated paper**	20·00	
		Ey. Phosphor omitted	2·00	
		Ee. Deep blue	10	15
		Eey. Phosphor omitted	3·00	
736		6d. brt reddish purple (*shades*) (5.2.68)	20	25
		Ey. Phosphor omitted	6·50	
		Ea. Bright magenta	8·00	6·00
		Eb. Claret	50	45
		Eby. Phosphor omitted	15·00	
737	**282a**	7d. bright emerald (1.7.68)	40	35
		Ey. Phosphor omitted	95·00	
738		8d. bright vermilion (1.7.68)	20	45
		Ey. Phosphor omitted	£425	
739		8d. light turquoise-blue (6.1.69)	50	60
		Ey. Phosphor omitted	65·00	
740		9d. myrtle-green (8.8.67)	40	25
		Ey. Phosphor omitted	40·00	
		Ev. PVA gum (29.11.68)	50	
		Evy. Phosphor omitted	70·00	
741	**282**	10d. drab (1.7.68)	50	50
		a. Uncoated paper**	30·00	
		Ey. Phosphor omitted	55·00	
742		1s. light bluish violet (*shades*)	45	25
		Ey. Phosphor omitted	80·00	
		Ea. Pale bluish violet	2·25	50
		Ev. Ditto. PVA gum (26.4.68)	45	
		Evy. Phosphor omitted	3·50	
743		1s.6d. greenish blue and deep blue (*shades*) (8.8.67)	50	50
		a. Greenish blue omitted	£150	
		Ey. Phosphor omitted	6·00	
		Ev. PVA gum (28.8.68)	75	
		Eva. Greenish blue omitted	£200	
		Evy. Phosphor omitted	14·00	
		Evb. Prussian blue and indigo	2·25	1·50
		Evby. Phosphor omitted	11·00	
		c. Phosphorised paper (*Prussian blue and indigo*) (10.12.69)	80	80
		ca. Prussian blue omitted	£425	
744		1s.9d. dull orange and black (*shades*)	50	45
		Ey. Phosphor omitted	55·00	
		Ea. Bright orange and black	1·75	70
		Ev. PVA gum (*bright orange and black*) (16.11.70)	75	
Set of 16 (one of each value and colour)			4·00	4·00
Presentation Pack (one of each value) (1968)			12·00	
Presentation Pack (German) (1969)			£150	

*BOOKLET ERRORS. See note after No. 556.

** Uncoated paper. This does not respond to the chalky test, and may be further distinguished from the normal chalk-surfaced paper by the fibres which clearly show on the surface, resulting in the printing impression being rougher, and by the screening dots which are not so evident. The 1d., 4d. and 5d. come from the £1 "Stamps for Cooks" Booklet (1969); the 3d. and 10d. from sheets (1969). The 20p. and 50p. high values (Nos. 830/1) exist with similar errors.

†No. 724a occurs in a vertical strip of four, top stamp perforated on three sides, bottom stamp imperf three sides and the two middle stamps completely imperf.

††No. 735c comes from the original state of cylinder 15 which is identifiable by the screening dots which extend through the gutters of the stamps and into the margins of the sheet. This must not be confused with imperforate stamps from cylinder 10, a large quantity of which was stolen from the printers early in 1970.

The 1d. with centre band and PVA gum (725) only came in the September 1968 10s. booklet (No. XP6). The 1d., 2d. and 4d. with centre band and gum arabic (725Eg, 728 and 733Eg respectively) only came in the coil strip (725m). The 3d. (No. 730) appeared in booklets on 6.4.68, from coils during Dec 68 and from sheets in Jan 1969. The 4d. with one side band at left (734) came from 10s. (band at left) and £1 (band at left or right) booklet *se-tenant* panes, and the 4d. with one side band at right (734Eb) came from the £1 booklet *se-tenant* panes only.

The 4d. (731) in shades of washed-out grey are colour changelings which we understand are caused by the concentrated solvents used in modern dry cleaning methods.

For decimal issue, see Nos. X841, etc.

First Day Covers

5.6 67	4d., 1s., 1s.9d. (731, 742, 744)		3·00
8.8.67	3d., 9d., 1s.6d. (729, 740, 743)		3·00
5.2.68	½d., 1d., 2d., 6d. (723/4, 726, 736)		3·00
1.7.68	5d., 7d., 8d., 10d. (735, 737/8, 741)		3·00

283 "Master Lambton" (Sir Thomas Lawrence) **284** "Mares and Foals in a Landscape" (George Stubbs)

285 "Children Coming Out of School" (L. S. Lowry)

(Des S. Rose)

1967 (10 July). *British Paintings. Chalk-surfaced paper. Two phosphor bands. No wmk.* P 14×15 (4d.) or 15×14 (others).

748	**283**	4d. rose-red, lemon, brown, black, new blue and gold	10	10
		a. Gold (value and Queen's head) omitted	£325	
		b. New blue omitted	£17000	
		Ey. Phosphor omitted	7·00	
749	**284**	9d. Venetian red, ochre, grey-black, new blue, greenish yellow and black	15	15
		a. Black (Queen's head and value) omitted	£950	
		ab. Black (Queen's head only) omitted	£2200	
		Ey. Phosphor omitted	£450	
750	**285**	1s.6d. greenish yellow, grey, rose, new blue, grey-black and gold	25	35
		a. Gold (Queen's head) omitted	£280	
		b. New blue omitted	£280	
		c. Grey (clouds and shading) omitted	£150	
		Ey. Phosphor omitted	£300	
Set of 3			30	50
First Day Cover				2·50
Presentation Pack			5·50	

Special First Day of Issue Postmark

G.P.O. Philatelic Bureau, Edinburgh 1 (Type C) .... 5·00
 A First Day of Issue handstamp was provided at Bishop Auckland, Co. Durham, for this issue.

286 *Gypsy Moth IV*

(Des M. and Sylvia Goaman)

1967 (24 July). *Sir Francis Chichester's World Voyage. Chalk-surfaced paper. Three phosphor bands. No wmk.* P 15×14.

751	**286**	1s.9d. black, brown-red, light emerald and blue	20	20
First Day Cover				1·00

Special First Day of Issue Postmarks

G.P.O. Philatelic Bureau, Edinburgh 1	7·00
Greenwich, London SE10	7·00
Plymouth, Devon	7·00

 The Philatelic Bureau and Greenwich postmarks are similar in design to that for Plymouth. A First Day of Issue handstamp was provided at Chichester, Sussex for this issue.

287 Radar Screen   **288** *Penicillium notatum*

289 Vickers VC-10 Jet Engines   **290** Television Equipment

Broken scale (Cyl. 1c, R.10/2)

(Des C. Abbott (4d., 1s.), Negus-Sharland team (others))

1967 (19 Sept). *British Discovery and Invention. Chalk-surfaced paper. Three phosphor bands (4d.) or two phosphor bands (others).* W **179** *(sideways on 1s.9d.).* P 14×15 (1s.9d.) or 15×14 (others).

752	**287**	4d. greenish yellow, black and vermilion	10	10
		a. Broken scale	25·00	
		Ey. Phosphor omitted	5·00	
753	**288**	1s. blue-green, lt greenish blue, slate-purple and bluish violet	10	20
		Wi. Watermark inverted	20·00	
		Ey. Phosphor omitted	10·00	
754	**289**	1s.6d. black, grey, royal blue, ochre and turquoise-blue	20	25
		Wi. Watermark inverted	£225	
		Ey. Phosphor omitted	£500	
755	**290**	1s.9d. black, grey-blue, pale olive-grey, violet and orange	20	30
		a. Pale olive-grey omitted		£4500
		b. Orange (Queen's head) omitted	£500	
		Ey. Phosphor omitted	£500	
Set of 4			50	75
First Day Cover				2·00
Presentation Pack			4·00	

Special First of Issue Postmark

G.P.O. Philatelic Bureau, Edinburgh (Type C) .... 4·00

WATERMARK. All issues from this date are on unwatermarked paper *unless otherwise stated*

291 "The Adoration of the Shepherds" (School of Seville)   **292** "Madonna and Child" (Murillo)

293 "The Adoration of the Shepherds" (Louis le Nain)

(Des S. Rose)

1967. *Christmas. Chalk-surfaced paper. One phosphor band (3d.) or two phosphor bands (others).* P 15×14 (1s.6d.) or 14×15 (others).

756	**291**	3d. olive-yellow, rose, blue, black and gold (27.11)	10	15

		a. Gold (value and Queen's head)		
		omitted	£110	
		b. Printed on the gummed side	£600	
		c. Rose omitted	£3700	
		Ey. Phosphor omitted	1·00	
757	**292**	4d. bright purple, greenish yellow, new		
		blue, grey-black and gold (18.10)....	10	15
		a. Gold (value and Queen's head)		
		omitted	80·00	
		ab. Gold (Queen's head only) omitted ..	£4500	
		b. Gold ("4D" only) omitted	£3000	
		c. Greenish yellow (Child, robe and		
		Madonna's face) omitted	£7500	
		d. Greenish yellow and gold omitted .	£15000	
		Ey. Phosphor omitted	£125	
758	**293**	1s.6d. bright purple, bistre, lemon, black,		
		orange-red, ultramarine and gold		
		(27.11)	15	15
		a. Gold (value and Queen's head)		
		omitted	£15000	
		ab. Gold (face value only) omitted	£3000	
		b. Ultramarine omitted	£750	
		c. Lemon omitted	£20000	
		Ey. Phosphor omitted	12·00	
Set of 3			30	30
First Day Covers (2)				1·50

Distinct shades exist of the 3d. and 4d. values but are not listable as there are intermediate shades. For the 4d., stamps from one machine show a darker background and give the appearance of the yellow colour being omitted, but this is not so and these should not be confused with the true missing yellow No. 757c.

No. 757b comes from stamps in the first vertical row of a sheet.

The 3d. and 4d. values are known imperforate. They are of proof status.

Special First Day of Issue Postmarks

G.P.O. Philatelic Bureau, Edinburgh 1 (4d.) (18 Oct.) (Type C)..........	50
G.P.O. Philatelic Bureau, Edinburgh 1 (3d., 1s.6d.) (27 Nov.)	
(Type C)...	1·00
Bethlehem, Llandeilo, Carms (4d.) (18 Oct.) (Type C)......................	2·00
Bethlehem, Llandeilo, Carms (3d., 1s.6d.) (27 Nov.) (Type C)	3·00

Gift Pack 1967

1967 (27 Nov.). Comprises Nos. 715p/22p and 748/58.

GP758c Gift Pack	3·00

(Recess Bradbury, Wilkinson)

1967–68. No wmk. White paper. P 11×12.

759	**166**	2s.6d. black-brown (1.7.68)............................	30	45
760	**167**	5s. red (10.4.68)..	70	75
761	**168**	10s. bright ultramarine (10.4.68)	7·75	4·00
762	**169**	£1 black (4.12.67)..	7·50	4·50
Set of 4			15·00	8·00

PVA GUM. All the following issues from this date have PVA gum except where footnotes state otherwise.

294 Tarr Steps, Exmoor

295 Aberfeldy Bridge

296 Menai Bridge

297 M4 Viaduct

(Des A. Restall (9d.), L. Rosoman (1s.6d.), J. Matthews (others))

1968 (29 Apr.). British Bridges. Chalk surfaced paper. Two phosphor bands. P 15×14.

763	**294**	4d. black, bluish violet, turquoise-blue		
		and gold...	10	10
		a. Printed on gummed side....................	32·00	
		Ey. Phosphor omitted.............................		
764	**295**	9d. red-brown, myrtle-green,		
		ultramarine, olive-brown, black		
		and gold...	10	15
		a. Gold (Queen's head) omitted............	£225	
		b. Ultramarine omitted	†	£7000
		Ey. Phosphor omitted.............................	15·00	

765	**296**	1s.6d. olive-brown, red-orange, brt green,		
		turquoise-green and gold..................	15	25
		a. Gold (Queen's head) omitted	£350	
		b. Red-orange (rooftops) omitted.........	£375	
		Ey. Phosphor omitted.............................	50·00	
766	**297**	1s.9d. olive-brown, greenish yellow, dull		
		green, dp ultramarine and gold.......	20	30
		a. Gold (Queen's head) omitted............	£350	
		Ey. Phosphor omitted.............................	10·00	
		Eya. Gold (Queen's head) & Phosphor		
		omitted..		
Set of 4			50	70
First Day Cover				1·50
Presentation Pack			3·00	

No. 764b is only known on First Day Covers posted from Canterbury, Kent, or the Philatelic Bureau, Edinburgh.

Used examples of the 1s.6d. and 1s.9d. are known with both the gold and the phosphor omitted.

Special First Day of Issue Postmarks

297a

G.P.O.Philatelic Bureau, Edinburgh 1	5·00
Bridge, Canterbury, Kent	6·00
Aberfeldy, Perthshire (Type A) (9d. value only)	10·00
Menai Bridge, Anglesey (Type A) (1s.6d. value only)...........................	10·00

The Bridge, Canterbury, postmark is similar in design to that for the Philatelic Bureau.

298 "TUC" and Trades Unionists

299 Mrs. Emmeline Pankhurst (statue)

300 Sopwith Camel and English Electric Lightning Fighters

301 Captain Cook's Endeavour and Signature

(Des D. Gentleman (4d.), C. Abbott (others))

1968 (29 May). British Anniversaries. Events described on stamps. Chalk surfaced paper. Two phosphor bands. P 15×14.

767	**298**	4d. emerald, olive, blue and black	10	10
768	**299**	9d. reddish violet, bluish grey and		
		black...	10	15
		Ey. Phosphor omitted.............................	7·00	
769	**300**	1s. olive-brown, blue, red, slate-blue		
		and black...	15	15
		Ey. Phosphor omitted.............................	10·00	
770	**301**	1s.9d. yellow-ochre and blackish brown ...	35	35
		Ey. Phosphor omitted	£180	
Set of 4			50	50
First Day Cover				4·00
Presentation Pack			3·00	

Special First Day of Issue Postmarks

301a

301b

301c

301d

G.P.O. Philatelic Bureau, Edinburgh 1 (Type C)	7·00
Manchester (4d. value only)	1·00
Aldeburgh, Suffolk (9d. value only)	2·00
Hendon, London NW4 (1s. value only)	3·00
Whitby, Yorkshire (1s.9d. value only)	4·00

The Philatelic Bureau postmark was used on sets of four, but the other postmarks were only available on single stamps.

302 "Queen Elizabeth I" (unknown artist)

303 "Pinkie" (Sir Thomas Lawrence)

304 "Ruins of St. Mary Le Port" (John Piper)

305 "The Hay Wain" (John Constable)

(Des S. Rose)

1968 (12 Aug). *British Paintings. Queen's head embossed. Chalk-surfaced paper. Two phosphor bands.* P 15×14 (1s.9d.) or 14×15 (others).

771	**302**	4d. black, vermilion, greenish yellow, grey and gold	10	10
		a. Gold (value and Queen's head) omitted	£300	
		b. Vermilion omitted*	£600	
		Ec. Embossing omitted	80·00	
		Ey. Phosphor omitted	1·50	
		Eya. Gold (value and Queen's head) and phosphor omitted	£3700	
772	**303**	1s. mauve, new blue, greenish yellow, black, magenta and gold	10	20
		a. Gold (value and Queen's head) omitted	£7000	
		Eb. Gold (value and Queen's head), embossing and phosphor omitted.	£600	
		Ec. Embossing omitted		
		Ey. Phosphor omitted	7·00	
773	**304**	1s.6d. slate, orange, black, mauve, greenish yellow, ultramarine and gold	20	25
		a. Gold (value and Queen's head) omitted	£275	
		Eb. Embossing omitted	£300	
		Ey. Phosphor omitted	10·00	
774	**305**	1s.9d. greenish yellow, black, new blue, red and gold	25	40

	a. Gold (value and Queen's head) and embossing omitted	£850	
	b. Red omitted	£13000	
	Ec. Embossing omitted	£140	
	Ey. Phosphor omitted	20·00	
Set of 4		50	85
First Day Cover			2·00
Presentation Pack (P. O. Pack No. 1)		3·50	
Presentation Pack (German) (P. O. Pack No. 1)		12·00	

No. 774a is only known with the phosphor also omitted.
*The effect of this is to leave the face and hands white and there is more yellow and olive in the costume.
The 4d. also exists with the value only omitted resulting from a colour shift.

Special First Day of Issue Postmark

G.P.O. Philatelic Bureau, Edinburgh 1 (Type C)	5·00

Gift Pack 1968
1968 (16 Sept). Comprises Nos. 763/74.

GP774c	Gift Pack	6·00
GP774d	Gift Pack (German)	38·00

Collectors Pack 1968
1968 (16 Sept). Comprises Nos. 752/8 and 763/74.

CP774e	Collectors Pack	7·00

306 Boy and Girl with Rocking Horse

307 Girl with Doll's House

308 Boy with Train Set

(Des Rosalind Dease. Head printed in gold and then embossed)

1968 (25 Nov). *Christmas. Chalk-surfaced paper. One centre phosphor band (4d.) or two phosphor bands (others).* P 15×14 (4d.) or 14×15 (others).

775	**306**	4d. black, orange, vermilion, ultramarine, bistre and gold	10	15
		a. Gold omitted	£8000	
		b. Vermilion omitted*	£550	
		c. Ultramarine omitted	£450	
		d. Bistre omitted		
		Ed. Embossing omitted	6·00	
		Ey. Phosphor omitted	5·00	
776	**307**	9d. yellow-olive, black, brown, yellow, magenta, orange, turquoise-green and gold	15	25
		a. Yellow omitted	£150	
		b. Turquoise-green (dress) omitted	£20000	
		Ec. Embossing omitted	6·00	
		Ey. Phosphor omitted	10·00	
		Eya. Embossing and phosphor omitted	10·00	
777	**308**	1s.6d. ultramarine, yellow-orange, bright purple, blue-green, black and gold	15	50
		Ea. Embossing omitted		
		Ey. Phosphor omitted	15·00	
Set of 3			30	50
First Day Cover				1·00
Presentation Pack (P. O. Pack No. 4)		5·00	
Presentation Pack (German)		14·00	

*The effect of the missing vermilion is shown on the rocking horse, saddle and faces which appear orange instead of red.
A single used example of the 4d. exists with the bistre omitted.
No. 775c is only known with phosphor also omitted.
Two machines were used for printing for the 4d. value:
Stamps from cylinders 1A-1B-2C-1D-1E in combination with 1F, 2F or 3F (gold) were printed entirely on the Rembrandt sheet-fed machine. They invariably have the Queen's head level with the top of the boy's head and the sheets are perforated through the left side margin.

Stamps from cylinders 2A-2B-3C-2D-2E in combination with 1F, 2F, 3F or 4F (gold) were printed on the reel-fed Thrissell machine in five colours (its maximum colour capacity) and subsequently sheet-fed on the Rembrandt machine for the Queen's head and the embossing. The position of the Queen's head is generally lower than on the stamps printed at one operation but it varies in different parts of the sheet and is not, therefore, a sure indication for identifying single stamps. Another small difference is that the boy's grey pullover is noticeably "moth-eaten" in the Thrissell printings and is normal on the Rembrandt. The Thrissell printings are perforated through the top margin.

Special First Day of Issue Postmarks

G.P.O. Philatelic Bureau, Edinburgh 1 (Type C)	3·00
Bethlehem, Llandeilo, Carms (Type C)	7·00

309 *R.M.S. Queen Elizabeth 2*

310 Elizabethan Galleon   **311** East Indiaman

312 *Cutty Sark*

313 *S.S. Great Britain*

314 *R.M.S. Mauretania I*

(Des D. Gentleman)

1969 (15 Jan). *British Ships. Chalk-surfaced paper. Two vertical phosphor bands at right (1s.), one horizontal phosphor band (5d.) or two phosphor bands (9d.).* P 15×14.

778	**309**	5d. black, grey, red and turquoise	10	15
		a. Black (Queen's head, value, hull and inscr) omitted	£2800	
		b. Grey (decks, etc.) omitted	£225	
		c. Red (inscription) omitted	£250	
		Ey. Phosphor omitted	5·00	
		Eya. Red and phosphor omitted	£225	
779	**310**	9d. red, blue, ochre, brown, black and grey	10	25
		a. Strip of 3. Nos. 779/81	1·25	1·50
		ab. Red and blue omitted	£3500	
		ac. Blue omitted	£3500	
		Ey. Phosphor omitted	12·00	
		Eya. Strip of 3. Nos. 779/81. Phosphor omitted	40·00	
780	**311**	9d. ochre, brown, black and grey	10	25
		Ey. Phosphor omitted	12·00	
781	**312**	9d. ochre, brown, black and grey	10	25
		Ey. Phosphor omitted	12·00	
782	**313**	1s. brown, black, grey, green and greenish yellow	40	35
		a. Pair. Nos. 782/3	1·25	1·50
		ab. Greenish yellow omitted	£4000	
		Ey. Phosphor omitted	28·00	

		Eya. Pair. Nos. 782/3. Phosphor omitted	65·00	
783	**314**	1s. red, black, brown, carmine and grey	40	35
		a. Carmine (hull overlay) omitted	£35000	
		b. Red (funnels) omitted	£24000	
		c. Carmine and red omitted	£24000	
		Ey. Phosphor omitted	30·00	
Set of 6			2·50	3·00
First Day Cover				5·00
Presentation Pack (P. O. Pack No. 5)			4·50	
Presentation Pack (German) (P. O. Pack No. 5)			40·00	

The 9d. and 1s. values were arranged in horizontal strips of three and pairs respectively throughout the sheet. No. 779ab is known only with the phosphor also omitted.

Special First Day of Issue Postmark

G.P.O. Philatelic Bureau, Edinburgh 1 (Type C)	8·00

315 Concorde in Flight   **316** Plan and Elevation Views

317 Concorde's Nose and Tail

(Des M. and Sylvia Goaman (4d.), D. Gentleman (9d., 1s.6d.))

1969 (3 Mar). *First Flight of Concorde. Chalk-surfaced paper. Two phosphor bands.* P 15×14.

784	**315**	4d. yellow-orange, violet, greenish blue, blue-green and pale green	25	25
		a. Violet (value etc.) omitted	£600	
		b. Yellow-orange omitted	£600	
		Ey. Phosphor omitted	1·00	
		Eya. Yellow-orange and phosphor omitted	£600	
785	**316**	9d. ultramarine, emerald, red and grey-blue	55	75
		a. Face value and inscr omitted	£40000	
		Ey. Phosphor omitted	£100	
786	**317**	1s.6d. deep blue, silver-grey and light blue	75	1·00
		a. Silver-grey omitted	£600	
		Ey. Phosphor omitted	9·00	
Set of 3			1·00	1·50
First Day Cover				3·00
Presentation Pack (P. O. Pack No. 6)			12·00	
Presentation Pack (German)			40·00	

No. 785a is caused by a colour shift of the grey-blue. On the only known example the top of the Queen's head appears across the perforations at foot. No. 786a affects the Queen's head which appears in the light blue colour.

Special First Day of Issue Postmarks

G.P.O Philatelic Bureau, Edinburgh (Type C)	4·00
Filton, Bristol (Type C)	12·00

318 Queen Elizabeth II
(See also Type 357)

(Des after plaster cast by Arnold Machin. Recess Bradbury, Wilkinson)

1969 (5 Mar). P 12.

787	**318**	2s.6d. brown	35	30
788		5s. crimson-lake	1·75	60
789		10s. deep ultramarine	6·00	7·00
790		£1 bluish black	3·25	1·50
Set of 4			10·00	8·50
First Day Cover				9·50
Presentation Pack (P. O. Pack No. 7)			16·00	
Presentation Pack (German)			80·00	

Special First Day of Issue Postmarks
G.P.O. Philatelic Bureau (Type C) .... 12·00
Windsor, Berks (Type C) .... 18·00

For decimal issue, see Nos. 829/31b and notes after No. 831b.

319 Page from *Daily Mail*, and Vickers FB-27 Vimy Aircraft

320 Europa and CEPT Emblems

321 ILO Emblem

322 Flags of NATO Countries

323 Vickers FB-27 Vimy Aircraft and Globe showing Flight

(Des P. Sharland (5d., 1s., 1s.6d.), M. and Sylvia Goaman (9d., 1s.9d.))

1969 (2 Apr). *Anniversaries. Events described on stamps. Chalk-surfaced paper. Two phosphor bands.* P 15×14.

791	**319**	5d. black, pale sage-green, chestnut and new blue	10	15
		Ey. Phosphor omitted		
792	**320**	9d. pale turquoise, dp blue, lt emerald-green and black	15	25
		Ey. Phosphor omitted	18·00	
		a. Uncoated paper*	£1800	
		Ey. Phosphor omitted	18·00	
793	**321**	1s. brt purple, dp blue and lilac	15	25
		Ey. Phosphor omitted	10·00	
794	**322**	1s.6d. red, royal blue, yellow-green, black, lemon and new blue	15	30
		e. Black omitted	£120	
		f. Yellow-green (from flags) omitted ..	85·00	
		g. Lemon (from flags) omitted..............	†	£4500
		Ey. Phosphor omitted	9·00	
		Eya. Yellow-green and phosphor omitted	95·00	
795	**323**	1s.9d. yellow-olive, greenish yellow and pale turquoise-green	20	40
		a. Uncoated paper*	£275	
		Ey. Phosphor omitted	6·00	
	Set of 5		50	1·00
	First Day Cover			3·00
	Presentation Pack (P. O. Pack No. 9)		3·50	
	Presentation Pack (German)............................		65·00	

*Uncoated paper. The second note after No. 744 also applies here.
No. 794g is only known used on First Day Cover from Liverpool.
A trial of the 9d value in green and red is known.

Special First Day of Issue Postmark
G.P.O. Philatelic Bureau, Edinburgh (Type C).. 4·00

324 Durham Cathedral

325 York Minster

326 St. Giles, Edinburgh

327 Canterbury Cathedral

328 St. Paul's Cathedral

329 Liverpool Metropolitan Cathedral

(Des P. Gauld)

1969 (28 May). *British Architecture. Cathedrals. Chalk-surfaced paper. Two phosphor bands.* P 15×14.

796	**324**	5d. grey-black, orange, pale bluish violet and black............................	10	10
		a. Block of 4. Nos. 796/9....................	1·10	1·25
		ab. Block of 4. Uncoated paper†	£1000	
		b. Pale bluish violet omitted..................	£15000	
797	**325**	5d. grey-black, pale bluish violet, new blue and black............................	10	10
		b. Pale bluish violet omitted..................	£15000	
798	**326**	5d. grey-black, purple, green and black	10	10
		c. Green omitted*	£100	
799	**327**	5d. grey-black, green, new blue and black..	10	10
800	**328**	9d. grey-black, ochre, pale drab, violet and black..............................	25	30
		a. Black (value) omitted	£250	
		Ey. Phosphor omitted..............................	45·00	
		Eya. Black and phosphor omitted	£300	
801	**329**	1s.6d. grey-black, pale turquoise, pale reddish violet, pale yellow-olive and black..............................	25	35
		a. Black (value) omitted	£4700	
		b. Black (value) double	£4000	
		Ey. Phosphor omitted..............................	20·00	
	Set of 6		1·10	1·50
	First Day Cover			3·00
	Presentation Pack (P. O. Pack No. 10)............		3·25	
	Presentation Pack (German)............................		30·00	

*The missing green on the roof top is known on R. 2/5, R. 8/5 and R. 10/5 but all are from different sheets and it only occurred in part of the printing, being "probably caused by a batter on the impression cylinder". Examples are also known with the green partly omitted.
†Uncoated paper. The second note after No. 744 also applies here.
The 5d. values were issued together *se-tenant* in blocks of four throughout the sheet.

Special First Day of Issue Postmark
G.P.O. Philatelic Bureau, Edinburgh (Type C).. 4·00

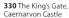

330 The King's Gate, Caernarvon Castle

331 The Eagle Tower, Caernarvon Castle

332 Queen Eleanor's Gate, Caernarvon Castle

333 Celtic Cross, Margam Abbey

Stay up to date with all things philatelic.
Subscribe to **Gibbons Stamp Monthly** – The UK's number one stamp magazine

334 H.R.H. The Prince of Wales (after photograph by G. Argent)

(Des D. Gentleman)

1969 (1 July). *Investiture of H.R.H. The Prince of Wales. Chalk-surfaced paper. Two phosphor bands.* P 14×15.

802	**330**	5d. dp olive-grey, lt olive-grey, dp grey, light grey, red, pale turquoise-green, black and silver	10	15
		a. Strip of 3. Nos. 802/4	50	1·00
		b. Black (value and inscr) omitted	£650	
		c. Red omitted*	£1250	
		d. Deep grey omitted**	£475	
		e. Pale turquoise-green omitted	£1100	
		f. Light grey omitted	£12000	
		Ey. Phosphor omitted	5·00	
		Eya. Strip of 3. Nos. 802/4. Phosphor omitted	15·00	
803	**331**	5d. dp olive-grey, lt olive-grey, dp grey, light grey, red, pale turquoise-green, black and silver	10	15
		b. Black (value and inscr) omitted	£650	
		c. Red omitted*	£1250	
		d. Deep grey omitted**	£475	
		e. Pale turquoise-green omitted	£1100	
		f. Light grey (marks on walls, window frames, etc) omitted	£12000	£8000
		Ey. Phosphor omitted	5·00	
804	**332**	5d. dp olive-grey, lt olive-grey, dp grey, lt grey, red, pale turquoise-green, black and silver	10	15
		b. Black (value and inscr) omitted	£650	
		c. Red omitted*	£1250	
		d. Deep grey omitted**	£475	
		e. Pale turquoise-green omitted	£1100	
		f. Light grey omitted	£12000	
		Ey. Phosphor omitted	5·00	
805	**333**	9d. dp grey, lt grey, black and gold	15	30
		Ey. Phosphor omitted	22·00	
806	**334**	1s. blackish yellow-olive and gold	15	30
		Ey. Phosphor omitted	15·00	
Set of 5			60	1·20
First Day Cover				1·50
Presentation Pack† (P. O. Pack No. 11)			3·00	
Presentation Pack (German)			30·00	

The 5d. values were issued together *se-tenant* in strips of three throughout the sheet.

*The 5d. value is also known with the red misplaced downwards and where this occurs the red printing does not take very well on the silver background and in some cases is so faint it could be mistaken for a missing red. However, the red can be seen under a magnifying glass and caution should therefore be exercised when purchasing copies of Nos. 802/4c.

**The deep grey affects the dark portions of the windows and doors.

†In addition to the generally issued Presentation Pack a further pack in different colours and with all texts printed in both English and Welsh was made available exclusively through Education Authorities for free distribution to all schoolchildren in Wales and Monmouthshire (Price £16).

No. 803f is only known commercially used on cover.

Special First Day of Issue Postmarks

G.P.O. Philatelic Bureau, Edinburgh 1 (Type C)	3·00
Day of Investiture, Caernarvon	5·00

335 Mahatma Gandhi

(Des B. Mullick)

1969 (13 Aug). *Gandhi Centenary Year. Chalk-surfaced paper. Two phosphor bands.* P 15×14.

807	**335**	1s.6d. black, green, red-orange and grey..	30	30

a. Printed on the gummed side	£1400	
Ey. Phosphor omitted	4·00	
First Day Cover		1 00

Special First Day of Issue Postmark

G.P.O.Philatelic Bureau, Edinburgh (Type C)	1·50

Collectors Pack 1969
1969 (15 Sept). Comprises Nos. 775/86 and 791/807.

CP807b	Collectors Pack	25·00

336 National Giro "G" Symbol

337 Telecommunications—International Subscriber Dialling

338 Telecommunications—Pulse Code Modulation

339 Postal Mechanisation—Automatic Sorting

(Des D. Gentleman. Litho De La Rue)

1969 (1 Oct). *Post Office Technology Commemoration. Chalk-surfaced paper. Two phosphor bands.* P 13½×14.

808	**336**	5d. new blue, greenish blue, lavender and black	10	10
		Ey. Phosphor omitted	5·00	
809	**337**	9d. emerald, violet-blue and black	20	25
810	**338**	1s. emerald, lavender and black	20	25
		Ey. Phosphor omitted	£300	
811	**339**	1s.6d. bright purple, light blue, grey-blue and black	25	50
Set of 4			70	1·00
First Day Cover				1·50
Presentation Pack (P. O. Pack No. 13)			3·00	

Special First Day of Issue Postmark

G.P.O.Philatelic Bureau, Edinburgh (Type C)	2·00

340 Herald Angel   **341** The Three Shepherds

342 The Three Kings

(Des F. Wegner. Queen's head (and stars 4d., 5d. and scrollwork 1s.6d.) printed in gold and then embossed)

1969 (26 Nov). *Christmas. Chalk-surfaced paper. Two phosphor bands (5d., 1s.6d.) or one centre band (4d.).* P 15×14.

812	**340**	4d. vermilion, new blue, orange, brt purple, light green, bluish violet, blackish brown and gold	10	10
		a. Gold (Queen's head etc.) omitted	£11000	
		Eb. Centre band 3½ mm	30	20
813	**341**	5d. magenta, light blue, royal blue, olive-brown, green, greenish yellow, red and gold	15	15
		a. Lt blue (sheep, etc.) omitted	£110	
		b. Red omitted*	£2500	
		c. Gold (Queen's head) omitted	£1000	
		d. Green omitted	£450	
		e. Olive-brown, red and gold omitted	£15000	
		Ef. Embossing omitted	22·00	
		Fy. Phosphor omitted	5 00	
814	**342**	1s.6d. greenish yellow, brt purple, bluish violet, dp slate, orange, green, new blue and gold	20	20

a. Gold (Queen's head etc.) omitted....	£170	
b. Deep slate (value) omitted................	£475	
c. Greenish yellow omitted	£450	
e. New blue omitted	£120	
Ef. Embossing omitted	10·00	
Ey. Phosphor omitted	6·00	
Eya. Embossing and phosphor omitted.	10·00	
Set of 3	30	30
First Day Cover		1·00
Presentation Pack (P. O. Pack No. 14)........................	3·00	

*The effect of the missing red is shown on the hat, leggings and purse which appear as dull orange.

No. 812 has one centre band 8mm. wide but this was of no practical use in the automatic facing machines and after about three-quarters of the stamps had been printed the remainder were printed with a 3½mm. band (No. 812Eb).

No. 813e was caused by a paper fold and also shows the phosphor omitted.

Used copies of the 5d. have been seen with the olive-brown or greenish yellow (tunic at left) omitted.

Special First Day of Issue Postmarks

P.O. Philatelic Bureau, Edinburgh (Type C)........................	2·00
Bethlehem, Llandeilo, Carms (Type C)........................	3·00

343 Fife Harling

344 Cotswold Limestone

345 Welsh Stucco

346 Ulster Thatch

(Des D. Gentleman (5d., 9d.), Sheila Robinson (1s., 1s.6d.))

1970 (11 Feb). *British Rural Architecture. Chalk-surfaced paper. Two phosphor bands.* P 15×14.

815	**343**	5d. grey, grey-black, black, lemon, greenish blue, orange-brown, ultramarine and green..........................	10	10
		a. Lemon omitted	£150	
		b. Grey (Queen's head and cottage shading) omitted................................		
		c. Greenish blue (door) omitted	† £4500	
		d. Grey black (inscription & face value) omitted	£18000	
		e. Grey black (face value only) omitted	£17000	
		f. Green omitted (cobblestones)		
		Ey. Phosphor omitted	2·00	
816	**344**	9d. orange-brown, olive-yellow, bright green, black, grey-black and grey ...	10	25
		Ey. Phosphor omitted	10·00	
817	**345**	1s. deep blue, reddish lilac, drab and new blue...	15	25
		a. New blue omitted	£130	
		Ey. Phosphor omitted	15·00	
818	**346**	1s.6d. greenish yellow, black, turquoise-blue and lilac.................................	20	40
		a. Turquoise-blue omitted......................	£18000	
		Ey. Phosphor omitted	5·00	
Set of 4			50	75
First Day Cover				1·50
Presentation Pack (P. O. Pack No. 15)........................			4·00	

Used examples of the 5d. exist, one of which is on piece, with the greenish blue colour omitted.

Special First Day of Issue Postmark

British Philatelic Bureau, Edinburgh (Type C)	2·00

347 Signing the Declaration of Arbroath

348 Florence Nightingale attending Patients

349 Signing of International Co-operative Alliance

350 Pilgrims and *Mayflower*

351 Sir William Herschel, Francis Baily, Sir John Herschel and Telescope

(Des F. Wegner (5d., 9d. and 1s.6d.), Marjorie Saynor (1s., 1s.9d.). Queen's head printed in gold and then embossed)

1970 (1 Apr). *Anniversaries. Events described on stamps. Chalk-surfaced paper. Two phosphor bands.* P 15×14.

819	**347**	5d. black, yellow-olive, blue, emerald, greenish yellow, rose-red, gold and orange-red..	10	10
		a. Gold (Queen's head) omitted............	£3500	
		b. Emerald omitted..................................	£500	
		Ey. Phosphor omitted	£350	
820	**348**	9d. ochre, deep blue, carmine, black, blue-green, yellow-olive, gold and blue..	15	15
		a. Ochre omitted.......................................	£500	
		Eb. Embossing omitted	15·00	
		Ey. Phosphor omitted	5·00	
821	**349**	1s. green, greenish yellow, brown, black, cerise, gold and lt blue............	20	25
		a. Gold (Queen's head) omitted............	90·00	
		Eb. Green and embossing omitted	£160	
		c. Green omitted	£160	
		d. Brown omitted	£300	
		Ee. Embossing omitted	12·00	
		Ey. Phosphor omitted	5·00	
		Eya. Brown and phosphor omitted..........	£300	
		Eyb. Embossing and phosphor omitted...	22·00	
822	**350**	1s.6d. greenish yellow, carmine, deep yellow-olive, emerald, black, blue, gold and sage-green............................	20	30
		a. Gold (Queen's head) omitted............	£300	
		b. Emerald omitted..................................	£160	
		Ec. Embossing omitted	6·00	
		Ey. Phosphor omitted	5·00	
823	**351**	1s.9d. black, slate, lemon, gold and bright purple..	25	30
		a. Lemon (trousers and document) omitted	£9000	
		Eb. Embossing omitted	75·00	
		Ey. Phosphor omitted	5·00	
Set of 5			75	1·00
First Day Cover				2·00
Presentation Pack (P. O. Pack No. 16)........................			3·00	

No. 823a is known mint, or used on First Day Cover postmarked London WC.

Special First Day of Issue Postmark

British Philatelic Bureau, Edinburgh (Type C)	2·50

First Day of Issue handstamps were provided at Arbroath, Angus; Billericay, Essex; Boston, Lincs and Rochdale, Lancs for this issue.

352 "Mr. Pickwick and Sam Weller" (*Pickwick Papers*)

353 "Mr. and Mrs. Micawber" (*David Copperfield*)

5_d
1812/1870
Charles Dickens

5_d
1812/1870
Charles Dickens

1/6
1770/1850
William Wordsworth

354 "David Copperfield and Betsy Trotwood" (*David Copperfield*)

355 "Oliver asking for more" (*Oliver Twist*)

356 "Grasmere" (from engraving by J. Farrington, R.A.)

T **352/5** were issued together *se-tenant* in blocks of four throughout the sheet.

(Des Rosalind Dease. Queen's head printed in gold and then embossed)

1970 (3 June). *Literary Anniversaries. Death Centenary of Charles Dickens (novelist) (5d.×4) and Birth Bicentenary of William Wordsworth (poet) (1s.6d.). Chalk-surfaced paper. Two phosphor bands.* P 14×15.

824	**352**	5d. black, orange, silver, gold and magenta		10	25
		a. Block of 4. Nos. 824/7		75	1·50
		ab. Imperf (block of four)		£2000	
		ac. Silver (inscr) omitted (block of four)	£40000		
825	**353**	5d. black, magenta, silver, gold and orange		10	25
826	**354**	5d. black, light greenish blue, silver, gold and yellow-bistre		10	25
		b. Yellow-bistre (value) omitted		£8500	
827	**355**	5d. black, yellow-bistre, silver, gold and light greenish blue		10	25
		b. Yellow-bistre (background) omitted		£20000	
		c. Lt greenish blue (value) omitted*		£800	
		d. Lt greenish blue and silver (inscr at foot) omitted		£30000	
828	**356**	1s.6d. yellow-olive, black, silver, gold and bright blue		25	50
		a. Gold (Queen's head) omitted		£6000	
		b. Silver ("Grasmere") omitted		£225	
		c. Bright blue (face value) omitted		£20000	
		d. Bright blue and silver omitted		£25000	
		Ee. Embossing omitted		6·00	
		Ey. Phosphor omitted		5·00	
		Eya. Embossing and phosphor omitted.		22·00	
Set of 5				1·00	1·50
First Day Cover					2·00
Presentation Pack (P. O. Pack No. 17)				3·00	

*No. 827c (unlike No. 826b) comes from a sheet on which the colour was only partially omitted so that, although No. 827 was completely without the light greenish blue colour, it was still partially present on No. 826.

Essays exist of Nos. 824/7 showing the Queen's head in silver and with different inscriptions.

Special First Day of Issue Postmarks

British Philatelic Bureau, Edinburgh (Type C)	3·00
Cockermouth, Cumberland (Type C) (No. 828 only)	4·00
Rochester, Kent (Type C) (Nos. 824/7)	4·00

A First Day of Issue handstamp was provided at Broadstairs, Kent, for this issue.

356a

357 (value redrawn)

(Des after plaster cast by Arnold Machin. Recess B.W.)

1970 (17 June)–**72**. *Decimal Currency. Chalk-surfaced paper or phosphorised paper (10p.).* P 12.

829	**356a**	10p. cerise	50	75
830		20p. olive-green	60	25
		Ea. Thinner uncoated paper*		
831		50p. deep ultramarine	1·50	40
		Ea. Thinner uncoated paper*	45·00	
831b	**357**	£1 bluish black (6.12.72)	3·50	80

Set of 4	6·00	2·00
First Day Cover (829/31)		2·75
First Day Cover (831b)		3·00
Presentation Pack No. 18 (829/31)	10·00	
Presentation Pack No. 38 (790 (or 831b), 830/1)	17·00	

*These are not as apparent as uncoated photogravure issues where there is normally a higher degree of chalk-surfacing. The 20p. is known only as a block of four with Plate No. 5. The 50p. comes from Plate No. 9.

The 10p. on phosphorised paper continued the experiments which started with the Machin 1s.6d. When the experiment had ended a quantity of the 50p. value was printed on the phosphorised paper to use up the stock. These stamps were issued on 1 February 1973, but they cannot be distinguished from No. 831 by the naked eye. (*Price* £2).

A £1 was also issued in 1970, but it is difficult to distinguish it from the earlier No. 790. In common with the other 1970 values it was issued in sheets of 100.

A whiter paper was introduced in 1973. The £1 appeared on 27 Sept. 1973, the 20p. on 30 Nov. 1973 and the 50p. on 20 Feb. 1974.

Imperforate examples of No. 831b are believed to be printer's waste.

Special First Day of Issue Postmarks

British Philatelic Bureau, Edinburgh (Type C) (Nos. 829/31)	4·00
Windsor, Berks (Type C) (Nos. 829/31)	8·00
Philatelic Bureau, Edinburgh (Type E) (No. 831b)	4·00
Windsor, Berks (Type E) (No. 831b)	10·00

IXth British Commonwealth Games Edinburgh 1970
5_d

IXth British Commonwealth Games Edinburgh 1970
1/6

358 Runners

359 Swimmers

IXth British Commonwealth Games Edinburgh 1970
1/9

360 Cyclists

(Des A. Restall. Litho D.L.R.)

1970 (15 July). *Ninth British Commonwealth Games. Chalk-surfaced paper. Two phosphor bands.* P 13½×14.

832	**358**	5d. pink, emerald, greenish yellow and deep yellow-green	25	25
		a. Greenish yellow omitted	£20000	
		Ey. Phosphor omitted	£200	
833	**359**	1s.6d. light greenish blue, lilac, bistre-brown and Prussian blue	50	50
		Ey. Phosphor omitted	60·00	
834	**360**	1s.9d. yellow-orange, lilac, salmon and deep red-brown	50	50
Set of 3			75	75
First Day Cover				1·20
Presentation Pack (P. O. Pack No. 19)			3·00	

Special First Day of Issue Postmark

British Philatelic Bureau, Edinburgh (Type C).	4·00

Collectors Pack 1970
1970 Sept 14 Comprises Nos. 808/28 and 832/4.

CP834a	Collectors Pack	35·00

5^d
Philympia 1970
POSTAGE
ONE PENNY
1840 first engraved issue

9^d
Philympia 1970
POSTAGE
ONE SHILLING
1847 first embossed issue

1/6
Philympia 1970
POSTAGE
FOUR PENCE
1855 first surface printed issue

361 1d. Black (1840)

362 1s. Green (1847)

363 4d. Carmine (1855)

(Des D. Gentleman)

1970 (18 Sept). *"Philympia 70" Stamp Exhibition. Chalk-surfaced paper. Two phosphor bands.* P 14×14½.

835	**361**	5d. grey-black, brownish bistre, black and dull purple	25	10
		a. Grey-black (Queen's head) omitted	£20000	
		Ey. Phosphor omitted	5·00	

836 **362** 9d. light drab, bluish green, stone,
black and dull purple 25 30
Ey. Phosphor omitted .... 11·00
837 **363** 1s.6d. carmine, light drab, black and dull
purple 25 45
Ey. Phosphor omitted .... 4·00
Set of 3 .... 50 75
First Day Cover .... 1·50
Presentation Pack (P. O. Pack No. 21).................... 3·00

Special First Day of Issue Postmark

British Post Office Philatelic Bureau, Edinburgh (Type D)................. 2·00

364 Shepherds and Apparition of the Angel

365 Mary, Joseph and Christ in the Manger

366 The Wise Men bearing gifts

(Des Sally Stiff after De Lisle Psalter. Queen's head printed in gold and then embossed)

1970 (25 Nov). *Christmas. Chalk-surfaced paper. One centre phosphor band (4d.) or two phosphor bands (others). P 14×15.*
838 **364** 4d. brown-red, turquoise-green, pale
chestnut, brown, grey-black, gold
and vermilion.. 15 10
Ea. Embossing omitted .... 50·00
Ey. Phosphor omitted .... 60·00
839 **365** 5d. emerald, gold, blue, brown-red,
ochre, grey-black and violet 15 15
a. Gold (Queen's head) omitted........... † £3500
b. Emerald omitted.................................. £130
c. Imperf (pair) £450
Ed. Embossing omitted .... 15·00
Ey. Phosphor omitted .... 5·00
840 **366** 1s.6d. gold, grey-black, pale turquoise-
green, salmon, ultramarine, ochre
and yellow-green 25 30
a. Salmon omitted £200
b. Ochre omitted £120
Ec. Embossing omitted .... 35·00
Ey. Phosphor omitted .... 5·00
Eya. Embossing and phosphor omitted.
Set of 3 .... 50 50
First Day Cover .... 1·00
Presentation Pack (P. O. Pack No. 22).................... 2·75

Special First Day of Issue Postmarks

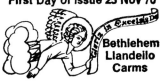

British Post Office Philatelic Bureau, Edinburgh (Type D) .... 1·50
Bethlehem, Llandeilo, Carms.. 2·00

For Nos. X841/1058 see Decimal Machin Definitives section.

(New Currency. 100 new pence = £1)

368 "A Mountain Road" (T. P. Flanagan)

369 "Deer's Meadow" (Tom Carr) **370** "Slieve na brock" (Colin Middleton)

(Colin Middleton)

1971 (16 June). *"Ulster 1971" Paintings. Chalk-surfaced paper. Two phosphor bands. P 15×14.*
881 **368** 3p. yellow-buff, pale yellow, Venetian
red, black, blue and drab 25 25
Ey. Phosphor omitted .... 6·00
a. Venetian red omitted .... —
882 **369** 7½p. olive-brown, brownish grey, pale
olive-grey, deep blue, cobalt and
grey-blue 50 50
a. Pale olive-grey omitted*.................... £350
Ey. Phosphor omitted .... 22·00
883 **370** 9p. greenish yellow, orange, grey,
lavender-grey, bistre, black, pale
ochre-brown and ochre-brown 50 50
a. Orange (flowers) omitted £4200
Ey. Phosphor omitted .... 22·00
Set of 3 .... 1·00 1·00
First Day Cover .... 1·75
Presentation Pack (P.O. Pack No. 26a).................... 6·00

*This only affects the boulder in the foreground, which appears whitish and it only applied to some stamps in the sheet.

Special First Day of Issue Postmarks

**FIRST DAY OF ISSUE
16 JUNE 1971
BELFAST**

British Post Office Philatelic Bureau, Edinburgh (Type D, see
Introduction) .... 2·50
Belfast .... 8·00
First Day of Issue handstamps, in the same design as that for Belfast, were provided at Armagh, Ballymena, Coleraine, Cookstown, Enniskillen, Londonderry, Newry, Omagh and Portadown for this issue.

371 John Keats (150th Death Anniv)

372 Thomas Gray (Death Bicentenary)

373 Sir Walter Scott (Birth Bicentenary)

(Des Rosalind Dease. Queen's head printed in gold and then embossed)

1971 (28 July). *Literary Anniversaries. Chalk-surfaced paper. Two phosphor bands.* P 15×14.

884	**371**	3p. black, gold and greyish blue	25	10
		a. Gold (Queen's head) omitted...........	£225	
		Ey. Phosphor omitted..........................	5·00	
885	**372**	5p. black, gold and yellow-olive...........	45	50
		a. Gold (Queen's head) omitted...........	£1200	
		Ey. Phosphor omitted..........................	32·00	
886	**373**	7½p. black, gold and yellow-brown	45	45
		Eb. Embossing omitted	40·00	
		Ey. Phosphor omitted..........................	22·00	
Set of 3			1·00	1·10
First Day Cover				2·00
Presentation Pack (P.O. Pack No. 32)			6·00	

374 Servicemen and Nurse of 1921

375 Roman Centurion

376 Rugby Football, 1871

(Des F. Wegner)

1971 (25 Aug). *British Anniversaries. Events described on stamps. Chalk-surfaced paper. Two phosphor bands.* P 15×14.

887	**374**	3p. red-orange, grey, dp blue, olive-green, olive-brown, black, rosine and violet-blue	25	25
		a. Deep blue omitted*............................	£950	
		b. Red-orange (nurse's cloak) omitted	£700	
		c. Olive-brown (faces, etc.) omitted	£600	
		d. Black omitted....................................		
		e. Grey omitted.....................................		£5500
		f. Olive-green omitted...........................		£5500
		Ey. Phosphor omitted..........................	3·00	
888	**375**	7½p. grey, yellow-brown, vermilion, mauve, grey-black, black, silver, gold and ochre	50	50
		a. Grey omitted	£275	
		b. Ochre omitted		
		Ey. Phosphor omitted..........................	15·00	
889	**376**	9p. new blue, myrtle-green, grey-black, lemon, olive-brown, magenta and yellow-olive	50	50
		a. Olive-brown omitted	£275	
		b. New blue omitted	£12000	
		c. Myrtle-green omitted.........................		£3250
		d. Lemon (jerseys) omitted....................		£4500
		Ey. Phosphor omitted..........................	£425	
Set of 3			1·00	1·00
First Day Cover				1·50
Presentation Pack (P.O. Pack No. 32A).....................			6·00	

*The effect of the missing deep blue is shown on the sailor's uniform, which appears as grey.

377 Physical Sciences Building, University College of Wales, Aberystwyth

378 Faraday Building, Southampton University

379 Engineering Department, Leicester University

380 Hexagon Restaurant, Essex University

(Des N. Jenkins)

1971 (22 Sept). *British Architecture. Modern University Buildings. Chalk-surfaced paper. Two phosphor bands.* P 15×14.

890	**377**	3p. olive-brown, ochre, lemon, black and yellow-olive	10	10
		a. Lemon omitted	†	£8000
		b. Black (windows) omitted...................	£15000	
		Ey. Phosphor omitted..........................	8·00	
891	**378**	5p. rose, black, chestnut and lilac.........	25	20
		Ey. Phosphor omitted..........................	70·00	
892	**379**	7½p. ochre, black and purple-brown........	45	55
		Ey. Phosphor omitted..........................	12·00	
893	**380**	9p. pale lilac, black, sepia-brown and dp blue..	75	80
		a. Pale lilac omitted	£6000	
		Ey. Phosphor omitted..........................	18·00	
Set of 4			1·25	1·50
First Day Cover				2·00
Presentation Pack (P.O. Pack No. 33)			8·00	

Mint examples of the 5p. exist with a larger "P" following the face value.
No. 890a is only known used on commercial cover from Wantage.
No. 890b is only a partial omission with traces of black on the wall at the far right.

Special First Day of Issue Postmarks

British Post Office Philatelic Bureau, Edinburgh (Type D, see
Introduction) .... 2·50
Aberystwyth.. 12·00
Colchester.. 12·00
Leicester... 12·00
Southampton... 12·00

Collectors Pack 1971
1971 (29 Sept). Comprises Nos. 835/40 and 881/93.
CP893a Collectors Pack... 60·00

381 "Dream of the Wise Men"   **382** "Adoration of the Magi"

383 "Ride of the Magi"

(Des Clarke-Clements-Hughes design team, from stained-glass
windows, Canterbury Cathedral. Queen's head printed in gold and
then embossed)

1971 (13 Oct). *Christmas. Ordinary paper. One centre phosphor band
(2½p.) or two phosphor bands (others). P 15×14.*
894	381	2½p. new blue, black, lemon, emerald, reddish violet, carmine-red, carmine-rose and gold	10	10
		a. Imperf (pair)	£675	
		Eb. Embossing omitted		
895	382	3p. black, reddish violet, lemon, new blue, carmine-rose, emerald, ultramarine and gold	10	10
		a. Gold (Queen's head) omitted	£2200	
		b. Carmine-rose omitted	£5500	
		c. Lemon (window panels) omitted	£325	
		d. New blue omitted	†	£7000
		e. Reddish violet (tunics etc) omitted	£7500	
		f. Carmine-rose and lemon omitted		£8000
		g. Reddish violet and embossing omitted		£5500
		Eh. Embossing omitted	15·00	
		Ey. Phosphor omitted	5·00	
		Eya. Embossing and phosphor omitted.	£100	
896	383	7½p. black, lilac, lemon, emerald, new blue, rose, green and gold	55	75
		a. Gold (Queen's head) omitted	£275	
		b. Lilac omitted	£1300	
		c. Emerald omitted	£700	
		d. Lemon omitted		£4500
		Ef. Embossing omitted	50·00	
		Ef. Embossing double	50·00	
		Ey. Phosphor omitted	12·00	

		Eya. Embossing and phosphor omitted.	32·00	
	Set of 3		55	75
	First Day Cover			2·00
	Presentation Pack (P.O. Pack No. 35)		4·50	

Special First Day of Issue Postmarks

British Post Office Philatelic Bureau, Edinburgh (Type D, see
Introduction) .... 2·50
Bethlehem, Llandeilo, Carms... 10·00
Canterbury.. 10·00

WHITE CHALK-SURFACED PAPER. From No. 897 all issues, with the
exception of Nos. 904/8, were printed on fluorescent white paper, giving
a stronger chalk reaction than the original cream paper.

384 Sir James Clark Ross   **385** Sir Martin Frobisher

386 Henry Hudson   **387** Capt. Scott

(Des Marjorie Saynor. Queen's head printed in gold and then
embossed)

1972 (16 Feb). *British Polar Explorers. Two phosphor bands. P 14×15.*
897	384	3p. yellow-brown, indigo, slate-black, flesh, lemon, rose, brt blue & gold	10	10
		a. Gold (Queen's head) omitted	£180	
		b. Slate-black (hair, etc.) omitted	£7500	
		c. Lemon omitted	£13000	
		Ed. Embossing omitted	45·00	
		Ee. Gold (Queen's head) and embossing omitted	£275	
		Ey. Phosphor omitted	5·00	
		Eya. Embossing and phosphor omitted.	35·00	
898	385	5p. salmon, flesh, purple-brown, ochre, black and gold	15	15
		a. Gold (Queen's head) omitted	£275	
		Eb. Embossing omitted	25·00	
		Ey. Phosphor omitted	12·00	
		Eya. Gold and phosphor omitted	£300	
		Eyb. Embossing and phosphor omitted.		
899	386	7½p. reddish violet, blue, deep slate, yellow-brown, buff, black and gold	45	50

		a. Gold (Queen's head) omitted............	£500		
		Ey. Phosphor omitted................................	20·00		
900	**387**	9p. dull blue, ultramarine, black, greenish yellow, pale pink, rose-red and gold..............		70	85
		Ey. Phosphor omitted................................	£325		
Set of 4				1·25	1·50
First Day Cover					2·50
Presentation Pack (P.O. Pack No. 39)				5·25	

An example of the 3p. is known used on piece with the flesh colour omitted.

391 St. Andrew's, Greensted-juxta-Ongar, Essex

392 All Saints, Earls Barton, Northants

Special First Day of Issue Postmarks

Philatelic Bureau, Edinburgh	5·00
London WC	12·00

388 Statuette of Tutankhamun   **389** 19th-century Coastguard

393 St. Andrew's, Letheringsett, Norfolk

394 St. Andrew's, Helpringham, Lincs

390 Ralph Vaughan Williams and Score

395 St. Mary the Virgin, Huish Episcopi, Somerset

(Des Rosalind Dease (3p.), F. Wegner (7½p.), C. Abbott (9p.). Queen's head printed in gold and then embossed (7½p., 9p.))

1972 (26 Apr). *Anniversaries. Events described on stamps. Two phosphor bands.* P 15×14.

901	**388**	3p. black, grey, gold, dull bistre-brown, blackish brown, pale stone and light brown		25	25
		a. Face value omitted	£15000		
902	**389**	7½p. pale yellow, new blue, slate-blue, violet-blue, slate and gold.................		50	50
		Ea. Embossing omitted	£200		
		Ey. Phosphor omitted................................	£250		
903	**390**	9p. bistre-brown, black, sage-green, dp slate, yellow-ochre, brown and gold		50	50
		a. Gold (Queen's head) omitted........	£3500		
		b. Brown (facial features) omitted........	£4500		
		c. Deep slate omitted	£20000		
		Ed. Embossing omitted			
		Ey. Phosphor omitted................................	32·00		
Set of 3				1·00	1·00
First Day Cover					2·25
Presentation Pack (P.O. Pack No. 40)				4·25	

Special First Day of Issue Postmarks

Philatelic Bureau, Edinburgh	3·00
London EC	7·00

(Des R. Maddox. Queen's head printed in gold and then embossed)

1972 (21 June). *British Architecture. Village Churches. Ordinary paper. Two phosphor bands.* P 14×15.

904	**391**	3p. violet-blue, black, lt yellow-olive, emerald-green, orange-vermilion and gold...................................		10	10
		a. Gold (Queen's head) omitted............	£225		
		b. Orange-vermilion omitted................			£5500
		Ec. Embossing omitted	35·00		
		Ey. Phosphor omitted................................	6·00		
		Eya. Gold (Queen's head) and phosphor omitted	£300		
		Eyb. Embossing and phosphor omitted.	20·00		
905	**392**	4p. deep yellow-olive, black, emerald, violet-blue, orange-vermilion and gold		10	20
		a. Gold (Queen's head) omitted............	£6500		
		b. Violet-blue omitted............................	£250		
		Ec. Embossing omitted	12·00		
		Eya. Phosphor omitted............................	18·00		
906	**393**	5p. deep emerald, black, royal blue, light yellow-olive, orange-vermilion and gold..............................		15	20
		a. Gold (Queen's head) omitted............	£275		
		Eb. Embossing omitted	50·00		
		Ey. Phosphor omitted................................	25·00		
907	**394**	7½p. orange-red, black, dp yellow-olive, royal blue, lt emerald and gold		50	75
		Ey. Phosphor omitted................................	18·00		
		Eya. Embossing and phosphor omitted.	48·00		
908	**395**	9p. new blue, black, emerald-green, dp yellow-olive, orange-vermilion and gold		50	80
		Ea. Embossing omitted	20·00		
		Ey. Phosphor omitted................................	22·00		
Set of 5				1·25	1·90
First Day Cover					2·75
Presentation Pack (P.O. Pack No. 41)				10·00	

Nos. 905a and 906a only exist with the phosphor omitted.

Special First Day of Issue Postmarks

Philatelic Bureau, Edinburgh	3·50
Canterbury	8·00

"Belgica 72" Souvenir Pack

1972 (24 June). Comprises Nos. 894/6 and 904/8.
CP908b Souvenir Pack .... 10·00
  This pack was specially produced for sale at the "Belgica '72" Stamp Exhibition, held in Brussels between 24 June and 9 July. It contains information on British stamps with a religious theme with text in English, French and Flemish, and was put on sale at Philatelic Bureaux in Britain on 26 June.

396 Microphones, 1924–69   **397** Horn Loudspeaker

398 T.V. Camera, 1972   **399** Oscillator and Spark Transmitter, 1897

(Des D. Gentleman)

1972 (13 Sept). *Broadcasting Anniversaries. 75th Anniv of Marconi and Kemp's Radio Experiments (9p.), and 50th Anniv of Daily Broadcasting by the B.B.C. (others). Two phosphor bands.* P 15×14.

909	**396**	3p. pale brown, black, grey, greenish yellow and brownish slate	10	10
		a. Greenish yellow (terminals) omitted	£6000	
910	**397**	5p. brownish slate, lake-brown, salmon, lt brown, black and red-brown	10	20
		Ey. Phosphor omitted	6·00	
		Eya. Phosphor on back but omitted on front	45·00	
911	**398**	7½p. lt grey, slate, brownish slate, magenta and black	45	50
		a. Brownish slate (Queen's head) omitted	†	£4500
		Eya. Phosphor on back but omitted on front	45·00	
		Ey. Phosphor omitted	12·00	
912	**399**	9p. lemon, brown, brownish slate, deep brownish slate, bluish slate and black	50	50
		a. Brownish slate (Queen's head) omitted	£7000	
		Ey. Phosphor omitted	13·00	
Set of 4			1·00	1·25
First Day Cover				2·75
Presentation Pack (P.O. Pack No. 43)			4·25	

  In addition to the generally issued Presentation Pack a further pack exists inscribed "1922–1972". This pack of stamps commemorating the 50th Anniversary of the B.B.C. was specially produced as a memento of the occasion for the B.B.C. staff. It was sent with the good wishes of the Chairman and Board of Governors, the Director-General and Board of Management. The pack contains Nos. 909/11 only (Price £35).
  No. 911a is only found in first day covers posted from the Philatelic Bureau in Edinburgh.

Special First Day of Issue Postmarks

Philatelic Bureau, Edinburgh	3·50
London W1	10·00

400 Angel holding Trumpet   **401** Angel playing Lute

402 Angel playing Harp

(Des Sally Stiff. Photo and embossing)

1972 (18 Oct). *Christmas. One centre phosphor band (2½p.) or two phosphor bands (others).* P 14×15.

913	**400**	2½p. cerise, pale reddish brown, yellow-orange, orange-vermilion, lilac, gold, red-brown and deep grey	10	10
		a. Gold omitted	£1500	
		Eb. Embossing omitted	15·00	
		c. Deep grey omitted	£3000	
		Ey. Phosphor omitted	12·00	
914	**401**	3p. ultramarine, lavender, lt turquoise-blue, brt green, gold, red-brown and bluish violet	10	10
		a. Red-brown omitted	£1000	
		b. Bright green omitted	£275	
		c. Bluish violet omitted	£275	
		d. Lavender omitted		
		e. Gold omitted	£2000	
		Ef. Embossing omitted	9·00	
		Ey. Phosphor omitted	6·00	
		Eya. Embossing and phosphor omitted	15·00	
915	**402**	7½p. dp brown, pale lilac, lt cinnamon, ochre, gold, red-brown and blackish violet	50	45
		a. Ochre omitted	£275	
		b. Blackish violet (shadow) omitted		
		Ec. Embossing omitted	18·00	
		Ey. Phosphor omitted	12·00	
		Eya. Embossing and phosphor omitted	30·00	
Set of 3			60	45
First Day Cover				1·50
Presentation Pack (P.O. Pack No. 44)			4·00	

  The gold printing on the 3p. is from two cylinders: 1E and 1F. Examples have been seen with the gold of the 1F cylinder omitted, but these are difficult to detect on single stamps.

Special First Day of Issue Postmarks

Philatelic Bureau, Edinburgh .... 2·00
Bethlehem, Llandeilo, Carms.................................... 6·50

403 Queen Elizabeth and
Duke of Edinburgh
404 "Europe"

(Des J. Matthews from photo by N. Parkinson)

1972 (20 Nov). *Royal Silver Wedding. "All-over" phosphor (3p.) or without phosphor (20p.).* P 14×15.

I. "Rembrandt" Machine

916	**403**	3p. brownish black, dp blue & silver	25	25
		a. Silver omitted.............................	£650	
917		20p. brownish black, reddish purple and silver...........................	1·00	1·00

II. "Jumelle" Machine

918	**403**	3p. brownish black, dp blue & silver	40	10
Set of 2			1·00	1·00
Gutter Pair (No. 918)...			80	
Traffic Light Gutter Pair			20·00	
First Day Cover..				1·50
Presentation Pack (P.O. Pack No. 45)			4·00	
Presentation Pack (Japanese)			9·50	
Souvenir Book..			4·00	

The souvenir book is a twelve-page booklet containing photographs of the Royal Wedding and other historic events of the royal family and accompanying information. The 3p. "JUMELLE" has a lighter shade of the brownish black than the 3p. "REMBRANDT". It also has the brown cylinders less deeply etched, which can be distinguished in the Duke's face which is slightly lighter, and in the Queen's hair where the highlights are sharper.

3p. "REMBRANDT". Cyls. 3A-1B-11C no dot. Sheets of 100 (10×10).
3p. "JUMELLE". Cyls. 1A-1B-3C dot and no dot. Sheets of 100 (two panes 5×10, separated by gutter margin).

Special First Day of Issue Postmarks

Philatelic Bureau, Edinburgh .... 2·00
Windsor, Berks.. 6·00

Collectors Pack 1972

1972 (20 Nov). Comprises Nos. 897/917.
CP918a Collectors Pack.. 35·00

(Des P. Murdoch)

1973 (3 Jan). *Britain's Entry into European Communities. Two phosphor bands.* P 14×15.

919	**404**	3p. dull orange, bright rose-red, ultramarine, lt lilac and black............	25	25
920		5p. new blue, brt rose-red, ultramarine, cobalt-blue and black	25	50
		a. Pair. Nos. 920/1	1·00	1·00

921		5p. lt emerald-green, brt rose-red, ultramarine, cobalt-blue & black	25	50
Set of 3			1·00	1·00
First Day Cover..				2·00
Presentation Pack (P.O. Pack No. 48)			3·00	

Nos. 920/1 were printed horizontally *se-tenant* throughout the sheet.

Special First Day of Issue Postmark

Philatelic Bureau, Edinburgh .... 2·50

405 Oak Tree

(Des D. Gentleman)

1973 (28 Feb). *Tree Planting Year. British Trees (1st issue). Two phosphor bands.* P 15×14.

922	**405**	9p. brownish black, apple-green, deep olive, sepia, blackish green and brownish grey.............................	35	40
		a. Brownish black (value and inscr) omitted	£700	
		b. Brownish grey (Queen's head) omitted	£650	
		Ey. Phosphor omitted................................	90·00	
First Day Cover..				1·75
Presentation Pack (P.O. Pack No. 49)			2·75	

See also No. 949.

Special First Day of Issue Postmark

Philatelic Bureau, Edinburgh .... 2·00

CHALK-SURFACED PAPER. The following issues are printed on chalk-surfaced paper but where "all-over" phosphor has been applied there is no chalk reaction except in the sheet margins outside the phosphor area.

406 David Livingstone   **407** H. M. Stanley

T **406/7** were printed together, horizontally *se-tenant* within the sheet.

408 Sir Francis Drake

409 Walter Raleigh

410 Charles Sturt

(Des Marjorie Saynor. Queen's head printed in gold and then embossed)

1973 (18 Apr). *British Explorers. "All-over" phosphor.* P 14×15.

923	**406**	3p.	orange-yellow, light orange-brown, grey-black, light turquoise-blue, turquoise-blue and gold	40	25
		a.	Pair. Nos. 923/4	80	1·00
		b.	Gold (Queen's head) omitted	£135	
		c.	Turquoise-blue (background and inscr) omitted	£2000	
		d.	Light orange-brown omitted	£1300	
		Ee.	Embossing omitted	35·00	
924	**407**	3p.	orange-yellow, light orange-brown, grey-black, light turquoise-blue, turquoise-blue and gold	40	25
		b.	Gold (Queen's head) omitted	£135	
		c.	Turquoise-blue (background and inscr) omitted	£2000	
		d.	Light orange-brown omitted	£1300	
		Ee.	Embossing omitted	35·00	
925	**408**	5p.	light flesh, chrome-yellow, orange-yellow, sepia, brownish grey, grey-black, violet-blue and gold	40	50
		a.	Gold (Queen's head) omitted	£250	
		b.	Grey-black omitted	£4500	
		c.	Sepia omitted	£5000	
		Ed.	Embossing omitted	9·00	
926	**409**	7½p.	light flesh, reddish brown, sepia, ultramarine, grey-black, bright lilac and gold	40	50
		a.	Gold (Queen's head) omitted	£10000	
		b.	Ultramarine (eyes) omitted	—	£5000
927	**410**	9p.	flesh, pale stone, grey-blue, grey-black, brown-grey, Venetian red, brown-red and gold	40	75
		a.	Gold (Queen's head) omitted	£225	
		b.	Brown-grey printing double from	£850	
		c.	Grey-black omitted	£5000	
		d.	Brown-red (rivers on map) omitted	£1500	
		Ee.	Embossing omitted	40·00	
Set of 5				1·50	2·50
First Day Cover					2·50
Presentation Pack (P.O. Pack No. 50)				4·50	

Caution is needed when buying missing gold heads in this issue as they can be removed by using a hard eraser, etc., but this invariably affects the "all-over" phosphor. Genuine examples have the phosphor intact. Used examples off cover cannot be distinguished as much of the phosphor is lost in the course of floating.

In the 5p. value the missing grey-black affects the doublet, which appears as brownish grey, and the lace ruff, which is entirely missing. The missing sepia affects only Drake's hair, which appears much lighter.

The double printing of the brown-grey (cylinder 1F) on the 9p., is a most unusual type of error to occur in a multicoloured photogravure issue. Two sheets are known and it is believed that they stuck to the cylinder and went through a second time. This would result in the following two sheets missing the colour but at the time of going to press this error has not been reported. The second print is slightly askew and more prominent in the top half of the sheets. Examples from the upper part of the sheet showing a clear double impression of the facial features are worth a substantial premium over the price quoted.

Special First Day of Issue Postmark

Philatelic Bureau, Edinburgh .... 3·00

First Day of Issue handstamps were provided at Blantyre, Glasgow, and Denbigh for this issue.

411 **412** **413** (T **411**/**13** show sketches of W.G. Grace by Harry Furniss)

(Des E. Ripley. Queen's head printed in gold and then embossed)

1973 (16 May). *County Cricket 1873–1973. "All-over" phosphor.* P 14×15.

928	**411**	3p.	black, ochre and gold	25	25
		a.	Gold (Queen's head) omitted	£6000	
		Eb.	Embossing omitted	20·00	
929	**412**	7½p.	black, light sage-green and gold	75	75
		Eb.	Embossing omitted	30·00	
930	**413**	9p.	black, cobalt and gold	1·25	1·00
		Eb.	Embossing omitted	80·00	
Set of 3				1·75	1·50
First Day Cover					3·00
Presentation Pack (P.O. Pack No. 51)				4·50	
Souvenir Book				7·00	
P.H.Q. Card (No. 928) (1)				70·00	£275

Nos. 928/30 with two phosphor bands are known.

The souvenir book is a 24-page illustrated booklet containing a history of County Cricket with text by John Arlott.

The P.H.Q. card did not become available until mid-July. The used price quoted is for an example used in July or August 1973.

Special First Day of Issue Postmarks

Philatelic Bureau, Edinburgh .... 3·00
Lords, London NW .... 8·00

414 "Self-portrait" (Reynolds)

415 "Self-portrait" (Raeburn)

416 "Nelly O'Brien"
(Reynolds)

417 "Rev. R. Walker
(The Skater)" (Raeburn)

(Des S. Rose. Queen's head printed in gold and then embossed)

1973 (4 July). *British Paintings. 250th Birth Anniv of Sir Joshua Reynolds and 150th Death Anniv of Sir Henry Raeburn. "All-over" phosphor.* P 14×15.

931	**414**	3p. rose, new blue, jet-black, magenta, greenish yellow, black, ochre and gold	10	10
		a. Gold (Queen's head) omitted	£135	
		Ec. Gold (Queen's head) and embossing omitted	£150	
932	**415**	5p. cinnamon, greenish yellow, new blue, light magenta, black, yellow-olive and gold	30	30
		a. Gold (Queen's head) omitted	£150	
		b. Greenish yellow omitted	£1200	
		Ec. Embossing omitted	30·00	
933	**416**	7½p. greenish yellow, new blue, light magenta, black, cinnamon and gold	30	30
		a. Gold (Queen's head) omitted	£200	
		b. Cinnamon omitted	£20000	
		Ec. Embossing omitted	25·00	
934	**417**	9p. brownish rose, black, dull rose, pale yellow, brownish grey, pale blue and gold	60	60
		b. Brownish rose omitted	£160	
		Ec. Embossing omitted	£150	
Set of 4			1·20	1·20
First Day Cover				2·00
Presentation Pack (P.O. Pack No. 52)			3·25	

Special First Day of Issue Postmark

Philatelic Bureau, Edinburgh .... 2·50

418 Court Masque Costumes

419 St. Paul's Church, Covent Garden

420 Prince's Lodging, Newmarket

421 Court Masque Stage Scene

T **418/19** and T **420/1** were printed horizontally *se-tenant* within the sheet.

(Des Rosalind Dease. Litho and typo B.W.)

1973 (15 Aug). *400th Birth Anniv of Inigo Jones (architect and designer). "All-over" phosphor.* P 15×14.

935	**418**	3p. deep mauve, black and gold	10	25

		a. Pair. Nos. 935/6	30	50
		ab. Face values omitted	£14000	
		Eac. Deep mauve ptg double (pair)	£6500	
		Ec. 9 mm. phosphor band*	15·00	
936	**419**	3p. deep brown, black and gold	10	25
937	**420**	5p. blue, black and gold	35	50
		a. Pair. Nos. 937/8	1·00	1·00
		Ec. 9 mm. phosphor band*	18·00	
938	**421**	5p. grey-olive, black and gold	35	50
Set of 4			1·25	1·25
First Day Cover				2·00
Presentation Pack (P.O. Pack No. 53)			3·50	
P.H.Q. Card (No. 936) (2)			£200	£200

No. 935ab is caused by the omission of virtually all the black printing from one horizontal row.

*On part of the printings for both values the "all-over" phosphor band missed the first vertical row and a 9 mm. phosphor band was applied to correct this.

Special First Day of Issue Postmark

Philatelic Bureau, Edinburgh .... 3·00

422 Palace of Westminster seen from Whitehall

423 Palace of Westminster seen from Millbank

(Des R. Downer. Recess and typo B.W.)

1973 (12 Sept). *19th Commonwealth Parliamentary Conference. "All-over" phosphor.* P 15×14.

939	**422**	8p. black, brownish grey and stone	45	50
940	**423**	10p. gold and black	45	40
Set of 2			75	75
First Day Cover				1·50
Presentation Pack (P.O. Pack No. 54)			3·00	
Souvenir Book			7·00	
P.H.Q. Card (No. 939) (3)			40·00	£150

The souvenir book is a twelve-page booklet containing a history of the Palace of Westminster.

Special First Day of Issue Postmark

Philatelic Bureau, Edinburgh .... 2·00

424 Princess Anne and Capt. Mark Phillips

(Des C. Clements and E. Hughes from photo by Lord Lichfield)

1973 (14 Nov). *Royal Wedding. "All-over" phosphor.* P 15×14.

941	**424**	3½p. dull violet and silver	25	25
		a. Imperf (horiz pair)	£6000	
942		20p. deep brown and silver	1·00	75
		a. Silver omitted	£5500	
Set of 2			1·00	75

Set of 2 Gutter Pairs	2·75	
Set of 2 Traffic Light Gutter Pairs	£110	
First Day Cover		1·50
Presentation Pack (P.O. Pack No. 56)	2·75	
P.H.Q. Card (No. 941) (4)	9·00	50·00

Special First Day of Issue Postmarks

Philatelic Bureau, Edinburgh	2·00	
Westminster Abbey, London SW1	5·00	
Windsor, Berks	5·00	

425

426

427

428

429

T **425/9** depict the carol "Good King Wenceslas" and were printed horizontally *se-tenant* within the sheet.

430 Good King Wenceslas, the Page and Peasant

(Des D. Gentleman)

1973 (28 Nov). *Christmas. One centre phosphor band (3p.) or "all-over" phosphor (3½p.).* P 15×14.

943	**425**	3p. grey-black, violet-blue, slate, brown, rose-red, rosy mauve, turquoise-green, salmon-pink and gold	20	25
		a. Strip of 5. Nos. 943/7	2·25	2·50
		ab. Rosy mauve omitted (strip of 5)	£13000	
		b. Imperf (horiz strip of 5)	£6500	

		c. Black (face value) omitted*	£10000	
		Eg. Gum arabic	25	
		Ega. Strip of 5. Nos. 943Eg/7Eg	3·00	
		Egb. Imperf (strip of 5. Nos. 943 Eg/7Eg)	£6500	
944	**426**	3p. grey-black, violet-blue, slate, brown, rose-red, rosy mauve, turquoise-green, salmon-pink and gold	20	25
		Eg. Gum arabic	25	
945	**427**	3p. grey-black, violet-blue, slate, brown, rose-red, rosy-mauve, turquoise-green, salmon-pink and gold	20	25
		Eg. Gum arabic	25	
946	**428**	3p. grey-black, violet-blue, slate, brown, rose-red, rosy mauve, turquoise-green, salmon-pink and gold	20	25
		Eg. Gum arabic	25	
947	**429**	3p. grey-black, violet-blue, slate, brown, rose-red, rosy-mauve, turquoise-green, salmon-pink and gold	20	25
		Eg. Gum arabic	25	
948	**430**	3½p. salmon-pink, grey-black, red-brown, blue, turquoise-green, brt rose-red, rosy mauve, lavender-grey and gold	20	25
		a. Imperf (pair)	£575	
		b. Grey-black (value, inscr, etc.) omitted	£170	
		c. Salmon-pink omitted	£110	
		d. Blue (leg, robes) omitted	£275	
		e. Rosy mauve (robe at right) omitted	£150	
		f. Blue and rosy mauve omitted	£650	
		g. Brt rose-red (King's robe) omitted	£160	
		h. Red-brown (logs, basket, etc.) omitted		
		i. Turquoise-green (leg, robe, etc.) omitted	£5500	
		j. Gold (background) omitted	†	£2800
Set of 6			2·25	2·50
First Day Cover				2·50
Presentation Pack (P.O. Pack No. 57)			4·00	

Examples of No. 948j are only known used on covers from Gloucester. The 3½p. has also been seen with the lavender-grey omitted used on piece.

The 3p. and 3½p. are normally with PVA gum with added dextrin, but the 3½p. also exists with normal PVA gum.

*No. 943c is known in a corner marginal strip of five showing a progressive dry print of black leaving a total omission on the first stamp. Adjacent similar strips of five all show traces of black.

Special First Day of Issue Postmarks

Philatelic Bureau, Edinburgh	3·00	
Bethlehem, Llandeilo, Carms	6·00	

Collectors Pack 1973

1973 (28 Nov). Comprises Nos. 919/48.

CP948k Collectors Pack	27·00

431 Horse Chestnut

(Des D. Gentleman)

1974 (27 Feb). *British Trees (2nd issue). "All-over" phosphor.* P 15×14.

949	**431**	10p. light emerald, bright green, greenish yellow, brown-olive, black and brownish grey	40	35

Gutter Pair	2·00	
Traffic Light Gutter Pair	65·00	
First Day Cover		1·25
Presentation Pack (P.O. Pack No. 59)	2·50	
P.H.Q. Card (5)	£150	£150

The pack number is stated to be 58 on the reverse but the correct number is 59.

Special First Day of Issue Postmark

Philatelic Bureau, Edinburgh .... 1·50

432 First Motor Fire-engine, 1904   **433** Prize-winning Fire-engine, 1863

434 First Steam Fire-engine, 1830   **435** Fire-engine, 1766

(Des D. Gentleman)

1974 (24 Apr). *Bicentenary of the Fire Prevention (Metropolis) Act. "All-over" phosphor.* P 15×14.

950	432	3½p. grey-black, orange-yellow, greenish yellow, dull rose, ochre and grey	25	10
		a. Imperf (pair)	£1000	
951	433	5½p. greenish yellow, dp rosy magenta, orange-yellow, lt emerald, grey-black and grey	25	30
952	434	8p. greenish yellow, lt blue-green, greenish blue, lt chestnut, grey-black and grey	50	50
953	435	10p. grey-black, pale reddish brown, lt brown, orange-yellow and grey	50	50
Set of 4			1·25	1·25
Set of 4 Gutter Pairs			4·00	
Set of 4 Traffic Light Gutter Pairs			60·00	
First Day Cover				3·00
Presentation Pack (P.O. Pack No. 60)			3·00	
P.H.Q. Card (No. 950) (6)			£140	£150

The 3½p. exists with ordinary PVA gum.

Special First Day of Issue Postmark

Philatelic Bureau, Edinburgh .... 3·50

436 P & O Packet, *Peninsular,* 1888   **437** Farman H.F. III Biplane, 1911

438 Airmail-blue Van and Postbox, 1930   **439** Imperial Airways Short S.21 Flying Boat *Maia,* 1937

(Des Rosalind Dease)

1974 (12 June). *Centenary of Universal Postal Union. "All over" phosphor.* P 15×14.

954	436	3½p. dp brownish grey, brt mauve, grey-black and gold	25	10
955	437	5½p. pale orange, lt emerald, grey-black and gold	25	30
956	438	8p. cobalt, brown, grey-black & gold	25	35
957	439	10p. dp brownish grey, orange, grey-black and gold	50	40
Set of 4			1·00	1·00
Set of 4 Gutter Pairs			3·00	
Set of 4 Traffic Light Gutter Pairs			45·00	
First Day Cover				2·00
Presentation Pack (P.O. Pack No. 64)			3·00	

Special First Day of Issue Postmark

Philatelic Bureau, Edinburgh .... 2·50

440 Robert the Bruce   **441** Owain Glyndwr

442 Henry the Fifth   **443** The Black Prince

(Des F. Wegner)

1974 (10 July). *Medieval Warriors. "All-over" phosphor.* P 15×14.

958	440	4½p. greenish yellow, vermilion, slate-blue, red-brown, reddish brown, lilac-grey and gold	25	10
959	441	5½p. lemon, vermilion, slate-blue, red-brown, reddish brown, olive-drab and gold	25	35
960	442	8p. dp grey, vermilion, greenish yellow, new blue, red-brown, dp cinnamon and gold	50	50
961	443	10p. vermilion, greenish yellow, new blue, red-brown, reddish brown, lt blue and gold	50	50
Set of 4			1·25	1·25

Set of 4 Gutter Pairs	4·00	
Set of 4 Traffic Light Gutter Pairs	60·00	
First Day Cover		3·00
Presentation Pack (P.O. Pack No. 65)	4·00	
P.H.Q. Cards (set of 4) (7)	28·00	65·00

Imperforate pairs of SG961 are known and thought to be of proof status (£700 per pair).

Special First Day of Issue Postmark

Philatelic Bureau, Edinburgh	3·50

444 Churchill in Royal Yacht Squadron Uniform

445 Prime Minister, 1940

446 Secretary for War and Air, 1919

447 War Correspondent, South Africa, 1899

(Des C. Clements and E. Hughes)

1974 (9 Oct). Birth Centenary of Sir Winston Churchill. "All-over" phosphor. P 14×15.

962	**444**	4½p. Prussian blue, pale turquoise-green and silver	20	15
963	**445**	5½p. sepia, brownish grey and silver	35	35
964	**446**	8p. crimson, lt claret and silver	60	50
965	**447**	10p. lt brown, stone and silver	60	50
Set of 4			1·60	1·50
Set of 4 Gutter Pairs			4·00	
Set of 4 Traffic Light Gutter Pairs			34·00	
First Day Cover				2·00
Presentation Pack (P.O. Pack No. 66)			3·50	
Souvenir Book			3·00	
P.H.Q. Card (No. 963) (8)			6·00	32·00

The souvenir book consists of an illustrated folder containing a biography of Sir Winston.

Nos. 962/5 come with PVA gum containing added dextrin, but the 8p. also exists with normal PVA.

Special First Day of Issue Postmarks

Philatelic Bureau, Edinburgh	3·50
Blenheim, Woodstock, Oxford	10·00
House of Commons, London SW	10·00

448 "Adoration of the Magi" (York Minster, circa 1355)

449 "The Nativity" (St. Helen's Church, Norwich, circa 1480)

450 "Virgin and Child" (Ottery St. Mary Church, circa 1350)

451 "Virgin and Child" (Worcester Cathedral, circa 1224)

(Des Peter Hatch Partnership)

1974 (27 Nov). Christmas. Church Roof Bosses. One phosphor band (3½p.) or "all-over" phosphor (others). P 15×14.

966	**448**	3½p. gold, lt new blue, lt brown, grey-black and lt stone	10	10
		a. Light stone (background shading) omitted	£40000	
		Ey. Phosphor omitted	12·00	
967	**449**	4½p. gold, yellow-orange, rose-red, lt brown, grey-black & lt new blue	10	10
968	**450**	8p. blue, gold, lt brown, rose-red, dull green and grey-black	25	50
969	**451**	10p. gold, dull rose, grey-black, lt new blue, pale cinnamon and lt brown	50	50
Set of 4			1·00	1·00
Set of 4 Gutter Pairs			3·50	
Set of 4 Traffic Light Gutter Pairs			36·00	
First Day Cover				2·00
Presentation Pack (P.O. Pack No. 67)			3·00	

The phosphor band on the 3½p. was first applied down the centre of the stamp but during the printing this was deliberately placed to the right between the roof boss and the value; however, intermediate positions, due to shifts, are known.

Two used examples of the 3½p. have been reported with the light brown colour omitted.

Special First Day of Issue Postmarks

Philatelic Bureau, Edinburgh	2·50
Bethlehem, Llandeilo, Carms	5·00

Collectors Pack 1974
1974 (27 Nov). Comprises Nos. 949/69.

CP969a Collectors Pack	13·00

452 Invalid in Wheelchair

(Des P. Sharland)

1975 (22 Jan). *Health and Handicap Funds. "All-over" phosphor.* P 15×14.

970	**452**	4½p. +1½p. azure and grey-blue	25	25
		Gutter Pair	50	
		Traffic Light Gutter Pair	2·25	
		First Day Cover		1·00

Special First Day of Issue Postmark

Philatelic Bureau, Edinburgh .... 1·50

453 "Peace-Burial at Sea"

454 "Snowstorm-Steamer off a Harbour's Mouth"

455 "The Arsenal, Venice"

456 "St. Laurent"

(Des S. Rose)

1975 (19 Feb). *Birth Bicentenary of J. M. W. Turner (painter). "All-over" phosphor.* P 15×14.

971	**453**	4½p. grey-black, salmon, stone, blue and grey	25	25
972	**454**	5½p. cobalt, greenish yellow, lt yellow brown, grey-black and rose	25	25
973	**455**	8p. pale yellow-orange, greenish yellow, rose, cobalt and grey-black	25	50
974	**456**	10p. dp blue, lt yellow-ochre, lt brown, dp cobalt and grey-black	50	50
		Set of 4	1·00	1·00
		Set of 4 Gutter Pairs	2·25	
		Set of 4 Traffic Light Gutter Pairs	8·00	
		First Day Cover		1·50
		Presentation Pack (P.O. Pack No. 69)	3·00	
		P.H.Q. Card (No. 972) (9)	42·00	34·00

Special First Day of Issue Postmarks

London WC .... 5·00
Philatelic Bureau, Edinburgh .... 2·00

457 Charlotte Square, Edinburgh

458 The Rows, Chester

T **457/8** were printed horizontally *se-tenant* within the sheet.

459 Royal Observatory, Greenwich

460 St. George's Chapel, Windsor

461 National Theatre, London

(Des P. Gauld)

1975 (23 Apr). *European Architectural Heritage Year. "All over" phosphor.* P 15×14.

975	**457**	7p. greenish yellow, brt orange, grey-black, red-brown, new blue, lavender and gold	15	15
		a. Pair. Nos. 975/6	90	1·00
976	**458**	7p. grey-black, greenish yellow, new blue, brt orange, red-brown and gold	15	15
977	**459**	8p. magenta, dp slate, pale magenta, lt yellow-olive, grey-black and gold	40	30
978	**460**	10p. bistre-brown, greenish yellow, dp slate, emerald-green, grey-black and gold	40	30
979	**461**	12p. grey-black, new blue, pale magenta and gold	40	35
		Set of 5	1·50	1·40
		Set of 5 Gutter Pairs	5·50	
		Set of 5 Traffic Light Gutter Pairs	22·00	
		First Day Cover		2·50
		Presentation Pack (P.O. Pack No. 70)	3·00	
		P.H.Q. Cards (Nos. 975/7) (10)	11·00	40·00

Special First Day of Issue Postmark

Philatelic Bureau, Edinburgh .... 3·00

462 Sailing Dinghies

463 Racing Keel Yachts

464 Cruising Yachts

465 Multihulls

(Des A. Restall. Recess and photo)

1975 (11 June). *Sailing. "All-over" phosphor. P 15×14.*

980	**462**	7p. black, bluish violet, scarlet, orange-vermilion, orange and gold	25	20
981	**463**	8p. black, orange-vermilion, orange, lavender, brt mauve, brt blue, dp ultramarine and gold	35	40
		a. Black omitted	£125	
982	**464**	10p. black, orange, bluish emerald, lt olive-drab, chocolate and gold	35	45
983	**465**	12p. black, ultramarine, turquoise-blue, rose, grey, steel-blue and gold	50	50
Set of 4			1·25	1·25
Set of 4 Gutter Pairs			2·50	
Set of 4 Traffic Light Gutter Pairs			25·00	
First Day Cover				2·00
Presentation Pack (P.O. Pack No. 71)			2·50	
P.H.Q. Card (No. 981) (11)			5·75	30·00

On No. 981a the recess-printed black colour is completely omitted.

Special First Day of Issue Postmark

Philatelic Bureau, Edinburgh	2·50

A First Day of Issue handstamp was provided at Weymouth for this issue.

1825 Stockton and Darlington Railway
466 *Stephenson's Locomotion*, 1825

1876 North British Railway Drummond
467 *Abbotsford*, 1876

1923 Great Western Railway Castle Class
468 *Caerphilly Castle*, 1923

1975 British Rail Inter-City Service HST
469 High Speed Train, 1975

(Des B. Craker)

1975 (13 Aug). *150th Anniv of Public Railways. "All-over" phosphor. P 15×14.*

984	**466**	7p. red-brown, grey-black, greenish yellow, grey and silver	25	25
985	**467**	8p. brown, orange-yellow, vermilion, grey-black, grey and silver	50	50
986	**468**	10p. emerald-green, grey-black, yellow-orange, vermilion, grey and silver	50	50
987	**469**	12p. grey-black, pale lemon, vermilion, blue, grey and silver	40	50
Set of 4			1·50	1·50
Set of 4 Gutter Pairs			3·00	
Set of 4 Traffic Light Gutter Pairs			12·00	
First Day Cover				2·50
Presentation Pack (P.O. Pack No. 72)			3·00	
Souvenir Book			4·00	
P.H.Q. Cards (set of 4) (12)			70·00	72·00

The souvenir book is an eight-page booklet containing a history of the railways.

Special First Day of Issue Postmarks

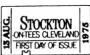

Philatelic Bureau, Edinburgh	3·00
Darlington, Co. Durham	12·00
Shildon, Co. Durham	15·00
Stockton-on-Tees, Cleveland	12·00

470 Palace of Westminster

(Des R. Downer)

1975 (3 Sept). *62nd Inter-Parliamentary Union Conference. "All-over" phosphor. P 15×14.*

988	**470**	12p. lt new blue, black, brownish grey and gold	50	40
Gutter Pair			1·00	
Traffic Light Gutter Pair			3·00	
First Day Cover				80
Presentation Pack (P.O. Pack No. 74)			1·75	

Special First Day of Issue Postmark

Philatelic Bureau, Edinburgh	1·25

471 Emma and Mr. Woodhouse (*Emma*)

472 Catherine Morland (*Northanger Abbey*)

473 Mr. Darcy (*Pride and Prejudice*)

474 Mary and Henry Crawford (*Mansfield Park*)

(Des Barbara Brown)

1975 (22 Oct). *Birth Bicentenary of Jane Austen (novelist). "All-over" phosphor.* P 14×15.

989	**471**	8½p. blue, slate, rose-red, lt yellow, dull green, grey-black and gold	25	20
990	**472**	10p. slate, brt magenta, grey, lt yellow, grey-black and gold	45	45
991	**473**	11p. dull blue, pink, olive-sepia, slate, pale greenish yellow, grey-black and gold	45	45
992	**474**	13p. brt magenta, lt new blue, slate, buff, dull blue-green, grey-black & gold	50	50
Set of 4			1·50	1·25
Set of 4 Gutter Pairs			2·50	
Set of 4 Traffic Light Gutter Pairs			7·00	
First Day Cover				2·50
Presentation Pack (P.O. Pack No. 75)			3·00	
P.H.Q. Cards (set of 4) (13)			24·00	42·00

Special First Day of Issue Postmarks

Philatelic Bureau, Edinburgh	3·00
Steventon, Basingstoke, Hants	6·00

475 Angels with Harp and Lute   **476** Angel with Mandolin

477 Angel with Horn   **478** Angel with Trumpet

(Des R. Downer)

1975 (26 Nov). *Christmas. One phosphor band (6½p.), phosphor-inked background (8½p.), "all-over" phosphor (others).* P 15×14.

993	**475**	6½p. bluish violet, brt reddish violet, light lavender and gold	25	25
994	**476**	8½p. turquoise-green, brt emerald-green, slate, lt turquoise-green and gold	25	40
995	**477**	11p. vermilion, cerise, pink and gold	50	45
996	**478**	13p. drab, brown, brt orange, buff and gold	50	45
Set of 4			1·25	1·25
Set of 4 Gutter Pairs			2·75	
Set of 4 Traffic Light Gutter Pairs			9·00	
First Day Cover				1·50
Presentation Pack (P.O. Pack No. 76)			3·00	

The 6½p. exists with both ordinary PVA gum and PVA containing added dextrin.

Special First Day of Issue Postmarks

Philatelic Bureau, Edinburgh	2·00
Bethlehem, Llandeilo, Dyfed	3·00

Collectors Pack 1975

1975 (26 Nov). Comprises Nos. 970/96.

CP996a Collectors Pack	9·00

479 Housewife   **480** Policeman

481 District Nurse   **482** Industrialist

(Des P. Sharland)

1976 (10 Mar). *Telephone Centenary. "All-over" phosphor.* P 15×14.

997	**479**	8½p. greenish blue, deep rose, black and blue	25	20
		a. Deep rose (vase and picture frame) omitted	£5500	
998	**480**	10p. greenish blue, black and yellow-olive	40	40
999	**481**	11p. greenish blue, deep rose, black and bright mauve	50	50
1000	**482**	13p. olive-brown, deep rose, black and orange-red	60	60
Set of 4			1·50	1·50
Set of 4 Gutter Pairs			2·75	
Set of 4 Traffic Light Gutter Pairs			9·00	
First Day Cover				1·50
Presentation Pack (P.O. Pack No. 78)			3·00	

Special First Day of Issue Postmark

Philatelic Bureau, Edinburgh	2·00

483 Hewing Coal (Thomas Hepburn)   **484** Machinery (Robert Owen)

485 Chimney Cleaning (Lord Shaftesbury)   **486** Hands clutching Prison Bars (Elizabeth Fry)

(Des D. Gentleman)

1976 (28 Apr). *Social Reformers. "All-over" phosphor.* P 15×14.

1001	**483**	8½p. lavender-grey, grey-black, black and slate-grey	25	20
1002	**484**	10p. lavender-grey, grey-black, grey and slate-violet	40	40

1003	**485**	11p. black, slate-grey and drab..................	50	50
1004	**486**	13p. slate-grey, black & dp dull green	60	60
Set of 4			1·50	1·50
Set of 4 Gutter Pairs...			2·75	
Set of 4 Traffic Light Gutter Pairs			9·00	
First Day Cover				1·50
Presentation Pack (P.O. Pack No. 79)			2·75	
P.H.Q. Card (No. 1001) (14)			6·00	20·00

Special First Day of Issue Postmark

Philatelic Bureau, Edinburgh .... 2·00

487 Benjamin Franklin (bust by Jean-Jacques Caffieri)

(Des P. Sharland)

1976 (2 June). *Bicentenary of American Revolution. "All over" phosphor. P 14×15.*

1005	**487**	11p. pale bistre, slate-violet, pale blue-green, black and gold	50	50
Gutter Pair			75	
Traffic Light Gutter Pair			2·50	
First Day Cover..				1·50
Presentation Pack (P.O. Pack No. 80)			1·50	
P.H.Q. Card (15)			5·00	20·00

Special First Day of Issue Postmark

Philatelic Bureau, Edinburgh .... 2·00

488 "Elizabeth of Glamis"   **489** "Grandpa Dickson"

Stay up to date with all things philatelic.
Subscribe to **Gibbons Stamp Monthly** –
The UK's number one stamp magazine

490 "Rosa Mundi"   **491** "Sweet Briar"

(Des Kristin Rosenberg)

1976 (30 June). *Centenary of Royal National Rose Society. "All-over" phosphor. P 14×15.*

1006	**488**	8½p. brt rose-red, greenish yellow, emerald, grey-black and gold..........	15	10
1007	**489**	10p. greenish yellow, brt green, reddish brown, grey-black and gold	40	40
1008	**490**	11p. brt magenta, greenish yellow, emerald, grey-blue, grey-black and gold...	50	50
1009	**491**	13p. rose-pink, lake-brown, yellow-green, pale greenish yellow, grey-black and gold........................	65	65
		a. Value omitted*	£95000	
Set of 4			1·50	1·50
Set of 4 Gutter Pairs..			3·00	
Set of 4 Traffic Light Gutter Pairs			10·00	
First Day Cover				1·50
Presentation Pack (P.O. Pack No. 81)			3·00	
P.H.Q. Cards (set of 4) (16)			30·00	38·00

*During repairs to the cylinder the face value on R.1/9 was temporarily covered with copper. This covering was inadvertently left in place during printing, but the error was discovered before issue and most examples were removed from the sheets. Two mint and one used examples have so far been reported, but only one of the mint remains in private hands.

Special First Day of Issue Postmark

Philatelic Bureau, Edinburgh .... 2·00

492 Archdruid   **493** Morris Dancing

494 Scots Piper   **495** Welsh Harpist

(Des Marjorie Saynor)

1976 (4 Aug). *British Cultural Traditions. "All-over" phosphor. P 14×15.*

1010	**492**	8½p. yellow, sepia, bright rose, dull ultramarine, black and gold	25	20
1011	**493**	10p. dull ultramarine, brt rose-red, sepia, greenish yellow, black and gold........	40	40
1012	**494**	11p. bluish green, yellow-brown, yellow-orange, black, brt rose-red and gold	45	45

1013	**495**	13p. dull violet-blue, yellow-orange, yellow, black, bluish green and gold	60	60
Set of 4			1·50	1·50
Set of 4 Gutter Pairs			3·00	
Set of 4 Traffic Light Gutter Pairs			12·00	
First Day Cover				2·00
Presentation Pack (P.O. Pack No. 82)			2·50	
P.H.Q. Cards (set of 4) (17)			18·00	30·00

The 8½p. and 13p. commemorate the 800th anniversary of the Royal National Eisteddfod.

Special First Day of Issue Postmarks

Philatelic Bureau, Edinburgh		2·50
Cardigan, Dyfed		5·00

496 Woodcut from *The Canterbury Tales* **497** Extract from *The Tretyse of Love*

498 Woodcut from *The Game and Playe of Chesse* **499** Early Printing Press

(Des R. Gay. Queen's head printed in gold and then embossed)

1976 (29 Sept). *500th Anniv of British Printing.* "All-over" phosphor. P 14×15.

1014	**496**	8½p. black, lt new blue and gold	25	20
1015	**497**	10p. black, olive-green and gold	40	40
1016	**498**	11p. black, brownish grey and gold	45	45
1017	**499**	13p. chocolate, pale ochre and gold	60	60
Set of 4			1·50	1·50
Set of 4 Gutter Pairs			3·00	
Set of 4 Traffic Light Gutter Pairs			7·00	
First Day Cover				1·75
Presentation Pack (P.O. Pack No. 83)			2·75	
P.H.Q. Cards (set of 4) (18)			10·00	28·00

Special First Day of Issue Postmarks

Philatelic Bureau, Edinburgh		2·00
London SW1		3·00

500 Virgin and Child **501** Angel with Crown

502 Angel appearing to Shepherds **503** The Three Kings

(Des Enid Marx)

1976 (24 Nov). *Christmas. English Medieval Embroidery.* One phosphor band (6½p.) or "all-over" phosphor (others). P 15×14.

1018	**500**	6½p. blue, bistre-yellow, brown and orange	25	25
		a. Imperf (pair)	£900	
1019	**501**	8½p. sage-green, yellow, brown-ochre, chestnut and olive-black	35	25
1020	**502**	11p. dp magenta, brown-orange, new blue, black and cinnamon	40	45
		a. Uncoated paper*	75·00	30·00
1021	**503**	13p. bright purple, new blue, cinnamon, bronze-green and olive-grey	45	50
Set of 4			1·25	1·25
Set of 4 Gutter Pairs			2·75	
Set of 4 Traffic Light Gutter Pairs			7·00	
First Day Cover				1·50
Presentation Pack (P.O. Pack No. 87)			2·75	
P.H.Q. Cards (set of 4) (19)			4·50	26·00

*See footnote after No. 744.

Special First Day of Issue Postmarks

Philatelic Bureau, Edinburgh		2·50
Bethlehem, Llandeilo, Dyfed		3·50

Collectors Pack 1976
1976 (24 Nov). Comprises Nos. 997/1021.

CP1021a Collectors Pack		13·50

504 Lawn Tennis **505** Table Tennis

506 Squash **507** Badminton

(Des A. Restall)

1977 (12 Jan). *Racket Sports. Phosphorised paper.* P 15×14.

1022	**504**	8½p. emerald-green, black, grey and bluish green	25	20
		a. Imperf (horiz pair)	£3000	

1023	**505**	10p. myrtle-green, black, grey-black and deep blue-green	40	40
1024	**506**	11p. orange, pale yellow, black, slate-black and grey	45	40
		a. Imperf (horiz pair)	£10000	
1025	**507**	13p. brown, grey-black, grey and brt reddish violet	45	50
Set of 4			1·25	1·25
Set of 4 Gutter Pairs			3·00	
Set of 4 Traffic Light Gutter Pairs			7·50	
First Day Cover				2·00
Presentation Pack (P.O. Pack No. 89)			3·00	
P.H.Q. Cards (set of 4) (20)			8·00	24·00

The only known example of No. 1024a is cut close at left.

Special First Day of Issue Postmark

507a

Philatelic Bureau, Edinburgh .... 2·50

508

1977 (2 Feb)–**87**. P 14×15.

1026	**508**	£1 brt yellow-green and blackish olive	3·00	25
		a. Imperf (pair)	£1500	
1026b		£1.30 pale drab and deep greenish blue (3.8.83)	5·50	6·00
1026c		£1.33 pale mauve and grey-black (28.8.84)	7·50	8·00
1026d		£1.41 pale drab and deep greenish blue (17.9.85)	8·50	8·50
1026e		£1.50 pale mauve and grey-black (2.9.86)	6·00	5·00
1026f		£1.60 pale drab and deep greenish blue (15.9.87)	6·50	7·00
1027		£2 light emerald and purple-brown	9·00	50
		a. Imperf (pair)	£3500	
1028		£5 salmon and chalky blue	22·00	3·00
		a. Imperf (vert pair)	£7000	
Set of 8			60·00	32·00
Set of 8 Gutter Pairs			£140	
Set of 8 Traffic Light Gutter Pairs			£170	

Gutter pairs			
	Plain	Traffic Light	First Day Cover
1026, 1027/8	70·00	75·00	14·00
1026b	13·00	20·00	6·50
1026c	15·00	20·00	8·00
1026d	17·00	25·00	9·00
1026e	12·00	15·00	6·50
1026f	13·00	16·00	8·50

Presentation Pack (P.O. Pack No. 91 (small size)) (1026, 1027/8)	48·00
Presentation Pack (P.O. Pack No. 13 (large size)) (1026, 1027/8)	£180
Presentation Pack (P.O. Pack No. 14) (large size) (1026f)	22·00

Special First Day of Issue Postmarks
(for illustrations see Introduction)

Philatelic Bureau, Edinburgh (Type F) (£1, £2, £5)	14·00
Windsor, Berks (Type F) (£1, £2, £5)	20·00
Philatelic Bureau, Edinburgh (Type F) (£1.30)	6·50
Windsor, Berks (Type F) (£1.30)	10·00
British Philatelic Bureau, Edinburgh (Type F) (£1.33)	8·00
Windsor, Berks (Type F) (£1.33)	10·00
British Philatelic Bureau, Edinburgh (Type G) (£1.41)	9·00
Windsor, Berks (Type G) (£1.41)	9·00
British Philatelic Bureau, Edinburgh (Type G) (£1.50)	6·50

Windsor, Berks (Type G) (£1.50)	6·50
British Philatelic Bureau, Edinburgh (Type G) (£1.60)	8·50
Windsor, Berks (Type G) (£1.60)	8·50

509 Steroids—Conformational Analysis   **510** Vitamin C—Synthesis

511 Starch—Chromatography   **512** Salt—Crystallography

(Des J. Karo)

1977 (2 Mar). *Royal Institute of Chemistry Centenary. "All over" phosphor.* P 15×14.

1029	**509**	8½p. rosine, new blue, olive-yellow, brt mauve, yellow-brown, black and gold	25	20
		a. Imperf (horiz pair)	£4500	
1030	**510**	10p. brt orange, rosine, new blue, brt blue, black and gold	45	45
1031	**511**	11p. rosine, greenish yellow, new blue, deep violet, black and gold	45	45
1032	**512**	13p. new blue, brt green, black and gold	45	45
Set of 4			1·25	1·25
Set of 4 Gutter Pairs			3·00	
Set of 4 Traffic Light Gutter Pairs			7·00	
First Day Cover				1·50
Presentation Pack (P.O. Pack No. 92)			3·00	
P.H.Q. Cards (set of 4)			8·00	18·00

Special First Day of Issue Postmark

Philatelic Bureau, Edinburgh .... 2·75

513

514

515   516

T **513/16** differ in the decorations of "ER".

(Des R. Guyatt)

1977 (11 May–15 June). *Silver Jubilee. "All-over" phosphor.* P 15×14.

1033	**513**	8½p. blackish green, black, silver, olive-grey and pale turquoise-green	25	25
		a. Imperf (pair)	£1000	
1034		9p. maroon, black, silver, olive-grey and lavender (15 June)	25	25

1035	**514**	10p. blackish blue, black, silver, olive-grey and ochre	25	25
		a. Imperf (horiz pair)	£3200	
1036	**515**	11p. brown-purple, black, silver, olive-grey and rose-pink	50	50
		a. Imperf (horiz pair)	£3200	
1037	**516**	13p. sepia, black, silver, olive-grey and bistre-yellow	50	50
		a. Imperf (pair)	£2000	
Set of 5			1·75	1·75
Set of 5 Gutter Pairs			3·50	
Set of 5 Traffic Light Gutter Pairs			6·00	
First Day Covers (2)				2·50
Presentation Pack (Nos. 1033, 1035/7) (P.O. Pack No. 94)			2·00	
Souvenir Book			3·00	
P.H.Q. Cards (set of 5) (22)			14·00	20·00

The Souvenir book is a 16-page booklet containing a history of the Queen's reign.

Special First Day of Issue Postmarks

Philatelic Bureau, Edinburgh (1033, 1035/7) (11 May)	1·50
Philatelic Bureau, Edinburgh (1034) (15 June)	1·00
Windsor, Berks (1033, 1035/7) (11 May)	2·00
Windsor, Berks (1034) (15 June)	1·00

517 "Gathering of Nations"

(Des P. Murdoch. Recess and photo)

1977 (8 June). *Commonwealth Heads of Government Meeting, London. "All-over" phosphor.* P 14×15.

1038	**517**	13p. black, blackish green, rose-carmine and silver	50	50
Gutter Pair			1·00	
Traffic Light Gutter Pair			1·50	
First Day Cover				1·50
Presentation Pack (P.O. Pack No. 95)			1·50	
P.H.Q. Card (23)			5·00	6·00

Special First Day of Issue Postmarks

Philatelic Bureau, Edinburgh	1·50
London SW	2·00

518 Hedgehog
519 Brown Hare

520 Red Squirrel
521 Otter

522 Badger

T **518/22** were printed horizontally *se-tenant* within the sheet.

(Des P. Oxenham)

1977 (5 Oct). *British Wildlife. "All-over" phosphor.* P 14×15.

1039	**518**	9p. reddish brown, grey-black, pale lemon, brt turquoise-blue, brt magenta and gold	25	20
		a. Horiz strip of 5. Nos. 1039/43	1·50	1·75
		b. Imperf (vert pair)	£2500	
		c. Imperf (horiz pair. Nos. 1039/40)	£3750	
1040	**519**	9p. reddish brown, grey-black, pale lemon, brt turquoise-blue, brt magenta and gold	25	20
1041	**520**	9p. reddish brown, grey-black, pale lemon, brt turquoise-blue, brt magenta and gold	25	20
1042	**521**	9p. reddish brown, grey-black, pale lemon, brt turquoise-blue, brt magenta and gold	25	20
1043	**522**	9p. grey-black, reddish brown, pale lemon, brt turquoise-blue, brt magenta and gold	25	20
Set of 5			1·50	1·75
Gutter Strip of 10			3·00	
Traffic Light Gutter Strip of 10			5·00	
First Day Cover				3·00
Presentation Pack (P.O. Pack No. 96)			2·50	
P.H.Q. Cards (set of 5) (25)			3·00	7·00

Special First Day of Issue Postmark

Philatelic Bureau, Edinburgh ....3·50

523 "Three French Hens, Two Turtle Doves and a Partridge in a Pear Tree"
524 "Six Geese-a-laying, Five Gold Rings, Four Colly Birds"

For a full range of Stanley Gibbons catalogues, please visit **www.stanleygibbons.com**

525 "Eight Maids-a-milking, Seven Swans-a-swimming"

526 "Ten Pipers piping, Nine Drummers drumming"

527 "Twelve Lords a-leaping, Eleven Ladies dancing"

T **523/7** depict the carol "The Twelve Days of Christmas" and were printed horizontally *se-tenant* within the sheet.

528 "A Partridge in a Pear Tree"

(Des D. Gentleman)

1977 (23 Nov). *Christmas. One centre phosphor band (7p.) or "all-over" phosphor (9p.).* P 15×14.

1044	**523**	7p. slate, grey, brt yellow-green, new blue, rose-red and gold	20	15
		a. Horiz strip of 5. Nos. 1044/8	1·50	1·50
		ab. Imperf (strip of 5. Nos. 1044/8)	£4500	
1045	**524**	7p. slate, brt yellow-green, new blue and gold	20	15
1046	**525**	7p. slate, grey, brt yellow-green, new blue, rose-red and gold	20	15
1047	**526**	7p. slate, grey, brt yellow-green, new blue, rose-red and gold	20	15
1048	**527**	7p. slate, grey, brt yellow-green, new blue, rose-red and gold	20	15
1049	**528**	9p. pale brown, pale orange, bright emerald, pale greenish yellow, slate-black and gold	35	30
		a. Imperf (pair)	£2250	
Set of 6			1·25	1·50
Set of 6 Gutter Pairs			3·00	
Traffic Light Gutter Pairs			5·50	
First Day Cover				2·25
Presentation Pack (P.O. Pack No. 97)			2·25	
P.H.Q. Cards (set of 6) (26)			3·00	6·00

Special First Day of Issue Postmarks

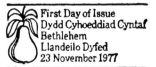

First Day of Issue
Dydd Cyhoeddiad Cyntaf
Bethlehem
Llandeilo Dyfed
23 November 1977

Philatelic Bureau, Edinburgh	2·50
Bethlehem, Llandeilo, Dyfed	3·00

Collectors Pack 1977
1977 (23 Nov). Comprises Nos. 1022/5 and 1029/49.
CP1049b Collectors Pack .... 9·00

529 Oil–North Sea

530 Coal–Modern Pithead Production Platform

531 Natural Gas–Flame Rising from Sea

532 Electricity–Nuclear Power Station and Uranium Atom

(Des P. Murdoch)

1978 (25 Jan). *Energy Resources. "All-over" phosphor.* P 14×15.

1050	**529**	9p. dp brown, orange-vermilion, grey-black, greenish yellow, rose-pink, new blue and silver	25	25
1051	**530**	10½p. lt emerald-green, grey-black, red-brown, slate-grey, pale apple-green and silver	25	25
1052	**531**	11p. greenish blue, brt violet, violet-blue, blackish brown, grey-black and silver	50	50
1053	**532**	13p. orange-vermilion, grey-black, dp brown, greenish yellow, lt brown, lt blue and silver	50	50
Set of 4			1·25	1·25
Set of 4 Gutter Pairs			2·75	
Set of 4 Traffic Light Gutter Pairs			4·50	
First Day Cover				1·50
Presentation Pack (P.O. Pack No. 99)			2·00	
P.H.Q. Cards (set of 4) (27)			3·00	6·00

Special First Day of Issue Postmark

Philatelic Bureau, Edinburgh	2·50

533 The Tower of London

534 Holyroodhouse

535 Caernarvon Castle

536 Hampton Court Palace

(Des R. Maddox (stamps), J. Matthews (miniature sheet))

1978 (1 Mar). *British Architecture. Historic Buildings. "All over" phosphor.*
P 15×14.

1054	**533**	9p. black, olive-brown, new blue, brt green, lt yellow-olive and rose-red .	25	20
1055	**534**	10½p. black, brown-olive, orange-yellow, brt green, lt yellow-olive and violet-blue...........................	25	40
1056	**535**	11p. black, brown-olive, violet-blue, brt green, lt yellow-olive and dull blue	60	40
1057	**536**	13p. black, orange-yellow, lake-brown, brt green and light yellow- olive......	60	40

Set of 4	1·50	1·25
Set of 4 Gutter Pairs...	3·00	
Set of 4 Traffic Light Gutter Pairs..................	4·50	
First Day Cover...		1·50
Presentation Pack (P.O. Pack No. 100)...........	2·00	
P.H.Q. Cards (set of 4) (28)	3·00	6·00
MS1058 121×89 mm. Nos. 1054/7 (sold at 53½p.)	1·50	1·75
a. Imperforate..	£17000	
b. Lt yellow-olive (Queen's head) omitted..........	£25000	
c. Rose-red (Union Jack on 9p.) omitted.............	£8500	
d. Orange-yellow omitted......................	£12500	
e. New blue (Union Jack on 9p.) omitted		
First Day Cover...		2·00

The premium on No. **MS**1058 was used to support the London 1980 International Stamp Exhibition. No. **MS**1058d is most noticeable on the 10½p. (spheres absent on towers) and around the roadway and arch on the 13p.

Special First Day of Issue Postmarks

Philatelic Bureau, Edinburgh (stamps)..2.00	
Philatelic Bureau, Edinburgh (miniature sheet). 2.50	
London EC (stamps)...2.50	
London EC (miniature sheet)..3.00	

537 State Coach   **538** St. Edward's Crown

539 The Sovereign's Orb   **540** Imperial State Crown

(Des J. Matthews)

1978 (31 May). *25th Anniv of Coronation. "All-over" phosphor.* P 14×15.

1059	**537**	9p. gold and royal blue...........................	35	25
1060	**538**	10½p. gold and brown-lake.....................	45	45
1061	**539**	11p. gold and dp dull green....................	45	45
1062	**540**	13p. gold and reddish violet...................	50	50

Set of 4	1·50	1·50
Set of 4 Gutter Pairs...	3·00	
Set of 4 Traffic Light Gutter Pairs..................	4·25	
First Day Cover...		1·50
Presentation Pack (P.O. Pack No. 101)	2·00	
Souvenir Book	3·00	
P.H.Q. Cards (set of 4) (29)	3·00	6·00

The souvenir book is a 16-page booklet illustrated with scenes from the Coronation.

Special First Day of Issue Postmarks

Philatelic Bureau, Edinburgh 2.00	
London SW1 ....2.50	

541 Shire Horse   **542** Shetland Pony

543 Welsh Pony   **544** Thoroughbred

(Des P. Oxenham)

1978 (5 July). *Horses. "All-over" phosphor.* P 15×14.

1063	**541**	9p. black, pale reddish brown, grey-black, greenish yellow, lt blue, vermilion and gold...........................	20	10
		a. Imperf (vert pair)	—	
1064	**542**	10½p. pale chestnut, magenta, brownish grey, greenish yellow, greenish blue, grey-black and gold..................	35	40
1065	**543**	11p. reddish brown, black, lt green, greenish yellow, bistre, grey-black and gold...	35	45
1066	**544**	13p. reddish brown, pale reddish brown, emerald, greenish yellow, grey-black and gold...........................	45	50

Set of 4	1·25	1·25
Set of 4 Gutter Pairs...	3·00	
Set of 4 Traffic Light Gutter Pairs..................	4·50	
First Day Cover...		1·50
Presentation Pack (P.O. Pack No. 102)	1·75	
P.H.Q. Cards (set of 4) (30)	2·25	5·75

Special First Day of Issue Postmarks

Philatelic Bureau, Edinburgh 2.00	
Peterborough 2.50	

545 "Penny-farthing" and 1884 Safety Bicycle   **546** 1920 Touring Bicycles

547 Modern Small-wheel Bicycles **548** 1978 Road-racers

(Des F. Wegner)

1978 (2 Aug). *Centenaries of Cyclists' Touring Club and British Cycling Federation.* "All-over" phosphor. P 15×14.

1067	**545**	9p. brown, dp dull blue, rose-pink, pale olive, grey-black and gold	25	20
		a. Imperf (pair)	£800	
1068	**546**	10½p. olive, pale yellow-orange, orange-vermilion, rose-red, lt brown, grey-black and gold..............................	35	40
1069	**547**	11p. orange-vermilion, greenish blue, lt brown, pale greenish yellow, dp grey, grey-black and gold..................	40	40
1070	**548**	13p. new blue, orange-vermilion, lt brown, olive-grey, grey-black and gold..	50	50
		a. Imperf (pair)	£2400	
Set of 4			1·25	1·25
Set of 4 Gutter Pairs			2·75	
Set of 4 Traffic Light Gutter Pairs			4·50	
First Day Cover				1·50
Presentation Pack (P.O. Pack No. 103)			1·75	
P.H.Q. Cards (set of 4) (31)			2·25	5·00

Special First Day of Issue Postmarks

Philatelic Bureau, Edinburgh ....2·00
Harrogate, North Yorkshire ....2·50

549 Singing Carols round the Christmas Tree **550** The Waits

551 18th-century Carol Singers **552** "The Boar's Head Carol"

(Des Faith Jaques)

1978 (22 Nov). *Christmas.* One centre phosphor band (7p.) or "all-over" phosphor (others). P 15×14.

1071	**549**	7p. brt green, greenish yellow, magenta, new blue, black and gold	25	25
		a. Imperf (pair)	£900	
1072	**550**	9p. magenta, greenish yellow, new blue, sage-green, black and gold	25	25
		a. Imperf (pair)	£2200	
1073	**551**	11p. magenta, new blue, greenish yellow, yellow-brown, black and gold	50	50
		a. Imperf (horiz pair)	£2200	
1074	**552**	13p. salmon-pink, new blue, greenish yellow, magenta, black and gold.....	50	50

Set of 4	1·25	1·25
Set of 4 Gutter Pairs	2·50	
Set of 4 Traffic Light Gutter Pairs	4·25	
First Day Cover		1·50
Presentation Pack (P.O. Pack No. 104)	1·75	
P H Q Cards (set of 4) (32)..	2·25	5·00

Special First Day of Issue Postmarks

Philatelic Bureau, Edinburgh .... 2·00
Bethlehem, Llandeilo, Dyfed ....2·50

Collectors Pack 1978
1978 (22 Nov). Comprises Nos. 1050/7 and 1059/74.
CP1074a Collectors Pack.. 10·00

553 Old English Sheepdog **554** Welsh Springer Spaniel

555 West Highland Terrier **556** Irish Setter

(Des P. Barrett)

1979 (7 Feb). *Dogs.* "All-over" phosphor. P 15×14.

1075	**553**	9p. grey-black, sepia, turquoise-green, pale greenish yellow, pale greenish blue and grey	25	20
1076	**554**	10½p. grey-black, lake-brown, apple-green, pale greenish yellow, pale greenish blue and grey	40	40
1077	**555**	11p. grey-black, claret, yellowish green, pale greenish yellow, cobalt and grey..	40	40
		a. Imperf (horiz pair)	£5500	
1078	**556**	13p. grey-black, lake-brown, green, pale greenish yellow and dp turquoise-blue..	40	50
Set of 4			1·25	1·25
Set of 4 Gutter Pairs			2·50	
Set of 4 Traffic Light Gutter Pairs			4·25	
First Day Cover				1·50
Presentation Pack (P.O. Pack No. 106)			1·75	
P.H.Q. Cards (set of 4) (33)			2·50	5·00

Special First Day of Issue Postmarks

Philatelic Bureau, Edinburgh .... 2·00
London SW ....2·50

557 Primrose

558 Daffodil

559 Bluebell

560 Snowdrop

(Des P. Newcombe)

1979 (21 Mar). *Spring Wild Flowers.* "All-over" phosphor. P 14×15.

1079	**557**	9p. slate-black, dp brown, pale greenish yellow, dp olive, pale new blue and silver	25	20
		a. Imperf (pair)	£750	
1080	**558**	10½p. greenish yellow, grey-green, steel-blue, slate-black, new blue and silver	25	45
		a. Imperf (vert pair)	£3500	
1081	**559**	11p. slate-black, dp brown, ultramarine, lt greenish blue, pale greenish yellow and silver	50	45
		a. Imperf (horiz pair)	£3000	
1082	**560**	13p. slate-black, indigo, grey-green, sepia, ochre and silver	50	40
		a. Imperf (horiz pair)	£2250	
Set of 4			1·25	1·25
Set of 4 Gutter Pairs			2·50	
Set of 4 Traffic Light Gutter Pairs			4·25	
First Day Cover				1·50
Presentation Pack (P.O. Pack No. 107)			1·75	
P.H.Q. Cards (set of 4) (34)			2·50	4·50

Special First Day of Issue Postmark

Philatelic Bureau, Edinburgh ....2·00

561

562

563

564

T **561/4** show Hands placing National Flags in Ballot Boxes.

(Des S. Cliff)

1979 (9 May). *First Direct Elections to European Assembly.* Phosphorised paper. P 15×14.

1083	**561**	9p. grey black, vermilion, cinnamon, pale greenish yellow, pale turquoise-green and dull ultramarine	25	20
1084	**562**	10½p. grey-black, vermilion, cinnamon, pale greenish yellow, dull ultramarine, pale turquoise-green and chestnut	35	35
1085	**563**	11p. grey-black, vermilion, cinnamon, pale greenish yellow, dull ultramarine, pale turquoise-green and grey-green	40	40
1086	**564**	13p. grey-black, vermilion, cinnamon, pale greenish yellow, dull ultramarine, pale turquoise-green and brown	45	40
Set of 4			1·25	1·25
Set of 4 Gutter Pairs			2·50	
Set of 4 Traffic Light Gutter Pairs			4·25	
First Day Cover				1·50
Presentation Pack (P.O. Pack No. 108)			1·75	
P.H.Q. Cards (set of 4) (35)			2·25	4·50

Special First Day of Issue Postmarks

Philatelic Bureau, Edinburgh ....2·00
London SW .... 2·50

565 "Saddling 'Mahmoud' for the Derby, 1936" (Sir Alfred Munnings)

566 "The Liverpool Great National Steeple Chase, 1839" (aquatint by F. C. Turner)

567 "The First Spring Meeting, Newmarket, 1793" (J. N. Sartorius)

568 "Racing at Dorsett Ferry, Windsor, 1684" (Francis Barlow)

(Des S. Rose)

1979 (6 June). *Horseracing Paintings. Bicentenary of the Derby (9p.).* "All-over" phosphor. P 15×14.

1087	**565**	9p. lt blue, red-brown, rose-pink, pale greenish yellow, grey-black and gold	25	25
1088	**566**	10½p. bistre-yellow, slate-blue, salmon-pink, lt blue, grey black and gold	25	25
1089	**567**	11p. rose, vermilion, pale greenish yellow, new blue, grey-black and gold	50	50
1090	**568**	13p. bistre-yellow, rose, turquoise, grey-black and gold	50	50
Set of 4			1·25	1·25
Set of 4 Gutter Pairs			2·50	
Set of 4 Traffic Light Gutter Pairs			4·25	
First Day Cover				1·50
Presentation Pack (P.O. Pack No. 109)			1·75	
P.H.Q. Cards (set of 4) (36)			2·25	4·50

Special First Day of Issue Postmarks

Philatelic Bureau, Edinburgh ....2·00
Epsom, Surrey...2·50

569 *The Tale of Peter Rabbit* (Beatrix Potter)

570 *The Wind in the Willows* (Kenneth Grahame)

571 *Winnie-the-Pooh* (A. A. Milne)

572 *Alice's Adventures in Wonderland* (Lewis Carroll)

(Des E. Hughes)

1979 (11 July). *International Year of the Child. Children's Book Illustrations. "All-over" phosphor.* P 14×15.

1091	**569**	9p. dp bluish green, grey-black, bistre-brown, brt rose, greenish yellow and silver	30	25
1092	**570**	10½p. dull ultramarine, grey-black, olive-brown, brt rose, yellow-orange, pale greenish yellow and silver	35	35
1093	**571**	11p. drab, grey-black, greenish yellow, new blue, yellow-orange, agate and silver	40	40
1094	**572**	13p. pale greenish yellow, grey-black, brt rose, dp bluish green, olive-brown, new blue and silver	60	60

Set of 4 ....1·50 1·50
Set of 4 Gutter Pairs...3·50
Set of 4 Traffic Light Gutter Pairs ....4·25
First Day Cover ....1·50
Presentation Pack (P.O. Pack No. 110) ....1·75
P.H.Q. Cards (set of 4) (37) ....2·50 4·50

Special First Day of Issue Postmark

Philatelic Bureau, Edinburgh ....2·00
    First Day of Issue handstamps were provided at Hartfield, East Sussex and Stourbridge, West Midlands for this issue.

573 Sir Rowland Hill

574 Postman, circa 1839

575 London Postman, circa 1839

576 Woman and Young Girl with Letters, 1840

(Des E. Stemp)

1979 (22 Aug–24 Oct). *Death Centenary of Sir Rowland Hill. "All-over" phosphor.* P 14×15.

1095	**573**	10p. grey-black, brown-ochre, myrtle-green, pale greenish yellow, rosine, brt blue and gold	25	20
		a. Imperf (horiz pair)	£8000	
1096	**574**	11½p. grey-black, brown-ochre, brt blue, rosine, bistre-brown, pale greenish yellow and gold	25	35
1097	**575**	13p. grey-black, brown-ochre, brt blue, rosine, bistre-brown, pale greenish yellow and gold	50	45
1098	**576**	15p. grey-black, brown-ochre, myrtle-green, bistre-brown, rosine, pale greenish yellow and gold	75	50

Set of 4 ....1·50 1·50
Set of 4 Gutter Pairs...3·00
Set of 4 Traffic Light Gutter Pairs ....4·25
First Day Cover ....1·50
Presentation Pack (P.O. Pack No. 111) ....1·50
P.H.Q. Cards (set of 4) (38) ....2·25 4·25
MS1099 89×121 mm. Nos. 1095/8 (sold at 59½p.) (24 Oct) ....1·25 1·50

a. Imperforate	£9500	
b. Brown-ochre (15p. background, etc.) omitted	£10000	
c. Gold (Queen's head) omitted	£950	
d. Brown-ochre, myrtle-green and gold omitted	£17000	
e. Brt blue (13p. background, etc.) omitted	£17000	
f. Myrtle-green (10p. (background), 15p.) omitted	£9000	
g. Pale greenish yellow omitted	£850	
h. Rosine omitted	£2500	
i. Bistre-brown omitted	£2500	
j. Grey-black and pale greenish yellow omitted	£75000	

First Day Cover ....1·50
    The premium on No. **MS**1099 was used to support the London 1980 International Stamp Exhibition.
    Examples of No. **MS**1099 showing face values on the stamps of 9p., 10½p., 11p. and 13p., with a sheet price of 53½p., were prepared, but not issued. (Price £40,000).

Special First Day of Issue Postmarks

Philatelic Bureau, Edinburgh (stamps) (22 Aug)...2·00
Philatelic Bureau, Edinburgh (miniature sheet) (24 Oct)........................2·00
London EC (stamps) (22 Aug) ....2·00
London EC (miniature sheet) (24 Oct)...2·00

First Day of Issue handstamps were provided at Kidderminster, Worcs on 22 August (pictorial) and 24 October (Type C) and at Sanquhar, Dumfriesshire on 22 August and 24 October (both Type C).

577 Policeman on the Beat

578 Policeman directing Traffic

579 Mounted Policewoman

580 River Patrol Boat

(Des B. Sanders)

1979 (26 Sept). *150th Anniv of Metropolitan Police. Phosphorised paper.* P 15×14.

1100	**577**	10p. grey-black, red-brown, emerald, greenish yellow, brt blue and magenta	30	20
1101	**578**	11½p. grey-black, brt orange, purple-brown, ultramarine, greenish yellow and deep bluish green	35	35
1102	**579**	13p. grey-black, red-brown, magenta, olive-green, greenish yellow and deep dull blue	40	55
1103	**580**	15p. grey-black, magenta, brown, slate-blue, dp brown and greenish black	60	55
Set of 4			1·50	1·50
Set of 4 Gutter Pairs			3·00	
Set of 4 Traffic Light Gutter Pairs			4·25	
First Day Cover				1·50
Presentation Pack (P.O. Pack No. 112)			1·75	
PHQ Cards (set of 4) (39)			2·25	4·25

Special First Day of Issue Postmarks

Philatelic Bureau, Edinburgh ....2·00
London SW ....2·00

581 The Three Kings

582 Angel appearing to the Shepherds

583 The Nativity

584 Mary and Joseph travelling to Bethlehem

585 The Annunciation

(Des F. Wegner)

1979 (21 Nov). *Christmas. One centre phosphor band (8p.) or phosphorised paper (others).* P 15×14.

1104	**581**	8p. blue, grey-black, ochre, slate-violet and gold	25	20
		a. Imperf (pair)	£850	
1105	**582**	10p. brt rose-red, grey-black, chestnut, chrome-yellow, dp violet and gold	25	25
		a. Imperf between (vert pair)	£2000	
		b. Imperf (pair)	£1600	
1106	**583**	11½p. orange-vermilion, steel-blue, drab, grey-black, dp blue-green and gold	25	35
1107	**584**	13p. brt blue, orange-vermilion, bistre, grey-black and gold	50	50
1108	**585**	15p. orange-vermilion, blue, bistre, grey-black, green and gold	50	50
Set of 5			1·50	1·50
Set of 5 Gutter Pairs			3·50	
Set of 5 Traffic Light Gutter Pairs			4·50	
First Day Cover				1·50
Presentation Pack (P.O. Pack No. 113)			2·00	
P.H.Q. Cards (set of 5) (40)			2·50	4·25

Special First Day of Issue Postmarks

Philatelic Bureau, Edinburgh ....2·00
Bethlehem, Llandeilo, Dyfed ....2·00

Collectors Pack 1979
1979 (21 Nov). Comprises Nos. 1075/98 and 1100/8.
CP1108a Collectors Pack ....12·00

586 Common Kingfisher

587 Dipper

588 Moorhen

589 Yellow Wagtails

(Des M. Warren)

1980 (16 Jan). *Centenary of Wild Bird Protection Act. Phosphorised paper.* P 14½×15.

1109	**586**	10p. brt blue, brt yellow-green, vermilion, pale greenish yellow, grey-black and gold	20	10

1110	587	11½p. sepia, grey-black, dull ultramarine, vermilion, grey-green, pale greenish yellow and gold..................	40	35
1111	588	13p. emerald-green, grey-black, brt blue, vermilion, pale greenish yellow and gold	50	55
1112	589	15p. greenish yellow, brown, lt green, slate-blue, grey-black and gold........	50	55
Set of 4			1·50	1·50
Set of 4 Gutter Pairs........			3·50	
First Day Cover				1·50
Presentation Pack (P.O. Pack No. 115)			1·50	
P.H.Q. Cards (set of 4) (41)			2·25	4·50

Special First Day of Issue Postmarks

Philatelic Bureau, Edinburgh	2·00
Sandy, Beds	2·50

590 *Rocket* approaching Moorish Arch, Liverpool

591 First and Second Class Carriages passing through Olive Mount Cutting

592 Third Class Carriage and Sheep Truck crossing Chat Moss

593 Horsebox and Carriage Truck near Bridgewater Canal

594 Goods Truck and Mail-Coach at Manchester

T **590/4** were printed together, *se-tenant*, in horizontal strips of 5 throughout the sheet.

(Des D. Gentleman)

1980 (12 Mar). *150th Anniv of Liverpool and Manchester Railway.* Phosphorised paper. P 15×14.

1113	590	12p. lemon, lt brown, rose-red, pale blue and grey-black........	20	15
		a. Strip of 5. Nos. 1113/17	1·75	1·75
		ab. Imperf (horiz strip of 5. Nos. 1113/17)	£6500	
		ac. Lemon omitted (horiz strip of 5. Nos. 1113/17)	£45000	
1114	591	12p. rose-red, lt brown, lemon, pale blue and grey-black........	20	15
1115	592	12p. pale blue, rose-red, lemon, lt brown and grey-black........	20	15
1116	593	12p. lt brown, lemon, rose-red, pale blue and grey-black........	20	15
1117	594	12p. lt brown, rose-red, pale blue, lemon and grey-black........	20	15
Set of 5			1·75	1·75
Gutter Block of 10			3·75	
First Day Cover				1·75

Presentation Pack (P.O. Pack No. 116)	2·00	
P.H.Q. Cards (set of 5) (42)	3·25	4·50

Special First Day of Issue Postmarks

Philatelic Bureau, Edinburgh	2·00
Liverpool	2·25
Manchester	2·25

INTERNATIONAL STAMP EXHIBITION
595 Montage of London Buildings

During the printing of No. 1118 the die was re-cut resulting in the following two types:

Type I (original). Top and bottom lines of shading in portrait oval broken. Hatched shading below left arm of Tower Bridge and hull of ship below right arm. Other points: Hatched shading on flag on Westminster Abbey, bottom right of Post Office Tower and archway of entrance to Westminster Abbey.

Type II (re-engraved). Lines in oval unbroken. Solid shading on bridge and ship. Also solid shading on flag, Post Office Tower and archway.

(Des J. Matthews. Eng G. Holt. Recess)

1980 (9 Apr). *"London 1980" International Stamp Exhibition. Phosphorised paper.* P 14½×14.

1118	**595**	50p. agate (I)	1·50	1·50
		Ea. Type II	1·25	1·25
Gutter Pair			3·25	
First Day Cover				1·50
Presentation Pack (P.O. Pack No. 117)			1·75	
P.H.Q. Card (43)			2·25	3·00
MS1119 90×123 mm. No. 1118Ea (sold at 75p.) (7 May)			1·50	1·75
		a. Error. Imperf	£6200	
First Day Cover				2·00

Examples of No. 1118 are known in various shades of green.

Such shades result from problems with the drying of the printed sheets on the press, but are not listed as similar colours can be easily faked.

598 Royal Opera House **599** Hampton Court

600 Kensington Palace

(Des Sir Hugh Casson)

1980 (7 May). *London Landmarks. Phosphorised paper.* P 14×15.

1120	**596**	10½p. grey, pale blue, rosine, pale greenish yellow, yellowish green and silver	25	10
1121	**597**	12p. grey-black, bistre, rosine, yellowish green, pale greenish yellow and silver	25	15
		a. Imperf (vert pair)	£4000	
1122	**598**	13½p. grey-black, pale salmon, pale olive-green, slate-blue and silver	40	50
		a. Imperf (pair)	£4000	
1123	**599**	15p. grey-black, pale salmon, slate-blue, dull yellowish green, olive-yellow and silver	50	75
1124	**600**	17½p. grey, slate-blue, red-brown, sepia, yellowish green, pale greenish yellow and silver	75	75
		a. Silver (Queen's head) omitted	£1400	
Set of 5			2·00	2·00
Set of 5 Gutter Pairs			4·25	
First Day Cover				2·00
Presentation Pack (P.O. Pack No. 118)			2·00	
P.H.Q. Cards (set of 5) (43)			2·25	3·00

No. 1124a shows the Queen's head in pale greenish yellow, this colour being printed beneath the silver for technical reasons.

Special First Day of Issue Postmarks

Philatelic Bureau, Edinburgh (stamp) (9 Apr.)	2·00
Philatelic Bureau, Edinburgh (miniature sheet) (7 May)	2·50
London SW (stamp) (9 Apr.)	2·50
London SW (miniature sheet) (7 May)	2·50

Special First Day of Issue Postmarks

Philatelic Bureau, Edinburgh	2·25
Kingston-upon-Thames	2·50

T **601/4** show authoresses and scenes from their novels. T **601/2** also include the "Europa" C.E.P.T. emblem.

596 Buckingham Palace

597 The Albert Memorial

601 Charlotte Brontë (*Jane Eyre*)

602 George Eliot (*The Mill on the Floss*)

603 Emily Brontë (*Wuthering Heights*)   **604** Mrs Gaskell (*North and South*)

(Des Barbara Brown)

1980 (9 July). *Famous Authoresses. Phosphorised paper.* P 15×14.

1125	**601**	12p. red-brown, brt rose, brt blue, greenish yellow, grey and gold	35	20
		Ea. Missing "p" in value (R. 4/6)	25·00	
1126	**602**	13½p. red-brown, dull vermilion, pale blue, pale greenish yellow, grey and gold .	40	45
		a. Pale blue omitted	£3750	
1127	**603**	15p. red-brown, vermilion, blue, lemon, grey and gold...........................	40	45
1128	**604**	17½p. dull vermilion, slate-blue, ultramarine, pale greenish yellow, grey and gold...........................	50	50
		a. Imperf and slate-blue omitted (pair).	£900	
Set of 4			1·50	1·50
Set of 4 Gutter Pairs........................			3·75	
First Day Cover........................				1·50
Presentation Pack (P.O. Pack No. 119)........................			1·75	
P.H.Q. Cards (set of 4) (44)			2·50	3·00

Special First Day of Issue Postmarks

Philatelic Bureau, Edinburgh .... 2·00
Haworth, Keighley, W. Yorks .... 2·50

605 Queen Elizabeth the Queen Mother

(Des J. Matthews from photograph by N. Parkinson)

1980 (4 Aug). *80th Birthday of Queen Elizabeth the Queen Mother. Phosphorised paper.* P 14×15.

1129	**605**	12p. brt rose, greenish yellow, new blue, grey and silver	75	75
		a. Imperf (horiz pair)	£2700	
Gutter Pair........................			1·50	
First Day Cover........................				1·50
P.H.Q. Card (45)........................			2·25	2·00

Special First Day of Issue Postmarks

Philatelic Bureau, Edinburgh .... 2·00
Glamis Castle, Forfar .... 3·00

606 Sir Henry Wood   **607** Sir Thomas Beecham

608 Sir Malcolm Sargent   **609** Sir John Barbirolli

(Des P. Gauld)

1980 (10 Sept). *British Conductors. Phosphorised paper.* P 14×15.

1130	**606**	12p. slate, rose-red, greenish yellow, bistre and gold	30	10
1131	**607**	13½p. grey-black, vermilion, greenish yellow, pale carmine-rose and gold	45	40
1132	**608**	15p. grey-black, brt rose-red, greenish yellow, turquoise-green and gold...	50	55
1133	**609**	17½p. black, brt rose-red, greenish yellow, dull violet-blue and gold	50	55
Set of 4			1·50	1·50
Set of 4 Gutter Pairs........................			3·75	
First Day Cover........................				1·75
Presentation Pack (P.O. Pack No. 120)			1·75	
P.H.Q. cards (set of 4) (46)........................			2·25	3·75

Special First Day of Issues

Postmarks Philatelic Bureau, Edinburgh .... 2·00
London SW .... 2·25

610 Running   **611** Rugby

612 Boxing   **613** Cricket

(Des R. Goldsmith. Litho Questa)

1980 (10 Oct). *Sport Centenaries. Phosphorised paper.* P 14×14½.

1134	**610**	12p. pale new blue, greenish yellow, magenta, lt brown, reddish purple and gold		25	20
		a. Gold (Queen's head) omitted		£45000	
1135	**611**	13½p. pale new blue, olive-yellow, brt purple, orange-vermilion, blackish lilac and gold		50	50
1136	**612**	15p. pale new blue, greenish yellow, brt purple, chalky blue & gold		50	45
		a. Gold (Queen's head) omitted		£25000	
1137	**613**	17½p. pale new blue, greenish yellow, magenta, dp olive, grey-brown and gold		50	50

Set of 4	1·50	1·50
Set of 4 Gutter Pairs	3·75	
First Day Cover		1·75
Presentation Pack (P.O. Pack No. 121)	1·75	
P.H.Q. Cards (set of 4) (47)	2·25	3·75

Centenaries:−12p. Amateur Athletics Association; 13½p. Welsh Rugby Union; 15p. Amateur Boxing Association; 17½p. First England-Australia Test Match. Nos. 1134a and 1136a were caused by paper folds.

Special First Day of Issue Postmarks

Philatelic Bureau, Edinburgh	2·00
Cardiff	2·25

614 Christmas Tree

615 Candles

616 Apples and Mistletoe

617 Crown, Chains and Bell

618 Holly

(Des J. Matthews)

1980 (19 Nov). *Christmas. One centre phosphor band (10p.) or phosphorised paper (others).* P 15×14.

1138	**614**	10p. black, turquoise-green, greenish yellow, vermilion and blue		20	10
		a. Imperf (horiz pair)		£2700	
1139	**615**	12p. grey, magenta, rose-red, greenish grey and pale orange		20	20
1140	**616**	13½p. grey-black, dull yellow-green, brown, greenish yellow and pale olive-bistre		40	40
1141	**617**	15p. grey-black, bistre-yellow, brt orange, magenta and new blue		55	50
1142	**618**	17½p. black, vermilion, dull yellowish green and greenish yellow		55	50

Set of 5	1·75	1·50
Set of 5 Gutter Pairs	4·50	
First Day Cover		1·75
Presentation Pack (P.O. Pack No. 122)	2·00	
P.H.Q. Cards (set of 5) (48)	2·25	4·00

Special First Day of Issue Postmarks

Philatelic Bureau, Edinburgh	2·00
Bethlehem, Llandeilo, Dyfed	2·50

Collectors Pack 1980

1980 (19 Nov). Comprises Nos. 1109/18 and 1120/42.

CP1142a Collectors Pack		15·00

619 St. Valentine's Day	620 Morris Dancers

621 Lammastide	622 Medieval Mummers

T **619/20** also include the "Europa" C.E.P.T. emblem.

(Des F. Wegner)

1981 (6 Feb). *Folklore. Phosphorised paper.* P 15×14.

1143	**619**	14p. cerise, green, yellow-orange, salmon-pink, black and gold		25	25
1144	**620**	18p. dull ultramarine, lemon, lake-brown, brt green, black and gold		50	50
1145	**621**	22p. chrome-yellow, rosine, brown, new blue, black and gold		75	80
1146	**622**	25p. brt blue, red-brown, brt rose-red, greenish yellow, black and gold		1·00	1·10

Set of 4	2·25	2·50
Set of 4 Gutter Pairs	5·25	
First Day Cover		2·00
Presentation Pack (P.O. Pack No. 124)	2·25	
P.H.Q. Cards (set of 4) (49)	2·25	3·25

Special First Day of Issue Postmarks

Philatelic Bureau, Edinburgh	2·25
London WC	2·50

623 Blind Man with Guide Dog	624 Hands spelling "Deaf" in Sign Language

625 Disabled Man in Wheelchair　**626** Disabled Artist with Foot painting

(Des J. Gibbs)

1981 (25 Mar). *International Year of the Disabled. Phosphorised paper.* P 15×14.

1147	**623**	14p. drab, greenish yellow, brt rose-red, dull purple and silver	50	25
		a. Imperf (pair)	£800	
1148	**624**	18p. dp blue-green, brt orange, dull vermilion, grey-black and silver	50	50
1149	**625**	22p. brown-ochre, rosine, purple-brown, greenish blue, black and silver	75	85
1150	**626**	25p. vermilion, lemon, pale salmon, olive-brown, new blue, black and silver	1·00	1·00
Set of 4			2·25	2·50
Set of 4 Gutter Pairs			4·25	
First Day Cover				2·50
Presentation Pack (P.O. Pack No. 125)			2·25	
P.H.Q. Cards (set of 4) (50)			2·25	3·25

All known examples of No. 1147a are creased.

Special First Day of Issue Postmarks

Philatelic Bureau, Edinburgh	2·50
Windsor	2·50

627 *Aglais urticae*　**628** *Maculinea arion*

629 *Inachis io*　**630** *Carterocephalus palaemon*

(Des G. Beningfield)

1981 (13 May). *Butterflies. Phosphorised paper.* P 14×15.

1151	**627**	14p. greenish yellow, yellow-green, brt rose, brt blue, emerald and gold	25	20
		a. Imperf (pair)	£9000	
1152	**628**	18p. black, greenish yellow, dull yellowish green, dull blue, brt green and gold	75	70
1153	**629**	22p. black, greenish yellow, bronze-green, rosine, ultramarine, lt green and gold	70	85
1154	**630**	25p. black, greenish yellow, bronze-green, brt rose-red, ultramarine, brt emerald and gold	75	85

Set of 4	2·25	2·50
Set of 4 Gutter Pairs	4·75	
First Day Cover		2·50
Presentation Pack (P.O. Pack No. 126)	2·25	
P.H.Q. Cards (set of 4) (51)	2·25	6·00

Special First Day of Issue Postmarks

Philatelic Bureau, Edinburgh	2·50
London SW	3·00

631 Glenfinnan, Scotland　**632** Derwentwater, England

633 Stackpole Head, Wales　**634** Giant's Causeway, Northern Ireland

635 St. Kilda, Scotland

(Des M. Fairclough)

1981 (24 June). *50th Anniv of National Trust for Scotland. British Landscapes. Phosphorised paper.* P 15×14.

1155	**631**	14p. lilac, dull blue, reddish brown, bistre-yellow, black and gold	15	25
1156	**632**	18p. bottle green, brt blue, brown, bistre-yellow, black and gold	45	50
1157	**633**	20p. dp turquoise-blue, dull blue, greenish yellow, reddish brown, black and gold	70	75
1158	**634**	22p. chrome-yellow, reddish brown, new blue, yellow-brown, black and gold	75	1·00
1159	**635**	25p. ultramarine, new blue, olive-green, olive-grey and gold	90	1·00

Set of 5	2·50	3·00
Set of 5 Gutter Pairs	6·00	
First Day Cover		3·25
Presentation Pack (P.O. Pack No. 127)	3·00	
P.H.Q. Cards (set of 5) (52)	2·50	5·00

Special First Day of Issue Postmarks

Philatelic Bureau, Edinburgh .... 3·25
Glenfinnan .... 3·50
Keswick .... 3·50

636 Prince Charles and
Lady Diana Spencer

(Des J. Matthews from photograph by Lord Snowdon)
1981 (22 July). *Royal Wedding. Phosphorised paper.* P 14×15.
1160	**636**	14p. grey-black, greenish yellow, brt rose-red, ultramarine, pale blue, blue and silver	75	25
1161		25p. drab, greenish yellow, brt rose-red, ultramarine, grey-brown, grey-black and silver.....................	1·50	1·50

Set of 2 .... 2·25 — 1·50
Set of 2 Gutter Pairs .... 4·00
First Day Cover .... — 2·75
Presentation Pack (P.O. Pack No. 127a)................. 3·00
Souvenir Book .... 3·00
P.H.Q. Cards (set of 2) (53) .... 2·50 — 5·00

The souvenir book is a 12-page illustrated booklet with a set of mint stamps in a sachet attached to the front cover.

Special First Day of Issue Postmarks

Philatelic Bureau, Edinburgh .... 3·00
Caernarfon, Gwynedd .... 4·00
London EC .... 3·50

637 "Expeditions"   **638** "Skills"

639 "Service"   **640** "Recreation"

(Des P. Sharland. Litho J.W.)
1981 (12 Aug). *25th Anniv of Duke of Edinburgh's Award Scheme. Phosphorised paper.* P 14.
1162	**637**	14p. greenish yellow, magenta, pale new blue, black, emerald and silver	25	20
1163	**638**	18p. greenish yellow, magenta, pale new blue, black, cobalt and gold.....	45	50
1164	**639**	22p. greenish yellow, magenta, pale new blue, black, red-orange and gold......	80	80
1165	**640**	25p. brt orange, mauve, pale new blue, black, flesh and bronze	90	1·00

Set of 4 .... 2·25 — 2·50
Set of 4 Gutter Pairs .... 5·00
First Day Cover .... — 2·50
Presentation Pack (P.O. Pack No. 128) .... 2·50
P.H.Q. Cards (set of 4) (54) .... 2·50 — 4·50

Special First Day of Issue Postmarks

Philatelic Bureau, Edinburgh .... 2·50
London W2 .... 2·75

641 Cockle-dredging from *Linsey II*   **642** Hauling in Trawl Net

643 Lobster Potting   **644** Hoisting Seine Net

(Des B. Sanders)
1981 (23 Sept). *Fishing Industry. Phosphorised paper.* P 15×14.
1166	**641**	14p. slate, greenish yellow, magenta, new blue, orange-brown, olive-grey and bronze-green	25	25
1167	**642**	18p. slate, greenish yellow, brt crimson, ultramarine, black and greenish slate	50	50
1168	**643**	22p. grey, greenish yellow, brt rose, dull ultramarine, reddish lilac and black	85	85
1169	**644**	25p. grey, greenish yellow, brt rose, cobalt and black......................	85	85

Set of 4 .... 2·25 — 2·50
Set of 4 Gutter Pairs .... 5·00
First Day Cover .... — 2·00
Presentation Pack (P.O. Pack No. 129) .... 2·50
P.H.Q. Cards (set of 4) (55) .... 2·25 — 4·50

Nos. 1166/9 were issued on the occasion of the centenary of the Royal National Mission to Deep Sea Fishermen.

Special First Day of Issue Postmarks

Philatelic Bureau, Edinburgh ....2·50
Hull ....2·75

645 Father Christmas **646** Jesus Christ

647 Flying Angel **648** Joseph and Mary arriving at Bethlehem

649 Three Kings approaching Bethlehem

(Des Samantha Brown (11½p.), Tracy Jenkins (14p.), Lucinda Blackmore (18p.), Stephen Moore (22p.), Sophie Sharp (25p.))

1981 (18 Nov). *Christmas. Children's Pictures. One phosphor band (11½p.) or phosphorised paper (others).* P 15×14.

1170	**645**	11½p. ultramarine, black, red, olive-bistre, brt green and gold..............................	25	20
1171	**646**	14p. bistre-yellow, brt magenta, blue, greenish blue, brt green, black and gold...	35	20
1172	**647**	18p. pale blue-green, bistre-yellow, brt magenta, ultramarine, black and gold...	50	60
1173	**648**	22p. dp turquoise-blue, lemon, magenta, black and gold..................	75	75
1174	**649**	25p. royal blue, lemon, brt magenta, black and gold..............................	85	85
Set of 5			2·50	2·50
Set of 5 Gutter Pairs..			5·50	
First Day Cover				2·75
Presentation Pack (P.O. Pack No. 130)			3·00	
P.H.Q. Cards (set of 5) (56)			2·25	5·50

Special First Day of Issue Postmarks

Philatelic Bureau, Edinburgh ....2·75
Bethlehem, Llandeilo, Dyfed ....2·75

Collectors Pack 1981
1981 (18 Nov). Comprises Nos. 1143/74.
CP1174a Collectors Pack.. 17·50

650 Charles Darwin and Giant Tortoises **651** Darwin and Marine Iguanas

652 Darwin, Cactus Ground Finch and Large Ground Finch **653** Darwin and Prehistoric Skulls

(Des D. Gentleman)

1982 (10 Feb). *Death Centenary of Charles Darwin. Phosphorised paper.* P 15×14.

1175	**650**	15½p. dull purple, drab, bistre, black and grey-black...	50	20
1176	**651**	19½p. violet-grey, bistre-yellow, slate-black, red-brown, grey-black and black..	50	60
1177	**652**	26p. sage green, bistre-yellow, orange, chalky blue, grey-black, red-brown and black....................................	75	85
1178	**653**	29p. grey-brown, yellow-brown, brown-ochre, black and grey-black..............	95	90
Set of 4			2·50	2·50
Set of 4 Gutter Pairs..			5·25	
First Day Cover				2·75
Presentation Pack (P.O. Pack No. 132)			3·00	
P.H.Q. Cards (set of 4) (57)			2·50	6·00

Special First Day of Issue Postmarks

Philatelic Bureau, Edinburgh ....2·75
Shrewsbury ....2·75

654 Boys' Brigade **655** Girls' Brigade

656 Boy Scout Movement **657** Girl Guide Movement

(Des B. Sanders)

1982 (24 Mar). *Youth Organizations. Phosphorised paper.* P 14×15.

1179	**654**	15½p. gold, greenish yellow. pale orange. mauve, dull blue and grey-black	25	15
1180	**655**	19½p. gold, greenish yellow, pale orange, brt rose, dp ultramarine, olive-bistre and grey-black	50	50
1181	**656**	26p. gold, greenish yellow, olive-sepia, rosine, dp blue, dp dull green and grey-black	85	85
1182	**657**	29p. gold, yellow, dull orange, cerise, dull ultramarine, chestnut and grey-black	1·00	1·10
Set of 4			2·50	2·50
Set of 4 Gutter Pairs			5·50	
First Day Cover				2·75
Presentation Pack (P.O. Pack No. 133)			3·00	
P.H.Q. Cards (set of 4) (58)			2·50	6·00

Nos. 1179/82 were issued on the occasion of the 75th anniversary of the Boy Scout Movement; the 125th birth anniversary of Lord Baden-Powell and the centenary of the Boys' Brigade (1983).

Special First Day of Issue Postmarks

Edinburgh Philatelic Bureau	2·75
Glasgow	3·00
London SW	3·00

15½ᴾ · 19½ᴾ

658 Ballerina   **659** Harlequin

26ᴾ · 29ᴾ

660 Hamlet   **661** Opera Singer

(Des A. George)

1982 (28 Apr). *Europa. British Theatre. Phosphorised paper.* P 14×15.

1183	**658**	15½p. carmine-lake, greenish blue, greenish yellow, grey-black, bottle green and silver	25	15
1184	**659**	19½p. rosine, new blue, greenish yellow, black, ultramarine and silver	50	50
1185	**660**	26p. carmine-red, brt rose-red, greenish yellow, black, dull ultramarine, lake-brown and silver	1·25	1·00
1186	**661**	29p. rose-red, greenish yellow, brt blue, grey-black and silver	1·50	1·00
Set of 4			3·25	2·50
Set of 4 Gutter Pairs			8·00	
First Day Cover				2·75
Presentation Pack (P.O. Pack No. 134)			3·00	
P.H.Q. Cards (set of 4) (59)			2·50	6·00

Special First Day of Issue Postmarks

Philatelic Bureau, Edinburgh	2·75
Stratford-upon-Avon	3·00

15½ᴾ   HENRY VIII/MARY ROSE   19½ᴾ   ADMIRAL BLAKE/TRIUMPH

662 Henry VIII and *Mary Rose*   **663** Admiral Blake and *Triumph*

24ᴾ   LORD NELSON/HMS VICTORY   26ᴾ   LORD FISHER/HMS DREADNOUGHT

664 Lord Nelson and H.M.S. *Victory*   **665** Lord Fisher and H.M.S. *Dreadnought*

29ᴾ   VISCOUNT CUNNINGHAM/HMS WARSPITE

666 Viscount Cunningham and H.M.S. *Warspite*

(Des Marjorie Saynor. Eng C. Slania. Recess and photo)

1982 (16 June). *Maritime Heritage. Phosphorised paper.* P 15×14.

1187	**662**	15½p. black, lemon, brt rose, pale orange, ultramarine and grey	35	25
		a. Imperf (pair)	£3500	
1188	**663**	19½p. black, greenish yellow, brt rose-red, pale orange, ultramarine and grey	50	50
1189	**664**	24p. black, orange-yellow, brt rose-red, lake-brown, dp ultramarine and grey	75	85
1190	**665**	26p. black, orange-yellow, brt rose, lemon, ultramarine and grey	75	85
		a. Imperf (pair)	£7500	
1191	**666**	29p. black, olive-yellow, brt rose, orange-yellow, ultramarine and grey	1·00	1·00
Set of 5			3·00	3·50
Set of 5 Gutter Pairs			7·00	
First Day Cover				3·75
Presentation Pack (P.O. Pack No. 136)			3·50	
P.H.Q. Cards (set of 5) (60)			2·50	6·00

Nos. 1187/91 were issued on the occasion of Maritime England Year, the Bicentenary of the Livery Grant by the City of London to the Worshipful Company of Shipwrights and the raising of the Mary Rose from Portsmouth Harbour.

Several used examples of the 15½p. have been seen with the black recess (ship and waves) omitted £1750

Special First Day of Issue Postmarks

Philatelic Bureau, Edinburgh ....3·75
Portsmouth ....3·75

667 "Strawberry Thief" (William Morris)

668 Untitled (Steiner and Co)

669 "Cherry Orchard" (Paul Nash)

670 "Chevron" (Andrew Foster)

(Des Peter Hatch Partnership)

1982 (23 July). *British Textiles. Phosphorised paper.* P 14×15.

1192	**667**	15½p. blue, olive-yellow, rosine, dp blue-green, bistre and Prussian blue		25	25
		a. Imperf (horiz pair)		£3500	
1193	**668**	19½p. olive-grey, greenish yellow, brt magenta, dull green, yellow-brown and black		75	75
		a. Imperf (vert pair)		£3500	
1194	**669**	26p. brt scarlet, dull mauve, dull ultramarine and brt carmine		75	1·00
1195	**670**	29p. bronze-green, orange-yellow, turquoise-green, stone, chestnut and sage-green		1·00	1·25
Set of 4				2·50	2·75
Set of 4 Gutter Pairs				5·50	
First Day Cover					3·00
Presentation Pack (P.O. Pack No. 137)				2·75	
P.H.Q. Cards (set of 4) (61)				2·50	6·00

Nos. 1192/5 were issued on the occasion of the 250th birth anniversary of Sir Richard Arkwright (inventor of spinning machine).

Special First Day of Issue Postmarks

Philatelic Bureau, Edinburgh ....3·00
Rochdale ....3·00

671 Development of Communications

672 Modern Technological Aids

(Des Delaney and Ireland)

1982 (8 Sept). *Information Technology. Phosphorised paper.* P 14×15.

1196	**671**	15½p. black, greenish yellow, brt rose-red, bistre-brown, new blue and lt ochre		50	25
		a. Imperf (pair)		£550	
1197	**672**	26p. black, greenish yellow, brt rose-red, olive-bistre, new blue and lt olive-grey		75	1·00
		a. Imperf (pair)		£3800	
Set of 2				1·25	1·25
Set of 2 Gutter Pairs				2·75	
First Day Cover					1·75
Presentation Pack (P.O. Pack No. 138)				1·50	
P.H.Q. cards (set of 2) (62)				2·00	5·25

Special First Day of Issue Postmarks

Philatelic Bureau, Edinburgh ....2·00
London WC ....2·50

673 Austin "Seven" and "Metro"

674 Ford "Model T" and "Escort"

675 Jaguar "SS 1" and "XJ6"

676 Rolls-Royce "Silver Ghost" and "Silver Spirit"

(Des S. Paine. Litho Questa)

1982 (13 Oct). *British Motor Cars. Phosphorised paper.* P 14½×14.

1198	**673**	15½p. slate, orange-vermilion, brt orange, drab, yellow-green, olive-yellow, bluish grey and black		50	25
1199	**674**	19½p. slate, brt orange, olive-grey, rose-red, dull vermilion, grey and black		75	75
		Ea. Rose-red, grey and black ptgs double		£1600	
1200	**675**	26p. slate, red-brown, brt orange, turquoise-green, myrtle-green, dull blue-green, grey and olive		75	75
1201	**676**	29p. slate, brt orange, carmine-red, reddish purple, grey and black		1·00	1·00
		Ea Black ptg quadruple		£1500	
		Eb Brt orange, carmine-red, grey and black ptgs double		£2200	
Set of 4				2·50	2·50
Set of 4 Gutter Pairs				6·25	
First Day Cover					2·50
Presentation Pack (P.O. Pack No. 139)				3·00	
P.H.Q. cards (set of 4) (63)				2·50	6·00

Special First Day of Issue Postmarks

Philatelic Bureau, Edinburgh ....3·00
Birmingham ....3·75
Crewe ....3·75

677 "While Shepherds Watched"   678 "The Holly and the Ivy"

679 "I Saw Three Ships"   680 "We Three Kings"

681 "Good King Wenceslas"

(Des Barbara Brown)

1982 (17 Nov). *Christmas. Carols. One phosphor band (12½p.) or phosphorised paper (others).* P 15×14.

1202	677	12½p. black, greenish yellow, brt scarlet, steel blue, red-brown and gold........	25	20
1203	678	15½p. black, bistre-yellow, brt rose-red, brt blue, brt green and gold.............	50	20
		a. Imperf (pair)	£6000	
1204	679	19½p. black, bistre-yellow, brt rose-red, dull blue, dp brown and gold	65	75
		a. Imperf (pair)	£6000	
1205	680	26p. black, bistre-yellow, brt magenta, brt blue, chocolate, gold and orange-red	75	90
1206	681	29p. black, bistre-yellow, magenta, brt blue, chestnut, gold and brt magenta......................................	1·00	1·00
Set of 5			3·00	2·75
Set of 5 Gutter Pairs...			5·25	
First Day Cover...				2·50
Presentation Pack (P.O. Pack No. 140)			3·25	
P.H.Q. cards (set of 5) (64)			2·50	6·00

Special Day of Issue Postmarks

Philatelic Bureau, Edinburgh ....2·75
Bethlehem, Llandeilo, Dyfed ....3·00

Collectors Pack 1982

1982 (Nov 17). Comprises Nos. 1175/1206.
CP1206a Collectors Pack... 26·00

682 Atlantic Salmon   683 Northern Pike

684 Brown Trout   685 Eurasian Perch

(Des A. Jardine)

1983 (26 Jan). *British River Fish. Phosphorised paper.* P 15×14.

1207	682	15½p. grey-black, bistre-yellow, brt purple, new blue and silver	30	25
		a Imperf (pair)	£4000	
1208	683	19½p. black, bistre-yellow, olive-bistre, dp claret, silver and dp bluish green.....	60	60
1209	684	26p. grey-black, bistre-yellow, chrome-yellow, magenta, silver and pale blue...	75	85
		a. Imperf (pair)	£4000	
1210	685	29p. black, greenish yellow, brt carmine, new blue and silver..........................	1·00	1·10
Set of 4			2·50	2·50
Set of 4 Gutter Pairs...			5·00	
First Day Cover...				2·50
Presentation Pack (P.O. Pack No. 142)			2·75	
P.H.Q. Cards (set of 4) (65)			3·00	7·00

All known examples of No. 1209a are creased.

Special First Day of Issue Postmarks

Philatelic Bureau, Edinburgh ....2·75
Peterborough ....3·00

686 Tropical Island   687 Desert

688 Temperate Farmland

689 Mountain Range

(Des D. Fraser)

1983 (9 Mar). *Commonwealth Day. Geographical Regions. Phosphorised paper.* P 14×15.

1211	**686**	15½p. greenish blue, greenish yellow, brt rose, lt brown, grey-black, dp claret and silver	40	25
1212	**687**	19½p. brt lilac, greenish yellow, magenta, dull blue, grey-black, dp dull blue and silver	75	75
1213	**688**	26p. lt blue, greenish yellow, brt magenta, new blue, grey-black, violet and silver	75	75
1214	**689**	29p. dull violet-blue, reddish violet, slate-lilac, new blue, myrtlegreen, black and silver	1·00	1·00
Set of 4			2·50	2·50
Set of 4 Gutter Pairs			6·00	
First Day Cover				2·50
Presentation Pack (P.O. Pack No. 143)			3·00	
P.H.Q. Cards (set of 4) (66)			2·50	6·50

Special First Day of Issue Postmarks

Philatelic Bureau, Edinburgh	2·75
London SW	3·00

690 Humber Bridge

691 Thames Flood Barrier

692 *Iolair* (oilfield emergency support vessel)

(Des M. Taylor)

1983 (25 May). *Europa. Engineering Achievements. Phosphorised paper.* P 15×14.

1215	**690**	16p. silver, orange-yellow, ultramarine, black and grey	50	25
1216	**691**	20½p. silver, greenish yellow, brt purple, blue, grey-black and grey	1·00	1·00
1217	**692**	28p. silver, lemon, brt rose-red, chestnut, dull ultramarine, black and grey	1·00	1·00
Set of 3			2·25	2·00
Set of 3 Gutter Pairs			7·00	
First Day Cover				2·25
Presentation Pack (P.O. Pack No. 144)			2·50	
P.H.Q. Cards (set of 3) (67)			2·50	5·75

Special First Day of Issue Postmarks

Philatelic Bureau, Edinburgh	2·50
Hull	2·75

693 Musketeer and Pikeman

694 Fusilier and Ensign, The Royal Scots (1633) The Royal Welch Fusiliers (mid-18th century)

695 Riflemen, 95th Rifles (The Royal Green Jackets) (1805)

696 Sergeant (khaki service) and Guardsman (full dress), The Irish Guards (1900)

697 Paratroopers, The Parachute Regiment (1983)

(Des E. Stemp)

1983 (6 July). *British Army Uniforms. Phosphorised paper.* P 14×15.

1218	**693**	16p. black, buff, dp brown, slate-black, rose-red, gold and new blue	50	10
1219	**694**	20½p. black, buff, greenish yellow, slate-black, brown-rose, gold and brt blue	50	60
1220	**695**	26p. black, buff, slate-purple, green, bistre and gold	75	90
		a. Imperf (pair)	£7000	
1221	**696**	28p. black, buff, lt brown, grey, dull rose, gold and new blue	75	90
		a. Imperf (pair)	£5000	
1222	**697**	31p. black, buff, olive-yellow, grey, dp magenta, gold and new blue	75	85
Set of 5			3·00	3·25
Set of 5 Gutter Pairs			7·50	
First Day Cover				3·25
Presentation Pack (P.O. Pack No. 145)			3·50	
P.H.Q. Cards (set of 5) (68)			3·50	6·50

Nos. 1218/22 were issued on the occasion of the 350th anniversary of the Royal Scots, the senior line regiment of the British Army.

Special First Day of Issue Postmarks

Philatelic Bureau, Edinburgh ....3·50
Aldershot ....3·75

698 20th-century Garden, Sissinghurst

699 19th-century Garden, Biddulph Grange

700 18th-century Garden, Blenheim

701 17th-century Garden, Pitmedden

(Des Liz Butler. Litho J.W.)

1983 (24 Aug). *British Gardens. Phosphorised paper.* P 14.

1223	**698**	16p. greenish yellow, brt purple, new blue, black, brt green and silver.......	50	10
1224	**699**	20½p. greenish yellow, brt purple, new blue, black, brt green and silver.......	50	55
1225	**700**	28p. greenish yellow, brt purple, new blue, black, brt green and silver.......	75	1·00
1226	**701**	31p. greenish yellow, brt purple, new blue, black, brt green and silver.......	1·00	1·00

Set of 4 .... 2·50 2·50
Set of 4 Gutter Pairs... 6·00
First Day Cover .... 2·25
Presentation Pack (P.O. Pack No. 146) .... 3·00
P.H.Q. Cards (set of 4) (69) .... 3·00 6·25

Nos. 1223/6 were issued on the occasion of the death bicentenary of "Capability" Brown (landscape gardener).

Special First Day of Issue Postmarks

Philatelic Bureau, Edinburgh ....3·00
Oxford ....3·50

702 Merry-go-round

703 Big Wheel, Helter-skelter and Performing Animals

704 Side Shows

705 Early Produce Fair

(Des A. Restall)

1983 (5 Oct). *British Fairs. Phosphorised paper.* P 15×14.

1227	**702**	16p. grey-black, greenish yellow, orange-red, ochre and turquoise-blue..............	35	25
1228	**703**	20½p. grey-black, yellow-ochre, yellow-orange, brt magenta, violet and black..............	75	75
1229	**704**	28p. grey-black, bistre-yellow, orange-red, violet and yellow-brown	75	1·00
1230	**705**	31p. grey-black, greenish yellow, red, dp turquoise-green, slate-violet and brown	1·00	1·00

Set of 4 .... 2·50 2·75
Set of 4 Gutter Pairs... 6·00
First Day Cover .... 3·00
Presentation Pack (P.O. Pack No. 147) .... 3·00
P.H.Q. Cards (set of 4) (70) .... 3·00 6·25

Special First Day of Issue Postmarks

Philatelic Bureau, Edinburgh ....3·00
Nottingham ....3·00

706 "Christmas Post" (pillar-box)

707 "The Three Kings" (chimney-pots)

708 "World at Peace" (Dove and Blackbird)

709 "Light of Christmas"(street lamp)

710 "Christmas Dove" (hedge sculpture)

(Des T. Meeuwissen)

1983 (16 Nov). *Christmas. One phosphor band (12½p.) or phosphorised paper (others).* P 15×14.

1231	**706**	12½p. black, greenish yellow, brt rose-red, brt blue, gold and grey-black...	25	25
		a. Imperf (horiz pair)	£4000	
1232	**707**	16p. black, greenish yellow, brt rose, pale new blue, gold and brown-purple.....	50	25
		a. Imperf (pair)	£2750	

1233	**708**	20½p.	black, greenish yellow, brt rose, new blue, gold and blue......................	75	1·00
1234	**709**	28p.	black, lemon, brt carmine, bluish violet, gold, dp turquoise-green and purple...........................	75	1·00
1235	**710**	31p.	black, greenish yellow, brt rose, new blue, gold, green and brown-olive..................	1·25	1·25

Set of 5	3·25	3·25
Set of 5 Gutter Pairs..........................	6·50	
First Day Cover..........................		3·50
Presentation Pack (P.O. Pack No. 148)	3·50	
P.H.Q. Cards (set of 5) (71)	3·00	6·25

Special First Day of Issue Postmarks

Philatelic Bureau, Edinburgh	3·50
Bethlehem, Llandeilo, Dyfed	3·50

Collectors Pack 1983
1983 (Nov 16). Comprises Nos. 1207/35.
CP1235a Collectors Pack.......................... 32·00

711 Arms of the College of Arms

712 Arms of King Richard III (founder)

713 Arms of the Earl Marshal of England

714 Arms of the City of London

(Des J. Matthews)

1984 (17 Jan). 500th Anniv of College of Arms. Phosphorised paper. P 14½.

1236	**711**	16p.	black, chrome-yellow, reddish brown, scarlet-vermillion, brt blue and grey-black..........................	50	15
1237	**712**	20½p.	black, chrome-yellow, rosine, brt blue and grey-black..........................	50	65
1238	**713**	28p.	black, chrome-yellow, rosine, brt blue, dull green and grey-black	1·00	1·10
1239	**714**	31p.	black, chrome-yellow, rosine, brt blue and grey-black..........................	1·25	1·25
			a. Imperf (horiz pair)	£12000	

Set of 4	3·00	3·00
Set of 4 Gutter Pairs..........................	6·25	
First Day Cover..........................		3·00
Presentation Pack (P.O. Pack No. 150)	3·25	
P.H.Q. Cards (set of 4) (72)..........................	3·00	6·50

Special First Day of Issue Postmarks

Philatelic Bureau, Edinburgh	3·00
London EC	3·50

715 Highland Cow

716 Chillingham Wild Bull

717 Hereford Bull

718 Welsh Black Bull

719 Irish Moiled Cow

(Des B. Driscoll)

1984 (6 Mar). British Cattle. Phosphorised paper. P 15×14.

1240	**715**	16p.	grey-black, bistre-yellow, rosine, yellow-orange, new blue and pale drab	35	15
			a. Imperf (vert pair)	£9000	
1241	**716**	20½p.	grey-black, greenish yellow, magenta, bistre, dull blue-green, pale drab and lt green	60	60
1242	**717**	26p.	black, chrome-yellow, rosine, reddish brown, new blue and pale drab	80	80
1243	**718**	28p.	black, greenish yellow, brt carmine, orange-brown, dp dull blue and pale drab..........................	90	90
1244	**719**	31p.	grey-black, bistre-yellow, rosine, red-brown, lt blue and pale drab.....	1·00	1·20
			a. Imperf (pair)	—	

Set of 5	3·50	3·50
Set of 5 Gutter Pairs..........................	7·25	
First Day Cover..........................		3·50
Presentation Pack (P.O. Pack No. 151)	4·00	
P.H.Q. Cards (set of 5) (73)	3·00	6·50

Nos. 1240/4 were issued on the occasion of the centenary of the Highland Cattle Society and the bicentenary of the Royal Highland and Agricultural Society of Scotland.

Special First Day of Issue Postmarks

Philatelic Bureau, Edinburgh	3·50
Oban, Argyll	4·50

720 Garden Festival Hall, Liverpool

721 Milburngate Centre, Durham

722 Bush House, Bristol

723 Commercial Street Development, Perth

(Des R. Maddox and Trickett and Webb Ltd)

1984 (10 Apr). *Urban Renewal. Phosphorised paper.* P 15×14.

1245	**720**	16p. brt emerald, greenish yellow, cerise, steel-blue, black, silver and flesh	30	10
1246	**721**	20½p. brt orange, greenish yellow, dp dull blue, yellowish green, azure, black and silver	50	60
		a. Imperf (horiz pair)	£9000	
1247	**722**	28p. rosine, greenish yellow, Prussian blue, pale blue-green, black and silver	1·25	1·25
1248	**723**	31p. blue, greenish yellow, cerise, grey-blue, bright green, black and silver	1·25	1·25
		a. Imperf (pair)	£7500	
Set of 4			3·00	3·00
Set of 4 Gutter Pairs			6·50	
First Day Cover				2·50
Presentation Pack (P.O. Pack No. 152)			3·00	
P.H.Q. Cards (set of 4) (74)			3·00	6·25

Nos. 1245/8 were issued on the occasion of 150th anniversaries of the Royal Institute of British Architects and the Chartered Institute of Building, and to commemorate the first International Gardens Festival, Liverpool.

Special First Day of Issue Postmarks

Philatelic Bureau, Edinburgh	3·00
Liverpool	3·50

724 C.E.P.T. 25th Anniversary Logo

725 Abduction of Europa

(Des J. Larrivière (T **724**), F. Wegner (T **725**))

1984 (15 May). *25th Anniv of C.E.P.T. ("Europa") (T **724**) and Second Elections to European Parliament (T **725**). Phosphorised paper.* P 15×14.

1249	**724**	16p. greenish slate, dp blue and gold	50	25
		a. Horiz pair. Nos. 1249/50	1·50	1·50
		ab Imperf (horiz pair)	£6500	
1250	**725**	16p. greenish slate, dp blue, black and gold	50	25
1251	**724**	20½p. Venetian red, dp magenta and gold	70	40
		a. Horiz pair. Nos. 1251/2	2·50	2·50
		ab. Imperf (horiz pair)	£8000	
1252	**725**	20½p. Venetian red, dp magenta, black and gold	70	40
Set of 4			3·00	3·00
Set of 2 Gutter Blocks of 4			8·00	
First Day Cover				3·50
Presentation Pack (P.O. Pack No. 153)			4·00	
P.H.Q. Cards (set of 4) (75)			3·00	6·25

Nos. 1249/50 and 1251/2 were each printed together, *se-tenant*, in horizontal pairs throughout the sheets.

Special First Day of Issue Postmarks

Philatelic Bureau, Edinburgh	4·00
London SW	4·50

726 Lancaster House

(Des P. Hogarth)

1984 (5 June). *London Economic Summit Conference. Phosphorised paper.* P 14×15.

1253	**726**	31p. silver, bistre-yellow, brown-ochre, black, rosine, brt blue and reddish lilac	1·25	1·25
Gutter Pair			2·50	
First Day Cover				2·25
P.H.Q. Card (76)			1·00	3·50

Special First Day of Issue Postmarks

Philatelic Bureau, Edinburgh	2·50
London SW	2·50

727 View of Earth from "Apollo 11"

728 Navigational Chart of English Channel

729 Greenwich Observatory

730 Sir George Airy's Transit Telescope

(Des H. Waller. Litho Questa)

1984 (26 June). *Centenary of the Greenwich Meridian. Phosphorised paper.* P 14×14½.

1254	727	16p. new blue, greenish yellow, magenta, black, scarlet and blue-black	50	25
		Ea. Black ptg double	†	£1900
1255	728	20½p. olive-sepia, lt brown, pale buff, black and scarlet	75	80
1256	729	28p. new blue, greenish yellow, scarlet, black and brt purple	1·00	1·00
1257	730	31p. dp blue, cobalt, scarlet & black	1·00	1·10
Set of 4			3·00	3·00
Set of 4 Gutter Pairs			6·50	
First Day Cover				3·00
Presentation Pack (P.O. Pack No. 154)			3·50	
P.H.Q. Cards (set of 4) (77)			3·00	6·25

On Nos. 1254/7 the Meridian is represented by a scarlet line.

Special First Day of Issue Postmarks

Philatelic Bureau, Edinburgh .... 3·00
London SE10 .... 3·25

731 Bath Mail Coach, 1784   **732** Attack on Exeter Mail, 1816

733 Norwich Mail in Thunderstorm, 1827   **734** Holyhead and Liverpool Mails leaving London, 1828

735 Edinburgh Mail Snowbound, 1831

(Des K. Bassford and S. Paine. Eng C. Slania. Recess and photo)

1984 (31 July). *Bicentenary of First Mail Coach Run, Bath and Bristol to London. Phosphorised paper.* P 15×14.

1258	731	16p. pale stone, black, grey-black and brt scarlet	40	35
		a. Horiz strip of 5. Nos. 1258/62	2·50	2·75
		ab. Imperf (horiz pair. Nos. 1261/2)	£7500	
1259	732	16p. pale stone, black, grey-black and brt scarlet	40	35
1260	733	16p. pale stone, black, grey-black and brt scarlet	40	35
1261	734	16p. pale stone, black, grey-black and brt scarlet	40	35
1262	735	16p. pale stone, black, grey-black and brt scarlet	40	35
Set of 5			2·50	2·75
Gutter Block of 10			6·50	
First Day Cover				3·00
Presentation Pack (P.O. Pack No. 155)			3·00	
Souvenir Book			7·50	
P.H.Q. Cards (set of 5) (78)			3·00	6·50

Nos. 1258/62 were printed together, se-tenant, in horizontal strips of 5 throughout the sheet.
No. 1258ab also includes No. 1260 perforated at left only.
The souvenir book is a 24-page illustrated booklet with a set of mint stamps in a sachet attached to the front cover.

Special First Day of Issue Postmarks

Philatelic Bureau, Edinburgh .... 3·50
Bristol .... 4·00

736 Nigerian Clinic   **737** Violinist and Acropolis, Athens

738 Building Project, Sri Lanka   **739** British Council Library, Middle East

(Des F. Newell and J. Sorrell)

1984 (25 Sept). *50th Anniv of the British Council. Phosphorised paper.* P 15×14.

1263	736	17p. grey-green, greenish yellow, brt purple, dull blue, black, pale green and yellow-green	50	25
1264	737	22p. crimson, greenish yellow, brt rose-red, dull green, black, pale drab and slate-purple	85	1·00
1265	738	31p. sepia, olive-bistre, red, black, pale stone and olive-brown	85	1·00
1266	739	34p. steel blue, yellow, rose-red, new blue, black, azure and pale blue	1·00	1·00
Set of 4			3·00	3·00
Set of 4 Gutter Pairs			6·50	
First Day Cover				3·00
Presentation Pack (P.O. Pack No. 156)			3·25	
P.H.Q. Cards (set of 4) (79)			3·00	6·25

Special First Day of Issue Postmarks

London SW .... 3·50
Philatelic Bureau, Edinburgh .... 3·50

740 The Holy Family   **741** Arrival in Bethlehem

742 Shepherd and Lamb   **743** Virgin and Child

744 Offering of Frankincense

(Des Yvonne Gilbert)

1984 (20 Nov). *Christmas. One phosphor band (13p.) or phosphorised paper (others).* P 15×14.

1267	**740**	13p. pale cream, grey-black, bistre-yellow, magenta, red-brown and lake-brown	25	25
		Eu. Underprint Type 4	70	
1268	**741**	17p. pale cream, grey-black, yellow, magenta, dull blue and dp dull blue	50	50
		a. Imperf (pair)	£5000	
1269	**742**	22p. pale cream, grey-black, olive-yellow, brt magenta, brt blue and brownish grey	75	75
1270	**743**	31p. pale cream, grey-black, bistre-yellow, magenta, dull blue and lt brown	1·00	1·00
1271	**744**	34p. pale cream, olive-grey, bistre-yellow, magenta, turquoise-green and brown-olive	1·00	1·00
Set of 5			3·25	3·25
Set of 5 Gutter Pairs			7·00	
First Day Cover				3·25
Presentation Pack (P.O. Pack No. 157)			3·75	
P.H.Q. Cards (set of 5) (80)			3·00	6·25

Examples of No. 1267Eu from the 1984 Christmas booklet (No. FX7) show a random pattern of blue double-lined stars printed on the reverse over the gum.

Special First Day of Issue Postmarks

Philatelic Bureau, Edinburgh	3·50
Bethlehem, Llandeilo, Dyfed	3·50

Collectors Pack 1984

1984 (Nov 20). Comprises Nos. 1236/71.

CP1271a Collectors Pack .... 37·00

Post Office Yearbook

1984. Comprises Nos. 1236/71 in 24-page hardbound book with slip case, illustrated in colour .... 85·00

745 "Flying Scotsman"   **746** "Golden Arrow"

747 "Cheltenham Flyer"   **748** "Royal Scot"

749 "Cornish Riviera"

(Des T. Cuneo)

1985 (22 Jan). *Famous Trains. Phosphorised paper.* P 15×14.

1272	**745**	17p. black, lemon, magenta, dull blue, grey-black and gold	75	25
		a. Imperf (pair)	£4500	
1273	**746**	22p. black, greenish yellow, brt rose, dp dull blue, grey-black and gold	75	1·00
1274	**742**	29p. black, greenish yellow, magenta, blue, grey-black and gold	1·00	1·25
1275	**748**	31p. black, bistre-yellow, brt rose, new blue, slate-black and gold	1·25	1·50
1276	**749**	34p. black, greenish yellow, brt rose, blue, slate-black and gold	2·50	2·50
Set of 5			6·00	6·00
Set of 5 Gutter Pairs			12·00	
First Day Cover				6·00
Presentation Pack (P.O. Pack No. 159)			6·00	
P.H.Q. Cards (set of 5) (81)			6·00	15·00

Nos. 1272/6 were issued on the occasion of the 150th anniversary of the Great Western Railway Company.

Special First Day of Issue Postmarks

Philatelic Bureau, Edinburgh	6·50
Bristol	8·00

750 *Bombus terrestris* (bee)   **751** *Coccinella septempunctata* (ladybird)

752 *Decticus verrucivorus* (bush-cricket)   **753** *Lucanus cervus* (stag beetle)

754 *Anax imperator*
(dragonfly)

(Des G. Beningfield)

1985 (12 Mar). *Insects. Phosphorised paper.* P 14×15.

1277	**750**	17p. black, greenish yellow, magenta, blue, azure, gold and slate-black.....	40	10
1278	**751**	22p. black, greenish yellow, brt rose-red, dull blue-green, slate-black and gold....................	60	55
1279	**752**	29p. black, greenish yellow, brt rose, greenish blue, grey-black, gold and bistre-yellow........................	85	90
1280	**753**	31p. black, greenish yellow, rose, pale new blue and gold........................	1·00	1·00
1281	**754**	34p. black, greenish yellow, magenta, greenish blue, grey-black & gold.....	1·00	90
		a. Imperf (vert pair)	£20000	
Set of 5		....	3·25	3·25
Set of 5 Gutter Pairs		....	8·75	
First Day Cover		....		3·50
Presentation Pack (P.O. Pack No. 160)		....	4·50	
P.H.Q. Cards (set of 5) (82)		....	3·00	7·50

Nos. 1277/81 were issued on the occasion of the centenaries of the Royal Entomological Society of London's Royal Charter, and of the Selborne Society.

Special First Day of Issue Postmarks

Philatelic Bureau, Edinburgh .... 4·00
London SW .... 4·50

SEVENTEEN·PENCE

WATER·MUSIC
George Frideric Handel
755 "Water Music" (George Frederick Handel)

TWENTY·TWO·PENCE

THE·PLANETS·SUITE
Gustav Holst
756 "The Planets Suite" (Gustav Holst)

THIRTY·ONE·PENCE

THE·FIRST·CUCKOO
Frederick Delius
757 "The First Cuckoo" (Frederick Delius)

THIRTY·FOUR·PENCE

SEA·PICTURES
Edward Elgar
758 "Sea Pictures" (Edward Elgar)

(Des W. McLean)

1985 (14 May). *Europa. European Music Year. British Composers. Phosphorised paper.* P 14×14½.

1282	**755**	17p. black, brt yellow-green, deep magenta, new blue, grey & gold..........	55	10
		a. Imperf (vert pair)...................	£6500	
1283	**756**	22p. black, greenish yellow, brt magenta, new blue, grey-black and gold.............	75	90
		a. Imperf (pair)...................	£6500	
1284	**757**	31p. black, greenish yellow, magenta, greenish blue, grey-black & gold	1·50	1·25
1285	**758**	34p. black, olive-yellow, bistre, turquoise-blue, slate and gold.....................	1·50	1·25
Set of 4		....	4·00	3·25
Set of 4 Gutter Pairs		....	10·00	
First Day Cover		....		4·00
Presentation Pack (P.O. Pack No. 161)		....	4·75	
P.H.Q. Cards (set of 4) (83)		....	3·00	6·50

Nos. 1282/5 were issued on the occasion of the 300th birth anniversary of Handel.

Special First Day of Issue Postmarks

Philatelic Bureau, Edinburgh .... 4·50
Worcester .... 4·75

759 R.N.L.I. Lifeboat and Signal Flags

760 Beachy Head Lighthouse and Chart

761 "Marecs A" Communications Satellite and Dish Aerials

762 Buoys

(Des F. Newell and J. Sorrell. Litho J.W.)

1985 (18 June). *Safety at Sea. Phosphorised paper.* P 14.

1286	**759**	17p. black, azure, emerald, ultramarine, orange-yellow, vermilion, brt blue and chrome-yellow............................	40	25
1287	**760**	22p. black, azure, emerald, ultramarine, orange-yellow, vermilion, brt blue and chrome-yellow............................	60	75
1288	**761**	31p. black, azure, emerald, ultramarine, orange-yellow, vermilion and brt blue............................	1·00	1·00
1289	**762**	34p. black, azure, emerald, ultramarine, orange-yellow, vermilion, brt blue and chrome-yellow............................	1·50	1·25
Set of 4		....	3·00	3·00
Set of 4 Gutter Pairs		....	7·00	
First Day Cover		....		3·00
Presentation Pack (P.O. Pack No. 162)		....	3·75	
P.H.Q. Cards (set of 4) (84)		....	3·00	6·50

Nos. 1286/9 were issued on the occasion of the bicentenary of the unimmersible lifeboat and the 50th anniversary of radar.

Special First Day of Issue Postmarks

Philatelic Bureau, Edinburgh .... 3·50
Eastbourne.. 3·50

763 Datapost Motorcyclist, City of London

764 Rural Postbus

765 Parcel Delivery in Winter

766 Town Letter Delivery

(Des P. Hogarth)

1985 (30 July). *350 Years of Royal Mail Public Postal Service. Phosphorised paper.* P 14×15.

1290	**763**	17p. black, greenish yellow, brt carmine, greenish blue, yellow-brown, grey-black and silver	50	10
		a. Imperf on 3 sides (vert pair)	£3250	
		Eu. Underprint Type **5**	1·00	
1291	**764**	22p. black, greenish yellow, cerise, steel-blue, lt green, grey-black and silver	75	70
		a. Imperf (vert pair)	£20000	
1292	**765**	31p. black, greenish yellow, brt carmine, dull blue, drab, grey-black and silver	1·00	1·00
		a. Imperf	£4000	
1293	**766**	34p. black, greenish yellow, cerise, ultramarine, lt brown, grey-black and silver	1·50	1·50
		a. Imperf between (vert pair)	£1750	
		b. Imperf (vert pair)	—	
Set of 4			3·00	3·00
Set of 4 Gutter Pairs			7·00	
First Day Cover				3·25
Presentation Pack (P.O. Pack No. 163)			3·75	
P.H.Q. Cards (set of 4) (85)			3·00	6·50

No. 1290a shows perforation indentations at right, but is imperforate at top, bottom and on the left-hand side.

Examples of No. 1290Eu from the 1985 £1.70 booklet (sold at £1.53) (No. FT4) show a blue double-lined D in a random pattern, on the reverse over the gum.

Special First Day of Issue Postmarks

Philatelic Bureau, Edinburgh ....3·50
Bagshot, Surrey ....3·75

767 King Arthur and Merlin

768 Lady of the Lake

769 Queen Guinevere and Sir Lancelot

770 Sir Galahad

(Des Yvonne Gilbert)

1985 (3 Sept). *Arthurian Legends. Phosphorised paper.* P 15×14.

1294	**767**	17p. grey-black, lemon, brown-lilac, ultramarine, grey-black & silver	50	25
		a. Imperf (pair)	£8000	
1295	**768**	22p. black, lemon, brown-lilac, pale blue, grey-black, silver and grey-black	75	75
1296	**769**	31p. black, lemon, magenta, turquoise-blue, grey-black, silver and grey-black	1·25	1·25
1297	**770**	34p. grey, lemon, magenta, new blue, grey-black, silver and grey-black	1·25	1·25
Set of 4			3·50	3·00
Set of 4 Gutter Pairs			7·00	
First Day Cover				3·50
Presentation Pack (P.O. Pack No. 164)			4·00	
P.H.Q. Cards (set of 4) (86)			3·00	6·50

Nos. 1294/7 were issued on the occasion of the 500th anniversary of the printing of Sir Thomas Malory's *Morte d'Arthur*.

Trials are known with face value and inscription in a different type face.

Special First Day of Issue Postmarks

Philatelic Bureau, Edinburgh ....4·00
Tintagel, Cornwall ....4·00

771 Peter Sellers (from photo by Bill Brandt)

772 David Niven (from photo by Cornell Lucas)

773 Charlie Chaplin (from photo by Lord Snowdon)

774 Vivien Leigh (from photo by Angus McBean)

775 Alfred Hitchcock (from photo by Howard Coster)

(Des K. Bassford)

1985 (8 Oct). *British Film Year. Phosphorised paper.* P 14½.

1298	**771**	17p. grey-black, olive-grey, gold and silver	45	25
1299	**772**	22p. black, brown, gold and silver	60	75
1300	**773**	29p. black, lavender, gold and silver	1·00	1·25
1301	**774**	31p. black, pink, gold and silver	1·10	1·50
1302	**775**	34p. black, greenish blue, gold and silver	1·40	1·50

Set of 5	4·00	4·50
Set of 5 Gutter Pairs	10·50	
First Day Cover		5·00
Presentation Pack (P.O. Pack No. 165)	5·50	
Souvenir Book	11·50	
P.H.Q. Cards (set of 5) (87)	3·00	8·50

The souvenir book is a 24-page illustrated booklet with a set of mint stamps in a sachet attached to the front cover.

Philatelic Bureau, Edinburgh	5·50
London WC	5·50

776 Principal Boy

777 Genie

778 Dame

779 Good Fairy

780 *Pantomime* Cat

(Des A. George)

1985 (19 Nov). *Christmas. Pantomine Characters.* One phosphor band (12p.) or phosphorised paper (others). P 15×14.

1303	**776**	12p. new blue, greenish yellow, brt rose, gold, grey-black and silver	50	15
		a. Imperf (pair)	£4000	
		Eu. Underprint Type 4	1·00	
1304	**777**	17p. emerald, greenish yellow, brt rose, new blue, grey, gold and silver	50	25
		a. Imperf (pair)	£7000	
1305	**778**	22p. brt carmine, greenish yellow, pale new blue, grey, gold and silver	75	1·10
1306	**779**	31p. brt orange, lemon, rose, slate-purple, silver and gold	1·25	1·40
1307	**780**	34p. brt reddish violet, brt blue, brt rose, black, grey-brown, gold & silver	1·25	1·40
Set of 5			4·00	4·00

Set of 5 Gutter Pairs	8·00	
First Day Cover		4·50
Presentation Pack (P.O. Pack No. 166)	4·25	
P.H.Q. Cards (set of 5) (88)	3·00	6·50
Christmas Folder (contains No. 1303×50)	35·00	

Examples of No. 1303Eu from the 1985 Christmas booklet (No. FX8) show a random pattern of blue double-lined stars printed on the reverse over the gum.

Philatelic Bureau, Edinburgh	4·75
Bethlehem, Llandeilo, Dyfed	5·00

Collectors Pack 1985

1985 Nov 19 Comprises Nos. 1272/1307.

CP1307a Collectors Pack	35·00

Post Office Yearbook

1985. Comprises Nos. 1272/1307 in 32-page hardbound book with slip case, illustrated in colour ... 75·00

17 PENCE · INDUSTRY YEAR 1986
781 Light Bulb and North Sea Oil Drilling Rig (Energy)

22 PENCE · INDUSTRY YEAR 1986
782 Thermometer and Pharmaceutical Laboratory (Health)

31 PENCE · INDUSTRY YEAR 1986
783 Garden Hoe Steelworks (Steel)

34 PENCE · INDUSTRY YEAR 1986
784 Loaf of Bread and Cornfield (Agriculture)

(Des K. Bassford. Litho Questa)

1986 (14 Jan). *Industry Year. Phosphorised paper.* P 14½×14.

1308	**781**	17p. gold, black, magenta, greenish yellow and new blue	75	25
1309	**782**	22p. gold, pale turquoise-green, black, magenta, greenish yellow & blue	50	75
1310	**783**	31p. gold, black, magenta, greenish yellow and new blue	1·25	1·40
1311	**784**	34p. gold, black, magenta, greenish yellow and new blue	1·25	1·40

Set of 4	3·50	3·50
Set of 4 Gutter Pairs	7·00	
First Day Cover		3·50
Presentation Pack (P.O. Pack No. 168)	3·75	
P.H.Q. Cards (set of 4) (89)	3·50	6·50

Philatelic Bureau, Edinburgh	3·50
Birmingham	4·00

785 Dr. Edmond Halley as Comet

786 *Giotto* Spacecraft approaching Comet

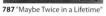

787 "Maybe Twice in a Lifetime"

788 Comet orbiting Sun and Planets

(Des R. Steadman)

1986 (18 Feb). *Appearance of Halley's Comet. Phosphorised paper.* P 15×14.

1312	**785**	17p. black, bistre, rosine, blue, grey-black, gold and dp brown	50	25
		a. Imperf (pair)	£15000	
1313	**786**	22p. orange-vermilion, greenish yellow, brt purple, new blue, black and gold	75	75
1314	**787**	31p. black, greenish yellow, brt purple, dp turquoise-blue, grey-black and gold	1·25	1·25
		a. Imperf (pair)	£17500	
1315	**788**	34p. blue, greenish yellow, magenta, dp turquoise-blue, black & gold	1·25	1·40
Set of 4			3·50	3·50
Set of 4 Gutter Pairs			7·00	
First Day Cover				3·50
Presentation Pack (P.O. Pack No. 168)			3·75	
P.H.Q. Cards (set of 4) (90)			3·50	6·50

The presentation pack was incorrectly numbered '168'.

Special First Day of Issue Postmarks

Philaelic Bureau, Edinburgh	4·00
London SE10	4·50

789 Queen Elizabeth in 1928, 1942 and 1952

790 Queen Elizabeth in 1958, 1973 and 1982

T **789/90** were printed horizontally *se-tenant* within the sheet

(Des J. Matthews)

1986 (21 Apr). *60th Birthday of Queen Elizabeth II. Phosphorised paper.* P 15×14.

1316	**789**	17p. grey-black, turquoise-green, brt green, green and dull blue	60	25
		a. Pair. Nos. 1316/17	1·50	1·50
1317	**790**	17p. grey-black, dull blue, greenish blue and indigo	60	25
1318	**789**	34p. grey-black, dp dull purple, yellow-orange and red	70	50
		a. Pair. Nos. 1318/19	3·00	4·00
1319	**790**	34p. grey-black, olive-brown, yellow-brown, olive-grey and red	70	50

Set of 4		4·50	5·00
Set of 2 Gutter Blocks of 4		11·00	
First Day Cover			5·00
Presentation Pack (P.O. Pack No. 170)		5·50	
Souvenir Book		8·50	
P.H.Q. Cards (set of 4) (91)		5·00	6·50

The souvenir book is a special booklet, fully illustrated and containing a mint set of stamps.

Special First Day of Issue Postmarks

Philatelic Bureau, Edinburgh	5·00
Windsor	5·00

791 Barn Owl

792 Pine Marten

793 Wild Cat

794 Natterjack Toad

(Des K. Lilly)

1986 (20 May). *Europa. Nature Conservation—Endangered Species. Phosphorised paper.* P 14½×14.

1320	**791**	17p. gold, greenish yellow, rose, yellow-brown, olive-grey, new blue and black	40	10
1321	**792**	22p. gold, greenish yellow, reddish brown, olive-yellow, turquoise-blue, grey-black and black	80	1·00
1322	**793**	31p. gold, brt yellow-green, magenta, lt brown, ultramarine, olive-brown and black	1·50	1·25
1323	**794**	34p. gold, greenish yellow, brt rose-red, brt green, grey-black and black	1·65	1·40
Set of 4			4·00	3·50
Set of 4 Gutter Pairs			10·00	
First Day Cover				4·00
Presentation Pack (P.O. Pack No. 171)			4·00	
P.H.Q. Cards (set of 4) (92)			3·50	6·50

Special First Day of Issue Postmarks

Philatelic Bureau, Edinburgh	4·50
Lincoln	4·75

795 Peasants working in Fields

796 Freemen working at Town Trades

797 Knight and Retainers

798 Lord at Banquet

(Des Tayburn Design Consultancy)

1986 (17 Jun). *900th Anniv of Domesday Book. Phosphorised paper.* P 15×14.

1324	**795**	17p. yellow-brown, vermilion, lemon, brt emerald, orange-brown, grey and brownish grey	40	10
1325	**796**	22p. yellow-ochre, red, greenish blue, chestnut, grey-black and brownish grey	85	85
1326	**797**	31p. yellow-brown, vermilion, green, Indian red, grey-black and brownish grey	1·25	1·40
1327	**798**	34p. yellow-ochre, bright scarlet, grey-brown, new blue, lake-brown, grey-black and grey	1·25	1·40
Set of 4			3·50	3·50
Set of 4 Gutter Pairs			7·00	
First Day Cover				4·00
Presentation Pack (P.O. Pack No. 172)			4·00	
P.H.Q. Cards (set of 4) (93)			3·50	6·50

Special First Day of Issue Postmarks

Philatelic Bureau, Edinburgh	4·50
Gloucester	4·50

799 Athletics

800 Rowing

801 Weightlifting

802 Rifle Shooting

803 Hockey

(Des N. Cudworth)

1986 (15 July). *Thirteenth Commonwealth Games, Edinburgh and World Hockey Cup for Men, London (34p.). Phosphorised paper.* P 15×14.

1328	**799**	17p. black, greenish yellow, orange-vermilion, ultramarine, chestnut and emerald	40	25
1329	**800**	22p. black, lemon, scarlet, new blue, royal blue, chestnut and dp ultramarine	55	75
		a. Imperf (pair)		—
1330	**801**	29p. grey-black, greenish yellow, scarlet, new blue, brown-ochre, brown-rose and pale chestnut	75	1·00
1331	**802**	31p. black, greenish yellow, rose, blue, dull yellow-green, chestnut and yellow-green	1·50	1·75
1332	**803**	34p. black, lemon, scarlet, brt blue, brt emerald, red-brown and vermilion.	1·75	1·75
		a. Imperf (pair)	£6000	
Set of 5			4·00	4·00
Set of 5 Gutter Pairs			8·75	
First Day Cover				3·50
Presentation Pack (P.O. Pack No. 173)			4·00	
P.H.Q. Cards (set of 5) (94)			3·50	7·50

No. 1332 also commemorates the centenary of the Hockey Association.

Special First Day of Issue Postmarks

Philatelic Bureau, Edinburgh	4·00
Head Post Office, Edinburgh	5·00

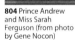

804 Prince Andrew and Miss Sarah Ferguson (from photo by Gene Nocon)

805 Prince Andrew and Miss Sarah Ferguson (from photo by Gene Nocon)

(Des J. Matthews)

1986 (22 July). *Royal Wedding. One phosphor band (12p.) or phosphorised paper (17p.).* P 14×15.

1333	**804**	12p. lake, greenish yellow, cerise, ultramarine, black and silver	50	30
1334	**805**	17p. steel blue, greenish yellow, cerise, ultramarine, black & gold	1·00	1·25
		a. Imperf (pair)	£1400	
Set of 2			1·50	1·50
Set of 2 Gutter Pairs			3·00	
First Day Cover				2·00
Presentation Pack (P.O. Pack No. 174)			1·75	
P.H.Q. Cards (set of 2) (95)			2·25	5·00

Special First Day of Issue Postmarks

Philatelic Bureau, Edinburgh	2·50
London, SW1	2·75

806 Stylized Cross on Ballot Paper

(Des J. Gibbs. Litho Questa)

1986 (19 Aug). *32nd Commonwealth Parliamentary Association Conference. Phosphorised paper.* P 14×14½.

1335	806	34p. pale grey-lilac, black, vermilion, yellow and ultramarine	1·25	1·25
		a. Imperf between (vert pair)	£4000	
Gutter Pair			2·75	
First Day Cover				1·75
P.H.Q. Card (96)			1·00	3·00

Special First Day of Issue Postmarks

Philatelic Bureau, Edinburgh		2·00
London, SW1		2·00

807 Lord Dowding and Hawker Hurricane Mk I

808 Lord Tedder and Hawker Typhoon IB

809 Lord Trenchard and De Havilland D.H.9A

810 Sir Arthur Harris and Avro Type 683 Lancaster

811 Lord Portal and De Havilland D.H.98 Mosquito

(Des B. Sanders)

1986 (16 Sept). *History of the Royal Air Force. Phosphorised paper.* P 14½.

1336	807	17p. pale blue, greenish yellow, brt rose, blue, black and grey-black	50	10
		a. Imperf (pair)	£5000	
1337	808	22p. pale turquoise-green, greenish yellow, magenta, new blue, black and grey-black	75	95
		a. Face value omitted*	£1200	

		b. Queen's head omitted*	£1200	
1338	809	29p. pale drab, olive-yellow, magenta, blue, grey-black and black	1·25	1·25
1339	810	31p. pale flesh, greenish yellow, magenta, ultramarine, black and grey-black	1·75	1·60
1340	811	34p. buff, greenish yellow, magenta, blue, grey-black and black	1·75	1·90
Set of 5			5·00	5·50
Set of 5 Gutter Pairs			12·00	
First Day Cover				5·50
Presentation Pack (P.O. Pack No. 175)			5·50	
P.H.Q. Cards (set of 5) (97)			4·50	10·00

Nos. 1336/40 were issued to celebrate the 50th anniversary of the first R.A.F. Commands.

*Nos. 1337a/b come from three consecutive sheets on which the stamps in the first vertical row are without the face value and those in the second vertical row the Queen's head.

Special First Day of Issue Postmarks

Philatelic Bureau, Edinburgh		6·00
Farnborough		6·00

812 The Glastonbury Thorn

813 The Tanad Valley Plygain

814 The Hebrides Tribute

815 The Dewsbury Church Knell

816 The Hereford Boy Bishop

(Des Lynda Gray)

1986 (18 Nov–2 Dec). *Christmas. Folk Customs. One phosphor band (12p., 13p.) or phosphorised paper (others).* P 15×14.

1341	812	12p. gold, greenish yellow, vermilion, dp brown, emerald and dp blue (2.12)	50	50
		a. Imperf (pair)	£4250	
1342		13p. dp blue, greenish yellow, vermilion, dp brown, emerald and gold	25	15
		Eu. Underprint Type 4 (2.12)	1·00	
1343	813	18p. myrtle-green, yellow, vermilion, dp blue, black, reddish brown and gold	50	15
1344	814	22p. vermilion, olive-bistre, dull blue, dp brown, dp green and gold	1·00	1·00
1345	815	31p. dp brown, yellow, vermilion, violet, dp dull green, black and gold	1·25	1·00
1346	816	34p. violet, lemon, vermilion, dp dull blue, reddish brown and gold	1·25	1·10
Set of 6			3·75	3·50
Set of 6 Gutter Pairs			9·00	
First Day Covers (2)				3·75

Presentation Pack (Nos. 1342/6) (P.O. Pack No. 176) .... 3·75
P.H.O. Cards (Nos. 1342/6) (set of 5) (98) .... 3·50   6·50
Christmas Folder (contains No. 1342Eu×36)........................ 17·00

No. 1341 represented a discount of 1p., available between 2 and 24 December 1986, on the current second class postage rate.

Special First Day of Issue Postmarks

Philatelic Bureau, Edinburgh (Nos. 1342/6) (18 Nov) ....3·00
Bethlehem, Llandeilo, Dyfed (Nos. 1342/6) (18 Nov) ....4·00
Philatelic Bureau, Edinburgh (No. 1341) (2 Dec) ....1·00

Collectors Pack 1986
1986 Nov 18 Comprises Nos. 1308/40 and 1342/6.
CP1346a Collectors Pack... 37·00

Post Office Yearbook
1986 Nov 18 Comprises Nos. 1308/46 in 32-page hardbound book with slip case, illustrated in colour... 70·00

817 North American   **818** Globe Thistle
Blanket Flower

819 Echeveria   **820** Autumn Crocus

(Adapted J. Matthews)

1987 (20 Jan). *Flower Photographs by Alfred Lammer. Phosphorised paper.* P 14½×14.

1347	**817**	18p. silver, greenish yellow, rosine, dp green and black	40	10
1348	**818**	22p. silver, greenish yellow, new blue, greenish blue and black......................	70	85
1349	**819**	31p. silver, greenish yellow, scarlet, blue-green, dp green and black.......	1·10	1·25
		a. Imperf (pair)	£8500	
1350	**820**	34p. silver, greenish yellow, magenta, dull blue, dp green and black	1·10	1·25
Set of 4			3·25	3·25
Set of 4 Gutter Pairs...			7·50	
First Day Cover				3·50
Presentation Pack (P.O. Pack No. 178)			4·00	
P.H.Q. Cards (set of 4) (99)			3·00	7·00

Special First Day of Issue Postmarks

Philatelic Bureau, Edinburgh ....4·00
Richmond, Surrey..4·50

821 The Principia   **822** Motion of Bodies
Mathematica   in Ellipses

823 Optick Treatise   **824** The System of the
World

(Des Sarah Godwin)

1987 (24 Mar–2 Dec). *300th Anniv of "The Principia Mathematica" by Sir Isaac Newton. Phosphorised paper.* P 14×15.

1351	**821**	18p. black, greenish yellow, cerise, blue-green, grey-black and silver..............	50	15
		a. Imperf (pair)	£8000	
1352	**822**	22p. black, greenish yellow, brt orange, blue, brt emerald, silver and bluish violet	75	75
1353	**823**	31p. black, greenish yellow, scarlet, new blue, bronze-green, silver and slate-green	1·25	1·50
1354	**824**	34p. black, greenish yellow, red, brt blue, grey-black and silver	1·25	1·25
Set of 4			3·50	3·25
Set of 4 Gutter Pairs...			8·00	
First Day Cover				3·75
Presentation Pack (P.O. Pack No. 179)			4·00	
P.H.Q. Cards (set of 4) (100)			3·00	6·50

Special First Day of Issue Postmarks

Philatelic Bureau, Edinburgh .... 4·00
Woolsthorpe, Lincs .... 4·25

825 Willis Faber and Dumas   **826** Pompidou Centre, Paris
Building, Ipswich

827 Staatsgalerie, Stuttgart   **828** European Investment Bank,
Luxembourg

(Des B. Tattersfield)

1987 (12 May). *Europa. British Architects in Europe. Phosphorised paper.*
P 15×14.

1355	**825**	18p. black, bistre-yellow, cerise, brt blue, dp grey and grey-black	50	15
1356	**826**	22p. black, greenish yellow, carmine, brt blue, dp grey and grey-black	75	75
1357	**827**	31p. grey-black, bistre-yellow, cerise, brt blue, brt green, black and dull violet	1·25	1·25
		a. Imperf (horiz pair)	£8500	
1358	**828**	34p. black, greenish yellow, cerise, brt blue, grey-black and dp grey	1·75	1·25
Set of 4			4·00	3·25
Set of 4 Gutter Pairs...............................			9·50	
First Day Cover				3·75
Presentation Pack (P.O. Pack No. 180) ...			4·00	
P.H.Q. Cards (set of 4) (101)			3·00	6·50

Special First Day of Issue Postmarks

Philatelic Bureau, Edinburgh ....4·00
Ipswich ....4·00

829 Brigade Members with Ashford Litter, 1887

830 Bandaging Blitz Victim, 1940

831 Volunteer with fainting Girl, 1965

832 Transport of Transplant Organ by Air Wing, 1987

(Des Debbie Cook. Litho Questa)

1987 (16 June). *Centenary of St. John Ambulance Brigade. Phosphorised paper.* P 14×14½.

1359	**829**	18p. new blue, greenish yellow, magenta, black, silver and pink....................	40	25
		Ea. Black ptg double..................................	†	£1200
		Eb. Black ptg triple....................................	†	£1700
1360	**830**	22p. new blue, greenish yellow, magenta, black, silver and cobalt.................	60	75
1361	**831**	31p. new blue, greenish yellow, magenta, black, silver and bistre-brown	1·25	1·25
1362	**832**	34p. new blue, greenish yellow, magenta, black, silver and greenish grey	1·25	1·25
Set of 4			3·25	3·25
Set of 4 Gutter Pairs...............................			7·50	
First Day Cover				3·75
Presentation Pack (P.O. Pack No. 181) ...			4·00	
P.H.Q. Cards (set of 4) (102)			3·00	6·50

Special First Day of Issue Postmarks

Philatelic Bureau, Edinburgh ....4·00
London, EC1 ....4·00

833 Arms of the Lord Lyon King of Arms

834 Scottish Heraldic Banner of Prince Charles

835 Arms of Royal Scottish Academy of Painting, Sculpture and Architecture

836 Arms of Royal Society of Edinburgh

(Des J. Matthews)

1987 (21 July). *300th Anniv of Revival of Order of the Thistle. Phosphorised paper.* P 14½.

1363	**833**	18p. black, lemon, scarlet, blue, dp green, slate and brown......................	50	10
1364	**834**	22p. black, greenish yellow, carmine, new blue, dp green, grey and lake-brown	75	90
1365	**835**	31p. black, greenish yellow, scarlet, new blue, dull green, grey and grey-black	1·40	1·40
1366	**836**	34p. black, greenish yellow, scarlet, dp ultramarine, dull green, grey and yellow-brown	1·50	1·40
Set of 4			3·75	3·50
Set of 4 Gutter Pairs...............................			8·00	
First Day Cover				3·75
Presentation Pack (P.O. Pack No. 182) ...			4·00	
P.H.Q. Cards (set of 4) (103)			3·00	6·50

Special First Day of Issue Postmarks

Philatelic Bureau, Edinburgh ....4·00
Rothesay, Isle of Bute ....4·50

837 Crystal Palace, "Monarch of the Glen" (Landseer) and Grace Darling

838 *Great Eastern, Beeton's Book of Household Management* and Prince Albert

839 Albert Memorial, Ballot Box and Disraeli

840 Diamond Jubilee Emblem, Newspaper Placard for Relief of Mafeking and Morse Key

(Des M. Dempsey. Eng C. Slania. Recess and photo)

1987 (8 Sept). *150th Anniv of Queen Victoria's Accession. Phosphorised paper.* P 15×14.

1367	**837**	18p. pale stone, dp blue, lemon, rose, greenish blue, brown-ochre and grey-black	50	10
1368	**838**	22p. pale stone, dp brown, lemon, rose, grey-black & brown-ochre	80	75
1369	**839**	31p. pale stone, dp lilac, lemon, cerise, brown-ochre, greenish blue and grey-black	1·25	1·50
1370	**840**	34p. pale stone, myrtle-green, yellow-ochre, reddish brown and brown-ochre	1·35	1·60

Set of 4 .... 3·50 3·50
Set of 4 Gutter Pairs .... 9·00
First Day Cover .... 3·75
Presentation Pack (P.O. Pack No. 183) .... 4·25
P.H.Q. Cards (set of 4) (104) .... 3·00 6·50

Special First Day of Issue Postmarks

Philatelic Bureau, Edinburgh .... 4·00
Newport, Isle of Wight .... 4·50

841 Pot by Bernard Leach

842 Pot by Elizabeth Fritsch

843 Pot by Lucie Rie

844 Pot by Hans Coper

(Des T. Evans)

1987 (13 Oct). *Studio Pottery. Phosphorised paper.* P 14½×14.

1371	**841**	18p. gold, lemon, lt red-brown, chestnut, lt grey and black	50	25
1372	**842**	26p. blue over silver, yellow-orange, brt purple, lavender, bluish violet, grey-brown and black	70	75
1373	**843**	31p. rose-lilac over silver, greenish yellow, cerise, new blue, grey-lilac and black	1·25	1·25
1374	**844**	34p. copper, yellow-brown, reddish brown, grey-lilac and black	1·40	1·50
		a. Imperf (pair)	£6500	

Set of 4 .... 3·50 3·50
Set of 4 Gutter Pairs .... 8·50

First Day Cover .... 3·75
Presentation Pack (P.O. Pack No. 184) .... 3·50
P.H.Q. Cards (set of 4) (105) .... 3·00 6·50

Special First Day of Issue Postmarks

Philatelic Bureau, Edinburgh .... 4·00
St. Ives, Cornwall .... 4·00

845 Decorating the Christmas Tree

846 Waiting for Father Christmas

847 Sleeping Child and Father Christmas in Sleigh

848 Child reading

849 Child playing Recorder and Snowman

(Des M. Foreman)

1987 (17 Nov). *Christmas. One phosphor band (13p.) or phosphorised paper (others).* P 15×14.

1375	**845**	13p. gold, greenish yellow, rose, greenish blue and black	30	10
		Eu. Underprint Type 4	95	
1376	**846**	18p. gold, greenish yellow, brt purple, greenish blue, brt blue and black	40	20
1377	**847**	26p. gold, greenish yellow, brt purple, new blue and black	80	1·00
1378	**848**	31p. gold, greenish yellow, scarlet, brt magenta, dull rose, greenish blue and black	1·10	1·25
1379	**849**	34p. gold, greenish yellow, dull rose, greenish blue, brt blue and black	1·25	1·50

Set of 5 .... 3·50 3·75
Set of 5 Gutter Pairs .... 8·50
First Day Cover .... 3·75
Presentation Pack (P.O. Pack No. 185) .... 3·50
P.H.Q. Cards (set of 5) (106) .... 3·00 6·50
Christmas Folder (contains No. 1375Eu×36) .... 17·00

Examples of the 13p. value from special folders, containing 36 stamps and sold for £4.60, show a blue underprint of doublelined stars printed on the reverse over the gum.

Special First Day of Issue Postmarks

Philatelic Bureau, Edinburgh ....4·00
Bethlehem, Llandeilo, Dyfed .... 4·50

Collectors Pack 1987
1987 Nov 17 Comprises Nos. 1347//79.
CP1379a Collectors Pack .... 37·00

Post Office Yearbook
1987 Nov 17 Comprises Nos. 1347/79 in 32-page
hardbound book with slip case, illustrated in
colour .... 35·00

850 Short-spined Seascorpion ("Bull-rout") (Jonathan Couch)

851 Yellow Waterlily (Major Joshua Swatkin)

852 Whistling ("Bewick's") Swan (Edward Lear)

853 *Morchella esculenta* (James Sowerby)

(Des. E. Hughes)

1988 (19 Jan). *Bicentenary of Linnean Society. Archive Illustrations.*
Phosphorised paper. P 15×14.

1380	**850**	18p. grey-black, stone, orange-yellow, brt purple, olive-bistre and gold......	55	10
1381	**851**	26p. black, stone, bistre-yellow, dull orange, greenish blue, gold and pale bistre....................	85	1·00
1382	**852**	31p. black, stone, greenish yellow, rose-red, dp blue, gold and olive-bistre..	1·10	1·25
		a. Imperf (horiz pair)..........................	£5500	
1383	**853**	34p. black, stone, yellow, pale bistre, olive-grey, gold and olive-bistre......	1·25	1·40
Set of 4		....	3·25	3·25
Set of 4 Gutter Pairs		....	8·00	
First Day Cover		....		3·75
Presentation Pack (P.O. Pack No. 187)		....	4·00	
P.H.Q. Cards (set of 4) (107)		....	3·00	6·50

Special First Day of Issue Postmarks

Philatelic Bureau, Edinburgh ....4·00
London, W1 .... 4·50

854 Revd William Morgan (Bible translator, 1588)

855 William Salesbury (New Testament translator, 1567)

856 Bishop Richard Davies (New Testament translator, 1567)

857 Bishop Richard Parry (editor of Revised Welsh Bible, 1620)

(Des K. Bowen)

1988 (1 Mar). *400th Anniv of Welsh Bible. Phosphorised paper.* P 14½×14.

1384	**854**	18p. grey-black, greenish yellow, cerise, blue, black and emerald..................	40	10
		a. Imperf (pair)..................................	£6000	
1385	**855**	26p. grey-black, yellow, brt rose-red, turquoise-blue, black and orange...	70	95
1386	**856**	31p. black, chrome-yellow, carmine, new blue, grey-black and blue.........	1·25	1·25
1387	**857**	34p. grey-black, greenish yellow, cerise, turquoise-green, black and brt violet..	1·40	1·25
Set of 4		....	3·25	3·25
Set of 4 Gutter Pairs		....	8·00	
First Day Cover		....		3·75
Presentation Pack (P.O. Pack No. 188)		....	4·00	
P.H.Q. Cards (set of 4) (108)		....	3·00	6·50

Special First Day of Issue Postmarks

Philatelic Bureau, Edinburgh ....4·00
Ty Mawr, Wybrnant, Gwynedd...4·50

858 Gymnastics (Centenary of British Amateur Gymnastics Association)

859 Downhill Skiing (Ski Club of Great Britain)

860 Tennis (Centenary of Lawn Tennis Association)

861 Football (Centenary of Football League)

(Des J. Sutton)

1988 (22 Mar). *Sports Organizations. Phosphorised paper.* P 14½.

1388	**858**	18p. violet-blue, greenish yellow, rosine, brt rose, new blue and silver............	40	15
		a. Imperf (pair).................................		
1389	**859**	26p. violet-blue, greenish yellow, vermilion, carmine, yellow-orange and silver.....................................	70	80
1390	**860**	31p. violet-blue, greenish yellow, rose, blue, pale greenish blue, silver and brt orange..................................	1·10	1·25
1391	**861**	34p. violet-blue, greenish yellow, vermilion, blue, brt emerald, silver and pink..	1·25	1·25

Set of 4	3·25	3·25
Set of 4 *Gutter Pairs*	8·00	
First Day Cover		3·50
Presentation Pack *(P.O. Pack No. 189)*	4·00	
P.H.Q. Cards *(set of 4) (109)*	2·50	6·00

Philatelic Bureau, Edinburgh	4·00
Wembley	5·00

862 *Mallard* and Mailbags on Pick-up Arms

863 Loading Transatlantic Mail on Liner *Queen Elizabeth*

864 Glasgow Tram No. 1173 and Pillar Box

865 Imperial Airways Handley Page H.P.45 *Horatius* and Airmail Van

(Des M. Dempsey)

1988 (10 May). *Europa. Transport and Mail Services in 1930s. Phosphorised paper.* P 15×14.

1392	**862**	18p. brown, yellow, rose-red, dull blue, dp brown, reddish violet and black	50	15
1393	**863**	26p. brown, yellow, orange-vermilion, dull blue, violet-blue, brt emerald and black	1·00	1·00
1394	**864**	31p. brown, yellow-orange, carmine, dull purple, violet-blue, brt green and black	1·25	1·25
1395	**865**	34p. brown, orange-yellow, carmine-rose, bluish violet, brt blue, sepia and black	1·60	1·50
Set of 4			4·00	3·50
Set of 4 *Gutter Pairs*			11·00	
First Day Cover				3·75
Presentation Pack *(P.O. Pack No. 190)*			4·25	
P.H.Q. Cards *(set of 4) (110)*			2·25	6·00

Trials exist with alternative face values; 19p, 27p, 32p and 35p.

Philatelic Bureau, Edinburgh	4·00
Glasgow	4·50

866 Early Settler and Sailing Clipper

867 Queen Elizabeth II with British and Australian Parliament Buildings

868 W. G. Grace (cricketer) and Tennis Racquet

869 Shakespeare, John Lennon (entertainer) and Sydney Opera House

(Des G. Emery. Litho Questa)

1988 (21 June). *Bicentenary of Australian Settlement. Phosphorised paper.* P 14½.

1396	**866**	18p. deep ultramarine, orange-yellow, scarlet, black, bluish grey and emerald	30	25
		a. Horiz pair. Nos. 1396/7	1·25	1·50
1397	**867**	18p. deep ultramarine, orange-yellow, black, bluish grey and emerald	30	25
1398	**868**	34p. deep ultramarine, orange-yellow, scarlet, black, bluish grey and emerald	60	50
		a. Horiz pair. Nos. 1398/9	2·50	2·50
1399	**869**	34p. deep ultramarine, orange-yellow, black, bluish grey and emerald	60	50
Set of 4			3·50	3·50
Set of 2 *Gutter Blocks of 4*			8·25	
First Day Cover				3·75
Presentation Pack *(P.O. Pack No. 191)*			4·00	
Souvenir Book			15·00	
P.H.Q. Cards *(set of 4) (111)*			2·25	6·00

Nos. 1396/7 and 1398/9 were each printed together, *se-tenant*, in horizontal pairs throughout the sheets, each pair showing a background design of the Australian flag.

The 40 page souvenir book contains the British and Australian sets which were issued on the same day in similar designs.

Philatelic Bureau, Edinburgh	3·75
Portsmouth	4·00

870 Spanish Galeasse off The Lizard

871 English Fleet leaving Plymouth

872 Engagement off Isle of Wight

873 Attack of English Fire-ships, Calais

874 Armada in Storm, North Sea

(Des G. Evernden)

1988 (19 July). *400th Anniv of Spanish Armada. Phosphorised paper.* P 15×14.

1400	**870**	18p. slate-black, yellow-orange, brt carmine, brt blue, turquoise-blue, yellow-green and gold	30	25
		a. Horiz strip of 5. Nos. 1400/4	3·00	3·00
1401	**871**	18p. slate-black, yellow-orange, brt carmine, brt blue, turquoise-blue, yellow-green and gold	30	25
1402	**872**	18p. slate-black, yellow-orange, brt carmine, brt blue, turquoise-blue, yellow-green and gold	30	25
1403	**873**	18p. slate-black, yellow-orange, brt carmine, brt blue, turquoise-blue, yellow-green and gold	30	25
1404	**874**	18p. slate-black, yellow-orange, brt carmine, brt blue, turquoise-blue, yellow-green and gold	30	25
Set of 5			3·00	3·00
Gutter Block of 10			8·00	
First Day Cover				3·75
Presentation Pack (P.O. Pack No. 192)			3·75	
P.H.Q. Cards (set of 5) (112)			2·75	7·00

Nos. 1400/4 were printed together, *se-tenant*, in horizontal strips of 5 throughout the sheet, forming a composite design.

Special First Day of Issue Postmarks

Philatelic Bureau, Edinburgh .... 4·00
Plymouth .... 5·50

875 "The Owl and the Pussy-cat"

876 "Edward Lear as a Bird" (self-portrait)

877 "Cat" (from alphabet book)

878 "There was a Young Lady whose Bonnet..." (limerick)

(Des M. Swatridge and S. Dew)

1988 (6–27 Sept). *Death Centenary of Edward Lear (artist and author). Phosphorised paper.* P 15×14.

1405	**875**	19p. black, pale cream and carmine	65	20
1406	**876**	27p. black, pale cream and yellow	1·00	1·00
1407	**877**	32p. black, pale cream and emerald	1·25	1·40
1408	**878**	35p. black, pale cream and blue	1·40	1·40
Set of 4			4·00	3·50
Set of 4 Gutter Pairs			9·00	
First Day Cover				3·75
Presentation Pack (P.O. Pack No. 193)			4·25	
P.H.Q. Cards (set of 4) (113)			2·25	6·00
MS1409 122×90 mm. Nos. 1405/8 (sold at £1.35) (27 Sept)			7·00	8·50
First Day Cover				8·50

The premium on No. **MS**1409 was used to support the "Stamp World London 90" International Stamp Exhibition.

Special First Day of Issue Postmarks

Philatelic Bureau, Edinburgh (stamps) (6 Sept).................................4·00
Philatelic Bureau, Edinburgh (miniature sheet) (27 Sept).................9·00
London N7 (stamps) (6 Sept)...5·00
London N22 (miniature sheet) (27 Sept)...9·50

CARRICKFERGUS CASTLE
879 Carrickfergus Castle

CAERNARFON CASTLE
880 Caernarfon Castle

EDINBURGH CASTLE
881 Edinburgh Castle

WINDSOR CASTLE
882 Windsor Castle

(Des from photos by Prince Andrew, Duke of York. Eng C. Matthews. Recess Harrison)

1988 (18 Oct). *Ordinary paper.* P 15×14.

1410	**879**	£1 dp green	4·25	60
1411	**880**	£1.50 maroon	4·50	1·25
1412	**881**	£2 indigo	8·00	1·50
1413	**882**	£5 dp brown	21·00	5·50
Set of 4			35·00	8·00
Set of 4 Gutter Pairs (vert or horiz)			70·00	
First Day Cover				35·00
Presentation Pack (P.O. Pack No. 18)			35·00	

For similar designs, but with silhouette of Queen's head see Nos. 1611/14 and 1993/6.

Special First Day of Issue Postmarks

(For illustrations see Introduction)

Philatelic Bureau Edinburgh (Type H) ....40·00
Windsor, Berkshire (Type 1)..45·00

883 Journey to Bethlehem

884 Shepherds and Star

885 Three Wise Men

886 Nativity

887 The Annunciation

(Des L. Trickett)

1988 (15 Nov). *Christmas. Christmas Cards. One phosphor band (14p.) or phosphorised paper (others)*. P 15×14.

1414	**883**	14p. gold, orange-yellow, brt mauve, bluish violet, brt blue and grey-black	45	25
		a. Error. "13p" instead of "14p"	£10000	
		b. Imperf (pair)	£3000	
1415	**884**	19p. gold, yellow-orange, brt violet, ultramarine, rose-red, grey-black and brt blue	50	25
		a. Imperf (pair)	£1900	
1416	**885**	27p. gold, red, dp lavender, dp lilac, emerald, grey-black and brt blue	90	1·00
1417	**886**	32p. gold, orange-yellow, brt rose, dp mauve, violet, grey-black and brt blue	1·10	1·25
1418	**887**	35p. gold, green, reddish violet, brt blue, brt purple and grey-black	1·40	1·25
Set of 5			4·00	3·75
Set of 5 Gutter Pairs			9·50	
First Day Cover				3·75
Presentation Pack (P.O. Pack No. 194)			4·00	
P.H.Q. Cards (set of 5) (114)			3·00	6·00

Examples of No. 1414a were found in some 1988 Post Office Yearbooks.

Special First Day of Issue Postmarks

Philatelic Bureau, Edinburgh	4·00
Bethlehem, Llandeilo, Dyfed	4·50

Collectors Pack 1988
1988 Nov 15 Comprises Nos. 1380/1408, 1414/18.
CP1418a Collectors Pack .... 35·00

Post Office Yearbook
1988 Nov 15 Comprises Nos. 1380/1404, MS1409, 1414/18 in 32-page hardbound book with slip case, illustrated in colour .... 37·00

888 Atlantic Puffin

889 Avocet

890 Oystercatcher

891 Northern Gannet

(Des D. Cordery)

1989 (17 Jan). *Centenary of Royal Society for the Protection of Birds. Phosphorised paper*. P 14×15.

1419	**888**	19p. grey, orange-yellow, orange-red, dull ultramarine, grey-black and silver	25	20
1420	**889**	27p. grey, bistre, rose, steel-blue, lavender, silver and grey-black	1·25	1·25
1421	**890**	32p. grey, bistre, scarlet, orange-red, lavender, silver and black	1·25	1·25
1422	**891**	35p. grey, lemon, rose-carmine, green, new blue, silver and black	1·25	1·25
Set of 4			3·50	3·50
Set of 4 Gutter Pairs			9·50	
First Day Cover				4·00
Presentation Pack (P.O. Pack No. 196)			4·00	
P.H.Q. Cards (set of 4) (115)			3·00	7·00

Special First Day of Issue Postmarks

Philatelic Bureau, Edinburgh	4·00
Sandy, Bedfordshire	5·00

892 Rose

893 Cupid

894 Yachts

895 Fruit

896 Teddy Bear

(Des P. Sutton)

1989 (31 Jan). *Greetings Stamps. Phosphorised paper.* P 15×14.

1423	892	19p. black, greenish yellow, brt rose, red, new blue, lt green and gold......	60	50
		a. Booklet pane. Nos. 1423/7×2 plus 12 half stamp-size labels....................	50·00	
		b. Horiz strip of 5. Nos. 1423/7........	25·00	25·00
1424	893	19p. black, greenish yellow, brt rose, red, new blue, lt green and gold......	60	50
1425	894	19p. black, greenish yellow, brt rose, red, new blue, lt green and gold......	60	50
1426	895	19p. black, greenish yellow, brt rose, red, new blue, lt green and gold......	60	50
1427	896	19p. black, greenish yellow, brt rose, red, new blue, lt green and gold......	60	50
Set of 5			25·00	25·00
First Day Cover				25·00

Nos. 1423/7 were only issued in £1.90 booklets.

Special First Day of Issue Postmarks

Philatelic Bureau, Edinburgh .... 25·00
Lover, Salisbury, Wilts .... 25·00

897 Fruit and Vegetables   **898** Meat Products

899 Dairy Products   **900** Cereal Products

(Des Sedley Place Ltd)

1989 (7 Mar). *Food and Farming Year. Phosphorised paper.* P 14×14½.

1428	897	19p. brownish grey, greenish yellow, rose, new blue, black, pale grey and emerald	45	15
1429	898	27p. brownish grey, greenish yellow, brt carmine, new blue, black, pale grey and brt orange	90	95
1430	899	32p. brownish grey, greenish yellow, rose-red, new blue, black, pale grey and bistre-yellow..............................	1·25	1·40
1431	900	35p. brownish grey, greenish yellow, brt carmine, new blue, black, pale grey and brown-red......................	1·40	1·50
Set of 4			3·50	3·50
Set of 4 Gutter Pairs..................................			8·50	
First Day Cover				3·75
Presentation Pack (P.O. Pack No. 197)			4·00	
P.H.Q. Cards (set of 4) (116)..			2·25	6·50

Special First Day of Issue Postmarks

Philatelic Bureau, Edinburgh .... 4·00
Stoneleigh, Kenilworth, Warwicks .... 4·50

901 Mortar Board (150th Anniv of Public Education in England)   **902** Cross on Ballot Paper (3rd Direct Elections to European Parliament)

903 Posthorn (26th Postal, Telegraph and Telephone International Congress, Brighton)   **904** Globe (Inter-Parliamentary Union Centenary Conference, London)

(Des Lewis Moberly from firework set-pieces. Litho Questa)

1989 (11 Apr). *Anniversaries. Phosphorised paper.* P 14×14½.

1432	901	19p. new blue, greenish yellow, magenta and black	50	25
		a. Horiz pair. Nos. 1432/3..........................	1·50	1·50
1433	902	19p. new blue, greenish yellow, magenta and black	50	25
1434	903	35p. new blue, greenish yellow, magenta and black	75	50
		a. Horiz pair. Nos. 1434/5..........................	2·50	2·50
1435	904	35p. new blue, greenish yellow, magenta and black	75	50
Set of 4			3·50	3·50
Set of 2 Gutter Strips of 4			9·00	
First Day Cover				4·50
Presentation Pack (P.O. Pack No. 198)			4·00	
P.H.Q. Cards (set of 4) (117)..			2·25	6·50

Nos. 1432/3 and 1434/5 were each printed together, *se-tenant,* in horizontal pairs throughout the sheets. Stamps as No. 1435, but inscribed "ONE HUNDREDTH CONFERENCE" were prepared, but not issued.

Special First Day of Issue Postmarks

Philatelic Bureau, Edinburgh .... 5·00
London SW .... 6·00

905 Toy Train and Aeroplanes

906 Building Bricks

907 Dice and Board Games

908 Toy Robot, Boat and Doll's House

(Des D. Fern)

1989 (16 May). *Europa. Games and Toys. Phosphorised paper.* P 14×15.

1436	**905**	19p. black, greenish yellow, vermilion, blue-green, blue, gold and pale ochre	65	25
1437	**906**	27p. black, greenish yellow, reddish orange, blue-green, blue and gold	95	1·00
1438	**907**	32p. black, greenish yellow, orange-red, blue-green, blue, gold and pale ochre	1·40	1·25
1439	**908**	35p. black, greenish yellow, reddish orange, blue-green, blue, gold and stone	1·50	1·25
Set of 4			4·00	3·50
Set of 4 Gutter Strips			10·50	
First Day Cover				3·75
Presentation Pack (P.O. Pack No. 199)			4·25	
P.H.Q. Cards (set of 4) (118)			2·25	6·50

Special First Day of Issue Postmarks

Philatelic Bureau, Edinburgh	4·00
Leeds	5·00

909 Ironbridge, Shropshire

910 Tin Mine, St. Agnes Head, Cornwall

NEW INFORMATION

The editor is always interested to correspond with people who have new information that will improve or correct this catalogue

911 Cotton Mills, New Lanark, Strathclyde

912 Pontcysyllte Aqueduct, Clwyd

912a Horizontal versions of T **909/12**

(Des R. Maddox)

1989 (4–25 July). *Industrial Archaeology. Phosphorised paper.* P 14×15.

1440	**909**	19p. black, bistre-yellow, rose-red, apple-green, lt blue, grey-black and emerald	60	15
1441	**910**	27p. black, bistre-yellow, rose-red, apple-green, lt blue, grey-black and dull blue	1·00	1·10
1442	**911**	32p. black, yellow-orange, apple-green, yellow, dull blue, grey-black and dp reddish violet	1·10	1·25
1443	**912**	35p. black, yellow, brt rose, apple-green, dull blue, grey-black and vermilion	1·25	1·50
Set of 4			3·50	3·50
Set of 4 Gutter Pairs			8·50	
First Day Cover				3·75
Presentation Pack (P.O. Pack No. 200)			4·00	
P.H.Q. Cards (set of 4) (119)			2·25	6·50
MS1444	**912a**	122×90 mm. As Nos. 1440/3, but horizontal. Each black, olive-yellow, brt rose-red, dull blue, apple-green, grey-black and vermilion (*sold at £1.40*) (25 July)	6·00	6·50
First Day Cover				6·50

The premium on No. **MS**1444 was used to support the "Stamp World London 90" International Stamp Exhibition.

Special First Day of Issue Postmarks

Philatelic Bureau, Edinburgh (stamps) (4 July) ....4·00
Philatelic Bureau, Edinburgh (miniature sheet) (25 July) ....7·00
Telford (stamps) (4 July) ....5·00
New Lanark (miniature sheet) (25 July) ....7·50

For Nos. 1445/52 see Decimal Machin Definitives section.

915 Snowflake (×10)

916 *Calliphora erythrocephala* (×5) (fly)

917 Blood Cells (×500)

918 Microchip (×600)

(Des K. Bassford. Litho Questa)

1989 (5 Sept). *150th Anniv of Royal Microscopical Society. Phosphorised paper.* P 14½×14.

1453	**915**	19p. gold, lemon, pale blue, grey, black and grey-black........................	45	25
1454	**916**	27p. gold, lemon, drab, black and grey-black........................	95	1·00
1455	**917**	32p. gold, lemon, orange-vermilion, flesh, black and grey-black............	1·10	1·25
1456	**918**	35p. gold, lemon, black, brt green and grey-black........................	1·25	1·25
Set of 4			3·50	3·50
Set of 4 Gutter Pairs			8·50	
First Day Cover				3·50
Presentation Pack (P.O. Pack No. 201)			4·00	
P.H.Q. Cards (set of 4) (120)			2·25	6·50

Special First Day of Issue Postmarks

Philatelic Bureau, Edinburgh ....4·00
Oxford..4·50

919 Royal Mail Coach

920 Escort of Blues and Royals

921 Lord Mayor's Coach

922 Passing St. Paul's

923 Blues and Royals Drum Horse

(Des P. Cox)

1989 (17 Oct). *Lord Mayor's Show, London. Phosphorised paper.* P 14×15.

1457	**919**	20p. gold, lemon, rose, orange, pale blue and black........................	40	30
		a. Horiz strip of 5. Nos. 1457/61............	3·00	3·00
		ab. Imperf (horiz strip of 5. Nos. 1457/61)........................	£15000	
		ac. Imperf (horiz strip of 4. Nos. 1457/60)........................	£12000	
		ad. Imperf (horiz strip of 3. Nos. 1457/9)........................	£9000	
1458	**920**	20p. gold, lemon, rose, orange, pale blue and black........................	40	30
1459	**921**	20p. gold, lemon, rose, orange, pale blue and black........................	40	30
1460	**922**	20p. gold, lemon, rose, orange, pale blue and black........................	40	30
1461	**923**	20p. gold, lemon, rose, orange, pale blue and black........................	40	30
Set of 5			3·00	3·00
Gutter Strip of 10			8·00	
First Day Cover				3·50
Presentation Pack (P.O. Pack No. 202)			3·00	
P.H.Q. Cards (set of 5) (121)			3·00	6·50

Nos. 1457/61 were printed together, *se-tenant*, in horizontal strips of 5 throughout the sheet. This issue commemorates the 800th anniversary of the installation of the first Lord Mayor of London.

Nos. 1457ab/ad come from a sheet partly imperf at left. Stamps of Types **919/23**, but each with face value of 19p., were prepared but not issued. One mint *se-tenant* strip has been recorded.

Special First Day of Issue Postmarks

Philatelic Bureau, Edinburgh .... 4·00
London, EC4 .... 4·50

924 14th-century Peasants from Stained-glass Window

925 Arches and Roundels, West Front

926 Octagon Tower

927 Arcade from West Transept

928 Triple Arch from West Front

(Des D. Gentleman)

1989 (14 Nov). *Christmas. 800th Anniv of Ely Cathedral. One phosphor band (15p., 15p.+1p.) or phosphorised paper (others). P 15×14.*

1462	**924**	15p. gold, silver and blue	40	15
1463	**925**	15p. +1p. gold, silver and blue	50	40
		a. Imperf (pair)	£3750	
1464	**926**	20p. +1p. gold, silver and rosine	65	80
		a. Imperf (pair)	£3750	
1465	**927**	34p. +1p. gold, silver and emerald	1·25	1·75
1466	**928**	37p. +1p. gold, silver and yellow-olive	1·40	1·90
Set of 5			3·75	4·50
Set of 5 Gutter Pairs			9·00	
First Day Cover				4·50
Presentation Pack (P.O. Pack No. 203)			4·50	
P.H.Q. Cards (set of 5) (122)			3·00	6·00

Trials are known showing different values and including an additional design.

Special First Day of Issue Postmarks

Philatelic Bureau, Edinburgh	4·50
Bethlehem, Llandeilo, Dyfed	4·50
Ely	5·00

Collectors Pack 1989

1989 Nov 14 Comprises Nos. 1419/22, 1428/43 and 1453/66.

CP1466a Collectors Pack	38·00

Post Office Yearbook

1989 (14 Nov). Comprises Nos. 1419/22, 1428/44 and 1453/66 in hardbound book with slip case, illustrated in colour .... 42·00

929 Queen
Victoria and
Queen Elizabeth II

(Des J. Matthews (after Wyon and Machin))

1990 (10 Jan–12 June). *150th Anniv of the Penny Black.*

(a) Photo Harrison. P 15×14.

1467	**929**	15p. bright blue (1 centre band)	80	80

		a. Imperf (pair)	£2500	
		l. Booklet pane. No. 1467×10 with horizontal edges of pane imperf (30.1.90)	10·00	
1468		15p. brt blue (1 side band at left) (30.1.90)	3·75	3·75
		Ea. Band at right (20.3.90)	3·25	3·25
		l. Booklet pane. No. 1468×2 and 1470 plus label	9·50	
1469		20p. brownish black and cream (phosphorised paper)	1·00	1·00
		a. Imperf (pair)	£2000	
		l. Booklet pane. No. 1469×5 plus label with vertical edges of pane imperf (30.1.90)	8·00	
		m. Booklet pane. No. 1469×10 with horizontal edges of pane imperf (30.1.90)	11·00	
		n. Booklet pane. No. 1469×6 with margins all round (20.3.90)	5·00	
		r. Booklet pane. No. 1469×4 with three edges of pane imperf (17.4.90)	8·00	
1470		20p. brownish black and cream (2 bands) (30.1.90)	2·75	2·75
1471		29p. dp mauve (phosphorised paper)	1·75	1·75
1472		29p. dp mauve (2 bands) (20.3.90)	9·00	9·00
1473		34p. dp bluish grey (phosphorised paper)	2·00	2·00
1474		37p. rosine (phosphorised paper)	2·25	2·25

(b) Litho Walsall. P 14 (from booklets).

1475	**929**	15p. brt blue (1 centre band) (30.1.90)	1·50	1·75
		l. Booklet pane. No. 1475×4 with three edges of pane imperf	7·00	
		m. Booklet pane. No. 1475×10 with three edges of pane imperf (12.6.90)	12·00	
1476		20p. brownish black and cream (phosphorised paper) (30.1.90)	1·60	1·75
		l. Booklet pane. No. 1476×5 plus label with vertical edges of pane imperf	12·00	
		m. Booklet pane. No. 1476×4 with three edges of pane imperf	10·00	
		n. Booklet pane. No. 1476×10 with three edges of pane imperf (12.6.90)	15·00	

(c) Litho Questa. P 15×14 (from booklets).

1477	**929**	15p. brt blue (1 centre band) (17.4.90)	2·25	2·25
1478		20p. brownish black (phosphorised paper) (17.4.90)	2·00	2·25
Set of 5 (Nos. 1467, 1469, 1471, 1473/4)			7·00	7·00
First Day Cover (Nos. 1467, 1469, 1471, 1473/4)				7·00
Presentation Pack (Nos. 1467, 1469, 1471, 1473/4) (P.O. Pack No. 21)			9·00	

Nos. 1475/6 do not exist perforated on all four sides, but come with either one or two adjacent sides imperforate.

Nos. 1468, 1468Ea, 1470, 1472 and 1475/8 were only issued in stamp booklets. Nos. 1468Ea, 1470 and 1472 occur in the *se-tenant* pane from the 1990 London Life £5 booklet. This pane is listed as No. X906m.

For illustrations showing the difference between photogravure and lithography see beneath Type **367**.

For No. 1469 in miniature sheet see No. **MS**1501.

For Type **929** redrawn with "1st" face value see No. 2133.

Colour trials are known denominated 19p. in several colours.

Special First Day of Issue Postmark

Philatelic Bureau, Edinburgh (in red)	7·50
Windsor, Berks (Type G, see Introduction) (in red)	8·00

930 Kitten

931 Rabbit

932 Duckling   **933** Puppy

(Des T. Evans. Litho Questa)

1990 (23 Jan). *150th Anniv of Royal Society for Prevention of Cruelty to Animals. Phosphorised paper.* P 14×14½.

1479	**930**	20p. new blue, greenish yellow, brt magenta, black and silver..................	75	50
		a. Silver (Queen's head and face value) omitted	£475	
1480	**931**	29p. new blue, greenish yellow, brt magenta, black and silver..................	1·25	1·25
		a. Imperf (horiz pair).................	£7500	
1481	**932**	34p. new blue, greenish yellow, brt magenta, black and silver..................	1·25	1·50
		a. Silver (Queen's head and face value) omitted	£950	
1482	**933**	37p. new blue, greenish yellow, brt magenta, black and silver..................	1·50	1·50
Set of 4			4·50	4·25
Set of 4 Gutter Pairs			9·50	
First Day Cover				4·25
Presentation Pack (P.O. Pack No. 205)			4·50	
P.H.Q. Cards (set of 4) (123).....................................			3·00	7·50

Special First Day of Issue Postmarks

Philatelic Bureau, Edinburgh ....4·25	
Horsham .... 5·00	

934 Teddy Bear   **935** Dennis the Menace

936 Punch   **937** Cheshire Cat

938 The Man in the Moon   **939** The Laughing Policeman

940 Clown   **941** Mona Lisa

942 Queen of Hearts   **943** Stan Laurel (comedian)

(Des Michael Peters and Partners Ltd)

1990 (6 Feb). *Greetings Stamps. "Smiles". Two phosphor bands.* P 15×14.

1483	**934**	20p. gold, greenish yellow, brt rose-red, new blue and grey-black	70	60
		a. Booklet pane. Nos. 1483/92 with margins all round	30·00	26·00
1484	**935**	20p. gold, greenish yellow, brt rose-red, new blue, dp blue and grey-black....	70	60
1485	**936**	20p. gold, greenish yellow, brt rose-red, new blue, dp blue and grey-black....	70	60
1486	**937**	20p. gold, greenish yellow, brt rose-red, new blue and grey-black	70	60
1487	**938**	20p. gold, greenish yellow, brt rose-red, new blue and grey-black	70	60
1488	**939**	20p. gold, greenish yellow, brt rose-red, new blue and grey-black	70	60
1489	**940**	20p. gold, greenish yellow, brt rose-red, new blue and grey-black	70	60
1490	**941**	20p. gold, greenish yellow, brt rose-red, new blue and grey-black	70	60
1491	**942**	20p. gold, greenish yellow, brt rose-red, new blue and grey-black	70	60
1492	**943**	20p. gold and grey-black............................	70	60
Set of 10..			30·00	26·00
First Day Cover				28·00

Nos. 1483/92 were only issued in £2 booklets. The design of Nos. 1483, 1485/7, 1489 and 1492 extend onto the pane margin.

For Types **934/43** inscribed (1st), see Nos. 1550/59.

SET PRICES. Please note that set prices for booklet greetings stamps are for complete panes. Sets of single stamps are worth much less.

Special First Day of Issue Postmarks

Philatelic Bureau, Edinburgh .... 28·00	
Giggleswick, North Yorkshire .... 28·00	

944 Alexandra Palace ("Stamp World London 90" Exhibition)   **945** Glasgow School of Art

946 British Philatelic
Bureau, Edinburgh

947 Templeton Carpet
Factory, Glasgow

(Des P. Hogarth)

1990 (6–20 Mar). *Europa (Nos. 1493 and 1495) and "Glasgow 1990 European City of Culture" (Nos. 1494 and 1496). Phosphorised paper.* P 14×15.

1493	**944**	20p. silver, lemon, flesh, grey-brown, blue, grey-black and black	50	25
		a. Booklet pane. No. 1493×4 with margins all round (20 Mar)	3·50	
1494	**945**	20p. silver, greenish yellow, dull orange, blue, grey-black and black	50	25
1495	**946**	29p. silver, stone, orange, olive-sepia, grey-blue, grey-black and black	1·25	1·75
1496	**947**	37p. silver, greenish-yellow, brt emerald, salmon, olive-sepia, brt blue and black	1·50	1·75
Set of 4			3·50	3·50
Set of 4 Gutter Pairs			10·00	
First Day Cover				3·50
Presentation Pack (P.O. Pack No. 206)			4·25	
P.H.Q. Cards (set of 4) (124)			3·00	6·00

Special First Day of Issue Postmarks

Philatelic Bureau, Edinburgh		4·00
Glasgow		5·00

948 Export Achievement
Award

949 Technological
Achievement Award

(Des S. Broom. Litho Questa)

1990 (10 Apr). *25th Anniv of Queen's Awards for Export and Technology.* P 14×14½.

1497	**948**	20p. new blue, greenish yellow, magenta, black and silver	40	30
		a. Horiz pair. Nos. 1497/8	1·40	1·60
1498	**949**	20p. new blue, greenish yellow, magenta, black and silver	40	30
1499	**948**	37p. new blue, greenish yellow, magenta, black and silver	50	50
		a. Horiz pair. Nos. 1499/500	3·00	3·00
1500	**949**	37p. new blue, greenish yellow, magenta, black and silver	50	50
Set of 4			4·00	4·25
Set of 2 Gutter Strips of 4			8·50	
First Day Cover				4·50
Presentation Pack (P.O. Pack No. 207)			4·50	
P.H.Q. Cards (set of 4) (125)			3·00	6·00

Nos. 1497/8 and 1499/1500 were each printed together, *se-tenant*, in horizontal pairs throughout the sheets.

Special First Day of Issue Postmarks

Philatelic Bureau, Edinburgh		4·50
London, SW		5·00

949a

(Des Sedley Place Design Ltd. Eng C. Matthews. Recess and photo Harrison)

1990 (3 May). *"Stamp World London '90" International Stamp Exhibition. Sheet 122×89 mm containing No. 1469. Phosphorised paper.* P 15×14.

MS1501 **949a**	20p. brownish black and cream (sold at £1)	5·50	5·50
	a. Error. Imperf	£15000	
	b. Black (recess-printing) omitted	£65000	
	c. Black (recess-printing) inverted	—	
First Day Cover			5·75
Souvenir Book (Nos. 1467, 1469, 1471, 1473/4 and MS1501)		20·00	

The premium on No. **MS**1501 was used to support the "Stamp World London '90" International Stamp Exhibition. In No. **MS**1501 only the example of the 20p. is perforated.

No. **MS**1501b shows an albino impression on the reverse. The 1d. black and Seahorse background are omitted due to one sheet becoming attached to the underside of another prior to recessprinting. No. **MS**1501c shows the recess part of the design inverted in relation to the photogravure of Type **929**.

Special First Day of Issue Postmarks

Philatelic Bureau, Edinburgh (in red)		6·00
City of London (in red)		6·00

A First Day of Issue handstamp as Type B was provided at Alexandra Palace, London N22 for this issue.

950 Cycad and Sir
Joseph Banks Building

951 Stone Pine and
Princess of Wales
Conservatory

952 Willow Tree and Palm House

953 Cedar Tree and Pagoda

(Des P. Leith)

1990 (5 June). *150th Anniv of Kew Gardens. Phosphorised paper.* P 14×15.

1502	**950**	20p. black, brt emerald, pale turquoise-green, lt brown and lavender...........	55	15
1503	**951**	29p. black, brt emerald, turquoise-green, reddish-orange and grey-black..........	75	1·00
1504	**952**	34p. Venetian red, brt green, cobalt, dull purple, turquoise-green and yellow-green...................	1·25	1·60
1505	**953**	37p. pale violet-blue, brt emerald, red-brown, steel-blue and brown-rose..	1·50	1·50

Set of 4 .... 3·50 3·75
Set of 4 Gutter Pairs .... 9·00
First Day Cover.. 3·75
Presentation Pack (P.O. Pack No. 208) .... 4·00
P.H.Q. Cards (set of 4) (126)............................. 3·00 6·00

Special First Day of Issue Postmarks

Philatelic Bureau, Edinburgh .... 4·00
Kew, Richmond .... 5·00

954 Thomas Hardy and Clyffe Clump, Dorset

(Des J. Gibbs)

1990 (10 July). *150th Birth Anniv of Thomas Hardy (author). Phosphorised paper.* P 14×15.

1506	**954**	20p. vermilion, greenish yellow, pale lake-brown, dp brown, lt red-brown and black...................	80	75
		a. Imperf (pair)	£7000	

Gutter Pair.. 1·75
First Day Cover.. 1·50
Presentation Pack (P.O. Pack No. 209) .... 1·50
P.H.Q. Card (127) .... 1·00 2·25

Special First Day of Issue Postmarks

Philatelic Bureau, Edinburgh ....2·00
Dorchester .... 2·50

955 Queen Elizabeth the Queen Mother

956 Queen Elizabeth

957 Elizabeth, Duchess of York

958 Lady Elizabeth Bowes-Lyon

(Des J. Gorham from photographs by N. Parkinson (20p.), Dorothy Wilding (29p.), B. Park (34p.), Rita Martin (37p.))

1990 (2 Aug). *90th Birthday of Queen Elizabeth the Queen Mother. Phosphorised paper.* P 14×15.

1507	**955**	20p. silver, greenish yellow, magenta, turquoise-blue and grey-black.........	95	25
1508	**956**	29p. silver, indigo and grey-blue	1·40	1·50
1509	**957**	34p. silver, lemon, red, new blue and grey-black........................	2·00	2·50
1510	**958**	37p. silver, sepia and stone........................	2·25	2·50

Set of 4 .... 6·00 6·25
Set of 4 Gutter Pairs .... 15·00
First Day Cover.. 6·25
Presentation Pack (P.O. Pack No. 210) .... 7·00
P.H.Q. Cards (set of 4) (128)............................. 5·50 8·00

For these designs with Queen's head and frame in black see Nos. 2280/3.

Special First Day of Issue Postmarks

Philatelic Bureau, Edinburgh .... 6·25
Westminster, SW1 .... 7·00

For Nos. 1511/16 see Decimal Machin Definitives section.

959 Victoria Cross

960 George Cross

961 Distinguished Service Cross and Distinguished Service Medal

962 Military Cross and Military Medal

963 Distinguished Flying Cross and Distinguished Flying Medal

(Des J. Gibbs and J. Harwood)

1990 (11 Sept). *Gallantry Awards. Phosphorised paper.* P 14×15 (vert) or 15×14 (horiz).

1517	**959**	20p. grey-black, pale stone, stone, bistre-brown and brt carmine	80	75
1518	**960**	20p. grey-black, pale stone, flesh, grey and ultramarine	80	75
1519	**961**	20p. grey-black, pale stone, flesh, pale blue and ultramarine	80	75
		a. Imperf (pair)	£3000	
1520	**962**	20p. grey-black, pale stone, ochre, pale blue, ultramarine, scarlet and violet	80	75
1521	**963**	20p. grey-black, pale stone, yellow-brown, bluish grey and purple	80	75
Set of 5			3·75	3·50
Set of 5 Gutter Pairs			9·25	
First Day Cover				3·75
Presentation Pack (P.O. Pack No. 211)			4·00	
P.H.Q. Cards (set of 5) (129)			3·00	8·00

For Type **959** with "all-over" phosphor and perf 14×14½ see No. 2666.

Philatelic Bureau, Edinburgh	4·00
Westminster, SW1	4·75

964 Armagh Observatory, Jodrell Bank Radio Telescope and La Palma Telescope

965 Newton's Moon and Tides Diagram and Early Telescopes

966 Greenwich Old Observatory and Early Astronomical Equipment

967 Stonehenge, Gyroscope and Navigation by Stars

(Des J. Fisher. Litho Questa)

1990 (16 Oct). *Astronomy. Phosphorised paper.* P 14×14½.

1522	**964**	22p. cream, grey, dull blue-green, slate-blue, blue-green, orange-red, gold & black	65	15
		a. Gold (Queen's head) omitted	£800	
1523	**965**	26p. black, yellow, dull purple, pale cream, brown-rose, new blue, greenish yellow, vermilion and gold	1·00	1·10

1524	**966**	31p. black, cream, pale cream, yellow-orange, salmon, lemon, vermilion and gold	1·25	1·40
1525	**967**	37p. black, pale buff, olive-bistre, pale cream, pale flesh, flesh, grey, rose-red and gold	1·50	1·40
Set of 4			3·75	3·75
Set of 4 Gutter Pairs			9·25	
First Day Cover				4·00
Presentation Pack (P.O. Pack No. 212)			4·50	
P.H.Q. Cards (set of 4) (130)			3·00	7·00

Philatelic Bureau, Edinburgh	4·50
Armagh	5·25

968 Building a Snowman

969 Fetching the Christmas Tree

970 Carol Singing

971 Tobogganing

972 Ice-skating

(Des J. Gorham and A. Davidson)

1990 (13 Nov). *Christmas. One phosphor band (17p.) or phosphorised paper (others).* P 15×14.

1526	**968**	17p. gold, greenish yellow, rose, new blue and grey-black	50	15
		a. Imperf (pair)	£3500	
		b. Booklet pane of 20	10·00	
1527	**969**	22p. gold, greenish yellow, magenta, new blue and black	70	20
		a. Imperf (horiz pair)	£3500	
1528	**970**	26p. gold, olive-yellow, pale magenta, agate, new blue, dull violet-blue and black	70	1·10
1529	**971**	31p. gold, greenish yellow, brt rose-red, dull mauve, new blue, turquoise-blue and grey-black	1·25	1·50
1530	**972**	37p. gold, greenish yellow, rose, new blue and slate-green	1·25	1·50
Set of 5			4·00	4·00
Set of 5 Gutter Pairs			10·00	
First Day Cover				4·00
Presentation Pack (P.O. Pack No. 213)			4·50	
P.H.Q. Cards (set of 5) (131)			3·00	7·00

Booklet pane No. 1526b has the horizontal edges of the pane imperforate.

Special First Day of Issue Postmarks

Philatelic Bureau, Edinburgh ....4·50
Bethlehem, Llandeilo, Dyfed ....5·00

Special First Day of Issue Postmarks

Philatelic Bureau, Edinburgh ....5·50
Birmingham ....5·50

Collectors Pack 1990
1990 (13 Nov). Comprises Nos. 1479/82, 1493/1510 and 1517/30.
CP1530a Collectors Pack .... 40·00

Post Office Yearbook
1990 (13 Nov). Comprises Nos. 1479/82, 1493/1500,
1502/10, 1517/30 in hardbound book with slip
case, illustrated in colour YB1530a Yearbook.......... 45·00

978 Thrush's Nest   **979** Shooting Star and Rainbow

973 "King Charles Spaniel"   **974** "A Pointer"

975 "Two Hounds in a
Landscape"   **976** "A Rough Dog"

980 Magpies and Charm Bracelet   **981** Black Cat

982 Common Kingfisher with Key   **983** Mallard and Frog

977 "Fino and Tiny"

(Des Carroll, Dempsey and Thirkell Ltd)

1991 (8 Jan). *Dogs. Paintings by George Stubbs. Phosphorised paper.*
P 14×14½.

1531	**973**	22p. gold, greenish yellow, magenta, new blue, black and drab	50	15
		a. Imperf (pair)	£2800	
1532	**974**	26p. gold, greenish yellow, magenta, new blue, black and drab	75	1·25
1533	**975**	31p. gold, greenish yellow, magenta, new blue, black and drab	1·00	1·25
		a. Imperf (pair)	£4000	
1534	**976**	33p. gold, greenish yellow, magenta, new blue, black and drab	1·25	1·25
1535	**977**	37p. gold, greenish yellow, magenta, new blue, black and drab	1·25	1·25
Set of 5			4·50	4·50
Set of 5 Gutter Pairs.................................			11·00	
First Day Cover				5·00
Presentation Pack (P.O. Pack No. 215)			5·00	
P.H.Q. Cards (set of 5) (132)			3·50	7·00

984 Four-leaf Clover in Boot and
Match Box   **985** Pot of Gold at End of
Rainbow

986 Heart-shaped Butterflies   **987** Wishing Well and Sixpence

(Des T. Meeuwissen)

1991 (5 Feb). *Greetings Stamps. "Good Luck". Two phosphor bands.*
P 15×14.

1536	**978**	(1st) silver, greenish yellow, magenta, new blue, olive-brown and black	70	60
		a. Booklet pane. Nos. 1536/45 plus 12 half stamp-size labels with margins on 3 sides..	15·00	17·00
1537	**979**	(1st) silver, greenish yellow, magenta, new blue, olive-brown and black	70	60
1538	**980**	(1st) silver, greenish yellow, magenta, new blue, olive-brown and black	70	60

1539	**981**	(1st) silver, greenish yellow, magenta, new blue, olive-brown and black....	70	60
1540	**982**	(1st) silver, greenish yellow, magenta, new blue, olive-brown and black....	70	60
1541	**983**	(1st) silver, greenish yellow, magenta, new blue, olive-brown and black....	70	60
1542	**984**	(1st) silver, greenish yellow, magenta, new blue, olive-brown and black....	70	60
1543	**985**	(1st) silver, greenish yellow, magenta, new blue, olive-brown and black....	70	60
1544	**986**	(1st) silver, greenish yellow, magenta, new blue, olive-brown and black....	70	60
1545	**987**	(1st) silver, greenish yellow, magenta, new blue, olive-brown and black....	70	60
Set of 10			15·00	17·00
First Day Cover				19·00

Nos. 1536/45 were only issued in £2.20 booklets (sold at £2.40 from 16 September 1991).

The backgrounds of the stamps form a composite design.

Special First Day of Issue Postmarks

Philatelic Bureau, Edinburgh	19·00
Greetwell, Lincs	19·00

988 Michael Faraday (inventor of electric motor) (Birth Bicentenary)

989 Charles Babbage (computer science pioneer) (Birth Bicentenary)

990 Radar Sweep of East Anglia (50th Anniv of Operational Radar Network)

991 Gloster Whittle E28/39 over East Anglia (50th Anniv of First Flight of Sir Frank Whittle's Jet Engine)

(Des P. Till (Nos. 1546/7), J. Harwood (Nos. 1548/9))

1991 (5 Mar). *Scientific Achievements. Phosphorised paper.* P 14×15.

1546	**988**	22p. silver, olive-brown, greenish yellow, magenta, slate-blue, grey and black	60	50
		a. Imperf (pair)	£750	
1547	**989**	22p. silver, chrome-yellow, red, grey-black, brownish grey and sepia	60	50
1548	**990**	31p. silver, dp turquoise-green, violet-blue, steel-blue and dp dull blue	1·20	1·50
1549	**991**	37p. silver, olive-bistre, rose-red, turquoise-blue, new blue and grey-black	1·40	1·75
Set of 4			3·50	4·00
Set of 4 Gutter Pairs			8·50	
First Day Cover				4·00
Presentation Pack (P.O. Pack No. 216)			4·25	
P.H.Q. Cards (set of 4) (133)			3·50	7·00

Special First Day of Issue Postmarks

Philatelic Bureau, Edinburgh	4·00
South Kensington, London, SW7	4·75

992 Teddy Bear

(Des Michael Peters and Partners Ltd)

1991 (26 Mar). *Greeting Stamps. "Smiles".* As Nos. 1483/92, but inscribed "1st" as T **992**. Two phosphor bands. P 15×14.

1550	**992**	(1st) gold, greenish yellow, brt rose-red, new blue and grey-black	70	60
		a. Booklet pane. Nos. 1550/9 plus 12 half stamp-size labels with margins on 3 sides	12·00	13·00
1551	**935**	(1st) gold, greenish yellow, brt rose-red, new blue, dp blue and grey-black...	70	60
1552	**936**	(1st) gold, greenish yellow, brt rose-red, new blue, dp blue and grey-black...	70	60
1553	**937**	(1st) gold, greenish yellow, bright rose-red, new blue and grey-black	70	60
1554	**938**	(1st) gold, greenish yellow, brt rose-red, new blue and grey-black	70	60
1555	**939**	(1st) gold, greenish yellow, brt rose-red, new blue and grey-black	70	60
1556	**940**	(1st) gold, greenish yellow, brt rose-red, new blue and grey-black	70	60
1557	**941**	(1st) gold, greenish yellow, brt rose-red, new blue and grey-black	70	60
1558	**942**	(1st) gold, greenish yellow, brt rose-red, new blue and grey-black	70	60
1559	**943**	(1st) gold and grey-black	70	60
Set of 10			12·00	13·00
First Day Cover				13·00

Nos. 1550/9 were originally issued in £2.20 booklets (sold at £2.40 from 16 September 1991 and at £2.50 from 1 November 1993). The designs of Nos. 1550, 1552/4, 1556 and 1559 extend onto the pane margin.

The stamps were re-issued in sheets of 10, printed in photogravure by Questa, each with *se-tenant* label on 22 May 2000 in connection with "customised" stamps available at "Stamp Show 2000". The labels show either a pattern of ribbons at £2.95 (LS1), or a personal photograph for £5.95.

A similar sheet, but printed in lithography by Questa instead of photogravure, appeared on 3 July 2001 (LS5). Stamps from this sheet were perforated 14½×14 instead of the previous 15×14. Sheets showing greetings on the labels were available from the Bureau or Postshops at £2.95 each or with personal photographs at £12.95 for two. Similar sheets each containing ten examples of Nos. 1550/1 and 1555/7 were only available with personal photograph. From 29 October 2001 sheets with personal photographs could also be purchased, on an experimental basis, from photo-booths situated at six post offices.

On 1 October 2002 three further sheets appeared printed in lithography by Questa. One contained Nos. 1550/1 each ×10 with greetings labels and cost £5.95 (LS9). Both designs were also available in sheets of 20 with personal photographs at £14.95 a sheet.

SET PRICES. Please note that set prices for booklet greetings stamps are for complete panes. Sets of single stamps are worth much less.

Special First Day of Issue Postmarks

Philatelic Bureau, Edinburgh .... 14·00
Laugherton, Lincs .... 14·00

993 Man Looking at Space   **994** Man Looking at Space

995 Space Looking at Man   **996** Space Looking at Man

(Des J. M. Folou)

1991 (23 Apr). *Europa. Europe in space. Phosphorised paper.* P 14½×14.

1560	**993**	22p. silver-mauve, greenish yellow, scarlet, violet-blue, brt blue, brt green and black	40	30
		a. Horiz pair. Nos 1560/1	1·50	1·50
1561	**994**	22p. silver-mauve, greenish yellow, scarlet, violet-blue, brt blue and black	40	30
1562	**995**	37p. silver-mauve, bistre-yellow, dull vermilion, blue and black	50	40
		a. Horiz pair. Nos 1562/3	3·50	3·00
1563	**996**	37p. silver-mauve, bistre-yellow, dull vermilion, blue and black	50	40
Set of 4			4·00	3·50
Set of 2 Gutter Pairs of 4			12·00	
First Day Cover				4·50
Presentation Pack (P.O. Pack No. 217)			5·00	
P.H.Q. Cards (set of 4) (134)			3·00	7·00

Special First Day of Issue Postmarks

Philatelic Bureau, Edinburgh .... 4·50
Cambridge .... 5·50

997 Fencing   **998** Hurdling

999 Diving   **1000** Rugby

(Des Huntley Muir Partners)

1991 (11 June). *World Student Games, Sheffield (Nos. 1564/6) and World Cup Rugby Championship, London (No. 1567). Phosphorised paper.* P 14½×14.

1564	**997**	22p. black, greenish yellow, vermilion, brt orange, ultramarine and grey	60	20
1565	**998**	26p. pale blue, greenish yellow, red, brt blue and black	1·00	1·00
1566	**999**	31p. brt blue, bistre-yellow, rose, vermilion, new blue and black	1·25	1·25
1567	**1000**	37p. yellow-orange, greenish yellow, rose, brt blue, emerald and black	1·50	1·50
Set of 4			3·50	3·50
Set of 4 Gutter Pairs			9·00	
First Day Cover				4·00
Presentation Pack (P.O. Pack No. 218)			4·50	
P.H.Q. Cards (set of 4) (135)			3·00	7·00

Special First Day of Issue Postmarks

Philatelic Bureau, Edinburgh .... 4·25
Sheffield .... 4·75

1001 "Silver Jubilee"   **1002** "Mme Alfred Carrière"

1003 Rosa moyesii   **1004** "Harvest Fayre"

1005 "Mutabilis"

(Des Yvonne Skargon. Litho Questa)

1991 (16 July). *Ninth World Congress of Roses, Belfast. Phosphorised paper.* P 14½×14.

1568	**1001**	22p. new blue, greenish yellow, magenta, black and silver	50	20
		a. Silver (Queen's head) omitted	£3250	
		Eb. Black printing double	£6500	£4500
1569	**1002**	26p. new blue, greenish yellow, magenta, black and silver	75	1·25
1570	**1003**	31p. new blue, greenish yellow, magenta, black and silver	1·00	1·25

1571	**1004**	33p. new blue, greenish yellow, magenta, black and silver..................	1·25	1·50
1572	**1005**	37p. new blue, greenish yellow, magenta, black and silver..................	1·50	1·50
Set of 5			4·50	5·00
Set of 5 Gutter Pairs....................................			11·00	
First Day Cover...				5·00
Presentation Pack (P.O. Pack No. 219).......................			5·00	
P.H.Q. Cards (set of 5) (136).................................			3·00	9·00

Special First Day of Issue Postmarks

Philatelic Bureau, Edinburgh ....6·00
Belfast .... 7·00

1006 Iguanodon

1007 Stegosaurus

1008 Tyrannosaurus

1009 Protoceratops

1010 Triceratops

(Des B. Kneale)

1991 (20 Aug). *150th Anniversary of Dinosaurs' Identification by Owen. Phosphorised paper.* P 14½×14.

1573	**1006**	22p. grey, pale blue, magenta, brt blue, dull violet and grey-black..................	60	20
		a. Imperf (pair)	£4000	
1574	**1007**	26p. grey, greenish yellow, pale emerald, brt blue-green, pale brt blue, grey-black and black	1·10	1·25
1575	**1008**	31p. grey, lt blue, magenta, brt blue, pale blue, brown and grey-black.....	1·25	1·25
1576	**1009**	33p. grey, dull rose, pale brt blue, brt rose-red, yellow-orange, grey-black and black	1·50	1·50
1577	**1010**	37p. grey, greenish yellow, turquoise-blue, dull violet, yellow-brown and black....................................	1·60	1·50
Set of 5			5·75	5·00
Set of 5 Gutter Pairs....................................			12·00	
First Day Cover...				5·50
Presentation Pack (P.O. Pack No. 220).......................			6·00	
P.H.Q. Cards (set of 5) (137).................................			3·00	9·00

Special First Day of Issue Postmarks

Philatelic Bureau, Edinburgh ....6·00
Plymouth .... 7·00

1011 Map of 1816

1012 Map of 1906

1013 Map of 1959

1014 Map of 1991

(Des H. Brown. Recess and litho Harrison (24p.), litho Harrison (28p.), Questa (33p., 39p.))

1991 (17 Sept). *Bicentenary of Ordnance Survey. Maps of Hamstreet, Kent. Phosphorised paper.* P 14½×14.

1578	**1011**	24p. black, magenta and cream..................	60	20
		Ea. Black (litho) printing treble and magenta printing double..................	£1800	
		Eb. Black (litho) and magenta printing double	£2800	
		Ec. Black (litho) printing double	£2800	
1579	**1012**	28p. black, brt yellow-green, new blue, reddish orange, magenta, olive-sepia and cream....................................	1·00	95
1580	**1013**	33p. dull blue-green, orange-brown, magenta, olive-grey, greenish yellow, vermilion, greenish grey, pale blue, blue, dull orange, apple green and black	1·25	1·40
1581	**1014**	39p. black, magenta, greenish yellow and new blue	1·50	1·40
Set of 4			3·50	3·50
Set of 4 Gutter Pairs....................................			10·00	
First Day Cover...				4·25
Presentation Pack (P.O. Pack No. 221).......................			4·50	
P.H.Q. Cards (set of 4) (138).................................			3·00	7·00

Mint examples of Type **1012** exist with a face value of 26p. (*Price* £6500).

Special First Day of Issue Postmarks

Philatelic Bureau, Edinburgh .... 4·50
Southampton ....5·50

1015 Adoration of the Magi

1016 Mary and Jesus in Stable

1017 Holy Family and Angel

1018 The Annunciation

1019 The Flight into Egypt

(Des D. Driver)

1991 (12 Nov). *Christmas. Illuminated Letters from "Acts of Mary and Jesus" Manuscript in Bodleian Library, Oxford. One phosphor band (18p.) or phosphorised paper (others).* P 15×14.

1582	1015	18p. steel-blue, greenish yellow, rose-red, orange-red, black and gold.......	75	10
		a. Imperf (pair)	£8000	
		b. Booklet pane of 20..............	8·25	
1583	1016	24p. brt rose-red, greenish yellow, vermilion, slate-blue, yellow-green, grey-black and gold............................	90	10
1584	1017	28p. reddish brown, bistre-yellow, orange-vermilion, orange-red, deep dull blue, grey-black and gold	95	1·25
1585	1018	33p. green, greenish yellow, red, orange-red, blue, grey and gold	1·10	1·50
		a. Imperf (pair............................	£10000	
1586	1019	39p. orange-red, greenish yellow, orange-vermilion, dp dull blue, olive-sepia, black and gold	1·25	1·75
Set of 5			4·50	4·50
Set of 5 Gutter Pairs			11·00	
First Day Cover				4·50
Presentation Pack (P.O. Pack No. 222)			4·50	
P.H.Q. Cards (set of 5) (139).....................................			3·00	7·50

Booklet pane No. 1582b has margins at left, top and bottom.

Special First Day of Issue Postmarks

Philatelic Bureau, Edinburgh .... 5·00
Bethlehem, Landeilo, Dyfed... 5·50

Collectors Pack 1991
1991 (12 Nov). Comprises Nos. 1531/5, 1546/9 and 1560/86.
CP1586a Collectors Pack................................ 40·00

Post Office Yearbook
1991 (13 Nov). Comprises Nos. 1531/5, 1546/9 and 1560/86 in hardbound book with slip case, illustrated in colour .... 45·00

1020 Fallow Deer in Scottish Forest

1021 Hare on North Yorkshire Moors

1022 Fox in the Fens

1023 Redwing and Home Counties Village

1024 Welsh Mountain Sheep in Snowdonia

(Des J. Gorham and K. Bowen)

1992 (14 Jan–25 Feb). *The Four Seasons. Wintertime. One phosphor band (18p.) or phosphorised paper (others).* P 15×14.

1587	1020	18p. silver, greenish yellow, grey, dull rose, new blue and black..................	55	25
1588	1021	24p. silver, lemon, rose, blue and grey-black..	75	25
		a. Imperf (pair)	£750	
1589	1022	28p. silver, greenish yellow, bright rose, steel-blue and grey-black.................	1·00	1·25
1590	1023	33p. silver, greenish yellow, brt orange, brt purple, greenish blue and grey .	1·25	1·50
1591	1024	39p. silver, yellow, yellow-orange, grey, vermilion, new blue and black	1·40	1·75
		a. Booklet pane. No. 1591×4 with margins all round (25 Feb)	4·75	
Set of 5			4·50	4·50
Set of 5 Gutter Pairs			11·00	
First Day Cover				4·50
Presentation Pack (P.O. Pack No. 224)			4·50	
P.H.Q. Cards (set of 5) (140).....................................			3·00	8·00

Booklet pane No. 1591a comes from the £6 "Cymru-Wales" booklet.

Special First Day of Issue Postmarks

Philatelic Bureau, Edinburgh .... 4·75
Brecon... 5·50

1025 Flower Spray

1026 Double Locket

1027 Key

1028 Model Car and Cigarette Cards

1029 Compass and Map

1030 Pocket Watch

1031 1854 1d. Red Stamp and Pen

1032 Pearl Necklace and Pen

1033 Marbles

1034 Bucket, Spade and Starfish

(Des Trickett and Webb Ltd)

1992 (28 Jan). *Greetings Stamps. "Memories". Two phosphor bands.* P 15×14.

1592	**1025**	(1st) gold, greenish yellow, magenta, ochre, lt blue and grey-black	70	60
		a. Booklet pane. Nos. 1592/1601 plus 12 half stamp-size labels with margins on 3 sides	13·00	13·00
1593	**1026**	(1st) gold, greenish yellow, magenta, ochre, lt blue and grey-black	70	60
1594	**1027**	(1st) gold, greenish yellow, magenta, ochre, lt blue and grey-black	70	60
1595	**1028**	(1st) gold, greenish yellow, magenta, ochre, lt blue and grey-black	70	60
1596	**1029**	(1st) gold, greenish yellow, magenta, ochre, lt blue and grey-black	70	60
1597	**1030**	(1st) gold, greenish yellow, magenta, ochre, lt blue and grey-black	70	60
1598	**1031**	(1st) gold, greenish yellow, magenta, ochre, lt blue and grey-black	70	60
1599	**1032**	(1st) gold, greenish yellow, magenta, ochre, lt blue and grey-black	70	60
1600	**1033**	(1st) gold, greenish yellow, magenta, ochre, lt blue and grey-black	70	60
1601	**1034**	(1st) gold, greenish yellow, magenta, ochre, lt blue and grey-black	70	60
Set of 10			13·00	13·00
First Day Cover				13·00
Presentation Pack (P.O. Pack No. G1)			17·00	

Nos. 1592/1601 were only issued in £2.40 booklets (sold at £2.50 from 1 November 1993 and at £2.60 from 8 July 1996).

The backgrounds of the stamps form a composite design.

Stay up to date with all things philatelic. Subscribe to **Gibbons Stamp Monthly** – The UK's number one stamp magazine

Philatelic Bureau, Edinburgh	13·50
Whimsey, Gloucestershire	14·00

1035 Queen Elizabeth in Coronation Robes and Parliamentary Emblem

1036 Queen Elizabeth in Garter Robes and Archiepiscopal Arms

1037 Queen Elizabeth with Baby Prince Andrew and Royal Arms

1038 Queen Elizabeth at Trooping the Colour and Service Emblems

1039 Queen Elizabeth and Commonwealth Emblem

(Des Why Not Associates. Litho Questa)

1992 (6 Feb). *40th Anniv of Accession. Two phosphor bands.* P 14½×14.

1602	**1035**	24p. new blue, greenish yellow, magenta, black, silver and gold	50	50
		a. Horiz strip of 5. Nos. 1602/6	6·00	6·50
1603	**1036**	24p. new blue, greenish yellow, magenta, black, silver and gold	50	50
1604	**1037**	24p. new blue, greenish yellow, magenta, black and silver	50	50
1605	**1038**	24p. new blue, greenish yellow, magenta, black, silver and gold	50	50
1606	**1039**	24p. new blue, greenish yellow, magenta, black, silver and gold	50	50
Set of 5			6·00	6·50
Gutter Block of 10			15·00	
First Day Cover				6·00
Presentation Pack (P.O. Pack No. 225)			7·00	
P.H.Q. Cards (set of 5) (141)			3·00	7·50

Nos. 1602/6 were printed together, *se-tenant*, in horizontal strips of five throughout the sheet.

Philatelic Bureau, Edinburgh	6·50
Buckingham Palace, London SW1	7·50

1040 Tennyson in 1888 and "The Beguiling of Merlin" (Sir Edward Burne-Jones)

1041 Tennyson in 1856 and "April Love" (Arthur Hughes)

1042 Tennyson in 1864 and "I am Sick of the Shadows" (John Waterhouse)

1043 Tennyson as a Young Man and "Mariana" (Dante Gabriel Rossetti)

(Des Irene von Treskow)

1992 (10 Mar). *Death Centenary of Alfred, Lord Tennyson (poet). Phosphorised paper.* P 14½×14.

1607	**1040**	24p. gold, greenish yellow, magenta, new blue and black	60	20
1608	**1041**	28p. gold, greenish yellow, magenta, new blue and black	85	85
1609	**1042**	33p. gold, greenish yellow, magenta, new blue, bistre and black	1·40	1·60
1610	**1043**	39p. gold, greenish yellow, magenta, new blue, bistre and black	1·50	1·60
Set of 4			4·00	3·75
Set of 4 Gutter Pairs			10·00	
First Day Cover				4·25
Presentation Pack (P.O. Pack No. 226)			4·50	
P.H.Q. Cards (Set of 4) (142)			3·00	7·00

Special First Day of Issue Postmarks

| Philatelic Bureau, Edinburgh | 4·50 |
| Isle of Wight | 4·50 |

CARRICKFERGUS CASTLE
1044 Carrickfergus Castle

Elliptical hole in vertical perforations

CASTLE

Harrison Plates (Nos. 1611/14)

CASTLE

Enschedé Plates (Nos. 1993/6)

(Des from photos by Prince Andrew, Duke of York. Eng C. Matthews. Recess Harrison)

1992 (24 Mar)–**95**. *Designs as Nos. 1410/13, but showing Queen's head in silhouette as T* **1044**. P 15×14 (with one elliptical hole in each vertical side).

1611	**1044**	£1 bottle green and gold†	5·50	1·00
1612	**880**	£1.50 maroon and gold†	6·00	1·20
1613	**881**	£2 indigo and gold†	8·00	1·20
1613a	**1044**	£3 reddish violet and gold† (22.8.95)	19·00	3·00
1614	**882**	£5 deep brown and gold†	18·00	3·00
		a. Gold† (Queen's head) omitted	£450	
Set of 5			50·00	8·00
Set of 5 Gutter Pairs (vert or horiz)			98·00	
First Day Cover (Nos. 1611/13, 1614)				35·00
First Day Cover (No. 1613a)				10·00
Presentation Pack (P.O. Pack No. 27) (Nos. 1611/13, 1614)			38·00	
Presentation Pack (P.O. Pack No. 33) (No. 1613a)			30·00	
P.H.Q. Cards†† (Nos. 1611/13, 1614) (D2–5)			15·00	15·00
P.H.Q. Cards (No. 1613a) (D8)			10·00	25·00

†The Queen's head on these stamps is printed in optically variable ink which changes colour from gold to green when viewed from different angles.

††The P.H.Q. cards for this issue did not appear until 16 February 1993. The Bureau FDI cancellation is 3 March 1993 (the date of issue of the £10).

The £1.50 (5 March 1996), £2 (2 May 1996), £3 (February 1997) and £5 (17 September 1996) subsequently appeared on PVA (white gum) instead of the tinted PVAD previously used.

See also Nos. 1993/6.

Special First Day of Issue Postmarks

(for illustrations see Introduction)

Philatelic Bureau, Edinburgh (Type H) (£1, £1.50, £2, £5)	35·00
Windsor, Berkshire (Type I) (£1, £1.50, £2, £5)	35·00
Philatelic Bureau, Edinburgh (Type H) (£3)	12·00
Carrickfergus, Antrim (as Type I) (£3)	15·00

OLYMPICS '92 BARCELONA

1045 British Olympic Association Logo (Olympic Games, Barcelona)

PARALYMPICS '92 BARCELONA

1046 British Paralympic Association Symbol (Paralympics '92, Barcelona)

LANDFALL IN THE AMERICAS 1492
CHRISTOPHER COLUMBUS

1047 *Santa Maria* (500th Anniv of Discovery of America by Columbus)

GRAND REGATTA COLUMBUS 1992
OPERATION RALEIGH

1048 *Kaisei* (Japanese cadet brigantine) (Grand Regatta Columbus, 1992)

EXPO '92 SEVILLE

1049 British Pavilion, "EXPO '92", Seville

(Des K. Bassford (Nos. 1615/16, 1619), K. Bassford and S. Paine. Eng C. Matthews (Nos. 1617/18). Litho Questa (Nos. 1615/16, 1619) or recess and litho Harrison (Nos. 1617/18))

1992 (7 Apr). *Europa. International Events. Phosphorised paper.* P 14×14½.

| 1615 | **1045** | 24p. new blue, lemon, magenta & black | 50 | 40 |
| | | a. Horiz pair. Nos. 1615/16 | 2·25 | 1·75 |

1616	**1046**	24p. new blue, lemon, magenta & black	50	40
1617	**1047**	24p. black, grey, carmine, cream & gold .	1·00	75
		a. Cream omitted		
1618	**1048**	39p. black, grey, carmine, cream & gold .	1·40	1·50
1619	**1049**	39p. new blue, lemon, magenta & black	1·40	1·50

Set of 5 .... 4·50   4·50
Set of 3 Gutter Pairs and a Gutter Strip of 4 .... 13·00
First Day Cover........................ 5·00
Presentation Pack (P.O. Pack No. 227) .... 5·25
PHQ Cards (set of 5) (143) .... 3·00   7·00
Nos. 1615/16 were printed together, *se-tenant*, throughout the sheet.

Special First Day of Issue Postmarks

Philatelic Bureau, Edinburgh ....5·00
Liverpool..................................5·50

1050 Pikeman   **1051** Drummer

1052 Musketeer   **1053** Standard Bearer

(Des J. Sancha)

1992 (16 June). *350th Anniv of the Civil War. Phosphorised paper.* P 14½×14.

1620	**1050**	24p. black, stone, bistre, scarlet, indigo, grey-green and yellow-ochre............	60	20
		a. Imperf (pair)	£650	
1621	**1051**	28p. black, yellow-ochre, ochre, rose-pink, blue, dull yellow-green and slate-lilac....................	85	85
1622	**1052**	33p. black, ochre, pale orange, lemon, reddish orange, new blue and olive-green........................	1·40	1·50
1623	**1053**	39p. black, yellow-ochre, yellow, greenish yellow, vermilion, indigo and orange-brown...............	1·50	1·75

Set of 4 .... 4·00   4·00
Set of 4 Gutter Pairs.................. 10·50
First Day Cover....................... 4·00
Presentation Pack (P.O. Pack No. 228) .... 4·50
P.H.Q. Cards (set of 4) (144)............. 3·00   7·00

Special First Day of Issue Postmarks

Philatelic Bureau, Edinburgh ....4·50
Banbury, Oxfordshire ....4·50

1054 *The Yeomen of the Guard*   **1055** *The Gondoliers*

1056 *The Mikado*   **1057** *The Pirates of Penzance*

1058 *Iolanthe*

(Des Lynda Gray)

1992 (21 July). *150th Birth Anniv of Sir Arthur Sullivan (composer). Gilbert and Sullivan Operas. One phosphor band (18p.) or phosphorised paper (others).* P 14½×14.

1624	**1054**	18p. bluish violet, bistre-yellow, scarlet, stone, blue and grey-black................	50	20
1625	**1055**	24p. purple-brown, lemon, scarlet, stone, blue, olive-bistre and black ..	80	20
		a. Imperf (pair)	£700	
1626	**1056**	28p. rose-red, lemon, stone, new blue, bluish violet, brt emerald and black	95	1·00
1627	**1057**	33p. blue-green, orange-yellow, scarlet, olive-bistre, blue, brown-purple and black....................	1·50	1·60
1628	**1058**	39p. dp blue, lemon, scarlet, stone, lavender, olive-bistre and lake-brown................	1·60	1·60

Set of 5 .... 4·50   4·25
Set of 5 Gutter Pairs.................. 10·50
First Day Cover....................... 4·50
Presentation Pack (P.O. Pack No. 229) .... 4·50
P.H.Q. Cards (set of 5) (145).............. 3·00   6·25

Special First Day of Issue Postmarks

Philatelic Bureau, Edinburgh ....5·00
Birmingham ....5·25

1059 "Acid Rain Kills"   **1060** "Ozone Layer"

1061 "Greenhouse Effect"

1062 "Bird of Hope"

(Des Christopher Hall (24p.), Lewis Fowler (28p.), Sarah Warren (33p.), Alice Newton-Mold (39p.). Adapted Trickett and Webb Ltd)

1992 (15 Sept). *Protection of the Environment. Children's Paintings. Phosphorised paper.* P 14×14½.

1629	**1059**	24p. emerald, greenish yellow, pale olive-yellow, brt carmine and black..	70	25
1630	**1060**	28p. vermilion, lemon, brt blue, new blue, brt green, ultramarine and black........	1·10	1·25
1631	**1061**	33p. greenish blue, greenish yellow, brt rose-red, brt green, emerald, blue and black	1·25	1·50
1632	**1062**	39p. emerald, greenish yellow, brt magenta, brt orange, brt blue and black	1·40	1·50
Set of 4			4·00	4·00
Set of 4 Gutter Pairs			10·00	
First Day Cover				4·00
Presentation Pack (P.O. Pack No. 230)			4·50	
P.H.Q. Cards (set of 4) (146)			3·00	6·25

Special First Day of Issue Postmarks

Philatelic Bureau, Edinburgh (in green) ....4·50
Torridon (in green)...5·00

1063 European Star

(Des D. Hockney)

1992 (13 Oct). *Single European Market. Phosphorised paper.* P 15×14.

1633	**1063**	24p. gold, greenish yellow, brt magenta, dull ultramarine and black	1·00	1·00
Gutter Pair			2·25	
First Day Cover				1·50
Presentation Pack (P.O. Pack No. 231)			1·50	
P.H.Q. Card (147)			1·50	4·00

Special First Day of Issue Postmarks

Philatelic Bureau, Edinburgh ....1·75
Westminster ....2·50

1064 "Angel Gabriel", St. James's, Pangbourne

1065 "Madonna and Child", St. Mary's, Bibury

1066 "King with Gold", Our Lady and St. Peter, Leatherhead

1067 "Shepherds", All Saints, Porthcawl

1068 "Kings with Frankincense and Myrrh", Our Lady and St. Peter, Leatherhead

(Des Carroll, Dempsey and Thirkell Ltd from windows by Karl Parsons (18, 24, 33p.) and Paul Woodroffe (28p. 39p.))

1992 (10 Nov). *Christmas. Stained Glass Windows.* One centre band (18p.) or phosphorised paper (others). P 15×14.

1634	**1064**	18p. black, greenish yellow, mauve, ultramarine, brt emerald and gold .	50	15
		a. Booklet pane of 20	7·50	
		b. Imperf (pair)	£150	
1635	**1065**	24p. black, greenish yellow, brt purple, ultramarine, new blue, brt greenish yellow and gold	75	15
1636	**1066**	28p. black, lemon, rosine, ultramarine, reddish lilac, red-orange and gold..	1·00	1·10
1637	**1067**	33p. brt ultramarine, greenish yellow, rosine, brown, yellow-orange, black and gold	1·25	1·50
1638	**1068**	39p. black, lemon, rosine, brt blue, dp violet, yellow-orange and gold	1·25	1·50
Set of 5			4·25	4·00
Set of 5 Gutter Pairs			10·00	
First Day Cover				4·50
Presentation Pack (P.O. Pack No. 232)			4·50	
P.H.Q. Cards (set of 5) (148)			3·00	7·50

Booklet pane No. 1634a comes from a special £3 Christmas booklet and has margins at left, top and bottom.

Special First Day of Issue Postmarks

Philatelic Bureau, Edinburgh ....4·75
Bethlehem, Llandeilo, Dyfed ....5·00
Pangbourne ....5·50

Collectors Pack 1992

1992 (10 Nov). Comprises Nos. 1587/91, 1602/10 and 1615/38.
CP1638a Collectors Pack..45·00

Post Office Yearbook

1992 (11 Nov). Comprises Nos. 1587/91, 1602/10 and 1615/38 in hardbound book with slip case, illustrated in colour .... 55·00

1069 Mute Swan Cob and St. Catherine's Chapel, Abbotsbury

1070 Cygnet and Decoy

1071 Swans and Cygnet

1072 Eggs in Nest and Tithe Barn, Abbotsbury

1073 Young Swan and the Fleet

(Des D. Gentleman)

1993 (19 Jan). *600th Anniv of Abbotsbury Swannery. One phosphor band (18p.) or phosphorised paper (others). P 14×15.*

1639	1069	18p. gold, greenish yellow, bistre, green, vermilion and black	1·25	25
1640	1070	24p. gold, cream, brt green, grey-brown, dull blue and grey-black......	1·10	25
1641	1071	28p. gold, greenish grey, yellow-brown, myrtle-green, brown, vermilion and black	1·40	2·25
1642	1072	33p. gold, ochre, apple-green, olive-brown, brt orange and grey-black ..	1·75	2·50
1643	1073	39p. gold, cream, brt green, cobalt, lt brown and black	1·90	2·50
Set of 5			6·50	7·50
Set of 5 Gutter Pairs			15·00	
First Day Cover				7·50
Presentation Pack (P.O. Pack No. 234)			7·00	
P.H.Q. Cards (set of 5) (149)			4·25	8·50

Special First Day of Issue Postmarks

Philatelic Bureau, Edinburgh ....7·50
Abbotsbury, Dorset..7·50

1074 Long John Silver and Parrot (*Treasure Island*)

1075 Tweedledum and Tweedledee (*Alice Through the Looking-Glass*)

1076 William (*William* books)

1077 Mole and Toad (*The Wind in the Willows*)

1078 Teacher and Wilfrid ("*The Bash Street Kids*")

1079 Peter Rabbit and Mrs. Rabbit (*The Tale of Peter Rabbit*)

1080 Snowman (*The Snowman*) and Father Christmas (*Father Christmas*)

1081 The Big Friendly Giant and Sophie (*The BFG*)

1082 Bill Badger and Rupert Bear

1083 Aladdin and the Genie

(Des Newell and Sorell)

1993 (2 Feb–10 Aug). *Greetings Stamps. "Gift Giving". Two phosphor bands. P 15×14 (with one elliptical hole in each horizontal side).*

1644	1074	(1st) gold, greenish yellow, magenta, pale brown, light blue and black......	70	50
		a. Booklet pane. Nos. 1644/53................	11·00	12·00
1645	1075	(1st) gold, cream and black	70	50
1646	1076	(1st) gold, greenish yellow, magenta, cream, new blue and black...............	70	50
1647	1077	(1st) gold, greenish yellow, magenta, cream, new blue and black...............	70	50
1648	1078	(1st) gold, greenish yellow, magenta, cream, new blue and black...............	70	50
1649	1079	(1st) gold, greenish yellow, magenta, cream, new blue and black...............	70	50
		a. Booklet pane. No. 1649×4 with margins all round (10 Aug)	4·75	
1650	1080	(1st) gold, greenish yellow, magenta, cream, new blue and black................	70	50
1651	1081	(1st) gold, greenish yellow, magenta, cream, new blue and black................	70	50
1652	1082	(1st) gold, greenish yellow, magenta, cream, new blue and black................	70	50
1653	1083	(1st) gold, greenish yellow, magenta, cream, new blue and black................	70	50
Set of 10			11·00	12·00
First Day Cover				12·00
Presentation Pack (P.O. Pack No. G2).........................			16·00	
P.H.Q. Cards (set of 10) (GS1).......................................			16·00	30·00

Nos. 1644/53 were issued in £2.40 booklets (sold at £2.50 from 1 November 1993), together with a pane of 20 half stamp-sized labels. The stamps and labels were affixed to the booklet cover by a common gutter margin.

Booklet pane No. 1649a comes from the £6 (£5.64) Beatrix Potter booklet.

> **SET PRICES.** Please note that set prices for booklet greetings stamps are for complete panes. Sets of single stamps are worth much less.

Special First Day of Issue Postmarks

Philatelic Bureau, Edinburgh (No. 1644a) (2 Feb)......................................12·00
Greetland (No. 1644a) (2 Feb).. 12·00
Philatelic Bureau, Edinburgh (No. 1649a) (10 Aug) ....6·00
Keswick (No. 1649a) (10 Aug)...6·00

1084 Decorated Enamel Dial

1085 Escapement, Remontoire and Fusée

1086 Balance, Spring and Temperature Compensator

1087 Back of Movement

(Des H. Brown and D. Penny. Litho Questa)

1993 (16 Feb). *300th Birth Anniv of John Harrison (inventor of the marine chronometer). Details of "H4" Clock.* Phosphorised paper. P 14½×14.

1654	**1084**	24p. new blue, greenish yellow, magenta, black, grey-black and grey cream	60	25
1655	**1085**	28p. new blue, greenish yellow, magenta, black, grey-black and pale cream	1·00	1·25
1656	**1086**	33p. new blue, greenish yellow, magenta, black, grey-black and pale cream	1·10	1·25
1657	**1087**	39p. new blue, greenish yellow, magenta, black, grey-black and pale cream	1·50	1·50

Set of 4 .... 4·00 | 4·00
Set of 4 Gutter Pairs .... 10·00
First Day Cover .... | 4·00
Presentation Pack (P.O. Pack No. 235) .... 4·25
P.H.Q. Cards (set of 4) (150).. 4·25 | 7·00

Special First Day of Issue Postmarks

Philatelic Bureau, Edinburgh ....4·25
Greenwich...4·75

1088 Britannia

(Des B. Craddock, adapted Roundel Design Group. Litho (silver die-stamped, Braille symbol for "10" embossed) Questa)

1993 (2 Mar). *Granite paper.* P 14×14½ (with two elliptical holes in each horizontal side).

1658	**1088**	£10 greenish grey, rosine, yellow, new blue, reddish violet, vermilion, violet, brt green and silver	40·00	12·00
		a. Silver omitted..	£4000	
		b. Braille symbol for "10" omitted		

First Day Cover .... | 25·00
Presentation Pack (P.O. Pack No. 28) .... 45·00
P.H.Q. Card (D1) .... 8·00 | 60·00

The paper used for No. 1658 contains fluorescent coloured fibres which, together with the ink used on the shield, react under U.V. light.

Special First Day of Issue Postmarks

Philatelic Bureau, Edinburgh .... 26·00
Windsor.. 28·00

1089 *Dendrobium hellwigianum*

1090 *Paphiopedilum Maudiae "Magnificum"*

1091 *Cymbidium lowianum*

1092 *Vanda Rothschildiana*

1093 *Dendrobium vexillarius var albiviride*

(Des Pandora Sellars)

1993 (16 Mar). *14th World Orchid Conference, Glasgow. One phosphor band (18p.) or phosphorised paper (others).* P 15×14.

1659	**1089**	18p. green, greenish yellow, magenta, pale blue, apple-green and slate.....	45	25
		a. Imperf (pair)	£7000	
1660	**1090**	24p. green, greenish yellow, brt green and grey-black..................................	75	25
1661	**1091**	28p. green, greenish yellow, red, brt turquoise-blue and drab...................	1·00	1·25
1662	**1092**	33p. green, greenish yellow, pale magenta, brt violet, brt green and grey..	1·25	1·50
		a. Copyright logo and "1993" omitted (R. 10/6, dot pane)............................	15·00	15·00
1663	**1093**	39p. green, greenish yellow, red, pale olive-yellow, brt green, violet and grey-black.......................................	1·60	1·50
Set of 5			4·50	4·50
Set of 5 Gutter Pairs			10·00	
First Day Cover				4·50
Presentation Pack (P.O. Pack No. 236)			5·00	
P.H.Q. Cards (set of 5) (151).................................			4·50	7·00

Special First Day of Issue Postmarks

Philatelic Bureau, Edinburgh	4·50
Glasgow	5·50

For Nos. 1664/72 and Y1667/1803 see Decimal Machin Definitives section.

1094 "Family Group" (bronze sculpture) (Henry Moore)

1095 "Kew Gardens" (lithograph) (Edward Bawden)

1096 "St. Francis and the Birds" (Stanley Spencer)

1097 "Still Life: Odyssey I" (Ben Nicholson)

(Des. A. Dastor)

1993 (11 May). *Europa. Contemporary Art. Phosphorised paper.* P 14×14½.

1767	**1094**	24p. brownish grey, lemon, magenta, turquoise-blue and grey-black...........	60	20
1768	**1095**	28p. brownish grey, buff, lt green, yellow-brown, brt orange, new blue and grey-black..................................	90	1·00

1769	**1096**	33p. brownish grey, cream, greenish yellow, magenta, new blue and grey-black..	1·25	1·40
1770	**1097**	39p. brownish grey, cream, yellow ochre, rose-lilac, red, lt blue and grey-black.	1·75	1·75
Set of 4			4·00	4·00
Set of 4 Gutter Pairs...			10·00	
First Day Cover				4·50
Presentation Pack (P.O. Pack No. 237)			4·50	
PHQ Cards (set of 4) (152)			4·00	7·00

Special First Day of Issue Postmarks

British Philatelic Bureau, Edinburgh	4·75
London SW	5·00

1098 Emperor Claudius (from gold coin)

1099 Emperor Hadrian (bronze head)

1100 Goddess Roma (from gemstone)

1101 Christ (Hinton St. Mary mosaic)

(Des J. Gibbs)

1993 (15 June). *Roman Britain. Phosphorised paper with two phosphor bands.* P 14×14½.

1771	**1098**	24p. black, pale orange, lt brown and silver	60	20
1772	**1099**	28p. black, greenish yellow, brt rose-red, silver, brt blue and grey-black..	90	1·00
1773	**1100**	33p. black, greenish yellow, brt rose-red, silver and grey........................	1·30	1·50
1774	**1101**	39p. black, greenish yellow, rosine, silver, pale violet and grey.................	1·50	1·60
Set of 4			4·00	4·00
Set of 4 Gutter Pairs...			10·00	
First Day Cover				4·00
Presentation Pack (P.O. Pack No. 238)			4·50	
PHQ Cards (set of 4) (153)			4·25	7·00

Special First Day of Issue Postmarks

British Philatelic Bureau, Edinburgh	4·50
Caerllion	4·50

1102 *Midland Maid* and other Narrow Boats, Grand Junction Canal

1103 *Yorkshire Lass* and other Humber Keels, Stainforth and Keadby Canal

1104 *Valley Princess* and other Horse-drawn Barges, Brecknock and Abergavenny Canal

1105 Steam Barges, including *Pride of Scotland*, and Fishing Boats, Crinan Canal

(Des T. Lewery. Litho Questa)

1993 (20 July). *Inland Waterways*. Two phosphor bands. P 14½×14.

1775	**1102**	24p.	new blue, greenish yellow, brt magenta, black, blue, vermilion, brownish grey and sage-green	50	20
1776	**1103**	28p.	new blue, greenish yellow, brt magenta, black, blue, bluish grey, vermilion and sage-green	1·00	1·00
1777	**1104**	33p.	new blue, greenish yellow, brt magenta, black, blue, vermilion, greenish grey and sage-green	1·25	1·25
1778	**1105**	39p.	new blue, greenish yellow, brt magenta, black, blue, vermilion, sage-green and dull mauve	1·50	1·40

Set of 4 .... 3·75 3·50
Set of 4 Gutter Pairs .... 9·00
First Day Cover .... 3·75
Presentation Pack (P.O. Pack No. 239) .... 4·50
PHQ Cards (set of 4) (154) .... 4·25 7·00

Nos. 1775/8 commemorate the bicentenary of the Acts of Parliament authorising the canals depicted.

Special First Day of Issue Postmarks

British Philatelic Bureau, Edinburgh .... 4·00
Gloucester .... 4·50

1106 Horse Chestnut

1107 Blackberry

1108 Hazel

1109 Rowan

1110 Pear

(Des Charlotte Knox)

1993 (14 Sept). *The Four Seasons. Autumn. Fruits and Leaves*. One phosphor band (18p.) or phosphorised paper (others). P 15×14.

1779	**1106**	18p.	black, greenish yellow, cerise, brt green, gold and chestnut	50	20
1780	**1107**	24p.	black, lemon, cerise, myrtle-green, gold, brt green and brown	75	20
1781	**1108**	28p.	grey, lemon, emerald, lake-brown and gold	1·10	1·25
1782	**1109**	33p.	grey-black, greenish yellow, rosine, lt green, gold and brown	1·40	1·50
1783	**1110**	39p.	myrtle-green, greenish yellow, rosine, olive-sepia, gold, apple-green and dp myrtle-green	1·50	1·50

Set of 5 .... 4·75 4·50
Set of 5 Gutter Pairs .... 10·50
First Day Cover .... 4·50
Presentation Pack (P.O. Pack No. 240) .... 4·75
PHQ Cards (set of 5) (155) .... 4·50 7·00

Special First Day of Issue Postmarks

British Philatelic Bureau, Edinburgh .... 5·00
Taunton .... 5·25

SHERLOCK HOLMES & DR. WATSON
"THE REIGATE SQUIRE"
1111 *The Reigate Squire*

SHERLOCK HOLMES & SIR HENRY
"THE HOUND OF THE BASKERVILLES"
1112 *The Hound of the Baskervilles*

SHERLOCK HOLMES & LESTRADE
"THE SIX NAPOLEONS"
1113 *The Six Napoleons*

SHERLOCK HOLMES & MYCROFT
"THE GREEK INTERPRETER"
1114 *The Greek Interpreter*

SHERLOCK HOLMES & MORIARTY
"THE FINAL PROBLEM"
1115 *The Final Problem*

(Des A. Davidson. Litho Questa)

1993 (12 Oct). *Sherlock Holmes. Centenary of the Publication of "The Final Problem". Phosphorised paper.* P 14×14½.

1784	**1111**	24p. new blue, greenish yellow, magenta, black and gold..................	50	40
		a. Horiz strip of 5. Nos. 1784/8.............	5·00	5·25
1785	**1112**	24p. new blue, greenish yellow, magenta, black and gold..................	50	40
1786	**1113**	24p. new blue, greenish yellow, magenta, black and gold..................	50	40
1787	**1114**	24p. new blue, greenish yellow, magenta, black and gold..................	50	40
1788	**1115**	24p. new blue, greenish yellow, magenta, black and gold..................	50	40

Set of 5	5·00	5·25
Gutter strip of 10	11·00	
First Day Cover.............		5·50
Presentation Pack (P.O. Pack No. 241)	5·00	
PHQ Cards (set of 5) (156)	4·50	8·00

Nos. 1784/8 were printed together, *se-tenant*, in horizontal strips of 5 throughout the sheet.

Special First Day of Issue Postmarks

British Philatelic Bureau, Edinburgh	6·00
London NW1	7·50

A First Day of Issue handstamp was provided at Autumn Stampex, London SW1, for this issue.

For Nos. 1789 see Decimal Machin Definitives section.

1117 Bob Cratchit and Tiny Tim   **1118** Mr. and Mrs. Fezziwig

1119 Scrooge   **1120** The Prize Turkey

1121 Mr. Scrooge's Nephew

(Des Q. Blake)

1993 (9 Nov). *Christmas. 150th Anniv of Publication of "A Christmas Carol" by Charles Dickens. One phosphor band (19p.) or phosphorised paper (others).* P 15×14.

1790	**1117**	19p. new blue, yellow, magenta, salmon, brt emerald and grey-black	60	15
		a. Imperf (pair)..	£8000	
1791	**1118**	25p. yellow-orange, brown-lilac, steel-blue, lake-brown, lt green, grey-black and black..................	90	15
1792	**1119**	30p. cerise, bistre-yellow, dull blue, brown-rose, pale green, grey-black and black..................	1·25	1·50

1793	**1120**	35p. dp turquoise-green, lemon, vermilion, dull ultramarine, Indian red, bluish grey and black..................	1·40	1·60
1794	**1121**	41p. reddish purple, lemon, purple, lt blue, salmon, brt green and black....	1·40	1·60

Set of 5	4·50	4·50
Set of 5 Gutter Pairs..	11·00	
First Day Cover..		5·00
Presentation Pack (P.O. Pack No. 242)..	5·00	
PHQ Cards (set of 5) (157)	4·50	8·00

Special First Day of Issue Postmarks

British Philatelic Bureau, Edinburgh	5·25
Bethlehem, Llandeilo	5·50

A First Day of Issue handstamp (pictorial) was provided at the City of London for this issue.

Collectors Pack 1993

1993 (9 Nov). *Comprises Nos. 1639/43, 1654/7, 1659/63, 1767/88 and 1790/4.*

CP1794a Collectors Pack..	45·00

Post Office Yearbook

1993 (9 Nov). *Comprises Nos. 1639/43, 1654/7, 1659/63, 1767/88 and 1790/4 in hardbound book with slip case, illustrated in colour.................* 65·00

1122 Class 5 No. 44957 and Class B1 No. 61342 on West Highland Line

1123 Class A1 No. 60149 *Amadis* at Kings Cross

1124 Class 4 No. 43000 on Turntable at Blyth North

1125 Class 4 No. 42455 near Wigan Central

1126 Class "Castle" No. 7002 *Devizes Castle* on Bridge crossing Worcester and Birmingham Canal

(Des B. Delaney)

1994 (18 Jan). *The Age of Steam. Railway Photographs by Colin Gifford. One phosphor band (19p.) or phosphorised paper with two bands (others).* P 14½.

1795	**1122**	19p. dp blue-green, grey-black & black..	55	25
1796	**1123**	25p. slate-lilac, grey-black and black........	90	95
1797	**1124**	30p. lake-brown, grey-black & black........	1·40	1·50
1798	**1125**	35p. dp claret, grey-black and black	1·75	1·80
1799	**1126**	41p. indigo, grey-black and black	1·80	1·90

Set of 5	6·00	6·00
Set of 5 Gutter Pairs...	12·00	
First Day Cover		6·00
Presentation Pack (P.O. Pack No. 244)	5·75	
PHQ Cards (set of 5) (158)	5·75	11·00

Nos. 1796/9 are on phosphorised paper and also show two phosphor bands.

Special First Day of Issue Postmarks

Philatelic Bureau, Edinburgh ....6·00	
York..6·00	

A First Day of Issue handstamp (pictorial) was provided at Bridge of Orchy for this issue.

1127 Dan Dare and the Mekon

1128 The Three Bears

1129 Rupert Bear

1130 Alice (*Alice in Wonderland*)

1131 Noggin and the Ice Dragon

1132 Peter Rabbit posting Letter

1133 Red Riding Hood and the Wolf

1134 Orlando Marmalade Cat

1135 Biggles

1136 Paddington Bear on Station

(Des Newell and Sorrell)

1994 (1 Feb). Greetings Stamps. "Messages". Two phosphor bands. P 15×14 (with one elliptical hole in each vertical side).

1800	**1127**	(1st) gold, greenish yellow, brt purple, bistre-yellow, new blue and black...	70	50
		a. Booklet pane. Nos. 1800/9	13·00	12·00
1001	**1128**	(1st) gold, greenish yellow, brt purple, bistre-yellow, new blue and black...	70	50
1802	**1129**	(1st) gold, greenish yellow, brt purple, bistre-yellow, new blue and black...	70	50

1803	**1130**	(1st) gold, bistre-yellow and black............	70	50
1804	**1131**	(1st) gold, greenish yellow, brt purple, bistre-yellow, new blue and black...	70	50
1805	**1132**	(1st) gold, greenish yellow, brt purple, bistre-yellow, new blue and black...	70	50
1806	**1133**	(1st) gold, greenish yellow, brt purple, bistre-yellow, new blue and black...	70	50
1807	**1134**	(1st) gold, greenish yellow, brt purple, bistre-yellow, new blue and black...	70	50
1808	**1135**	(1st) gold, greenish yellow, brt purple, bistre-yellow, new blue and black...	70	50
1809	**1136**	(1st) gold, greenish yellow, brt purple, bistre-yellow, new blue and black...	70	50
Set of 10..			13·00	12·00
First Day Cover				12·00
Presentation Pack (P.O. Pack No. G3)..............			18·00	
PHQ Cards (set of 10) (GS2)			16·00	30·00

Nos. 1800/9 were issued in £2.50 stamp booklets (sold at £2.60 from 8 July 1996), together with a pane of 20 half stampsized labels.

The stamps and labels were attached to the booklet cover by a common gutter margin.

Special First Day of Issue Postmarks

British Philatelic Bureau, Edinburgh .... 13·00	
Penn, Wolverhampton .... 15·00	

1137 Castell Y Waun (Chirk Castle), Clwyd, Wales

1138 Ben Arkle, Sutherland, Scotland

1139 Mourne Mountains, County Down, Northern Ireland

1140 Dersingham, Norfolk, England

1141 Dolwyddelan, Gwynedd, Wales

1994 (1 Mar – 26 July). 25th Anniv of Investiture of the Prince of Wales. Paintings by Prince Charles. One phosphor band (19p.) or phosphorised paper (others). P 15×14.

1810	**1137**	19p. grey-black, greenish yellow, magenta, new blue, black & silver...	55	20
1811	**1138**	25p. grey-black, orange-yellow, brt magenta, new blue, silver & black...	1·00	20
1812	**1139**	30p. grey-black, greenish yellow, magenta, new blue, silver & black...	1·10	1·50
		a. Booklet pane. No. 1812×4 with margins all round (26 July)............	5·00	
1813	**1140**	35p. grey-black, greenish yellow, magenta, new blue, silver & black...	1·40	1·75
1814	**1141**	41p. grey-black, lemon, magenta, new blue, silver & black...	1·50	1·75
Set of 5			5·00	5·00
Set of 5 Gutter Pairs...			11·00	
First Day Cover				5·00
Presentation Pack (P.O. Pack No. 245)			5·00	
PHQ Cards (set of 5) (159)			5·75	11·50

Booklet pane No. 1812a comes from the £6.04 "Northern Ireland" booklet.

British Philatelic Bureau, Edinburgh ....5·50
Caernarfon ....5·50

1142 Bather at Blackpool

1143 "Where's my Little Lad?"

1144 "Wish You were Here!"

1145 Punch and Judy Show

1146 "The Tower Crane" Machine

(Des M. Dempsey and B. Dare. Litho Questa)

1994 (12 Apr). *Centenary of Picture Postcards. One side band (19p.) or two phosphor bands (others). P 14×14½.*
1815	**1142**	19p. new blue, greenish yellow, magenta & black....................	60	20
1816	**1143**	25p. new blue, greenish yellow, magenta & black....................	90	20
1817	**1144**	30p. new blue, greenish yellow, magenta & black....................	1·10	1·50
1818	**1145**	35p. new blue, greenish yellow, magenta & black....................	1·40	1·75
1819	**1146**	41p. new blue, greenish yellow, magenta & black....................	1·50	1·75

Set of 5 .... 5·00 5·00
Set of 5 Gutter Pairs .... 11·00
First Day Cover .... 5·00
Presentation Pack (P.O. Pack No. 246) ...... 5·00
PHQ Cards (set of 5) (160) .... 5·75 11·50

British Philatelic Bureau, Edinburgh ....5·00
Blackpool ....5·00

1147 British Lion and French Cockerel over Tunnel

1148 Symbolic Hands over Train

(Des G. Hardie (T **1147**), J.-P. Cousin (T **1148**))

1994 (3 May). *Opening of Channel Tunnel. Phosphorised paper.* P 14×14½
1820	**1147**	25p. ultramarine, brt orange, scarlet, new blue, emerald, turquoise-blue & silver ...	50	40
		a. Horiz pair. Nos. 1820/1	1·75	2·00
1821	**1148**	25p. ultramarine, scarlet, new blue, emerald & silver..............	50	40
1822	**1147**	41p. new blue, brt orange, scarlet, turquoise-blue, emerald, ultramarine & silver.......	60	50
		a. Horiz pair. Nos. 1822/3........	3·25	2·50
		ab. Imperf (horiz pair)	£5000	
1823	**1148**	41p. ultramarine, scarlet, new blue, emerald & silver..............	60	50

Set of 4 .... 4·50 4·50
First Day Cover .... 5·25
First Day Covers (2) (UK and French stamps)...... 20·00
Presentation Pack (P.O. Pack No. 247) ...... 5·00
Presentation Pack (UK and French Stamps)........... 25·00
Souvenir Book .... 50·00
PHQ Cards (set of 4) (161) .... 5·75 9·00

Nos. 1820/1 and 1822/3 were printed together, *se-tenant*, in horizontal pairs throughout the sheets.

Stamps in similar designs were also issued by France. These are included in the joint presentation pack and souvenir book.

British Philatelic Bureau, Edinburgh ....5·50
Folkestone ....8·00

1149 Groundcrew replacing Smoke Canisters on Douglas Boston of 88 Sqn

1150 H.M.S. *Warspite* (battleship) shelling Enemy Positions

1151 Commandos landing on Gold Beach

1152 Infantry regrouping on Sword Beach

1153 Tank and Infantry advancing, Ouistreham

(Des K. Bassford from contemporary photographs. Litho Questa)

1994 (6 June). *50th Anniv of D-Day. Two phosphor bands.* P 14½×14.

1824	**1149**	25p. pink, greenish yellow, blackish lilac, slate-black, brt scarlet & silver-grey	50	40
		a. Horiz strip of 5. Nos. 1824/8	4·25	5·00
1825	**1150**	25p. pink, greenish yellow, blackish lilac, slate-black, brt scarlet & silver-grey	50	40
1826	**1151**	25p. pink, greenish yellow, blackish lilac, slate-black, brt scarlet & silver-grey	50	40
1827	**1152**	25p. pink, greenish yellow, blackish lilac, slate-black, brt scarlet & silver-grey	50	40
1828	**1153**	25p. pink, greenish yellow, blackish lilac, slate-black, brt scarlet & silver-grey	50	40
Set of 5			4·25	5·00
Gutter block of 10			11·00	
First Day Cover				5·50
Presentation Pack (P.O. Pack No. 248)			5·50	
PHQ Cards (set of 5) (162)			5·00	11·50

Nos. 1824/8 were printed together, *se-tenant*, in horizontal strips of 5 throughout the sheet.

Special First Day of Issue Postmarks

British Philatelic Bureau, Edinburgh ....5·50
Portsmouth...5·50

1154 The Old Course, St. Andrews

1155 The 18th Hole, Muirfield

1156 The 15th Hole ("Luckyslap"), Carnoustie

1157 The 8th Hole ("The Postage Stamp"), Royal Troon

1158 The 9th Hole, Turnberry

(Des P. Hogarth)

1994 (5 July). *Scottish Golf Courses. One phosphor band (19p.) or phosphorised paper (others).* P 14½×14.

1829	**1154**	19p. yellow-green, olive-grey, orange-vermilion, apple-green, blue & grey-black	50	20
1830	**1155**	25p. yellow-green, lemon, brt orange, apple-green, blue, magenta & grey-black	75	20
1831	**1156**	30p. yellow-green, yellow, rosine, emerald, blue-green, new blue & grey-black	1·10	1·40
1832	**1157**	35p. yellow-green, yellow, rosine, apple-green, new blue, dull blue & grey-black	1·25	1·40
1833	**1158**	41p. yellow-green, lemon, magenta, apple-green, dull blue, new blue & grey-black	1·40	1·40
Set of 5			4·50	4·25
Set of 5 Gutter Pairs			11·50	
First Day Cover				4·75
Presentation Pack (P.O. Pack No. 249)			4·75	
PHQ Cards (set of 5) (163)			5·75	11·50

Nos. 1829/33 commemorate the 250th anniversary of golf's first set of rules produced by the Honourable Company of Edinburgh Golfers.

Special First Day of Issue Postmarks

British Philatelic Bureau, Edinburgh ....5·00
Turnberry ....5·50

1159 Royal Welsh Show, Llanelwedd

1160 All England Tennis Championships, Wimbledon

1161 Cowes Week

1162 Test Match, Lord's

1163 Braemar Gathering

(Des M. Cook)

1994 (2 Aug). *The Four Seasons. Summertime. One phosphor band (19p.) or phosphorised paper (others).* P 15×14.

1834	**1159**	19p. black, greenish yellow, brt magenta, brown, yellow-brown & new blue	50	20

1835	**1160**	25p. black, greenish yellow, magenta, reddish violet, yellow-green, myrtle-green & new blue	75	20
1836	**1161**	30p. black, greenish yellow, brt magenta, yellow-ochre, dp slate-blue, blue-green & blue	1·10	1·25
1837	**1162**	35p. black, greenish yellow, magenta, slate-lilac, yellow-green, dp bluish green & brt blue................................	1·25	1·60
1838	**1163**	41p. black, greenish yellow, brt magenta, dp claret, lt brown, myrtle-green & brt blue	1·40	1·60

Set of 5	4·50	4·25
Set of 5 Gutter Pairs...................................	11·50	
First Day Cover		4·75
Presentation Pack (P.O. Pack No. 250)	4·75	
PHQ Cards (set of 5) (164)	5·75	11·50

Special First Day of Issue Postmarks

British Philatelic Bureau, Edinburgh	5·00
Wimbledon	5·00

1164 Ultrasonic Imaging

1165 Scanning Electron Microscopy

1166 Magnetic Resonance Imaging

1167 Computed Tomography

(Des P. Vermier and J.-P. Tibbles. Photo Enschedé)

1994 (27 Sept). *Europa. Medical Discoveries. Phosphorised paper.* P 14×14½.

1839	**1164**	25p. greenish yellow, brt magenta, new blue, black & silver.............................	75	25
		a. Imperf (vert pair)	£8000	
1840	**1165**	30p. greenish yellow, brt magenta, new blue, black & silver.............................	1·00	1·25
1841	**1166**	35p. greenish yellow, brt magenta, new blue, black & silver.............................	1·50	1·75
1842	**1167**	41p. greenish yellow, brt magenta, new blue, black & silver.............................	1·75	1·75

Set of 4	4·50	4·50
Set of 4 Gutter Pairs...................................	11·00	
First Day Cover		4·75
Presentation Pack (P.O. Pack No. 251)	4·75	
PHQ Cards (set of 4) (165)	5·75	10·00

Special First Day of Issue Postmarks

British Philatelic Bureau, Edinburgh	5·00
Cambridge	5·00

1168 Mary and Joseph

1169 Three Wise Men

1170 Mary with Doll

1171 Shepherds

1172 Angels

(Des Yvonne Gilbert)

1994 (1 Nov). *Christmas. Children's Nativity Plays. One phosphor band (19p.) or phosphorised paper (others).* P 15×14.

1843	**1168**	19p. turquoise-green, greenish yellow, brt magenta, new blue, dull blue & grey-black..	50	15
		a. Imperf (pair)	£175	
1844	**1169**	25p. orange-brown, greenish yellow, brt magenta, new blue, lt blue, bistre & grey-black..	75	15
1845	**1170**	30p. lt brown, greenish yellow, brt magenta, blue, turquoise-blue, new blue & brownish grey	1·00	1·50
		a. Imperf (pair)	—	
1846	**1171**	35p. dp grey-brown, greenish yellow, brt magenta, turquoise-blue, dull violet-blue, ochre & brown	1·25	1·50
1847	**1172**	41p. blue, greenish yellow, brt magenta, turquoise-blue, lt blue & dp grey....	1·50	1·75

Set of 5	4·50	4·75
Set of 5 Gutter Pairs...................................	10·50	
First Day Cover		4·75
Presentation Pack (P.O. Pack No. 252)	4·75	
PHQ Cards (set of 5) (166)	5·75	11·50

Special First Day of Issue Postmarks

British Philatelic Bureau, Edinburgh	5·00
Bethlehem, Llandeilo	5·00

Collectors Pack 1994
1994 (14 Nov). *Comprises Nos. 1795/1847.*

CP1847*a* Collectors Pack..	55·00

Post Office Yearbook
1994 (14 Nov). *Comprises Nos. 1795/9 and 1810/47 in hardbound book with slip case, illustrated in colour* 55·00

1173 Sophie (black cat)

1174 Puskas (Siamese) and Tigger (tabby)

1175 Chloe (ginger cat)

1176 Kikko (tortoiseshell) and Rosie (Abyssinian)

1177 Fred (black and white cat)

(Des Elizabeth Blackadder. Litho Questa)

1995 (17 Jan). *Cats. One phosphor band (19p.) or two phosphor bands (others).* P 14½×14.

1848	**1173**	19p. new blue, greenish yellow, magenta, black & brown-red............	75	20
1849	**1174**	25p. new blue, greenish yellow, magenta, black & dull yellowgreen	75	25
1850	**1175**	30p. new blue, greenish yellow, magenta, black & yellow-brown......	1·00	1·50
1851	**1176**	35p. new blue, greenish yellow, magenta, black & yellow....................	1·25	1·50
1852	**1177**	41p. new blue, greenish yellow, magenta, black & reddish orange ...	1·50	1·50
Set of 5			4·75	4·75
Set of 5 *Gutter Pairs*			11·00	
First Day Cover				4·75
Presentation Pack (P.O. Pack No. 254)			5·50	
PHQ Cards *(set of 5) (167)*			6·00	11·50

Special First Day of Issue Postmarks

British Philatelic Bureau, Edinburgh	5·00
Kitts Green	5·50

1178 Dandelions

1179 Chestnut Leaves

1180 Garlic Leaves

1181 Hazel Leaves

1182 Spring Grass

1995 (14 Mar). *The Four Seasons. Springtime. Plant Sculptures by Andy Goldsworthy. One phosphor band (19p.) or two phosphor bands (others).* P 15×14.

1853	**1178**	19p. silver, greenish yellow, magenta, green & grey black.................	75	15
1854	**1179**	25p. silver, greenish yellow, magenta, new blue & black.....................	75	15
1855	**1180**	30p. silver, greenish yellow, magenta, new blue & black.....................	1·00	1·50
1856	**1181**	35p. silver, greenish yellow, magenta, new blue & black.....................	1·25	1·50
1857	**1182**	41p. silver, greenish yellow, magenta, new blue, blue-green & black..........	1·50	1·75
Set of 5			4·75	4·75
Set of 5 *Gutter Pairs*			11·50	
First Day Cover				4·75
Presentation Pack (P.O. Pack No. 255)			5·00	
PHQ Cards *(set of 5) (168)*			6·00	11·50

Special First Day of Issue Postmarks

British Philatelic Bureau, Edinburgh	5·00
Springfield..	5·50

1183 "La Danse à la Campagne" (Renoir)

1184 "Troilus and Criseyde" (Peter Brookes)

1185 "The Kiss" (Rodin)

1186 "Girls on the Town" (Beryl Cook)

1187 "Jazz" (Andrew Mockett)

1188 "Girls performing a Kathak Dance" (Aurangzeb period)

1189 "Keppel with her Daughter" (Alice Hughes)

1190 "Children Playing" (L. S. Lowry)

1191 "Circus Clowns" (Emily Firmin and Justin Mitchell)

1192 Decoration from "All the Love Poems of Shakespeare" (Eric Gill)

(Des Newell and Sorrell. Litho Walsall)

1995 (21 Mar). *Greetings Stamps. "Greetings in Art". Two phosphor bands.* P 14½×14 (with one elliptical hole in each vertical side).

1858	**1183**	(1st) greenish yellow, new blue, magenta, black & silver	70	50
		a. Booklet pane. Nos. 1858/67	11·50	11·00
		ab. Silver (Queen's head and "1ST") and phosphor omitted	£15000	
1859	**1184**	(1st) greenish yellow, new blue, magenta, black & silver	70	50
1860	**1185**	(1st) greenish yellow, new blue, magenta, black & silver	70	50
1861	**1186**	(1st) greenish yellow, new blue, magenta, black & silver	70	50
1862	**1187**	(1st) greenish yellow, new blue, magenta, black & silver	70	50
1863	**1188**	(1st) greenish yellow, new blue, magenta, black & silver	70	50
1864	**1189**	(1st) purple-brown & silver	70	50
1865	**1190**	(1st) greenish yellow, new blue, magenta, black & silver	70	50
1866	**1191**	(1st) greenish yellow, new blue, magenta, black & silver	70	50
1867	**1192**	(1st) black, greenish yellow & silver	70	50
Set of 10			11·50	11·00
First Day Cover				11·50
Presentation Pack (P.O. Pack No. G4)			12·00	
PHQ Cards (set of 10) (GS3)			16·00	30·00

Nos. 1858/67 were issued in £2.50 stamp booklets (sold at £2.60 from 8 July 1996), together with a pane of 20 half stampsized labels.

The stamps and labels were attached to the booklet cover by a common gutter margin.

Special First Day of Issue Postmarks

British Philatelic Bureau, Edinburgh .... 12·00
Lover .... 13·00

The National Trust
Celebrating 100 Years **19**
1193 Fireplace Decoration, Attingham Park, Shropshire

The National Trust
Protecting Land **25**
1194 Oak Seedling

The National Trust
Conserving Art **30**
1195 Carved Table Leg, Attingham Park

The National Trust
Saving Coast **35**
1196 St. David's Head, Dyfed, Wales

The National Trust
Repairing Buildings **41**
1197 Elizabethan Window, Little Moreton Hall, Cheshire

(Des T. Evans)

1995 (11 – 25 Apr). *Centenary of The National Trust. One phosphor band (19p.), two phosphor bands (25p., 35p.) or phosphorised paper (30p., 41p.).* P 14×15.

1868	**1193**	19p. grey-green, stone, grey-brown, grey-black & gold	60	20
1869	**1194**	25p. grey-green, greenish yellow, magenta, new blue, gold & black	80	20
		a. Booklet pane. No. 1869×6 with margins all round (25 Apr)	4·50	
1870	**1195**	30p. grey-green, greenish yellow, magenta, new blue, gold, black & slate-black	1·00	1·50
1871	**1196**	35p. grey-green, greenish yellow, magenta, blue, gold & black	1·25	1·50
1872	**1197**	41p. grey-green, greenish yellow, brt green, slate-green, gold, blackish brown & black	1·40	1·75
Set of 5			4·50	4·75
Set of 5 Gutter Pairs			11·00	
First Day Cover				4·75
Presentation Pack (P.O. Pack No. 256)			4·75	
PHQ Cards (set of 5) (169)			6·00	11·50

Booklet pane No. 1869a comes from the £6 "National Trust" booklet.

Special First Day of Issue Postmarks

British Philatelic Bureau, Edinburgh .... 5·00
Alfriston .... 5·25

1198 British Troops and French Civilians celebrating

1199 Symbolic Hands and Red Cross

1200 St. Paul's Cathedral and Searchlights

1201 Symbolic Hand releasing Peace Dove

1202 Symbolic Hands

(Des J. Gorham (Nos. 1873, 1875), J-M. Folon (others))

1995 (2 May). *Europa. Peace and Freedom. One phosphor band (Nos. 1873/4) or two phosphor bands (others).* P 14½×14.

1873	**1198**	19p. silver, bistre-brown & grey-black	70	40
1874	**1199**	19p. silver, bistre-yellow, brt rose-red, vermilion, brt blue & slate-blue	70	40
1875	**1200**	25p. silver, blue & grey-black	1·00	1·00
1876	**1201**	25p. silver, vermilion, brt blue & grey-black	1·00	1·00
		a. Imperf (vert pair)	£20000	

1877 **1202** 30p. silver, bistre-yellow, brt magenta,
pale greenish blue, grey-black & flesh 1·25 2·25
Set of 5 .... 4·25 4·25
Set of 5 Gutter Pairs.................................. 10·50
First Day Cover .... 4·75
Presentation Pack (P.O. Pack No. 257) .... 5·00
PHQ Cards (set of 5) (170) .... 6·00 11·50

Nos. 1873 and 1875 commemorate the 50th anniversary of the end of the Second World War, No. 1874 the 125th anniversary of the British Red Cross Society and Nos. 1876/7 the 50th anniversary of the United Nations. Nos. 1876/7 include the "EUROPA" emblem.

For No. 1875 with the face value expressed as "1st" see No. **MS**2547.

Special First Day of Issue Postmarks

British Philatelic Bureau, Edinburgh .... 5·00
London SW .... 5·50

A First Day of Issue handstamp (pictorial) was provided at London EC4 for this issue.

1203 *The Time Machine*

1204 *The First Men in the Moon*

1205 *The War of the Worlds*

1206 *The Shape of Things to Come*

(Des Siobhan Keaney. Litho Questa)

1995 (6 June). *Science Fiction. Novels by H. G. Wells. Two phosphor bands.* P 14½×14.
1878 **1203** 25p. new blue, greenish yellow,
magenta, black & rosine...................... 75 25
1879 **1204** 30p. new blue, greenish yellow, black,
rosine & violet................................... 1·25 1·50
1880 **1205** 35p. rosine, greenish yellow, violet,
black & lt blue-green......................... 1·25 1·60
1881 **1206** 41p. new blue, greenish yellow,
magenta, black & rosine...................... 1·50 1·60
Set of 4 .... 4·25 4·50
Set of 4 Gutter Pairs.. 10·00
First Day Cover .... 4·75
Presentation Pack (P.O. Pack No. 258) .... 5·00
PHQ Cards (set of 4) (171) .... 6·00 11·50

Nos. 1878/81 commemorate the centenary of publication of Wells's *The Time Machine.*

Special First Day of Issue Postmarks

British Philatelic Bureau, Edinburgh .... 5·00
Wells .... 5·50

1207 The Swan, 1595

1208 The Rose, 1592

1209 The Globe, 1599

1210 The Hope, 1613

1211 The Globe, 1614

(Des C. Hodges. Litho Walsall)

1995 (8 Aug). *Reconstruction of Shakespeare's Globe Theatre. Two phosphor bands.* P 14½.
1882 **1207** 25p. brownish grey, black, magenta,
new blue & greenish yellow 50 40
a. Horiz strip of 5. Nos. 1882/6.............. 4·50 4·75
1883 **1208** 25p. brownish grey, black, magenta,
new blue & greenish yellow 50 40
1884 **1209** 25p. brownish grey, black, magenta,
new blue & greenish yellow 50 40
1885 **1210** 25p. brownish grey, black, magenta,
new blue & greenish yellow 50 40
1886 **1211** 25p. brownish grey, black, magenta,
new blue & greenish yellow 50 40
Set of 5 .... 4·50 4·75
Gutter Strip of 10.. 10·50
First Day Cover .... 5·50
Presentation Pack (P.O. Pack No. 259) .... 5·00
PHQ Cards (set of 5) (172) .... 6·00 11·50

Nos. 1882/6 were issued together, *se-tenant*, in horizontal strips of 5 throughout the sheet with the backgrounds forming a composite design.

Special First Day of Issue Postmarks

British Philatelic Bureau, Edinburgh ....5·75
Stratford-upon-Avon...5·75

NEW INFORMATION

The editor is always interested to correspond with people who have new information that will improve or correct this catalogue

1212 Sir Rowland Hill and Uniform Penny Postage Petition

1213 Hill and Penny Black

1214 Guglielmo Marconi and Early Wireless

1215 Marconi and Sinking of *Titanic* (liner)

(Des The Four Hundred, Eng C. Slania. Recess and litho Harrison)

1995 (5 Sept). *Pioneers of Communications. One phosphor band (19p.) or phosphorised paper (others)*. P 14½×14.

1887	**1212**	19p. silver, red & black	75	30
1888	**1213**	25p. silver, brown & black..........................	1·00	50
		a. Silver (Queen's head and face value) omitted	£900	
1889	**1214**	41p. silver, grey-green & black....................	1·50	1·75
1890	**1215**	60p. silver, dp ultramarine & black.............	1·75	2·25
Set of 4			4·50	4·50
Set of 4 Gutter Pairs			11·00	
First Day Cover				4·75
Presentation Pack (P.O. Pack No. 260)			5·00	
PHQ Cards (set of 4) (173)			5·75	11·50

Nos. 1887/8 mark the birth bicentenary of Sir Rowland Hill and Nos. 1889/90 the centenary of the first radio transmissions.

Special First Day of Issue Postmarks

British Philatelic Bureau, Edinburgh .... 5·00
London EC .... 5·00

1216 Harold Wagstaff

1217 Gus Risman

1218 Jim Sullivan

1219 Billy Batten

1220 Brian Bevan

(Des C. Birmingham)

1995 (3 Oct). *Centenary of Rugby League. One phosphor band (19p.) or two phosphor bands (others)*. P 14½×14.

1891	**1216**	19p. blue, greenish yellow, magenta, new blue, grey-black & black	75	25
1892	**1217**	25p. slate-purple, greenish yellow, magenta, new blue, grey-black & black..	75	30
1893	**1218**	30p. slate-green, greenish yellow, brt purple, new blue, grey-black & black..	1·00	1·50
1894	**1219**	35p. slate-black, greenish yellow, magenta, new blue & black	1·00	1·60
1895	**1220**	41p. bluish grey, orange-yellow, magenta, new blue, grey-black & black..	1·50	1·60
Set of 5			4·75	4·75
Set of 5 Gutter Pairs			11·00	
First Day Cover				4·75
Presentation Pack (P.O. Pack No. 261)			5·50	
PHQ Cards (set of 5) (174)			6·00	11·50

Special First Day of Issue Postmarks

British Philatelic Bureau, Edinburgh .... 5·00
Huddersfield.. 5·75

A First Day of Issue handstamp (pictorial) was provided at Headingly, Leeds for this issue.

1221 European Robin in Mouth of Pillar Box

1222 European Robin on Railings and Holly

1223 European Robin on Snow-covered Milk Bottles

1224 European Robin on Road Sign

1225 European Robin on Door Knob and Christmas Wreath

(Des K. Lilly)

1995 (30 Oct). *Christmas. Christmas Robins. One phosphor band (19p.) or two phosphor bands (others).* P 15×14.

1896	**1221**	19p. silver, greenish yellow, vermilion, orange-vermilion, bistre & black......	60	20
1897	**1222**	25p. silver, greenish yellow, scarlet, pale blue, ochre & black....................	85	30
1898	**1223**	30p. silver, greenish yellow, rose-carmine, lt green, olive-brown & grey...	1·25	1·50
1899	**1224**	41p. silver, greenish yellow, rose-red, dull blue, bistre & black..........	1·60	1·75
1900	**1225**	60p. silver, orange-yellow, red-orange, bistre & black..........................	1·75	1·90

Set of 5	5·50	5·50
Set of 5 Gutter Pairs........................	12·00	
First Day Cover..................................		5·50
Presentation Pack (P.O. Pack No. 262)	5·75	
PHQ Cards (set of 5) (175)................	6·00	11·50

The 19p. value was re-issued on 3 October 2000 in sheets of 20, each with a *se-tenant* label showing Christmas greetings (sold for £3.99) (L52) or a personal photograph (sold for £7.99). These sheets were printed in photogravure by Questa and were sold by the Philatelic Bureau and selected philatelic outlets. Similar sheets were available from 9 October 2001 when the price for a personalised version was increased to £8.75. These could also be purchased, on an experimental basis, from photo-booths at six post offices.

Special First Day of Issue Postmarks

British Philatelic Bureau, Edinburgh	5·50
Bethlehem, Llandeilo	5·50

Collectors Pack 1995

1995 (30 Oct). *Comprises Nos. 1848/1900.*

CP1900a Collectors Pack.................	55·00

Post Office Yearbook

1995 (30 Oct). *Comprises Nos. 1848/57 and 1868/1900 in hardback book with slip case, illustrated in colour* | 55·00

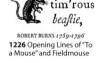

1226 Opening Lines of "To a Mouse" and Fieldmouse

1227 "O my Luve's like a red, red rose" and Wild Rose

1228 "Scots, wha hae wi Wallace bled" and Sir William Wallace

1229 "Auld Lang Syne" and Highland Dancers

(Des Tayburn Design Consultancy. Litho Questa)

1996 (25 Jan). *Death Bicentenary of Robert Burns (Scottish poet). One phosphor band (19p.) or two phosphor bands (others).* P 14½.

1901	**1226**	19p. cream, bistre-brown & black	75	25
1902	**1227**	25p. cream, bistre-brown, black, magenta, bistre-yellow & new blue	1·00	30
1903	**1228**	41p. cream, bistre-brown, black, magenta, bistre-yellow & new blue	1·50	2·00
1904	**1229**	60p. cream, bistre-brown, black, magenta, bistre-yellow & new blue	1·75	2·50

Set of 4	4·50	4·50
Set of 4 Gutter Pairs........................	10·50	
First Day Cover..................................		4·75
Presentation Pack (P.O. Pack No. 264)	5·00	
PHQ Cards (set of 4) (176)................	6·00	11·50

Special First Day of Issue Postmarks

British Philatelic Bureau, Edinburgh	5·00
Dumfries	5·25

1230 "MORE! LOVE" (Mel Calman)   **1231** "Sincerely" (Charles Barsotti)

1232 "Do you have something for the HUMAN CONDITION?" (Leo Cullum)   **1233** "MENTAL FLOSS" (Mel Calman)

1234 "4.55 P.M." (Charles Barsotti)   **1235** "Dear lottery prize winner" (Larry)

1236 "I'm writing to you because...." (Mel Calman)   **1237** "FETCH THIS, FETCH THAT" (Charles Barsotti)

1238 "My day starts before I'm ready for it" (Mel Calman)   **1239** "THE CHEQUE IN THE POST" (Jack Ziegler)

(Des M. Wolff. Litho Walsall)

1996 (26 Feb–11 Nov). *Greetings Stamps. Cartoons. "All over" phosphor.* P 14½×14 (with one elliptical hole in each vertical side).

1905	**1230**	(1st) black & bright mauve......................	70	40
		a. Booklet pane. Nos. 1905/14..............	10·00	11·00
		p. Two phosphor bands (11 Nov)	1·00	60
		pa. Booklet pane. Nos. 1905p/14p	38·00	36·00
1906	**1231**	(1st) black & blue-green...........................	70	10
		p. Two phosphor bands (11 Nov)	1·00	60
1907	**1232**	(1st) black & new blue	70	40

		p. Two phosphor bands (11 Nov)	1·00	60
1908	**1233**	(1st) black & brt violet	70	40
		p. Two phosphor bands (11 Nov)	1·00	60
1909	**1234**	(1st) black & vermilion	70	40
		p. Two phosphor bands (11 Nov)	1·00	60
1910	**1235**	(1st) black & new blue	70	40
		p. Two phosphor bands (11 Nov)	1·00	60
1911	**1236**	(1st) black & vermilion	70	40
		p. Two phosphor bands (11 Nov)	1·00	60
1912	**1237**	(1st) black & brt violet	70	40
		p. Two phosphor bands (11 Nov)	1·00	60
1913	**1238**	(1st) black & blue-green	70	40
		p. Two phosphor bands (11 Nov)	1·00	60
1914	**1239**	(1st) black & brt mauve	70	40
		p. Two phosphor bands (11 Nov)	1·00	60
Set of 10 (Nos. 1905/14)			10·00	11·00
Set of 10 (Nos. 1905p/14p)			38·00	36·00
First Day Cover (1905/14)				11·00
Presentation Pack (1905/14) (P.O. Pack No. G5)			16·00	
PHQ Cards (set of 10) (GS4)			16·00	30·00

Nos. 1905/14 were issued in £2.50 stamp booklets, Nos. KX8/a (sold at £2.60 from 8 July 1996), together with a pane of twenty half stamp-sized labels. The stamps and labels were attached to the booklet cover by a common gutter margin.

These designs were re-issued on 18 December 2001 in sheets of 10, each with a *se-tenant* label showing cartoon comments (sold for £2.95) (LS6). They were re-issued again on 29 July 2003 in sheets of 20 sold for £6.15 containing two of each design, each stamp accompanied by a half stamp-size label showing a crossword grid (clues printed on the bottom sheet margin) (LS13). Sheets of 20 with personal photographs on the labels and a crossword puzzle in the bottom sheet margin were also available, at £14.95 a sheet from Royal Mail, Edinburgh and Post Office philatelic outlets, or £15 a sheet from photo booths.

All these sheets were printed in lithography by Questa with two phosphor bands and perforated 14½×14 (without elliptical holes), and were available from the bureau and other selected philatelic outlets.

Special First Day of Issue Postmarks

British Philatelic Bureau, Edinburgh .... 11·00
Titterhill, Haytons Bent, Ludlow .... 11·00

1240 "Muscovy Duck"

1241 "Lapwing"

1242 "White-fronted Goose"

1243 "Bittern"

1244 "Whooper Swan"

(Des Moseley Webb)

1996 (12 Mar). *50th Anniv of the Wildfowl and Wetlands Trust. Bird Paintings by C. F. Tunnicliffe. One phosphor band (19p.) or phosphorised paper (others).* P 14×14½.

1915	**1240**	19p. sepia, orange-yellow, brown, pale buff, grey & gold	70	25
1916	**1241**	25p. bistre-brown, greenish yellow, magenta, new blue, pale buff, gold & black	90	30
1917	**1242**	30p. bistre-brown, greenish yellow, magenta, new blue, pale buff, gold & grey-black	1·00	1·25
1918	**1243**	35p. sepia, pale orange, lake-brown, brown-olive, pale buff, gold & grey-black	1·10	1·50
1919	**1244**	41p. sepia, greenish yellow, magenta, new blue, pale buff, gold & grey-black	1·50	1·60
Set of 5			4·75	4·50
Set of 5 Gutter Pairs			10·50	
First Day Cover				5·75
Presentation Pack (P.O. Pack No. 265)			5·00	
PHQ Cards (set of 5) (177)			6·00	11·50

Special First Day of Issue Postmarks

British Philatelic Bureau, Edinburgh .... 6·00
Slimbridge, Gloucester .... 6·50

1245 The Odeon, Harrogate

1246 Laurence Olivier and Vivien Leigh in *Lady Hamilton* (film)

1247 Old Cinema Ticket

1248 Pathé News Still

1249 Cinema Sign, The Odeon, Manchester

(Des The Chase)

1996 (16 Apr). *Centenary of Cinema. One phosphor band (19p.) or two phosphor bands (others).* P 14×14½.

1920	**1245**	19p. black, greenish yellow, silver, brt magenta & new blue	50	25
1921	**1246**	25p. black, greenish yellow, silver, brt magenta & new blue	70	30
1922	**1247**	30p. black, greenish yellow, silver, brt magenta & new blue	1·00	1·75
1923	**1248**	35p. black, red & silver	1·25	2·00

1924	**1249**	41p. black, greenish yellow, silver, brt magenta & new blue	1·50	2·25
		Set of 5	4·75	4·75
		Set of 5 Gutter Pairs	11·00	
		First Day Cover		5·75
		Presentation Pack (P.O. Pack No. 266)	5·50	
		PHQ Cards (set of 5) (178)	6·00	11·50

Special First Day of Issue Postmarks

British Philatelic Bureau, Edinburgh ....6·00
London, WC2 ....6·50

1250 Dixie Dean

1251 Bobby Moore

1252 Duncan Edwards

1253 Billy Wright

1254 Danny Blanchflower

(Des H. Brown. Litho Questa)

1996 (14 May). *European Football Championship. One phosphor band (19p.) or two phosphor bands (others).* P 14½×14.

1925	**1250**	19p. vermilion, black, pale grey & grey ...	50	20
		a. Booklet pane. No. 1925×4 with margins all round	3·25	
1926	**1251**	25p. brt emerald, black, pale grey & grey	75	20
		a. Booklet pane. No. 1926×4 with margins all round	3·25	
1927	**1252**	35p. orange-yellow, black, pale grey & grey	1·25	1·75
		a. Booklet pane. Nos. 1927/9, each ×2, with margins all round	8·00	
1928	**1253**	41p. new blue, black, pale grey & grey	1·50	1·75
1929	**1254**	60p. brt orange, black, pale grey & grey	1·75	2·00
		Set of 5	5·50	5·75
		Set of 5 Gutter Pairs	12·00	
		First Day Cover		5·75
		Presentation Pack (P.O. Pack No. 267)	5·75	
		PHQ Cards (set of 5) (179)	6·00	11·50

Special First Day of Issue Postmarks

British Philatelic Bureau, Edinburgh ....6·00
Wembley...6·00

1255 Athlete on Starting Blocks

1256 Throwing the Javelin

1257 Basketball

1258 Swimming

1259 Athlete celebrating and Olympic Rings

(Des N. Knight. Litho Questa)

1996 (9 July). *Olympic and Paralympic Games, Atlanta. Two phosphor bands.* P 14½×14.

1930	**1255**	26p. greenish grey, silver, rosine, black, magenta, bistre-yellow & new blue	50	40
		a. Horiz strip of 5. Nos. 1930/4	4·50	4·50
1931	**1256**	26p. greenish grey, silver, rosine, black, magenta, bistre-yellow & new blue	50	40
1932	**1257**	26p. greenish grey, silver, rosine, black, magenta, bistre-yellow & new blue	50	40
1933	**1258**	26p. greenish grey, silver, rosine, black, magenta, bistre-yellow & new blue	50	40
1934	**1259**	26p. greenish grey, silver, rosine, black, magenta, bistre-yellow & new blue	50	40
		Set of 5	4·50	4·50
		Gutter Strip of 10	11·00	
		First Day Cover		5·00
		Presentation Pack (P.O. Pack No. 268)	4·50	
		PHQ Cards (set of 5) (180)	6·00	11·50

Nos. 1930/4 were printed together, *se-tenant*, in horizontal strips of 5 throughout the sheet.

For these designs with face value expressed as "1st" see **MS**2554.

Special First Day of Issue Postmarks

British Philatelic Bureau, Edinburgh ....5·50
Much Wenlock ....6·00

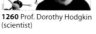

1260 Prof. Dorothy Hodgkin (scientist)

1261 Dame Margot Fonteyn (ballerina)

1262 Dame Elisabeth Frink (sculptress)

1263 Dame Daphne du Maurier (novelist)

1264 Dame Marea Hartman (sports administrator)

(Des Stephanie Nash)

1996 (6 Aug). *Europa. Famous Women. One phosphor band (20p.) or two phosphor bands (others).* P 14½.

1935	**1260**	20p. dull blue-green, brownish grey & black	60	25
1936	**1261**	26p. dull mauve, brownish grey & black	75	25
		a. Imperf (horiz pair)	£800	
1937	**1262**	31p. bronze, brownish grey & black	1·10	1·10
1938	**1263**	37p. silver, brownish grey & black	1·25	1·40
1939	**1264**	43p. gold, brownish grey & black	1·50	1·50
Set of 5			4·75	4·50
Set of 5 Gutter Pairs			12·00	
First Day Cover				5·00
Presentation Pack (P.O. Pack No. 269)			4·75	
PHQ Cards (set of 5) (181)			6·00	11·50

Nos. 1936/7 include the "EUROPA" emblem.

Special First Day of Issue Postmarks

British Philatelic Bureau, Edinburgh ....5·50
Fowey...6·00

1265 *Muffin the Mule*   **1266** *Sooty*

1267 *Stingray*   **1268** *The Clangers*

1269 *Dangermouse*

(Des Tuttsels. Photo Harrison (No. 1940a) or Enschedé (others))

1996 (3 Sept)–**97**. *50th Anniv of Children's Television. One phosphor band (20p.) or two phosphor bands (others).* P 14½×14.

1940	**1265**	20p. dp claret, black, magenta, rosine & greenish yellow	55	20
		a. Perf 15×14 (23.9.97)	2·00	2·00
		ab. Booklet pane. No. 1940a×4 with margins all round	8·00	
1941	**1266**	26p. brt blue, black, dp grey-blue, magenta & greenish yellow	80	20
1942	**1267**	31p. greenish blue, black, new blue, magenta & greenish yellow	1·00	1·50
1943	**1268**	37p. dull violet-blue, black, new blue, magenta & greenish yellow	1·40	1·75
1944	**1269**	43p. brt purple, black, new blue, magenta & greenish yellow	1·60	2·00
Set of 5			4·75	4·75
Set of 5 Gutter Pairs			10·50	
First Day Cover				4·75
Presentation Pack (P.O. Pack No. 270)			4·75	
PHQ Cards (set of 5) (182)			6·00	11·50

No. 1940a comes from the 1997 £6.15 B.B.C. stamp booklet.

Special First Day of Issue Postmarks

British Philatelic Bureau, Edinburgh ....5·00
Alexandra Palace, London ....6·00

1270 Triumph TR3   **1271** MG TD

1272 Austin-Healey 100   **1273** Jaguar XK120

1274 Morgan Plus 4

(Des S. Clay)

1996 (1 Oct). *Classic Sports Cars. One phosphor band (20p.) or two phosphor bands (others).* P 14½.

1945	**1270**	20p. silver, greenish yellow, brt scarlet, vermilion, new blue & black	55	20
1946	**1271**	26p. silver, greenish yellow, magenta, greenish blue & black	1·10	20
		a. Imperf (pair)	£5000	
1947	**1272**	37p. silver, greenish yellow, brt magenta, dp turquoise-blue, new blue & black	1·40	1·90
		a. Imperf (pair)	£2000	
1948	**1273**	43p. silver, greenish yellow, magenta, greenish blue & black	1·60	1·90
		a. Imperf (horiz pair)	£3500	
1949	**1274**	63p. silver, greenish yellow, magenta, greenish blue, stone & black	1·75	2·00

Set of 5	5·75	6·00
Set of 5 Gutter Pairs	13·00	
First Day Cover		6·00
Presentation Pack (P.O. Pack No. 271)	6·00	
PHQ Cards (set of 5) (183)	6·00	11·50

On Nos. 1946/9 the right-hand phosphor band on each stamp is three times the width of that on the left.

Special First Day of Issue Postmarks

British Philatelic Bureau, Edinburgh	6·00
Beaulieu, Brockenhurst	6·25

A pictorial First Day of Issue handstamp was provided at London E1 for this issue.

1275 The Three Kings   **1276** The Annunciation

1277 The Journey to Bethlehem   **1278** The Nativity

1279 The Shepherds

(Des Laura Stoddart)

1996 (28 Oct). *Christmas. One phosphor band (2nd) or two phosphor bands (others).* P 15×14.

1950	**1275**	(2nd) gold, greenish yellow, magenta, blue, black & lt brown	75	20
1951	**1276**	(1st) gold, yellow, cerise, new blue, black & lt brown	1·00	35
1952	**1277**	31p. gold, orange-yellow, cerise, blue, black & lt brown	1·25	1·75
1953	**1278**	43p. gold, greenish yellow, magenta, new blue, grey-black & lt brown	1·25	1·75
1954	**1279**	63p. gold, greenish yellow, magenta, new blue, black & lt brown	1·50	2·00
Set of 5			5·50	5·50
Set of 5 Gutter Pairs			13·00	
First Day Cover				6·00
Presentation Pack (P.O. Pack No. 272)			5·75	
PHQ Cards (set of 5) (184)			6·00	11·50

Special First Day of Issue Postmarks

British Philatelic Bureau, Edinburgh	6·25
Bethlehem, Llandeilo	6·25

Collectors Pack 1996
1996 (28 Oct). *Comprises Nos. 1901/54.*
CP1954a Collectors Pack .... 60·00

Post Office Yearbook
1996 (28 Oct). *Comprises Nos. 1901/4 and 1915/54 in hardback book with slip case, illustrated in colour....* 60·00

1280 *Gentiana acaulis* (Georg Ehret)   **1281** *Magnolia grandiflora* (Ehret)

1282 *Camellia japonica* (Alfred Chandler)   **1283** *Tulipa* (Ehret)

1284 *Fuchsia "Princess of Wales"* (Augusta Withers)   **1285** *Tulipa gesneriana* (Ehret)

1286 *Gazania splendens* (Charlotte Sowerby)   **1287** *Iris latifolia* (Ehret)

1288 *Hippeastrum rutilum* (Pierre-Joseph Redoute)   **1289** *Passiflora coerulea* (Ehret)

(Des Tutssels. Litho Walsall)

1997 (6 Jan). *Greeting Stamps. 19th-century Flower Paintings. Two phosphor bands.* P 14½×14 (with one elliptical hole in each vertical side).

1955	**1280**	(1st) greenish yellow, new blue, magenta, black, blue-green & gold	70	40
		a Booklet pane Nos. 1955/64	11·00	11·00
		ab. Gold, blue-green and phosphor omitted	£28000	
1956	**1281**	(1st) greenish yellow, new blue, magenta, black, blue-green & gold	70	40
1957	**1282**	(1st) greenish yellow, new blue, magenta, black, blue-green & gold	70	40
1958	**1283**	(1st) greenish yellow, new blue, magenta, black, blue-green & gold	70	40
1959	**1284**	(1st) greenish yellow, new blue, magenta, black, blue-green & gold	70	40
1960	**1285**	(1st) greenish yellow, new blue, magenta, black, blue-green & gold	70	40

1961	**1286**	(1st) greenish yellow, new blue,		
		magenta, black, blue-green & gold	70	40
1962	**1287**	(1st) greenish yellow, new blue,		
		magenta, black, blue-green & gold	70	40
1963	**1288**	(1st) greenish yellow, new blue,		
		magenta, black, blue-green & gold	70	40
1964	**1289**	(1st) greenish yellow, new blue,		
		magenta, black, blue-green & gold	70	40

Set of 10..	11·00	11·00
First Day Cover.....................................		11·50
Presentation Pack (P.O. Pack No. G6)........................	16·00	
PHQ Cards (set of 10) (GS5)................................	16·00	30·00

Nos. 1955/64 were issued in £2.60 stamp booklets together with a pane of twenty half-sized labels. The stamps and labels were attached to the booklet cover by a common gutter margin.

Nos. 1955/64 were re-issued on 21 January 2003 in *se-tenant* sheets of 20, each accompanied by a label showing further flowers (sold at £5.95) (LS11) or personal photographs (sold at £14.95). These stamps were printed in lithography by Questa and are without elliptical holes in the perforations.

For booklet stamps in designs as Nos. 1955, 1958 and 1962 and perf 15×14, printed by Enschedé see Nos. 2463/5.

Special First Day of Issue Postmarks

British Philatelic Bureau, Edinburgh .... 12·00
Kew, Richmond, Surrey .... 13·00

1290 "King Henry VIII"   **1291** "Catherine of Aragon"

1292 "Anne Boleyn"   **1293** "Jane Seymour"

1294 "Anne of Cleves"   **1295** "Catherine Howard"

For a full range of Stanley Gibbons catalogues, please visit **www.stanleygibbons.com**

1296 "Catherine Parr"

(Des Kate Stephens from contemporary paintings)

1997 (21 Jan). *450th Death Anniv of King Henry VIII. Two phosphor bands.* P 15 (No. 1965) or 14×15 (others).

1965	**1290**	26p. gold, greenish yellow, brt purple,		
		new blue and black	50	40
		a. Imperf (vert pair)	£8000	
1966	**1291**	26p. gold, greenish yellow, brt carmine,		
		new blue and black	50	40
		a. Horiz strip of 6. Nos. 1966/71	8·00	8·50
1967	**1292**	26p. gold, greenish yellow, brt carmine,		
		new blue and black	50	40
1968	**1293**	26p. gold, greenish yellow, brt carmine,		
		new blue and black	50	40
1969	**1294**	26p. gold, greenish yellow, brt carmine,		
		new blue and black	50	40
1970	**1295**	26p. gold, greenish yellow, brt carmine,		
		new blue and black	50	40
1971	**1296**	26p. gold, greenish yellow, brt carmine,		
		new blue and black	50	40

Set of 7	8·00	8·50
Set of 1 Gutter Pair and a Gutter Strip of 12	17·00	
First Day Cover..		9·50
Presentation Pack (P.O. Pack No. 274)......................	10·00	
PHQ Cards (set of 7) (185)	10·00	18·00

Nos. 1966/71 were printed together, *se-tenant*, in horizontal strips of 6 throughout the sheet.

Special First Day of Issue Postmarks

British Philatelic Bureau, Edinburgh .... 10·00
Hampton Court, East Molesey .... 11·00

1297 St. Columba in Boat   **1298** St. Columba on Iona

1299 St. Augustine with King Ethelbert   **1300** St. Augustine with Model of Cathedral

(Des Claire Melinsky. Photo Enschedé)

1997 (11 Mar). *Religious Anniversaries. Two phosphor bands.* P 14½.

| 1972 | **1297** | 26p. greenish yellow, magenta, new | | |
| | | blue, grey-black and gold.................. | 75 | 35 |

		a. Imperf (pair)	£1750	
1973	1298	37p. greenish yellow, magenta, new blue, grey-black and gold...............	1·10	1·50
1974	1299	43p. greenish yellow, magenta, new blue, grey-black and gold...............	1·50	1·50
1975	1300	63p. greenish yellow, magenta, new blue, grey-black and gold...............	2·00	2·10
Set of 4			4·75	5·00
Set of 4 Gutter Pairs			11·50	
First Day Cover				5·75
Presentation Pack (P.O. Pack No. 275)			5·25	
PHQ Cards (set of 4) (186)			5·75	11·50

Nos. 1972/3 commemorate the 1400th death anniversary of St. Columba and Nos. 1974/5 the 1400th anniversary of the arrival of St. Augustine of Canterbury in Kent.

Special First Day of Issue Postmarks

British Philatelic Bureau, Edinburgh .... 6·00
Isle of Iona .... 6·00

For Nos. 1976/7 see Decimal Machin Definitives section.

Dracula
1303 *Dracula*

Frankenstein
1304 *Frankenstein*

Dr Jekyll and Mr Hyde
1305 *Dr. Jekyll and of Mr. Hyde*

The Hound of the Baskervilles
1306 *The Hound the Baskervilles*

(Des I. Pollock. Photo Walsall)

1997 (13 May). *Europa. Tales and Legends. Horror Stories.* Two phosphor bands. P 14×15.

1980	1303	26p. grey-black, black, new blue, magenta and greenish yellow	1·00	40
1981	1304	31p. grey-black, black, new blue, magenta and greenish yellow	1·10	1·50
1982	1305	37p. grey-black, black, new blue, magenta and greenish yellow	1·30	1·75
1983	1306	43p. grey-black, black, new blue, magenta and greenish yellow	2·00	1·95
Set of 4			5·00	5·50
Set of 4 Gutter Pairs			12·00	
First Day Cover				5·50
Presentation Pack (P.O. Pack No. 276)			5·25	
PHQ Cards (set of 4) (187)			5·75	11·50

Nos. 1980/3 commemorate the birth bicentenary of Mary Shelley (creator of Frankenstein) with the 26p. and 31p. values incorporating the "EUROPA" emblem. Each value has features printed in fluorescent ink which are visible under ultra-violet light.

Special First Day of Issue Postmarks

British Philatelic Bureau, Edinburgh .... 6·00
Whitby .... 6·00

1307 Reginald Mitchell and Supermarine Spitfire MkIIA

1308 Roy Chadwick and Avro Lancaster MkI

1309 Ronald Bishop and De Havilland Mosquito B MkXVI

1310 George Carter and Gloster Meteor T Mk7

1311 Sir Sidney Camm and Hawker Hunter FGA Mk9

(Des Turner Duckworth)

1997 (10 June). *British Aircraft Designers.* One phosphor band (20p.) or two phosphor bands (others). P 15×14.

1984	1307	20p. silver, greenish yellow, magenta, new blue, black and grey..................	75	40
1985	1308	26p. silver, greenish yellow, magenta, new blue, black and grey..................	1·10	1·25
1986	1309	37p. silver, greenish yellow, magenta, new blue, black and grey..................	1·40	1·25
1987	1310	43p. silver, greenish yellow, magenta, new blue, black and grey..................	1·50	1·60
1988	1311	63p. silver, greenish yellow, magenta, new blue, black and grey..................	2·00	2·00
Set of 5			6·00	6·50
Set of 5 Gutter Pairs			15·00	
First Day Cover				6·50
Presentation Pack (P.O. Pack No. 277)			6·50	
PHQ Cards (set of 5) (188)			6·00	13·00

Special First Day of Issue Postmarks

British Philatelic Bureau, Edinburgh .... 6·50
Duxford, Cambridge .... 6·50

1312 Carriage Horse and Coachman

1313 Lifeguards Horse and Trooper

1314 Blues and Royals Drum Horse and Drummer

1315 Duke of Edinburgh's Horse and Groom

(Des J.-L. Benard. Litho Walsall)

1997 (8 July). *"All the Queen's Horses". 50th Anniv of the British Horse Society. One phosphor band (20p.) or two phosphor bands (others).* P 14½.

1989	**1312**	20p. scarlet-vermilion, black, magenta, new blue and greenish yellow..........	80	45
1990	**1313**	26p. scarlet-vermilion, black, magenta, new blue and greenish yellow..........	1·10	1·50
1991	**1314**	43p. scarlet-vermilion, black, magenta, new blue and greenish yellow..........	1·50	1·50
1992	**1315**	63p. scarlet-vermilion, black, magenta, new blue and greenish yellow..........	2·00	2·00

Set of 4 .... 5·00 5·25
Set of 4 Gutter Pairs.................................. 12·00
First Day Cover .... 5·75
Presentation Pack (P.O. Pack No. 278) .... 5·50
PHQ Cards (set of 4) (189) .... 5·75 11·50

Special First Day of Issue Postmarks

British Philatelic Bureau, Edinburgh .... 6·00
Windsor, Berks .... 6·00

CASTLE

Harrison plates (Nos. 1611/14)

CASTLE

Enschedé plates (Nos. 1993/6)

Differences between Harrison and Enschedé:
Harrison- "C" has top serif and tail of letter points to right. "A" has flat top. "S" has top and bottom serifs.
Enschedé- "C" has no top serif and tail of letter points upwards. "A" has pointed top. "S" has no serifs.

Harrison plates (Nos. 1611/14) Enschedé plates (Nos. 1993/6)

(Des from photos by Prince Andrew, Duke of York. Eng Inge Madle Recess (Queen's head by silk screen process) Enschedé)

1997 (29 July). *Designs as Nos. 1611/14 with Queen's head in silhouette as T **1044**, but re-engraved with differences in inscription as shown above.* P 15×14 (with one elliptical hole in each vertical side).

1993	**880**	£1·50 deep claret and gold†.........................	12·00	6·00
		a. Gold (Queen's head) omitted............	19·00	—

1994	**881**	£2 indigo and gold†.................................	14·00	2·25
		a. Gold (Queen's head) omitted............	£750	
1995	**1044**	£3 violet and gold†.................................	30·00	3·50
		a. Gold (Queen's head) omitted............	£2500	
1996	**882**	£5 deep brown and gold†.......................	36·00	10·00
		a. Gold (Queen's head) omitted............	£5500	

Set of 4 .... 75·00 18·00
Set of 4 Gutter Pairs (vert or horiz) £175
Presentation Pack (P.O. Pack No. 40)................... £150
   †The Queen's head on these stamps is printed in optically variable ink which changes colour from gold to green when viewed from different angles. No. 1996a occurs on R. 5/8 and 6/8 from some sheets.

1316 Haroldswick, Shetland

1317 Painswick, Gloucestershire

1318 Beddgelert, Gwynedd

1319 Ballyroney, County Down

(Des T. Millington. Photo Enschedé)

1997 (12 Aug). *Sub-Post Offices. One phosphor band (20p.) or two phosphor bands (others).* P 14½.

1997	**1316**	20p. greenish yellow, bright magenta, new blue, grey-black, rosine and blue-green	75	50
1998	**1317**	26p. greenish yellow, bright magenta, new blue, grey-black, rosine and blue-green	1·00	1·00
1999	**1318**	43p. greenish yellow, bright magenta, new blue, grey-black, rosine and blue-green	1·50	1·50
2000	**1319**	63p. greenish yellow, bright magenta, new blue, grey-black, rosine and blue-green	2·25	2·25

Set of 4 .... 5·50 5·00
Set of 4 Gutter Pairs.................................. 12·00
First Day Cover .... 5·75
Presentation Pack (P.O. Pack No. 279) .... 5·00
PHQ Cards (set of 4) (190) .... 5·75 11·50
   Nos. 1997/2000 were issued on the occasion of the Centenary of the National Federation of Sub-Postmasters.

Special First Day of Issue Postmarks

British Philatelic Bureau, Edinburgh .... 6·00
Wakefield .... 6·00

PRINTERS. Harrison and Sons Ltd became De La Rue Security Print on 8 September 1997. This was not reflected in the sheet imprints until mid-1998.

Enid Blyton's *Noddy*
1320 *Noddy*

Enid Blyton's *Famous Five*
1321 *Famous Five*

Enid Blyton's *Secret Seven*
1322 *Secret Seven*

Enid Blyton's *Faraway Tree*
1323 *Faraway Tree*

Enid Blyton's *Malory Towers*
1324 *Malory Towers*

(Des C. Birmingham. Photo Enschedé)

1997 (9 Sept). *Birth Centenary of Enid Blyton (children's author). One phosphor band (20p.) or two phosphor bands (others).* P 14×14½.

2001	**1320**	20p. greenish yellow, magenta, new blue, grey-black and deep grey-blue	50	45
2002	**1321**	26p. greenish yellow, magenta, new blue, grey-black and deep grey-blue	1·00	1·25
2003	**1322**	37p. greenish yellow, magenta, new blue, grey-black and deep grey-blue	1·25	1·25
2004	**1323**	43p. greenish yellow, magenta, new blue, grey-black and deep grey-blue	1·50	2·00
2005	**1324**	63p. greenish yellow, magenta, new blue, grey-black and deep grey-blue	1·75	2·00
Set of 5			5·50	6·00
Set of 5 Gutter Pairs			12·00	
First Day Cover				6·00
Presentation Pack (P.O. Pack No. 280)			5·75	
PHQ Cards (set of 5) (191)			6·00	13·00

Special First Day of Issue Postmarks

British Philatelic Bureau, Edinburgh ....6·50
Beaconsfield..6·50

1325 Children and Father Christmas pulling Cracker

1326 Father Christmas with Traditional Cracker

1327 Father Christmas riding Cracker

1328 Father Christmas on Snowball

1329 Father Christmas and Chimney

(Des J. Gorham and M. Thomas (1st), J. Gorham (others))

1997 (27 Oct). *Christmas. 150th Anniv of the Christmas Cracker. One phosphor band (2nd) or two phosphor bands (others).* P 15×14.

2006	**1325**	(2nd) gold, greenish yellow, bright magenta, new blue and grey-black	75	20
		a. Imperf (pair)	£3000	
2007	**1326**	(1st) gold, greenish yellow, bright magenta, new blue and grey-black	90	30
2008	**1327**	31p. gold, greenish yellow, bright magenta, new blue, bright blue and grey-black	1·00	1·50
		a. Imperf (pair)	£4000	
2009	**1328**	43p. gold, greenish yellow, bright magenta, pale new blue and grey-black	1·25	1·75
2010	**1329**	63p. gold, greenish yellow, bright magenta, new blue and grey-black	1·60	2·00
Set of 5			5·50	5·00
Set of 5 Gutter Pairs			12·00	
First Day Cover				6·00
Presentation Pack (P.O. Pack No. 282)			5·75	
PHQ Cards (set of 5) (192)			6·00	13·00

The 1st value was re-issued on 3 October 2000 in sheets of 10, each with a *se-tenant* label showing Christmas greetings (sold for £2.95) (LS3) or a personal photograph (sold for £5.95). These sheets were printed in photogravure by Questa and were sold by the Philatelic Bureau and selected philatelic outlets. Similar sheets were available from 9 October 2001 when the price for the personalised version was increased to £12.95 for two sheets. These could also be purchased, on an experimental basis, from photo-booths situated at six post offices. From 1 October 2002 the size of the sheet was increased to 20 either with greetings labels (sold at £5.95) (LS10) or personal photographs (sold at £14.95). These stamps were printed by Questa in lithography and perforated 14½×14.

Special First Day of Issue Postmarks

British Philatelic Bureau, Edinburgh ....6·25
Bethlehem, Llandeilo ....6·25

1330 Wedding Photograph, 1947

1331 Queen Elizabeth II and Prince Philip, 1997

(Des D. Driver (20p., 43p.), Lord Snowdon (26p., 63p.))

1997 (13 Nov). *Royal Golden Wedding. One phosphor band (20p.) or two phosphor bands (others).* P 15.

2011	**1330**	20p. gold, yellow-brown and grey-black	85	45
		a. Imperf (pair)	£10000	
		b. Face value ommitted	£15000	
2012	**1331**	26p. gold, bistre-yellow, magenta, new blue, grey-black and greenish grey	1·10	70
		a. Imperf (vert pair)	£7500	
2013	**1330**	43p. gold, bluish green and grey-black...	1·90	2·25
2014	**1331**	63p. gold, bistre-yellow, magenta, new blue, grey-black and lavender-grey	2·50	3·00
Set of 4			5·75	5·75
Set of 4 Gutter Pairs			12·00	
First Day Cover				8·25
Presentation Pack (P.O. Pack No. 281)			6·25	
Souvenir Book (contains Nos. 1668, 1989/92 and 2011/14)			50·00	
PHQ Cards (set of 4) (192)			5·75	11·50

For 26p. and (1st) Machin printed in gold, see Nos. 1668 and Y1686.

Special First Day of Issue Postmarks

British Philatelic Bureau, Edinburgh .... 9·00
London, SW1 .... 10·00

Collectors Pack 1997
1997 (13 Nov). *Comprises Nos. 1965/75, 1980/92 and 1997/ 2014.*
CP2014*a* Collectors Pack.. 65·00

Post Office Yearbook
1997 (13 Nov). *Comprises Nos. 1965/75, 1980/92 and 1997/ 2014 in hardback book with slip case* .... 65·00

20 ENDANGERED SPECIES
Common dormouse
Muscardinus avellanarius
1332 Common Dormouse

26 ENDANGERED SPECIES
Lady's slipper orchid
Cypripedium calceolus
1333 Lady's Slipper Orchid

31 ENDANGERED SPECIES
Song thrush
Turdus philomelos
1334 Song Thrush

37 ENDANGERED SPECIES
Shining ram's-horn snail
Segmentina nitida
1335 Shining Ram's-horn Snail

43 ENDANGERED SPECIES
Mole cricket
Gryllotalpa gryllotalpa
1336 Mole Cricket

63 ENDANGERED SPECIES
Devil's bolete
Boletus satanas
1337 Devil's Bolete

(Des R. Maude. Litho Questa)

1998 (20 Jan). *Endangered Species. One side phosphor band (20p.) or two phosphor bands (others).* P 14×14½.

2015	**1332**	20p. black, new blue, magenta, greenish yellow, deep blue and pale lavender grey	60	40
2016	**1333**	26p. black, new blue, magenta, greenish yellow, deep blue and pale yellow-olive	75	40
2017	**1334**	31p. black, new blue, magenta, greenish yellow, deep blue and pale bluish grey	1·00	2·00
2018	**1335**	37p. black, new blue, magenta, greenish yellow, deep blue and pale greenish grey	1·25	1·25
2019	**1336**	43p. black, new blue, magenta, greenish yellow, deep blue and pale dull mauve	1·40	1·75
2020	**1337**	63p. black, new blue, magenta, greenish yellow, deep blue and pale grey-brown	1·90	2·25
Set of 6			6·25	6·50
Set of 6 Gutter Pairs			15·00	
First Day Cover				6·50
Presentation Pack (P.O. Pack No. 284)			6·75	
PHQ Cards (set of 6) (194)			6·00	14·00

Special First Day of Issue Postmarks

British Philatelic Bureau, Edinburgh ....6·50
Selborne, Alton ....7·00

1338 Diana, Princess of Wales (photo by Lord Snowdon)

1339 At British Lung Foundation Function, April 1997 (photo by John Stillwell)

1340 Wearing Tiara, 1991 (photo by Lord Snowdon)

1341 On Visit to Birmingham, October 1995 (photo by Tim Graham)

1342 In Evening Dress, 1987 (photo by Terence Donavan)

(Des B. Robinson)

1998 (3 Feb). *Diana, Princess of Wales Commemoration. Two phosphor bands.* P 14×15.

2021	**1338**	26p. purple, greenish yellow, magenta, new blue and black	50	40
		a. Horiz strip of 5. Nos. 2021/5	4·50	4·50
		ab. Imperf (horiz strip of 5. Nos. 2021/5)	£20000	
		ac. Imperf (horiz strip of 4. Nos. 2021/4)	£15000	
		ad. Imperf (horiz strip of 3. Nos. 2021/3)	£10000	
2022	**1339**	26p. purple, greenish yellow, magenta, new blue and black	50	40
2023	**1340**	26p. purple, greenish yellow, magenta, new blue and black	50	40
2024	**1341**	26p. purple, greenish yellow, magenta, new blue and black	50	40
2025	**1342**	26p. purple, greenish yellow, magenta, new blue and black	50	40
Set of 5			4·50	4·50
Gutter Strip of 10..			10·00	
First Day Cover				5·50
Presentation Pack (unnumbered)			16·00	
Presentation Pack (Welsh)			£150	

Nos. 2021/5 were printed together, *se-tenant*, in horizontal strips of 5 throughout the sheet.

No. 2021ac shows No. 2025 perforated at right only. In addition to the generally issued Presentation Pack a further pack with all text printed in English and Welsh was available.

Special First Day of Issue Postmarks

British Philatelic Bureau, Edinburgh	6·00
Kensington, London	6·00

1343 Lion of England and Griffin of Edward III

1344 Falcon of Plantagenet and Bull of Clarence

1345 Lion of Mortimer and Yale of Beaufort

1346 Greyhound of Richmond and Dragon of Wales

1347 Unicorn of Scotland and Horse of Hanover

(Des J. Matthews. Recess and litho Harrison)

1998 (24 Feb). *650th Anniv of the Order of the Garter. The Queen's Beasts. Two phosphor bands.* P 15×14.

2026	**1343**	26p. silver, green, bright blue, carmine-red, vermilion, lemon, grey-black and black..	90	90
		a. Horiz strip of 5. Nos. 2026/30	4·50	4·50
		ab. Missing green (on Nos. 2026, 2028/9) (horiz strip of 5)......................	£35000	

		Eay. Horiz strip of 5. Phosphor omitted..	25·00	
2027	**1344**	26p. silver, bright blue, carmine-red, vermilion, lemon, grey, grey-black and black...	90	90
2028	**1345**	26p. silver, green, bright blue, carmine-red, vermilion, lemon, grey, grey-black and black..................................	90	90
2029	**1346**	26p. silver, green, bright blue, carmine-red, vermilion, lemon, grey, grey-black and black..................................	90	90
2030	**1347**	26p. silver, green, bright blue, vermilion, lemon, grey, grey-black and black ..	90	90
Set of 5			4·00	4·00
Gutter Block of 10			10·00	
First Day Cover				5·25
Presentation Pack (P.O. Pack No. 285)			5·00	
PHQ Cards (set of 5) (195)			6·00	13·00

Nos. 2026/30 were printed together, *se-tenant*, in horizontal strips of 5 throughout the sheet. The phosphor bands on Nos. 2026/30 are only half the height of the stamps and do not cover the silver parts of the designs.

Special First Day of Issue Postmarks

British Philatelic Bureau, Edinburgh	5·50
London SW1	5·50

1348

(Des G. Knipe, adapted Dew Gibbons Design Group. Photo Walsall)

1998 (10 Mar). *As T* **157** *(Wilding Definitive of 1952–54) but with face values in decimal currency as T* **1348**. *One side phosphor band (20p.) or two phosphor bands (others).* P 14 (with one elliptical hole in each vertical side).

2031	**1348**	20p. light green (1 band at right)	70	75
		Ea. Band at left..	70	75
		b. Booklet pane. Nos. 2031/Ea each ×3 with margins all round	4·75	
		c. Booklet pane. Nos. 2031/Ea and 2032/3, all×2, and central label with margins all round	9·50	
2032		26p. red-brown	90	95
		a. Booklet pane. No. 2032×9 with margins all round	9·50	
		b. Booklet pane. Nos. 2032/3, each ×3 with margins all round	9·50	
2033		37p. light purple	2·75	2·75
Set of 3 (cheapest)			4·00	4·00
First Day Cover (No. 2031c)				7·00

Nos. 2031/3 were only issued in the 1998 £7.49 Wilding Definitives stamp booklet No. DX20.

For further Wilding designs with decimal face values and on paper watermarked W **1565** see Nos. 2258/9, **MS**2326, **MS**2367 and 2378/9.

Special First Day of Issue Postmarks

British Philatelic Bureau, Edinburgh	7·00
London SW1	7·00

1349 St. John's Point Lighthouse, County Down

1350 Smalls Lighthouse, Pembrokeshire

1351 Needles Rock Lighthouse, Isle of Wight, c 1900

1352 Bell Rock Lighthouse, Arbroath, mid-19th-century

1353 Original Eddystone Lighthouse, Plymouth, 1698

(Des D. Davis and J. Boon. Litho Questa)

1998 (24 Mar). *Lighthouses. One side phosphor band (20p.) or two phosphor bands (others).* P 14½×14.

2034	**1349**	20p. gold, greenish yellow, magenta, new blue and black	50	40
2035	**1350**	26p. gold, greenish yellow, magenta, new blue and black	75	50
2036	**1351**	37p. gold, greenish yellow, magenta, new blue and black	1·10	1·50
2037	**1352**	43p. gold, greenish yellow, magenta, new blue and black	1·50	1·75
2038	**1353**	63p. gold, greenish yellow, magenta, new blue and black	2·10	2·50
Set of 5			5·50	6·00
Set of 5 Gutter Pairs			13·50	
First Day Cover				6·00
Presentation Pack (P.O. Pack No. 286)			6·00	
PHQ Cards (set of 5) (196)			6·00	13·00

Nos. 2034/8 commemorate the 300th anniversary of the first Eddystone Lighthouse and the final year of manned lighthouses.

Special First Day of Issue Postmarks

British Philatelic Bureau, Edinburgh	6·00
Plymouth	6·00

For Nos. 2039/40 see Decimal Machin Definitives section.

1354 Tommy Cooper

1355 Eric Morecambe

1356 Joyce Grenfell

1357 Les Dawson

1358 Peter Cook

(Des G. Scarfe. Litho Walsall)

1998 (23 Apr). *Comedians. One side phosphor band (20p.) or two phosphor bands (others).* P 14½×14.

2041	**1354**	20p. vermilion, black, rose-pink, new blue and greenish yellow	50	50
		Ea. Vermilion printed double		£1500
		Eb. Vermilion and black both printed quadruple with rose-pink and new blue both printed double	†	£2500
		Ec. Vermilion and black both printed double	†	£2000
2042	**1355**	26p. vermilion, black, rose-pink and new blue	75	85
		Ea. Vermilion printed double	£600	
		Eb. Vermilion printed triple	£1000	
		Ec. Black printed double, vermilion printed triple	£2500	
		Ed. Black and vermilion printed triple	£2500	
2043	**1356**	37p. vermilion, black, rose-pink, new blue and greenish yellow	1·25	1·25
2044	**1357**	43p. vermilion, black, rose-pink, new blue and pale orange	1·50	1·50
2045	**1358**	63p. vermilion, black, deep rose-pink, new blue and greenish yellow	1·75	2·10
Set of 5			5·25	5·50
Set of 5 Gutter Pairs			13·50	
First Day Cover				6·00
Presentation Pack (P.O. Pack No. 287)			6·00	
PHQ Cards (set of 5) (197)			6·00	13·00

Stamps as Type **1356**, but with a face value of 30p., were prepared but not issued. Mint examples and a first day cover have been reported (*Price £2750*).

Special First Day of Issue Postmarks

British Philatelic Bureau, Edinburgh	6·50
Morecambe	6·50

1359 Hands forming Heart

1360 Adult and Child holding Hands

1361 Hands forming Cradle   **1362** Hand taking Pulse

(Des V. Frost from photos by A. Wilson. Litho Questa)

1998 (23 June). *50th Anniv of the National Health Service. One side phosphor band (20p.) or two phosphor bands (others).* P 14×14½.

2046	**1359**	20p. deep claret, black, grey-brown, pale cream and cream	50	50
2047	**1360**	26p. deep grey-green, black, grey-brown, pale cream and cream	90	90
2048	**1361**	43p. deep lilac, black, grey-brown, pale cream and cream	1·50	1·50
2049	**1362**	63p. deep dull blue, black, grey-brown, pale cream and cream	2·10	2·10
Set of 4			4·50	4·50
Set of 4 Gutter Pairs			11·00	
First Day Cover				5·75
Presentation Pack (P.O. Pack No. 288)			5·50	
PHQ Cards (set of 4) (198)			5·75	11·50

Special First Day of Issue Postmarks

British Philatelic Bureau, Edinburgh .... 5·75
Tredegar, Wales ....5·75

1363 The Hobbit (J. R. R. Tolkien)   **1364** The Lion, The Witch and the Wardrobe (C. S. Lewis)

1365 The Phoenix and the Carpet (E. Nesbit)   **1366** The Borrowers (Mary Norton)

1367 Through the Looking Glass (Lewis Carroll)

(Des P. Malone. Photo D.L.R.)

1998 (21 July). *Famous Children's Fantasy Novels. One centre phosphor band (20p.) or two phosphor bands (others).* P 15×14.

2050	**1363**	20p. silver, greenish yellow, bright magenta, new blue, black and gold	50	45
2051	**1364**	26p. silver, greenish yellow, bright magenta, new blue, black and gold	75	55
	a. Imperf (pair)		£3750	
2052	**1365**	37p. silver, greenish yellow, bright magenta, new blue, black and gold	1·25	1·50
2053	**1366**	43p. silver, greenish yellow, bright magenta, new blue, black and gold	1·50	1·50
2054	**1367**	63p. silver, greenish yellow, bright magenta, new blue, black and gold	2·10	2·00
Set of 5			5·75	5·75
Set of 5 Gutter Pairs			13·00	
First Day Cover				5·75
Presentation Pack (P.O. Pack No. 289)			6·00	
PHQ Cards (set of 5) (199)			6·00	13·00

Nos. 2050/4 commemorate the birth centenary of C. S. Lewis and the death centenary of Lewis Carroll.

The PHQ card showing the Type **1363** design is known incorrectly inscribed "Tolkein".

Special First Day of Issue Postmarks

British Philatelic Bureau, Edinburgh ....6·00
Oxford . ...6·50

1368 Woman in Yellow Feathered Costume   **1369** Woman in Blue Costume and Headdress

1370 Group of Children in White and Gold Robes   **1371** Child in "Tree" Costume

(Des T. Hazael. Photo Walsall)

1998 (25 Aug). *Europa. Festivals. Notting Hill Carnival. One centre phosphor band (20p.) or two phosphor bands (others).* P 14×14½.

2055	**1368**	20p. gold, black, new blue, bright magenta and greenish yellow	75	45
	a. Imperf (pair)		£950	
2056	**1369**	26p. gold, grey-black, new blue, bright magenta and greenish yellow	95	55
2057	**1370**	43p. gold, grey-black, new blue, bright magenta and bistre-yellow	1·50	2·00
2058	**1371**	63p. gold, grey-black, new blue, bright magenta and greenish yellow	2·00	2·75
Set of 4			4·75	4·75
Set of 4 Gutter Pairs			12·50	
First Day Cover				5·75
Presentation Pack (P.O. Pack No. 290)			5·25	
PHQ Cards (set of 4) (200)			5·75	11·50

The 20p. and 26p. incorporate the "EUROPA" emblem.

Special First Day of Issue Postmarks

British Philatelic Bureau, Edinburgh ....6·00
London W11 ....6·50

1372 Sir Malcolm Campbell's *Bluebird*, 1925   **1373** Sir Henry Segrave's *Sunbeam*, 1926

1374 John G. Parry Thomas's *Babs*, 1926   **1375** John R. Cobb's *Railton Mobil Special*, 1947

1376 Donald Campbell's *Bluebird CN7*, 1964

(Des Roundel Design Group. Photo De La Rue)

1998 (29 Sept–13 Oct). *British Land Speed Record Holders. One phosphor band (20p.) or two phosphor bands (others)*. P 15×14.

2059	1372	20p. rosine, greenish yellow, magenta, new blue, black and silver (1 centre band)	50	25
		a. Perf 14½×13½ (1 side band at right) (13.10.98)	1·40	1·20
		aEb. Band at left	1·00	1·00
		ac. Booklet pane. Nos. 2059a and 2059aEb, each ×2, with margins all round	5·00	
2060	1373	26p. rosine, greenish yellow, magenta, new blue, black and silver	75	30
		a. Rosine (face value) omitted	£4700	
		Eb. "2" from face value omitted	£3700	
		Ec. "6" from face value omitted	£3700	
2061	1374	30p. rosine, greenish yellow, magenta, new blue, black and silver	1·25	1·50
2062	1375	43p. rosine, greenish yellow, magenta, new blue, black and silver	1·50	1·60
2063	1376	63p. rosine, greenish yellow, magenta, new blue, black and silver	2·00	2·40
Set of 5			5·50	5·50
Set of 5 Gutter Pairs			13·00	
First Day Cover				6·00
Presentation Pack (P.O. Pack No. 291)			6·25	
PHQ Cards (set of 5) (201)			6·00	13·00

Nos. 2059/63 commemorate the 50th death anniversary of Sir Malcolm Campbell.

Nos. 2060a/Ec occur on the fourth vertical row of several sheets. Other examples show one or other of the figures partially omitted. Nos. 2059a/aEb come from the £6.16 British Land Speed Record Holders stamp booklet, No. DX21, and were printed by Walsall. There are minor differences of design between No. 2059 (sheet stamp printed by De La Rue) and Nos. 2059a/aEb (booklet stamps printed by Walsall), which omit the date and copyright symbol.

Special First Day of Issue Postmarks

British Philatelic Bureau, Edinburgh ....6·50
Pendine ....6·50

The mis-spelling 'PHILALETIC' in the Bureau datestamp was later corrected; same price, either spelling.

1377 Angel with Hands raised in Blessing   **1378** Angel praying

1379 Angel playing Flute   **1380** Angel playing Lute

1381 Angel praying

(Des Irene von Treskow. Photo De La Rue)

1998 (2 Nov). *Christmas. Angels. One centre phosphor band (20p.) or two phosphor bands (others)*. P 15×14.

2064	1377	20p. gold, greenish yellow, magenta, new blue and grey-black	50	50
		a. Imperf (pair)	£1100	
2065	1378	26p. gold, greenish yellow, magenta, new blue and grey-black	75	60
		a. Imperf (pair)	£3700	
2066	1379	30p. gold, greenish yellow, magenta, new blue and grey-black	1·25	1·50
		a. Imperf (pair)	£900	
2067	1380	43p. gold, greenish yellow, magenta, new blue and grey-black	1·50	1·60
		a. Imperf (pair)	£5000	
2068	1381	63p. gold, greenish yellow, magenta, new blue and grey-black	2·00	2·25
Set of 5			5·75	5·75
Set of 5 Gutter Pairs			13·00	
First Day Cover				6·00
Presentation Pack (P.O. Pack No. 292)			6·50	
PHQ Cards (set of 5) (202)			6·00	13·00

Special First Day of Issue Postmarks

British Philatelic Bureau, Edinburgh ....6·25
Bethlehem.................................6·25

Collectors Pack 1998
1998 (2 Nov). *Comprises Nos. 2015/30, 2034/8 and 2041/68.*
CP2068a Collectors Pack ....95·00

Post Office Yearbook
1998 (2 Nov). *Comprises Nos. 2015/30, 2034/8 and 2041/68 in hardback book with slip case* ....85·00

1382 Greenwich Meridian and Clock (John Harrison's chronometer)

1383 Industrial Worker and Blast Furnace (James Watt's discovery of steam power)

1384 Early Photos of Leaves (Henry Fox-Talbot's photographic experiments)

1385 Computer inside Human Head (Alan Turing's work on computers)

(Des D. Gentleman (20p.), P. Howson (26p.), Z. and Barbara Baran (43p.), E. Paolozzi (63p.). Photo Enschedé (26p.), Questa (63p. No. 2072a) or De La Rue (others))

1999 (12 Jan – 21 Sept). *Millennium Series. The Inventors' Tale.* One centre phosphor band (20p.) or two phosphor bands (others). P 14×14½.

2069	1382	20p. silver, deep grey, pale olive-grey, greenish grey, grey-black and bright rose-red	75	70
		a. Imperf (horiz pair)	£4000	
2070	1383	26p. silver, black, new blue, bright magenta and greenish yellow	95	1·00
2071	1384	43p. silver, greenish yellow, bright crimson, new blue, black and bright magenta	1·50	1·60
2072	1385	63p. greenish blue, greenish yellow, cerise, new blue, black and pale lemon	2·25	2·40
		a. Perf 13½×14 (21 Sept)	3·50	3·50
		ab. Booklet pane. No. 2072a×4 with margins all round	10·00	
Set of 4			5·25	5·25
Set of 4 Gutter Pairs			13·00	
First Day Cover (Philatelic Bureau) (Type J, see Introduction)				14·00
First Day Cover (Greenwich, London SE)				14·00
Presentation Pack (P.O. Pack No. 294)			7·50	
PHQ Cards (set of 4) (203)			8·50	13·00

No. 2072a comes from the £6.99 World Changers booklet, No. DX23.

Special First Day of Issue Postmark

FIRST DAY OF ISSUE
GREENWICH | LONDON SE
12-1-1999

1386 Airliner hugging Globe (International air travel)

1387 Woman on Bicycle (Development of the bicycle)

1388 Victorian Railway Station (Growth of public transport)

1389 Captain Cook and Maori (Captain James Cook's voyages)

(Des G. Hardie (20p.), Sara Fanelli (26p.), J. Lawrence (43p.), A. Klimowski (63p.). Photo Enschedé (20p., 63p.) or De La Rue (26p.). Litho Enschedé (43p.))

1999 (2 Feb). *Millennium Series. The Travellers' Tale.* One centre phosphor band (20p.) or two phosphor bands (others). P 14×14½.

2073	1386	20p. silver, vermilion, grey-black, bluish violet, greenish blue and pale grey	75	70
2074	1387	26p. silver, greenish yellow, cerise, new black and vermilion	95	1·00
2075	1388	43p. grey-black, stone and bronze	1·50	1·60
2076	1389	63p. silver, grey-black, new blue, bright magenta and greenish yellow	2·25	2·40
Set of 4			5·25	5·25
Set of 4 Gutter Pairs			13·00	
First Day Cover (Philatelic Bureau) (Type J, see Introduction)				8·00
First Day Cover (Coventry)				8·50
Presentation Pack (P.O. Pack No. 295)			7·50	
PHQ Cards (set of 4) (204)			8·50	13·00

Special First Day of Issue Postmark

FIRST DAY OF ISSUE COVENTRY
2-2-1999

1390

1999 (16 Feb).

(a) Embossed and litho Walsall. Self-adhesive. Die-cut perf 14×15.

2077	1390	(1st) grey (face value) (Queen's head in colourless relief) (phosphor background around head)	3·00	2·50
		l. Booklet pane. No. 2077×4 with margins all round	10·00	

(b) Eng C. Slania. Recess Enschedé. P 14×14½.

2078	1390	(1st) grey-black (2 phosphor bands)	3·00	2·50
		l. Booklet pane. No. 2078×4 with margins all round	10·00	

(c) Typo Harrison. P 14×15.

2079	1390	(1st) black (2 phosphor bands)	3·00	2·50
		Ey. Phosphor omitted	£1250	
		l. Booklet pane. No. 2078×4 with margins all round	10·00	
		LEy. Booklet pane.Phosphor omitted		
First Day Covers (3 covers with Nos. 2077l, 2078l, 2079l) (Philatelic Bureau)				12·00
First Day Covers (3 covers with Nos. 2077l, 2078l, 2079l) (London SW1)				12·00

Nos. 2077/9 were only issued in the £7.54 "Profile on Print" booklet, No. DX22.

For a full range of Stanley Gibbons catalogues, please visit **www.stanleygibbons.com**

Special First Day of Issue Postmarks

16 FEBRUARY 1999

16 FEBRUARY 1999

1395 Dove and Norman Settler (medieval migration to Scotland)

1396 Pilgrim Fathers and Red Indian (17th-century migration to America)

1391 Vaccinating Child (pattern in cow markings) (Jenner's development of smallpox vaccine)

1392 Patient on Trolley (nursing care)

1397 Sailing Ship and Aspects of Settlement (19th-century migration to Australia)

1398 Hummingbird and Superimposed Stylized Face (20th-century migration to Great Britain)

(Des J. Byrne (20p.), W. McLean (26p.), J. Fisher (43p.), G. Powell (63p.). Litho (20p.) or photo (others) Walsall)

1999 (6 Apr – 12 May). *Millennium Series. The Settlers' Tale. One centre phosphor band (20p.) or two phosphor bands (others).* P 14×14½.

2084	**1395**	20p. gold, silver, black, magenta, blue and greenish yellow	75	70
2085	**1396**	26p. greenish yellow, magenta, new blue, grey-black and silver	95	1·00
		a. Booklet pane. Nos. 2085 and 2089 with margins all round (12 May)	6·50	
2086	**1397**	43p. greenish yellow, magenta, new blue, grey-black, gold and chocolate	2·00	1·75
2087	**1398**	63p. greenish yellow, magenta, new blue, reddish violet, deep reddish violet and gold	3·00	3·00
Set of 4			5·75	5·75
Set of 4 Gutter Pairs			13·00	
First Day Cover (Philatelic Bureau) (Type J, see Introduction)				8·00
First Day Cover (Plymouth)				8·50
Presentation Pack (P.O. Pack No. 297)			7·50	
PHQ Cards (set of 4) (206)			8·50	13·00

No. 2085a comes from the £2.60 booklet, No. HBA1.

Imperf pairs of Nos. 2085 and 2089 are known and believed to be of proof status (Price £750).

Imperf pairs of No. 2085 with silver and phosphor omitted are known and believed to be of proof status (Price £350).

Imperf pairs of No. 2086 are known with gold, chocolate and phosphor omitted and believed to be of proof status (Price £350).

1393 Penicillin Mould (Fleming's discovery of penicillin)

1394 Sculpture of Test-tube Baby (development of in-vitro fertilization)

(Des P. Brookes (20p.), Susan Macfarlane (26p.), M. Dempsey (43p.), A. Gormley (63p.). Photo Questa)

1999 (2 Mar – 21 Sept). *Millennium Series. The Patients' Tale. One centre phosphor band (20p.) or two phosphor bands (others).* P 13½×14.

2080	**1391**	20p. greenish yellow, bright magenta, new blue, black and silver	75	70
		a. Booklet pane. No. 2080×4 with margins all round (21 Sept)	2·50	
2081	**1392**	26p. greenish yellow, bright magenta, new blue, black, silver and deep turquoise-blue	95	1·00
		a. Imperf (pair)	£7000	
2082	**1393**	43p. greenish yellow, bright magenta, new blue, black, deep bluish green and silver	1·50	1·60
2083	**1394**	63p. greenish yellow, bright magenta, new blue, black, silver and blueblack	2·25	2·40
Set of 4			5·25	5·25
Set of 4 Gutter Pairs			13·00	
First Day Cover (Philatelic Bureau) (Type J, see Introduction)				8·00
First Day Cover (Oldham)				8·50
Presentation Pack (P.O. Pack No. 296)			7·50	
PHQ Cards (set of 4) (205)			8·50	13·00

No. 2080a comes from the £6.99 World Changers booklet, No. DX23.

Special First Day of Issue Postmark

6-4-1999

Special First Day of Issue Postmark

2-3-1999

1399 Woven Threads (woollen industry)

1400 Salts Mill, Saltaire (worsted cloth industry)

1401 Hull on Slipway (shipbuilding)

1402 Lloyd's Building (City of London finance centre)

(Des P. Collingwood (19p.), D. Hockney (26p.), B. Sanderson (44p.), B. Neiland (64p.). Litho (19p.) or photo (others) De La Rue)

1999 (4 May). *Millennium Series. The Workers' Tale.* One centre phosphor band (19p.) or two phosphor bands (others). P 14×14½.

2088	**1399**	19p. drab, greenish yellow, cerise, new blue, grey-black and bronze..............	75	70
		a. Bronze (Queen's head) omitted........	£525	
		aEy. Bronze and phosphor omitted.........	£525	
2089	**1400**	26p. silver, greenish yellow, rosine, new blue and grey-black............................	95	1·00
2090	**1401**	44p. silver, greenish yellow, orangered, bright blue, yellow-brown and grey-black.................................	1·75	1·60
2091	**1402**	64p. silver, greenish yellow, rosine, new blue and grey-black...........................	2·25	2·40
Set of 4			5·25	5·25
Set of 4 Gutter Pairs			13·00	

First Day Cover (Philatelic Bureau) (Type J, see Introduction).. 8·00
First Day Cover (Belfast)... 8·50
Presentation Pack (P.O. Pack No. 298) .... 7·50
PHQ Cards (set of 4) (207) .... 8·50 13·00

For No. 2089, printed by Walsall in photogravure, see booklet pane No. 2085a.

Special First Day of Issue Postmark

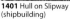

FIRST DAY OF ISSUE BELFAST
4-5-1999

1403 Freddie Mercury (lead singer of Queen) ("Popular Music")

1404 Bobby Moore with World Cup, 1966 ("Sport")

1405 Dalek from Dr. Who (science-fiction series) ("Television")

1406 Charlie Chaplin (film star) ("Cinema")

(Des P. Blake (19p.), M. White (26p.), Lord Snowdon (44p.), R. Steadman (64p.). Photo Enschedé)

1999 (1 June). *Millennium Series. The Entertainers' Tale.* One centre phosphor band (19p.) or two phosphor bands (others). P 14×14½.

2092	**1403**	19p. greenish yellow, bright magenta, new blue, grey-black and gold........	75	70
2093	**1404**	26p. greenish yellow, bright magenta, new blue, grey-black, gold and stone	95	1·00
2094	**1405**	44p. greenish yellow, bright magenta, new blue, grey-black and silver........	1·50	1·60

2095	**1406**	64p. greenish yellow, bright magenta, new blue, grey-black and silver........	2·25	2·40
Set of 4			5·25	5·25
Set of 4 Gutter Pairs			13·00	

First Day Cover (Philatelic Bureau) (Type J, see Introduction).. 8·00
First Day Cover (Wembley) .... 8·50
Presentation Pack (P.O. Pack No. 299) .... 7·50
PHQ Cards (set of 4) (208) .... 8·50 13·00

Special First Day of Issue Postmark

FIRST DAY OF ISSUE WEMBLEY
1-6-1999

1407 Prince Edward and Miss Sophie Rhys-Jones (from photos by John Swannell)

1408

(Adapted J. Gibbs. Photo De La Rue)

1999 (15 June). *Royal Wedding.* Two phosphor bands. P 15×14.

2096	**1407**	26p. vermilion, black, grey-black and silver	85	85
		a. Imperf (pair)	£2800	
2097	**1408**	64p. new blue, black, grey-black and silver	2·50	2·50
Set of 2			3·00	3·00
Set of 2 Gutter Pairs			7·00	

First Day Cover (Philatelic Bureau)............................ 4·75
First Day Cover (Windsor) .... 5·25
Presentation Pack (P.O. Pack No. M01).................... 4·00
PHQ Cards (set of 2) (PSM1) .... 8·50 6·75

Special First Day of Issue Postmarks

British Philatelic Bureau / Edinburgh
edward & sophie
15.6.1999

First Day of Issue / Windsor
e&s
15.6.1999

1409 Suffragette behind Prison Window (Equal Rights for Women)

1410 Water Tap (Right to Health)

1411 Generations of School Children (Right to Education)

1412 "MAGNA CARTA" (Human Rights)

(Des Natasha Kerr (19p.), M. Craig-Martin (26p.), A. Drummond (44p.), A. Kitching (64p.). Photo De La Rue)

1999 (6 July). *Millennium Series. The Citizens' Tale. One centre phosphor band (19p.) or two phosphor bands (others).* P 14×14½.

2098	**1409**	19p. silver, greenish yellow, cerise, new blue and grey-black	75	70
2099	**1410**	26p. grey-black, new blue, bright mauve, rosine, turquoise-green and apple-green	95	1·00
2100	**1411**	44p. bright blue, greenish yellow, cerise, new blue and grey-black	1·75	1·60
2101	**1412**	64p. gold, greenish yellow, cerise, new blue and grey-black	2·50	2·40

Set of 4	5·75	5·25
Set of 4 Gutter Pairs	13·00	
First Day Cover (Philatelic Bureau) (Type J, see Introduction)		8·00
First Day Cover (Newtown, Powis)		8·50
Presentation Pack (P.O. Pack No. 300)	7·50	
PHQ Cards (set of 4) (209)	8·50	13·00

Special First Day of Issue Postmark

1413 Molecular Structures (DNA Decoding)

1414 Galapagos Finch and Fossilized Skeleton (Darwin's Theory of Evolution)

1415 Rotation of Polarized Light by Magnetism (Faraday's work on Electricity)

1416 Saturn (development of astronomical telescopes)

(Des M. Curtis (19p.), R. Harris Ching (26p.), C. Gray (44p.), from Hubble Space Telescope photograph (64p.). Photo (19p., 44p.) or litho (26p., 44p.) Questa)

1999 (3 Aug – 21 Sept). *Millennium Series. The Scientists' Tale. One centre phosphor band (19p.) or two phosphor bands (others).* P 13½×14 (19p., 64p.) or 14×14½ (26p., 44p.).

2102	**1413**	19p. bright magenta, greenish yellow, new blue, black and silver	75	70
2103	**1414**	26p. greenish yellow, bright magenta, new blue, black, bronze and reddish violet	1·50	1·00
		a. Imperf (pair)	£1500	
		b. Perf 14½×14 (21 Sept)	2·50	2·50
		ba. Booklet pane. No. 2103b×4 with margins all round	8·00	
2104	**1415**	44p. bright magenta, greenish yellow, new blue, black and gold	1·50	1·60
		a. Perf 14½×14 (21 Sept)	2·75	2·75
		ab. Booklet pane. No. 2104a×4 with margins all round	9·00	
2105	**1416**	64p. bright magenta, greenish yellow, new blue, black and silver	2·25	2·40

Set of 4	5·25	5·25
Set of 4 Gutter Pairs	13·00	
First Day Cover (Philatelic Bureau) (Type J, see Introduction)		8·00
First Day Cover (Cambridge)		8·50

Presentation Pack (P.O. Pack No. 301)	7·50	
PHQ Cards (set of 4) (210)	8·50	13·00

Nos. 2103b and 2104a come from the £6.99 World Changers booklet, No. DX23.

Special First Day of Issue Postmark

3-8-1999

(Photo De La Rue)

1999 (11 Aug). *Solar Eclipse. Sheet 89×121 mm. Two phosphor bands.* P 14×14½.

MS2106 T	**1416**×4 (sold at £2.56)		22·00	22·00
	a. Imperf		£15000	
First Day Cover (Philatelic Bureau)				22·00
First Day Cover (Falmouth)				22·00

Special First Day of Issue Postmarks

11-8-1999

11-8-1999

1417 Upland Landscape (Strip Farming)

1418 Horse-drawn Rotary Seed Drill (Mechanical Farming)

1419 Man peeling Potato (Food Imports)

1420 Aerial View of Combine Harvester (Satellite Agriculture)

(Des D. Tress (19p.), C. Wormell (26p.), Tessa Traeger (44p.), R. Cooke (64p.). Photo Walsall (No. 2108a) or De La Rue (others))

1999 (7 – 21 Sept). *Millennium Series. The Farmers' Tale. One centre phosphor band (19p.) or two phosphor bands (others).* P 14×14½.

2107	**1417**	19p. grey-black, greenish yellow, cerise, new blue and silver	75	70
2108	**1418**	26p. chestnut, orange-brown, violet-blue, grey-black, pale turquoise-green and silver	95	1·00
		a. Booklet pane. No. 2108×2 with margins all round (21 Sept)	6·50	
2109	**1419**	44p. silver, yellow-brown, brown and grey-black	2·00	1·60
2110	**1420**	64p. deep brown, greenish yellow, magenta, new blue and silver	2·50	2·40

Set of 4	5·75	5·25
Set of 4 Gutter Pairs	13·00	
First Day Cover (Philatelic Bureau) (Type J, see Introduction)		8·00
First Day Cover (Laxton, Newark)		8·50
Presentation Pack (P.O. Pack No. 302)	7·50	
PHQ Cards (set of 4) (211)	8·50	13·00

The 19p. includes the "EUROPA" emblem. No. 2108a comes from the £2.60 booklet, No. HBA2.

Special First Day of Issue Postmark

1421 Robert the Bruce (Battle of Bannockburn, 1314)

1422 Cavalier and Horse (English Civil War)

1423 War Graves Cemetery, The Somme (World Wars)

1424 Soldiers with Boy (Peace-keeping)

(Des A. Davidson (19p.), R. Kelly (26p.), D. McCullin (44p.), C. Corr (64p.). Litho (19p.) or photo (others) Walsall)

1999 (5 Oct). *Millennium Series. The Soldiers' Tale.* One centre phosphor band (19p.) or two phosphor bands (others). P 14×14½.

2111	**1421**	19p. black, stone and silver	75	70
2112	**1422**	26p. lemon, black, grey, silver and gold..	95	1·00
2113	**1423**	44p. grey-black, black and silver	2·00	1·60
2114	**1424**	64p. greenish yellow, red-orange, bright magenta, pale new blue, black and bright blue	2·50	2·40

Set of 4 .... 5·75 5·25
Set of 4 *Gutter Pairs*........................ 13·00
First Day Cover (Philatelic Bureau) (Type J, see Introduction)........................ 8·00
First Day Cover (London SW)........................ 8·50
Presentation Pack (P.O. Pack No. 303) .... 7·50
PHQ Cards (set of 4) (212) .... 8·50 13·00

The presentation pack was numbered 302 in error.

Special First Day of Issue Postmark

1425 "Hark the herald angels sing" and Hymn book (John Wesley)

1426 King James I and Bible (Authorised Version of Bible)

1427 St. Andrews Cathedral, Fife ("Pilgrimage")

1428 Nativity ("First Christmas")

(Des B. Neuenschwander (19p.), Clare Melinsky (26p.), Catherine Yass (44p.), C. Aitchison (64p.). Photo De La Rue)

1999 (2 Nov). *Millennium Series. The Christians' Tale.* One centre phosphor band (19p.) or two phosphor bands (others). P 14×14½.

2115	**1425**	19p. gold, stone, greenish yellow, bright crimson, deep dull blue, black and yellow-ochre	75	70
		a. Imperf (pair)	£750	
2116	**1426**	26p. gold, greenish yellow, bright scarlet, emerald, dull violet and black	95	1·00
2117	**1427**	44p. gold, greenish yellow, bright magenta, new blue, black and ultramarine	1·50	1·60
2118	**1428**	64p. gold, bistre-yellow, cerise, bright emerald, bistre, slate-blue, pale new blue and black	2·25	2·40

Set of 4 .... 5·25 5·25
Set of 4 *Gutter Pairs*........................ 13·00
First Day Cover (Philatelic Bureau) (Type J, see Introduction)........................ 8·00
First Day Cover (St. Andrews, Fife) .... 8·50
Presentation Pack (P.O. Pack No. 304) .... 7·50
PHQ Cards (set of 4) (213) .... 8·50 13·00

Special First Day of Issue Postmark

1429 "World of the Stage" (Allen Jones)

1430 "World of Music" (Bridget Riley)

1431 "World of Literature" (Lisa Milroy)

1432 "New Worlds" (Sir Howard Hodgkin)

(Photo Walsall)

1999 (7 Dec). *Millennium Series. The Artists' Tale.* One centre phosphor band (19p.) or two phosphor bands (others). P 14×14½.

2119	**1429**	19p. greenish yellow, bright magenta, new blue, black and silver	75	70
2120	**1430**	26p. lemon, orange, pale new blue, violet-blue and black	95	1·00
2121	**1431**	44p. greenish yellow, bright magenta, new blue, black and gold	1·50	1·60
2122	**1432**	64p. greenish yellow, yellow, bright turquoise-green, bright magenta, new blue, black, gold and silver	2·25	2·40

Set of 4		5·25	5·25
Set of 4 Gutter Pairs		13·00	
First Day Cover (Philatelic Bureau) (Type J, see Introduction)			8·00
First Day Cover (Stratford -upon- Avon)			8·50
Presentation Pack (P.O. Pack No. 305)		7·50	
PHQ Cards (set of 4) (214)		8·50	13·00

Special First Day of Issue Postmark

Collectors Pack 1999

1999 (7 Dec). *Comprises Nos. 2069/76, 2080/105 and 2107/22.*
CP2122a Collectors Pack £125

Post Office Yearbook

1999 (7 Dec). *Comprises Nos. 2069/76, 2080/105 and*
2107/22 *in hardback book with slip case* £130

1433a

(Des D. Gentleman. Photo De La Rue)

1999 (14 Dec). *Millennium Series. "Millennium Timekeeper". Sheet 120×89 mm. Each design silver, deep grey, pale olive-grey, greenish grey, grey-black and bright rose-red. Two phosphor bands.* P 14×14½.

MS2123 **1433a** 64p. Clock face and map of North America; 64p. Clock face and map of Asia; 64p. Clock face and map of Middle East; 64p. Clock face and map of Europe .... 26·00 26·00

First Day Cover (Philatelic Bureau)		26·00
First Day Cover (Greenwich SE)		26·00
Presentation Pack (P.O. Pack No. M02)	30·00	
PHQ Cards (set of 5) (PSM02)	14·00	32·00

No. **MS**2123 also exists overprinted "EARLS COURT, LONDON 22-28 MAY 2000 THE STAMP SHOW 2000" from Exhibition Premium Passes, costing £10, available from 1 March 2000 (*Price £35*).

Special First Day of Issue Postmarks

For No. 2124 see Decimal Machin Definitives section.

1438 Barn Owl (World Owl Trust, Muncaster) Science Centre, Leicester)

1439 Night Sky (National Space

1440 River Goyt and Textile Mills (Torrs Walkway, New Mills)

1441 Gannets (Seabird Centre, North Berwick)

(Litho (44p.), photo (others) Walsall (No. 2126a/ab) or Questa (others))

2000 (18 Jan)–**02**. *Millennium Projects (1st series). "Above and Beyond".* One centre phosphor band (19p.) or two phosphor bands (others). P 14×14½ (1st, 44p.) or 13½×14 (others).

2125	**1438**	19p. greenish yellow, magenta, pale new blue, black and silver		1·25	70
		a. Imperf (pair)		£1700	
2126	**1439**	26p. greenish yellow, magenta, pale new blue, black and silver		95	1·00
		aa. Imperf (pair)		£1700	
2126a		(1st) greenish yellow, magenta, pale new blue, black and silver (26.5.00)		5·25	4·50
		ab. Booklet pane. Nos. 2126a and 2139 with margins all round		7·00	
		ac. Booklet pane. No. 2126a×4 with margins all round (24.9.02)		15·00	
2127	**1440**	44p. black, bistre-brown, buff and silver		1·50	1·75
2128	**1441**	64p. greenish yellow, magenta, blue, black, silver and orange		2·50	2·50

Set of 4 (ex No. 2126a)	5·75	6·00
Set of 4 Gutter Pairs	13·00	
First Day Cover (Nos. 2125/8) (Philatelic Bureau) (Type J, see Introduction)		8·00
First Day Cover (Nos. 2125/8) (Muncaster, Ravenglass)		8·50
First Day Cover (No. 2126ab) (Philatelic Bureau)		7·00
First Day Cover (No. 2126ab) (Leicester)		7·00
Presentation Pack (P.O. Pack No. 307)	7·00	
PHQ Cards (set of 4) (215)	8·50	13·00

No. 2126a comes from the £2.70 Millennium booklet, No. HBA3, and the "Across the Universe" sponsored booklet, No. DX29.

Imperforate pairs of No. 2125 with Queen's head in gold, Nos. 2126 and 2139 with inscriptions in an alternative typeface and No. 2128 with inscriptions in silver are all of proof status (Prices from £200).

Special First Day of Issue Postmarks

1442 Millennium Beacon (Beacons across The Land)

1443 Garratt Steam Locomotive No. 143 pulling Train (Rheilffordd Eryri, Welsh Highland Railway)

1444 Lightning (Dynamic Earth Centre, Edinburgh)

1445 Multicoloured Lights (Lighting Croydon's Skyline)

(Photo De La Rue)

2000 (1 Feb). *Millennium Projects (2nd series). "Fire and Light". One centre phosphor band (19p.) or two phosphor bands (others). P 14×14½.*

2129	**1442**	19p. silver, greenish yellow, bright magenta, new blue and black	75	70
2130	**1443**	26p. silver, greenish yellow, bright magenta, new blue and black	1·25	1·00
2131	**1444**	44p. silver, greenish yellow, bright magenta, new blue and black	1·50	1·50
2132	**1445**	64p. silver, greenish yellow, bright magenta, pale greenish blue and black..........	2·25	2·50

Set of 4	5·50	5·50
Set of 4 Gutter Pairs	13·00	
First Day Cover (Philatelic Bureau) (Type J, see Introduction)		8·00
First Day Cover (Edinburgh 3°10′W)		8·50
Presentation Pack (P.O. Pack No. 308)	7·00	
PHQ Cards (set of 4) (216)	8·50	13·00

Special First Day of Issue Postmark

1446 Queen Victoria and Queen Elizabeth II

(Des J. Matthews. Photo Walsall)

2000 (15 Feb). *T **929** redrawn with "1st" face value as T **1446**. Two phosphor bands. P 14 (with one elliptical hole in each vertical side).*

2133	**1446**	(1st) brownish black and cream................	1·50	1·25
		l. Booklet pane. No. 2133×6 with margins all round	8·00	

First Day Cover (No. 2133l) (Philatelic Bureau)		4·00
First Day Cover (No. 2133l) (London SW5)		4·00

No. 2133 was only issued in £7.50 stamp booklets. For illustrations of first day cover cancellations see below No. 2124.

1447 Beach Pebbles (Turning the Tide, Durham Coast)

1448 Frog's Legs and Water Lilies (National Pondlife Centre, Merseyside)

1449 Cliff Boardwalk (Parc Arfordirol, Llanelli Coast)

1450 Reflections in Water (Portsmouth Harbour Development)

(Litho (44p.), photo (others) Walsall)

2000 (7 Mar). *Millennium Projects (3rd series). "Water and Coast". One centre phosphor band (19p.) or two phosphor bands (others). P 14×14½.*

2134	**1447**	19p. silver, black, dull blue, sagegreen, olive-grey, orange-yellow and pale grey................	75	70
2135	**1448**	26p. new blue, silver, black, greenish yellow and magenta................	1·25	1·00
2136	**1449**	44p. black, grey and silver................	1·50	1·50
2137	**1450**	64p. black, grey, deep bluish green, greenish blue, cobalt, grey-green and brownish grey	2·25	2·50

Set of 4	5·50	5·50
Set of 4 Gutter Pairs	13·00	
First Day Cover (Philatelic Bureau) (Type J, see Introduction)		8·00
First Day Cover (Llanelli)		8·50
Presentation Pack (P.O. Pack No. 309)	7·00	
PHQ Cards (set of 4) (217)	8·50	13·00

Special First Day of Issue Postmark

1451 Reed Beds, River Braid (ECOS, Ballymena)

1452 South American Leafcutter Ants ("Web of Life" Exhibition, London Zoo)

1453 Solar Sensors (Earth Centre, Doncaster)

1454 Hydroponic Leaves (Project SUZY, Teesside)

(Photo De La Rue)

2000 (4 Apr). *Millennium Projects (4th series). "Life and Earth". One centre phosphor band (2nd) or two phosphor bands (others). P 14×14½.*

2138	**1451**	(2nd) silver, greenish yellow, magenta, new blue, black and grey................	75	70
2139	**1452**	(1st) silver, greenish yellow, magenta, new blue and black	1·25	1·00
2140	**1453**	44p. silver, greenish yellow, magenta, new blue and black	1·50	1·50
2141	**1454**	64p. silver, greenish yellow, magenta, new blue and grey-black................	2·25	1·50

Set of 4	5·50	5·50
Set of 4 Gutter Pairs	13·00	

First Day Cover (Philatelic Bureau) (Type J, see
Introduction).. 8·00
First Day Cover (Doncaster).. 8·50
Presentation Pack (P.O. Pack No. 310) .... 7·00
PHQ Cards (set of 4) (218) .... 8·50 13·00
For No. 2139 printed by Walsall in photogravure, see booklet pane
No. 2126ab.
Types **1453/4** with face values of 45p. and 65p. were prepared, but
not issued.

Special First Day of Issue Postmark

1455 Pottery Glaze (Ceramica
Museum, Stoke-on-Trent)

1456 Bankside Galleries
(Tate Modern, London)

1457 Road Marking (Cycle
Network Artworks)

1458 People of Salford (Lowry
Centre, Salford)

(Photo Enschedé)

2000 (2 May). *Millennium Projects (5th series). "Art and Craft". One
centre phosphor band (2nd) or two phosphor bands (others).*
P 14×14½.

2142	**1455**	(2nd)	greenish yellow, magenta, new blue, black, silver and greybrown....	75	70
2143	**1456**	(1st)	greenish yellow, magenta, new blue, black and silver.............	1·25	1·00
2144	**1457**	45p.	greenish yellow, magenta, new blue, black and silver.............	1·50	1·50
2145	**1458**	65p.	greenish yellow, magenta, new blue, black, dull silver and silver.......	2·25	2·50

Set of 4 .... 5·50 5·50
Set of 4 Gutter Pairs.. 13·00
First Day Cover (Philatelic Bureau) (Type J, see
Introduction) .... 8·00
First Day Cover (Salford)...................................... 8·50
Presentation Pack (P.O. Pack No. 311) .... 7·50
PHQ Cards (set of 4) (219) .... 8·50 13·00

Special First Day of Issue Postmark

For Nos. **MS**2146/7 see Decimal Machin Definitives section.

1460 Children playing
(Millennium Greens Project)

1461 Millennium Bridge,
Gateshead

1462 Daisies (Mile End Park,
London)

1463 African Hut and
Thatched Cottage ("On the
Meridian Line" Project)

(Photo (2nd, 45p.) or litho (1st, 65p.) Walsall)

2000 (6 June). *Millennium Projects (6th series). "People and Places".
One centre phosphor band (2nd) or two phosphor bands (others).*
P 14×14½.

2148	**1460**	(2nd)	bistre-yellow, bright magenta, new blue, grey-black and silver	75	70
2149	**1461**	(1st)	deep ultramarine, silver, black, new blue, bright magenta and greenish yellow	1·25	1·00
2150	**1462**	45p.	greenish yellow, magenta, pale new blue, grey-black, silver and deep turquoise-green.....................	1·50	1·50
2151	**1463**	65p.	silver, black, new blue, bright magenta and greenish yellow	2·25	2·50

Set of 4 .... 5·50 5·50
Set of 4 Gutter Pairs.. 13·00
First Day Cover (Philatelic Bureau) (Type J, see
Introduction) .... 8·00
First Day Cover (Gateshead)................................ 8·50
Presentation Pack (P.O. Pack No. 312) .... 7·50
PHQ Cards (set of 4) (220) .... 8·50 13·00

Special First Day of Issue Postmark

1464 Raising the Stone
(Strangford Stone, Killyleagh)

1465 Horse's Hooves (Trans
Pennine Trail, Derbyshire)

1466 Cyclist (Kingdom of Fife
Cycle Ways, Scotland)

1467 Bluebell Wood
(Groundwork's "Changing
Places" Project)

(Photo Walsall (Nos. 2153a, 2155a) or Enschedé (others))

2000 (4 July–18 Sept). *Millennium Projects (7th series). "Stone and Soil".*
One centre phosphor band (2nd) or two phosphor bands (others).
P 14×14½

2152	**1464**	(2nd) brownish black, grey-black and silver	75	70
2153	**1465**	(1st) greenish yellow, bright magenta, new blue, grey-black, silver and grey	1·25	1·00
		a. Booklet pane. Nos. 2153 and 2157 with margins all round (18 Sept)	9·00	
2154	**1466**	45p. brownish black, grey-black, black and silver	1·50	1·75
2155	**1467**	65p. greenish yellow, bright magenta, new blue, black and silver	2·50	2·50
		a. Booklet pane. No. 2155×2 with margins all round (18 Sept)	5·00	

Set of 4 .... 5·50 5·75
Set of 4 *Gutter Pairs* .... 13·00
First Day Cover (Philatelic Bureau) (Type J, see
Introduction) .... 8·00
First Day Cover (Killyleagh) .... 8·50
Presentation Pack (P.O. Pack No. 313) .... 7·50
PHQ Cards (set of 4) (221) .... 8·50 13·00
No. 2155a comes from the £7 Treasury of Trees booklet, No. DX26.

Special First Day of Issue Postmark

4-7-2000

1468 Tree Roots ("Yews for the Millennium" Project)

1469 Sunflower ("Eden" Project, St. Austell)

1470 Sycamore Seeds (Millennium Seed Bank, Wakehurst Place, West Sussex)

1471 Forest, Doire Dach ("Forest for Scotland")

(Photo Walsall (Nos. 2156a, 2158a, 2159a) or De La Rue (others))

2000 (1 Aug – 18 Sept). *Millennium Projects (8th series). "Tree and Leaf".*
One centre phosphor band (2nd) or two phosphor bands (others)).
P 14×14½.

2156	**1468**	(2nd) silver, greenish yellow, magenta, new blue and black	75	70
		a. Booklet pane. No. 2156×4 with margins all round (18 Sept)	4·00	
2157	**1469**	(1st) greenish yellow, magenta, new blue, black and silver	1·25	1·00
2158	**1470**	45p. black, greenish yellow, magenta, new blue, grey-black and silver	1·50	1·60
		a. Booklet pane. No. 2158×4 with margins all round (18 Sept)	6·00	
2159	**1471**	65p. silver, greenish yellow, magenta, new blue and black	2·50	2·50
		a. Booklet pane. No. 2159×2 with margins all round (18 Sept)	5·00	

Set of 4 .... 5·50 5·50
Set of 4 *Gutter Pairs* .... 13·00
First Day Cover (Philatelic Bureau) (Type J, see
Introduction) .... 8·00
First Day Cover (St Austell) .... 8·50
Presentation Pack (P.O. Pack No. 314) .... 7·50

PHQ Cards (set of 4) (222) .... 8·50 13·00
Nos. 2156a, 2158a and 2159a come from the £7 Treasury of Trees booklet, No. DX26. For No. 2157 printed by Walsall in photogravure, see booklet pane No. 2153a.

Special First Day of Issue Postmark

1-8-2000

1472 Queen Elizabeth the Queen Mother

1472a Royal Family on Queen Mother's 99th Birthday

(Des J. Gibbs from photo by J. Swannell. Photo Questa (Nos. 2160, **MS**2161a) or De La Rue (No. **MS**2161))

2000 (4 Aug). *Queen Elizabeth the Queen Mother's 100th Birthday.*
Phosphorised paper plus two phosphor bands. P 14½.

2160	**1472**	27p. silver, greenish yellow, magenta, new blue and black	2·50	2·75
		a. Booklet pane. No. 2160×4 with margins all round	9·00	
MS2161		121×89mm. **1472a** 27p.×4, silver, greenish yellow, magenta, new blue and black	11·00	11·00
		a. Booklet pane. As No. **MS**2161, but larger, 150×95 mm, and with additional silver frame	10·00	8·00

First Day Cover (No. 2160a) (Philatelic Bureau) .... 8·00
First Day Cover (No. 2160a) (London SW1) .... 8·00
First Day Cover (**MS**2161) (Philatelic Bureau) .... 12·00
First Day Cover (**MS**2161) (London SW1) .... 12·00
Presentation Pack (**MS**2161) (P.O. Pack No. M04) .... 38·00
PHQ Cards (set of 5) (PSM04) .... 11·00 24·00
No. 2160 was only issued in £7.03 stamp booklets and as part of Nos. **MS**2161/a.
The complete miniature sheet is shown on one of the PHQ cards with the others depicting individual stamps.

Special First Day of Issue Postmarks

1473 Head of Gigantiops *destructor* (Ant) (Wildscreen at Bristol)

1474 Gathering Water Lilies on Broads (Norfolk and Norwich Project)

1475 X-ray of Hand holding Computer Mouse (Millennium Point, Birmingham)

1476 Tartan Wool Holder (Scottish Cultural Resources Access Network)

(Litho Walsall)

2000 (5 Sept). *Millennium Projects (9th series). "Mind and Matter".* One centre phosphor band (2nd) or two phosphor bands (others). P 14×14½.

2162	**1473**	(2nd) black, orange-yellow, slate-green and silver	75	70
2163	**1474**	(1st) black, sage-green, ochre and gold..	1·25	1·00
2164	**1475**	45p. silver, black, new blue, magenta and greenish yellow	1·50	1·75
2165	**1476**	65p. silver, black, new blue, magenta and greenish yellow	2·25	2·50
Set of 4			5·50	5·75
Set of 4 Gutter Pairs			13·00	
First Day Cover (Philatelic Bureau) (Type J, see Introduction)				8·00
First Day Cover (Norwich)				8·50
Presentation Pack (P.O. Pack No. 315)			7·50	
PHQ Cards (set of 4) (223)			8·50	13·00

Special First Day of Issue Postmark

5-9-2000

1477 Acrobatic Performers (Millennium Dome)

1478 Football Players (Hampden Park, Glasgow)

1479 Bather (Bath Spa Project)

1480 Hen's Egg under Magnification (Centre for Life, Newcastle)

(Litho (2nd) or photo (others) Questa)

2000 (3 Oct). *Millennium Projects (10th series). "Body and Bone".* One centre phosphor band (2nd) or two phosphor bands (others). P 14×14½ (2nd) or 13½×14 (others).

2166	**1477**	(2nd) black, slate-blue and silver	75	70
2167	**1478**	(1st) magenta, new blue, greenish yellow, black and silver	1·25	1·00
2168	**1479**	45p. mauve, olive-grey, greenish yellow, grey-black and silver	1·50	1·50
2169	**1480**	65p. magenta, pale new blue, greenish yellow, grey-black and silver	2·25	2·50
Set of 4			5·50	5·75
Set of 4 Gutter Pairs			13·00	
First Day Cover (Philatelic Bureau) (Type J, see Introduction)				8·00
First Day Cover (Glasgow)				8·50
Presentation Pack (P.O. Pack No. 316)			7·50	
PHQ Cards (set of 4) (224)			8·50	13·00

Special First Day of Issue Postmark

3-10-2000

1481 Virgin and Child Stained Glass Window, St. Edmundsbury Cathedral (Suffolk Cathedral Millennium Project)

1482 Floodlit Church of St. Peter and St. Paul, Overstowey (Church Floodlighting Trust)

1483 12th-cent Latin Gradual (St. Patrick Centre, Downpatrick)

1484 Chapter House Ceiling, York Minster (York Millennium Mystery Plays)

(Photo De La Rue)

2000 (7 Nov). *Millennium Projects (11th series). "Spirit and Faith".* One centre phosphor band (2nd) or two phosphor bands (others). P 14×14½.

2170	**1481**	(2nd) gold, greenish yellow, cerise, new blue and grey-black	75	70
		a. Imperf pair	£800	
2171	**1482**	(1st) gold, greenish yellow, cerise, new blue, bright blue, black and grey-black	1·25	1·00
		a. Imperf (pair)	£750	
2172	**1483**	45p. deep reddish purple, olive-sepia, red, black and gold	1·50	1·50
2173	**1484**	65p. gold, greenish yellow, cerise, new blue, grey-black and black	2·25	2·50
Set of 4			5·50	5·50
Set of 4 Gutter Pairs			13·00	
First Day Cover (Philatelic Bureau) (Type J, see Introduction)				8·00
First Day Cover (Downpatrick)				8·50
Presentation Pack (P.O. Pack No. 317)			7·50	
PHQ Cards (set of 4) (225)			8·50	13·00

No. 2173 has been reported with the gold omitted, leaving the Queen's head in yellow. It is only known used.

Special First Day of Issue Postmark

Post Office Yearbook

2000 (Nov 7). Comprises Nos. 2125/6, 2127/32, 2134/45, 2148/59 and **MS**2161/77 in hardback book with slip case £110

The last two issues in the Millennium Projects Series were supplied for insertion into the above at a later date.

1485 Church Bells (Ringing in the Millennium)

1486 Eye (Year of the Artist)

1487 Top of Harp (Canolfan Mileniwm, Cardiff)

1488 Silhouetted Figure within Latticework (TS2K Creative Enterprise Centres, London)

(Photo De La Rue)

2000 (5 Dec). Millennium Projects (12th series). "Sound and Vision". One centre phosphor band (2nd) or two phosphor bands (others). P 14×14½.

2174	**1485**	(2nd) silver, greenish yellow, magenta, new blue and black	75	70
2175	**1486**	(1st) silver, magenta, blue, black and brownish grey..	1·25	1·00
2176	**1487**	45p. silver, greenish yellow, magenta, new blue and black	1·50	1·50
2177	**1488**	65p. black, greenish yellow, magenta, new blue, grey-black and silver........	2·25	2·50

Set of 4 .... 5·50 5·50
Set of 4 Gutter Pairs... 13·00
First Day Cover (Philatelic Bureau) (Type J, see Introduction).. 8·00
First Day Cover (Cardiff) .... 8·50
Presentation Pack (P.O. Pack No. 318) .... 7·50
PHQ Cards (set of 4) (226) .... 8·50 13·00

Special First Day of Issue Postmark

Collectors Pack 2000

2000 (Dec 5) Comprises Nos. 2125/6, 2127/32, 2134/45, 2148/59 and **MS**2161/77.
CP2181a Collectors Pack... £120

1489 "Flower" ("Nurture Children")

1490 "Tiger" ("Listen to Children")

1491 "Owl" ("Teach Children")

1492 "Butterfly" ("Ensure Children's Freedom")

(Des Why Not Associates. Photo De La Rue)

2001 (16 Jan). New Millennium. Rights of the Child. Face Paintings. One centre phosphor band (2nd) or two phosphor bands (others). P 14×14½.

2178	**1489**	(2nd) bright violet, greenish yellow, cerise, new blue, rosine, grey-black and silver	75	75
2179	**1490**	(1st) lemon, greenish yellow, cerise, new blue, emerald, grey-black and silver	1·00	1·10
2180	**1491**	45p. orange-yellow, greenish yellow, cerise, new blue, pale violet-blue, grey-black and silver	1·60	1·75
2181	**1492**	65p. bright violet, greenish yellow, cerise, new blue, lemon, grey-black and silver	2·40	2·50

Set of 4 .... 5·75 5·75
Set of 4 Gutter Pairs... 14·00
First Day Cover (Philatelic Bureau).................... 7·50
First Day Cover (Hope, Hope Valley) .... 8·00
Presentation Pack (P.O. Pack No. 319) .... 7·50
PHQ Cards (set of 4) (227) .... 7·50 10·00

Special First Day of Issue Postmarks

1493 "Love"

1494 "THANKS"

1495 "abc" (New Baby)

1496 "WELCOME"

1497 " Cheers"

(Des Springpoint Design. Photo Enschedé)

2001 (6 Feb). *Greetings Stamps. "Occasions".* Two phosphor bands.
P 14×14½.

2182	**1493**	(1st)	silver, greenish yellow, magenta, pale greenish blue, black and silver-grey ..	1·30	1·30
2183	**1494**	(1st)	silver, greenish yellow, magenta, pale greenish blue, black and silver-grey ..	1·30	1·30
2184	**1495**	(1st)	silver, greenish yellow, magenta, pale greenish blue, black and silver-grey ..	1·30	1·30
2185	**1496**	(1st)	silver, greenish yellow, magenta, pale greenish blue, black and silver-grey ...	1·30	1·30
2186	**1497**	(1st)	silver, greenish yellow, magenta, pale greenish blue, black and silver-grey ..	1·30	1·30

Set of 5	5·75	5·75
Set of 5 Gutter Pairs	13·00	
First Day Cover (Philatelic Bureau)		7·50
First Day Cover (Merry Hill, Wolverhampton)		8·00
Presentation Pack (13 Feb) (P.O. Pack No. M05)	10·00	
PHQ Cards (set of 5) (PSM05)	8·50	11·00

The silver-grey backgrounds are printed in Iriodin ink which gives a shiny effect.

Further packs of Nos. 2182/6 were sold from 3 July 2001. These comprised the listed stamps in blocks of ten (from sheets) with an insert describing the occasion (*Price* £10 *per pack*).

Nos. 2182/6 were re-issued on 1 May 2001 in sheets of 20 printed by Questa in lithography instead of photogravure, in connection with the "customised" stamps scheme. Such sheets contained twenty examples of either Nos. 2182, 2184 or 2185, or ten each of Nos. 2183 and 2186. Sheets with personal photographs printed on the labels were available from Royal Mail in Edinburgh at £12 each. From 5 June 2001 a similar sheet (LS4) containing four of each design in horizontal strips, with postal symbols on the labels, was sold at £5.95.

Special First Day of Issue Postmarks

1498 Dog and Owner on Bench

1499 Dog in Bath

1500 Boxer at Dog Show

1501 Cat in Handbag

1502 Cat on Gate

1503 Dog in Car

1504 Cat at Window

1505 Dog Behind Fence

1506 Cat watching Bird

1507 Cat in Washbasin

(Des johnson banks. Photo Walsall)

2001 (13 Feb). *Cats and Dogs. Self-adhesive.* Two phosphor bands.
P 15×14 die-cut.

2187	**1498**	(1st)	black, grey and silver	80	50
		a.	Sheetlet. Nos. 2187/96	15·00	15·00
		aa.	Imperf (sheetlet)	£20000	
		b.	Booklet pane. Nos. 2187/96 plus No. 2040×2	30·00	
		ba.	Imperf (pane)		
2188	**1499**	(1st)	black, grey and silver	80	50
2189	**1500**	(1st)	black, grey and silver	80	50
2190	**1501**	(1st)	black, grey and silver	80	50
2191	**1502**	(1st)	black, grey and silver	80	50
2192	**1503**	(1st)	black, grey and silver	80	50
2193	**1504**	(1st)	black, grey and silver	80	50
2194	**1505**	(1st)	black, grey and silver	80	50
2195	**1506**	(1st)	black, grey and silver	80	50
2196	**1507**	(1st)	black, grey and silver	80	50

2187/96 Set of 10	15·00	15·00
First Day Cover (Philatelic Bureau)		15·00
First Day Cover (Petts Wood, Orpington)		16·00
Presentation Pack (P.O. Pack No. 320)	20·00	
PHQ Cards (set of 10) (228)	14·00	30·00

Nos. 2187/96 were printed together in sheetlets of 10 (5×2), with the surplus self-adhesive paper around each stamp retained. The pane has vertical roulettes between rows 2/3 and 4/5 with the design on the reverse of the backing paper similar to Booklet No. PM1.

Special First Day of Issue Postmarks

1508 "RAIN"

1509 "FAIR"

1510 "STORMY"

1511 "VERY DRY"

(Des H. Brown and T. Meeuwissen. Photo De La Rue)

2001 (13 Mar). *The Weather.* One side phosphor band (19p.) or two phosphor bands (others). P 14½.

| 2197 | **1508** | 19p. | black, greenish yellow, bright magenta, new blue and gold | 70 | 75 |

Did you miss the boat or did you take our advice?

In 1973 we recommended and sold the British definitive 1/2p (SGX842) with one phosphor band on side. We told our customers to buy them at 25p each. WE WERE RIGHT!! Today this stamp is catalogued at £55.00 each. If you had taken our advice, for an outlay of only £50 in1973, the current catalogue value of your investment would be a staggering total of £11,000.00.

In 1999 we recommended our customers to buy the Princess Diana Welsh Language Presentation Packs. The catalogue value was only £2.50 each, but we were telling our customers to buy them for up to double catalogue value £5 each. Within only 6 years they had increased by 5,900%.

As everyone knows, investments can go down as well as up and the past in not necessarily a guide to the future. However, being selective and taking sound advice is the best way to make your hobby pay for itself.

In 2003 we recommended our customers to buy the Coronation £1 Green (SG 2380) which was catalogued by Stanley Gibbons at £1.50 per stamp. Within 1 year the catalogue value had increased to £50 per stamp, an increase of over 3,200%.

In 2004 we told our customers to buy the Fruit & Veg Presentation Pack – it was catalogued at £4.50. We said ignore the catalogue value, it's cheap at even treble the catalogue value – this pack increased in Stanley Gibbons Catalogue to £60

within two years; an increase of well over 1,200%. We hope that you took our advice in 2004. We recommended you to buy the Locomotives Miniature Sheet (SG.MS.2423). The Stanley Gibbons Catalogue value was £3.75 each. Within 1 year the Stanley Gibbons Catalogue had increased to £25 each - An increase of over 550% in only one year.

In 2005 we recommended the 2003 Rugby Presentation Pack. The 2005 Stanley Gibbons concise catalogue listed this at £6 and, within 3 years, the catalogue value had soared. The 2008 Concise Catalogue value for the Rugby Presentation Pack was £35 each, a truly massive increase. We hope you took our advice.

In 2008 we recommended the 2002 Bridges of London Presentation pack (number 338). At the time the catalogue value was £8 each. Within 2 years of our recommendation the catalogue value of the Presentation Pack increased to £25 each. This year the catalogue value increased once again from £25 per pack to £55 per pack.

Earlier this year we recommended our customers to buy the Nobel Prizes Presentation Pack. The catalogue value was £10 each. After our recommendation the price zoomed in the latest catalogue to a staggering £50 each. Our customers have complimented us and said once again "You were right!"

We now strongly recommend you to buy the 2001 Flags Presentation pack, pack number MO6, at the best possible price.

PLEASE LISTEN TO US NOW!
**For our most recent up to the minute recommendations
Please telephone 01273 326994**

12 Prince Albert Street, Brighton,
Sussex BN1 1HE
Tel: 01273 326994

2198	**1509**	27p. black, greenish yellow, bright magenta, new blue and gold............	85	1·00
2199	**1510**	45p. black, greenish yellow, bright magenta, new blue and gold............	1·50	1·50
2200	**1511**	65p. black, greenish yellow, bright magenta, new blue and gold............	2·40	2·50

Set of 4	5·00	5·50
Set of 4 Gutter Pairs...	14·00	
First Day Cover (Philatelic Bureau).................		7·50
First Day Cover (Fraserburgh)...........................		8·00
Presentation Pack (P.O. Pack No. 321).............	14·00	
MS2201 105×105 mm. Nos. 2197/200	18·00	18·00
First Day Cover (Philatelic Bureau).................		19·00
First Day Cover (Fraserburgh)...........................		20·00
PHQ Cards (set of 5) (229)	8·50	20·00

Nos. 2197/200 show the four quadrants of a barometer dial which are combined on the miniature sheet. The reddish violet on both the 27p. and the miniature sheet is printed in thermochromic ink which changes from reddish violet to light blue when exposed to heat. The PHQ cards depict the four values and the miniature sheet.

Special First Day of Issue Postmarks

1512 *Vanguard* Class Submarine, 1992

1513 *Swiftsure* Class Submarine, 1973

1514 *Unity* Class Submarine, 1939

1515 "Holland" Type Submarine, 1901

1516 White Ensign

1517 Union Jack

1518 Jolly Roger flown by H.M.S. *Proteus* (submarine)

1519 Flag of Chief of Defence Staff

(Des. D. Davis. Photo Questa)

2001 (10 Apr – 22 Oct). *Centenary of Royal Navy Submarine Service. One centre phosphor band (2nd) or two phosphor bands (others).* P 15×14.

(a) Submarines. Ordinary gum.

2202	**1512**	(2nd) black, brownish black, dull purple and gold..	80	75
		a. Perf 15½×15 (22 Oct)	3·75	3·00
		ab. Booklet pane. Nos. 2202a and 2204a, each ×2, with margins all round	12·00	
2203	**1513**	(1st) black, azure, slate-blue and gold.....	1·00	90

		a. Perf 15½×15 (22 Oct)......................	3·75	3·00
		b. Imperf (pair)	£1500	
		ab. Booklet pane. Nos. 2203a and 2205a, each ×2, with margins all round	12·00	
2204	**1514**	45p. magenta, chrome yellow, new blue, black and gold........................	1·75	1·60
		a. Perf 15½×15 (22 Oct)	3·75	3·00
2205	**1515**	65p. magenta, chrome yellow, new blue, black and gold........................	2·40	2·50
		a. Perf 15½×15 (22 Oct)	3·75	3·00

Set of 4	5·25	5·25
Set of 4 Gutter Pairs...	13·50	
First Day Cover (Philatelic Bureau).................		7·50
First Day Cover (Portsmouth)...........................		8·00
Presentation Pack (P.O. Pack No. 322).............	20·00	
PHQ Cards (set of 4) (230)	7·50	12·00

(b) Flags. Ordinary gum. P 14½.

MS2206 92×97 mm. **1516** (1st) bright scarlet, blue and silver; **1517** (1st) bright scarlet, blue and silver; **1518** (1st) black, blue and silver; **1519** (1st) bright scarlet, blue, greenish yellow, black and silver (22 Oct)............	9·00	9·00
a. Booklet pane. As No. **MS**2206 but larger, 152×96 mm	9·00	9·00
First Day Cover (Tallents House)....................		11·00
First Day Cover (Rosyth, Dunfermline).........		12·00
Presentation Pack (P.O. Pack No. M06)...........	30·00	
PHQ Cards (set of 5) (PSM07)...........................	12·00	15·00

(c) Self-adhesive. Die-cut P 15½×14 (No. 2207) or 14½ (others).

2207	**1513**	(1st) black, azure, slate-blue and gold (17 Apr)......................................	50·00	40·00
		a. Booklet pane. No. 2207×2 plus No. 2040×4	£100	
		ab. Booklet pane. Imperf	£4500	
2208	**1516**	(1st) bright scarlet, blue and silver (22 Oct)......................................	15·00	15·00
		a. Booklet pane. Nos. 2208/9 plus No. 2040×4	22·00	
		ab. Booklet pane. Imperf		
2209	**1518**	(1st) black, blue and silver (22 Oct)...........	15·00	15·00

The five PHQ cards depict the four designs and the complete miniature sheet.

Nos. 2202a/5a were only issued in the £6.76 "Unseen and Unheard" booklet, No. DX27, and Nos. 2207/9 only come from two different £1.62 self-adhesive booklets, Nos. PM2 and PM4.

Type **1516** was re-issued on 21 June 2005 in sheets of 20, printed in lithography by Cartor and sold at £6.55, containing four vertical rows of five stamps alternated with half stamp-size printed labels showing signal flags (LS25). These sheets with personalised photographs were available at £14.95 from the Royal Mail.

Type **1517** was re-issued on 27 July 2004 in sheets of 20, printed in lithography by Walsall and sold at £6.15, containing vertical strips of five stamps alternated with half stamp-size printed labels (LS20). These sheets with personalised photographs were available at £14.95 from the Royal Mail in Edinburgh.

See also Nos. 2581 and 2805.

Special First Day of Issue Postmarks

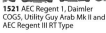

1520 Leyland X2 Open-top, London General B Type, Leyland Titan TD1 and AEC Regent 1

1521 AEC Regent 1, Daimler COG5, Utility Guy Arab Mk II and AEC Regent III RT Type

1522 AEC Regent III RT Type, Bristol KSW5G Open-top, AEC Routemaster and Bristol Lodekka FSF6G

1523 Bristol Lodekka FSF6G, Leyland Titan PD3/4, Leyland Atlantean PDR1/1 and Daimler Fleetline CRG6LX-33

1524 Daimler Fleetline CRG6LX-33, MCW Metrobus DR102/43, Leyland Olympian ONLXB/1R and Dennis Trident

(Des M. English. Litho Questa)

2001 (15 May). *150th Anniv of First Double-decker Bus. "All-over" phosphor.* P 14½×14.

2210	**1520**	(1st) new blue, greenish yellow, magenta, black and grey		75	50
		a. Horiz strip of 5. Nos. 2210/14		6·00	6·00
		ab. Imperf (horiz strip of 5)		£5000	
		b. Grey omitted		—	
2211	**1521**	(1st) new blue, greenish yellow, magenta, black and grey		75	50
2212	**1522**	(1st) new blue, greenish yellow, magenta, black and grey		75	50
		a. Grey omitted		—	
2213	**1523**	(1st) new blue, greenish yellow, magenta, black and grey		75	50
		a. Grey omitted		—	
2214	**1524**	(1st) new blue, greenish yellow, magenta, black and grey		75	50
		a. Grey omitted		—	
Set of 5				6·00	6·00
Gutter Strip of 10				12·00	
First Day Cover (Philatelic Bureau)					6·50
First Day Cover (Covent Garden, London WC2)					7·00
Presentation Pack (P.O. Pack No. 323)				10·00	
PHQ Cards (set of 6) (231)				14·00	16·00
MS2215 120×105 mm. Nos. 2210/14				10·50	10·50
First Day Cover (Philatelic Bureau)					15·00
First Day Cover (Covent Garden, London WC2)					15·00

Nos. 2210/14 were printed together, *se-tenant*, in horizontal strips of 5 throughout the sheet. The illustrations of the first bus on No. 2210 and the last bus on No. 2214 continue onto the sheet margins.

In No. **MS**2215 the illustrations of the AEC Regent III RT Type and the Daimler Fleetline CRG6LX-33 appear twice.

The six PHQ cards show the five stamps and **MS**2215.

Special First Day of Issue Postmarks

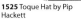

1525 Toque Hat by Pip Hackett

1526 Butterfly Hat by Dai Rees

1527 Top Hat by Stephen Jones

1528 Spiral Hat by Philip Treacy

(Des Rose Design from photos by N. Knight. Litho Enschedé)

2001 (19 June). *Fashion Hats. "All-over" phosphor.* P 14½.

2216	**1525**	(1st) greenish yellow, bright magenta, new blue, grey-black and silver		85	90
2217	**1526**	(E) greenish yellow, bright magenta, new blue, grey-black and silver		1·10	1·25
2218	**1527**	45p. greenish yellow, bright magenta, new blue, grey-black and silver		1·60	1·60
2219	**1528**	65p. greenish yellow, bright magenta, new blue, grey-black and silver		2·50	2·50
Set of 4				5·50	5·50
Set of 4 Gutter Pairs				13·00	
First Day Cover (Tallents House)					7·25
First Day Cover (Ascot)					7·50
Presentation Pack (P.O. Pack No. 324)				7·50	
PHQ Cards (set of 4) (232)				8·50	14·00

Special First Day of Issue Postmarks

1529 Common Frog

1530 Great Diving Beetle

1531 Three-Spined Stickleback

1532 Southern Hawker Dragonfly

(Des J. Gibbs. Photo De La Rue)

2001 (10 July). *Europa. Pond Life. Two phosphor bands.* P 15×14.

2220	**1529**	(1st) black, greenish yellow, bright magenta, new blue, bluish silver and silver		1·00	1·00
2221	**1530**	(E) black, greenish yellow, bright magenta, new blue, bluish silver and silver		1·25	1·25
2222	**1531**	45p. black, greenish yellow, bright magenta, new blue, bluish silver, dull silver and silver		1·50	1·50
2223	**1532**	65p. black, greenish yellow, bright magenta, new blue, bluish silver and silver		2·00	2·25
Set of 4				5·50	5·75
Set of 4 Gutter Pairs				13·00	
First Day Cover (Tallents House)					11·00
First Day Cover (Oundle, Peterborough)					12·00
Presentation Pack (P.O. Pack No. 325)				7·50	
PHQ Cards (set of 4) (233)				8·50	14·00

The 1st and E values incorporate the "EUROPA" emblem. The bluish silver on all four values is in Iriodin ink and was used as a background for those parts of the design below the water line.

Special First Day of Issue Postmarks

1533 Policeman

1534 Clown

1535 Mr. Punch

1536 Judy

1537 Beadle

1538 Crocodile

(Des K. Bernstein from puppets by Bryan Clarkez)

2001 (4 Sept). *Punch and Judy Show Puppets. Two phosphor bands.* P 14×15.

(a) Photo Walsall. Ordinary gum.

2224	**1533**	(1st) greenish yellow, bright magenta, new blue, grey-black, violet, deep magenta, ultramarine and silver......	75	50
		a. Horiz strip of 6. Nos. 2224/9..............	6·50	6·50
2225	**1534**	(1st) greenish yellow, bright magenta, new blue, grey-black, violet, deep magenta, ultramarine and silver......	75	50
2226	**1535**	(1st) greenish yellow, bright magenta, new blue, grey-black, violet, deep magenta, ultramarine and silver......	75	50
2227	**1536**	(1st) greenish yellow, bright magenta, new blue, grey-black, violet, deep magenta, ultramarine and silver......	75	50
2228	**1537**	(1st) greenish yellow, bright magenta, new blue, grey-black, violet, deep magenta, ultramarine and silver......	75	50
2229	**1538**	(1st) greenish yellow, bright magenta, new blue, grey-black, violet, deep magenta, ultramarine and silver......	75	50
Set of 6			6·50	5·50
Gutter Block of 12			13·00	
First Day Cover (Tallents House)................				7·00
First Day Cover (Blackpool)				7·50
Presentation Pack (P.O. Pack No. 326)			7·00	
PHQ Cards (set of 6) (234)			8·50	18·00

(b) Photo Questa. Self-adhesive. Die-cut P 14×15½.

2230	**1535**	(1st) greenish yellow, bright magenta, new blue, grey-black, violet, deep magenta, ultramarine and silver (4 Sept)	17·00	17·00

		a. Booklet pane. Nos. 2230/1 plus No. 2040×4	18·00	
2231	**1536**	(1st) greenish yellow, bright magenta, new blue, grey-black, violet, deep magenta, ultramarine and silver (4 Sept)	17·00	17·00

Nos. 2224/9 were printed together, *se-tenant*, as horizontal strips of 6 in sheets of 60 (6×10).

Nos. 2230/1 were only issued in £1.62 stamp booklets, No. PM3.

Imperforate strips of 6 with alternative background colours to 2224, 2228 and 2229 are of proof status (*Price* £3000).

Special First Day of Issue Postmarks

1539 Carbon 60 Molecule (Chemistry)

1540 Globe (Economic Sciences)

1541 Embossed Dove (Peace)

1542 Crosses (Physiology or Medicine)

1543 Poem "The Addressing of Cats" by T. S. Eliot in Open Book (Literature)

1544 Hologram of Boron Molecule (Physics)

(Des P. Vermier. Eng Ing Madle (1st). Litho and silk-screen ptg (2nd), litho and recess (1st), litho and embossed (E), litho (45p.), litho and hologram (65p.) Enschedé)

2001 (2 Oct). *Centenary of Nobel Prizes. One side phosphor band (2nd) or phosphor frame (others).* P 14½.

2232	**1539**	(2nd) black, silver and grey-black...............	75	65
2233	**1540**	(1st) black, silver, dull mauve, blue and rosine	1·50	90
2234	**1541**	(E) black, silver and bright green	1·50	1·50
2235	**1542**	40p. black, silver, new blue and greenish yellow	2·00	1·50
2236	**1543**	45p. black, silver, yellow-ochre and pale grey......................................	3·00	2·00
2237	**1544**	65p. black and silver..........................	5·00	2·50
Set of 6			12·00	8·00
Set of 6 Gutter Pairs			24·00	
First Day Cover (Tallents House)				9·50
First Day Cover (Cambridge)....................				10·00
Presentation Pack (P.O. Pack No. 327)			50·00	
PHQ Cards (set of 6) (235)			10·00	14·00

The grey-black on No. 2232 is printed in thermochromic ink which temporarily changes to pale grey when exposed to heat. The centre of No. 2235 is coated with a eucalyptus scent.

Trials, differing slightly from the issued stamps, are known for all values.

Special First Day of Issue Postmarks

1545 Robins with Snowman   1546 Robins on Bird Table

1547 Robins skating on Bird Bath   1548 Robins with Christmas Pudding

1549 Robins in Paper Chain Nest

(Des A. Robins and H. Brown. Photo De La Rue)

2001 (6 Nov). *Christmas. Robins. Self-adhesive. One centre phosphor band (2nd) or two phosphor bands (others). Die-cut p 14½.*

2238	1545	(2nd) new blue, blue, greenish yellow, bright magenta, vermilion and black	75	70
		a. Booklet pane. No. 2238×24	12·00	
		b. Imperf (pair)	£950	
2239	1546	(1st) red-orange, blue, greenish yellow, bright magenta, new blue and black	1·00	1·00
		a. Booklet pane. No. 2239×12	8·00	
2240	1547	(E) indigo, azure, greenish yellow, bright magenta, new blue, vermilion and black	1·50	1·50
2241	1548	45p. bright purple, blue, greenish yellow, bright magenta, new blue, vermilion and black	2·00	2·00
2242	1549	65p. greenish blue, blue, greenish yellow, bright magenta, new blue, vermilion and black	3·00	3·00
		a. Imperf (pair) (die-cut perforations and roulettes omitted)	£1300	
		ab. Imperf (pair) (die-cut perforations only omitted)	£750	
		b. Imperf backing paper (pair) (roulettes omitted)	£275	
Set of 5			7·50	7·50
First Day Cover (Tallents House)				9·50
First Day Cover (Bethlehem, Llandeilo)				10·00
Presentation Pack (P.O. Pack No. 328)			8·00	
PHQ Cards (set of 5) (236)			11·00	16·00

Nos. 2238/40 were each printed in sheets of 50 with the surplus backing paper around each stamp retained and separated by gauge 9 roulettes.

The 1st value was re-issued on 30 September 2003 in sheets of 20 (sold at £6.15) printed in lithography instead of photogravure, each stamp accompanied by a stamp-size label showing a snowman (LS14). Sheets with personal photographs printed on the labels were available from Royal Mail, Edinburgh for £14.95 or photobooths at selected post offices and Safeway stores for £15.

The 2nd and 1st values were re-issued together on 1 November 2005 in sheets of 20, printed in lithography by Cartor, sold at £5.60, containing ten 2nd class and ten 1st class, each stamp accompanied by a label showing a snowman (LS27). Separate sheets of 20 2nd class and 20 1st class were available with personalised photographs at £9.95 (2nd) or £14.95 (1st) from Royal Mail.

No. 2238b shows both the die-cut perforations and the roulettes omitted. Stamps from booklet panes Nos. 2238a and 2239a differ from those in sheets by omitting the roulettes in the backing paper between each stamp. Instead there are roulettes after the first and then every alternate horizontal row to assist with the folding of the booklets.

Trials of (2nd) and (1st) stamps in alternative designs are known.

Special First Day of Issue Postmarks

Collectors Pack 2001
2001 (6 Nov). *Comprises Nos. 2178/2200, 2202/6, 2210/14, 2216/29 and 2232/42.*
CP2242a Collectors Pack £120

Post Office Yearbook
2001 (6 Nov) *Comprises Nos.* 2178/96, **MS**2201/6, 2210/14, 2216/29 *and* 2232/42 *in hardback book with slip case* £110

1550 "How the Whale got his Throat"   1551 "How the Camel got his Hump"

1552 "How the Rhinoceros got his Skin"   1553 "How the Leopard got his Spots"

1554 "The Elephant's Child"   1555 "The Sing-Song of Old Man Kangaroo"

1556 "The Beginning of the Armadillos"   1557 "The Crab that played with the Sea"

1558 "The Cat that walked by Himself"　　**1559** "The Butterfly that stamped"

(Des I. Cohen. Photo Walsall)

2002 (15 Jan). *Centenary of Publication of Rudyard Kipling's Just So Stories. Self-adhesive. Two phosphor bands.* Die-cut P 15×14.

2243	**1550**	(1st) new blue, magenta, greenish yellow and black	75	45
		a. Sheetlet. Nos. 2243/52	12·00	10·00
2244	**1551**	(1st) new blue, magenta, greenish yellow and black	75	45
2245	**1552**	(1st) new blue, magenta, greenish yellow and black	75	45
2246	**1553**	(1st) new blue, magenta, greenish yellow and black	75	45
2247	**1554**	(1st) new blue, magenta, greenish yellow and black	75	45
2248	**1555**	(1st) new blue, magenta, greenish yellow and black	75	45
2249	**1556**	(1st) new blue, magenta, greenish yellow and black	75	45
2250	**1557**	(1st) new blue, magenta, greenish yellow and black	75	45
2251	**1558**	(1st) new blue, magenta, greenish yellow and black	75	45
2252	**1559**	(1st) new blue, magenta, greenish yellow and black	75	45
Set of 10			12·00	10·00
First Day Cover (Tallents House)				11·00
First Day Cover (Burwash, Etchingham)				12·00
Presentation Pack (P.O. Pack No. 330)			16·00	
PHQ Cards (set of 10) (237)			10·00	28·00

Nos. 2243/52 were printed together in sheetlets of 10 (5×2), with the surplus self-adhesive paper around each stamp retained. The pane shows vertical roulettes between rows 2/3 and 4/5 and has illustrations on the reverse of the backing paper.

Special First Day of Issue Postmarks

1560 Queen Elizabeth II, 1952 (Dorothy Wilding)　　**1561** Queen Elizabeth II, 1968 (Cecil Beaton)

1562 Queen Elizabeth II, 1978 (Lord Snowdon)　　**1563** Queen Elizabeth II, 1984 (Yousef Karsh)

1564 Queen Elizabeth II, 1996 (Tim Graham)　　**1565**

(Des Kate Stephens. Photo De La Rue)

2002 (6 Feb). *Golden Jubilee. Studio portraits of Queen Elizabeth II by photographers named. One centre phosphor band (2nd) or two phosphor bands (others).* W **1565** (sideways). P 14½×14.

2253	**1560**	(2nd) silver, pale turquoise-green, black and deep grey	75	55
		a. Watermark upright	4·00	70
		b. Booklet pane. Nos. 2253a/6a with margins all round	13·00	
2254	**1561**	(1st) silver, pale turquoise-green, black and grey-black	1·00	80
		a. Watermark upright	2·50	1·00
		b. Booklet pane. Nos. 2254a/7a with margins all round	15·00	
2255	**1562**	(E) silver, pale turquoise-green, black and grey-black	1·50	1·50
		a. Watermark upright	2·75	1·40
2256	**1563**	45p. silver, pale turquoise-green, black and grey-black	1·75	2·00
		a. Watermark upright	3·50	1·50
2257	**1564**	65p. silver, pale turquoise-green, black and grey-black	2·75	3·00
		a. Watermark upright	6·00	2·25
Set of 5			7·00	7·00
Set of 5 Gutter Pairs			16·00	
First Day Cover (Tallents House)				9·00
First Day Cover (Windsor)				9·00
Presentation Pack (P.O. Pack No. 331)			9·00	
PHQ Cards (set of 5) (238)			4·50	14·00

The turquoise-green is used as an underlay for the black colour on all five values.

Nos. 2253a/7a were only available in £7.29 stamp booklets.

Trials, including dates and with values in a different typeface, are known for all values.

Special First Day of Issue Postmarks

1566

(Des M. Farrar-Bell (2nd), Enid Marx (1st). Photo Enschedé)

2002 (6 Feb). *As T* **154/5** *(Wilding definitive of 1952-54), but with service indicator as T* **1566**. *One centre phosphor band (2nd) or two phosphor bands (1st).* W **1565**. *Uncoated paper.* P 15×14 (with one elliptical hole in each vertical side).

2258	**1566**	(2nd) carmine-red	1·20	1·00
		Ea. Watermark diagonal	4·50	3·25
		b. Booklet pane. Nos. 2258×4, 2258Ea and 2259×4 with centre blank label and margins all round	14·00	
2259	–	(1st) green	1·25	1·25
First Day Cover (No. 2258b) (Tallents House)				10·00
First Day Cover (No. 2258b) (Windsor)				10·00

Nos. 2258/9 were only issued in the £7.29 "A Gracious Accession" booklet, No. DX28.

No. 2258b contains a block of 8, four of each value, with a blank central label, plus an additional 2nd value shown to the left at such an angle so as to produce a diagonal watermark. First day cover postmarks were as Nos. 2253/7.

1567 Rabbits ("a new baby")

1568 "LOVE"

1569 Aircraft Sky-writing "hello"

1570 Bear pulling Potted Topiary Tree (Moving Home)

1571 Flowers ("best wishes")

(Des I. Bilbey (Nos. 2260, 2264), A. Kitching (No. 2261), Hoop Associates (No. 2262) and G. Percy (No. 2263))

2002 (5 Mar)–*03. Greetings Stamps. "Occasions". Two phosphor bands.*

(a) Litho Questa. Ordinary gum. P 15×14.

2260	**1567**	(1st) greenish yellow, magenta, new blue, black and lilac	1·25	1·10
2261	**1568**	(1st) greenish yellow, magenta, new blue, black and silver	1·25	1·10
2262	**1569**	(1st) greenish yellow, magenta, new blue and black	1·25	1·10
2263	**1570**	(1st) greenish yellow, magenta, new blue and black	1·25	1·10
2264	**1571**	(1st) greenish yellow, magenta, new blue, black and cobalt	1·25	1·10

Set of 5	6·00	5·00
Set of 5 Gutter Pairs	11·00	
First Day Cover (Tallents House)		6·75
First Day Cover (Merry Hill, Wolverhampton)		7·00
Presentation Pack (P.O. Pack No. M07)	6·50	
PHQ Cards (set of 5) (PSM08)	4·50	14·00

(b) Photo Questa. Self-adhesive. Die-cut P 15×14.

2264a	**1569**	(1st) greenish yellow, magenta, new blue and black (4.3.03)	6·00	6·00
		ab. Booklet pane. No. 2264a×2 plus No. 2295×4	14·00	

Nos. 2260/4 were re-issued on 23 April 2002 in sheets of 20 with half stamp-size labels, with either the five designs *se-tenant* with greetings on the labels (LS7, sold at £5.95) or in sheets of one design with personal photographs on the labels (sold at £12.95). These stamps, printed by Questa in lithography, were perforated 14 instead of 15×14.

Type **1569** was re-issued in sheets of 20 with half stamp-size *se-tenant* labels all printed in lithography as follows: on 30 January 2004 for Hong Kong Stamp Expo (LS17, Walsall), on 21 April 2005 for Pacific Explorer 2005 World Stamp Expo (LS24, Walsall, p14), on 25 May 2006 for Washington 2006 International Stamp Exhibition (LS30, Cartor, p 14) on 14 November 2006 for Belgica 2006 International Stamp Exhibition (LS36, Cartor, p14), on 5 August 2008 for Beijing 2008 Olympic Expo (LS48, Cartor, p14), on 3 August 2009 for Thaipex 09 Stamp Exhibition (LS64, Cartor, p14), on 21 October 2009 for Italia 2009 International Stamp Exhibition (LS66, Cartor, p14) and on 4 December 2009 for MonacoPhil International Stamp Exhibition (LS69, Cartor, p14).

No. 2264a was only issued in £1.62 stamp booklets, No. PM8, in which the surplus self-adhesive paper around each stamp was removed.

Special First Day of Issue Postmarks

1572 Studland Bay, Dorset

1573 Luskentyre, South Harris

1574 Cliffs, Dover, Kent

1575 Padstow Harbour, Cornwall

1576 Broadstairs, Kent

1577 St. Abb's Head, Scottish Borders

1578 Dunster Beach, Somerset

1579 Newquay Beach, Cornwall

1580 Portrush, County Antrim

1581 Sand-spit, Conwy

(Des R. Cooke. Litho Walsall)

2002 (19 Mar). *British Coastlines. Two phosphor bands.* P 14½.

2265	**1572**	27p. silver, black, greenish yellow, bright magenta and new blue	60	50
		a. Block of 10. Nos. 2265/74	8·75	8·75
		b. Silver omitted (block of 10)	£9000	
2266	**1573**	27p. silver, black, greenish yellow, bright magenta and new blue	60	50
2267	**1574**	27p. silver, black, greenish yellow, bright magenta and new blue	60	50
2268	**1575**	27p. silver, black, greenish yellow, bright magenta and new blue	60	50
2269	**1576**	27p. silver, black, greenish yellow, bright magenta and new blue	60	50
2270	**1577**	27p. silver, black, greenish yellow, bright magenta and new blue	60	50
2271	**1578**	27p. silver, black, greenish yellow, bright magenta and new blue	60	50
2272	**1579**	27p. silver, black, greenish yellow, bright magenta and new blue	60	50
2273	**1580**	27p. silver, black, greenish yellow, bright magenta and new blue	60	50
2274	**1581**	27p. silver, black, greenish yellow, bright magenta and new blue	60	50

Set of 10	8·75	8·75
Gutter Block of 20	18·00	
First Day Cover (Tallents House)		11·50

First Day Cover (Poolewe, Achnasheen) .... 12·00
Presentation Pack (P.O. Pack No. 332) .... 10·50
PHQ Cards (set of 10) (239)... 9·25   28·00
Nos. 2265/74 were printed together, *se tenant*, in blocks of 10 (5×2) throughout the sheet.

1582 Slack Wire Act   **1583** Lion Tamer

1584 Trick Tri-cyclists   **1585** Krazy Kar

1586 Equestrienne

(Des R. Fuller. Photo Questa)

2002 (10 Apr*). *Europa. Circus.* One centre phosphor band (2nd) or two phosphor bands (others). P 14½.

2275   **1582** (2nd) greenish yellow, magenta, new
                  blue, black, bright orange, emerald
                  and silver   50   60
2276   **1583** (1st) greenish yellow, magenta, new
                  blue, black, bright orange, emerald
                  and silver   75   85
       a. Imperf (vert pair) £3000
2277   **1584** (E) greenish yellow, magenta, new
                  blue, black, bright orange, emerald
                  and silver .... 1·00   1·25
       a. Imperf (pair) £3500
2278   **1585** 45p. greenish yellow, magenta, new
                  blue, black, bright orange, emerald
                  and silver .... 1·75   1·50
2279   **1586** 65p. greenish yellow, magenta, new
                  blue, black, bright orange, emerald
                  and silver .... 2·75   2·25
Set of 5 .... 6·00   6·00
Set of 5 Gutter Pairs... 14·00
First Day Cover (Tallents House).......................................   8·00
First Day Cover (Clowne, Chesterfield)............................   9·00
Presentation Pack (P.O. Pack No. 333) .... 7·50
PHQ Cards (set of 5) (240) .... 4·50   14·00
The 1st and E values incorporate the "EUROPA" emblem.
*Due to the funeral of the Queen Mother, the issue of Nos. 2275/9 was delayed from 9 April, the date which appears on first day covers.

1587 Queen Elizabeth
the Queen Mother

(Des J. Gorham from photographs by N. Parkinson (1st), Dorothy Wilding (E), B. Park (45p.), Rita Martin (65p.). Photo De La Rue)

2002 (25 Apr). *Queen Elizabeth the Queen Mother Commemoration.* Vert designs as T **955/8** with changed face values and showing both the Queen's head and frame in black as in T **1587**. Two phosphor bands. P 14×15.

2280   **1587** (1st) black, greenish yellow, magenta,
                  new blue and grey-black................... 1·00   85
2281   **956** (E) black and indigo .... 1·25   1·10
2282   **957** 45p. black, greenish yellow, magenta,
                  new blue and grey-black................... 1·50   1·50
2283   **958** 65p. black, stone and sepia .... 2·00   2·25
Set of 4 .... 5·50   5·50
Set of 4 Gutter Pairs... 14·00
First Day Cover (Tallents House).......................................   8·00
First Day Cover (London SW1)..   9·00
Presentation Pack (P.O. Pack No. M08).......................... 7·00

1588 Airbus A340-600 (2002)   **1589** Concorde (1976)

1590 Trident (1964)   **1591** VC10 (1964)

1592 Comet (1952)

(Des Roundel)

2002 (2 May). *50th Anniv of Passenger Jet Aviation. Airliners. One centre phosphor band (2nd) or two phosphor bands (others).* P 14½.

(a) Photo De La Rue. Ordinary gum.

2284	**1588**	(2nd)	greenish yellow, bright magenta, new blue, black and silver	75	55
2285	**1589**	(1st)	greenish yellow, bright magenta, new blue, black and silver	1·25	1·00
2286	**1590**	(E)	greenish yellow, bright magenta, new blue, black and silver	1·50	1·50
2287	**1591**	45p.	greenish yellow, bright magenta, new blue, black and silver	2·00	2·00
2288	**1592**	65p.	greenish yellow, bright magenta, new blue, black and silver	3·00	3·00

Set of 5	8·00	7·50
Set of 5 Gutter Pairs	14·00	
First Day Cover (Tallents House)		8·00
First Day Cover (Heathrow Airport, London)		9·00
Presentation Pack (P.O. Pack No. 334)	10·00	
MS2289 120×105 mm. Nos. 2284/8	12·00	11·00
First Day Cover (Tallents House)		12·00
First Day Cover (Heathrow Airport, London)		12·00
PHQ Cards (set of 6) (241)	5·25	18·00

(b) Photo Questa. Self-adhesive. Die-cut P 14½.

2290	**1589**	(1st)	greenish yellow, bright magenta, new blue, black and silver	7·00	7·00
			a. Booklet pane. No. 2040×4 and No. 2290×2	15·00	

No. 2290 was only issued in £1.62 stamp booklets, No. PM5.

Special First Day of Issue Postmarks

1593 Crowned Lion with Shield of St. George

1594 Top Left Quarter of English Flag, and Football

1595 Top Right Quarter of English Flag, and Football

1596 Bottom Left Quarter of English Flag, and Football

1597 Bottom Right Quarter of English Flag, and Football

(Des Sedley Place (No. 2291), H. Brown (No. **MS**2292). Photo Walsall)

2002 (21 May). *World Cup Football Championship, Japan and Korea. Two phosphor bands.* P 14½×14.

(a) Ordinary gum.

2291	**1593**	(1st)	deep turquoise-blue, scarlet-vermilion and silver	2·50	2·50
			Gutter Pair	12·00	

MS2292 145×74 mm. No. 2291; **1594** (1st) deep turquoise-blue, indigo, deep blue, black, silver, scarlet-vermilion and pale bluish grey; **1595** (1st) deep turquoise-blue, indigo, deep blue, black, silver, scarlet-vermilion and pale bluish grey; **1596** (1st) deep turquoise-blue, indigo, deep blue, black, silver, scarlet-vermilion and pale bluish grey; **1597** (1st) deep turquoise-blue, indigo, deep blue, black, silver, scarlet-vermilion and pale bluish grey. P 14½ (square) or 15×14 (horiz)

	7·50	6·50
First Day Cover (**MS**2292) (Tallents House)		9·00
First Day Cover (**MS**2292) (Wembley)		9·00
Presentation Pack (**MS**2292) (P. O. Pack No. 335)	8·50	
PHQ Cards (set of 6) (242)	5·25	15·00

(b) Self-adhesive. Die-cut P 15×14.

2293	**1594**	(1st)	deep turquoise-blue, indigo, deep blue, black, silver, scarlet-vermilion and pale bluish grey	6·00	6·00
			a. Booklet pane. Nos. 2293/4 plus No. 2040×4	14·00	14·00
2294	**1595**	(1st)	deep turquoise-blue, indigo, deep blue, black, silver, scarlet-vermilion and pale bluish grey	6·00	6·00

The complete miniature sheet is shown on one of the PHQ cards with the others depicting individual stamps from No. **MS**2292 and No. 2291. Nos. 2293/4 were only issued in £1.62 stamp booklets, No. PM6.

Stamps as Type **1597** also exist in sheets of 20 with *se-tenant* labels, printed in lithography by Questa (LS8). Such sheets, with the labels showing match scenes or supporters, were available at £5.95 from philatelic outlets, or with personal photographs at £12.95 from Royal Mail in Edinburgh.

Stamps as Type **1593** but with "WORLD CUP 2002" inscription omitted were issued on 17 May 2007 in sheets of 20 with *se-tenant* labels showing scenes from Wembley Stadium, printed in lithography by Cartor (LS39).

Special First Day of Issue Postmarks

For Nos. 2295/8 see Decimal Machin Definitives section.

1598 Swimming

1599 Running

1600 Cycling

1601 Long Jumping

1602 Wheelchair Racing

(Des Madeleine Bennett. Photo Enschedé)

2002 (16 July). *17th Commonwealth Games, Manchester. One side phosphor band (2nd) or two phosphor bands (others).* P 14½.

2299	**1598**	(2nd) greenish yellow, magenta, greenish blue, black, silver and new blue.......	75	55
2300	**1599**	(1st) greenish yellow, magenta, new blue, black and silver..........................	1·00	80
2301	**1600**	(E) greenish yellow, magenta, new blue, black and silver..........................	1·25	1·25
2302	**1601**	47p. greenish yellow, magenta, new blue, black and silver..........................	1·50	1·50
2303	**1602**	68p. greenish yellow, magenta, new blue, black and silver..........................	2·00	2·25

Set of 5	6·00	6·00
Set of 5 Gutter Pairs..	14·00	
First Day Cover (Tallents House)...............................		8·00
First Day Cover (Manchester)		9·00
Presentation Pack (P.O. Pack No. 336)	7·50	
PHQ Cards (set of 5) (243)	4·75	16·00

On Nos. 2300/3 the phosphor bands appear at the right and the centre of each stamp.

Special First Day of Issue Postmarks

1603 Tinkerbell

1604 Wendy, John and Michael Darling in front of Big Ben

1605 Crocodile and Alarm Clock

1606 Captain Hook

1607 Peter Pan

(Des Tutssels. Photo De La Rue.)

2002 (20 Aug). *150th Anniv of Great Ormond Street Children's Hospital. "Peter Pan" by Sir James Barrie. One centre phosphor band (2nd) or two phosphor bands (others).* P 15×14.

2304	**1603**	(2nd) gold, deep ultramarine, greenish yellow and grey-black..........................	75	55
2305	**1604**	(1st) gold, purple, greenish yellow, deep violet and grey-black..........................	1·00	80
2306	**1605**	(E) gold, blue-green, greenish yellow, bright carmine, new blue grey-black and orange-brown	1·25	1·25
2307	**1606**	47p. gold, pale new blue, greenish yellow, bright carmine and grey-black............	1·50	1·50

2308	**1607**	68p. gold, bright rose-red, orange-brown, emerald and grey-black.......	2·00	2·25

Set of 5	6·00	6·00
Set of 5 Gutter Pairs..	14·00	
First Day Cover (Tallents House)...............................		8·00
First Day Cover (I look)		8·50
Presentation Pack (P.O. Pack No. 337)	7·50	
PHQ Cards (set of 5) (244)	4·75	15·00

Special First Day of Issue Postmarks

1608 Millennium Bridge, 2001

1609 Tower Bridge, 1894

1610 Westminster Bridge, 1864

1611 "Blackfriars Bridge, c1800" (William Marlow)

1612 "London Bridge, c1670" (Wenceslaus Hollar)

(Des Sarah Davies and R. Maude)

2002 (10 Sept). *Bridges of London. One centre phosphor band (2nd) or two phosphor bands (others).*

(a) Litho Questa. Ordinary gum. P 15×14.

2309	**1608**	(2nd) greenish yellow, magenta, new blue and black	75	55
2310	**1609**	(1st) grey-brown, black, brown-purple and pale grey-brown...........................	1·00	80
2311	**1610**	(E) greenish yellow, magenta, new blue, black and reddish brown........	2·00	1·50
2312	**1611**	47p. greenish yellow, magenta, new blue and black	2·50	2·00
2313	**1612**	68p. greenish yellow, magenta, new blue, black and reddish brown........	3·50	3·00

Set of 5	9·00	7·50
Set of 5 Gutter Pairs..	20·00	
First Day Cover (Tallents House)...............................		9·00
First Day Cover (London SE1)		10·00
Presentation Pack (P.O. Pack No. 338)	60·00	
PHQ Cards (set of 5) (245)	4·00	12·00

(b) Photo Questa. Self-adhesive. Die-cut P 15×14.

2314	**1609**	(1st) grey-brown, black, brown-purple and pale grey-brown...........................	6·00	6·00
		a. Booklet pane. No. 2314×2, and No. 2295×4	14·00	

No. 2314 was only issued in £1.62 stamp booklets in which the surplus self-adhesive paper around each stamp was removed, No. PM7.

Special First Day of Issue Postmarks

'Praise the
BRIDGE *that*
carried
you over'
GEORGE COLMAN
10-9-2002

'The
THAMES *is*
liquid
history'
JOHN BURNS
10-9-2002

1618 Modern Style
Box, 1980

(Des Silk Pearce. Eng C. Slania. Recess and litho Enschedé)

2002 (8 Oct). *150th Anniv of the First Pillar Box. One centre phosphor band (2nd) or two phosphor bands (others).* P 14×14½.

2316	**1614**	(2nd) greenish black, new blue, bright magenta, greenish yellow, grey and silver	75	55
2317	**1615**	(1st) deep blue, new blue, bright magenta, greenish yellow, grey and silver	1·00	80
2318	**1616**	(E) deep blue, new blue, bright magenta, greenish yellow, grey and silver	1·75	1·75
2319	**1617**	47p. brown-purple, new blue, bright magenta, greenish yellow, grey and silver	2·00	2·50
2320	**1618**	68p. deep brown-red, new blue, bright magenta, greenish yellow, grey and silver	2·50	3·00
Set of 5			7·50	7·50
Set of 5 Gutter Pairs			16·00	
First Day Cover (Tallents House)				8·50
First Day Cover (Bishops Caundle, Sherborne)				9·00
Presentation Pack (P.O. Pack No. 340)			8·00	
PHQ Cards (set of 5) (247)			4·75	16·00

1613a Galaxies and Nebulae (*Illustration reduced. Actual size* 120×89 mm)

(Des Rose Design. Photo Questa)

2002 (24 Sept). *Astronomy. Sheet 120×89 mm. Multicoloured. Two phosphor bands.* P 14½×14.

MS2315	**1613a**	(1st) Planetary nebula in Aquila; (1st) Seyfert 2 galaxy in Pegasus; (1st) Planetary nebula in Norma; (1st) Seyfert 2 galaxy in Circinus	5·25	5·25
		a. Booklet pane. As No. **MS**2315, but larger, 150×95 mm	1·60	
First Day Cover (Tallents House)				6·00
First Day Cover (Star, Glenrothes)				6·00
Presentation Pack (P.O. Pack No. 339)			20·00	
PHQ Cards (set of 5) (246)			4·75	18·00

The five PHQ cards depict the four designs and the complete miniature sheet.

Special First Day of Issue Postmarks

1619 Blue Spruce Star

1620 Holly

24-9-2002
24-9-2002

1621 Ivy

1622 Mistletoe

1614 Green Pillar Box, 1857

1615 Horizontal Aperture Box, 1874

1623 Pine Cone

(Des Rose Design. Photo De La Rue)

2002 (5 Nov). *Christmas. Self-adhesive. One centre phosphor band (2nd) or two phosphor bands (others).* Die-cut p 14½×14.

2321	**1619**	(2nd) lilac, greenish yellow, bright carmine, new blue and black	75	55

1616 Air Mail Box, 1934

1617 Double Aperture Box, 1939

		a. Booklet pane. No. 2321×24	6·75		
		b. Imperf (pair)	80·00		
2322	**1620**	(1st) greenish grey, greenish yellow, bright carmine, new blue and black	1·00	80	
		a. Booklet pane. No. 2322×12	4·75		
		b. Impert (pair)	£325		
2323	**1621**	(E) dull mauve, greenish yellow, bright carmine, new blue and black	1·50	1·50	
2324	**1622**	47p. silver, greenish yellow, bright carmine, new blue and black	2·00	1·75	
2325	**1623**	68p. light blue, greenish yellow, bright carmine, new blue and black	3·00	2·75	

Set of 5 .... 8·00 7·50
First Day Cover (Tallents House) .... 8·50
First Day Cover (Bethlehem, Llandeilo) .... 9·00
Presentation Pack (P.O. Pack No. 341) .... 7·50
PHQ Cards (set of 5) (248) .... 4·75 16·00

Nos. 2321/5 were each printed in sheets of 50, with the surplus backing paper around each stamp retained, separated by gauge 9 roulettes. Nos. 2321b and 2322b show both the die-cut perforations and the roulettes omitted.

Special First Day of Issue Postmarks

Collectors Pack 2002
2002 (5 Nov). *Comprises Nos. 2243/57, 2260/4, 2265/88, **MS**2292, 2299/313 and **MS**2315/25.*
CP2325a Collectors Pack £110

Post Office Yearbook
2002 (5 Nov). *Comprises Nos. 2243/57, 2260/4, 2265/88, 2291/2, 2299/313 and **MS**2315/25 in hardback book with slip case* £100

(Des Rose Design. Photo De La Rue)

2002 (5 Dec). *50th Anniv of Wilding Definitives (1st issue). Sheet 124×70 mm containing designs as T **154/5** and **157/60** (1952–54 issue), but with values in decimal currency as T **1348** or with service indicator as T **1566**, printed on pale cream. One centre phosphor band (2nd) or two phosphor bands (others). W **1565**. P 15×14 (with one elliptical hole in each vertical side).*
MS2326 1p. orange-red; 2p. ultramarine; 5p. red-brown; (2nd) carmine-red; (1st) green; 33p. brown; 37p. magenta; 47p. bistre-brown; 50p. green and label showing national emblems .... 10·00 10·00
First Day Cover (Tallents House) .... 10·00
First Day Cover (Windsor) .... 11·00
Presentation Pack (P.O. Pack No. 59) £100
PHQ Cards (set of 5) (D21) .... 3·00 12·00
The five PHQ cards depict the 1st, 2nd, 33p., 37p. and 47p. stamps.

Special First Day of Issue Postmarks

1624 Barn Owl landing

1625 Barn Owl with folded Wings and Legs down

1626 Barn Owl with extended Wings and Legs down

1627 Barn Owl in Flight with Wings lowered

1628 Barn Owl in Flight with Wings raised

1629 Kestrel with Wings folded

1630 Kestrel with Wings fully extended upwards

1631 Kestrel with Wings horizontal

1632 Kestrel with wings partly extended downwards

1633 Kestrel with wings fully extended downwards

(Des J. Gibbs from photographs by S. Dalton. Litho Walsall)

2003 (14 Jan). *Birds of Prey. Phosphor background. P 14½.*

2327	**1624**	(1st) brownish grey, black, greenish yellow, magenta and new blue		80	50
		a. Block of 10. Nos. 2327/36		12·00	10·00
		ab. Brownish grey and phosphor omitted		£3000	
2328	**1625**	(1st) brownish grey, black, greenish yellow and new blue		80	50
2329	**1626**	(1st) brownish grey, black, greenish yellow and new blue		80	50
2330	**1627**	(1st) brownish grey, black, greenish yellow and new blue		80	50
2331	**1628**	(1st) brownish grey, black, greenish yellow and new blue		80	50
2332	**1629**	(1st) brownish grey, black, greenish yellow and new blue		80	50
2333	**1630**	(1st) brownish grey, black, greenish yellow and new blue		80	50
2334	**1631**	(1st) brownish grey, black, greenish yellow and new blue		80	50
2335	**1632**	(1st) brownish grey, black, greenish yellow and new blue		80	50
2336	**1633**	(1st) brownish grey, black, greenish yellow and new blue		80	50

Set of 10 .... 12·00 10·00
Gutter Block of 20 .... 24·00
First Day Cover (Tallents House) .... 11·00
First Day Cover (Hawkshead Ambleside) .... 12·00
Presentation Pack (P.O. Pack No. 343) .... 15·00
PHQ Cards (set of 10) (249) .... 9·25 28·00

Nos. 2327/36 were printed together, *se-tenant*, in blocks of 10 (5×2) throughtout the sheet.

No. 2327ab shows the owl white on Nos. 2327/31, and the face value with Queen's head omitted on Nos. 2332/6.

Special First Day of Issue Postmarks (applied in silver)

1634 "Gold star, See me, Playtime" **1635** "I♥U, XXXX, S.W.A.L.K."

 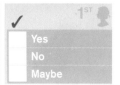

1636 "Angel, Poppet, Little terror" **1637** "Yes, No, Maybe"

 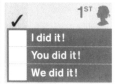

1638 "Oops!, Sorry, Will try harder" **1639** "I did it!, You did it!, We did it!"

(Des UNA, Sara Wiegand and M. Exon. Litho Questa)

2003 (4 Feb). *Greetings Stamps. "Occasions". Two phosphor bands.* P 14½×14.

2337	**1634**	(1st) lemon and new blue	80	50
		a. Block of 6. Nos. 2337/42	6·50	6·00
		b. Imperf (block of 6)	£4000	
2338	**1635**	(1st) red and deep ultramarine	80	50
2339	**1636**	(1st) purple and bright yellow-green	80	50
2340	**1637**	(1st) bright yellow-green and red	80	50
2341	**1638**	(1st) deep ultramarine and lemon	80	50
2342	**1639**	(1st) new blue and purple	80	50
Set of 6			6·50	6·00
Gutter Block of 12			14·00	
First Day Cover (Tallents House)				9·00
First Day Cover (Merry Hill, Wolverhampton)				9·00
Presentation Pack (P.O. Pack No. M09)			10·00	
PHQ Cards (set of 6) (PSM09)			5·25	18·00

Nos. 2337/42 were printed together, *se-tenant*, in blocks of 6 (3×2) throughout the sheet.

Nos. 2337/42 were also issued in sheets of 20 (containing four of Nos. 2338 and 2340 and three each of the others) with *se-tenant* labels (LS12). Such sheets with the labels showing printed faces were available at £5.95 from philatelic outlets, or with personalised photographs at £14.95 from Royal Mail in Edinburgh.

Special First Day of Issue Postmarks

1640 Completing the Genome Jigsaw **1641** Ape with Moustache and Scientist

1642 DNA Snakes and Ladders **1643** "Animal Scientists"

1644 Genome Crystal Ball

(Des Williams Murray Hamm and P. Brookes. Litho Enschedé)

2003 (25 Feb). *50th Anniv of Discovery of DNA. One centre phosphor band (2nd) or two phosphor bands (others).* P 14½.

2343	**1640**	(2nd) azure, black, new blue, magenta and greenish yellow	1·00	55
		a. Booklet pane. Nos. 2343/4, each ×2, with margins all round	3·00	
2344	**1641**	(1st) bright apple-green, black, new blue, magenta and greenish yellow	1·00	80
2345	**1642**	(E) yellow-orange, black, new blue, magenta and greenish yellow	1·25	1·25
		a. Booklet pane. No. 2345×4 with margins all round	5·00	
2346	**1643**	47p. bistre-yellow, black, new blue, magenta and greenish yellow	1·50	1·50
2347	**1644**	68p. lavender, black, new blue, magenta and greenish yellow	2·00	2·25
Set of 5			6·50	6·00
Set of 5 Gutter Pairs			15·00	
First Day Cover (Tallents House)				10·00
First Day Cover (Cambridge)				10·00
Presentation Pack (P.O. Pack No. 344)			9·00	
PHQ Cards (set of 5) (250)			4·75	18·00

Special First Day of Issue Postmarks

1645 Strawberry **1646** Potato

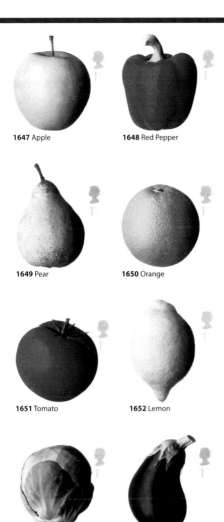

1647 Apple

1648 Red Pepper

1649 Pear

1650 Orange

1651 Tomato

1652 Lemon

1653 Brussels Sprout

1654 Aubergine

(Des Johnson Banks. Photo Walsall)

2003 (25 Mar). *Fruit and Vegetables. Self-adhesive. Two phosphor bands.* P 14½×14 die-cut (without teeth around protruding tops or bottoms of the designs).

2348	**1645**	(1st) greenish yellow, magenta, new blue, black and silver.............................	80	50
		a. Sheetlet. Nos. 2348/57 and pane of decorative labels.................................	12·00	10·00
		ab. Imperf (block of 10)	£4000	
2349	**1646**	(1st) greenish yellow, magenta, new blue, black and silver.............................	80	50
2350	**1647**	(1st) greenish yellow, magenta, new blue, black and silver.............................	80	50
2351	**1648**	(1st) greenish yellow, magenta, new blue, black and silver.............................	80	50
2352	**1649**	(1st) greenish yellow, magenta, new blue, black and silver.............................	80	50
2353	**1650**	(1st) greenish yellow, magenta, new blue, black and silver.............................	80	50
2354	**1651**	(1st) greenish yellow, magenta, new blue, black and silver.............................	80	50
2355	**1652**	(1st) greenish yellow, magenta, new blue, black and silver.............................	80	50
2356	**1653**	(1st) greenish yellow, magenta, new blue, black and silver.............................	80	50
2357	**1654**	(1st) greenish yellow, magenta, new blue, black and silver.............................	80	50
Set of 10..			12·00	10·00
First Day Cover (Tallents House)...............................				12·00
First Day Cover (Pear Tree, Derby)...........................				12·00
Presentation Pack (P.O. Pack No. 345)			50·00	
PHQ Cards (set of 10) (251)....................................			9·25	25·00

Nos. 2348/57 were printed together in sheets of 10 with the surplus self-adhesive paper around each stamp retained. The stamp pane is accompanied by a similar-sized pane of self-adhesive labels showing ears, eyes, mouths, hats etc which are intended for the adornment of fruit and vegetables depicted. This pane is separated from the stamps by a line of roulettes.

Nos. 2348/57 were re-issued on 7th March 2006 in sheets of 20, containing two of each of the ten designs accompanied by *se-tenant* labels with speech bubbles and stickers showing eyes, hats, etc. in the sheet margin (LS29). These sheets were printed in lithography by Cartor and sold for £6.55.

No. 2355 was also available in sheets of 20 with personal photographs on the labels at £14.95 per sheet from Royal Mail, Edinburgh.

Special First Day of Issue Postmarks

For Nos. 2357a (Overseas Booklet Stamps) see Decimal Machin Definitives sections

1656 Amy Johnson (pilot) and Bi-plane

1657 Members of 1953 Everest Team

1658 Freya Stark (traveller and writer) and Desert

1659 Ernest Shackleton (Antarctic explorer) and Wreck of *Endurance*

1660 Francis Chichester (yachtsman) and *Gipsy Moth IV*

1661 Robert Falcon Scott (Antarctic explorer) and Norwegian Expedition at the Pole

(Des H. Brown)

2003 (29 Apr). *Extreme Endeavours (British Explorers). One centre phosphor band (2nd) or two phosphor bands (others).* P 15×14½.

(a) Photo Questa. Ordinary gum.

2360	**1656**	(2nd) gold, black, magenta, greenish yellow and new blue	50	50
2361	**1657**	(1st) gold, black, magenta, greenish yellow and new blue	75	75
2362	**1658**	(E) gold, black, magenta, greenish yellow and new blue	1·50	1·50
2363	**1659**	42p. gold, black, magenta, greenish yellow and new blue	1·75	1·75
2364	**1660**	47p. gold, black, magenta, greenish yellow and new blue	2·00	2·00
2365	**1661**	68p. gold, black, magenta, greenish yellow and new blue	2·50	2·50
Set of 6			8·00	8·50
Set of 6 Gutter Pairs			17·00	
First Day Cover (Tallents House)				12·00
First Day Cover (Plymouth)				12·00
Presentation Pack (P.O. Pack No. 346)			10·00	
PHQ Cards (set of 6) (252)			3·25	14·00

(b) Photo De La Rue. Self-adhesive. Die-cut P 14½.

2366	**1657**	(1st) gold, black, magenta, greenish yellow and new blue	5·00	5·00
		a. Booklet pane. No. 2366×2 plus No. 2295×4	12·00	

The phosphor bands on Nos. 2361/5 are at the centre and right of each stamp.

No. 2366 was only issued in £1.62 stamp booklets, No. PM9, in which the surplus self-adhesive paper around each stamp was removed.

Gummed perforated trials with alternative face values and/or designs are known (*Price from £500*).

Special First Day of Issue Postmarks

Des Rose Design. Photo De La Rue)

2003 (20 May). *50th Anniv of Wilding Definitives (2nd issue). Sheet 124×70 mm, containing designs as T **155/8** and **160** (1952–54 issue), but with values in decimal currency as T **1348** or with service indicator as T **1566**, printed on pale cream. One centre phosphor band (20p.) or two phosphor bands (others).* W **1565**. P 15×14 (with one elliptical hole in each vertical side).

MS2367	4p. deep lilac; 8p. ultramarine; 10p. reddish purple; 20p. bright green; 28p. bronze-green; 34p. brown-purple; (E) chestnut; 42p. Prussian blue; 68p. grey-blue and label showing national emblems	10·50	11·25
First Day Cover (Tallents House)			13·00
First Day Cover (Windsor)			14·00
Presentation Pack (P.O. Pack No. 61)		18·00	

Special First Day of Issue Postmarks

1662 Guardsmen in Coronation Procession

1663 East End Children reading Coronation Party Poster

1664 Queen Elizabeth II in Coronation Chair with Bishops of Durham and Bath and Wells

1665 Children in Plymouth working on Royal Montage

1666 Queen Elizabeth II in Coronation Robes (photograph by Cecil Beaton)

1667 Children's Race at East End Street Party

1668 Coronation Coach passing through Marble Arch

1669 Children in Fancy Dress

1670 Coronation Coach outside Buckingham Palace

1671 Children eating at London Street Party

(Des Kate Stephens. Photo De La Rue (sheets) or Walsall (booklets))

2003 (2 June). *50th Anniv of Coronation.* W **1565**. *Two phosphor bands.* P 14½×14.

2368	**1662**	(1st) greenish yellow, bright magenta, new blue, grey-black, deep turquoise-blue and gold	70	50
		a. Block of 10. Nos. 2368/77	12·00	10·00
		b. Booklet pane. Nos. 2368, 2370, 2373 and 2375 with margins all round	1·70	
2369	**1663**	(1st) black and gold	70	50
		b. Booklet pane. Nos. 2369, 2372, 2374 and 2377 with margins all round	1·70	
2370	**1664**	(1st) greenish yellow, bright magenta, new blue, grey-black, deep turquoise-blue and gold	70	50
2371	**1665**	(1st) black and gold	70	50
2372	**1666**	(1st) greenish yellow, bright magenta, new blue, grey-black and deep turquoise-blue	70	50
2373	**1667**	(1st) black and gold	70	50
2374	**1668**	(1st) greenish yellow, bright magenta, new blue, grey-black, deep turquoise-blue and gold	70	50
2375	**1669**	(1st) black and gold	70	50
2376	**1670**	(1st) greenish yellow, bright magenta, new blue, grey-black, deep turquoise-blue and gold	70	50

2377	**1671**	(1st)	black and gold	70	50

Set of 10 ..... 12·00 10·00
Gutter Block of 20 ..... 25·00
First Day Cover (Tallents House) ..... 12·00
First Day Cover (London SW1) ..... 12·00
Presentation Pack (P.O. Pack No. 347) ..... 25·00
PHQ Cards (set of 10) (253) ..... 9·25 20·00

Nos. 2368/77 were printed together, *se-tenant*, as blocks of 10 (5×2) in sheets of 60 (2 panes of 30). No. 2372 does not show a silhouette of the Queen's head in gold as do the other nine designs.

Special First Day of Issue Postmarks

(Photo Walsall)

2003 (2 June). *50th Anniv of Coronation. Booklet stamps. Designs as T* **160** *(Wilding definitive of 1952) and* **163** *(Coronation commemorative of 1953), but with values in decimal currency as T* **1348**. *W* **1565**. *Two phosphor bands. P* 15×14 (with one elliptical hole in each vertical side for Nos. 2378/9).

2378	**160**	47p. bistre-brown		5·00	2·50
		a. Booklet pane. Nos. 2378/9, each ×2, and 2380 with margins all round		65·00	
2379		68p. grey-blue		5·00	2·50
2380	**163**	£1 deep yellow-green		50·00	45·00

Set of 3 ..... 55·00 45·00

Nos. 2378/80 were only available in £7.46 stamp booklets, No. DX31. Stamps as Nos. 2378/9, but on pale cream, were also included in the Wilding miniature sheets, Nos. **MS**2326 or **MS**2367. A £1 design as No. 2380, but on phosphorised paper, was previously included in the "Stamp Show 2000" miniature sheet, No. **MS**2147.

1672 Prince William in September 2001 (Brendan Beirne)

1673 Prince William in September 2000 (Tim Graham)

1674 Prince William in September 2001 (Camera Press)

1675 Prince William in September 2001 (Tim Graham)

(Des Madeleine Bennett. Photo Walsall)

2003 (17 June). *21st Birthday of Prince William of Wales. Phosphor backgrounds. P* 14½.

2381	**1672**	28p. silver, black, grey-black and light green		1·00	50
2382	**1673**	(E) dull mauve, grey-black and light green		2·25	1·50
2383	**1674**	47p. greenish grey, grey-black, black and light green		2·75	2·00
2384	**1675**	68p. sage-green, black and bright green		4·00	2·50

Set of 4 ..... 9·00 6·00
Set of 4 Gutter Pairs ..... 13·00
First Day Cover (Tallents House) ..... 10·00
First Day Cover (Cardiff) ..... 10·00
Presentation Pack (P.O. Pack No. 348) ..... 25·00
PHQ Cards (set of 4) (254) ..... 7·50 20·00

Special First Day of Issue Postmarks

1676 Loch Assynt, Sutherland

1677 Ben More, Isle of Mull

1678 Rothiemurchus, Cairngorms

1679 Dalveen Pass, Lowther Hills

1680 Glenfinnan Viaduct, Lochaber

1681 Papa Little, Shetland Islands

(Des Phelan Barker. Photo De La Rue)

2003 (15 July). *A British Journey: Scotland. One centre phosphor band (2nd) or two phosphor bands (others). P* 14½.

(a) Ordinary gum.

2385	**1676**	(2nd)	silver, black, bright magenta, greenish yellow and new blue	50	35
2386	**1677**	(1st)	silver, black, bright magenta, greenish yellow and new blue	75	50
2387	**1678**	(E)	silver, black, bright magenta, greenish yellow and new blue	1·25	1·25
2388	**1679**	42p.	silver, black, bright magenta, greenish yellow and new blue	1·25	1·50
2389	**1680**	47p.	silver, black, bright magenta, greenish yellow and new blue	1·50	2·00
2390	**1681**	68p.	silver, black, bright magenta, greenish yellow and new blue	2·00	2·50

Set of 6 ..... 7·00 7·75
Set of 6 Gutter Pairs ..... 16·00
First Day Cover (Tallents House) ..... 11·00
First Day Cover (Baltasound, Unst, Shetland) ..... 11·00
Presentation Pack (P.O. Pack No. 349) ..... 9·50
PHQ Cards (set of 6) (255) ..... 3·00 14·00

(b) Self-adhesive. Die-cut perf 14½.

2391	**1677**	(1st)	silver, black, bright magenta, greenish yellow and new blue	6·00	6·00
		a. Booklet pane. No. 2391×2, and No. 2295×4		14·00	

Perforated trials of this set with alternative face values or designs are known.

No. 2391 was only issued in £1.68 stamp booklets, No. PM10, in which the surplus self-adhesive paper around each stamp was removed.

Special First Day of Issue Postmarks

1682 "The Station"
(Andrew Davidson)

1683 "Black Swan"
(Stanley Chew)

1684 "The Cross Keys"
(George Mackenney)

1685 "The Mayflower"
(Ralph Ellis)

1686 "The Barley
Sheaf" (Joy Cooper)

(Des Elmwood. Photo De La Rue)

2003 (12 Aug). *Europa. British Pub Signs. Two phosphor bands.* P 14×14½.

2392	**1682**	(1st) silver, black, magenta, greenish yellow and new blue	75	50
		a. Booklet pane. No. 2392×4 with margins all round (16.3.04)	3·75	
2393	**1683**	(E) silver, black, magenta, greenish yellow and new blue	2·00	2·00
2394	**1684**	42p. silver, black, magenta, greenish yellow and new blue	1·50	1·50
2395	**1685**	47p. silver, black, magenta, greenish yellow and new blue	1·75	2·00
2396	**1686**	68p. silver, black, magenta, greenish yellow and new blue	2·00	2·25
Set of 5			7·50	7·75
Set of 5 Gutter Pairs			17·00	
First Day Cover (Tallents House)				11·00
First Day Cover (Cross Keys, Hereford)				11·00
Presentation Pack (P.O. Pack No. 350)			11·00	
PHQ Cards (set of 5) (256)			3·00	12·00

The 1st and E values include the "EUROPA" emblem. No. 2392a comes from the £7.44 "Letters by Night" booklet, No. DX32.

Special First Day of Issue Postmarks

1687 Meccano Constructor
Biplane, c.1931

1688 Wells-Brimtoy Clockwork
Double-decker Omnibus, c.1938

1689 Hornby M1 Clockwork
Locomotive and Tender, c.1948

1690 Dinky Toys Ford Zephyr,
c. 1956

1691 Mettoy Friction Drive Space
Ship Eagle, c.1960

(Des Trickett and Webb)

2003 (18 Sept). *Classic Transport Toys. Two phosphor bands.*

(a) Photo Enschedé. Ordinary gum. P 14½×14.

2397	**1687**	(1st) silver, blue-black, black, new blue, magenta and greenish yellow	75	50
2398	**1688**	(E) silver, blue-black, black, new blue, magenta and greenish yellow	1·25	1·25
2399	**1689**	42p. silver, blue-black, black, new blue, magenta and greenish yellow	1·50	1·50
2400	**1690**	47p. silver, blue-black, black, new blue, magenta and greenish yellow	1·75	1·75
2401	**1691**	68p. silver, blue-black, black, new blue, magenta and greenish yellow	2·50	2·50
Set of 5			7·50	7·50
Set of 5 Gutter Pairs			16·00	
First Day Cover (Tallents House)				10·00
First Day Cover (Toye, Downpatrick)				10·00
Presentation Pack (P.O. Pack No. 351)			12·00	
PHQ Cards (set of 6) (257)			3·00	14·00
MS2402 115×105mm.Nos. 2397/401			8·00	8·25
First Day Cover				14·00

(b) Photo De La Rue. Self-adhesive. Die-cut P 14½×14.

2403	**1687**	(1st) silver, blue-black, black, new blue, magenta and greenish yellow	6·00	6·00
		a. Booklet pane. No. 2403×2 and No. 2295×4	14·00	

The complete miniature sheet is shown on one of the PHQ cards with the others depicting individual stamps.

No. 2403 was only issued in £1.60 stamp booklets, No. PM11, in which the surplus self-adhesive paper around each stamp was removed.

Special First Day of Issue Postmarks

Special First Day of Issue Postmarks

1692 Coffin of Denytenamun, Egyptian, c.900BC

1693 Alexander the Great, Greek, c.200BC

1698 Ice Spiral

1699 Icicle Star

1694 Sutton Hoo Helmet, Anglo-Saxon, c.AD600

1695 Sculpture of Parvati, South Indian, c.AD1550

1700 Wall of Ice Blocks

1701 Ice Ball

1696 Mask of Xiuhtecuhtli, Mixtec-Aztec, c.AD1500

1697 Hoa Hakananai'a, Easter Island, c.AD1000

1702 Ice Hole

1703 Snow Pyramids

(Des Rose Design. Photo Walsall)

2003 (7 Oct). *250th Anniv of the British Museum. One side phosphor band (2nd), two phosphor bands ((1st), (E), 47p.) or phosphor background at left and band at right (42p., 68p.). P 14×14½.*

2404	**1692**	(2nd)	brownish grey, black, greenish yellow, magenta and pale new blue	50	35
2405	**1693**	(1st)	brownish grey, black, greenish yellow, magenta and pale new blue	75	50
2406	**1694**	(E)	brownish grey, black, greenish yellow, magenta and pale new blue	1·25	1·25
2407	**1695**	42p.	brownish grey, black, greenish yellow, magenta and pale new blue	1·50	1·50
2408	**1696**	47p.	brownish grey, black, greenish yellow, magenta and pale new blue	2·00	2·00
2409	**1697**	68p.	brownish grey, black, greenish yellow, magenta and pale new blue	2·75	2·75

Set of 6	8·00	8·00
Set of 6 Gutter Pairs	16·00	
First Day Cover (Tallents House)		11·00
First Day Cover (London WC1)		11·00
Presentation Pack (P.O. Pack No. 352)	11·00	
PHQ Cards (set of 6) (258)	3·00	14·00

(Des D. Davis. Photo De La Rue)

2003 (4 Nov). *Christmas. Ice Sculptures by Andy Goldsworthy. Self-adhesive. One side phosphor band (2nd), "all-over" phosphor (1st) or two bands (others). Die-cut perf 14½×14.*

2410	**1698**	(2nd)	magenta, greenish yellow, new blue and black	75	35
			a. Booklet pane. No. 2410×24	7·25	
2411	**1699**	(1st)	magenta, greenish yellow, new blue and black	1·25	50
			a. Booklet pane. No. 2411×12	5·00	
2412	**1700**	(E)	magenta, greenish yellow, new blue and black	1·50	1·50
2413	**1701**	53p.	magenta, greenish yellow, new blue and black	2·00	2·00
2414	**1702**	68p.	magenta, greenish yellow, new blue and black	2·50	2·50
2415	**1703**	£1.12	magenta, greenish yellow, new blue and black	3·00	3·00

Set of 6	10·00	10·00
First Day Cover (Tallents House)		12·50
First Day Cover (Bethlehem, Llandeilo)		12·50
Presentation Pack (P.O. Pack No. 353)	12·00	
PHQ Cards (set of 6) (259)	4·00	14·00

Nos. 2410/15 were each printed in sheets of 50 with the surplus backing paper around each stamp removed.

The 2nd and 1st class were also issued in separate sheets of 20 printed in lithography instead of photogravure, each stamp accompanied by a half stamp-size *se-tenant* label showing either ice sculptures (2nd) or animals (1st) (LS15/16). Both sheets have the backing paper around each stamp retained. The 2nd class sheet was sold for £4.20 and the 1st class for £6.15. These sheets were also available with personal photographs instead of labels at £9.95 (2nd) or £14.95 (1st) from Royal Mail, Edinburgh or £15 from photo-booths at selected post offices and Safeway stores.

Special First Day of Issue Postmarks

Collectors Pack 2003

2003 (4 Nov). *Comprises Nos. 2327/57, 2360/5, 2368/77, 2381/90, 2392/401 and 2404/15*

CP2415a Collectors Pack... £120

Post Office Yearbook

2003 (4 Nov). *Comprises Nos. 2327/57, 2360/5, 2368/77, 2381/90, 2392/401 and 2404/15 in hardback book with slipcase*.. £100

1704 (*Illustration reduced. Actual size 115×88 mm*)

(Des Why Not Associates. Litho Walsall)

2003 (19 Dec). *England's Victory in Rugby World Cup Championship, Australia. Sheet 115×85 mm. Multicoloured. Two phosphor bands. P 14.*

MS2416 **1704** (1st) England flags and fans; (1st) England team standing in circle before match; 68p. World Cup trophy; 68p. Victorious England players after match... 14·00 14·00

First Day Cover (Tallents House)................................... 14·00
First Day Cover (Twickenham)...................................... 14·00
Presentation Pack (P.O. Pack No. M9B).......... 35·00

Special First Day of Issue Postmarks

1705 *Dolgoch*, Rheilffordd Talyllyn Railway, Gwynedd

1706 CR Class 439, Bo'ness and Kinneil Railway, West Lothian

1707 GCR Class 8K, Leicestershire

1708 GWR Manor Class *Bradley Manor*, Severn Valley Railway, Worcestershire

1709 SR West Country Class *Blackmoor Vale*, Bluebell Railway, East Sussex

1710 BR Standard Class, Keighley and Worth Valley Railway, Yorkshire

(Des Roundel. Litho De La Rue)

2004 (13 Jan–16 Mar). *Classic Locomotives. One side phosphor band (20p.) or two phosphor bands (others). P 14½.*

2417	**1705**	20p. greenish yellow, magenta, new blue, silver and black..........................	65	65
2418	**1706**	28p. greenish yellow, magenta, new blue, silver and black..........................	90	90
		a. Booklet pane. Nos. 2418/20 with margins all round (16 Mar).............	3·50	
2419	**1707**	(E) greenish yellow, magenta, new blue, silver and black..........................	1·20	1·20
2420	**1708**	42p. greenish yellow, magenta, new blue, silver and black..........................	1·50	1·50
2421	**1709**	47p. greenish yellow, magenta, new blue, silver and black..........................	2·00	2·00
		a. Imperf (pair)...............................	£2800	
2422	**1710**	68p. greenish yellow, magenta, new blue, silver and black..........................	3·00	3·50

Set of 6 .... 8·00 8·50
Set of 6 Gutter Pairs... 15·00
First Day Cover (Tallents House)................................... 12·00
First Day Cover (York) .... 12·00
Presentation Pack (P.O. Pack No. 355) .... 35·00
PHQ Cards (set of 7) (260) .... 8·50 15·00
MS2423 190×67 mm. Nos. 2417/22 .... 35·00 35·00
First Day Cover (Tallents House)................................... 35·00
First Day Cover (York) .... 35·00

No. 2418a comes from the £7.44 "Letters by Night" booklet, No. DX32. The seven PHQ cards depict the six individual stamps and the miniature sheet.

Special First Day of Issue Postmarks

1711 Postman   **1712** Face

1713 Duck

1714 Baby

1715 Aircraft

(Des S. Kambayashi. Litho De La Rue)

2004 (3 Feb). *Occasions. Two phosphor bands.* P 14½×14.

2424	**1711**	(1st) bright mauve and black	70	50
		a. Horiz strip of 5. Nos. 2424/8	6·00	6·00
		ab. Imperf strip of 5		
2425	**1712**	(1st) magenta and black	70	50
2426	**1713**	(1st) lemon and black	70	50
2427	**1714**	(1st) pale turquoise-green and black	70	50
2428	**1715**	(1st) bright new blue and black	70	50

Set of 5	6·00	6·00
Gutter Block of 10	13·00	
First Day Cover (Tallents House)		8·00
First Day Cover (Merry Hill, Wolverhampton)		8·00
Presentation Pack (P.O. Pack No. M10)	8·00	
PHQ Cards (set of 5) (PSM10)	4·75	12·00

Nos. 2424/8 were printed together, *se-tenant*, as horizontal strips of 5 in sheets of 25 (5×5). Nos. 2424/8 were also issued in sheets of 20 containing vertical strips of the five designs alternated with half stamp-size labels (LS18). These sheets with printed labels were available at £6.15 from philatelic outlets, or with personalised photographs at £14.95 from Royal Mail in Edinburgh.

Special First Day of Issue Postmarks

1716 Map showing Middle Earth

1717 Forest of Lothlórien in Spring

1718 Dust-jacket for *The Fellowship of the Ring*

1719 Rivendell

1720 The Hall at Bag End

1721 Orthanc

1722 Doors of Durin

1723 Barad-dûr

1724 Minas Tirith

1725 Fangorn Forest

(Des HGV Design. Litho Walsall)

2004 (26 Feb). *50th Anniv of Publication of The Fellowship of the Ring and The Two Towers by J. R. R. Tolkien. Two phosphor bands.* P 14½.

2429	**1716**	(1st) pale stone, sepia, black, greenish yellow, magenta and new blue	70	50
		a. Block of 10. Nos. 2429/38	12·00	10·00
2430	**1717**	(1st) pale stone, sepia, black, greenish yellow, magenta and new blue	70	50
2431	**1718**	(1st) pale stone, sepia, black, greenish yellow, magenta and new blue	70	50
2432	**1719**	(1st) pale stone, sepia, black, greenish yellow, magenta and new blue	70	50
2433	**1720**	(1st) pale stone, sepia, black, greenish yellow, magenta and new blue	70	50
2434	**1721**	(1st) pale stone, sepia, black, greenish yellow, magenta and new blue	70	50
2435	**1722**	(1st) pale stone, sepia, black, greenish yellow, magenta and new blue	70	50
2436	**1723**	(1st) pale stone, sepia, black, greenish yellow, magenta and new blue	70	50
2437	**1724**	(1st) pale stone, sepia, black, greenish yellow, magenta and new blue	70	50
2438	**1725**	(1st) pale stone, sepia, black, greenish yellow, magenta and new blue	70	50

Set of 10	12·00	10·00
Gutter Block of 20	24·00	
First Day Cover (Tallents House)		10·00
First Day Cover (Oxford)		10·00
Presentation Pack (P.O. Pack No. 356)	25·00	
PHQ Cards (set of 10) (261)	9·75	18·00

Nos. 2429/38 were printed together, *se-tenant*, in blocks of 10 (5×2) throughout the sheet.

Special First Day of Issue Postmarks

1726 Ely Island, Lower Lough Erne

1727 Giant's Causeway, Antrim Coast

1728 Slemish, Antrim Mountains

1729 Banns Road, Mourne Mountains

1730 Glenelly Valley, Sperrins

1731 Islandmore, Strangford Lough

(Des Phelan Barker. Photo Enschedé (sheets) or De La Rue (booklet))

2004 (16 Mar). *A British Journey: Northern Ireland. One side phosphor band (2nd) or two phosphor bands (others).* P 14½.

(a) Ordinary gum.

2439	**1726**	(2nd) silver, black, new blue, magenta and greenish yellow	65	65
2440	**1727**	(1st) silver, black, new blue, magenta and greenish yellow	90	90
2441	**1728**	(E) silver, black, new blue, magenta and greenish yellow	1·20	1·20
2442	**1729**	42p. silver, black, new blue, magenta and greenish yellow	1·30	1·30
2443	**1730**	47p. silver, black, new blue, magenta and greenish yellow	1·50	1·50
2444	**1731**	68p. silver, black, new blue, magenta and greenish yellow	2·20	2·20

Set of 6	7·75	7·75
Set of 6 Gutter Pairs	16·00	
First Day Cover (Tallents House)		12·50
First Day Cover (Garrison, Enniskillen)		12·50
Presentation Pack (P.O. Pack No. 357)	14·00	
PHQ Cards (set of 6) (262)	5·75	14·00

(b) Self-adhesive. Die-cut perf 14½.

2445	**1727**	(1st) silver, black, new blue, magenta and greenish yellow	6·00	6·00
		a. Booklet pane. No. 2445×2 and No. 2295×4	14·00	
		ab. Imperf (pane)	£5000	

No. 2445 was only issued in £1·68 stamp booklets No. PM12 in which the surplus self-adhesive paper around each stamp was removed.

Special First Day of Issue Postmarks

1732 "Lace 1 (trial proof) 1968" (Sir Terry Frost)

1733 "Coccinelle" (Sonia Delaunay)

(Des Rose Design. Photo Walsall)

2004 (6 Apr). *Centenary of the Entente Cordiale. Contemporary Paintings. Two phosphor bands.* P 14×14½.

2446	**1732**	28p. grey, black and rosine	1·00	85
2447	**1733**	57p. grey, black, grey-brown, rosine, new blue, orange-yellow and bright crimson	2·25	2·00

Set of 2	3·00	2·75
Set of 2 Gutter Pairs	7·00	
Set of 2 Traffic Light Gutter Blocks of 4	15·00	
First Day Cover (Tallents House)		4·50
First Day Cover (London SW1)		4·50
First Day Cover (UK and French stamps)		12·00
Presentation Pack (P.O. Pack No. 358)	35·00	
Presentation Pack (UK and French stamps)	35·00	
PHQ Cards (set of 2) (263)	3·50	6·00

Stamps in similar designs were issued by France and these are included in the joint Presentation Pack.

Special First Day of Issue Postmarks

1734 "RMS *Queen Mary 2*, 2004" (Edward D. Walker)

1735 "SS *Canberra*, 1961" (David Cobb)

1736 "RMS *Queen Mary*, 1936" (Charles Pears)

1737 "RMS *Mauretania*, 1907" (Thomas Henry)

1738 "SS *City of New York*, 1888" (Raphael Monleaon y Torres)

1739 "PS *Great Western*, 1838" (Joseph Walter)

(Des J. Gibbs. Photo De La Rue)

2004 (13 Apr). *Ocean Liners. Two phosphor bands.* P 14½×14.

(a) Ordinary gum.

2448	**1734**	(1st)	gold, black, magenta, greenish yellow and new blue	90	90
2449	**1735**	(E)	gold, black, magenta, greenish yellow and new blue	1·30	1·30
			a. Imperf (pair)	£1000	
2450	**1736**	42p.	gold, black, magenta, greenish yellow and new blue	1·30	1·30
2451	**1737**	47p.	gold, black, magenta, greenish yellow and new blue	1·50	1·50
2452	**1738**	57p.	gold, black, magenta, greenish yellow and new blue	1·80	1·80
2453	**1739**	68p.	gold, black, magenta, greenish yellow and new blue	2·20	2·20
Set of 6				9·00	9·00
Set of 6 Gutter Pairs				20·00	
First Day Cover (Tallents House)					12·00
First Day Cover (Southampton)					12·00
Presentation Pack (P.O. Pack No. 359)				11·00	
PHQ Cards (set of 7) (264)				6·75	20·00
MS2454 114×104mm. Nos. 2448/53				18·00	18·00
First Day Cover (Tallents House)					18·00
First Day Cover (Southampton)					18·00

(b) Self-adhesive. Die-cut perf 14½×14.

2455	**1734**	(1st)	gold, black, magenta, greenish yellow and new blue	6·00	6·00
			a. Booklet pane. No. 2455×2 and No. 2295×4	14·00	

Nos. 2448/55 commemorate the introduction to service of the *Queen Mary 2.*

The complete miniature sheet is shown on one of the PHQ cards with the others depicting individual stamps. No. 2455 was only issued in £1.68 stamp booklets No. PM13 in which the surplus self-adhesive paper around each stamp was removed.

No. **MS**2454 is known to exist with a face value of "53" on No. 2452. It is known perforated and imperforate.

Special First Day of Issue Postmarks

1740 Dianthus Allwoodii Group

1741 Dahlia "Garden Princess"

1742 Clematis "Arabella"

1743 Miltonia "French Lake"

1744 Lilium "Lemon Pixie"

1745 Delphinium "Clifford Sky"

(Des Rose Design. Photo Enschedé)

2004 (25 May). *Bicentenary of the Royal Horticultural Society (1st issue). One side phosphor band (2nd) or "all-over" phosphor (others).* P 14½.

2456	**1740**	(2nd)	sage-green, black, new blue, magenta and greenish yellow	70	70
			a. Booklet pane. Nos. 2456, 2458/9 and 2461 with margins all round	5·50	
2457	**1741**	(1st)	sage-green, black, new blue, magenta and greenish yellow	90	90
			a. Booklet pane. Nos. 2457 and 2460, each ×2, with margins all round	4·75	
2458	**1742**	(E)	sage-green, black, new blue, magenta and greenish yellow	1·30	1·30
2459	**1743**	42p.	sage-green, black, new blue, magenta and greenish yellow	2·00	2·00
2460	**1744**	47p.	sage-green, black, new blue, magenta and greenish yellow	2·50	2·50
2461	**1745**	68p.	sage-green, black, new blue, magenta and greenish yellow	3·50	3·50
Set of 6				10·00	10·00
Set of 6 Gutter Pairs				22·00	
First Day Cover (Tallents House)					12·00
First Day Cover (Wisley, Woking)					12·00
Presentation Pack (P.O. Pack No. 360)				11·00	
PHQ Cards (set of 7) (265)				6·75	20·00
MS2462 115×105 mm. Nos. 2456/61				14·00	14·00
First Day Cover (Tallents House)					16·00
First Day Cover (Wisley, Woking)					16·00

The complete miniature sheet is shown on one of the PHQ cards with the others depicting individual stamps.

The 1st class stamp was also issued in sheets of 20, printed in lithography by Walsall and sold at £6.15, containing vertical strips of five stamps alternated with printed labels giving information about dahlias. These sheets with personalised photographs were available at £14.95 from the Royal Mail in Edinburgh.

Special First Day of Issue Postmarks

(Litho Enschedé)

2004 (25 May). *Bicentenary of the Royal Horticultural Society (2nd issue). Booklet stamps. Designs as Nos. 1955, 1958 and 1962 (1997 Greeting Stamps 19th-century Flower Paintings). Two phosphor bands.* P 15×14 (with one elliptical hole in each vert side).

2463	**1280**	(1st)	greenish yellow, new blue, magenta, black, blue-green and gold	8·00	8·00
			a. Booklet pane. Nos. 2463, 2464×2 and 2465 with margins all round	25·00	
2464	**1283**	(1st)	greenish yellow, new blue, magenta, black, blue-green and gold	4·00	4·00
2465	**1287**	(1st)	greenish yellow, new blue, magenta, black, blue-green and gold	8·00	8·00
Set of 3				18·00	18·00

On Nos. 2463/5 the phosphor bands appear at the left and the centre of each stamp. Nos. 2463/5 were only available in £7.23 stamp booklets, No. DX33.

1746 Barmouth Bridge

1747 Hyddgen, Plynlimon

1748 Brecon Beacons

1749 Pen-pych, Rhondda Valley

1750 Rhewl, Dee Valley · **1751** Marloes Sands

(Des Phelan Barker. Photo De La Rue)

2004 (15 June). *A British Journey: Wales.* One centre phosphor band (2nd), "all-over" phosphor (1st) or two phosphor bands (others). P 14½.

(a) Ordinary gum.

2466	**1746**	(2nd) silver, black, magenta, greenish yellow and new blue	70	70
		a. Imperf (pair)	£1000	
2467	**1747**	(1st) silver, black, magenta, greenish yellow and new blue	90	90
		a. Imperf (pair)	£1000	
2468	**1748**	40p. silver, black, magenta, greenish yellow and new blue	1·75	1·50
2469	**1749**	43p. silver, black, magenta, greenish yellow and new blue	2·00	2·00
2470	**1750**	47p. silver, black, magenta, greenish yellow and new blue	2·50	3·00
		a. Imperf (pair)	£750	
2471	**1751**	68p. silver, black, magenta, greenish yellow and new blue	3·50	4·00
		a. Imperf (pair)	£1000	
Set of 6			10·00	10·00
Set of 6 Gutter Pairs			22·00	
First Day Cover (Tallents House)				11·00
First Day Cover (Llanfair)				11·00
Presentation Pack (P.O. Pack No. 361)			11·00	
PHQ Cards (set of 6) (266)			5·75	12·00

(b) Self-adhesive. Die-cut perf 14½.

2472	**1747**	(1st) silver, black, magenta, greenish yellow and new blue	8·00	8·00
		a. Booklet pane. No. 2472×2 and No. 2295×4	12·00	

The 1st and 40p. values include the "EUROPA" emblem.

Imperf pairs of Type **1748** and Type **1749** with alternative face values are of proof status. (*Price* £1000 *per pair*).

No. 2472 was only issued in £1·68 stamp booklets, No. PM14, in which the surplus self-adhesive paper around each stamp was removed.

Special First Day of Issue Postmarks

1752 Sir Rowland Hill Award · **1753** William Shipley (Founder of Royal Society of Arts)

1754 "RSA" as Typewriter Keys and Shorthand · **1755** Chimney Sweep

1756 "Gill Typeface" · **1757** "Zero Waste"

(Des D. Birdsall. Litho Walsall)

2004 (10 Aug). *250th Anniv of the Royal Society of Arts.* Two phosphor bands. P 14.

2473	**1752**	(1st) silver, vermilion, blackish-brown and black	95	95
2474	**1753**	40p. silver, vermilion, grey-black, blackish-brown and black	1·30	1·30
2475	**1754**	43p. silver, new blue, vermilion and black	1·40	1·40
2476	**1755**	47p. silver, vermilion, blackish-brown and black	1·50	1·50
2477	**1756**	57p. silver, vermilion and black	2·20	2·20
2478	**1757**	68p. silver, vermilion and black	3·00	3·00
Set of 6			10·00	10·00
Set of 6 Gutter Pairs			22·00	
First Day Cover (Tallents House)				12·00
First Day Cover (London WC2)				12·00
Presentation Pack (P.O. Pack No. 362)			11·00	
PHQ Cards (set of 6) (267)			5·75	14·00

Special First Day of Issue Postmarks

1758 Pine Marten · **1759** Roe Deer

1760 Badger · **1761** Yellow-necked Mouse

1762 Wild Cat · **1763** Red Squirrel

1764 Stoat

1765 Natterer's Bat

1766 Mole

1767 Fox

(Des Kate Stephens. Photo Enschedé)

2004 (16 Sept). *Woodland Animals. Two phosphor bands.* P 14½.

2479	**1758**	(1st) ochre, black, bright new blue, magenta and lemon	70	50
		a. Block of 10. Nos. 2479/88	12·00	12·00
2480	**1759**	(1st) ochre, black, bright new blue, magenta and lemon	70	50
2481	**1760**	(1st) ochre, black, bright new blue, magenta and lemon	70	50
2482	**1761**	(1st) ochre, black, bright new blue, magenta and lemon	70	50
2483	**1762**	(1st) ochre, black, bright new blue, magenta and lemon	70	50
2484	**1763**	(1st) ochre, black, bright new blue, magenta and lemon	70	50
2485	**1764**	(1st) ochre, black, bright new blue, magenta and lemon	70	50
2486	**1765**	(1st) ochre, black, bright new blue, magenta and lemon	70	50
2487	**1766**	(1st) ochre, black, bright new blue, magenta and lemon	70	50
2488	**1767**	(1st) ochre, black, bright new blue, magenta and lemon	70	50
Set of 10			12·00	12·00
Gutter Block of 20			24·00	
First Day Cover (Tallents House)				13·00
First Day Cover (Woodland, Bishop Auckland)				14·00
Presentation Pack (P.O. Pack No. 363)			14·00	
PHQ Cards (set of 10) (268)			9·75	18·00

Nos. 2479/88 were printed together, *se-tenant*, in blocks of 10 (5×2) throughout sheets of 30.

1768 Pte. McNamara, 5th Dragoon Guards, Heavy Brigade charge, Battle of Balaklava

1769 Piper Muir, 42nd Regt of Foot, amphibious assault on Kerch

1770 Sgt. Maj. Edwards, Scots Fusilier Guards, gallant action, Battle of Inkerman

1771 Sgt. Powell, 1st Regt of Foot Guards, Battles of Alma and Inkerman

1772 Sgt. Maj. Poole, Royal Sappers and Miners, defensive line, Battle of Inkerman

1773 Sgt. Glasgow, Royal Artillery, gun battery besieged Sevastopol

(Des Atelier Works. Litho Walsall)

2004 (12 Oct). *150th Anniv of the Crimean War. One centre phosphor band (2nd) or two phosphor bands (others).* P 14.

2489	**1768**	(2nd) greyish silver, brownish grey, black and grey-black	70	70
		a. Greyish silver and phosphor omitted	£1100	
2490	**1769**	(1st) greyish silver, brownish grey, black and grey-black	90	90
2491	**1770**	40p. greyish silver, brownish grey, black and grey-black	2·00	2·00
2492	**1771**	57p. greyish silver, brownish grey, black and grey-black	2·50	2·50
		a. Imperf	£675	
2493	**1772**	68p. greyish silver, brownish grey, black and grey-black	2·75	3·00
		a. Imperf	£2000	
2494	**1773**	£1.12 greyish silver, brownish grey, black and grey-black	4·50	5·00
Set of 6			12·00	12·00
Set of 6 Gutter Pairs			25·00	
Set of 6 Traffic Light Gutter Pairs			30·00	
First Day Cover (Tallents House)				13·50
First Day Cover (London SW3)				13·50
Presentation Pack (P.O. Pack No. 364)			14·00	
PHQ Cards (set of 6) (269)			5·75	16·00

Nos. 2489/94 show "Crimean Heroes" photographs taken in 1856.

1774 Father Christmas on Snowy Roof

1775 Celebrating the Sunrise

1776 On Roof in Gale

1777 With Umbrella in Rain

1778 On Edge of Roof
with Torch

1779 Sheltering behind
Chimney

(Des R. Briggs. Photo De La Rue)

2004 (2 Nov). *Christmas. One centre phosphor band (2nd) or two phosphor bands (others).* P 14½×14.

(a) *Self-adhesive.*

2495	**1774**	(2nd) magenta, greenish yellow, new blue and black	70	70
		a. Booklet pane. No. 2495×24	16·00	
2496	**1775**	(1st) magenta, greenish yellow, new blue and black	90	90
		a. Booklet pane. No. 2496×12	11·00	
2497	**1776**	40p. magenta, greenish yellow, new blue and black	1·30	1·30
2498	**1777**	57p. magenta, greenish yellow, new blue and black	1·80	1·80
2499	**1778**	68p. magenta, greenish yellow, new blue and black	2·20	2·20
2500	**1779**	£1.12 magenta, greenish yellow, new blue and black	3·75	3·75
Set of 6			11·00	12·00
First Day Cover (Tallents House)......................				13·50
First Day Cover (Bethlehem, Llandeilo)................				13·50
Presentation Pack (P.O. Pack No. 365)................			12·50	
PHQ Cards (set of 7) (270)			6·75	18·00

(b) *Ordinary gum.*

MS2501 115×105 mm. As Nos. 2495/500............		12·00	13·00
First Day Cover (Tallents House)......................			13·50
First Day Cover (Bethlehem, Llandeilo)................			14·00

Nos. 2495/500 were each printed in sheets of 50 with the surplus backing paper around each stamp removed.

The seven PHQ cards depict the six individual stamps and the miniature sheet.

The 2nd and 1st class were also issued together in sheets of 20, sold at £5.40, containing ten 2nd class and ten 1st class, each value arranged in vertical rows of five alternated with rows of half stamp-size labels showing Father Christmas. Separate sheets of 20 2nd class and 20 1st class were available with personalised photographs at £9.95 (2nd class) or £14.95 (1st class) from Royal Mail, Edinburgh. These sheets were printed in lithography instead of photogravure and had the backing paper around the stamps retained.

Trials are known showing alternative face values.

Special First Day of Issue Postmarks

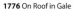

Collectors Pack 2004

2004 (2 Nov). *Comprises Nos.* 2417/22, 2424/44, 2446/53, 2456/61, 2466/71 *and* 2473/500.

CP2500a Collectors Pack....................................	£120

Post Office Yearbook

2004 (2 Nov). *Comprises Nos.* 2417/22, 2424/44, 2446/53, 2456/61, 2466/71 *and* 2473/500 *in hardback book with slipcase*............................ £110

1780 British Saddleback Pigs

1781 Khaki Campbell Ducks

1782 Clydesdale Mare and Foal

1783 Dairy Shorthorn Cattle

1784 Border Collie Dog

1785 Light Sussex Chicks

1786 Suffolk Sheep

1787 Bagot Goat

1788 Norfolk Black Turkeys

1789 Embden Geese

(Des C. Wormell. Photo Enschedé)

2005 (11 Jan). *Farm Animals. Two phosphor bands.* P 14½.

2502	**1780**	(1st) grey, grey-black, new blue, magenta and greenish yellow	70	60
		a. Block of 10. Nos. 2502/11	12·00	12·00
2503	**1781**	(1st) grey, grey-black, new blue, magenta and greenish yellow	70	60
2504	**1782**	(1st) grey, grey-black, new blue, magenta and greenish yellow	70	60
2505	**1783**	(1st) grey, grey-black, new blue, magenta and greenish yellow	70	60
2506	**1784**	(1st) grey, grey-black, new blue, magenta and greenish yellow	70	60
2507	**1785**	(1st) grey, grey-black, new blue, magenta and greenish yellow	70	60
2508	**1786**	(1st) grey, grey-black, new blue, magenta and greenish yellow	70	60
2509	**1787**	(1st) grey, grey-black, new blue, magenta and greenish yellow	70	60
2510	**1788**	(1st) grey, grey-black, new blue, magenta and greenish yellow	70	60
2511	**1789**	(1st) grey, grey-black, new blue, magenta and greenish yellow	70	60

Set of 10		12·00	12·00
Gutter Block of 20		24·00	
Traffic Light Gutter Block of 20		26·00	
First Day Cover (Tallents House)			12·00
First Day Cover (Paddock, Huddersfield)			12·00
Presentation Pack (P.O. Pack No. 367)		14·00	
PHQ Cards (set of 10) (271)		9·75	15·00

Nos. 2502/11 were printed together, *se-tenant*, in blocks of 10 (5×2) throughout sheets of 30. Nos. 2502/11 were also issued in sheets of 20, containing two of each of the ten designs, arranged in vertical strips of five alternated with printed labels showing black/white illustrations of farm scenes. These sheets were printed in lithography by Walsall and sold for £6.15.

They were also available with personal photographs on the labels at £14.95 per sheet from Royal Mail, Edinburgh.

Special First Day of Issue Postmarks

1790 Old Harry Rocks, Studland Bay **1791** Wheal Coates, St. Agnes

1792 Start Point, Start Bay **1793** Horton Down, Wiltshire

1794 Chiselcombe, Exmoor **1795** St. James's Stone, Lundy

(Des J. Phelan and Lissa Barker. Photo De La Rue)

2005 (8 Feb). *A British Journey: South West England. One centre phosphor band (2nd) or two phosphor bands (others).* P 14½.

2512	**1790**	(2nd)	silver, black, magenta, greenish yellow and new blue	60	50
2513	**1791**	(1st)	silver, black, magenta, greenish yellow and new blue	70	75
2514	**1792**	40p.	silver, black, magenta, greenish yellow and new blue	1·50	1·75
2515	**1793**	43p.	silver, black, magenta, greenish yellow and new blue	1·75	2·00
2516	**1794**	57p.	silver, black, magenta, greenish yellow and new blue	2·50	2·50
2517	**1795**	68p.	silver, black, magenta, greenish yellow and new blue	3·50	3·00
Set of 6				10·00	10·00
Set of 6 Gutter Pairs				21·00	
First Day Cover (Tallents House)					12·00
First Day Cover (The Lizard, Helston)					12·00
Presentation Pack (P.O. Pack No. 368)				11·00	
PHQ Cards (set of 6) (262)				4·25	14·00

Perforated examples of Type **1794** are known with face value of 47p are known (price £3000).

Special First Day of Issue Postmarks

1796 "Mr Rochester" **1797** "Come to Me"

1798 "In the Comfort of her Bonnet" **1799** "La Ligne des Rats"

1800 "Refectory" **1801** "Inspection"

(Des P. Willberg. Litho Walsall)

2005 (24 Feb). *150th Death Anniv of Charlotte Brontë. Illustrations of scenes from Jane Eyre by Paula Rego. One centre phosphor band (2nd), or two phosphor bands (others).* P 14×14½.

2518	**1796**	(2nd)	silver, sage-green, brownish grey and black	60	35
		a.	Booklet pane. Nos. 2518/19, both ×2, with margins all round	1·60	
2519	**1797**	(1st)	silver, lemon, magenta, new blue and black	70	45
2520	**1798**	40p.	silver, lemon, magenta, new blue and black	1·50	1·50
		a.	Booklet pane. Nos. 2520/3 with margins all round	13·00	
2521	**1799**	57p.	silver, brownish grey and black	3·00	2·50
2522	**1800**	68p.	silver, pale brownish grey, lemon, magenta, new blue and black	3·75	3·00
2523	**1801**	£1.12	silver, brownish grey and black	4·50	3·50
Set of 6				12·00	11·00
Set of 6 Gutter Pairs				24·00	
Set of 6 Traffic Light Gutter Blocks of 4				42·00	
First Day Cover (Tallents House)					12·00
First Day Cover (Haworth, Keighley)					12·00
Presentation Pack (P.O. Pack No. 369)				13·00	
PHQ Cards (set of 7) (273)				11·00	18·00
MS2524 114×105 mm. Nos. 2518/23				10·00	10·00
First Day Cover (Tallents House)					12·00
First Day Cover (Haworth, Keighley)					12·00

The complete miniature sheet is shown on one of the PHQ cards with the others depicting individual stamps.

Special First Day of Issue Postmarks

FERNDEAN MANOR
24.2.2005

HAWORTH PARSONAGE
24.2.2005

1802 Spinning Coin   RUB WITH A COIN FOR HEADS OR TAILS

1803 Rabbit out of Hat Trick   SLOWLY BRING THE STAMP TO YOUR NOSE

1804 Knotted Scarf Trick

1805 Card Trick   STARE AT DOT FOR 30 SECONDS THEN AT A WHITE WALL

RUB FEZZES WITH YOUR FINGER TO FIND PYRAMID

1806 Pyramid under Fez Trick

(Des G. Hardie and Tatham Design. Photo Walsall)

2005 (15 Mar). *Centenary of the Magic Circle. Two phosphor bands.* P 14½×14.

2525	**1802**	(1st) brownish grey, bright blue, yellow-orange and black	70	45
2526	**1803**	40p. brownish grey, turquoise-green, bright violet, yellow-orange and black	1·00	65
2527	**1804**	47p. brownish grey, bright mauve, bright violet, turquoise-green, yellow-orange and black	2·50	2·75
2528	**1805**	68p. brownish grey, turquoise-green, rosine and black	3·00	3·00
2529	**1806**	£1.12 brownish grey, bright mauve, new blue, lilac, reddish violet and black	3·50	3·50
Set of 5			10·00	10·00
Set of 5 *Gutter Pairs*			21·00	
First Day Cover (Tallents House)				11·75
First Day Cover (London NW1)				11·75
Presentation Pack (P.O. Pack No. 370)			15·00	
PHQ *Cards* (set of 5) (274)			5·00	12·00

Nos. 2525/9 are each printed with instructions for the illusion or trick on the stamp. No. 2525 can be rubbed with a coin to reveal the "head" or "tail" of a coin. The two versions, which appear identical before rubbing, are printed in alternate rows of the sheet, indicated by the letters H and T in the side margins of the sheet. Nos. 2526 and 2528 each show optical illusions. The bright mauve on No. 2527 and the bright mauve, new blue, and lilac on No. 2529 are printed in thermochromic inks which fade temporarily when exposed to heat, making the pyramid under the centre fez visible.

The 1st class stamp was also issued in sheets of 20, printed in lithography instead of photogravure and sold at £6.15, containing vertical rows of five stamps alternated with half stamp-size printed labels illustrating magic tricks. These sheets were also available with personal photographs on the labels at £14.95 per sheet from Royal Mail, Edinburgh.

Special First Day of Issue Postmarks

15.3.2005

15.3.2005

THE CASTLES DEFINITIVES

1806a (*Illustration reduced. Actual size* 127×73 mm)

(Des Sedley Place. Recess and litho Enschedé)

2005 (22 Mar). *50th Anniv of First Castles Definitives. Printed on pale cream. "All-over" phosphor.* P 11×11½.

MS2530 **1806a** 50p. brownish-black; 50p. black; £1 dull vermilion; £1 royal blue		10·00	10·00
First Day Cover (Tallents House)			12·00
First Day Cover (Windsor)			12·00
Presentation Pack (P.O. Pack No. 69)		18·00	
PHQ *Cards* (set of 5)		2·20	12·00

The five PHQ cards depict the whole miniature sheet and the four stamps it contains.

Special First Day of Issue Postmarks

1807 (*Illustration reduced. Actual size* 85×115 mm)

(Des Rose Design. Litho Enschedé)

2005 (9 Apr). *Royal Wedding. Sheet* 85×115 *mm. Multicoloured. "All-over" phosphor.* P 13½×14.

MS2531 30p.×2 Prince Charles and Mrs Camilla Parker Bowles laughing; 68p.×2 Prince Charles and Mrs Camilla Parker Bowles smiling into camera		8·00	10·00
First Day Cover (Tallents House)			10·00
First Day Cover (Windsor)			10·00
Presentation Pack (P.O. Pack No. M10)		18·00	

No. **MS**2531 was officially issued on 9th April. It was originally intended for issue on 8th April, and many post offices put it on sale on that day. Royal Mail first day covers were dated 8th April, but could be ordered with a 9th April Windsor handstamp. Our prices cover either date.

Special First Day of Issue Postmarks

1808 Hadrian's Wall, England

1809 Uluru-Kata Tjuta National Park, Australia

1810 Stonehenge, England

1811 Wet Tropics of Queensland, Australia

1812 Blenheim Palace, England

1813 Greater Blue Mountains Area, Australia

1814 Heart of Neolithic Orkney, Scotland

1815 Purnululu National Park, Australia

(Des J. Godfrey. Litho Enschedé)

2005 (21 Apr). *World Heritage Sites. One side phosphor band (2nd) or two phosphor bands (others).* P 14½.

2532	**1808**	2nd silver, black, magenta, new blue and greenish yellow	60	35
		a. Horiz pair. Nos. 2532/3	1·00	1·00
2533	**1809**	2nd silver, black, magenta, new blue and greenish yellow	60	35
2534	**1810**	1st silver, black, magenta, new blue and greenish yellow	75	45
		a. Horiz pair. Nos. 2534/5	2·00	1·50
2535	**1811**	1st silver, black, magenta, new blue and greenish yellow	75	45
2536	**1812**	47p. silver, black, magenta, new blue and greenish yellow	60	60
		a. Horiz pair. Nos. 2536/7	3·00	3·50
2537	**1813**	47p. silver, black, magenta, new blue and greenish yellow	60	60
2538	**1814**	68p. silver, black, magenta, new blue and greenish yellow	90	90
		a. Horiz pair. Nos. 2538/9	5·00	5·00

2539	**1815**	68p. silver, black, magenta, new blue and greenish yellow	90	90
Set of 8			11·00	11·00
Set of 4 Gutter Strips of 4			16·50	
Set of 4 Traffic Light Gutter Blocks of 8			35·00	
First Day Cover (Tallents House)				13·00
First Day Cover (Blenheim Palace, Woodstock)				14·00
First Day Covers (2) (UK and Australian stamps)				24·00
Presentation Pack (P.O. Pack No. 371)			12·00	
Presentation Pack (UK and Australian stamps)			16·00	
PHQ Cards (set of 8) (275)			5·00	16·00

The two designs of each value were printed together, *se-tenant*, in horizontal pairs in sheets of 30 (6×5).

Stamps in these designs were also issued by Australia and these are included in the joint Presentation Pack.

Special First Day of Issue Postmarks

1816 Ensign of the Scots Guards, 2002

1817 Queen taking the salute as Colonel-in-Chief of the Grenadier Guards, 1983

1818 Trumpeter of the Household Cavalry, 2004

1819 Welsh Guardsman, 1990s

1820 Queen riding side-saddle, 1972

1821 Queen and Duke of Edinburgh in carriage, 2004

(Des A. Altmann. Litho Walsall)

2005 (7 June). *Trooping the Colour. One phosphor band (2nd), two phosphor bands (others).* P 14½.

2540	**1816**	(2nd) silver, greenish yellow, bright carmine, new blue and black	70	80
2541	**1817**	(1st) silver, greenish yellow, bright carmine, new blue and black	75	90
2542	**1818**	42p. silver, greenish yellow, bright carmine, new blue and black	1·00	1·20
2543	**1819**	60p. silver, greenish yellow, bright carmine, new blue and black	2·00	2·00
2544	**1820**	68p. silver, greenish yellow, bright carmine, new blue and black	2·50	2·50
2545	**1821**	£1.12 silver, greenish yellow, bright carmine, new blue and black	3·50	3·50

Set of 6		10·00	10·00
Set of 6 Gutter Pairs		21·00	
First Day Cover (Tallents House)			12·00
First Day Cover (London SW1)			12·00
Presentation Pack (P.O. Pack No. 372)		14·00	
PHQ Cards (set of 7) (276)		5·00	20·00
MS2546 115×105 mm. Nos. 2540/5		11·00	11·00
First Day Cover (Tallents House)			12·00
First Day Cover (London SW1)			12·00

The seven PHQ cards show the six stamps and **MS**2546.

Special First Day of Issue Postmarks

1822 (*Illustration reduced. Actual size 115×105 mm*)

(Des J. Matthews. Photo Enschedé)

2005 (5 July). *60th Anniv of End of the Second World War. Sheet 115×105 mm containing design as T* **1200** *(1995 Peace and Freedom) but with service indicator and No. 1668×5. Two phosphor bands. P 15×14 (with one elliptical hole in each vert side) (1668) or 14½×14 (other).*

MS2547 **1822** (1st) gold×5; (1st) silver, blue and grey-black		6·50	6·00
First Day Cover (Tallents House)			8·00
First Day Cover (Peacehaven, Newhaven)			8·00

Special First Day of Issue Postmarks

1823 Norton F.1, Road Version of Race Winner (1991)

1824 BSA Rocket 3, Early Three Cylinder "Superbike" (1969)

1825 Vincent Black Shadow, Fastest Standard Motorcycle (1949)

1826 Triumph Speed Twin, Two Cylinder Innovation (1938)

1827 Brough Superior, Bespoke Luxury Motorcycle (1930)

1828 Royal Enfield, Small Engined Motor Bicycle (1914)

(Des I. Chilvers and M. English. Litho Walsall)

2005 (19 July). *Motorcycles. Two phosphor bands. P 14×14½.*

2548	**1823**	(1st) silver, greenish yellow, bright crimson, new blue and black	75	80
2549	**1824**	40p. silver, greenish yellow, bright crimson, new blue and black	90	1·00
2550	**1825**	42p. silver, greenish yellow, bright crimson, new blue and black	1·25	1·00
2551	**1826**	47p. silver, greenish yellow, bright crimson, new blue and black	1·75	2·00
2552	**1827**	60p. silver, greenish yellow, bright crimson, new blue and black	2·50	2·50
2553	**1828**	68p. silver, greenish yellow, bright crimson, new blue and black	3·00	3·00
Set of 6			9·00	9·00
Set of 6 Gutter Pairs			19·00	
First Day Cover (Tallents House)				12·00
First Day Cover (Solihull)				12·00
Presentation Pack (P.O. Pack No. 373)			15·00	
PHQ Cards (set of 6) (277)			5·00	14·00

Special First Day of Issue Postmarks

1829 (*Illustration reduced. Actual size 115×105 mm*)

(Des CDT Design. Litho Walsall)

2005 (5 Aug). *London's Successful Bid for Olympic Games, 2012. Sheet 115×105 mm containing designs as T* **1255/9**, *but with service indicator. Multicoloured. Two phosphor bands. P 14½.*

MS2554 **1829** (1st) Athlete celebrating×2; (1st) Throwing the javelin; (1st) Swimming; (1st) Athlete on starting blocks; (1st) Basketball		6·50	6·00

First Day Cover (Tallents House).. 8·00
First Day Cover (London E15) .... 8·00
Presentation Pack (P.O. Pack No. M11)............................... 12·00
    Stamps from **MS**2554 are all inscribed "London 2012—Host City" and
have imprint date "2005". The design as Type **1257** omits the Olympic
rings.

Special First Day of Issue Postmarks

Special First Day of Issue Postmarks

1836 Inspector Morse   **1837** Emmerdale

1830 African Woman eating
Rice

1831 Indian Woman
drinking Tea

1838 Rising Damp   **1839** The Avengers

1832 Boy eating Sushi   **1833** Woman eating Pasta

1840 The South Bank Show   **1841** Who Wants to be a
Millionaire

(Des Kate Stephens. Litho DLR)

2005 (15 Sept). *50th Anniversary of Independent Television. Classic ITV
Programmes. One side phosphor band (2nd) or two phosphor bands
(others).* P 14½×14.

2561	**1836**	(2nd) new blue, magenta, greenish yellow and brownish-black................	60	70
2562	**1837**	(1st) new blue, magenta, greenish yellow and brownish-black................	90	1·00
2563	**1838**	42p. new blue, magenta, greenish yellow and brownish-black................	1·30	1·40
2564	**1839**	47p. new blue, magenta, greenish yellow and brownish-black................	1·40	1·50
2565	**1840**	60p. new blue, magenta, greenish yellow and brownish-black................	2·00	1·90
2566	**1841**	68p. new blue, magenta, greenish yellow and brownish-black................	2·20	2·20

Set of 6 .... 8·00   8·00
Set of 6 Gutter Pairs.. 17·00
First Day Cover (Tallents House)...................................... 12·00
First Day Cover (London SE19)... 12·00
Presentation Pack (P.O. Pack No. 375)............ 9·00
PHQ Cards (set of 6) (279) .... 5·00   12·00
    The 1st class stamps were also issued in sheets of 20 sold at £6.55,
printed in lithography by Walsall, containing four vertical rows of
five stamps alternated with half stamp-size labels. These sheets with
personalised photographs were available at £14.95 from the Royal Mail.

1834 Woman eating Chips   **1835** Teenage Boy eating
Apple

(Des Catell Ronca and Rose Design. Photo Enschedé)

2005 (23 Aug). *Europa. Gastronomy. Changing Tastes in Britain. One
side phosphor band (2nd) or two phosphor bands (others).* P 14½.

2555	**1830**	(2nd) olive-grey, grey-black, new blue, magenta and greenish yellow	60	70
2556	**1831**	(1st) olive-grey, grey-black, new blue, magenta and greenish yellow	90	1·00
2557	**1832**	42p. olive-grey, grey-black, new blue, magenta and greenish yellow	1·30	1·40
2558	**1833**	47p. olive-grey, grey-black, new blue, magenta and greenish yellow	1·50	1·60
2559	**1834**	60p. olive-grey, grey-black, new blue, magenta and greenish yellow	2·00	1·90
2560	**1835**	68p. olive-grey, grey-black, new blue, magenta and greenish yellow	2·50	2·20

Set of 6 .... 8·00   8·00
Set of 6 Gutter Pairs.. 17·00
First Day Cover (Tallents House)...................................... 10·00
First Day Cover (Cookstown)... 10·00
Presentation Pack (P.O. Pack No. 374) .... 9·00
PHQ Cards (set of 6) (278) .... 5·00   12·00

Special First Day of Issue Postmarks

1842 *Gazania* **1842a** "LOVE"
splendens
(Charlotte
Sowerby)

(Photo Walsall)

2005 (4 Oct). *Smilers Booklet stamps (1st series). Designs as Types* **992**, **1221**, **1286**, **1517** *and* **1569** *but smaller, 20×23 mm and inscribed "1st" as T* **1842/a.** *Self-adhesive. Two phosphor bands. Die-cut. Perf 15×14.*

2567	**1842**	(1st) multicoloured	2·00	2·00
		a. Booklet pane. Nos. 2567/72	12·00	
2568	**1569**	(1st) multicoloured	2·00	2·00
2569	**1842a**	(1st) multicoloured	2·00	2·00
2570	**1517**	(1st) multicoloured	2·00	2·00
2571	**992**	(1st) multicoloured	2·00	2·00
2572	**1221**	(1st) multicoloured	2·00	2·00
Set of 6			12·00	12·00
First Day Cover (Tallents House) (Type K, see Introduction) ..				12·00
First Day Cover (Windsor) (Type K)				12·00

Nos. 2567/72 were only issued in stamp booklets, Nos. QA1 and QA2, in which the surplus backing paper around each stamp was removed.

Stamps in these designs in separate sheets printed in lithography by Cartor were available with personal photographs on the labels at £14.95 per sheet from Royal Mail, Edinburgh.

Nos. 2567/72 were issued on 4 July 2006 in sheets of 20 with *se-tenant* greetings labels, No. LS32, printed by Cartor in lithography instead of photogravure and sold at £6.95 per sheet.

Nos. 2568/70 were re-issued on 15 January 2008 in sheets of 20 with circular labels printed in lithography by Cartor and sold at £7.35 (LS45). These sheets were perforated with one elliptical hole on each vert side.

These three designs were available in separate sheets of 10 (sold at £8.95) or 20 (sold at £14.95) with personal photographs on the labels from Royal Mail, Edinburgh).

No. 2568 was issued on 30 April 2009 in sheets of 20 with *se-tenant* circular Jeremy Fisher labels, No. LS60, printed in lithography by Cartor and sold at £8.50. These sheets were perforated with one elliptical hole on each vertical side.

Similar sheets of 10 stamps and 10 *se-tenant* labels were only sold in packs for £7.95 each.

No. 2572 was issued on 8 May 2010 with other greetings stamps in sheets of 20 with *se-tenant* greetings labels, printed in lithography by Cartor, No. LS73, and sold for £10 per sheet. These sheets were printed with one elliptical hole in each vertical side.

For stamp as No. 2569 with elliptical perforations see No. 2693.

For stamps as Nos. 2567/8 and 2570 with elliptical perforations see Nos. 2819/21.

THE ASHES ENGLAND WINNERS 2005

1843 Cricket Scenes (*Illustration reduced. Actual size 115×90 mm*)

(Des Why Not Associates. Litho Cartor)

2005 (6 Oct). *England's Ashes Victory. Sheet 115×90 mm. Multicoloured. Two phosphor bands.* P 14½×14.

MS2573 **1843** (1st) England team with Ashes trophy; (1st) Kevin Pietersen, Michael Vaughan and Andrew Flintoff on opening day of First Test, Lords; 68p. Michael Vaughan, Third Test, Old Trafford; 68p. Second Test cricket, Edgbaston..........................	7·50	7·50
First Day Cover (Tallents House)................................		10·00
First Day Cover (London SE11)...................................		10·00
Presentation Pack (P.O. Pack No. M12)...................	10·00	

Special First Day of Issue Postmarks

1844 *Entrepreante* with dismasted British *Belle Isle*

1845 Nelson wounded on Deck of HMS *Victory*

1846 British Cutter *Entrepreante* attempting to rescue Crew of burning French *Achille*

1847 Cutter and HMS *Pickle* (schooner)

1848 British Fleet attacking in Two Columns

1849 Franco/Spanish Fleet putting to Sea from Cadiz

(Des D. Davis. Litho Cartor)

2005 (18 Oct). *Bicentenary of the Battle of Trafalgar (1st issue). Scenes from "Panorama of the Battle of Trafalgar" by William Heath. Two phosphor bands.* P 15×14½.

2574	**1844**	(1st) gold, deep bluish-green, greenish yellow, magenta, new blue and black..	70	45
		a. Horiz pair. Nos. 2574/5.......................	1·75	2·00
		b. Booklet pane. Nos. 2574, 2576 and 2578..	3·50	
2575	**1845**	(1st) gold, deep bluish-green, greenish yellow, magenta, new blue and black..	70	45
		b. Booklet pane. Nos. 2575, 2577 and 2570..	3·75	
2576	**1846**	42p. gold, deep bluish-green, greenish yellow, magenta, new blue and black..	65	65
		a. Horiz pair. Nos. 2576/7.......................	2·50	2·75
2577	**1847**	42p. gold, deep bluish-green, greenish yellow, magenta, new blue and black..	65	65
2578	**1848**	68p. gold, deep bluish-green, greenish yellow, magenta, new blue and black..	90	90
		a. Horiz pair. Nos. 2578/9.......................	4·00	4·40

2579 **1849** 68p. gold, deep bluish-green, greenish yellow, magenta, new blue and black... 90 90
Set of 6 .... 9·00 10·00
Set of 3 Gutter Strips of 4 .... 11·00
First Day Cover (Tallents House).......................... 11·00
First Day Cover (Portsmouth) .... 11·00
Presentation Pack (P.O. Pack No. 376) .... 12·00
PHQ Cards (set of 7) (280) .... 5·00 20·00
MS2580 190×68 mm. Nos. 2574/9................... 10·00 11·00
First Day Cover (Tallents House).......................... 11·00
First Day Cover (Portsmouth) .... 11·00

Nos. 2574/5, 2576/7 and 2578/9 were each printed together, *se-tenant*, in horizontal pairs throughout the sheets, each pair forming a composite design.

The phosphor bands are at just left of centre and at right of each stamp.

The seven PHQ cards depict the six individual stamps and the miniature sheet.

Special First Day of Issue Postmarks

(Litho Cartor or De La Rue)

2005 (18 Oct). *Bicentenary of the Battle of Trafalgar (2nd issue). Booklet stamp. Design as Type* **1516** *(2001 White Ensign from Submarine Centenary). Two phosphor bands.* P 14½.
2581 **1516** (1st) multicoloured .... 5·00 5·00
a. Booklet pane. No. 2581×3 with
margins all round .... 16·00

No. 2581 was issued in the £7.26 Trafalgar Bicentenary booklet, No. DX35, printed by Cartor, and also in the £7.40 James Bond booklet, No. DX41, which was printed by De La Rue (see booklet pane No. 2805a).

1850 Black Madonna and Child from Haiti

1851 "Madonna and Child" (Marianne Stokes)

1852 "The Virgin Mary with the Infant Christ"

1853 Choctaw Virgin Mother and Child (Fr. John Giuliani)

1854 "Madonna and the Infant Jesus" (from India)

1855 "Come let us adore Him" (Dianne Tchumut)

(Des Irene Von Treskow. Photo De La Rue)

2005 (1 Nov). *Christmas. Madonna and Child Paintings. One side phosphor band (2nd) or two phosphor bands (others).* P 14½×14.

(a) Self-adhesive
2582 **1850** (2nd) silver, magenta, greenish yellow, new blue and black 60 70
a. Booklet pane. No. 2582×24 .... 14·00
2583 **1851** (1st) silver, magenta, greenish yellow, new blue and black .... 90 1·00

a. Booklet pane. No. 2583×12 .... 10·50
2584 **1852** 42p. silver, magenta, greenish yellow, new blue and black .... 1·30 1·40
2585 **1853** 60p. silver, magenta, greenish yellow, new blue and black .... 1·80 1·90
2586 **1854** 68p. silver, magenta, greenish yellow, new blue and black .... 2·00 2·20
2587 **1855** £1.12 silver, magenta, greenish yellow, new blue and black .... 3·40 3·60
Set of 6 .... 10·00 11·00
First Day Cover (Tallents House).......................... 12·00
First Day Cover (Bethlehem, Llandeilo)............... 13·00
Presentation Pack (P.O. Pack No. 377) .... 12·00
PHQ Cards (set of 7) (281) .... 4·00 16·00

The seven PHQ cards depict the six individual stamps and the miniature sheet.

(b) Ordinary gum
MS2588 115×102 mm. As Nos. 2582/7 .... 10·50 11·00
First Day Cover (Tallents House).......................... 12·00
First Day Cover (Bethlehem, Llandeilo)............... 13·00

Special First Day of Issue Postmarks

Collectors Pack

2005 (1 Nov). Comprises Nos. 2502/23, 2525/9. **MS**2531/45, 2555/66, 2574/9 and 2582/7.
CP2587a Collectors Pack £110

Post Office Yearbook

2005 (1 Nov). Comprises Nos. 2502/23, 2525/9, **MS**2531/45, 2555/66, MS2574/9 and 2582/7.
YB2587a Yearbook.. 95·00

Miniature Sheet Collection

2005 (1 Nov). Comprises Nos. **MS**2524, **MS**2530/1, **MS**2546/7, **MS**2554, **MS**2573, **MS**2580 and **MS**2588.
MS2588*a* Miniature Sheet Collection .... 75·00

1856 *The Tale of Mr. Jeremy Fisher* (Beatrix Potter)

1857 *Kipper* (Mick Inkpen)

1858 *The Enormous Crocodile* (Roald Dahl)

1859 *More About Paddington* (Michael Bond)

1860 *Comic Adventures of Boots* (Satoshi Kitamura)

1861 *Alice's Adventures in Wonderland* (Lewis Carroll)

1862 *The Very Hungry Caterpillar* (Eric Carle)

1863 *Maisy's ABC* (Lucy Cousins)

(Des Rose Design. Litho DLR)

2006 (10 Jan). *Animal Tales*. One side phosphor band (2nd) or two phosphor bands (others). P 14½.

2589	**1856**	(2nd) brownish-black, new blue, magenta, greenish yellow and black	60	35
		a. Horiz pair. Nos. 2589/90	70	70
2590	**1857**	(2nd) brownish-black, new blue, magenta, greenish yellow and black	60	35
2591	**1858**	(1st) brownish-black, new blue, magenta, greenish yellow and black	70	50
		a. Horiz pair. Nos. 2591/2	1·50	1·50
2592	**1859**	(1st) brownish-black, new blue, magenta, greenish yellow and black	70	50
2593	**1860**	42p. brownish-black, new blue, magenta, greenish yellow and black	65	70
		a. Horiz pair. Nos. 2593/4	4·00	4·00
2594	**1861**	42p. brownish-black, new blue, magenta, greenish yellow and black	65	70
2595	**1862**	68p. brownish-black, new blue, magenta, greenish yellow and black	1·00	1·10
		a. Horiz pair. Nos. 2595/6	5·00	5·00
2596	**1863**	68p. brownish-black, new blue, magenta, greenish yellow and black	1·00	1·10
Set of 8			10·00	10·00
Set of 4 Gutter Strips of 4			13·00	
Set of 4 Traffic Light Gutter Blocks of 8			28·00	
First Day Cover (Tallents House)				11·00
First Day Cover (Mousehole, Penzance, Cornwall)				12·00
First Day Cover (Nos. 2595/6 UK and US stamps)				9·00
Presentation Pack (P.O. Pack No. 379)			12·00	
PHQ Cards (set of 8) (282)			4·50	16·00

Nos. 2589/90, 2591/2, 2593/4 and 2595/6 were printed together, *se-tenant*, in horizontal pairs in sheets of 60 (2 panes 6×5).

A design as No. 2592 but self-adhesive was issued in sheets of 20, printed in lithography by Cartor sold at £6.55, containing four vertical rows of five stamps alternated with printed labels. This sheet was also available with personal photographs on the labels at £14.95 from Royal Mail.

No. 2595 contains two die-cut holes.

Special First Day of Issue Postmarks

1864 Carding Mill Valley, Shropshire

1865 Beachy Head, Sussex

1866 St. Paul's Cathedral, London

1867 Brancaster, Norfolk

1868 Derwent Edge, Peak District

1869 Robin Hood's Bay, Yorkshire

1870 Buttermere, Lake District

1871 Chipping Campden, Cotswolds

1872 St. Boniface Down, Isle of Wight

1873 Chamberlain Square, Birmingham

(Des Phelan Barker Design Consultants. Photo DLR)

2006 (7 Feb). *A British Journey: England*. Two phosphor bands. P 14½.

2597	**1864**	(1st) silver, black, rosine, greenish yellow and new blue	70	50
		a. Block of 10. Nos. 2597/606	12·00	10·00
2598	**1865**	(1st) silver, black, rosine, greenish yellow and new blue	70	50
2599	**1866**	(1st) silver, black, rosine, greenish yellow and new blue	70	50
2600	**1867**	(1st) silver, black, rosine, greenish yellow and new blue	70	50
2601	**1868**	(1st) silver, black, rosine, greenish yellow and new blue	70	50
2602	**1869**	(1st) silver, black, rosine, greenish yellow and new blue	70	50
2603	**1870**	(1st) silver, black, rosine, greenish yellow and new blue	70	50
2604	**1871**	(1st) silver, black, rosine, greenish yellow and new blue	70	50
2605	**1872**	(1st) silver, black, rosine, greenish yellow and new blue	70	50
2606	**1873**	(1st) silver, black, rosine, greenish yellow and new blue	70	50
Set of 10			12·00	10·00
Gutter Block of 20			20·00	
First Day Cover (Tallents House)				11·00
First Day Cover (Tea Green, Luton)				12·00
Presentation Pack (P.O. Pack No. 380)			12·00	
PHQ Cards (set of 10) (283)			5·75	16·00

Nos. 2597/606 were printed together, *se-tenant*, as blocks of ten (5×2) in sheets of 60 (2 panes of 30).

First Day of Issue Postmarks

1874 Royal Albert Bridge

1875 Box Tunnel

1876 Paddington Station

1877 PSS *Great Eastern* (paddle steamer)

1878 Clifton Suspension Bridge Design

1879 Maidenhead Bridge

(Des Hat-trick Design. Litho Enschedé)

2006 (23 Feb). *Birth Bicentenary of Isambard Kingdom Brunel (engineer) (1st issue). Phosphor-coated paper (42p.) or two phosphor bands (others).* P 14×13½.

2607	**1874**	(1st) silver, black, new blue, magenta and greenish yellow	70	50
		a. Booklet pane. Nos. 2607, 2609 and 2612	3·00	
2608	**1875**	40p. silver, black, new blue, magenta and greenish yellow	75	75
		a. Booklet pane. Nos. 2608 and 2610/11	4·00	
2609	**1876**	42p. silver, black, new blue, magenta and greenish yellow	1·00	1·00
2610	**1877**	47p. silver, black, new blue, magenta and greenish yellow	1·50	1·00
		a. Booklet pane. No. 2610 and No. 2614×2	18·00	
2611	**1878**	60p. silver, black, new blue, magenta and greenish yellow	2·00	1·75
2612	**1879**	68p. silver, black, new blue, magenta and greenish yellow	2·50	2·25

Set of 6	7·50	8·50
Set of 6 Gutter Pairs	16·00	
First Day Cover (Tallents House)		9·00
First Day Cover (Bristol)		10·00
Presentation Pack (P.O. Pack No. 381)	10·00	
PHQ Cards (set of 7) (284)	4·00	14·00
MS2613 190×65 mm. Nos. 2607/12	8·50	8·50
a. Imperforate	—	
First Day Cover (Tallents House)		9·00
First Day Cover (Bristol)		10·00

The phosphor bands on Nos. 2607/8 and 2610/12 are at just left of centre and at right of each stamp.

The complete miniature sheet is shown on one of the PHQ Cards with the others depicting individual stamps.

First Day of Issue Postmarks

(Litho Enschedé)

2006 (23 Feb). *Birth Bicentenary of Isambard Kingdom Brunel (2nd issue). Booklet stamp. Design as Type* **1739** *("PS Great Western" from 2004 Ocean Liners). Two phosphor bands.* P 14½×14.

2614	**1739**	68p. multicoloured	12·00	12·50

No. 2614 was only available in stamp booklets, No. DX36.

1880 Sabre-tooth Cat   **1881** Giant Deer

1882 Woolly Rhino   **1883** Woolly Mammoth

1884 Cave Bear

(Des A. Davidson and H. Brown. Litho Enschedé)

2006 (21 Mar). *Ice Age Animals. Two phosphor bands.* P 14½.

2615	**1880**	(1st) black and silver	70	50
2616	**1881**	42p. black and silver	75	80
2617	**1882**	47p. black and silver	2·00	2·00
2618	**1883**	68p. black and silver	2·25	2·25
2619	**1884**	£1.12 black and silver	3·25	3·25

Set of 5	8·00	8·00
Set of 5 Gutter Pairs	16·00	
First Day Cover (Tallents House)		9·00
First Day Cover (Freezywater, Enfield)		10·00
Presentation Pack (P.O. Pack No. 382)	12·00	
PHQ Cards (set of 5) (285)	2·75	12·00

Special First Day of Issue Postmarks

1885 On Britannia, 1972

1886 At Royal Windsor Horse Show, 1985

1887 At Heathrow Airport, 2001

1888 As Young Princess Elizabeth with Duchess of York, 1931

1889 At State Banquet, Ottawa, 1951

1890 Queen in 1960

1891 As Princess Elizabeth, 1940

1892 With Duke of Edinburgh, 1951

(Des Sedley Place. Photo Enschedé)

2006 (18 Apr). *80th Birthday of Queen Elizabeth II. One side phosphor band (No. 2620), one centre phosphor band (No. 2621) or two phosphor bands (others).* P 14½.

2620	**1885**	(2nd) black, turquoise-green and grey ...	60	40
		a. Horiz pair. Nos. 2620/1	95	95
2621	**1886**	(2nd) black, turquoise-green and grey ...	60	40
2622	**1887**	(1st) black, turquoise-green and grey ...	70	45
		a. Horiz pair. Nos. 2622/3	1·75	1·75
2623	**1888**	(1st) black, turquoise-green and grey ...	70	50
2624	**1889**	44p. black, turquoise-green and grey ...	65	65
		a. Horiz pair. Nos. 2624/5	2·75	2·75
2625	**1890**	44p. black, turquoise-green and grey ...	65	65
2626	**1891**	72p. black, turquoise-green and grey ...	1·10	1·10
		a. Horiz pair. Nos. 2626/7	4·50	4·50
2627	**1892**	72p. black, turquoise-green and grey ...	1·10	1·10
Set of 8			9·50	9·50
Set of 4 Gutter Strips of 4			18·00	
First Day Cover (Tallents House)...............................				10·00
First Day Cover (Windsor)...				11·00
Presentation Pack (P.O. Pack No. 383)			12·00	
PHQ Cards (set of 8) (286)			4·50	16·00

Nos. 2620/1, 2622/3, 2624/5 and 2626/7 were each printed together, *se-tenant*, as horizontal pairs in sheets of 60 (2 panes 6×5).

1st
1893 England (1966)

42
1894 Italy (1934, 1938, 1982)

1895 Argentina (1978, 1986)

50
1896 Germany (1954, 1974, 1990)

44

64
1897 France (1998)

72
1898 Brazil (1958, 1962, 1970, 1994, 2002)

(Des Madeleine Bennett. Litho Walsall)

2006 (6 June). *World Cup Football Championship, Germany. World Cup Winners. Two phosphor bands.* P 14½.

2628	**1893**	(1st) lemon, deep brownish grey, greenish yellow, bright magenta, new blue and black	70	50
2629	**1894**	42p. lemon, deep brownish grey, greenish yellow, bright magenta, new blue and black	65	70
2630	**1895**	44p. lemon, deep brownish grey, greenish yellow, bright magenta, new blue and black	1·25	1·25
2631	**1896**	50p. lemon, deep brownish grey, greenish yellow, bright magenta, new blue and black	2·00	2·00
2632	**1897**	64p. lemon, deep brownish grey, greenish yellow, bright magenta, new blue and black	3·00	3·00
2633	**1898**	72p. lemon, deep brownish grey, greenish yellow, bright magenta, new blue and black	3·50	3·50
Set of 6			9·00	9·00
Set of 6 Gutter Pairs..			18·00	
First Day Cover (Tallents House)...............................				9·00
First Day Cover (Balls Park, Hertford)......................				10·00
Presentation Pack (P.O. Pack No. 384)			12·00	
PHQ Cards (set of 6) (287)..			4·00	12·00

The 1st class stamp was also issued in sheets of 20, sold for £6·95, printed in lithography by Cartor, containing four vertical rows of five stamps alternated with labels showing scenes from the 1966 World Cup final.

Special First Day of Issue Postmarks

Special First Day of Issue Postmarks

1899 30 St. Mary Axe, London

1900 Maggie's Centre, Dundee

1901 Selfridges, Birmingham

1902 Downland Gridshell, Chichester

1903 An Turas, Isle of Tiree

1904 The Deep, Hull

(Des Roundel. Photo Walsall)

2006 (20 June). *Modern Architecture. Two phosphor bands.* P 14½.

2634	**1899**	(1st)	greenish yellow, magenta, new blue and black	70	50
2635	**1900**	42p.	greenish yellow, magenta, new blue and black	65	70
2636	**1901**	44p.	greenish yellow, magenta, new blue and black	1·25	1·25
2637	**1902**	50p.	greenish yellow, magenta, new blue and black	2·00	2·00
2638	**1903**	64p.	greenish yellow, magenta, new blue and black	3·00	3·00
2639	**1904**	72p.	greenish yellow, magenta, new blue and black	3·50	3·50

Set of 6	9·00	9·00
Set of 6 Gutter Pairs	18·00	
First Day Cover (Tallents House)		9·00
First Day Cover (London EC3)		9·00
Presentation Pack (P.O. Pack No. 385)	12·00	
PHQ Cards (set of 6) (288)	4·00	12·00

Special First Day of Issue Postmarks

1905 "Sir Winston Churchill" (Walter Sickert)

1906 "Sir Joshua Reynolds" (self-portrait)

1907 "T. S. Eliot" (Patrick Heron)

1908 "Emmeline Pankhurst" (Georgina Agnes Brackenbury)

1909 Virginia Woolf (photo by George Charles Beresford)

1910 Bust of Sir Walter Scott (Sir Francis Leggatt Chantry)

1911 "Mary Seacole" (Albert Charles Challen)

1912 "William Shakespeare" (attrib to John Taylor)

1913 "Dame Cicely Saunders" (Catherine Goodman)

1914 "Charles Darwin" (John Collier)

(Des P. Willberg. Photo De La Rue)

2006 (18 July). *150th Anniversary of National Portrait Gallery, London. Two phosphor bands.* P 14½.

2640	**1905**	(1st)	silver, black, magenta, greenish yellow and new blue	70	50
		a.	Block of 10. Nos. 2640/9	12·00	9·00
2641	**1906**	(1st)	silver, black, magenta, greenish yellow and new blue	70	50
2642	**1907**	(1st)	silver, black, magenta, greenish yellow and new blue	70	50
2643	**1908**	(1st)	silver, black, magenta, greenish yellow and new blue	70	50
2644	**1909**	(1st)	silver, black, magenta, greenish yellow and new blue	70	50
2645	**1910**	(1st)	silver, black, magenta, greenish yellow and new blue	70	50
2646	**1911**	(1st)	silver, black, magenta, greenish yellow and new blue	70	50
2647	**1912**	(1st)	silver, black, magenta, greenish yellow and new blue	70	50
2648	**1913**	(1st)	silver, black, magenta, greenish yellow and new blue	70	50
2649	**1914**	(1st)	silver, black, magenta, greenish yellow and new blue	70	50

Set of 10	12·00	9·00
Gutter Block of 20	19·00	
Traffic Light Gutter Block of 20	25·00	
First Day Cover (Tallents House)		10·00
First Day Cover (London WC2)		10·00
Presentation Pack (P.O. Pack No. 386)	12·00	
PHQ Cards (set of 10) (289)	6·75	16·00

Nos. 2640/9 were printed together, *se-tenant*, as blocks of ten (5×2) in sheets of 60 (2 panes of 30).

Special First Day of Issue Postmarks

FIRST DAY
OF ISSUE
ROYAL MAIL
TALLENTS
HOUSE
EDINBURGH
18.7.2006

FIRST DAY
OF ISSUE
LONDON WC2
18.7.2006

For Nos. 2650/7 see Decimal Machin Definitives section.

1917 (Illustration reduced. Actual size 127×72 mm)

(Des Katja Thielan. Photo De La Rue)

2006 (31 Aug). *70th Anniversary of the Year of Three Kings. Sheet 127×72 mm containing No. Y1728. Multicoloured. Two phosphor bands.* P 15×14 (with one elliptical hole in each vertical side).

MS2658 **1917** £3 deep mauve		10·00	10·00
First Day Cover (Tallents House)			11·00
First Day Cover (Threekingham, Sleaford, Lincs)			11·00

Special First Day of Issue Postmarks

ROYAL MAIL TALLENTS HOUSE EDINBURGH
1936
31.8.2006

THREEKINGHAM SLEAFORD LINCS
1936
YEAR OF THE
III KINGS
31 AUGUST 2006

1918 Corporal Agansing Rai

1919 Boy Seaman Jack Cornwell

1920 Midshipman Charles Lucas

1921 Captain Noel Chavasse

1922 Captain Albert Ball

1923 Captain Charles Upham

(Des Atelier Works. Litho Enschedé)

2006 (21 Sept). *150th Anniv of the Victoria Cross (1st issue). One side phosphor band.* P 14½×14.

2659	**1918**	(1st) gold, black, new blue, magenta and greenish yellow	70	50
		a. Horiz pair. Nos. 2659/60	1·00	1·00
		b. Booklet pane. Nos. 2659, 2661 and 2663	3·75	
		ba. Booklet pane. Bronze and phosphor omitted	£17000	
2660	**1919**	(1st) gold, black, new blue. magenta and greenish yellow	70	50
		b. Booklet pane. Nos. 2660, 2662 and 2664	3·75	
		ba. Booklet pane. Bronze and phosphor omitted	£17000	
2661	**1920**	64p. gold, black, new blue, magenta and greenish yellow	1·25	1·25
		a. Horiz pair. Nos. 2661/2	5·00	5·00
2662	**1921**	64p. gold, black, new blue, magenta and greenish yellow	1·25	1·25
2663	**1922**	72p. gold, black, new blue, magenta and greenish yellow	2·00	2·25
		a. Horiz pair. Nos. 2663/4	7·00	7·00
2664	**1923**	72p. gold, black, new blue, magenta and greenish yellow	2·00	2·25

Set of 6	12·00	12·00
Set of 3 Gutter Strips of 4	16·00	
First Day Cover (Tallents House)		13·00
First Day Cover (Cuffley, Potters Bar, Herts)		13·00
Presentation Pack (P.O. Pack No. 387)	14·00	
MS2665 190×67 mm. Nos. 2659/64 and 2666	16·00	16·00
First Day Cover (Tallents House)		14·00
First Day Cover (Cuffley, Potters Bar, Herts)		14·00
PHQ Cards (set of 7) (290)	4·50	15·00

Nos. 2659/60, 2661/2 and 2663/4 were each printed together, *se-tenant*, as horizontal pairs in sheets of 60 (2 panes 6×5).

The seven PHQ Cards depict the six individual stamps and the miniature sheet.

Special First Day of Issue Postmarks

ROYAL MAIL TALLENTS HOUSE EDINBURGH
"Who would
true valour see,
Let him *come
hither*..."
JOHN BUNYAN
21·9·2006

FIRST DAY OF ISSUE CUFFLEY POTTERS BAR HERTS
"I only did
my job"
WILLIAM LEEFE
ROBINSON VC
21·9·2006

(Litho Enschedé)

2006 (21 Sept). *150th Anniv of the Victoria Cross (2nd issue). Booklet stamp. Design as No. 1517 (1990 Gallantry Awards). "All-over" phosphor.* P 14.

2666 **959** 20p. grey-black, pale stone, stone,
bistre-brown and bright carmine..... 10·00 10·00
a. Booklet pane. Nos. 2666×4................. 30·00 30·00

No. 2666 was only issued in No. **MS**2665 and in £7.44 stamp booklets, No. DX37.

1924 Sitar Player and Dancer   **1925** Reggae Bass Guitarist and African Drummer

1926 Fiddler and Harpist   **1927** Sax Player and Blues Guitarist

1928 Maraca Player and Salsa Dancers

(Des CDT Design. Litho Cartor)

2006 (3 Oct). *Europa. Integration. Sounds of Britain. "All-over" phosphor.* P 14½.

2667	**1924**	(1st) silver, greenish yellow, magenta, new blue and black	70	50
2668	**1925**	42p. silver, greenish yellow, magenta, new blue and black	1·00	1·00
2669	**1926**	50p. silver, greenish yellow, magenta, new blue and black	1·25	1·25
2670	**1927**	72p. silver, greenish yellow, magenta, new blue and black	1·75	1·75
2671	**1928**	£1.19 silver, greenish yellow, magenta, new blue and black	2·50	3·00

Set of 5 .... 6·25 6·75
Set of 5 Gutter Pairs.. 19·00
Set of 5 Traffic Light Gutter Blocks of 4 .... 38·00
First Day Cover (Tallents House).................................... 11·00
First Day Cover (Rock, Kidderminster, Worcs) .... 11·00
Presentation Pack (P.O. Pack No. 388) .... 12·00
PHQ Cards (set of 5) (291) .... 3·75 10·00

The 1st class and 50p. values include the "EUROPA" emblem.

Special First Day of Issue Postmarks

1929 "New Baby" (Alison Carmichael)   **1930** "Best Wishes" (Alan Kitching)   **1931** "THANK YOU" (Alan Kitching)

1932 Balloons (Ivan Chermayeff)   **1933** Firework (Kam Tang)   **1934** Champagne, Flowers and Butterflies (Olaf Hajek)

(Des NB Studio. Photo Walsall)

2006 (17 Oct). *Smilers Booklet stamps (2nd series). Occasions. Self-adhesive. Two phosphor bands. Die-cut perf 15×14.*

2672	**1929**	(1st) chrome-yellow	1·40	1·20
		a. Booklet pane. Nos. 2672/7	8·00	7·00
2673	**1930**	(1st) multicoloured	1·40	1·20
2674	**1931**	(1st) scarlet-vermilion, rosine and yellow	1·40	1·20
2675	**1932**	(1st) multicoloured	1·40	1·20
2676	**1933**	(1st) multicoloured	1·40	1·20
2677	**1934**	(1st) multicoloured	1·40	1·20

Set of 6... 8·00 7·00
First Day Cover (Tallents House)................................... 8·00
First Day Cover (Grinshill, Shrewsbury)............................. 8·00
Presentation Pack (P.O. Pack No. M13)........................ 18·00
PHQ Cards (set of 6) (D29)... 2·75 8·00

Nos. 2672/7 were issued in £1.92 stamp booklets, No. QA3, in which the surplus backing paper around each stamp was removed.

Nos. 2672/7 were also issued in sheets of 20, No. LS33, containing four of Nos. 2672 and 2677 and three of each of the other designs, each stamp accompanied by a *se-tenant* greetings label. These sheets were printed by Cartor in lithography instead of photogravure and sold at £6.95 each.

These designs were available in separate sheets with personal photographs printed on the labels from Royal Mail in Edinburgh at £14.95 each.

Stamps as No. 2672 but perforated with one elliptical hole on each vertical side were issued on 28 October 2008 in sheets of 20 with circular *se-tenant* Peter Rabbit labels, No. LS50. These sheets were printed by Cartor in lithography instead of photogravure and sold for £7.95 each

Similar sheets of 10 stamps and 10 *se-tenant* labels were sold in £7.95 packs.

No. 2674 was issued on 8 May 2010 with other greetings stamps in sheets of 20 with *se-tenant* greetings labels printed in lithography by Cartor, No. LS73, sold for £10 pre sheet. These sheets were printed with one elliptical hole in each vertical side.

Special First Day of Issue Postmarks

1935 Snowman   **1936** Father Christmas   **1937** Snowman

1938 Father Christmas   **1939** Reindeer   **1940** Christmas Tree

(Des T. Kiuchi, Rose Design and CDT Design. Photo De La Rue)

2006 (7 Nov). *Christmas. One centre phosphor band (No. 2678) or two phosphor bands (others).* P 15×14.

(a) Self-adhesive.

2678	**1935**	(2nd) silver, magenta, greenish yellow, new blue and black	60	40
		a. Booklet pane. No. 2678×12	4·00	
2679	**1936**	(1st) silver, magenta, greenish yellow, new blue and black	70	50
		a. Booklet pane. No. 2679×12	5·25	
2680	**1937**	(2nd Large) silver, deep new blue, magenta, greenish yellow, new blue and black	65	65
2681	**1938**	(1st Large) silver, gold, magenta, greenish yellow, new blue and black	75	75
2682	**1939**	72p. silver, magenta, greenish yellow, new blue and black	3·25	3·25
2683	**1940**	£1.19 silver, magenta, greenish yellow, new blue and black	4·50	4·50
Set of 6			9·00	9·00
First Day Cover (Tallents House)				9·50
First Day Cover (Bethlehem, Llandeilo)				9·50
Presentation Pack (P.O. Pack No. 389)			12·00	
PHQ Cards (set of 7) (292)			3·00	18·00

(b) Ordinary gum.

MS2684 115×102 mm. As Nos. 2678/83		9·00	9·00
First Day Cover (Tallents House)			10·00
First Day Cover (Bethlehem, Llandeilo)			10·00

The seven PHQ Cards depict the six individual stamps and the miniature sheet.

The 2nd and 1st class stamps were also issued together in sheets of 20 sold at £6, printed in lithography by Cartor, containing ten 1st class and ten 2nd class stamps, each value arranged in vertical rows of five alternated with rows of printed labels. Separate sheets of 20 1st or 20 2nd class were available with personalised photographs at £9.95 (2nd class) or £14.95 (1st class) from Royal Mail, Edinburgh. All these sheets had the backing paper around the stamps retained.

Special First Day of Issue Postmarks

1941 (Illustration reduced. Actual size 124×71 mm)

(Des Hat-trick Design. Photo De La Rue)

2006 (9 Nov). *"Lest We Forget" (1st issue). 90th Anniversary of the Battle of the Somme. Sheet 124×71 mm containing new stamp and designs as Nos. EN15, NI101, S118 and W107. Two phosphor bands.* P 14½ (1st) or 15×14 (with one elliptical hole in each vertical side) (72p).

MS2685	**1941**	(1st) Poppies on barbed wire stems; 72p.×4 As Nos. EN15, NI101, S118 and W107	9·00	9·00
First Day Cover (Tallents House)				9·50
First Day Cover (London SW1)				9·50
Presentation Pack (P.O. Pack No. 390)			12·00	

No. **MS**2685 (including the Northern Ireland stamp) is printed in gravure. The 1st class stamp was also issued in sheets of 20 with se-tenant labels showing war memorials, printed in lithography by Cartor.

For a full range of Stanley Gibbons catalogues, please visit **www.stanleygibbons.com**

Special First Day of Issue Postmarks

Collectors Pack

2006 (9 Nov). *Comprises Nos. 2589/612, 2615/49, 2659/64, 2667/71, 2678/83 and MS2685.*

CP2685a Collectors Pack		£120

Post Office Yearbook

2006 (9 Nov). *Comprises Nos. 2589/612, 2615/49, 2659/64, 2667/71, 2678/83 and MS2685.*

YB2685a Yearbook		£100

Miniature Sheet Collection

2006 (30 Nov). *Comprises Nos. MS2613, MS2658, MS2665, MS2684/5, MSS133 and MSW121.*

MS2685a Miniature Sheet Collection		50·00

1942 "with the beatles"	**1943** "Sgt Pepper's Lonely Hearts Club Band"

1944 "Help!"	**1945** "Abbey Road"

1946 "Revolver"	**1947** "Let It Be"

1948 Beatles Memorabilia (Illustration reduced. Actual size 115×89 mm)

(Des Johnson Banks)

2007 (9 Jan). *The Beatles. Album Covers. Two phosphor bands.*

(a) Self-adhesive. Photo Walsall. Die-cut irregular perf 13½–14½.

2686	**1942**	(1st) silver, greenish yellow, bright magenta, new blue and black	75	70
		a. Horiz pair. Nos. 2686/7	2·00	
2687	**1943**	(1st) silver, greenish yellow, bright magenta, new blue and black	75	70
2688	**1944**	64p. silver, greenish yellow, bright magenta, new blue and black	1·50	1·50
		a. Horiz pair. Nos. 2688/9	4·00	
2689	**1945**	64p. silver, greenish yellow, bright magenta, new blue and black	1·50	1·50

2690	**1946**	72p. greenish yellow, bright magenta, new blue and black	1·60	1·60
		a. Horiz pair. Nos. 2690/1	5·00	
2691	**1947**	72p. greenish yellow, bright magenta, new blue and black	1·60	1·60

Set of 6 .... 7·00 6·75
First Day Cover (Tallents House) .... 11·00
First Day Cover (Liverpool) .... 12·00
Presentation Pack (Nos. 2689/92) (P.O. Pack No. 392) .... 15·00
PHQ Cards (set of 11) (293) .... 5·00 18·00

(b) Ordinary gum. Litho Walsall. P 14.
MS2692 115×89 mm. **1948** (1st) Guitar; (1st) Yellow Submarine lunch-box and key-rings; (1st) Record "Love Me Do"; (1st) Beatles tea tray and badges .... 5·00 5·00
First Day Cover (Tallents House) .... 7·00
First Day Cover (Liverpool) .... 8·00

Nos. 2686/91 are all die-cut in the shape of a pile of records.
Nos. 2686/7, 2688/9 and 2690/1 were each printed together in sheets of 60 (2 panes of 30), with the two designs alternating horizontally and the surplus backing paper around each stamp removed.
Nos. 2686/92 commemorate the 50th anniversary of the first meeting of Paul McCartney and John Lennon.

Special First Day of Issue Postmarks

(Photo Walsall)

2007 (16 Jan)-**08**. *"Smilers" Booklet stamp (3rd series). "LOVE" design as No. 2569. Self-adhesive. Two phosphor bands. Die-cut perf 15×14 (with one elliptical hole in each vertical side).*

2693	**1842a**	(1st) multicoloured	20·00	20·00
		a. Booklet pane. No. 2655 × 5 and No. 2693	30·00	
		b. Booklet pane. No. 2693 × 2 with two attached labels and No. 1668 ×4 (15.1.08)	20·00	

No. 2693 was issued in stamp booklets, Nos. SA1 and SA2, in which the surplus backing paper around each stamp was removed.
No. 2693 was reissued on 8 May 2010 with other greetings stamps in sheets of 20 with *se-tenant* greetings labels printed in lithography by Cartor, No. LS73, sold for £10 pre sheet.

Nos. 2694/8 are left vacant.

1949 Moon Jellyfish   **1950** Common Starfish

1951 Beadlet Anemone   **1952** Bass

1953 Thornback Ray   **1954** Lesser Octopus

1955 Common Mussels   **1956** Grey Seal

1957 Shore Crab   **1958** Common Sun Star

(Des A. Ross. Litho Walsall)

2007 (1 Feb). *Sea Life. Two phosphor bands.* P 14½.

2699	**1949**	(1st) greyish silver, greenish yellow, magenta, new blue and black	75	80
		a. Block of 10. Nos. 2699/708	12·00	12·00
2700	**1950**	(1st) greyish silver, greenish yellow, magenta, new blue and black	75	80
2701	**1951**	(1st) greyish silver, greenish yellow, magenta, new blue and black	75	80
2702	**1952**	(1st) greyish silver, greenish yellow, magenta, new blue and black	75	80
2703	**1953**	(1st) greyish silver, greenish yellow, magenta, new blue and black	75	80
2704	**1954**	(1st) greyish silver, greenish yellow, magenta, new blue and black	75	80
2705	**1955**	(1st) greyish silver, greenish yellow, magenta, new blue and black	75	80
2706	**1956**	(1st) greyish silver, greenish yellow, magenta, new blue and black	75	80
2707	**1957**	(1st) greyish silver, greenish yellow, magenta, new blue and black	75	80
2708	**1958**	(1st) greyish silver, greenish yellow, magenta, new blue and black	75	80

Set of 10 .... 12·00 12·00
Gutter Block of 20 .... 24·00
First Day Cover (Tallents House) .... 11·00
First Day Cover (Seal Sands, Middlesbrough, Cleveland) ...... 11·00
Presentation Pack (P.O. Pack No. 393) .... 14·00
PHQ Cards (set of 10) (294) .... 4·50 14·00

Nos. 2699/708 were printed together, *se-tenant*, as blocks of ten (5×2) in sheets of 60 (2 panes of 30).

Special First Day of Issue Postmarks

1.2.2007   1.2.2007

1959 Saturn Nebula C55   **1960** Eskimo Nebula C39

1961 Cat's Eye Nebula C6   **1962** Helix Nebula C63

1963 Flaming Star Nebula C31   **1964** The Spindle C53

(Des D. Davis. Photo Walsall)

2007 (13 Feb). *50th Anniv of "The Sky at Night" (TV programme). Nebulae. Self-adhesive. Two phosphor bands. Die-cut perf 14½×14.*

2709	**1959**	(1st) greenish yellow, magenta, new blue and black	75	75
		a. Horiz pair. Nos. 2709/10	2·00	
2710	**1960**	(1st) greenish yellow, magenta, new blue and black	75	75
2711	**1961**	50p. greenish yellow, magenta, new blue and black	1·20	1·20
		a. Horiz pair. Nos. 2711/12	4·00	
2712	**1962**	50p. greenish yellow, magenta, new blue and black	1·20	1·20
2713	**1963**	72p. greenish yellow, magenta, new blue and black	1·70	1·70
		a. Horiz pair. Nos. 2713/14	5·00	
2714	**1964**	72p. greenish yellow, magenta, new blue and black	1·70	1·70

Set of 6	6·50	6·50
First Day Cover (Tallents House)		10·00
First Day Cover (Star, Glenrothes, Fife)		10·00
Presentation Pack (P.O. Pack No. 394)	14·00	
PHQ Cards (set of 6) (295)	4·50	14·00

Nos. 2709/10, 2711/12 and 2713/14 were each printed together in sheets of 60 (2 panes of 30), with the two designs alternating horizontally and the surplus backing paper around each stamp removed.

Special First Day of Issue Postmarks

13. 2. 2007   *13. 2. 2007*

1965 Iron Bridge (Thomas Telford)   **1966** Steam Locomotive and Railway Tracks

1967 Map of British Isles and Australia (telephone)   **1968** Camera and Television (John Logie Baird)

1969 Globe as Web (email and internet)   **1970** Couple with Suitcases on Moon (space travel)

(Des P. Willberg. Photo De La Rue)

2007 (1 Mar). *World of Invention (1st issue). Self-adhesive. Two phosphor bands. Die-cut perf 14½×14.*

2715	**1965**	(1st) olive-grey, magenta, greenish yellow, new blue and black	75	50
2716	**1966**	(1st) olive-grey, magenta, greenish yellow, new blue and black	75	50
2717	**1967**	64p. olive-grey, magenta, greenish yellow, new blue and black	1·25	1·25
2718	**1968**	64p. olive-grey, magenta, greenish yellow, new blue and black	1·25	1·25
2719	**1969**	72p. olive-grey, magenta, greenish yellow, new blue and black	2·00	2·25
2720	**1970**	72p. olive-grey, magenta, greenish yellow, new blue and black	2·00	2·25

Set of 6	7·25	7·25
First Day Cover (Tallents House)		11·00
First Day Cover (Pont Menai, Menai Bridge, Gwynedd)		11·00
Presentation Pack (P.O. Pack No. 395)	14·00	
PHQ Cards (set of 7) (296)	4·50	22·00

Nos. 2715/16, 2717/18 and 2719/20 were each printed together in sheets of 60 (2 panes of 30), with the two designs alternating horizontally and the surplus backing paper around each stamp removed.

The seven PHQ Cards depict the six individual stamps and **MS**2727.

Special First Day of Issue Postmarks

1·3·2007   *1·3·2007*

(Photo De La Rue)

2007 (1 Mar). *World of Invention (2nd issue). Two phosphor bands. P 14½×14.*

2721	**1965**	(1st) multicoloured	75	50
		a. Booklet pane. Nos. 2721/4	5·00	
		b. Booklet pane. Nos. 2721/2 and 2725/6	10·00	
2722	**1966**	(1st) multicoloured	75	50
2723	**1967**	64p. multicoloured	2·50	2·50
2724	**1968**	64p. multicoloured	2·50	2·50
2725	**1969**	72p. multicoloured	4·50	4·50
2726	**1970**	72p. multicoloured	4·50	4·50

Set of 6	14·00	14·00
MS2727 115×104 mm. Nos. 2721/6	14·00	14·00
First Day Cover (Tallents House)		11·00
First Day Cover (Pont Menai, Menai Bridge, Gwynedd)		11·00

Nos. 2721/6 were only issued in £7.49 stamp booklets, No. DX38 and in **MS**2727.

1971 William Wilberforce and Anti-slavery Poster   **1972** Olaudah Equiano and Map of Slave Trade Routes

1973 Granville Sharp and Slave Ship   **1974** Thomas Clarkson and Diagram of Slave Ship

1975 Hannah More
and Title Page of *The
Sorrows of Yamba*

1976 Ignatius Sancho
and Trade/Business
Card

(Des Howard Brown. Litho Cartor)

2007 (22 Mar). *Bicentenary of the Abolition of the Slave Trade. Two
phosphor bands.* P 14½.

2728	**1971**	(1st) grey-brown, pale stone, olive-bistre, bright reddish violet, deep blue-green and black......................	75	75
		a. Horiz pair. Nos. 2728/9......................	2·50	2·50
		ab. Gold and phosphor omitted	£2750	
2729	**1972**	(1st) grey-brown, pale stone, olive-bistre, bright reddish violet, deep blue-green and black......................	75	75
2730	**1973**	50p. grey-brown, pale stone, light blue, cinnamon, deep blue-green and black......................	1·20	1·20
		a. Horiz pair. Nos. 2730/1......................	4·00	4·00
2731	**1974**	50p. grey-brown, pale stone, light blue, cinnamon, deep blue-green and black......................	1·20	1·20
2732	**1975**	72p. grey-brown, pale stone, sage-green, brown-lilac, deep blue-green and black	1·70	1·70
		a. Horiz pair. Nos. 2732/3......................	5·00	5·00
2733	**1976**	72p. grey-brown, pale stone, sage-green, brown-lilac, deep blue-green and black	1·70	1·70
Set of 6........................			9·00	9·00
Set of 3 Gutter Strips of 4			14·00	
Set of 3 Traffic Light Gutter Strips of 4			16·00	
First Day Cover (Tallents House)				11·00
First Day Cover (Hull)				11·00
Presentation Pack (P.O. Pack No. 396)			12·00	
PHQ Cards (set of 6) (297)			4·50	14·00

Nos. 2728/9, 2730/1 and 2732/3 were each printed together, *se-tenant*,
in horizontal pairs throughout the sheets.

Special First Day of Issue Postmarks

1977 Ice Cream Cone

1978 Sandcastle

1979 Carousel Horse

1980 Beach Huts

1981 Deckchairs

1982 Beach Donkeys

(Des Phelan Barker. Photo De La Rue)

2007 (15 May). *"Beside the Seaside". Two phosphor bands.* P 14½.

2734	**1977**	1st magenta, greenish yellow, new blue and black	75	75
2735	**1978**	46p. magenta, greenish yellow, new blue and black	1·00	1·00
2736	**1979**	48p. magenta, greenish yellow, new blue and black	1·50	1·50
2737	**1980**	54p. magenta, greenish yellow, new blue and black	2·00	2·00
2738	**1981**	69p. magenta, greenish yellow, new blue and black	2·50	2·50
2739	**1982**	78p. magenta, greenish yellow, new blue and black	2·75	2·75
Set of 6........................			9·00	9·00
Set of 6 Gutter Pairs........................			18·00	
First Day Cover (Tallents House)				10·00
First Day Cover (Blackpool)				10·00
Presentation Pack (P.O. Pack No. 397)			12·00	
PHQ Cards (set of 6) (298)			4·50	14·00

Special First Day of Issue Postmarks

1983 *(Illustration reduced. Actual size
113×103 mm)*

(Des Roundel. Photo De La Rue)

2007 (17 May). *New Wembley Stadium, London. Sheet 113×103 mm
containing design as Type* **1593** *but with "WORLD CUP 2002"
inscription omitted, and Nos. EN6 and EN15, each×2. One centre
phosphor band (2nd) or two phosphor bands (others).* P 14½×14
(1st) or 15×14 (with one elliptical hole in each vertical side) (2nd,
78p.).

MS2740	**1983**	(1st) As Type **1593**; (2nd) No. EN6×2; 78p. No. EN15×2 and one central stamp-size label......	7·00	7·00
First Day Cover (Tallents House)				7·50
First Day Cover (Wembley)				8·00

The design as Type **1593** omits the "WORLD CUP 2002" inscription at
the left of the stamp.

Special First Day of Issue Postmarks

ARNOLD MACHIN 1911-1999

1984 Arnold Machin

FIRST MACHIN ISSUED 1967

1985 1967 4d. Machin

1986 *(Illustration reduced. Actual size 127×73 mm)*

(Des Jeffery Matthews and Together Design.
Photo and embossed De La Rue)

2007 (5 June). *40th Anniv of the First Machin Definitives. Sheet 127×73 mm containing new stamps and Nos. Y1725 and Y1725b. Two phosphor bands (£1). P 14½ (1st) or 15×14 (with one elliptical hole in each vertical side) (£1).*

2741	**1984**	(1st) multicoloured	4·50	4·50
		a. Booklet pane. Nos. 2741/2, each ×2, with margins all round	17·00	
2742	**1985**	(1st) multicoloured	4·50	4·50
MS2743	**1986**	Nos. 2741/2, Y1725 and Y1725b	12·00	12·00

First Day Cover (**MS**2743) (Tallents House) .... 12·00
First Day Cover (**MS**2743) (Windsor) .... 12·00
First Day Cover (**MS**2743) (Stoke-on-Trent) .... 12·00
Presentation Pack (**MS**2743) (P.O. Pack No. 398) ...... 14·00
PHQ Cards (set of 3) (Nos. 2741/**MS**2743) (299) .. 2·00 14·00

Nos. 2741/2 were only issued in £7.66 stamp booklets (No. DX39) and in **MS**2743. Stamps as Type **1984** but with phosphor frames were issued in sheets of 20 with se-tenant labels showing the 1967–9 Machin definitives (LS40). These sheets were sold for £7.35.

1989 Jim Clark in Lotus 25 Climax, 1963

1990 Jackie Stewart in Tyrrell 006/2, 1973

1991 James Hunt in McLaren M23, 1976

1992 Nigel Mansell in Williams FW11, 1986

(Des True North. Litho Cartor)

2007 (3 July). *Grand Prix. Racing Cars. Two phosphor bands. P 14½.*

2744	**1987**	(1st) grey-brown, greenish yellow, magenta, new blue and black	75	75
2745	**1988**	(1st) grey-brown, greenish yellow, magenta, new blue and black	75	75
2746	**1989**	54p. grey-brown, greenish yellow, magenta, new blue and black	2·00	2·00
2747	**1990**	54p. grey-brown, greenish yellow, magenta, new blue and black	2·00	2·00
2748	**1991**	78p. grey-brown, greenish yellow, magenta, new blue and black	2·50	2·50
2749	**1992**	78p. grey-brown, greenish yellow, magenta, new blue and black	2·50	2·50

Set of 6 .... 9·50 9·50
Set of 6 Gutter Pairs .... 19·00
First Day Cover (Tallents House) .... 10·00
First Day Cover (Silverstone, Towcester, Northants) ...... 11·00
Presentation Pack (P.O. Pack No. 399) .... 12·00
PHQ Cards (set of 6) (300) .... 4·50 14·00

Nos. 2744/9 commemorate the 50th anniversary of Stirling Moss' Victory in the British Grand Prix and the centenary of the opening of Brooklands race track.

1993 *Harry Potter and the Philosopher's Stone*

1994 *Harry Potter and the Chamber of Secrets*

1995 *Harry Potter and the Prisoner of Azkaban*

1996 *Harry Potter and the Goblet of Fire*

1997 *Harry Potter and the Order of the Phoenix*

1998 *Harry Potter and the Half-Blood Prince*

1987 Stirling Moss in Vanwall 2.5L, 1957

1988 Graham Hill in BRM P57, 1962

1999 *Harry Potter and the Deathly Hallows*

2000 Crests of Hogwarts School and its Four Houses
(illustration reduced. Actual size 123×70 mm)

(True North. Litho Walsall)

2007 (17 July). *Publication of Final Book in the Harry Potter Series.*

(a) Book Covers. "All-over" phosphor. P 14½.

2750	**1993**	(1st) gold, greenish yellow, magenta, new blue and black	75	75
		a. Horiz strip of 7. Nos. 2750/6	8·00	8·00
2751	**1994**	(1st) gold, greenish yellow, magenta, new blue and black	75	75
2752	**1995**	(1st) gold, greenish yellow, magenta, new blue and black	75	75
2753	**1996**	(1st) gold, greenish yellow, magenta, new blue and black	75	75
2754	**1997**	(1st) gold, greenish yellow, magenta, new blue and black	75	75
2755	**1998**	(1st) gold, greenish yellow, magenta, new blue and black	75	75
2756	**1999**	(1st) gold, greenish yellow, magenta, new blue and black	75	75

Set of 7	8·00	8·00
Gutter Block of 14	16·00	
Traffic Light Gutter Block of 14	20·00	
First Day Cover (Tallents House)		9·00
First Day Cover (Broom, Alcester, Warwickshire)		9·00
Presentation Pack (Nos. 2750/7) (P.O. Pack No. M16)	16·00	
PHQ Cards (set of 13) (HP)	7·50	27·00

(b) Crests of Hogwarts School and its Four Houses. Multicoloured. Two phosphor bands. P 15×14.

MS2757 123×70 mm. **2000** (1st) Gryffindor; (1st) Hufflepuff; (1st) Hogwarts; (1st) Ravenclaw; (1st) Slytherin	6·00	6·00
First Day Cover (Tallents House)		7·50
First Day Cover (Broom, Alcester, Warwickshire)		8·00

Nos. 2750/6 were printed together, *se-tenant*, as horizontal strips of seven stamps in sheets of 56 (2 panes 7×4).

The complete miniature sheet is shown on one of the thirteen PHQ cards with the others depicting individual stamps including those on **MS**2757.

Stamps as those within **MS**2757 but self-adhesive were issued in sheets of 20 containing the five designs *se-tenant* with labels depicting either magic spells (LS41, sold for £7.35) or personal photographs (sold for £14.95). The magic spells labels are printed in thermochromic ink which fades temporarily when exposed to heat, revealing the meaning of the spells.

Special First Day of Issue Postmarks

2001 Scout and Camp Fire

2002 Scouts Rock climbing

2003 Scout planting Tree

2004 Adult Volunteer teaching Scout Archery

2005 Scouts learning gliding

2006 Scouts from Many Nations

(Des Gez Fry and The Work Room. Litho Enschedé)

2007 (26 July). *Europa. Centenary of Scouting and 21st World Scout Jamboree, Chelmsford, Essex. Two phosphor bands.* P 14½×14.

2758	**2001**	(1st) silver, black, new blue, magenta and greenish yellow	75	75
2759	**2002**	46p. silver, black, new blue, magenta and greenish yellow	1·00	1·00
2760	**2003**	48p. silver, black, new blue, magenta and greenish yellow	1·50	1·50
2761	**2004**	54p. silver, black, new blue, magenta and greenish yellow	2·00	2·00
2762	**2005**	69p. silver, black, new blue, magenta and greenish yellow	2·50	2·50
2763	**2006**	78p. silver, black, new blue, magenta and greenish yellow	2·75	2·75

Set of 6	9·00	9·00
Set of 6 Gutter Pairs	18·00	
First Day Cover (Tallents House)		10·00
First Day Cover (Brownsea Island, Poole, Dorset)		10·00
Presentation Pack (P.O. Pack No. 400)	12·00	
PHQ Cards (set of 6) (301)	4·50	14·00

The 1st class and 48p. values include the "EUROPA" emblem.

Special First Day of Issue Postmarks

2007 White-tailed Eagle

2008 Bearded Tit

2009 Red Kite

2010 Cirl Bunting

2011 Marsh Harrier   **2012** Avocet

2013 Bittern   **2014** Dartford Warbler

2015 Corncrake   **2016** Peregrine Falcon

(Des Kate Stephens. Litho Da La Rue)

2007 (4 Sept). *"Action for Species"* (1st series). Birds. Two phosphor bands. P 14½.

2764	**2007**	(1st) stone, new blue, magenta, greenish yellow and black..............	75	75
		a. Block of 10. Nos. 2764/73	12·00	10·00
2765	**2008**	(1st) stone, new blue, magenta, greenish yellow and black..............	75	75
2766	**2009**	(1st) stone, new blue, magenta, greenish yellow and black..............	75	75
2767	**2010**	(1st) stone, new blue, magenta, greenish yellow and black..............	75	75
2768	**2011**	(1st) stone, new blue, magenta, greenish yellow and black..............	75	75
2769	**2012**	(1st) stone, new blue, magenta, greenish yellow and black..............	75	75
2770	**2013**	(1st) stone, new blue, magenta, greenish yellow and black..............	75	75
2771	**2014**	(1st) stone, new blue, magenta, greenish yellow and black..............	75	75
2772	**2015**	(1st) stone, new blue, magenta, greenish yellow and black..............	75	75
2773	**2016**	(1st) stone, new blue, magenta, greenish yellow and black..............	75	75

Set of 10	12·00	10·00
Gutter Block of 20	20·00	
First Day Cover (Tallents House)		10·00
First Day Cover (Dartford)		11·00
Presentation Pack (P.O. Pack No. 401)	14·00	
PHQ Cards (set of 10) (302)	6·00	16·00

Nos. 2764/73 were printed together, *se-tenant*, as blocks of ten (5×2) in sheets of 60 (2 panes of 30).

2017 NCO, Royal Military Police, 1999   **2018** Tank Commander, 5th Royal Tank Regiment, 1944

2019 Observer, Royal Field Artillery, 1917   **2020** Rifleman, 95th Rifles, 1813

2021 Grenadier, Royal Regiment of Foot of Ireland, 1704   **2022** Trooper, Earl of Oxford's Horse, 1661

(Des Graham Turner and Atelier Works. Litho Enschedé)

2007 (20 Sept). *Military Uniforms* (1st series). British Army Uniforms. Two phosphor bands. P 14½.

2774	**2017**	(1st) silver, black, new blue, magenta and greenish yellow	80	80
		a. Horiz strip of 3. Nos. 2774/6............	4·00	4·00
		b. Booklet pane. Nos. 2774/6 with margins all round	4·00	
2775	**2018**	(1st) silver, black, new blue, magenta and greenish yellow	80	80
2776	**2019**	(1st) silver, black, new blue, magenta and greenish yellow	80	80
2777	**2020**	78p. silver, black, new blue, magenta and greenish yellow	1·70	1·70
		a. Horiz strip of 3. Nos. 2777/9............	7·00	7·00
		b. Booklet pane. Nos. 2777/9 with margins all round	7·00	7·00
2778	**2021**	78p. silver, black, new blue, magenta and greenish yellow	1·70	1·70
2779	**2022**	78p. silver, black, new blue, magenta and greenish yellow	1·70	1·70

Set of 6	10·00	10·00
Set of 2 Gutter blocks of 6	20·00	
Set of 2 Traffic Light Gutter blocks of 6	24·00	
First Day Cover (Tallents House)		11·00
First Day Cover (Boot, Holmrook, Cumbria)		12·00
Presentation Pack (P.O. Pack No. 402)	14·00	
PHQ Cards (set of 6) (303)	4·50	14·00

Nos. 2774/6 and 2777/9 were each printed together, *se-tenant*, in horizontal strips of three stamps in sheets of 60 (2 panes 6×5).

Special First Day of Issue Postmarks

Special First Day of Issue Postmarks

2023 Leaving St. Paul's Cathedral after Thanksgiving Service, 2006

2024 Inspecting King's Troop Royal Horse Artillery, Regents Park, 1997

2025 At Garter Ceremony, Windsor, 1980

2026 At Royal Ascot, 1969

2027 At Premiere of *The Guns of Navarone*, 1961

2028 At Clydebank, 1947

2029 Photographs of the Royal Family
(illustration reduced. Actual size 115×89 mm)

(Des Studio David Hillman)

2007 (16 Oct). *Diamond Wedding of Queen Elizabeth II and Duke of Edinburgh.*

(a) Ordinary gum. Litho Cartor. "All-over" phosphor. P 14½×14.

2780	**2023**	(1st) blackish-brown and black	75	75
		a. Horiz pair. Nos. 2780/1	1·60	1·60
2781	**2024**	(1st) blackish-brown and black	75	75
2782	**2025**	54p. blackish-brown and black	1·20	1·20
		a. Horiz pair. Nos. 2782/3	3·75	3·75
2783	**2026**	54p. blackish-brown and black	1·20	1·20
2784	**2027**	78p. blackish-brown and black	1·90	1·90
		a. Horiz pair. Nos. 2784/5	5·50	5·50
2785	**2028**	78p. blackish-brown and black	1·90	1·90

Set of 6 .... 9·50 9·50
Set of 3 Gutter blocks of 4 .... 20·00
First Day Cover (Tallents House) .... 10·00
First Day Cover (Windsor, Berks) .... 10·00
Presentation Pack (Nos. 2780/**MS**2786) (P.O. Pack No. 403) .... 18·00
PHQ Cards (set of 11) (304) .... 6·00 27·00

(b) Self-adhesive. Photogravure Walsall. Two phosphor bands. P 14½.

MS2786 115×89 mm. (1st) Royal family, Balmoral, 1972; (1st) Queen and Prince Philip, Buckingham Palace, 2007; 69p. Royal family, Windsor Castle, 1965; 78p. Princess Elizabeth, Prince Philip, Prince Charles and Princess Anne, Clarence House, 1951 .... 6·00 6·00
First Day Cover (Tallents House) .... 8·50
First Day Cover (Windsor, Berks) .... 8·50

Nos. 2780/1, 2782/3 and 2784/5 were each printed together, se-tenant, in horizontal pairs throughout the sheets.

The complete miniature sheet is shown on one of the eleven PHQ cards with the others depicting individual stamps including those from **MS**2786.

Special First Day of Issue Postmarks

2030 *Madonna and Child* (William Dyce), c 1827

2031 *The Madonna of Humility* (Lippo di Dalmasio), c 1390–1400)

(Des Peter Willberg. Photo De La Rue)

2007 (6 Nov). *Christmas (1st issue). Paintings of the Madonna and Child. Self-adhesive.* One centre phosphor band (2nd) or two phosphor bands (1st). Die-cut perf 15×14 (with one elliptical hole in each vertical side).

2787	**2030**	(2nd) gold, magenta, greenish yellow, new blue and black	65	50
2788	**2031**	(1st) gold, magenta, greenish yellow, new blue and black	75	75

First Day Cover (Tallents House) .... 4·00
First Day Cover (Bethlehem, Llandeilo) .... 4·00

2032 Angel playing Trumpet ("PEACE")

2033 Angel playing Lute ("GOODWILL")

2034 Angel playing Trumpet ("PEACE")

2035 Angel playing Lute ("GOODWILL")

2036 Angel playing Flute ("JOY")

2037 Angel playing Tambourine ("GLORY")

(Des Marco Ventura and Rose Design. Photo De La Rue)

2007 (6 Nov). *Christmas (2nd issue). Angels.* One centre phosphor band (2789) or two phosphor bands (others). P 15×14.

(a) Self-adhesive

2789	**2032**	(2nd) gold, magenta, greenish yellow, new blue and black	65	55
		a. Booklet pane. No. 2789×12	6·50	
2790	**2033**	(1st) gold, magenta, greenish yellow, new blue and black	75	75
		a. Booklet pane. No. 2790×12	9·00	
2791	**2034**	(2nd Large) gold, magenta, greenish yellow, new blue and black	90	90
2792	**2035**	(1st Large) gold, magenta, greenish yellow, new blue and black	2·00	2·00
2793	**2036**	78p. gold, magenta, greenish yellow, new blue and black	3·00	3·00
2794	**2037**	£1·24 gold, magenta, greenish yellow, new blue and black	4·50	4·50

Set of 6 .... 9·50 9·50
First Day Cover (Tallents House) .... 10·00
First Day Cover (Bethlehem, Llandeilo) .... 10·00
Presentation Pack (Nos. 2787/94) (P.O. Pack No. 404) .... 14·00
PHQ Cards (set of 9) (305) .... 6·00 18·00

(b) Ordinary gum.

MS2795 115×102 mm. As Nos. 2789/94 .... 10·00 10·00
First Day Cover (Tallents House)....................................... 11·00
First Day Cover (Bethlehem, Llandello).......................... 11·00
The phosphor bands on Nos. 2791/2 are at the centre and right of each stamp.

The PHQ cards depict Nos. 2787/94 and **MS**2795.

The 2nd class, 1st class and 78p. stamps were also issued together in sheets of 20 sold at £8.30 containing eight 1st class, eight 2nd class and four 78p. stamps, arranged in vertical strips of five stamps alternated with printed labels (LS42). Separate sheets of 20 1st, 20 2nd or 10 78p. were available with personalised photographs from Royal Mail. These were sold at £9.95 for 20 2nd or £14.95 for 20 1st or 10 78p. All these sheets were printed in lithography by Cartor and had the backing paper around the stamps retained.

Special First Day of Issue Postmarks

2038 (illustration reduced. Actual size 124×70 mm)

(Des Hat-trick design. Litho De La Rue)

2007 (8 Nov). *"Lest We Forget" (2nd issue). 90th Anniv of the Battle of Passchendaele. Sheet 124×70 mm containing new stamp and designs as Nos. EN16, NI106, S119 and W108. Two phosphor bands. Perf 14½ (1st) or 15×14 (with one elliptical hole in each vertical side) (78p.).*

MS2796 **2038** (1st) Soldiers in poppy flower; 78p.×4
As Nos. EN16, NI106, S119 and W108 .... 10·00 10·00
First Day Cover (Tallents House)....................................... 11·00
First Day Cover (London SW1)... 11·00
Presentation Pack (P.O. Pack No. 405).................. 12·00
No. **MS**2796 (including the England, Northern Ireland, Scotland and Wales stamps) is printed in lithography.

A single example of the "Soldiers in Poppy" stamp from **MS** 2796 is known with the silver (Queen's head and value) omitted.

The 1st class stamp was also issued in sheets of 20 with *se-tenant* labels showing soldiers and their letters home, printed in lithography by Cartor and sold at £7.35 (LS43).

Special First Day of Issue Postmarks

Collectors Pack
2007 (8 Nov). *Comprises Nos. 2686/92, 2699/720, 2728/39, MS2743/94 and MS2796.*
CP2796a Collectors Pack £190

Post Office Yearbook
2007 (8 Nov). *Comprises Nos. 2686/92, 2699/720, 2728/39, MS2743/94 and MS2796.*
YB2796a Yearbook... £130

Miniature Sheet Collection
2007 (8 Nov). *Comprises Nos. MS2692, MS2727, MS2740, MS2743, MS2757, MS2786 and MS2795/6.*
MS2796a Miniature Sheet Collection .... 70·00

2039 Casino Royale

2040 Dr. No

2041 Goldfinger

2042 Diamonds are Forever

2043 For Your Eyes Only

2044 From Russia with Love

(Des A2. Litho De La Rue)

2008 (8 Jan). *Birth Centenary of Ian Fleming (author of James Bond books). Book Covers. Two phosphor bands. P 15×14½.*
2797	**2039**	(1st) gold, new blue, magenta, greenish yellow and black.............	75	75
		a. Booklet pane. Nos. 2797, 2799 and 2801 with margins all round..	5·00	
2798	**2040**	(1st) gold, new blue, magenta, greenish yellow and black.............	75	75
		a. Booklet pane. Nos. 2798, 2800 and 2802 with margins all round..	5·00	
		aa. Phosphor omitted..........................	£1250	
2799	**2041**	54p. gold, new blue, magenta, greenish yellow and black.............	2·00	1·20
2800	**2042**	54p. gold, new blue, magenta, greenish yellow and black.............	2·00	1·20
2801	**2043**	78p. gold, new blue, magenta, greenish yellow and black.............	3·00	3·00
2802	**2044**	78p. gold, new blue, magenta, greenish yellow and black.............	3·00	3·00

Set of 6.. 10·00 9·00
Set of 6 Gutter Pairs... 20·00
First Day Cover (Tallents House)................................... 11·00
First Day Cover (London SE1).. 11·00
Presentation Pack (P.O. Pack No. 407) .... 12·00
PHQ Cards (set of 7) (306) .... 4·75 20·00
MS2803 189×68 mm. Nos. 2797/802......... 10·00 10·00
First Day Cover (Tallents House)................................... 11·00
First Day Cover (London SE1).. 11·00

Special First Day of Issue Postmarks

(Litho De La Rue)

2008 (8 Jan). *Ian Fleming's James Bond. Booklet stamp. Design as Type* **1517** *(2001 Union Jack from Submarine Centenary). Two phosphor bands. P 14½.*
2805 **1517** (1st) multicoloured .... 4·25 4·25
a. Booklet pane. Nos. 2581 and 2805, each ×2, with margins all round .... 12·00
No. 2805 was only issued in £7.40 stamp booklets, No. DX41.

2045 Assistance Dog carrying Letter (Labrador "Rowan")

2046 Mountain Rescue Dog (Cross-bred "Merrick")

2047 Police Dog (German Shepherd "Max")

2048 Customs Dog (Springer Spaniel "Max")

2049 Sheepdog (Border Collie "Bob")

2050 Guide Dog (Labrador "Warwick")

(Des Redpath Design. Litho Cartor)

2008 (5 Feb). *Working Dogs. Two phosphor bands.* P 14½.

2806	**2045**	(1st) multicoloured	80	80
2807	**2046**	46p. multicoloured	1·00	1·00
2808	**2047**	48p. multicoloured	1·50	1·50
2809	**2048**	54p. multicoloured	2·00	2·00
2810	**2049**	69p. multicoloured	2·50	2·50
2811	**2050**	78p. multicoloured	2·75	2·75
Set of 6			9·00	9·00
Set of 6 Gutter Pairs			18·00	
First Day Cover (Tallents House)				10·00
First Day Cover (Hound Green, Basingstoke, Hants)				10·00
Presentation Pack (P.O. Pack No. 408)			12·00	
PHQ Cards (set of 6) (307)			4·50	14·00

The 1st class value includes the "EUROPA" emblem.

Special First Day of Issue Postmarks

2051 Henry IV (1399–1413)

2052 Henry V (1413–1422)

2053 Henry VI (1422–1461 & 1470–1)

2054 Edward IV (1461–1470 & 1471–1483)

2055 Edward V (1483)

2056 Richard III (1483–1485)

2057 The Age of Lancaster and York (Illustration reduced. Actual size 123×70 mm)

(Des Atelier Works. Litho Cartor)

2008 (28 Feb). *Kings and Queens (1st issue). Houses of Lancaster and York. Two phosphor bands.* P 14½.

2812	**2051**	(1st) slate, greenish yellow, magenta, new blue and black	80	80
2813	**2052**	(1st) slate, greenish yellow, magenta, new blue and black	80	80
2814	**2053**	54p. slate, greenish yellow, magenta, new blue and black	2·00	2·00
2815	**2054**	54p. slate, greenish yellow, magenta, new blue and black	2·00	2·00
2816	**2055**	69p. slate, greenish yellow, magenta, new blue and black	2·75	2·75
2817	**2056**	69p. slate, greenish yellow, magenta, new blue, and black	2·75	2·75
Set of 6			9·50	9·50
Set of 6 Gutter Pairs			20·00	
Set of 6 Traffic Light Gutter Blocks of 4			26·00	
First Day Cover (Tallents House)				10·00
First Day Cover (Tewkesbury)				10·00
Presentation Pack (P.O. Pack No. 409)			18·00	
PHQ Cards (set of 11) (308)			7·25	27·00

MS2818 123×70 mm. **2057** (1st) Owain Glyn Dwr ("Parliament"), 1404; (1st) Henry V's triumph at Battle of Agincourt, 1415; 78p. Yorkist victory at Battle of Tewkesbury, 1471; 78p. William Caxton, first English printer, 1477................ 6·50 / 6·50

First Day Cover (Tallents House) .... 8·00
First Day Cover (Tewkesbury) .... 8·00

The complete miniature sheet is shown on one of the eleven PHQ cards with the others depicting individual stamps including those from **MS**2818.

Special First Day of Issue Postmarks

(Photo Walsall)

2008 (28 Feb). *"Smilers" Booklet stamps (4th series). As Nos. 2567/8, 2570 and 2675/7. Self-adhesive. Two phosphor bands. Die-cut perf 15×14 (with one elliptical hole in each vertical side).*

2819	**1569**	(1st) multicoloured	75	75
		a. Booklet pane. Nos. 2819/24	9·00	
2820	**1842**	(1st) multicoloured	75	75
2821	**1517**	(1st) multicoloured	75	75
2822	**1932**	(1st) multicoloured	75	75
2823	**1933**	(1st) multicoloured	75	75
2824	**1934**	(1st) multicoloured	75	75
Set of 6			9·00	9·00

Nos. 2819/24 were issued in £2.04 booklets, No. QA4, in which the surplus backing paper around each stamp was removed.

No. 2819 was issued on 30 April 2009 in sheets of 20 with *se-tenant* circular Jeremy Fisher labels. No. LS60, printed in lithography by Cartor and sold at £8.50.

Similar sheets of 10 stamps and 10 *se-tenant* labels were only sold in packs for £7.95 each.

No. 2819 was re-issued again on 8 May 2010 for London 2010 Festival of Stamps in sheets of 20 *se-tenant* No. LS72 printed in lithography by Cartor and originally sold for £8.50 per sheet.

Nos. 2820 and 2822 were each issued on 28 October 2008 in separate sheets of 20, Nos. LS51/3, with circular *se-tenant* labels showing the Almond Blossom fairy (2820), Mr. Men or Noddy (2822). These sheets were printed in lithography by Cartor and originally sold for £9.95 per sheet.

Nos. 2819, 2820 and 2822 were issued again on 30 April 2009 in separate sheets of 20, Nos. LS61/3, with circular *se-tenant* labels showing Jeremy Fisher (2820), Wild Cherry fairy (2820), Little Miss Sunshine or Big Ears (2822), sold for £8.50 per sheet.

Similar sheets of 10 stamps and 10 *se-tenant* labels were sold in £7.95 packs.

Nos. 2821/3 were issued on 8 May 2010 with other greetings stamps in sheets of 20 with *se-tenant* greetings labels, No. LS73 sold for £10 per sheet.

No. 2821 was issued on 12 February 2011 in sheets of 20 with *se-tenant* labels for Indipex International Stamp Exhibition, No. LS76, sold at £8.50 per sheet.

All the above sheets were printed by Cartor in lithography instead of photogravure.

2058 Lifeboat, Barra

2059 Lifeboat approaching Dinghy, Appledore

2060 Helicopter Winchman, Portland

2061 Inshore lifeboat, St Ives

2062 Rescue Helicopter, Lee-on-Solent

2063 Launch of Lifeboat, Dinbych-y-Pysgod, Tenby

(Des Hat-trick Design. Litho Walsall)

2008 (13 Mar). Rescue at Sea. "All-over" phosphor. P 14½×14*.

2825	2058	(1st) bright orange, greenish yellow, magenta, new blue and black	75	75
2826	2059	46p. bright orange, greenish yellow, magenta, new blue and black	1·00	1·00
2827	2060	48p. bright orange, greenish yellow, magenta, new blue and black	1·50	1·50
2828	2061	54p. bright orange, greenish yellow, magenta, new blue and black	2·00	2·00
2829	2062	69p. bright orange, greenish yellow, magenta, new blue and black	2·50	2·50
2830	2063	78p. bright orange, greenish yellow, magenta, new blue and black	2·75	2·75
Set of 6			9·00	9·00
Set of 6 Gutter Pairs			18·00	
First Day Cover (Tallents House)				10·00
First Day Cover (Poole, Dorset)				10·00
Presentation Pack (P.O. Pack No. 411)			12·00	
PHQ Cards (set of 6) (309)			4·50	14·00

*Nos. 2825/30 have interrupted perforations along the top and bottom edges of the stamps, the gaps in the perforations forming the three dots and three dashes that spell out "SOS" in morse code.

Special First Day of Issue Postmarks

2064 *Lysandra bellargus* (Adonis blue)

2065 *Coenagrion mercuriale* (southern damselfly)

2066 *Formica rufibarbis* (red-barbed ant)

2067 *Pareulype berberata* (barberry carpet moth)

2068 *Lucanus cervus* (stag beetle)

2069 *Cryptocephalus coryli* (hazel pot beetle)

2070 *Gryllus campestris* (field cricket)

2071 *Hesperia comma* (silver-spotted skipper)

2072 *Pseudepipona herrichii* (Purbeck mason wasp)

2073 *Gnorimus nobilis* (noble chafer)

(Des Andrew Ross. Litho De La Rue)

2008 (15 Apr). "Action for Species" (2nd series). Insects. Phosphor background. P 14½.

2831	2064	(1st) brownish grey, new blue, magenta, greenish yellow and black	80	80
		a. Block of 10. Nos. 2831/40	12·00	10·00

2832	**2065**	(1st) brownish grey, new blue, magenta, greenish yellow and black	80	80
2833	**2066**	(1st) brownish grey, new blue, magenta, greenish yellow and black	80	80
2834	**2067**	(1st) brownish grey, new blue, magenta, greenish yellow and black	80	80
2835	**2068**	(1st) brownish grey, new blue, magenta, greenish yellow and black	80	80
2836	**2069**	(1st) brownish grey, new blue, magenta, greenish yellow and black	80	80
2837	**2070**	(1st) brownish grey, new blue, magenta, greenish yellow and black	80	80
2838	**2071**	(1st) brownish grey, new blue, magenta, greenish yellow and black	80	80
2839	**2072**	(1st) brownish grey, new blue, magenta, greenish yellow and black	80	80
2840	**2073**	(1st) brownish grey, new blue, magenta, greenish yellow and black	80	80

Set of 10	12·00	10·00
Gutter Block of 20	24·00	
First Day Cover (Tallents House)		10·00
First Day Cover (Crawley, W. Sussex)		11·00
Presentation Pack (P.O. Pack No. 412)	16·00	
PHQ Cards (set of 10) (310)	6·75	16·00

Nos. 2831/40 were printed together, se-tenant, as blocks of ten (5×2) in sheets of 60 (2 panes of 30).

Special First Day of Issue Postmarks

2074 Lichfield Cathedral

2075 Belfast Cathedral

2076 Gloucester Cathedral

2077 St. David's Cathedral

2078 Westminster Cathedral

2079 St. Magnus Cathedral, Kirkwall, Orkney

2080 St. Paul's Cathedral (Illustration reduced. Actual size 115×89 mm)

(Des Howard Brown. Litho Enschedé)

2008 (13 May). *Cathedrals. "All-over" phosphor.* P 14½.

2841	**2074**	(1st) black, blackish brown, brownish black and brownish grey	85	85
2842	**2075**	48p. black, brownish black, blackish brown and brownish grey	1·10	1·10
2843	**2076**	50p. black, brownish black, blackish brown and brownish grey	1·50	1·50
2844	**2077**	56p. black, brownish black, blackish brown and brownish grey	2·50	2·50
2845	**2078**	72p. black, brownish black, blackish brown and brownish grey	3·00	3·00
2846	**2079**	81p. black, blackish black, blackish brown and brownish grey	3·50	3·50

Set of 6	10·00	10·00
Set of 6 Gutter Pairs	20·00	
Set of 6 Traffic Light Gutter Pairs	22·00	
First Day Cover (Tallents House)		12·00
First Day Cover (London EC4)		12·00
Presentation Pack (P.O. Pack No. 413)	20·00	
PHQ Cards (set of 11) (311)	7·25	27·00
MS2847 115×89 mm. (1st) multicoloured; (1st) multicoloured; 81p. multicoloured; 81p. multicoloured. P 14½×14	6·00	6·00
First Day Cover (Tallents House)		7·50
First Day Cover (London EC4)		7·50

No. **MS**2847 commemorates the 300th anniversary of St. Paul's Cathedral.

The complete miniature sheet is shown on one of the eleven PHQ cards with the others depicting individual stamps including those from **MS**2847.

Special First Day of Issue Postmarks

(Photo Walsall)

2008 (13 May). *'Beside the Seaside' (2nd series). As Type* **1977** *but self-adhesive. Two phosphor bands. Die-cut perf* 14½.

2848	**1977**	(1st) multicoloured	2·00	2·00
		a. Booklet pane. No. 2848×2 and No. 2295×4	5·00	

No. 2848 was only issued in £2.16 booklets, No. PM15, in which the surplus self-adhesive paper was removed from around the 1st class gold stamps (No. 2295), but retained from around No. 2848.

2081 *Carry on Sergeant*

2082 *Dracula*

2083 *Carry on Cleo*

2084 *The Curse of Frankenstein*

2085 *Carry on Screaming*   **2086** *The Mummy*

(Des Elmwood. Litho Walsall)

2008 (10 June). *Posters for Carry On and Hammer Horror Films. Two phosphor bands.* P 14.

2849	**2081**	(1st) silver, greenish yellow, magenta, new blue and black	85	85
2850	**2082**	48p. silver, greenish yellow, magenta, new blue and black	1·10	1·10
2851	**2083**	50p. silver, greenish yellow, magenta, new blue and black	1·50	1·50
2852	**2084**	56p. silver, greenish yellow, magenta, new blue and black	2·50	2·50
2853	**2085**	72p. silver, greenish yellow, magenta, new blue and black	3·00	3·00
2854	**2086**	81p. silver, greenish yellow, magenta, new blue and black	3·50	3·50
Set of 6			10·00	10·00
Set of 6 Gutter Pairs			20·00	
First Day Cover (Tallents House)				11·00
First Day Cover (Bray, Maidenhead, Berks)				11·00
Presentation Pack (P.O. Pack No. 414)			15·00	
PHQ Cards (set of 6) (312)			4·50	14·00
PHQ Cards ('brick wall' background) and Stamps Set			9·00	

Nos. 2849/54 commemorate the 50th anniversary of *Dracula* and the first *Carry On* film (*Carry on Sergeant*).

Special First Day of Issue Postmarks

2087 Red Arrows, Dartmouth Regatta Airshow, 2006

2088 RAF Falcons Parachute Team, Biggin Hill, 2006

2089 Spectator watching Red Arrows, Farnborough, 2006

2090 Prototype Avro Vulcan Bombers and Avro 707s, Farnborough, 1953

2091 Parachutist Robert Wyndham on Wing of Avro 504, 1933

2092 Air Race rounding the Beacon, Hendon, c. 1912

(Des Roundel. Photo De La Rue)

2008 (17 July). *Air Displays. Two phosphor bands.* P 14½×14.

2855	**2087**	(1st) olive-grey, bright magenta, greenish yellow, new blue and black	85	85
2856	**2088**	48p. olive-grey, bright magenta, greenish yellow, new blue and black	1·10	1·10
2857	**2089**	50p. olive-grey, bright magenta, greenish yellow, new blue and black	1·50	1·50
2858	**2090**	56p. olive-grey, bright magenta, greenish yellow, new blue and black	2·50	2·50
2859	**2091**	72p. olive-grey, bright magenta, greenish yellow, new blue and black	3·00	3·00
2860	**2092**	81p. olive-grey, bright magenta, greenish yellow, new blue and black	3·50	3·50
Set of 6			10·00	10·00
Set of 6 Gutter Pairs			20·00	
First Day Cover (Tallents House)				11·00
First Day Cover (Farnborough, Hants)				11·00
Presentation Pack (P.O. Pack No. 415)			14·00	
PHQ Cards (set of 6) (313)			4·50	14·00

The 1st class stamp was also issued in sheets of 20 with *se-tenant* labels, printed in lithography by Cartor, and sold for £7.75 per sheet (LS47).

Special First Day of Issue Postmarks

2093 Landmarks of Beijing and London (Illustration reduced. Actual size 115×76 mm)

(Des Why Not Associates. Litho Walsall)

2008 (22 Aug). *Handover of Olympic Flag from Beijing to London. Sheet 115×76 mm. Phosphorised paper.* P 14½.

MS2861	**2093**	(1st) National Stadium, Beijing; (1st) London Eye; (1st) Tower of London; (1st) Corner Tower of the Forbidden City, Beijing	5·00	4·00
		a. UV varnish (Olympic Rings) omitted		4·00
First Day Cover (Tallents House)				4·00
First Day Cover (London E15)				4·00
Presentation Pack (P.O. Pack No. M17)			10·00	
PHQ Cards (set of 5) (OGH)			3·00	15·00

The Olympic rings overprinted on **MS**2861 are in silk-screen varnish.

The five PHQ cards show the four individual stamps and the complete miniature sheet.

Special First Day of Issue Postmarks

2094 Drum Major, RAF Central Band, 2007

2095 Helicopter Rescue Winchman, 1984

2096 Hawker Hunter Pilot, 1951

2097 Lancaster Air Gunner, 1944

2098 WAAF Plotter, 1940

2099 Pilot, 1918

(Des Graham Turner and Atelier Works. Litho Walsall)

2008 (18 Sept). *Military Uniforms (2nd series). RAF Uniforms. Two phosphor bands.* P 14.

2862	**2094**	(1st) silver, greenish yellow, bright magenta, new blue and black	80	80
		a. Horiz strip of 3. Nos. 2862/4...........	4·00	4·00
		b. Booklet pane. Nos. 2862/4 with margins all round	4·00	
2863	**2095**	(1st) silver, greenish yellow, bright magenta, new blue and black	80	80
2864	**2096**	(1st) silver, greenish yellow, bright magenta, new blue and black	80	80
2865	**2097**	81p. silver, greenish yellow, bright magenta, new blue and black	1·70	1·70
		a. Horiz strip of 3. Nos. 2865/7...........	6·50	6·50
		b. Booklet pane. Nos. 2865/7 with margins all round	6·50	
2866	**2098**	81p. silver, greenish yellow, bright magenta, new blue and black	1·70	1·70
2867	**2099**	81p. silver, greenish yellow, bright magenta, new blue and black	1·70	1·70
Set of 6			9·00	9·00
Set of 2 Gutter Strips of 6			18·00	
Set of 2 Traffic Light Gutter Blocks of 12....................			26·00	
First Day Cover (Tallents House)........................				9·00
First Day Cover (Hendon, London NW9)				9·00
Presentation Pack (P.O. Pack No. 416)			12·00	
PHQ Cards (set of 6) (314).................................			4·00	14·00

Nos. 2862/4 and 2865/7 were each printed together, *se-tenant*, as horizontal strips of three stamps in sheets of 60 (2 panes 6×5).

Special First Day of Issue Postmarks

(Litho Walsall)

2008 (18 Sept). *'Pilot to Plane'. RAF Uniforms. Booklet stamps. Designs as Types* **1307** *(Spitfire from 1997 British Aircraft Designers) and* **2087** *(Red Arrows from 2008 Air Displays). Two phosphor bands.* P 14.

2868	**1307**	20p. multicoloured	4·00	4·00

		a. Booklet pane. Nos. 2868/9, each ×2, with margins all round	14·00	
2869	**2087**	(1st) multicoloured	4·00	4·00

Nos. 2868/9 were only available from £7.15 stamp booklets, No. DX42.

2100 Millicent Garrett Fawcett (suffragist)

2101 Elizabeth Garrett Anderson (physician – women's health)

2102 Marie Stopes (family planning pioneer)

2103 Eleanor Rathbone (family allowance campaigner)

2104 Claudia Jones (civil rights activist)

2105 Barbara Castle (politician – Equal Pay Act)

(Des Together Design. Photo Walsall)

2008 (14 Oct). *Women of Distinction. "All-over" phosphor.* P 14×14½.

2870	**2100**	(1st) grey-black, grey, gold and black...	85	85
2871	**2101**	48p. grey-black, grey, gold and black...	1·10	1·10
2872	**2102**	50p. grey-black, grey, gold and black...	1·50	1·50
2873	**2103**	56p. grey-black, grey, gold and black...	2·50	2·50
2874	**2104**	72p. grey-black, grey, gold and black...	3·00	3·00
2875	**2105**	81p. grey-black, grey, gold and black...	3·50	3·50
Set of 6			10·00	10·00
Set of 6 Gutter Pairs..			20·00	
First Day Cover (Tallents House)........................				10·00
First Day Cover (Aldeburgh, Suffolk)..................				10·00
Presentation Pack (P.O. Pack No. 417)			14·00	
PHQ Cards (set of 6) (315).................................			4·50	14·00

Special First Day of Issue Postmarks

2106 Ugly Sisters from *Cinderella*

2107 Genie from *Aladdin*

2108 Ugly Sisters from *Cinderella*

2109 Captain Hook from *Peter Pan*

2110 Genie from *Aladdin*

2111 Wicked Queen from *Snow White*

(Des Steve Haskins. Photo De La Rue)

2008 (4 Nov). *Christmas. One centre band (2876) or two phosphor bands (others).* P 15×14.

(a) Self-adhesive

2876	**2106**	(2nd) bright magenta, greenish yellow, new blue and black	55	55
		a. Booklet pane. No. 2876×12	7·25	
2877	**2107**	(1st) bright magenta, greenish yellow, new blue and black	85	85
		a. Booklet pane. No. 2877×12	9·50	
2878	**2108**	(2nd Large) deep new blue, bright magenta, greenish yellow, new blue and black	90	90
2879	**2109**	50p. bright magenta, greenish yellow, new blue and black	1·10	1·10
2880	**2110**	(1st Large) gold, bright magenta, greenish yellow, new blue and black	1·30	1·30
2881	**2111**	81p. bright magenta, greenish yellow, new blue and black	2·00	2·00
Set of 6			6·00	6·00
First Day Cover (Tallents House)............................				9·00
First Day Cover (Bethlehem, Llandeilo).................				9·00
Presentation Pack (P.O. Pack No. 418)			14·00	
PHQ Cards (set of 7) (316)			4·50	26·00

(b) Ordinary gum

MS2882 114×102 mm. As Nos. 2876/81		8·00	8·00
First Day Cover (Tallents House)............................			9·00
First Day Cover (Bethlehem, Llandeilo).................			9·00

The phosphor bands on Nos. 2878/9 are at the centre and right of each stamp.

The seven PHQ cards depict the six stamps and **MS**2882.

The 2nd class, 1st class and 81p. stamps were also issued together in sheets of 20, sold for £8.85, containing eight 1st class, eight 2nd class and four 81p. stamps, arranged in vertical strips of five stamps alternated with printed labels (LS54). Separate sheets of 10 1st, 20 1st, 20 2nd or 10 81p. stamps were available with personalised photographs from Royal Mail, Edinburgh. These were sold at £7.50 for 10 1st, £8.50 for 20 2nd or £13.50 for 20 1st or 10 81p. All these sheets were printed in lithography by Cartor and had the backing paper around the stamps retained.

Special First Day of Issue Postmarks

1112 Poppies on Barbed Wire Stem

1113 Soldiers in Poppy Flower

2114 Soldier's Face in Poppy Flower

2115 (Illustration reduced. Actual size 124×70 mm)

(Des Hat Trick design. Litho De La Rue)

2008 (6 Nov). *'Lest We Forget' (3rd issue). 90th Anniv of the Armistice. Two phosphor bands.* P 14½ (1st) or 15×14 (with one elliptical hole in each vertical side) (81p.).

2883	**2112**	(1st) silver, new blue, bright magenta, greenish yellow and black...............	75	75
		a. Horiz strip of 3. Nos. 2883/5............	4·00	4·00
2884	**2113**	(1st) silver, new blue, bright magenta, greenish yellow and black...............	75	75
2885	**2114**	(1st) silver, new blue, bright magenta, greenish yellow and black...............	75	75
Set of 3			4·00	4·00
Gutter Strip of 6			8·00	
Traffic Light Gutter Block of 12			16·00	
MS2886 124×70 mm. **2115** No. 2885 and as Nos. EN17, NI107, S120 and W109...........		10·00	10·00
First Day Cover (Tallents House)............................				11·00
First Day Cover (London SW1)................................				11·00
PHQ Cards (set of 6) (317)			4·75	14·00
Presentation Pack (P.O. Pack No. 419).................			16·00	

Nos. 2883/5 were printed together, *se-tenant*, in horizontal strips of three stamps in sheets of 30.

No. **MS**2886 (including the Northern Ireland, Scotland and Wales stamps) is printed in lithography.

The six PHQ cards depict Nos. **MS**2685, **MS**2796 and 2883/**MS**2886.

The 1st class stamp was also issued in sheets of 20 with *se-tenant* labels showing artifacts from the trenches, printed in lithography by Cartor and sold at £7.75 (LS55).

No. 2885 has the two phosphor bands shaped around each side of the poppy.

A Miniature Sheet Collection containing Nos. **MS**2685, **MS**2796, **MS**2886 and a replica embroidered postcard in a folder was sold for £26.95.

Special First Day of Issue Postmarks

Collectors Pack

2008 (6 Nov). Comprises Nos. 2797/802, 2806/**MS**2818, 2825/**MS**2847, 1849/67, 2870/81, **MS**2886 and M3NI110

CP2886a Collectors Pack	£140

Post Office Yearbook

2008 (6 Nov). Comprises Nos. 2797/802, 2806/**MS**2818, 2825/**MS**2847, 2849/67, 2870/81, **MS**2886 and MSNI110

YB2886a Yearbook	£125

Miniature Sheet Collection

2008 (6 Nov). Comprises Nos. **MS**2803, **MS**2818, **MS**2847, **MS**2861, **MS**2882, **MS**2886 and MSN110/11

MS2886a Miniature Sheet Collection	75·00

2116 Supermarine Spitfire
(R. J. Mitchell)

2117 Mini Skirt (Mary Quant)

2118 Mini (Sir Alec Issigonis)

2119 Anglepoise Lamp
(George Carwardine)

2120 Concorde
(Aérospatiale-BAC)

2121 K2 Telephone Kiosk
(Sir Giles Gilbert Scott)

2122 Polypropylene Chair
(Robin Day)

2123 Penguin Books (Edward
Young)

2124 London Underground
Map (based on original
design by Harry Beck)

2125 Routemaster Bus
(design team led by AAM
Durrant)

(Des HGV Design. Litho Cartor)

2009 (13 Jan). *British Design Classics (1st series). Phosphor background.*
P 14½.

2887	**2116**	(1st) silver, greenish yellow, bright magenta, new blue and black		90	90
		a. Block of 10. Nos. 2887/96		12·00	12·00
		ab. Black printed treble		£10000	
		b. Booklet pane. Nos. 2887, 2889 and 2896×2		5·00	
2888	**2117**	(1st) silver, greenish yellow, bright magenta, new blue and black		90	90
		a. Booklet pane. Nos. 2888, 2890, 2892 and 2893/5		5·50	
2889	**2118**	(1st) silver, greenish yellow, bright magenta, new blue and black		90	90
2890	**2119**	(1st) silver, greenish yellow, bright magenta, new blue and black		90	90

2891	**2120**	(1st) silver, greenish yellow, bright magenta, new blue and black		90	90
		a. Booklet pane. Nos. 2891 and 2897, each ×2		16·00	
2892	**2121**	(1st) silver, greenish yellow, bright magenta, new blue and black		90	90
2893	**2122**	(1st) silver, greenish yellow, bright magenta, new blue and black		90	90
2894	**2123**	(1st) silver, greenish yellow, bright magenta, new blue and black		90	90
2895	**2124**	(1st) silver, greenish yellow, bright magenta, new blue and black		90	90
2896	**2125**	(1st) silver, greenish yellow, bright magenta, new blue and black		90	90
Set of 10				12·00	10·00
Gutter Block of 20				24·00	
First Day Cover (Tallents House)					11·00
First Day Cover (Longbridge, Birmingham)					12·00
Presentation Pack (P.O. Pack No. 421)				15·00	
PHQ Cards (set of 10) (318)				4·50	18·00

Nos. 2887/96 were printed together, *se-tenant*, in blocks of 10 (2×5) throughout sheets of 30 stamps.

No. 2889 was also issued in sheets of 20 with *se-tenant* labels, No. LS56, sold at £7.75 per sheet.

No. 2891 was also issued on 2 March 2009 in sheets of 20 with *se-tenant* labels, No. LS57, and sold at £7.75 per sheet.

No. 2887 was also issued on 15 September 2010 in sheets of 20 with *se-tenant* labels, No. LS74, sold at £8.50 per sheet.

The above sheets were all printed in lithography by Cartor and perforated 14×14½.

Special First Day of Issue Postmarks

(Litho Cartor)

2009 (13 Jan). *British Design Classics (2nd series). Booklet stamp. Design as No. 2285 (Concorde from 2002 Passenger Jet Aviation). Two phosphor bands.* P 14½.

2897	**1589**	(1st) multicoloured	8·00	6·00

No. 2897 was only issued in £7.68 booklets, No. DX44.

2126 Charles Darwin

2127 Marine Iguana

2128 Finches

2129 Atoll

2130 Bee Orchid

2131 Orang-utan

2132 Fauna and Map of the Galapagos Islands
(Illustration reduced. Actual size 115×89 mm)

(Des Hat-trick design (Nos. 2898/903) or Howard Brown (**MS**2904))

2009 (12 Feb). *Birth Bicentenary of Charles Darwin (naturalist and evolutionary theorist) (1st issue).*

(a) Self-adhesive. Photo De La Rue. "All-over" phosphor. P 14.

2898	2126	(1st) black, new blue, greenish yellow and bright magenta	85	85
2899	2127	48p. black, new blue, greenish yellow and bright magenta	1·10	1·10
2900	2128	50p. black, new blue, greenish yellow and bright magenta	1·50	1·50
2901	2129	56p. black, new blue, greenish yellow and bright magenta	2·00	2·00
2902	2130	72p. black, new blue, greenish yellow and bright magenta	2·50	2·50
2903	2131	81p. black, new blue, greenish yellow and bright magenta	3·00	3·00

Set of 6 .... 9·00 9·00
First Day Cover (Tallents House)................................ 12·00
First Day Cover (Shrewsbury) .... 12·00
Presentation Pack (P.O. Pack No. 423) .... 20·00
PHQ Cards (set of 11) (320).......................... 4·50 18·00

(b) Ordinary gum. Litho De La Rue. Two phosphor bands. P 14.
MS2904 115×89 mm. (1st) Flightless cormorant; (1st)
Giant tortoise and cactus finch; 81p. Marine iguana;
81p. Floreana mockingbird.................................. 6·50 6·50
First Day Cover (Tallents House) .... 8·00
First Day Cover (Shrewsbury) .... 8·00
a. Booklet pane. No. **MS**2904.............. 6·50

Nos. 2898/903 have "jigsaw" perforations on the two vertical sides.
The complete miniature sheet is shown on one of the eleven PHQ cards with the others depicting individual stamps, including those from the miniature sheet.

Special First Day of Issue Postmarks

(Photo De La Rue)

2009 (12 Feb). *Birth Bicentenary of Charles Darwin (naturalist and evolutionary theorist) (2nd issue). Phosphorised paper. P 14.*

2905	2126	(1st) multicoloured	4·50	4·50
		a. Booklet pane. Nos. 2905 and 2909/10	13·00	
2906	2127	48p. multicoloured............................	5·00	5·00
		a. Booklet pane. Nos. 2906/8	13·00	
2907	2128	50p. multicoloured............................	5·50	5·50
2908	2129	56p. multicoloured............................	6·00	6·00
2909	2130	72p. multicoloured............................	6·50	6·50
2910	2131	81p. multicoloured............................	7·00	7·00

Set of 6 .... 26·00 26·00
Nos. 2905/10 were only issued in £7.75 booklets, No. DX45. They also have "jigsaw" perforations on both vertical sides.

(Photo Walsall)

2009 (10 Mar)–2010. *British Design Classics (3rd series). Booklet stamps. Designs as Nos. 2887/9, 2891/2 and 2896. Self-adhesive.* Phosphor background. Die-cut perf 14½.

2911	2121	(1st) multicoloured	2·50	2·50
		a. Booklet pane. Nos. 2911/12 and U2949×4	5·00	
2912	2125	(1st) multicoloured	2·50	2·50
2913	2118	(1st) multicoloured (21.4.09).............	2·50	2·50
		a. Booklet pane. No. 2913×2 and U2949×4	5·00	
2914	2120	(1st) multicoloured (18.8.09).............	2·50	2·50
		a. Booklet pane. No. 2914×2 and U2949×4	5·00	
2915	2117	(1st) multicoloured (17.9.09).............	2·50	2·50
		a. Booklet pane. No. 2915×2 and U2949×4	5·00	
2915b	2116	(1st) multicoloured (15.9.10).............	2·50	2·50
		ba. Booklet pane. No. 2915b×2 and U2965×4	5·50	

Set of 6 .... 13·50 13·50
Nos. 2911/15b were only issued in booklets, Nos. PM16/17, PM19/20 and PM25, initially sold for £2.16 (PM16) or £2.34 (PM17, PM19/20) or £2.46 (PM25).

For Nos. U2911 etc see Decimal Machin Definitives section.

2133 Matthew Boulton and Factory (manufacturing)

2134 James Watt and Boulton & Watt Condensing Engine (steam engineering)

2135 Richard Arkwright and Spinning Machine (textiles)

2136 Josiah Wedgwood and Black Basalt Teapot and Vase (ceramics)

2137 George Stephenson and *Locomotion* (railways)

2138 Henry Maudslay and Table Engine (machine making)

2139 James Brindley and Bridgewater Canal Aqueduct (canal engineering)

2140 John McAdam (road building)

(Des Webb and Webb. Litho Enschedé)

2009 (10 Mar). *Pioneers of the Industrial Revolution. "All-over" phosphor.* P 14×14½.

2916	2133	(1st) gold, black, new blue, bright magenta and greenish yellow	85	85
		a. Horiz pair. Nos. 2916/17	2·50	2·50
2917	2134	(1st) gold, black, new blue, bright magenta and greenish yellow	85	85
2918	2135	50p. gold, black, new blue, bright magenta and greenish yellow	1·00	1·00
		a. Horiz pair. Nos. 2918/19	3·00	3·00
2919	2136	50p. gold, black, new blue, bright magenta and greenish yellow	1·00	1·00
2920	2137	56p. gold, black, new blue, bright magenta and greenish yellow	1·25	1·25
		a. Horiz pair. Nos. 2920/1..................	3·50	3·50
2921	2138	56p. gold, black, new blue, bright magenta and greenish yellow	1·25	1·25
2922	2139	72p. gold, black, new blue, bright magenta and greenish yellow	1·75	1·75

	a. Horiz pair. Nos. 2922/3......................	4·00	4·00
2923	**2140**	72p. gold, black, new blue, bright magenta and greenish yellow	1·75	1·75

Set of 8 .... 11·00 11·00
Set of 4 Gutter Strips of 4 .... 22·00
First Day Cover (Tallents House)................................... 12·00
First Day Cover (Steam Mills, Cinderford) .... 12·00
Presentation Pack (P.O. Pack No. 425)....................... 15·00
PHQ Cards (set of 8) (321).............................. 4·75 16·00

Nos. 2916/17, 2918/19, 2920/1 and 2922/3 were each printed together, *se-tenant*, as horizontal pairs in sheets of 60 (2 panes 6×5).

Special First Day of Issue Postmarks

2141 Henry VII (1485–1509)

2142 Henry VIII (1509–47)

2143 Edward VI (1547–53)

2144 Lady Jane Grey (1553)

2145 Mary I (1553–8)

2146 Elizabeth I (1558–1603)

2147 The Age of the Tudors (Illustration reduced. Actual size 123×70 mm)

(Des Atelier Works. Litho Cartor)

2009 (21 Apr.) *Kings and Queens (2nd issue). The House of Tudor. Two phosphor bands.* P 14.

2924	**2141**	(1st) blackish olive, greenish yellow, bright magenta, new blue and black........................	85	85
2925	**2142**	(1st) blackish olive, greenish yellow, bright magenta, new blue and black	85	85
2926	**2143**	62p. blackish olive, greenish yellow, bright magenta, new blue and black	1·40	1·40
2927	**2144**	62p. blackish olive, greenish yellow, bright magenta, new blue and black	1·40	1·40
2928	**2145**	81p. blackish olive, greenish yellow, bright magenta, new blue and black	1·75	1·75
2929	**2146**	81p. blackish olive, greenish yellow, bright magenta, new blue and black	1·75	1·75

Set of 6 .... 8·00 8·00
Set of 6 Gutter Pairs .... 16·00
Set of 6 Traffic Light Gutter Blocks of 4........................ 32·00
First Day Cover (Tallents House)................................... 10·00
First Day Cover (London SE10)..................................... 10·00
Presentation Pack (P.O. Pack No. 426) .... 18·00
PHQ Cards (set of 11) (322) .... 6·50 13·00

MS2930 123×70 mm. **2147** (1st) *Mary Rose* (galleon), 1510; (1st) Field of Cloth of Gold Royal Conference, 1520; 90p. Royal Exchange (centre of commerce), 1565; 90p. Francis Drake (circumnavigation), 1580 ..... 5·75 5·75
First Day Cover (Tallents House)................................... 7·50
First Day Cover (London SE10)..................................... 7·50

The complete miniature sheet is shown on one of the eleven PHQ cards with the others depicting individual stamps including those from **MS**2930.

The PHQ Card for the Royal Exchange design has the inscription for Sir Francis Drake and *vice versa*.

Special First Day of Issue Postmarks

2148 *Allium sphaerocephalon* (round-headed leek)

2149 *Luronium natans* (floating water-plantain)

2150 *Cypripedium calceolus* (lady's slipper orchid)

2151 *Polygala amarella* (dwarf milkwort)

2152 *Saxifraga hirculus* (marsh saxifrage)

2153 *Stachys germanica* (downy woundwort)

2154 *Euphorbia serrulata*
(upright spurge)

2155 *Pyrus cordata*
(Plymouth pear)

2156 *Polygonum maritimum*
(Sea knotgrass)

2157 *Dianthus armeria*
(Deptford pink)

2158 Royal Botanic Gardens, Kew (Illustration reduced. Actual size 115×89 mm)

(Des Studio Dempsey. Litho Cartor)

2009 (19 May). *"Action for Species" (3rd series). Plants.*

(a) Phosphor background. P 14½

2931	2148	(1st) brownish grey, greenish yellow, bright magenta, new blue and black	85	85
		a. Block of 10. Nos. 2931/40	12·00	10·00
2932	2149	(1st) brownish grey, greenish yellow, bright magenta, new blue and black	85	85
2933	2150	(1st) brownish grey, greenish yellow, bright magenta, new blue and black	85	85
2934	2151	(1st) brownish grey, greenish yellow, bright magenta, new blue and black	85	85
2935	2152	(1st) brownish grey, greenish yellow, bright magenta, new blue and black	85	85
2936	2153	(1st) brownish grey, greenish yellow, bright magenta, new blue and black	85	85
2937	2154	(1st) brownish grey, greenish yellow, bright magenta, new blue and black	85	85
2938	2155	(1st) brownish grey, greenish yellow, bright magenta, new blue and black	85	85
2939	2156	(1st) brownish grey, greenish yellow, bright magenta, new blue and black	85	85
2940	2157	(1st) brownish grey, greenish yellow, bright magenta, new blue and black	85	85
Set of 10			12·00	10·00
Gutter Block of 10			16·00	
First Day Cover (Tallents House)				11·00
First Day Cover (Kew, Richmond)				12·00
Presentation Pack (P.O. Pack No. 427)			20·00	
PHQ Cards (set of 15) (323)			8·75	15·00

(b) *250th Anniv of Royal Botanic Gardens, Kew. Multicoloured. Two phosphor bands. P 14×14½.*

MS2941 115×89 mm. **2158** (1st) Palm House, Kew Gardens; (1st) Millennium Seed Bank, Wakehurst Place; 90p. Pagoda, Kew Gardens; 90p. Sackler Crossing, Kew Gardens	5·75	5·75
First Day Cover (Tallents House)		7·50
First Day Cover (Kew, Richmond)		7·50

Nos. 2931/40 were printed together, *se-tenant*, as blocks of ten (5×2) in sheets of 60 (2 panes of 30).

The complete miniature sheet is shown on one of the fifteen PHQ cards with the others depicting individual stamps including those from **MS**2941.

Special First Day of Issue Postmarks

(Photo Walsall)

2009 (21 May). *50th Anniv of NAFAS (National Association of Flower Arrangement Societies). Booklet stamps. Designs as Nos. 1958 and 1962 (1997 Greeting Stamps 19th-century Flower Paintings). Self-adhesive. Two phosphor bands. Die-cut perf 14 (with one elliptical hole in each vert side).*

2942	1287	(1st) multicoloured	2·50	2·50
		a. Booklet pane. Nos. 2942/3 and U2932×4	5·00	
2943	1283	(1st) multicoloured	2·50	2·50

Nos. 2942/3 were only issued in stamp booklets, No. PM18.

2159 Dragon

2160 Unicorn

2161 Giant

2162 Pixie

2163 Mermaid

2164 Fairy

(Des Dave McKean and Morgan Radcliffe. Photo De La Rue)

2009 (16 June). *Mythical Creatures. "All-over" phosphor. P 14½.*

2944	2159	(1st) bright magenta, greenish yellow, new blue and black	85	85
2945	2160	(1st) bright magenta, greenish yellow, new blue and black	85	85
2946	2161	62p. bright magenta, greenish yellow, new blue and black	1·40	1·40
2947	2162	62p. bright magenta, greenish yellow, new blue and black	1·40	1·40
2948	2163	90p. bright magenta, greenish yellow, new blue and black	2·00	2·00

2949 **2164** 90p. bright magenta, greenish yellow,
new blue and black .... 2·00 2·00
Set of 6 .... 8·25 8·25
Set of 6 Gutter Pairs .... 16·00
First Day Cover (Tallents House) .... 11·00
First Day Cover (Dragonby, Scunthorpe) .... 11·00
Presentation Pack (P.O. Pack No. 428) .... 12·00
PHQ Cards (*set of 6*) (324) .... 2·50 12·00

Special First Day of Issue Postmarks

2165 George V
Type B Wall Letter Box,
1933–6

2166 Edward VII
Ludlow Letter Box,
1901–10

2167 Victorian Lamp
Letter Box, 1896

2168 Elizabeth II
Type A Wall Letter
Box, 1962–3

2169 Post Boxes (illustration reduced. Actual size 145×74 mm)

(Des Elmwood. Litho Cartor)

2009 (18 Aug). *Post Boxes (1st series).* "All-over" phosphor. P 14.
2950 **2165** (1st) multicoloured .... 1·50 1·50
a. Booklet pane. Nos. 2950/3 with
margins all round .... 8·50
2951 **2166** 56p. multicoloured .... 2·00 2·00
2952 **2167** 81p. multicoloured .... 2·50 2·50
2953 **2168** 90p. multicoloured .... 2·75 2·75
Set of 4 .... 8·50 8·50
MS2954 **2169** Nos. 2950/3 .... 8·50 8·50
First Day Cover (Tallents House) .... 8·25
First Day Cover (Wakefield, W. Yorkshire) .... 8·25
Presentation Pack (P.O. Pack No. 430) .... 10·00
PHQ Cards (*set of 5*) (325) .... 2·50 9·00
Nos. 2950/3 were only issued in £8.18 stamp booklets, No. DX46 and
in **MS**2954.
Type **2165** was also issued in sheets of 20 with *se-tenant* labels
showing post boxes, No. LS65, sold for £8.35 per sheet, No. LS65.

Special First Day of Issue Postmarks

FIRST DAY OF ISSUE ROYAL MAIL	FIRST DAY OF ISSUE
TUE	TUE
TALLENTS HOUSE EDINBURGH 18.8.2009	WAKEFIELD, W.YORKSHIRE 18.8.2009

(Litho Cartor)

2009 (18 Aug). *"Treasures of the Archive" (1st series).* Booklet stamps.
Designs as Types **929** (1990 150th anniv of the Penny Black) and
1446 (with redrawn 1st face value). Printed in lithography. Two
phosphor bands. P 14½×14 (with one elliptical hole in each vert
side).
2955 **929** 20p. brownish-black and grey-brown 45 45
a. Booklet pane. Nos. 2955/6, each ×4
with central label and margins all
round .... 5·25
2956 (1st) brownish-black and grey-brown 90 90
Nos. 2955/6 were only available from £8.18 stamp booklets, No. DX46.

(Litho Cartor)

2009 (18 Aug). *"Treasures of the Archive" (2nd series).* Booklet stamps.
Design as Type **919** (1989 Lord Mayor's Show). "All-over" phosphor.
P 14.
2957 **919** 20p. multicoloured .... 1·00 1·00
a. Booklet pane. No. 2957×4 with
margins all round .... 3·00
No. 2957 was only available from £8.18 stamp booklets, No. DX46.

2170 Firefighting

2171 Chemical Fire

2172 Emergency Rescue

2173 Flood Rescue

2174 Search and Rescue

2175 Fire Safety

(Des Rose Design. Photo De La Rue)

2009 (1 Sept). *Fire and Rescue Service.* "All-over" phosphor. P 14×14½.
2958 **2170** (1st) pale greenish yellow, bright
magenta, greenish yellow, new
blue and black 85 85
2959 **2171** 54p. pale greenish yellow, bright
magenta, greenish yellow, new
blue and black .... 1·10 1·10
2960 **2172** 56p. pale greenish yellow, bright
magenta, greenish yellow, new
blue and black .... 1·25 1·25
2961 **2173** 62p. pale greenish yellow, bright
magenta, greenish yellow, new
blue and black .... 1·40 1·40
2962 **2174** 81p. pale greenish yellow, bright
magenta, greenish yellow, new
blue and black .... 1·75 1·75

2963   **2175**   90p. pale greenish yellow, bright
                 magenta, greenish yellow, new
                 blue and black .... 2·00   2·00
Set of 6 .... 8·25   8·25
Set of 6 Gutter Pairs .... 16·00
First Day Cover (Tallents House).. 11·00
First Day Cover (Hose, Melton Mowbray)............................... 11·00
Presentation Pack (P.O. Pack No. 431) .... 12·00
PHQ Cards (set of 6) (326) .... 3·50   12·00

Special First Day of Issue Postmarks

2176 Flight Deck
Officer, 2009

2177 Captain, 1941

2178 Second Officer
WRNS, 1918

2179 Able Seaman,
1880

2180 Royal Marine,
1805

2181 Admiral, 1795

(Des Graham Turner and Atelier Works. Litho Cartor)

2009 (17 Sept). *Military Uniforms (3rd series). Royal Navy Uniforms.*
   Phosphor background. P 14.
2964   **2176**   (1st) silver, greenish yellow, magenta,
                new blue and black 85   85
            a. Horiz strip of 3. Nos. 2964/6............ 2·50   2·50
            b. Booklet pane. Nos. 2964/6 with
                margins all round .... 2·50
2965   **2177**   (1st) silver, greenish yellow, magenta,
                new blue and black 85   85
2966   **2178**   (1st) silver, greenish yellow, magenta,
                new blue and black 85   85
2967   **2179**   90p. silver, greenish yellow, magenta,
                new blue and black .... 2·00   2·00
            a. Horiz strip of 3. Nos. 2967/9............ 6·00   6·00
            b. Booklet pane. Nos. 2967/9 with
                margins all round .... 6·00
2968   **2180**   90p. silver, greenish yellow, magenta,
                new blue and black .... 2·00   2·00
2969   **2181**   90p. silver, greenish yellow, magenta,
                new blue and black .... 2·00   2·00
Set of 6 .... 8·50   8·50
Set of 2 Gutter Strips of 6 .... 16·00
Set of 2 Traffic Light Gutter Blocks of 12................................... 32·00

First Day Cover (Tallents House).. 11·00
First Day Cover (Portsmouth).. 11·00
Presentation Pack (P.O. Pack No. 432) .... 12·00
PHQ Cards (set of 6) (327) .... 3·50   12·00
       Nos. 2964/6 and 2967/9 were each printed together, se-tenant, as
horizontal strips of three in sheets of 60 (2 panes 6×5).

Special First Day of Postmarks

(Litho Cartor)

2009 (17 Sept). *Royal Navy Uniforms. Booklet stamp. Design as Type*
   1518 *(Jolly Roger flag from 2001 Submarine Centenary). Two*
   phosphor bands. P 14½.
2970   **1518**   (1st) multicoloured .... 5·00   5·00
            a. Booklet pane. Nos. 2970 and
                2581, each ×2 with margins all
                round .... 12·00
   No. 2970 was only issued in £7.93 stamp booklets, No. DX47.

2182 Fred Perry 1909–95
(lawn tennis champion)

2183 Henry Purcell 1659–95
(composer and musician)

2184 Sir Matt Busby
1909–94 (footballer and
football manager)

2185 William Gladstone
1809–98 (statesman and
Prime Minister)

2186 Mary Wollstonecraft
1759–97 (pioneering
feminist)

2187 Sir Arthur Conan
Doyle 1859–1930 (writer
and creator of Sherlock
Holmes)

2188 Donald Campbell
1921–67 (water speed
record broken 1959)

2189 Judy Fryd 1909–2000
(campaigner and founder
of MENCAP)

2190 Samuel Johnson 1709–84 (lexicographer, critic and poet)

2191 Sir Martin Ryle 1918–84 (radio survey of the Universe 1959)

(Des Together Design. Litho Cartor)

2009 (8 Oct). *Eminent Britons. Phosphor background.* P 14½.

2971	**2182**	(1st) silver, greenish yellow, magenta, new blue and black	85	85
		a. Horiz strip of 5. Nos. 2971/5............	6·00	6·00
2972	**2183**	(1st) silver, greenish yellow, magenta, new blue and black	85	85
2973	**2184**	(1st) silver, greenish yellow, magenta, new blue and black	85	85
2974	**2185**	(1st) silver, greenish yellow, magenta, new blue and black	85	85
2975	**2186**	(1st) silver, greenish yellow, magenta, new blue and black	85	85
2976	**2187**	(1st) silver, greenish yellow, magenta, new blue and black	85	85
		a. Horiz strip of 5. Nos. 2976/80	6·00	6·00
2977	**2188**	(1st) silver, greenish yellow, magenta, new blue and black	85	85
2978	**2189**	(1st) silver, greenish yellow, magenta, new blue and black	85	85
2979	**2190**	(1st) silver, greenish yellow, magenta, new blue and black	85	85
2980	**2191**	(1st) silver, greenish yellow, magenta, new blue and black	85	85

Set of 10..	12·00	12·00
Set of 2 Gutter Strips of 10...	16·00	
First Day Cover (Tallents House)......................................		12·00
First Day Cover (Britannia, Bacup, Lancashire).....................		12·00
Presentation Pack (P.O. Pack No. 433).............................	16·00	13·00
PHQ Cards (set of 10) (328)...	5·75	18·00

Nos. 2971/5 and 2976/80 were each printed together, *se-tenant*, as horizontal strips of five stamps in sheets of 50 (2 panes 5×5).

Special First Day of Issue Postmarks

2192 Canoe Slalom

2193 Paralympic Games Archery

2194 Athletics: Track

2195 Diving

2196 Paralympic Games Boccia

2197 Judo

2198 Paralympic Games Dressage

2199 Badminton

2200 Weightlifting

2201 Basketball

(Des John Royle (2981), George Hardie (2982), Nathalie Guinamard (2983), Julian Opie (2984), David Doyle (2985), Paul Slater (2986), Andrew Davidson (2987), David Holmes (2988), Guy Billout (2989), Huntley Muir (2990) and Studio David Hillman (all). Litho Cartor)

2009 (22 Oct). *Olympic and Paralympic Games, London (2012) (1st issue). "All-over" phosphor.* P 14½.

2981	**2192**	(1st) grey, greenish yellow, bright magenta, new blue and black	85	85
		a. Horiz strip of 5. Nos. 2981/5............	6·00	6·00
2982	**2193**	(1st) grey, greenish yellow, bright magenta, new blue and black	85	85
2983	**2194**	(1st) grey, greenish yellow, bright magenta, new blue and black	85	85
2984	**2195**	(1st) grey, greenish yellow, bright magenta, new blue and black	85	85
2985	**2196**	(1st) grey, greenish yellow, bright magenta, new blue and black	85	85
2986	**2197**	(1st) grey, greenish yellow, bright magenta, new blue and black	85	85
		a. Horiz strip of 5. Nos. 2986/90	6·00	6·00
2987	**2198**	(1st) grey, greenish yellow, bright magenta, new blue and black	85	85
2988	**2199**	(1st) grey, greenish yellow, bright magenta, new blue and black	85	85
2989	**2200**	(1st) grey, greenish yellow, bright magenta, new blue and black	85	85
2990	**2201**	(1st) grey, greenish yellow, bright magenta, new blue and black	85	85

Set of 10..	12·00	12·00
Set of 2 Gutter Strips of 10...	16·00	
First Day Cover (Tallents House)......................................		11·00
First Day Cover (Badminton, Glos)...................................		11·00
Presentation Pack (P.O. Pack No. M18)...........................	14·00	
PHQ Cards (set of 10) (OXPG1)..	5·75	12·00

Nos. 2981/5 and 2986/90 were each printed together, *se-tenant*, as horizontal strips of five stamps in sheets of 50 (2 panes 5×5).

Special First Day of Issue Postmarks

2202 Angel playing Lute (William Morris), Church of St. James, Staveley, Kendal, Cumbria

2203 Madonna and Child (Henry Holiday), Church of St. Michael, Great Yarmouth, Norfolk

2204 Angel playing Lute (William Morris), Church of St. James, Staveley, Kendal, Cumbria

2205 Joseph (Henry Holiday), Parish Church of St. Michael, Minehead, Somerset

2206 Madonna and Child (Henry Holiday), Church of Ormesby St. Michael, Ormesby, Great Yarmouth, Norfolk

2207 Wise Man (Sir Edward Burne-Jones), Church of St. Mary the Virgin, Rye, East Sussex

2208 Shepherd (Henry Holiday), St. Mary's Church, Upavon, Wiltshire

(Des Andrew Ross. Photo De La Rue)

2009 (3 Nov). *Christmas. Stained Glass Windows. One centre band (2202) or two phosphor bands (others). P 14½×14 (with one elliptical hole in each vert side).*

(a) Self-adhesive

2991	2202	(2nd) gold, bright magenta, greenish yellow, new blue, and black	60	60
		a. Booklet pane. No. 2991×12	8·00	
2992	2203	(1st) gold, bright magenta, greenish yellow, new blue and black	85	85
		a. Booklet pane. No. 2992×12	10·00	
2993	2204	(2nd Large) gold, bright magenta, greenish yellow, new blue and black	95	95
2994	2205	56p. gold, bright magenta, greenish yellow, new blue and black	1·25	1·25
2995	2206	(1st Large) gold, bright magenta, greenish yellow, new blue and black	1·25	1·25
2996	2207	90p. gold, bright magenta, greenish yellow, new blue and black	2·00	2·00
2997	2208	£1.35 gold, bright magenta, greenish yellow, new blue and black	2·75	2·75
Set of 7			9·50	9·50
First Day Cover (Tallents House)				11·50
First Day Cover (Bethlehem, Llandeilo)				11 50
Presentation Pack (P.O. Pack No. 434)			18·00	
PHQ Cards (set of 8) (328)			4·75	13·00

(b) Ordinary gum.

MS2998	115×102 mm. As Nos. 2991/7	9·50	9·50
First Day Cover (Tallents House)			11·50
First Day Cover (Bethlehem, Llandeilo)			11·50

The eight PHQ cards show the seven stamps and **MS**2998.

The 2nd class, 1st class, 50p and 81p stamps were also issued together in sheets of 20 (No. LS67), sold for £9, containing eight 2nd class, eight 1st class, two 50p and two 81p stamps, each stamp accompanied by a se-tenant label (LS67).

Separate sheets of 20 2nd, 20 1st, ten 1st, ten 56p and ten 90p were available with personal photographs from Royal Mail, Edinburgh. These were sold at £7.50 for 10 1st, £9.50 for 20 2nd or 10 56p or £13.50 for 20 1st or 10 90p.

All these sheets were printed in lithography by Cartor and had the backing paper around the stamps retained.

Special First Day of Issue Postmarks

Collectors Pack

2009 (3 Nov). Comprises Nos. 2887/96, 2898/**MS**2904, 2916/**MS**2941, 2944/9, **MS**2954, 2958/69, 2971/97, **MS**5137 and **MS**W125.

CP2998a Collectors Pack £120

Post Office Yearbook

2009 (3 Nov). Comprises Nos. 2887/96, 2898/**MS**2904, 2916/**MS**2941, 2944/9, **MS**2954, 2958/69 and 2971/97, **MS**5137 and **MS**W125.

YB2998a Yearbook.. £130

Miniature Sheet Collection

2009 (3 Nov). Comprises Nos. **MS**2904, **MS**2930, **MS**2941, **MS**2954, **MS**2998, **MS**S137 and **MS**W125.

MS2998a Miniature Sheet Collection .... 42·00

2209 *The Division Bell* (Pink Floyd)

2210 *A Rush of Blood to the Head* (Coldplay)

2211 *Parklife* (Blur)

2212 *Power Corruption and Lies* (New Order)

2213 *Let It Bleed* (Rolling Stones)

2214 *London Calling* (The Clash)

2215 *Tubular Bells* (Mike Oldfield)

2216 *IV* (Led Zeppelin)

2217 *Screamadelica* (Primal Scream)

2218 *The Rise and Fall of Ziggy Stardust and the Spiders from Mars* (David Bowie)

(Des Studio Dempsey)

2010 (7 Jan). *Classic Album Covers (1st issue). "All-over" phosphor.*

(a) *Self-adhesive. Photo De La Rue.* Die-cut perf 14½ (interrupted)

2999	**2209**	(1st) black, new blue, greenish yellow, bright magenta and silver.............	90	90
		a. Horiz strip of 5. Nos. 2999/3003	7·00	
3000	**2210**	(1st) black, new blue, greenish yellow, bright magenta and silver.............	90	90
3001	**2211**	(1st) black, new blue, greenish yellow, bright magenta and silver.............	90	90
3002	**2212**	(1st) black, new blue, greenish yellow, bright magenta and silver.............	90	90
3003	**2213**	(1st) black, new blue, greenish yellow, bright magenta and silver.............	90	90
3004	**2214**	(1st) black, new blue, greenish yellow, bright magenta and silver.............	90	90
		a. Horiz strip of 5. Nos. 3004/8...........	7·00	
3005	**2215**	(1st) black, new blue, greenish yellow, bright magenta and silver.............	90	90
3006	**2216**	(1st) black, new blue, greenish yellow, bright magenta and silver.............	90	90
3007	**2217**	(1st) black, new blue, greenish yellow, bright magenta and silver.............	90	90
3008	**2218**	(1st) black, new blue, greenish yellow, bright magenta and silver.............	90	90
Set of 10................			14·00	14·00
First Day Cover (Tallents House)................				14·00
First Day Cover (Oldfield, Keighley)................				15·00
Presentation Pack (P.O. Pack No. 435)................			18·00	
PHQ Cards (set of 10) (330)................			6·00	18·00

Nos. 2999/3003 and 3004/8 were each printed together, *se-tenant*, as horizontal strips of five stamps in sheets of 50 (2 panes of 25).

The right-hand edges of Nos. 2999/3008 are all cut around to show the vinyl disc protruding from the open edge of the album cover.

Special First Day of Issue Postmarks

2010 (7 Jan). *Classic Album Covers (2nd issue). "All-over" phosphor.* P 14½ (interrupted).

3009	**2213**	(1st) multicoloured..................	2·40	2·40
		a. Booklet pane. Nos. 3009/14..........	14·00	
3010	**2216**	(1st) multicoloured..................	2·40	2·40
3011	**2218**	(1st) multicoloured..................	2·40	2·40
3012	**2212**	(1st) multicoloured..................	2·40	2·40
3013	**2217**	(1st) multicoloured..................	2·40	2·40
3014	**2209**	(1st) multicoloured..................	2·40	2·40
3015	**2215**	(1st) multicoloured..................	2·40	2·40
		a. Booklet pane. Nos. 3015/18..........	10·00	
3016	**2214**	(1st) multicoloured..................	2·40	2·40
3017	**2211**	(1st) multicoloured..................	2·40	2·40
3018	**2210**	(1st) multicoloured..................	2·40	2·40
3009/18 *Set of 10*			12·00	12·00
MS3019 223×189 mm. Nos. 3009/18................			24·00	24·00
First Day Cover (Tallents House)................				12·00
First Day Cover (Oldfield, Keighley)................				13·00

Nos. 3009/18 were only issued in £8.06 stamp booklets (No. DX48) and miniature sheet **MS**3019.

The right-hand edges of Nos. 3009/18 and the miniature sheet **MS**3019 are all cut around in an imperforate section to show the vinyl disc protruding from the open edge of the album cover.

A miniature sheet containing No. 3014×10 *The Division Bell* (Pink Floyd) was issued on 6 March 2010 and sold for £4.75 per sheet.

(Photo Walsall)

2010 (7 Jan–25 Feb). *Olympic and Paralympic Games, London (2012) (2nd issue). Booklet stamps. Designs as Nos. 2982/3, 2986 and 2990. Self-adhesive. "All-over" phosphor. Die-cut perf 14½.*

3020	**2197**	(1st) multicoloured..................	2·75	2·75

		a. Booklet pane. Nos. 3020/1 and U2949×4................	5·25	
3021	**2193**	(1st) multicoloured..................	2·75	2·75
3022	**2194**	(1st) multicoloured (25 Feb)................	2·75	2·75
		a. Booklet pane. Nos. 3022/3 and U2949×4................	5·25	
3023	**2201**	(1st) multicoloured (25 Feb)................	2·75	2·75
Set of 4................			10·00	10·00

Nos. 3020/1 and 3022/3 were only issued in separate booklets, Nos. PM21/2, each sold for £2.34.

2219 (illustration reduced. Actual size 124×71 mm)

(Des Hat-trick Design. Litho Cartor)

2010 (26 Jan). *Business and Consumer Smilers. Sheet 124×71 mm. Multicoloured. Two phosphor bands. P 14½×14 (with one elliptical hole in each vertical side).*

MS3024	**2219**	(1st) Propeller driven airplane (Andrew Davidson); (1st) Vintage sports roadster (Andrew Davidson); (1st) Recreation of crown seal (Neil Oliver); (1st) Birthday cake (Annabel Wright); (1st) Steam locomotive (Andrew Davidson); (1st) Ocean liner (Andrew Davidson); (1st) As Type **2112**; (1st) Birthday present (Annabel Wright); (Europe up to 20 grams) Bird carrying envelope (Lucy Davey); (Worldwide up to 20 grams) "Hello" in plane vapour trail (Lucy Davey)................	15·00	15·00
First Day Cover (Tallents House)................				15·00
First Day Cover (Happy Valley, Malvern)................				14·00
Presentation Pack (P.O. Pack No. 435)................			18·00	
PHQ Cards (set of 11)................			6·50	18·00

MS3024 was sold for £4.58.

The eleven PHQ cards show the ten individual stamps and the complete miniature sheet.

Stamps in designs as within **MS**3024 but self-adhesive were available printed together, *se-tenant*, in sheets of 20 containing two of each design with greetings labels (No. LS70), sold for £9.70 per sheet.

The (1st) birthday cake, (1st) birthday present, Europe and Worldwide designs were also available in separate sheets with personal photographs.

The other 1st class designs were for the business customised service.

Stamps as the (1st) birthday cake (×4), (1st) birthday present (×4), Europe bird carrying envelope (×2) and Worldwide "Hello" in plane vapour trail (×2) designs but self-adhesive were issued together with Nos. 2572, 2674, 2693 and 2821/3 on 8 May 2010 in sheets of 20 stamps with *se-tenant* greetings labels printed in lithography by Cartor, No. LS73, and sold for £10 per sheet.

Special First Day of Issue Postmarks

Girlguiding UK

2220 Girlguiding UK (illustration reduced. Actual size 190×67 mm)

(Des Together Design. Litho Cartor)

2010 (2 Feb). *Centenary of Girlguiding. Sheet 190×67 mm. Multicoloured. Phosphor background. P 14×14½.*

MS3025	**2220**	(1st) Rainbows; 56p. Brownies; 81p. Guides; 90p. Senior Section members................	8·00	6·00

First Day Cover (Tallents House) .... 8·00
First Day Cover (Guide, Blackburn) .... 8·00
Presentation Pack (P.O. Pack No. 436) .... 12·00
PHQ Cards (set of 5) (331) .... 3·00   9·00

The five PHQ cards show the four individual stamps and the complete miniature sheet.

Special First Day of Issue Postmarks

2221 Sir Robert Boyle
(chemistry)

2222 Sir Isaac Newton
(optics)

2223 Benjamin Franklin
(electricity)

2224 Edward Jenner
(pioneer of smallpox
vaccination)

2225 Charles Babbage
(computing)

2226 Alfred Russel Wallace
(theory of evolution)

2227 Joseph Lister
(antiseptic surgery)

2228 Ernest Rutherford
(atomic structure)

2229 Dorothy Hodgkin
(crystallography)

2230 Sir Nicholas Shackleton
(earth sciences)

(Des Hat-trick Design. Litho Cartor)

2010 (25 Feb). *350th Anniv of the Royal Society.* "All-over" phosphor.
P 14½.

3026	**2221**	(1st) greenish yellow, bright magenta, new blue and black	90	90
		a. Block of 10. Nos. 3026/35	15·00	13·00
		b. Booklet pane. Nos. 3026, 3030/1 and 3035 with margins all round..	5·00	
3027	**2222**	(1st) greenish yellow, bright magenta, new blue and black	90	90
		a. Booklet pane. Nos. 3027/8 and 3033×2 with margins all round	5·00	
3028	**2223**	(1st) greenish yellow, bright magenta, new blue and black	90	90
3029	**2224**	(1st) greenish yellow, bright magenta, new blue and black	90	90
		a. Booklet pane. Nos. 3029×2, 3032 and 3034 with margins all round..	5·00	
3030	**2225**	(1st) greenish yellow, bright magenta, new blue and black	90	90
3031	**2226**	(1st) greenish yellow, bright magenta, new blue and black	90	90
3032	**2227**	(1st) greenish yellow, bright magenta, new blue and black	90	90
3033	**2228**	(1st) greenish yellow, bright magenta, new blue and black	90	90
3034	**2229**	(1st) greenish yellow, bright magenta, new blue and black	90	90
3035	**2230**	(1st) greenish yellow, bright magenta, new blue and black	90	90
Set of 10..			15·00	13·00
Gutter Block of 20			30·00	
First Day Cover (Tallents House)............................				13·00
First Day Cover (London SW1)..............................				14·00
Presentation Pack (P.O. Pack No. 437)..........			18·00	
PHQ Cards (set of 10) (332)...........................			6·00	15·00

Nos. 3026/35 were printed together, *se-tenant,* as blocks of ten (5×2) in sheets of 60 (2 panes of 30).

Special First Day of Issue Postmarks

2231 "Pixie" (mastiff cross)

2232 "Button"

2233 "Herbie" (mongrel)

2234 "Mr. Tumnus"

2235 "Tafka" (border collie)

2236 "Boris" (bulldog cross)

2237 "Casey" (lurcher)

2238 "Tigger"

2239 "Leonard" (Jack Russell cross)

2240 "Tia" (terrier cross)

(Des CDT Design. Litho Cartor)

2010 (11 Mar). *150th Anniv of Battersea Dogs and Cats Home. Phosphor background*. P 14½.

3036	**2231**	(1st) gold, greenish yellow, bright magenta, new blue and black	90	90
		a. Block of 10. Nos. 3036/45	15·00	13·00
3037	**2232**	(1st) gold, greenish yellow, bright magenta, new blue and black	90	90
3038	**2233**	(1st) gold, greenish yellow, bright magenta, new blue and black	90	90
3039	**2234**	(1st) gold, greenish yellow, bright magenta, new blue and black	90	90
3040	**2235**	(1st) gold, greenish yellow, bright magenta, new blue and black	90	90
3041	**2236**	(1st) gold, greenish yellow, bright magenta, new blue and black	90	90
3042	**2237**	(1st) gold, greenish yellow, bright magenta, new blue and black	90	90
3043	**2238**	(1st) gold, greenish yellow, bright magenta, new blue and black	90	90
3044	**2239**	(1st) gold, greenish yellow, bright magenta, new blue and black	90	90
3045	**2240**	(1st) gold, greenish yellow, bright magenta, new blue and black	90	90

Set of 10	15·00	13·00
Gutter Block of 20	30·00	
First Day Cover (Tallents House)...................................		13·00
First Day Cover (London SW8).....................................		14·00
Presentation Pack (P.O. Pack No. 438)	20·00	
PHQ Cards (set of 10) (333)......................................	6·00	15·00

Nos. 3036/45 were printed together, *se-tenant*, as blocks of ten (5×2) in sheets of 60 (2 panes of 30).

Special First Day of Issue Postmarks

2241 James I (1406–37)

2242 James II (1437–60)

2243 James III (1460–88)

2244 James IV (1488–1513)

2245 James V (1513–42)

2246 Mary (1542–67)

2247 James VI (1567–1625)

2248 The Age of the Stewarts (illustration reduced. Actual size 123×70 mm)

(Des Atelier Works. Litho Cartor)

2010 (23 Mar). *Kings and Queens (3rd issue). House of Stewart. Two phosphor bands*. P 14.

3046	**2241**	(1st) indigo, greenish yellow, bright magenta, new blue and black	90	90
3047	**2242**	(1st) indigo, greenish yellow, bright magenta, new blue and black	90	90
3048	**2243**	(1st) indigo, greenish yellow, bright magenta, new blue and black	90	90
3049	**2244**	62p. indigo, greenish yellow, bright magenta, new blue and black	1·40	1·40
3050	**2245**	62p. indigo, greenish yellow, bright magenta, new blue and black	1·40	1·40
3051	**2246**	81p. indigo, greenish yellow, bright magenta, new blue and black	1·75	1·75
3052	**2247**	81p. indigo, greenish yellow, bright magenta, new blue and black	1·75	1·75

Set of 7	9·00	9·00
Set of 7 Gutter Pairs..	18·00	
Set of 7 Traffic Light Gutter Blocks of 4	35·00	
First Day Cover (Tallents House)...................................		12·00
First Day Cover (Linlithgow, West Lothian).....................		12·00
Presentation Pack (P.O. Pack No. 439)	16·00	
PHQ Cards (set of 12) (334)......................................	7·25	15·00

MS3053 123×70 mm. **2248** (1st) Foundation of the University of St. Andrews, 1413; (1st) Foundation of the College of Surgeons, Edinburgh, 1505; 81p. Foundation of Court of Session, 1532; 81p. John Knox (Reformation, 1559)................ 5·25 5·25

First Day Cover (Tallents House)...................................		7·50
First Day Cover (Linlithgow, West Lothian).....................		7·50

The complete miniature sheet is shown on one of the twelve PHQ cards with the others depicting individual stamps including those from MS3053.

Special First Day of Issue Postmarks

2249 Humpback Whale
(*Megaptera novaeangliae*)

2250 Wildcat (*Felis silvestris*)

2251 Brown Long-eared Bat (*Plecotus auritus*)

2252 Polecat (*Mustela putorius*)

2253 Sperm Whale
(*Physeter macrocephalus*)

2254 Water Vole (*Arvicola terrestris*)

2255 Greater Horseshoe Bat (*Rhinolophus ferrumequinum*)

2256 Otter (*Lutra lutra*)

2257 Dormouse
(*Muscardinus avellanarius*)

2258 Hedgehog (*Erinaceus europaeus*)

(Des Jason Godfrey. Litho Cartor)

2010 (13 Apr). 'Action for Species' (4th series). Mammals. 'All-over' phosphor. P 14½.

3054	**2249**	(1st) greenish yellow, bright magenta, new blue and black		1·00	1·00
		a. Block of 10. Nos. 3054/63		9·25	9·25
3055	**2250**	(1st) greenish yellow, bright magenta, new blue and black		1·00	1·00
3056	**2251**	(1st) greenish yellow, bright magenta, new blue and black		1·00	1·00
3057	**2252**	(1st) greenish yellow, bright magenta, new blue and black		1·00	1·00
3058	**2253**	(1st) greenish yellow, bright magenta, new blue and black		1·00	1·00
3059	**2254**	(1st) greenish yellow, bright magenta, new blue and black		1·00	1·00
3060	**2255**	(1st) greenish yellow, bright magenta, new blue and black		1·00	1·00
3061	**2256**	(1st) greenish yellow, bright magenta, new blue and black		1·00	1·00
3062	**2257**	(1st) greenish yellow, bright magenta, new blue and black		1·00	1·00
3063	**2258**	(1st) greenish yellow, bright magenta, new blue and black		1·00	1·00
Set of 10				9·25	9·25
First Day Cover (Tallents House)					12·00
First Day Cover (Batts Corner, Farnham)					12·00
Presentation Pack (P.O. Pack No. 440)				10·50	
PHQ Cards (set of 10) (335)				6·00	16·00
Gutter Block of 20				19·00	

Nos. 3054/63 were printed together, *se-tenant*, as blocks of ten (5×2) in sheets of 60 (2 panes of 30).

Special First Day of Issue Postmarks

No. 3064, T **2259** are vacant.

2260 King George V and Queen Elizabeth II (1st); Two portraits of King George V (£1) (Illustration reduced. Actual size 141×74 mm)

(Des Sedley Place. Litho Cartor)

2010 (6 May). London 2010 Festival of Stamps and Centenary of Accession of King George V (1st issue). 'All-over' phosphor. P 14½×14.

MS3065	**2260**	(1st) rosine; £1 blackish brown, grey-brown and silver	3·25	3·25
First Day Cover (Tallents House)				4·75
First Day Cover (Sandringham, Norfolk)				4·75
Presentation Pack (**MS**3065 and **MS**3072) (P.O. Pack No. 441)			10·50	
PHQ Cards (set of 8) (336)			4·75	16·00

A miniature sheet as No. **MS**3065 but inscr 'BUSINESS DESIGN CENTRE, LONDON 8–15 MAY 2010' along the top right margin was only available at London 2010 Festival of Stamps.

The eight PHQ cards depict the individual stamps from **MS**3065 and **MS**3072 and the complete miniature sheets.

Special First Day of Issue Postmarks

2261 King George V and Queen Elizabeth II

2262 1924 British Empire Exhibition 1½d. Brown Stamp

2263 1924 British Empire Exhibition 1d. Scarlet Stamp

2264 Two Portraits of King George V

2265 1913 £1 Green 'Sea Horses' Design Stamp

2266 1913 10s. Blue 'Sea Horses' Design Stamp

LONDON 2010 FESTIVAL OF STAMPS

2267 (Illustration reduced. Actual size 115×90 mm)

(Des Sedley Place. Litho Cartor (Nos. 3066 and 3069) or recess and litho Enschedé (others))

2010 (6 May)–**10** (8 May). London 2010 Festival of Stamps and Centenary of Accession of King George V (2nd issue). 'All-over' phosphor. P 14½×14.

3066	**2261**	(1st) rosine (6 May)	1·00	1·00
		a. Booklet pane. Nos. 3066 and 3069, each ×3 with margins all round (8 May)	9·50	
3067	**2262**	(1st) multicoloured (8 May)	1·00	1·00
		a. Booklet pane. Nos. 3067/8, each ×2	3·75	
3068	**2263**	(1st) multicoloured (8 May)	1·00	1·00
3069	**2264**	£1 blackish brown, grey-brown and silver (8 May)	2·25	2·25
3070	**2265**	£1 multicoloured (8 May)	2·25	2·25
		a. Booklet pane. Nos. 3070/1 with margins all round	4·50	
3071	**2266**	£1 multicoloured (8 May)	2·25	2·25
3066/71		Set of 6	9·00	9·00
		Gutter Pair (No. 3066)		2·25
MS3072	**2267**	Nos. 3067/8 and 3070/1 (8 May)	6·50	6·50
		First Day Cover (MS3072) (Tallents House)		8·50
		First Day Cover (MS3072) (London N1)		8·50

No. 3066 was issued as a sheet stamp on 6 May 2010.

Nos. 3066/71 all come from £11.15 stamp booklet, No. DX50, issued on 8 May 2010.

Nos. 3066 and 3069 also come from miniature sheet MS3065, issued on 8 May 2010.

Nos. 3067/8 and 3070/1 also come from MS3072, issued on 8 May 2010.

For presentation pack and PHQ cards for No. MS3072 see under MS3065.

Special First Day of Issue Postmarks

For No. **MS**3073 see Decimal Machin Definitives section

2269 Winston Churchill

2270 Land Girl

2271 Home Guard

2272 Evacuees

2273 Air Raid Wardens

2274 Woman working in Factory

2275 Royal Broadcast by Princess Elizabeth and Princess Margaret

2276 Fire Service

(Des Why Not Associates. Litho Cartor)

2010 (13 May). 'Britain Alone' (1st issue). 'All-over' phosphor. P 14½.

3074	**2269**	(1st) pale stone, pale bistre and black	1·00	1·00
		a. Booklet pane. Nos. 3074/5 and 3079/80 with margins all round	5·50	

3075	**2270**	(1st) pale stone, pale bistre and black ..	1·00	1·00
3076	**2271**	60p. pale stone, pale bistre and black ..	1·50	1·50
		a. Booklet pane. Nos. 3076/8 and		
		3081	6·50	
3077	**2272**	60p. pale stone, pale bistre and black ..	1·50	1·50
3078	**2273**	67p. pale stone, pale bistre and black ..	1·60	1·60
3079	**2274**	67p. pale stone, pale bistre and black ..	1·60	1·60
3080	**2275**	97p. pale stone, pale bistre and black ..	2·40	2·40
3081	**2276**	97p. pale stone, pale bistre and black ..	2·40	2·40
Set of 8			12·00	12·00
First Day Cover (Tallents House)				15·00
First Day Cover (Dover, Kent)				15·00
Presentation Pack (P.O. Pack No. 442)			20·00	
PHQ Cards (set of 13) (337)			7·75	29·00
Set of 8 Gutter Pairs			24·00	

The thirteen PHQ cards depict Nos. 3074/85 and the complete miniature sheet **MS**3086.

Special First Day of Issue Postmarks

2277 Evacuation of British Soldiers from Dunkirk

2278 Vessels from Upper Thames Patrol in 'Operation Little Ships'

2279 Rescued Soldiers on Board Royal Navy Destroyer, Dover

2280 Steamship and Other Boat loaded with Troops

2281 Evacuation of British Troops from Dunkirk, 1940 (Illustration reduced. Actual size 115×80 mm)

(Des Why Not Associates. Litho Cartor)

2010 (13 May). 'Britain Alone' (2nd issue). 'All-over' phosphor. P 14½.

3082	**2277**	(1st) pale stone, pale bistre and black ..	1·00	1·00
		a. Booklet pane. Nos. 3082/5 with margins all round	6·50	
3083	**2278**	60p. pale stone, pale bistre and black ..	1·40	1·40
3084	**2279**	88p. pale stone, pale bistre and black ..	2·00	2·00
3085	**2280**	97p. pale stone, pale bistre and black ..	2·25	2·25
3082/5 *Set of 4*			6·00	6·00
MS3086	**2281**	Nos. 3082/5	6·50	6·50

First Day Cover (**MS**3086) (Tallents House)		8·50
First Day Cover (**MS**3086) (Dover, Kent)		8·50

Nos. 3082/5 were only issued in £9.76 booklets, No. DX51, and in **MS**3086.

2282 James I (1603–25)

2283 Charles I (1625–49)

2284 Charles II (1660–85)

2285 James II (1685–8)

2286 William III (1689–1702)

2287 Mary II (1689–94)

2288 Anne (1702–14)

2289 The Age of the Stuarts (Illustration reduced. Actual size 123×70 mm)

(Des Atelier Works. Litho Cartor)

2010 (15 June). Kings and Queens (4th issue). House of Stuart. Two phosphor bands. P 14.

3087	**2282**	(1st) reddish-brown, greenish yellow, bright magenta, new blue and black	1·00	1·00
3088	**2283**	(1st) reddish-brown, greenish yellow, bright magenta, new blue and black	1·00	1·00
3089	**2284**	60p. reddish-brown, greenish yellow, bright magenta, new blue and black	1·50	1·50

3090	**2285**	60p. reddish-brown, greenish yellow, bright magenta, new blue and black	1·50	1·50
3091	**2286**	67p. reddish-brown, greenish yellow, bright magenta, new blue and black	1·60	1·60
3092	**2287**	67p. reddish-brown, greenish yellow, bright magenta, new blue and black	1·60	1·60
3093	**2288**	88p. reddish-brown, greenish yellow, bright magenta, new blue and black	2·10	2·10

Set of 7 .... 9·50 9·50
First Day Cover (Tallents House)........................... 11·50
First Day Cover (Royal Oak, Filey)........................ 11·50
Presentation Pack (P.O. Pack No. 443) .... 17·00
PHQ Cards (set of 12) (338).......................... 7·25 24·00
Set of 7 Gutter Pairs .... 19·00
Set of 7 Traffic Light Gutter Blocks of 4 .... 38·00

MS3094 123×70 mm. **2289** (1st) William Harvey (discovery of blood circulation, 1628); 60p. Civil War Battle of Naseby, 1645; 88p. John Milton (*Paradise Lost*, 1667); 97p. Castle Howard (John Vanbrugh, 1712)......... 6·50 6·50
First Day Cover (Tallents House)........................ 8·00
First Day Cover (Royal Oak, Filey)..................... 8·00

The complete miniature sheet is shown on one of the twelve PHQ cards with the others depicting individual stamps including those from **MS**3094.

Special First Day of Issue Postmarks

(Photo Walsall)

2010 (15 June). Mammals. Booklet stamps. Designs as Nos. 3061 and 3063. Self-adhesive. Die-cut perf 14½.
3095 **2256** (1st) multicoloured .... 1·00 1·00
a. Booklet pane. Nos. 3095/6 and No. U2965×4 .... 5·50
3096 **2258** (1st) multicoloured .... 2·75 2·75

2290 Paralympic Games: Rowing

2291 Shooting

2292 Modern Pentathlon

2293 Taekwondo

2294 Cycling

2295 Paralympic Games: Table Tennis

2296 Hockey

2297 Football

2298 Paralympic Games: Goalball

2299 Boxing

(Des Marion Hill (3097), David Hillman (3098), Katherine Baxter (3099), James Fryer (3100), Matthew Dennis (3101), Michael Craig Martin (3102), Darren Hopes (3103), Alex Williamson (3104), Tobatron (3105), Stephen Ledwidge (3106), Studio David Hillman (all). Litho Cartor)

2010 (27 July). Olympic and Paralympic Games, London (2012) (3rd issue). 'All-over' phosphor. P 14½.

3097	**2290**	(1st) grey, greenish yellow, bright magenta, new blue and black	1·00	1·00
		a. Horiz strip of 5. Nos. 3097/101	5·50	5·50
3098	**2291**	(1st) grey, greenish yellow, bright magenta, new blue and black	1·00	1·00
3099	**2292**	(1st) grey, greenish yellow, bright magenta, new blue and black	1·00	1·00
3100	**2293**	(1st) grey, greenish yellow, bright magenta, new blue and black	1·00	1·00
3101	**2294**	(1st) grey, greenish yellow, bright magenta, new blue and black	1·00	1·00
3102	**2295**	(1st) grey, greenish yellow, bright magenta, new blue and black	1·00	1·00
		a. Horiz strip of 5. Nos. 3102/6	5·50	5·50
3103	**2296**	(1st) grey, greenish yellow, bright magenta, new blue and black	1·00	1·00
3104	**2297**	(1st) grey, greenish yellow, bright magenta, new blue and black	1·00	1·00
3105	**2298**	(1st) grey, greenish yellow, bright magenta, new blue and black	1·00	1·00
3106	**2299**	(1st) grey, greenish yellow, bright magenta, new blue and black	1·00	1·00

Set of 10.. 9·25 9·25
First Day Cover (Tallents House)........................ 12·00
First Day Cover (Rowington, Warwick).............. 12·00
Presentation Pack (P.O. Pack No. M20)......... 10·50
PHQ Cards (set of 10) (339)........................ 6·00 16·00
Set of 2 Gutter Strips of 10......................... 19·00

Nos. 3097/101 and 3102/6 were each printed together, *se-tenant*, in horizontal strips of five stamps in sheets of 50 (2 panes 5×5).

Special First Day of Issue Postmarks

(Photo Walsall)

2010 (27 July). Olympic and Paralympic Games, London (2012) (4th issue). Booklet stamps. Designs as Nos. 3097, 3101/2 and 3104. Self-adhesive. 'All-over' phosphor. Die-cut perf 14½.
3107 **2290** (1st) multicoloured .... 2·75 2·75
a. Booklet pane. Nos. 3107/8 and Nos. U2965×4 .... 5·50
3108 **2295** (1st) multicoloured .... 2·75 2·75
3108a **2297** (1st) multicoloured (12 Oct)......... 2·75 2·75
ab. Booklet pane. Nos. 3108a/b and U2965×4 .... 5·50
3108b **2294** (1st) multicoloured (12 Oct)......... 2·75 2·75

Nos. 3107/8 and 3108a/b were only issued in two separate stamp booklets, Nos. PM24 and PM26, each originally sold for £2.46.

2300 LMS Coronation Class Locomotive, Euston Station, 1938

2301 BR Class 9F Locomotive *Evening Star*, Midsomer Norton, 1962

2302 GWR King Class Locomotive *King William IV*, near Teignmouth, 1935

2303 LNER Class A1 Locomotive *Royal Lancer*, 1929

2304 SR King Arthur Class Locomotive *Sir Mador de la Porte*, Bournemouth Central Station, 1935–9

2305 LMS NCC Class WT No. 2, Larne Harbour, c. 1947

(Des Delaney Design Consultants. Photo De La Rue)

2010 (19 Aug). Great British Railways. 'All-over' phosphor. P 14.

3109	**2300**	(1st) gold, bluish grey and black	1·00	1·00
3110	**2301**	(1st) gold, bluish grey and black	1·00	1·00
3111	**2302**	67p. gold, bluish grey and black	1·60	1·60
3112	**2303**	67p. gold, bluish grey and black	1·60	1·60
3113	**2304**	97p. gold, bluish grey and black	2·25	2·25
3114	**2305**	97p. gold, bluish grey and black	2·25	2·25
Set of 6			9·00	9·00
First Day Cover (Tallents House)				11·50
First Day Cover (Swindon)				11·50
Presentation Pack (P.O. Pack No. 1)				10·00
PHQ Cards (set of 6) (340)			3·50	14·00
Set of 6 Gutter Pairs			19·00	

2308 Total Hip Replacement Operation (Sir John Charnley, 1962)

2309 Artificial Lens Implant Surgery (Sir Harold Ridley, 1949)

2310 Malaria Parasite transmitted by Mosquitoes (proved by Sir Ronald Ross, 1897)

2311 Computed Tomography Scanner (Sir Godfrey Hounsfield, 1971)

(Des Howard Brown. Litho Cartor)

2010 (16 Sept). Medical Breakthroughs. 'All-over' phosphor. P 14×14½.

3115	**2306**	(1st) grey-black, greenish yellow, bright magenta, new blue and black	1·00	1·00
3116	**2307**	58p. grey-black, greenish yellow, bright magenta, new blue and black	1·40	1·40
3117	**2308**	60p. grey-black, greenish yellow, bright magenta, new blue and black	1·50	1·50
3118	**2309**	67p. grey-black, greenish yellow, bright magenta, new blue and black	1·60	1·60
3119	**2310**	88p. grey-black, greenish yellow, bright magenta, new blue and black	2·10	2·10
3120	**2311**	97p. grey-black, greenish yellow, bright magenta, new blue and black	2·40	2·40
Set of 6			9·25	9·25
Set of 6 Gutter Pairs			18·00	
First Day Cover (Tallents House)				9·75
First Day Cover (Paddington, London W2)				9·75
Presentation Pack (P.O. Pack No. 446)				10·50
PHQ Cards (set of 6) (341)			3·50	12·50

Special First Day of Issue Postmarks

First Day of Issue Postmarks

2306 Heart-regulating Beta Blockers (Sir James Black, 1962)

2307 Antibiotic Properties of Penicillin (Sir Alexander Fleming, 1928)

Winnie-the-Pooh and Christopher Robin

2312 Winnie the Pooh and Christopher Robin (*Now we are Six*)

Winnie-the-Pooh and Piglet

2313 Winnie the Pooh and Piglet (*The House at Pooh Corner*)

60

Winnie-the-Pooh and Rabbit

2314 Winnie the Pooh and Rabbit (*Winnie the Pooh*)

67

Winnie-the-Pooh and Eeyore

2315 Winnie the Pooh and Eeyore (*Winnie the Pooh*)

88

Winnie-the-Pooh and Friends

2316 Winnie the Pooh and Friends (*Winnie the Pooh*)

97

Winnie-the-Pooh and Tigger

2317 Winnie the Pooh and Tigger (*The House at Pooh Corner*)

WINNIE
· THE ·
POOH

2318 Winnie the Pooh

(Des Magpie Studio. Litho Cartor)

2010 (12 Oct). Europa. Children's Books. *Winnie the Pooh* by A. A. Milne. Book Illustrations by E. H. Shepard. 'All-over' phosphor. P 14×14½.

3121	**2312**	(1st) yellow-brown, pale stone and black	1·00	1·00
3122	**2313**	58p. yellow-brown, pale stone and black	1·40	1·40
3123	**2314**	60p. yellow-brown, pale stone and black	1·50	1·50
3124	**2315**	67p. yellow-brown, pale stone and black	1·60	1·60
3125	**2316**	88p. yellow-brown, pale stone and black	2·10	2·10
3126	**2317**	97p. yellow-brown, pale stone and black	2·40	2·40
Set of 6			9·25	9·25
Set of 6 Gutter Pairs			18·00	
First Day Cover (Tallents House)				9·75
First Day Cover (Hartfield, East Sussex)				9·75
Presentation Pack (P.O. Pack No. 447)			10·50	
PHQ Cards (set of 11) (342)			6·50	15·00

MS3127 115×89 mm. **2318** (1st) Winnie the Pooh and Christopher Robin (from *Now we are Six*); 60p. Christopher Robin reads to Winnie the Pooh (from *Winnie the Pooh*); 88p. Winnie the Pooh and Christopher Robin sailing in umbrella (from *Winnie the Pooh*); 97p. Christopher Robin (putting on wellingtons) and Pooh (from *Winnie the Pooh*). P 14½.

	6·50	6·50
First Day Cover (Tallents House)		8·00
First Day Cover (Hartfield, East Sussex)		8·00

Stamps from **MS**3127 show lines from poem 'We Too' by A. A. Milne: 'Wherever I am, there's always Pooh' (1st); 'There's always Pooh and Me. Whatever I do, he wants to do' (60p.); 'Where are you going to-day?' says Pooh: "Well that's very odd 'cos I was too" (88p.); "Let's go together," says Pooh, says he. "Let's go together," says Pooh (97p.).

The eleven PHQ cards show the six stamps, the four individual stamps within **MS**3127 and the complete miniature sheet.

2319 Wallace and Gromit Carol singing

2320 Gromit posting Christmas Cards

2321 Wallace and Gromit Carol singing

2322 Wallace and Gromit decorating Christmas Tree

2323 Gromit posting Christmas Cards

2324 Gromit carrying Christmas Pudding

2325 Gromit wearing Oversized Sweater

(Photo De La Rue)

2010 (2 Nov). Christmas with Wallace and Gromit. One centre band (3128) or two bands (others). P 14½×14 (with one elliptical hole in each vert side).

(a) Self-adhesive

3128	**2319**	(2nd) bright magenta, greenish yellow, new blue and black	75	75
		a. Booklet pane. No. 3128×12	8·50	
3129	**2320**	(1st) bright magenta, greenish yellow, new blue and black	1·00	1·00
		a. Booklet pane. No. 3129×12	11·00	
3130	**2321**	(2nd bright magenta, greenish yellow, Large) new blue and black	1·25	1·25
3131	**2322**	60p. bright magenta, greenish yellow, new blue and black	1·50	1·50
3132	**2323**	(1st bright magenta, greenish yellow, Large) new blue and black	1·60	1·60
3133	**2324**	97p. bright magenta, greenish yellow, new blue and black	2·40	2·40
3134	**2325**	£1·46 bright magenta, greenish yellow, new blue and black	3·25	3·25
Set of 7			10·50	10·50
First Day Cover (Tallents House)				13·50
First Day Cover (Bethlehem, Llandeilo)				13·50
Presentation Pack (P.O. Pack No. 448)			12·00	
PHQ Cards (set of 8) (343)			4·75	17·00

(b) Ordinary gum.

MS3135 115×102 mm. Nos. 3128/34	10·50	10·50
First Day Cover (Tallents House)	13·50	
First Day Cover (Bethlehem, Llandeilo)	13·50	

The eight PHQ cards show the seven individual stamps and the miniature sheet.

The 2nd class, 1st class, 60p and 97p stamps were also issued together in sheets of 20 (No. LS75) sold for £9.30, containing eight 2nd class, eight 1st class, two 60p and two 97p stamps, each stamp accompanied by a *se-tenant* label.

Separate sheets of 20 2nd, 20 1st, ten 1st, ten 60p and ten 97p were available with personal photographs on the labels from Royal Mail, Edinburgh. These were sold at £7.80 for ten 1st, £9.95 for 20 2nd or ten 60p, £13.95 for 20 1st and £14.50 for ten 97p.

Special First Day of Issue Postmarks

2-11-2010   2-11-2010

Collectors Pack
2010 (2 Nov). Comprises Nos. 2999/3008, **MS**3025/63, **MS**3065, **MS**3072, 3074/94, 3097/106 and 3109/34.
CP3135a Collectors Pack £120

Post Office Yearbook
2010 (2 Nov). Comprises Nos. 2999/3008, **MS**3025/63, **MS**3065, **MS**3072, 3074/94, 3097/106 and 3109/34.
YB3135a Yearbook £130

Miniature Sheet Collection
2010 (2 Nov). Comprises Nos. **MS**3024, **MS**3025, **MS**3053, **MS**3065, **MS**3072, **MS**3086, **MS**3094, **MS**3197 and **MS**3135.
MS3135a Miniature Sheet Collection .... 48·00

2326 Joe 90   **2327** Captain Scarlet

2328 Thunderbird 2   **2329** Stingray
(Thunderbirds)

2330 Fireball XL5   **2331** Supercar

2332 Thunderbird 4; Thunderbird 3; Thunderbird 2; Thunderbird 1 (Illustration reduced. Actual size 116×89 mm)

(Des GBH)

2011 (11 Jan). 'F.A.B. The Genius of Gerry Anderson' (producer of TV programmes). 'All-over' phosphor.

(a) Ordinary gum. Litho Cartor. P 14

3136	**2326**	(1st) greenish yellow, bright magenta, new blue and black	1·00	1·00
3137	**2327**	a. Horiz strip of 3. Nos. 3136/8............	3·00	3·00
		(1st) greenish yellow, bright magenta, new blue and black	1·00	1·00
3138	**2328**	(1st) greenish yellow, bright magenta, new blue and black	1·00	1·00
3139	**2329**	97p. brownish grey, greenish yellow, bright magenta, new blue and black	2·40	2·40
		a. Horiz strip of 3. Nos. 3139/41	7·25	7·25
3140	**2330**	97p. brownish grey, greenish yellow, bright magenta, new blue and black	2·40	2·40
3141	**2331**	97p. brownish grey, greenish yellow, bright magenta, new blue and black	2·40	2·40

Set of 6 .... 9·25 9·25
Set of 2 Gutter Strips of 6 .... 19·00
First Day Cover (Tallents House) .... 12·50
First Day Cover (Slough) .... 12·50
Presentation Pack (P.O. Pack No. 450) .... 17·00
PHQ Cards (set of 11) (344) .... 7·50 20·00

(b) Microlenticular Cartor and Outer Aspect Ltd, New Zealand. P 14
MS3142 116×89 mm. **2332** 41p., 60p., 88p., 97p. multicoloured .... 6·50 6·50
First Day Cover (Tallents House) .... 9·00
First Day Cover (Slough) .... 9·00

(c) Self-adhesive. Photo Walsall. Die-cut perf 14

3143	**2328**	(1st) multicoloured	1·00	1·00
		a. Booklet pane. No. 3143×2 and U2965×4	5·50	

Nos. 3136/8 and 3139/41 were each printed together, se-tenant, as horizontal strips of three stamps in sheets of 60 (2 panes 6×5).
The stamps within **MS**3142 use microlenticular technology to show each vehicle's launch sequences when the miniature sheet is tilted.
The complete miniature sheet is shown on one of the eleven PHQ cards with the others depicting individual stamps including those from **MS**3142.
No. 3143 was only issued in booklets, No. PM27, sold for £1.46.

Special First Day of Issue Postmarks

11.1.2011   11.1.2011

2333

(Des Delaney Design Consultants. Litho Cartor)

2011 (1 Feb). Classic Locomotives (1st series). England. Sheet 180×74 mm. Multicoloured. 'All-over' phosphor. P 14.
MS3144 **2333** (1st) BR Dean Goods No. 2532; 60p. Peckett R2 Thor; 88p. Lancashire and Yorkshire Railway 1093 No. 1100; 97p. BR WD No. 90662 .... 6·75 6·75
First Day Cover (Tallents House) .... 9·25
First Day Cover (Liverpool) .... 9·25
Presentation Pack (P.O. Pack No. 451) .... 8·00
PHQ Cards (set of 5) (345) .... 3·25 11·00
The five PHQ cards show the four individual stamps and the complete miniature sheet.

Special First Day of Issue Postmarks

1.2.2011   1.2.2011

2334 *Oliver*

2335 *Blood Brothers*

2336 *We Will Rock You*

2337 *Spamalot*

2338 *Rocky Horror Show*

2339 *Me and My Girl*

2340 *Return to the Forbidden Planet*

2341 *Billy Elliot*

(Des Webb and Webb. Litho Cartor)

2011 (24 Feb). Musicals. 'All-over' phosphor. P 14.

3145	**2334**	(1st) greenish yellow, bright magenta, new blue and black		1·00	1·00
3146	**2335**	(1st) greenish yellow, bright magenta, new blue and black		1·00	1·00
3147	**2336**	(1st) greenish yellow, bright magenta, new blue and black		1·00	1·00
3148	**2337**	(1st) greenish yellow, bright magenta, new blue and black		1·00	1·00
3149	**2338**	97p. greenish yellow, bright magenta, new blue and black		2·40	2·40
3150	**2339**	97p. greenish yellow, bright magenta, new blue and black		2·40	2·40
3151	**2340**	97p. greenish yellow, bright magenta, new blue and black		2·40	2·40
3152	**2341**	97p. greenish yellow, bright magenta, new blue and black		2·40	2·40

Set of 8	12·50	12·50
Set of 8 Gutter Pairs	25·00	
Set of 8 Traffic Light Gutter Pairs	28·00	
First Day Cover (Tallents House)		16·50
First Day Cover (Dancers End, Tring)		16·50
Presentation Pack (P.O. Pack No. 452)		13·50
PHQ Cards (set of 8) (346)	5·50	20·00

Special First Day of Issue Postmarks

(Photo Walsall)

2011 (24 Feb). 50th Anniv of the British Heart Foundation. Booklet stamp. Design as No. 3115. Self-adhesive. 'All-over' phosphor. Die-cut perf 14×14½.

3153	**2306**	(1st) multicoloured		1·00	1·00
		a. Booklet pane. No. 3153×2 and U2932×4		5·50	

No. 3153 was only issued in booklets, No. PM28, sold for £2.46.

2342 Rincewind (Terry Pratchett's Discworld)

2343 Nanny Ogg (Terry Pratchett's Discworld)

2344 Michael Gambon as Dumbledore (J. K. Rowling's Harry Potter)

2345 Ralph Fiennes as Lord Voldemort (J. K. Rowling's Harry Potter)

2346 Merlin (Arthurian Legend)

2347 Morgan Le Fay (Arthurian Legend)

2348 Aslan (C. S. Lewis's Narnia)

2349 Tilda Swinton as The White Witch (C. S. Lewis's Narnia)

(Des So Design Consultants. Photo De La Rue)

2011 (8 Mar). Magical Realms. 'All-over' phosphor. P 14½.

3154	**2342**	(1st) brownish grey, bright magenta, greenish yellow, new blue and black		1·00	1·00
		a. Vert pair. Nos. 3154/5		2·00	2·00
3155	**2343**	(1st) brownish grey, bright magenta, greenish yellow, new blue and black		1·00	1·00
3156	**2344**	(1st) brownish grey, bright magenta, greenish yellow, new blue and black		1·00	1·00
		a. Vert pair. Nos. 3156/7		2·00	2·00
3157	**2345**	(1st) brownish grey, bright magenta, greenish yellow, new blue and black		1·00	1·00
3158	**2346**	60p. brownish grey, bright magenta, greenish yellow, new blue and black		1·50	1·50
		a. Vert pair. Nos. 3158/9		3·00	3·00
3159	**2347**	60p. brownish grey, bright magenta, greenish yellow, new blue and black		1·50	1·50

3160	**2348**	97p. brownish grey, bright magenta, greenish yellow, new blue and black		2·40	2·40
		a. Vert pair. Nos. 3160/1		4·75	4·75
3161	**2349**	97p. brownish grey, bright magenta, greenish yellow, new blue and black		2·40	2·40

Set of 8	11·00	11·00
Set of 4 Gutter Pairs	12·00	
First Day Cover (Tallents House)		14·00
First Day Cover (Merlins Bridge, Haverfordwest)		14·00
Presentation Pack (P.O. Pack No. 453)		12·00
PHQ Cards (set of 8) (347)	5·50	18·00

Nos. 3154/5, 3156/7, 3158/9 and 3160/1 were each printed together, se-tenant, as vertical pairs in sheets of 60 (2 panes 5×6).

Special First Day of Issue Postmarks

2358 African Wild Dog

2359 Golden Lion Tamarin

2360 Wildlife of the Amazon Rainforest

(Des Janice Nicholson and Rose Design (**MS**3172) or Rose Design Consultants (others). Litho Cartor)

2011 (22 Mar). 50th Anniv of the WWF. 'All-over' phosphor. P 14 (**MS**3172/a) or 14½ (others).

3162	**2350**	(1st) greenish yellow, bright magenta, new blue and black		1·00	1·00
		a. Horiz strip of 5. Nos. 3162/6		5·00	5·00
		b. 3162/3 and 3170/1 with margins all round		4·00	
3163	**2351**	(1st) greenish yellow, bright magenta, new blue and black		1·00	1·00
3164	**2352**	(1st) greenish yellow, bright magenta, new blue and black		1·00	1·00
		b. Booklet pane. Nos. 3164/9 with margins all round		6·00	
3165	**2353**	(1st) greenish yellow, bright magenta, new blue and black		1·00	1·00
3166	**2354**	(1st) greenish yellow, bright magenta, new blue and black		1·00	1·00
3167	**2355**	(1st) greenish yellow, bright magenta, new blue and black		1·00	1·00
		a. Horiz strip of 5. Nos. 3167/71		5·00	5·00
3168	**2356**	(1st) greenish yellow, bright magenta, new blue and black		1·00	1·00
3169	**2357**	(1st) greenish yellow, bright magenta, new blue and black		1·00	1·00
3170	**2358**	(1st) greenish yellow, bright magenta, new blue and black		1·00	1·00
3171	**2359**	(1st) greenish yellow, bright magenta, new blue and black		1·00	1·00

Set of 10	9·00	9·00
Set of 2 Gutter Strips of 10	19·00	
First Day Cover (Tallents House)		12·00
First Day Cover (Godalming, Surrey)		12·00
Presentation Pack (P.O. Pack No. 454)	10·50	
PHQ Cards (set of 15)	10·00	20·00

MS3172 115×89 mm. **2360** (1st) Spider monkey; 60p. Hyacinth macaw; 88p. Poison dart frog; 97p. Jaguar .. 6·75 6·75

First Day Cover (Tallents House)		9·25
First Day Cover (Godalming, Surrey)		9·25
a. Booklet pane. No. **MS**3172 but 125×96 mm with line of roulettes at left ..	6·75	

Nos. 3162/6 and 3167/71 were each printed together, se-tenant, as horizontal strips of five stamps in sheets of 50 (2 panes 5×5).

The complete miniature sheet is shown on one of the fifteen PHQ cards with the others depicting individual stamps including those from **MS**3172.

2350 African Elephant

2351 Mountain Gorilla

2352 Siberian Tiger

2353 Polar Bear

2354 Amur Leopard

2355 Iberian Lynx

2356 Red Panda

2357 Black Rhinoceros

NEW INFORMATION

The editor is always interested to correspond with people who have new information that will improve or correct this catalogue

Special First Day of Issue Postmarks

Decimal Machin Definitives
Denominated stamps, PVA, PVAD or gum arabic, 'standard' perforations

"X" NUMBERS. The following definitive series has been allocated "X" prefixes to the catalogue numbers to avoid renumbering all subsequent issues.

NO VALUE INDICATED. Stamps as Types **367/a** inscribed "2nd" or "1st" are listed as Nos. 1445/52, 1511/16, 1664/72, 2039/40 and 2295.

ELLIPTICAL PERFORATIONS. These were introduced in 1993 and stamps showing them will be found listed as Nos. Y1667 etc.

| 367 | 367a |

Printing differences

| Litho | Photo |

(Illustrations enlarged ×6)

Litho. Clear outlines to value and frame of stamp.
Photo. Uneven lines to value and frame formed by edges of screen.

Two types of the 3p., 10p. and 26p. (Nos. X930/c, X886/b and X971/b)

| I | II |

| I | II |

| I | II |

Figures of face value as I (all ptgs of 3p. bright magenta except the multi-value coil No. 930cl and sheets from 21.1.92 onwards, 10p. orange-brown except 1984 "Christian Heritage" £4 booklet and 26p. rosine except 1987 £1.04 barcode booklet).

Figures of face value narrower as in II (from coil No. X930cl and in sheets from 21.1.92 (3p.), 1984 "Christian Heritage" £4 booklet (10p.) or 1987 £1.04 barcode booklet (26p.)). This catalogue includes changes of figure styles on these stamps where there is no other listable difference. Similar changes have also taken place on other values, but only in conjuction with listed colour, paper or perforation changes.

1971 (15 Feb)–**96**. Decimal Currency. T **367**. Chalk-surfaced paper.
(a) Photo Harrison (except for some printings of Nos. X879 and X913 in sheets produced by Enschedé and issued on 12 Dec 1979 (8p.) and 19 Nov 1991 (18p.)). With phosphor bands. P 15×14.

X841	½p. turquoise-blue (2 bands)	10	10
	a. Imperf (pair)†	£3000	
	l. Booklet pane. No. X841×2 *se-tenant* vert with X849×2	6·00	
	lEy. Booklet pane. Phosphor omitted	£200	
	la. Booklet pane. No. X841×2 *se-tenant* horiz with X849×2 (14.7.71)	1·00	
	laEy. Booklet pane. Phosphor omitted	£350	
	m. Booklet pane. No. X841×5 plus label	2·75	
	mEy. Booklet pane. Phosphor omitted	£110	
	n. Coil strip. No. X849Eg, X841Eg×2 and X844Eg×2	3·50	
	nEy. Coil strip. Phosphor omitted	40·00	
	nEv. Coil strip. PVA gum. No. X849, X841×2 and X844×2 (4.74)	80	
	nEvy. Coil strip. Phosphor omitted	15·00	
	o. Booklet pane. No. X841, X851, X852, X852Ea, each×3 (24.5.72)	13·00	
	oEy. Booklet pane. Phosphor omitted	£1500	
	p. Booklet pane. No. X841×3, X842 and X852×2 (24.5.72)	60·00	
	pEy. Booklet pane. Phosphor omitted		
	q. Coil strip. No. X870, X849, X844 and X841×2 (3.12.75)	1·00	
	r. Booklet pane. No. X841×2, X844×3 and X870 (10.3.76)	75	
	s. Booklet pane. No. X841×2, X844×2, X873×2 and X881×4 (8½p. values at right) (26.1.77)	2·00	
	sa. Ditto, but No. X873Ea and 8½p. values at left	2·00	
	t. Booklet pane. No. X841, X844, X894×3 and X902 (14p. value at right) (26.1.81)	2·00	
	tEy. Booklet pane. Phosphor omitted	60·00	
	ta. Booklet pane. No. X841, X844, X894Ea×3 and X902 (14p. value at left)	1·90	
	taEy. Booklet pane. Phosphor omitted	60·00	
	u. Booklet pane. No. X841, X857×4 and X899×3 (12½p. values at left) (1.2.82)	3·00	
	ua. Ditto, but No. X899Ea and 12½p. values at right	3·00	
	Eg. Gum arabic (from coil strip, and on 22.9.72 from sheets)	40	
	Egy. Phosphor omitted	45·00	
X842	½p. turquoise-blue (1 side band at left) (24.5.72)	55·00	30·00
X843	½p. turquoise-blue (1 centre band) (14.12.77)	40	25
	l. Coil strip. No. X843×2, X875 and X845×2 (14.12.77)	85	
	m. Booklet pane. No. X843×2, X845×2 and X875 plus label (8.2.78)	60	
	mEy. Booklet pane. Phosphor omitted	40·00	
X844	1p. crimson (2 bands)	10	15
	a. Imperf (vert coil)		
	b. Pair, one imperf 3 sides (vert coil)		
	c. Imperf (pair)	£1400	
	l. Booklet pane. No. X844×2 *se-tenant* vert with X848×2	6·00	
	m. Ditto, but *se-tenant* horiz (14.7.71)	1·00	
	mEy. Booklet pane. Phosphor omitted	£150	
	n. Booklet pane. No. X844×2, X876×3 and X883×3 (9p. values at right) (13.6.77)	4·75	
	na. Ditto, but No. X876Ea and 9p. values at left	2·75	
	Eg. Gum arabic (from coil strip)	50	
	Egy. Phosphor omitted	45·00	
X845	1p. crimson (1 centre band) (14.12.77)	25	20
	l. Booklet pane. No. X879 and X845×2 plus label (17.10.79)	60	
	m. Coil strip. No. X879 and X845×2 plus 2 labels (16.1.80)	85	
	n. Booklet pane. No. X845×2, X860 and X898 each×3 (5.4.83)	6·50	
	nEy. Booklet pane. Phosphor omitted	20·00	
	p. Booklet pane. No. X845×3, X863×2 and X900×3 (3.9.84)	4·00	
	pEy. Booklet pane. Phosphor omitted	£225	
	q. Booklet pane. No. X845×2 and X896×4 (29.7.86)	9·00	

	s. Booklet pane. No. X845, X867×2 and X900×3 (20.10.86)	6·00	
	sa. Ditto, but with vertical edges of pane imperf (29.9.87)	3·00	
	saEy. Booklet pane. Phosphor omitted	£200	
X846	1p. crimson ("all-over") (10.10.79)	15	25
X847	1p. crimson (1 side band at left) (20.10.86) ...	1·00	1·25
	Ea. Band at right (3.3.87)........................	3·50	3·00
	l. Booklet pane. No. X847, X901 and X912×2 (20.10.86)	4·00	
	lEy. Booklet pane. Phosphor omitted.......	£100	
	m. Booklet pane. No. X847Ea, X901×2, X912×5 and X918 with margins all round (3.3.87)................................	16·00	
X848	1½p. black (2 bands)	15	25
	a. Uncoated paper*	£130	
	b. Imperf (pair)...................................		
	c. Imperf 3 sides (horiz pair)................		
	Ey. Phosphor omitted............................	55·00	
X849	2p. myrtle-green (2 bands)	15	20
	a. Imperf (horiz pair)...........................	£2700	
	l. Booklet pane. No. X849×2, X880×2 and X886×3 plus label (10p. values at right) (28.8.79)............................	2·50	
	la. Ditto, but No. X880Ea and 10p. values at left..	2·50	
	m. Booklet pane. No. X849×3, X889×2 and X895×2 plus label (12p. values at right) (4.2.80)...............................	2·50	
	mEy. Booklet pane. Phosphor omitted	50·00	
	ma. Booklet pane. No. X849×3, X889Ea×2 and X895×2 plus label (12p. values at left)..	2·50	
	maEy. Booklet pane. Phosphor omitted........	50·00	
	n. Booklet pane. No. X849, X888×3, X889Ea and X895×4 with margins all round (16.4.80)..............................	4·25	
	nEy. Booklet pane. Phosphor omitted.......	50·00	
	o. Booklet pane. No. X849×6 with margins all round (16.4.80)............	1·40	
	oEy. Booklet pane. Phosphor omitted........	55·00	
	p. Booklet pane. No. X849, X857, X898, X899×3 and X899Ea×3 with margins all round (19.5.82)........................	6·00	
	pEy. Booklet pane. Phosphor omitted	£150	
	Eg. Gum arabic (from coil strip)	2·25	
	Egy. Phosphor omitted............................	£200	
X850	2p. myrtle-green ("all-over") (10.10.79)	25	30
X851	2½p. magenta (1 centre band)	20	15
	a. Imperf (pair)†...................................	£325	
	Ey. Phosphor omitted............................	10·00	
	l. Booklet pane. No. X851×5 plus label	4·50	
	lEy. Booklet pane. Phosphor omitted	35·00	
	m. Booklet pane. No. X851×4 plus two labels	5·00	
	mEy. Booklet pane. Phosphor omitted	£150	
	n. Booklet pane. No. X851×3, X852Ea×3 and X855×6 (24.5.72)	8·00	
	nEy. Booklet pane. Phosphor omitted............		
	Eg. Gum arabic (13.9.72)........................	30	
X852	2½p. magenta (1 band at left)	1·50	1·75
	l. Booklet pane. No. X852×2 and X855×4 ..	6·00	
	lEy. Booklet pane. Phosphor omitted	£150	
	Ea. Band at right (24.5.72)	1·50	1·75
X853	2½p. magenta (1 band) (21.5.75).................	25	50
X854	2½p. rose-red (2 bands) (26.8.81)..............	40	60
	l. Booklet pane. No. X854×3, X862×2 and X894×3 (11½p. values at left)...........	5·25	
	la. Ditto, but No. X894Ea and 11½p. values at right	7·00	
X855	3p. ultramarine (2 bands)	20	25
	a. Imperf (coil strip of 5)	£2250	
	b. Imperf (pair)†...................................	£350	
	c. Uncoated paper*	45·00	
	Ey. Phosphor omitted............................	2·00	
	l. Booklet pane. No. X855×5 plus label	2·50	
	lEy. Booklet pane. Phosphor omitted	£375	
	n. Booklet pane. No. X855×12 (24.5.72)	5·00	
	nEy. Booklet pane. Phosphor omitted	£250	
	Eg. Gum arabic (23.8.72)........................	1·00	
	Egy. Phosphor omitted............................	10·00	
X856	3p. ultramarine (1 centre band) (10.9.73)	15	20
	a. Imperf (pair)†...................................	£300	
	b. Imperf between (vert pair)†.............	£400	
	c. Imperf horiz (vert pair)†..................	£250	
	Eg. Gum arabic....................................	50	
X857	3p. bright magenta (Type I) (2 bands) (1.2.82)...	35	35
X858	3½p. olive-grey (2 bands) (shades)...............	25	30
	a. Imperf (pair)	£525	
	Ey. Phosphor omitted............................	10·00	
	Eb. Bronze-green (18.7.73)	25	30
	Eby. Phosphor omitted............................	10·00	

X859	3½p. olive-grey (1 centre band) (24.6.74).........	30	35
X860	3½p. purple-brown (1 centre band) (5.4.83)	1·25	1·25
X861	4p. ochre-brown (2 bands).......................	20	25
	a. Imperf (pair)†...................................	£2000	
	Ey. Phosphor omitted............................	35·00	
	Eg. Gum arabic (1.11.72)	50	
X862	4p. greenish blue (2 bands) (26.8.81)........	1·75	2·00
X863	4p. greenish blue (1 centre band) (3.9.84).....	1·50	1·90
	a. Phosphor omitted	85·00	
X864	4p. greenish blue (1 band at right) (8.1.85)...	2·00	2·00
	Ea. Band at left	1·60	1·75
	l. Booklet pane. No. X864, X864Ea, X901×2, X901Ea×2, X909×2 and X920 with margins all round (8.1.85)............	14·00	
	lEy. Booklet pane. Phosphor omitted	£2500	
X865	4½p. grey-blue (2 bands) (24.10.73)	25	30
	a. Imperf (pair)	£475	
	Ey. Phosphor omitted............................	8·00	
X866	5p. pale violet (2 bands)	20	20
X867	5p. claret (1 centre band) (20.10.86)	2·00	2·25
	Ey. Phosphor omitted............................	80·00	
X868	5½p. violet (2 bands) (24.10.73)	25	30
X869	5½p. violet (1 centre band) (17.3.75)...........	25	30
	a. Uncoated paper*	£400	
	Ey. Phosphor omitted............................	18·00	
X870	6p. light emerald (2 bands)	25	20
	a. Uncoated paper*	20·00	
	Ey. Phosphor omitted............................	70·00	
	Eg. Gum arabic (6.6.73).........................	2·50	
X871	6½p. greenish blue (2 bands) (4.9.74).........	30	35
X872	6½p. greenish blue (1 centre band) (24.9.75) ..	25	20
	a. Imperf (vert pair)	£400	
	b. Uncoated paper*	£225	
	Ey. Phosphor omitted............................	13·00	
X873	6½p. greenish blue (1 band at right) (26.1.77)	70	75
	Ea. Band at left	60	60
X874	7p. purple-brown (2 bands) (15.1.75)........	30	35
	a. Imperf (pair)	£1000	
	Ey. Phosphor omitted............................	1·50	
X875	7p. purple-brown (1 centre band) (13.6.77)..	25	30
	a. Imperf (pair)	£140	
	l. Booklet pane. No. X875 and X883, each×10 (15.11.78)...........................	4·50	
X876	7p. purple-brown (1 band at right) (13.6.77)	50	50
	Ea. Band at left	45	50
X877	7½p. pale chestnut (2 bands)	25	35
	Ey. Phosphor omitted............................	20·00	
X878	8p. rosine (2 bands) (24.10.73)	30	30
	a. Uncoated paper*	15·00	
X879	8p. rosine (1 centre band) (20.8.79).........	30	30
	a. Uncoated paper*	£900	
	b. Imperf (pair)	£1000	
	Ey. Phosphor omitted............................	£450	
	l. Booklet pane. No. X879 and X886, each×10 (14.11.79)...........................	5·00	
X880	8p. rosine (1 band at right) (28.8.79).........	60	75
	Ea. Band at left	60	75
X881	8½p. light yellowish green (2 bands) (shades) (24.9.75)	30	30
	a. Imperf (pair)	£1400	
	Eb. Yellowish green (24.3.76)..................	35	35
X882	9p. yellow-orange and black (2 bands)	45	55
	Ey. Phosphor omitted............................	£100	
X883	9p. deep violet (2 bands) (25.2.76)............	35	30
	a. Imperf (pair)	£300	
	Ey. Phosphor omitted............................	4·00	
X884	9½p. purple (2 bands) (25.2.76).................	35	45
	Ey. Phosphor omitted............................	20·00	
X885	10p. orange-brown and chestnut (2 bands) (11.8.71)	35	35
	a. Orange-brown omitted.....................	£180	
	b. Imperf (horiz pair)	£3500	
	Ey. Phosphor omitted............................	10·00	
X886	10p. orange-brown (Type I) (2 bands) (25.2.76)..	35	30
	a. Imperf (pair)	£325	
	b. Type II (4.9.84).................................	22·00	22·00
	bl. Booklet pane. No. X886b, X901Ea and X909×7 with margins all round................	32·00	
	blEy. Booklet pane. Phosphor omitted	£2000	
X887	10p. orange-brown (Type I) ("all-over") (3.10.79)..	35	45
X888	10p. orange-brown (Type I) (1 centre band) (4.2.80)...	35	25
	a. Imperf (pair)	£325	
	l. Booklet pane. No. X888×9 with margins all round (16.4.80).............................	3·75	
	lEy. Booklet pane. Phosphor omitted	50·00	
	m. Booklet pane. No. X888 and X895, each×10 (12.11.80)...........................	5·50	

X889	10p. orange-brown (Type I) (1 band at right) (4.2.80)		70	80
	Fa. Band at left		70	80
X890	10½p. yellow (2 bands) (25.2.76)		40	45
X891	10½p. deep dull blue (2 bands) (26.4.78)		45	50
X892	11p. brown-red (2 bands) (25.2.76)		40	30
	a. Imperf (pair)	£3200		
X893	11½p. drab (1 centre band) (14.1.81)		40	35
	a. Imperf (pair)	£325		
	Ey. Phosphor omitted	6·00		
	l. Booklet pane. No. X893 and X902, each×10 (11.11.81)	8·50		
X894	11½p. drab (1 band at right) (26.1.81)		55	70
	Ea. Band at left		55	70
	l. Booklet pane. No. X894/Ea, each×2 & X902×6 (6.5.81)	6·50		
X895	12p. yellowish green (2 bands) (4.2.80)		45	45
	l. Booklet pane. No. X895×9 with margins all round (16.4.80)	4·00		
	lEy. Booklet pane. Phosphor omitted	40·00		
X896	12p. bright emerald (1 centre band) (29.10.85)		45	45
	a. Imperf (pair)	£1800		
	Eu. Underprint Type 4 (29.10.85)	55		
	Ey. Phosphor omitted	10·00		
	l. Booklet pane. No. X896×9 with margins all round (18.3.86)	4·75		
	lEy. Booklet pane. Phosphor omitted	£200		
X897	12p. bright emerald (1 band at right) (14.1.86)		80	85
	Ea. Band at left		80	85
	l. Booklet pane. No. X897/Ea, each×2 and X909×6 (12p. values at left) (14.1.86)	6·00		
	la. Ditto, but 12p. values at right	6·00		
	m. Booklet pane. No. X897/Ea, each×3, X909×2 and X919 with margins all round (18.3.86)	23·00		
	mEy. Booklet pane. Phosphor omitted	£1750		
X898	12½p. light emerald (1 centre band) (27.1.82)		45	40
	a. Imperf (pair)	£120		
	Eu. Underprint Type 1 (10.11.82)	60		
	Euy. Phosphor omitted	70·00		
	Ev. Underprint Type 2 (9.11.83)	60		
	Ey. Phosphor omitted	5·50		
	l. Booklet pane. No. X898Eu and X907Eu, each×10 (10.11.82)	10·00		
X899	12½p. light emerald (1 band at right) (1.2.82)		70	75
	Ea. Band at left		70	75
	l. Booklet pane. No. X899/Ea, each×2 and X907×6 (1.2.82)††	5·00		
	lEy. Booklet pane. Phosphor omitted			
	m. Booklet pane. No. X899/Ea, each×3 with margins all round (19.5.82)	3·25		
	mEy. Booklet pane. Phosphor omitted	40·00		
	n. Booklet pane. No. X899/Ea, each×2, and X908×6 (12½p. values at left) (5.4.83)	8·50		
	na. Ditto, but 12½p. values at right	8·50		
X900	13p. pale chestnut (1 centre band) (28.8.84)		40	40
	a. Imperf (pair)	£700		
	Eu. Underprint Type 2 (2.12.86)	90		
	Ey. Phosphor omitted	5·50		
	l. Booklet pane. No. X900×9 with margins all round (8.1.85)	4·50		
	lEy. Booklet pane. Phosphor omitted	£400		
	m. Booklet pane. No. X900×6 with margins all round (3.3.87)	3·75		
	n. Booklet pane. No. X900×4 with margins all round (4.8.87)	3·00		
	o. Booklet pane. No. X900×10 with margins all round (4.8.87)	7·00		
X901	13p. pale chestnut (1 band at right) (3.9.84)		50	60
	Ea. Band at left		50	60
	l. Booklet pane. No. X901/Ea, each×2, and X909×6 (13p. values at left)††	5·00		
	la. Ditto, but 13p. values at right	5·00		
	m. Booklet pane. No. X901/Ea, each×3 with margins all round (4.9.84)	4·50		
	mEy. Booklet pane. Phosphor omitted	£300		
	n. Booklet pane. No. X901Ea and X912×5 (20.10.86)	4·50		
	na. Ditto, but with vertical edges of pane imperf (29.9.87)	4·75		
X902	14p. grey-blue (2 bands) (26.1.81)		75	80
X903	14p. deep blue (1 centre band) (23.8.88)		45	50
	a. Imperf (pair)	£475		
	Ey. Phosphor omitted	7·00		
	l. Booklet pane. No. X903×4 with margins all round	6·00		
	lEy. Booklet pane. Phosphor omitted	£100		
	m. Booklet pane. No. X903×10 with margins all round	9·50		
	n. Booklet pane. No. X903×4 with horizontal edges of pane imperf (11.10.88)	6·50		
	p. Booklet pane. No. X903×10 with horizontal edges of pane imperf (11.10.88)	9·00		
	pEy. Booklet pane. Phosphor omitted	£150		
	q. Booklet pane. No. X903×4 with three edges of pane imperf (24.1.89)	32·00		
	qEy. Booklet pane. Phosphor omitted	35·00		
X904	14p. deep blue (1 band at right) (5.9.88)		4·00	4·00
	l. Booklet pane. No. X904 and X914×2 plus label	8·00		
	lEy. Booklet pane. Phosphor omitted	12·00		
	m. Booklet pane. No. X904×2 and X914×4 with vertical edges of pane imperf	6·50		
	mEy. Booklet pane. Phosphor omitted	£800		
X905	15p. bright blue (1 centre band) (26.9.89)		65	65
	a. Imperf (pair)	£575		
	Ey. Phosphor omitted	10·00		
X906	15p. brt blue (1 band at left) (2.10.89)		4·00	4·00
	Ea. Band at right (20.3.90)		3·00	3·00
	l. Booklet pane. No. X906×2 and X916 plus label	10·00		
	lEy. Booklet pane. Phosphor omitted	£500		
	m. Booklet pane. No. X906Ea, X916, X922, 1446, 1448, 1468Ea, 1470 and 1472 plus label with margins all round (20.3.90)	20·00		
X907	15½p. pale violet (2 bands) (1.2.82)		60	65
	Eu. Underprint Type 1 (10.11.82)	60		
	l. Booklet pane. No. X907×6 with margins all round (19.5.82)	4·00		
	lEy. Booklet pane. Phosphor omitted	80·00		
	m. Booklet pane. No. X907×9 with margins all round (19.5.82)	5·25		
	mEy. Booklet pane. Phosphor omitted	45·00		
X908	16p. olive-drab (2 bands) (5.4.83)		1·25	1·40
X909	17p. grey-blue (2 bands) (3.9.84)		60	60
	a. Phosphor omitted	£225		
	Eu. Underprint Type 4 (4.11.85)	70		
	Eua. Phosphor omitted	20·00		
	l. Booklet pane. No. X909Eu×3 plus label (4.11.85)	2·50		
	lEy. Booklet pane. Phosphor omitted	60·00		
	Ela. Booklet pane. No. X909×3 plus label (12.8.86)	3·00		
X910	17p. deep blue (1 centre band) (4.9.90)		80	85
	a. Imperf (pair)	£1400		
	Ey. Phosphor omitted	8·00		
X911	17p. deep blue (1 band at right) (4.9.90)		5·50	5·50
	Ea. Band at left		1·25	1·25
	l. Booklet pane. No. X911 and X911Ea×2 plus label	7·50		
	lEy. Booklet pane. Phosphor omitted	60·00		
	m. Booklet pane. No. X911×2 and X917×3 plus three labels with vertical edges of pane imperf	4·25		
	mEy. Booklet pane. Phosphor omitted	70·00		
X912	18p. deep olive-grey (2 bands) (20.10.86)		70	80
X913	18p. bright green (1 centre band) (10.9.91)		60	60
	a. Imperf (pair)	£450		
	Ey. Phosphor omitted	20·00		
X914	19p. brt orange-red (2 bands) (5.9.88)		1·50	1·50
X915	20p. dull purple (2 bands) (25.2.76)		1·20	90
X916	20p. brownish black (2 bands) (2.10.89)		1·50	1·60
X917	22p. brt orange-red (2 bands) (4.9.90)		1·50	1·25
X917a	25p. rose-red (2 bands) (6.2.96)		7·00	7·00
X918	26p. rosine (Type I) (2 bands) (3.3.87)		15·00	16·00
X919	31p. purple (2 bands) (18.3.86)		15·00	15·00
	a. Phosphor omitted	£1250		
X920	34p. ochre-brown (2 bands) (8.1.85)		7·00	7·50
	a. Phosphor omitted	£1250		
X921	50p. ochre-brown (2 bands) (2.2.77)		2·00	75
X922	50p. ochre (2 bands) (20.3.90)		4·50	4·50

(b) Photo Harrison. On phosphorised paper. P 15×14.

X924	½p. turquoise-blue (10.12.80)		10	15
	a. Imperf (pair)	£140		
	l. Coil strip. No. X924 and X932×3 (30.12.81)	75		
X925	1p. crimson (12.12.79)		10	15
	a. Imperf (pair)	£1400		
	l. Coil strip. No. X925 and X932Ea×3 (14.8.84)	90		
	m. Booklet pane. No. X925 and X969, each×2 (10.9.91)	2·00		
X926	2p. myrtle-green (face value as T **367**) (12.12.79)		15	20
	a. Imperf (pair)	£2400		
X927	2p. deep green (face value as T **367a**) (26.7.88)		20	20
	a. Imperf (pair)	£2700		

	I. Booklet pane. No. X927×2 and X969×4 plus 2 labels with vert edges of pane imperf (10.9.91)	3·25	
X928	7p. myrtle-green (face value as T **367a**) (5.9.88)	3·75	3·75
	I. Coil strip. No. X928 and X932Ea×3	5·00	
X929	2½p. rose-red (14.1.81)	15	20
	I. Coil strip. No. X929 and X930×3 (6.81)	1·00	
X930	3p. brt magenta (Type I) (22.10.80)	20	25
	a. Imperf (horiz pair)	£1700	
	b. Booklet pane. No. X930, X931×2 and X949×6 with margins all round (14.9.83)	6·50	
	c. Type II (10.10.89)	90	70
	cl. Coil strip. No. X930c and X933×3	2·25	
X931	3½p. purple-brown (30.3.83)	50	60
X932	4p. greenish blue (30.12.81)	25	40
	Ea. Pale greenish blue (14.8.84)	25	40
X933	4p. new blue (26.7.88)	20	25
	a. Imperf (pair)	£2500	
	I. Coil strip. No. X933×3 and X935 (27.11.90)	1·40	
	m. Coil strip. No. X933 and X935, each×2 (1.10.91)	1·00	
	n. Coil strip. No. X933 and X935×3 (31.1.95)	1·25	
X934	5p. pale violet (10.10.79)	30	35
X935	5p. dull red-brown (26.7.88)	25	30
	a. Imperf (pair)	£4000	
X936	6p. yellow-olive (10.9.91)	30	30
X937	7p. brownish red (29.10.85)	1·10	1·25
X938	8½p. yellowish green (24.3.76)	40	50
X939	10p. orange-brown (Type I) (11.79)	35	35
X940	10p. dull orange (Type II) (4.9.90)	40	35
X941	11p. brown-red (27.8.80)	70	80
X942	11½p. ochre-brown (15.8.79)	55	55
X943	12p. yellowish green (30.1.80)	45	45
X944	13p. olive-grey (15.8.79)	45	50
X945	13½p. purple-brown (30.1.80)	60	60
X946	14p. grey-blue (14.1.81)	50	50
X947	15p. ultramarine (15.8.79)	60	60
X948	15½p. pale violet (14.1.81)	60	50
	a. Imperf (pair)	£275	
X949	16p. olive-drab (30.3.83)	55	55
	a. Imperf (pair)	£200	
	Eu. Underprint Type 3 (10.8.83)	80	
	I. Booklet pane. No. X949×9 with margins all round (14.9.83)	5·00	
X950	16½p. pale chestnut (27.1.82)	80	80
X951	17p. light emerald (30.1.80)	60	60
X952	17p. grey-blue (30.3.83)	60	60
	a. Imperf (pair)	£375	
	Eu. Underprint Type 3 (5.3.85)	80	
	I. Booklet pane. No. X952×6 with margins all round (4.9.84)	4·50	
	m. Booklet pane. No. X952×9 with margins all round (8.1.85)	6·00	
X953	17½p. pale chestnut (30.1.80)	70	75
X954	18p. deep violet (14.1.81)	70	70
X955	18p. deep olive-grey (28.8.84)	75	60
	a. Imperf (pair)	£150	
	I. Booklet pane. No. X955×9 with margins all round (3.3.87)	7·50	
	m. Booklet pane. No. X955×4 with margins all round (4.8.87)	3·50	
	n. Booklet pane. No. X955×10 with margins all round (4.8.87)	8·00	
X956	19p. bright orange-red (23.8.88)	80	60
	a. Imperf (pair)	£450	
	I. Booklet pane. No. X956×4 with margins all round	7·00	
	m. Booklet pane. No. X956×10 with margins all round	12·00	
	n. Booklet pane. No. X956×4 with horizontal edges of pane imperf (11.10.88)	8·50	
	o. Booklet pane. No. X956×10 with horizontal edges of pane imperf (11.10.88)	12·00	
	q. Booklet pane. No. X956×4 with three edges of pane imperf (24.1.89)	32·00	
X957	19½p. olive-grey (27.1.82)	2·00	2·00
X958	20p. dull purple (10.10.79)	1·00	75
X959	20p. turquoise-green (23.8.88)	75	70
X960	20p. brownish black (26.9.89)	1·00	1·00
	a. Imperf (pair)	£850	
	I. Booklet pane. No. X960×5 plus label with vertical edges of pane imperf (2.10.89)	6·25	
X961	20½p. ultramarine (30.3.83)	1·25	1·25
	a. Imperf (pair)	£1700	
X962	22p. blue (22.10.80)	90	75

	a. Imperf (pair)	£275	
X963	22p. yellow-green (28.8.84)	90	80
	a. Imperf (horiz pair)	£2200	
X964	22p. bright orange-red (4.9.90)	90	80
	a. Imperf (pair)	£750	
X965	23p. brown red (30.3.83)	1·25	1·10
	a. Imperf (horiz pair)	£1600	
X966	23p. bright green (23.8.88)	1·10	1·10
X967	24p. violet (28.8.84)	1·40	1·50
X968	24p. Indian red (26.9.89)	2·00	1·60
	a. Imperf (pair)	£3500	
X969	24p. chestnut (10.9.91)	80	80
	a. Imperf (pair)	£260	
X970	25p. purple (14.1.81)	1·00	1·00
X971	26p. rosine (Type I) (27.1.82)	1·10	80
	a. Imperf (horiz pair)	£850	
	b. Type II (4.8.87)	3·50	4·00
	bl. Booklet pane. No. X971b×4 with margins all round	17·00	
X972	26p. drab (4.9.90)	1·50	1·25
X973	27p. chestnut (23.8.88)	1·25	1·25
	I. Booklet pane. No. X973×4 with margins all round	12·50	
	m. Booklet pane. No. X973×4 with horizontal edges of pane imperf (11.10.88)	30·00	
X974	27p. violet (4.9.90)	1·50	1·25
X975	28p. deep violet (30.3.83)	1·25	1·25
	a. Imperf (pair)	£2000	
X976	28p. ochre (23.8.88)	1·40	1·25
X977	28p. deep bluish grey (10.9.91)	1·40	1·25
	a. Imperf (pair)	£2500	
X978	29p. ochre-brown (27.1.82)	1·75	1·75
X979	29p. deep mauve (26.9.89)	1·75	1·75
X980	30p. deep olive-grey (26.9.89)	1·25	1·25
X981	31p. purple (30.3.83)	1·25	1·25
	a. Imperf (pair)	£1600	
X982	31p. ultramarine (4.9.90)	1·60	1·50
X983	32p. greenish blue (23.8.88)	1·90	1·75
	a. Imperf (pair)	£2500	
X984	33p. light emerald (4.9.90)	1·75	1·60
X985	34p. ochre-brown (28.8.84)	1·75	1·75
X986	34p. deep bluish grey (26.9.89)	2·00	1·90
X987	34p. deep mauve (10.9.91)	1·75	1·75
X988	35p. sepia (23.8.88)	1·60	1·60
	a. Imperf (pair)	£2500	
X989	35p. yellow (10.9.91)	1·75	1·60
X990	37p. rosine (26.9.89)	2·00	1·75
X991	39p. bright mauve (10.9.91)	1·75	1·75

(c) Photo Harrison. On ordinary paper. P 15×14.

X992	50p. ochre-brown (21.5.80)	1·75	70
	a. Imperf (pair)	£800	
X993	75p. grey-black (face value as T **367a**) (26.7.88)	3·25	1·50

(d) Photo Harrison. On ordinary or phosphorised paper. P 15×14.

X994	50p. ochre (13.3.90)	2·00	70
	a. Imperf (pair)	£2200	

(e) Litho J.W. P 14.

X996	4p. greenish blue (2 bands) (30.1.80)	25	35
	a. Phosphor omitted	£1250	
X997	4p. greenish blue (phosphorised paper) (11.81)	45	40
X998	20p. dull purple (2 bands) (21.5.80)	1·25	1·20
X999	20p. dull purple (phosphorised paper) (11.81)	1·75	1·20

(f) Litho Questa. P 14 (Nos. X1000, X1003/4 and X1023) or 15×14 (others).

X1000	2p. emerald-green (face value as T **367**) (phosphorised paper) (21.5.80)	20	25
	a. Perf 15×14 (10.7.84)	35	35
X1001	2p. brt green and dp green (face value as T **367a**) (phosphorised paper) (23.2.88)	75	70
X1002	4p. greenish blue (phosphorised paper) (13.5.86)	70	75
X1003	5p. light violet (phosphorised paper) (21.5.80)	40	40
X1004	5p. claret (phosphorised paper) (27.1.82)	50	50
	a. Perf 15×14 (21.2.84)	65	60
X1005	13p. pale chestnut (1 centre band) (9.2.88)	70	75
	I. Booklet pane. No. X1005×6 with margins all round	4·75	
X1006	13p. pale chestnut (1 side band at right) (9.2.88)	75	75
	Ea. Band at left	75	75
	I. Booklet pane. No. X1006/Ea each×3, X1010, X1015 and X1021 with margins all round	30·00	
	IEa. Grey-green (on 18p.) ptg double	£3500	
X1007	14p. deep blue (1 centre band) (11.10.88)	2·00	2·00
X1008	17p. deep blue (1 centre band) (19.3.91)	80	80

	Ey. Phosphor omitted	£225	
	l. Booklet pane. No. X1008×6 with margins all round	5·00	
	lEy. Booklet pane. Phosphor omitted	£1250	
X1009	18p. deep olive-grey (phosphorised paper) (9.2.88)	90	95
	l. Booklet pane. No. X1009×9 with margins all round	8·00	
	m. Booklet pane. No. X1009×6 with margins all round	5·50	
X1010	18p. deep olive-grey (2 bands) (9.2.88)	7·50	7·50
X1011	18p. bright green (1 centre band) (27.10.92)	75	75
	l. Booklet pane. No. X1011×6 with margins all round	5·00	
X1012	18p. bright green (1 side band at right) (27.10.92)	1·25	1·40
	Ea. Band at left (10.8.93)	1·80	2·00
	Eay. Phosphor omitted	£275	
	l. Booklet pane. No. X1012×2, X1018×2, X1022×2, 1451a, 1514a and centre label with margins all round	12·00	
	lEa. Bright blue (on 2nd) ptg treble		
	m. Booklet pane. No. X1012Ea, X1020, X1022 and 1451aEb, each×2, with centre label and margins all round (10.8.93)	13·00	
	mEy. Booklet pane. Phosphor omitted	£2000	
X1013	19p. bright orange-red (phosphorised paper) (11.10.88)	2·20	2·00
X1014	20p. dull purple (phosphorised paper) (13.5.86)	1·40	1·40
X1015	22p. yellow-green (2 bands) (9.2.88)	9·00	9·00
X1016	22p. bright orange-red (phosphorised paper) (19.3.91)	1·00	90
	l. Booklet pane. No. X1016×9 with margins all round	9·00	
	m. Booklet pane. No. X1016×6, X1019×2 and centre label with margins all round	9·00	
X1017	24p. chestnut (phosphorised paper) (27.10.92)	90	1·10
	l. Booklet pane. No. X1017×6 with margins all round	5·50	
X1018	24p. chestnut (2 bands) (27.10.92)	1·40	1·40
X1019	33p. light emerald (phosphorised paper) (19.3.91)	2·50	2·50
X1020	33p. lt emerald (2 bands) (25.2.92)	1·50	1·50
X1021	34p. bistre-brown (2 bands) (9.2.88)	7·50	7·50
X1022	39p. brt mauve (2 bands) (27.10.92)	1·50	1·60
	Ey. Phosphor omitted	£450	
X1023	75p. black (face value as T **367**) (ordinary paper) (30.1.80)	3·00	1·50
	a. Perf 15×14 (21.2.84)	4·00	2·25
X1024	75p. brownish grey and black (face value as T **367a**) (ordinary paper) (23.2.88)	9·00	8·50
	(g) Litho Walsall. P. 14.		
X1050	2p. deep green (phosphorised paper) (9.2.93)	1·50	1·40
	l. Booklet pane. No. X1050×2 and X1053×4 plus 2 labels with vert edges of pane imperf	7·50	
X1051	14p. deep blue (1 side band at right) (25.4.89)	4·50	4·50
	Ey. Phosphor omitted	£275	
	l. Booklet pane. No. X1051×2 and X1052×4 with vertical edges of pane imperf	10·00	
	lEy. Booklet pane. Phosphor omitted	£950	
X1052	19p. bright orange-red (2 bands) (25.4.89)	3·00	3·00
	Ey. Phosphor omitted	£225	
X1053	24p. chestnut (phosphorised paper) (9.2.93)	1·10	1·25
X1054	29p. dp mauve (2 bands) (2.10.89)	3·00	3·00
	l. Booklet pane. No. X1054×4 with three edges of pane imperf	15·00	
X1055	29p. deep mauve (phosphorised paper) (17.4.90)	4·50	4·50
	l. Booklet pane. No. X1055×4 with three edges of pane imperf	17·00	
X1056	31p. ultramarine (phosphorised paper) (17.9.90)	1·40	1·40
	l. Booklet pane. No. X1056×4 with horizontal edges of pane imperf	6·00	
X1057	33p. light emerald (phosphorised paper) (16.9.91)	1·25	1·25
	l. Booklet pane. No. X1057×4 with horiz edges of pane imperf	5·00	
X1058	39p. bright mauve (phosphorised paper) (16.9.91)	1·60	1·60
	l. Booklet pane. No. X1058×4 with horiz edges of pane imperf	6·00	

*See footnote after No. 744.

†These come from sheets with gum arabic.

††Examples of Booklet panes Nos. X899l, X901l and X901la are known on which the phosphor bands were printed on the wrong values in error with the result that the side bands appear on the 15½p. or 17p. and the two bands on the 12½p. or 13p. Similarly examples of the 1p. with phosphor band at right instead of left and of the 13p. with band at left

instead of right, exist from 50p. booklet pane No. X847l.

Nos. X844a/b come from a strip of eight of the vertical coil. It comprises two normals, one imperforate at sides and bottom, one completely imperforate, one imperforate at top, left and bottom and partly perforated at right due to the bottom three stamps being perforated twice. No. X844b is also known from another strip having one stamp imperforate at sides and bottom.

Nos. X848b/c come from the same sheet, the latter having perforations at the foot of the stamps only.

Multi-value coil strips Nos. X924l, X925l, X928l, X929l, X930cl and X933l/n were produced by the Post Office for use by a large direct mail marketing firm. From 2 September 1981 No. X929l was available from the Philatelic Bureau, Edinburgh, and, subsequently from a number of other Post Office counters. Later multi-value coil strips were sold at the Philatelic Bureau and Post Office philatelic counters.

In addition to booklet pane No. X1012m No. X1020 also comes from the *se-tenant* pane in the Wales £6 booklet. This pane is listed under No. W49a in the Wales Regional section.

PANES OF SIX FROM STITCHED BOOKLETS. Nos. X841m, X851l/m and X855l include one or two printed labels showing commercial advertisements. These were originally perforated on all four sides, but from the August 1971 editions of the 25p. and 30p. booklets (Nos. DH42, DQ59) and December 1971 edition of the 50p. (No. DT4) the line of perforations between the label and the binding margin was omitted. Similar panes, with the line of perforations omitted, exist for the 3p., 3½p. and 4½p. values (Nos. X856, X858 and X865), but these are outside the scope of this listing as the labels are blank.

PART-PERFORATED SHEETS. Since the introduction of the "Jumelle" press in 1972 a number of part perforated sheets, both definitives and commemoratives, have been discovered. It is believed that these occur when the operation of the press is interrupted. Such sheets invariably show a number of "blind" perforations, where the pins have failed to cut the paper. Our listings of imperforate errors from these sheets are for pairs showing no traces whatsoever of the perforations. Examples showing "blind" perforations are outside the scope of this catalogue.

In cases where perforation varieties affect *se-tenant* stamps, fuller descriptions will be found in Vols. 4 and 5 of the *G.B. Specialised Catalogue.*

WHITE PAPER. From 1972 printings appeared on fluorescent white paper giving a stronger chalk reaction than the original ordinary cream paper.

PHOSPHOR OMITTED ERRORS. These are listed for those stamps or booklet panes which were not subsequently issued on phosphorised paper. The following phosphor omitted errors also exist, but can only be identified by the use of an ultra-violet lamp. Prices quoted are for mint examples:

½p. X841 (£1)	8½p. X881 (£1·75)	18p. X912 (£27)
1p. X844 (£3)	10p. X886 (£1)	19p. X914 (£4)
2p. X849 (£5)	11p. X892 (£4)	20p. X916 (£425)
3p. X857 (£100)	12p. X895 (£6)	22p. X917 (£20)
3½p. X860 (£5·50)	14p. X902 (£28)	31p. X919 (£650)
4p. X863 (£85)	15½p. X907 (£4)	33p. X1020 (£375)
4p. X996	16p. X908 (£100)	34p. X920 (£750)
5p. X866 (£225)	17p. X909 (£150)	

No. X909Eu with underprint Type 4 also exists without phosphor (*price £10*).

"ALL-OVER" PHOSPHOR. To improve mechanised handling most commemoratives from the 1972 Royal Silver Wedding 3p. value to the 1979 Rowland Hill Death Centenary set had the phosphor applied by printing cylinder across the entire surface of the stamp, giving a matt effect. Printings of the 1, 2 and 10p. definitives, released in October 1979, also had "all-over" phosphor, but these were purely a temporary expedient pending the adoption of phosphorised paper. Nos. X883, X890 and X921 have been discovered with "all-over" phosphor in addition to the normal phosphor bands. These errors are outside the scope of this catalogue.

PHOSPHORISED PAPER. Following the experiments on Nos. 743c and 829 a printing of the 4½p. definitive was issued on 13 November 1974, which had, in addition to the normal phosphor bands, phosphor included in the paper coating. Because of difficulties in identifying this phosphorised paper with the naked eye this printing is not listed separately in this catalogue.

No. X938 was the first value printed on phosphorised paper without phosphor bands and was a further experimental issue to test the efficacy of this system. From 15 August 1979 phosphorised paper was accepted for use generally, this paper replacing phosphor bands on values other than those required for the second-class rate.

Stamps on phosphorised paper show a shiny surface instead of the matt areas of those printed with phosphor bands.

DEXTRIN GUM. From 1973 printings in photogravure appeared with PVA gum to which dextrin had been added. Because this is virtually colourless a bluish green colouring matter was added to distinguish it from the earlier pure PVA.

The 4p., 5p. (light violet), 20p. and 75p. printed in lithography exist with PVA and PVAD gum. From 1988 Questa printings were with PVAD gum, but did not show the bluish green additive.

VARNISH COATING. Nos. X841 and X883 exist with and without a varnish coating. This cannot easily be detected without the use of an ultra-violet lamp as it merely reduces the fluorescent paper reaction.

POSTAL FORGERIES. In mid-1993 a number of postal forgeries of the 24p. chestnut were detected in the London area. These forgeries, produced by lithography, can be identified by the lack of phosphor in the paper, screening dots across the face value and by the perforations which were applied by a line machine gauging 11.

First Day Covers

15.2.71	½p., 1p., 1½p., 2p., 2½p., 3p., 3½p., 4p., 5p., 6p., 7½p., 9p. (X841, X844, X848/9, X851, X855, X858, X861, X866, X870, X877, X882) (Covers carry "POSTING DELAYED BY THE POST OFFICE STRIKE 1971"cachet)	2·50
11.8.71	10p. (X885)	1·50
24.5.72	Wedgwood se-tenant pane ½p., 2½p. (X841p)	25·00
24.10.73	4½p., 5½p., 8p. (X865, X868, X878)	1·50
4.9.74	6½p. (X871)	1·50
15.1.75	7p. (X874)	1·00
24.9.75	8½p. (X881)	1·50
25.2.76	9p., 9½p., 10p., 10½p., 11p., 20p. (X883/4, X886, X890, X892, X915)	3·50
2.2.77	50p. (X921)	1·75
26.4.78	10½p. (X891)	1·20
15.8.79	11½p., 13p., 15p. (X942, X944, X947)	1·75
30.1.80	4p., 12p., 13½p., 17p., 17½p., 75p. (X996, X943, X945, X951, X953, X1023)	3·25
16.4.80	Wedgwood se-tenant pane 2p., 10p., 12p. (X849n)	2·25
22.10.80	3p., 22p. (X930, X962)	1·50
14.1.81	2½p., 11½p., 14p., 15½p., 18p., 25p. (X929, X893, X946, X948, X954, X970)	2·00
27.1.82	5p., 12½p., 16½p., 19½p., 26p., 29p. (X1004, X898, X950, X957, X971, X978)	3·50
19.5.82	Stanley Gibbons se-tenant pane 2p., 3p., 12½p. (X849p)	3·00
30.3.83	3½p., 16p., 17p., 20½p., 23p., 28p., 31p. (X931, X949, X952, X961, X965, X975, X981)	5·00
14.9.83	Royal Mint se-tenant pane 3p., 3½p., 16p. (X930b)	4·00
28.8.84	13p., 18p., 22p., 24p., 34p. (X900, X955, X963, X967, X985)	3·00
4.9.84	Christian Heritage se-tenant pane 10p., 13p., 17p. (X886bl)	20·00
8.1.85	The Times se-tenant pane 4p., 13p., 17p., 34p. (X864l)	9·50
29.10.85	7p., 12p. (X937, X896)	3·00
18.3.86	British Rail se-tenant pane 12p., 17p., 31p. (X897m)	12·00
3.3.87	P & O se-tenant pane 1p., 13p., 18p., 26p. (X847m)	9·00
9.2.88	Financial Times se-tenant pane 13p., 18p., 22p., 34p. (X1006l)	15·00
23.8.88	14p., 19p., 20p., 23p., 27p., 28p., 32p., 35p. (X903, X956, X959, X966, X973, X976, X983, X988)	6·00
26.9.89	15p., 20p., 24p., 29p., 30p., 34p., 37p. (X905, X960, X968, X979/80, X986, X990)	5·00
20.3.90	London Life se-tenant pane 15p., (2nd), 20p., (1st), 15p., 29p., 29p. (X906m)	10·00
4.9.90	10p., 17p., 26p., 27p., 31p., 33p. (X910, X940, X964, X972, X974, X982, X984)	5·50
19.3.91	Alias Agatha Christie se-tenant pane 22p., 33p. (X1016m)	8·00
10.9.91	6p., 18p., 24p., 28p., 34p., 35p., 39p. (X936, X913, X969, X977, X987, X989, X991)	6·00
27.10.92	Tolkien se-tenant pane 18p., (2nd), 24p., (1st), 39p. (X1012l)	8·00
10.8.93	Beatrix Potter se-tenant pane 18p., (2nd), 33p., 39p. (X1012m)	12·00

Post Office Presentation Packs

15.2.71	P.O. Pack No. 26. ½p. (2 bands), 1p. (2 bands), 1½p. (2 bands), 2p. (2 bands), 2½p. magenta (1 centre band), 3p. ultramarine (2 bands), 3½p. olive-grey (2 bands), 4p. ochre-brown (2 bands), 5p. pale violet (2 bands), 6p. light emerald (2 bands), 7½p. (2 bands), 9p. yellow-orange and black (2 bands). (Nos. X841, X844, X848/9, X851, X855, X858, X861, X866, X870, X877, X882)	5·00
15.4.71**	"Scandinavia 71". Contents as above	30·00
25.11.71	P.O. Pack No. 37. ½p. (2 bands), 1p. (2 bands), 1½p. (2 bands), 2p. (2 bands), 2½p. magenta (1 centre band), 3p. ultramarine (2 bands) or (1 centre band), 3½p. olive-grey (2 bands) or (1 centre band) 4p. ochre-brown (2 bands), 4½p. (2 bands), 5p. pale violet (2 bands), 5½p. (2 bands) or (1 centre band), 6p. (2 bands), 6½p. (2 bands) or (1 centre band), 7p. (2 bands), 7½p. (2 bands), 8p (2 bands), 9p. yellow-orange and black (2 bands), 10p. orange-brown and chestnut (2 bands). (Nos. X841, X844, X848/9, X851, X855 or X856, X858 or X859, X861, X865/6, X868 or X869, X870, X871 or X872, X874, X877/8, X882, X885) Later issues of this Pack contained the alternatives	30·00
2.2.77	P.O. Pack No. 90. ½p. (2 bands), 1p. (2 bands), 1½p (2 bands), 2p. (2 bands), 2½p. magenta (1 centre band), 3p. ultramarine (1 centre band), 5p. pale violet (2 bands), 6½p. (1 centre band), 7p. (2 bands) or (1 centre band), 7½p. (2 bands), 8p. (2 bands), 8½p. (2 bands), 9p. deep violet (2 bands), 9½p. (2 bands), 10p. orange-brown (2 bands), 10½p. yellow (2 bands), 11p. (2 bands), 20p. dull purple (2 bands), 50p. ochre-brown (2 bands) (Nos. X841, X844, X848/9, X851, X856, X866, X872, X874 or X875, X877/8, X881, X883/4, X886, X890, X892, X915, X921)	5·00

28.10.81	P.O. Pack No. 129a. 10½p. deep dull blue (2 bands), 11½p. (1 centre band), 2½p. (phos paper), 3p. (phos paper), 11½p. (phos paper), 12p. (phos paper), 13p. (phos paper), 13½p. (phos paper), 14p. (phos paper), 15p. (phos paper), 15½p. (phos paper), 17p. light emerald (phos paper), 17½p. (phos paper), 18p. deep violet (phos paper), 22p. blue (phos paper), 25p. (phos paper), 4p. greenish blue (litho, 2 bands), 75p. (litho) (Nos. X891, X893, X929/30, X942/8, X951, X953/4, X962, X970, X996, X1023)	20·00
3.8.83	P.O. Pack No. 1. 10p. orange-brown (1 centre band), 12½p. (1 centre band), ½p. (phos paper), 1p. (phos paper), 3p. (phos paper), 3½p. (phos paper), 16p. (phos paper), 16½p. (phos paper), 17p. grey-blue (phos paper), 20½p. (phos paper), 23p. brown-red (phos paper), 26p. prosine (phos paper), 28p. deep violet (phos paper), 31p. purple (phos paper), 50p (ord paper), 2p. (litho phos paper), 4p. (litho phos paper), 5p. claret (litho phos paper), 20p. (litho phos paper), 75p. (litho) (Nos. X888, X898, X924/5, X930/1, X949/50, X952, X961, X965, X971, X975, X981, X992, X997, X999, X1000, X1004, X1023)	40·00
23.10.84	P.O. Pack No. 5. 13p. (1 centre band), ½p. (phos paper), 1p. (phos paper), 3p. (phos paper), 10p. orange-brown (phos paper), 16p. (phos paper), 17p. grey-blue (phos paper), 18p. dp olive-grey (phos paper), 22p. yellow-green (phos paper), 24p. violet (phos paper), 26p. rosine (phos paper), 28p. deep violet (phos paper), 31p. purple (phos paper), 34p. ochre-brown (phos paper), 50p. (ord paper), 2p. (litho phos paper), 4p. (litho phos paper), 5p. claret (litho phos paper), 20p. (litho phos paper), 75p. (litho) (Nos. X900, X924/5, X930, X939, X949, X952, X955, X963, X967, X971, X975, X981, X985, X992, X1000a, X997, X1004a, X999, X1023a)	36·00
3.3.87	P.O. Pack No. 9. 12p. (1 centre band), 13p. (1 centre band), 1p. (phos paper), 3p. (phos paper), 7p. (phos paper), 10p. orange-brown (phos paper), 17p. grey-blue (phos paper), 18p. dp olive-grey (phos paper), 22p. yellow-green (phos paper), 24p. violet (phos paper), 26p. rosine (phos paper), 28p. deep violet (phos paper), 31p. purple (phos paper), 34p. ochre-brown (phos paper), 50p. (ord paper), 2p. (litho phos paper), 4p. (litho phos paper), 5p. claret (litho phos paper), 20p. (litho phos paper), 75p. (litho) (Nos. X896, X900, X925, X930, X937, X939, X952, X955, X963, X967, X971, X975, X981, X985, X992, X1000a, X997, X1004a, X999, X1023a)	40·00
23.8.88	P.O. Pack No. 15. 14p. (1 centre band), 19p. (phos paper), 20p. turquoise-green (phos paper), 23p. bright green (phos paper), 27p. chestnut (phos paper), 28p. ochre (phos paper), 32p. (phos paper), 35p. sepia (phos paper) (Nos. X903, X956, X959, X966, X973, X976, X983, X988)	12·00
26.9.89	P.O. Pack No. 19. 15p. (centre band), 20p. brownish black (phos paper), 24p. Indian red (phos paper), 29p. deep mauve (phos paper), 30p. (phos paper), 34p. deep bluish grey (phos paper), 37p. (phos paper) (Nos. X905, X960, X968, X979/80, X986, X990)	10·00
4.9.90	P.O. Pack No. 22. 10p. dull orange (phos paper), 17p. (centre band), 22p. bright orange-red (phos paper), 26p. drab (phos paper), 27p. violet (phos paper), 31p. ultramarine (phos paper), 33p. (phos paper) (Nos. X940, X910, X964, X972, X974, X9 82, X984)	9·00
14.5.91	P.O. Pack No. 24. 41p. (phos paper), 2½p. (phos paper), 3p. (phos paper), 4p. new blue (phos paper), 5p. dull red-brown (phos paper), 10p. dull orange (phos paper), 17p. (centre band), 20p. turquoise-green (phos paper), 22p. bright orange-red (phos paper), 26p. drab (phos paper), 27p. violet (phos paper), 30p. (phos paper), 31p. ultramarine (phos paper), 32p. (phos paper), 33p. (phos paper), 37p. (phos paper), 50p. (ord paper), 75p. (ord paper). (Nos. X925, X927, X930, X933, X935, X940, X910, X959, X964, X972, X974, X980, X982/4, X990, X994, X993)	30·00
10.9.91	P.O. Pack No. 25. 6p (phos paper), 18p. (centre band), 24p. chestnut (phos paper), 28p. deep bluish grey (phos paper), 34p. deep mauve (phos paper), 35p. yellow (phos paper), 39p. (phos paper) (Nos. X913, X936, X969, X977, X987, X989, X991)	9·00

**The "Scandinavia 71" was a special pack produced for sale during a visit to six cities in Denmark, Sweden and Norway by a mobile display unit between 15 April and 20 May 1971. The pack gives details of this tour and also lists the other stamps which were due to be issued in 1971, the text being in English. A separate insert gives translations in Danish, Swedish and Norwegian. The pack was also available at the Philatelic Bureau, Edinburgh.

For stamps of this design inscribed "2nd" and "1st" see Nos. 1445/51 and 1511/16, and for stamps with one elliptical perforation hole on each vertical side see Nos. 1664/71, Y1667/1803, 2039/40 and 2295/8.

Decimal Machin Index
(Denominated stamps with 'standard' perforations)

Those booklet stamps shown below with an * after the catalogue number do not exist with perforations on all four sides, but show one or two sides imperforate.

Value. Process		Colour	Phosphor	Cat. No.	Source
½p.	photo	turquoise-blue	2 bands	X841/Eg	(a) with P.V.A. gum–sheets, 5p. m/v coil (X841nEv), 10p.m/v coil (X841q), 10p. booklets (DN46/75, FA1/3), 25p. booklets (DH39/52), 50p. booklets (DT1/12, FB1, FB14/16, FB19/23), £1 Wedgwood booklet (DX1) (b) with gum arabic—sheets, 5p. m/v coil (X841n)
½p.	photo	turquoise-blue	1 band at left	X842	£1 Wedgwood booklet (DX1)
½p.	photo	turquoise-blue	1 centre band	X843	10p. m/v coil (X843l), 10p. booklets (FA4/9)
½p.	photo	turquoise-blue	phos paper	X924	sheets, 12½p. m/v coil (X924l)
1p.	photo	crimson	2 bands	X844/Eg	(a) with P.V.A. gum—sheets, vertical coils, 5p. m/v coil (X841nEv), 10p. m/v coil (X841q), 10p. booklets (DN46/75, FA1/3), 50p. booklets (FB1/8, FB14/16) (b) with gum arabic—vertical coils, 5p. m/v coil (X841n)
1p.	photo	crimson	1 centre band	X845	10p. m/v coils (X843l, X845m), 10p. booklets (FA4/11), 50p. booklets (FB24/30, 34/36, 43/6, 48, 50)
1p.	photo	crimson	"all-over"	X846	sheets
1p.	photo	crimson	phos paper	X925	sheets, horizontal and vertical coils, 13p. m/v coil (X925l), 50p. booklet (FB59/66)
1p.	photo	crimson	1 band at left	X847	50p. booklets (FB37/42, 47, 49)
1p.	photo	crimson	1 band at right	X847Ea	£5 P. & O. booklet (DX8)
1½p.	photo	black	2 bands	X848	sheets, 10p. booklets (DN46/75)
2p.	photo	myrtle-green	2 bands	X849/Eg	(a) with P.V.A. gum—sheets, 5p. m/v coil (X841nEv), 10p. m/v coil (X841q), 10p. booklets (DN46/75), 50p. booklets (FB9/13), £3 Wedgwood booklet (DX2), £4 SG booklet (DX3) (b) with gum arabic—5p. m/v coil (X841n)
2p.	photo	myrtle-green	"all-over"	X850	sheets
2p.	photo	myrtle-green	phos paper	X926	sheets
2p.	photo	myrtle-green	phos paper	X928	14p. m/v coil (X928l)
2p.	litho	emerald-green	phos paper	X1000/a	sheets
2p.	litho	brt grn and dp grn	phos paper	X1001	sheets
2p.	photo	dp green	phos paper	X927	sheets, £1 booklets (FH23/7)
2p.	litho	dp green	phos paper	X1050*	£1 booklets (FH28/30)
2½p.	photo	magenta	1 centre band	X851/Eg	(a) with P.V.A. gum—sheets, horizontal and vertical coils, 25p. booklets (DH39/52), 50p. booklets (DT1/12), £1 Wedgwood booklet (DX1) (b) with gum arabic—sheets, horizontal coils
2½p.	photo	magenta	1 side band	X852/Ea	(a) band at left—50p. booklets (DT1/12), £1 Wedgwood booklet (DX1) (b) band at right—£1 Wedgwood booklet (DX1)
2½p.	photo	magenta	2 bands	X853	sheets
2½p.	photo	rose-red	phos paper	X929	sheets, 11½p. m/v coil (X929l)
2½p.	photo	rose-red	2 bands	X854	50p. booklets (FB17/18)
3p.	photo	ultramarine	2 bands	X855/Eg	(a) with P.V.A. gum—sheets, horizontal and vertical coils, 30p. booklets (DQ56/72), 50p. booklets (DT1/12), £1 Wedgwood booklet (DX1) (b) with gum arabic—sheets, horizontal coils
3p.	photo	ultramarine	1 centre band	X856/Eg	(a) with P.V.A. gum—sheets, horizontal and vertical coils, 30p. booklets (DQ73/4), 50p. booklets (DT13/14) (b) with gum arabic—sheets
3p.	photo	brt magenta	phos paper	X930	Type I. sheets, 11½p. m/v coil (X929l), £4 Royal Mint booklet (DX4)
3p.	photo	brt magenta	phos paper	X930c	Type II. sheets (from 21.1.92), 15p. m/v coil (X930cl)
3p.	photo	brt magenta	2 bands	X857	Type I. 50p. booklets (FB19/23), £4 SG booklet (DX3)
3½p.	photo	olive-grey	2 bands	X858/Eb	sheets, horizontal and vertical coils, 35p. booklets (DP1/3), 50p. booklets (DT13/14)
3½p.	photo	olive-grey	1 centre band	X859	sheet, horizontal coils, 35p. booklet (DP4), 85p. booklet (DW1)
3½p.	photo	purple-brown	phos paper	X931	sheets, £4 Royal Mint booklet (DX4)
3½p.	photo	purple-brown	1 centre band	X860	50p. booklets (FB24/6)
4p.	photo	ochre-brown	2 bands	X861/Eg	(a) with P.V.A. gum—sheets. (b) with gum arabic—sheets
4p.	litho	greenish blue	2 bands	X996	sheets
4p.	photo	greenish blue	2 bands	X862	50p. booklets (FB17/18)
4p.	litho	greenish blue	phos paper	X997	sheets J.W. ptg.
				X1002	sheets Questa ptg.
4p.	photo	greenish blue	phos paper	X932	12½p. m/v coil (X924l)
				X932Ea	13p. m/v coil (X925l), 14p. m/v coil (X928l)
4p.	photo	greenish blue	1 centre band	X863	50p. booklets (FB27/30)
4p.	photo	greenish blue	1 side band	X864/Ea	(a) band at right—£5 Times booklet (DX6) (b) band at left—£5 Times booklet (DX6)
4p.	photo	new blue	phos paper	X933	sheets, 15p. m/v coil (X930cl), 17p. m/v coil (X933l), 18p. m/v coil (X933m), 19p m/v coil (X933n)
4½p.	photo	grey-blue	2 bands	X865	sheets, horizontal coils, 45p. booklets (DS1/2), 85p. booklet (DW1)
5p.	photo	pale violet	2 bands	X866	sheets
5p.	photo	pale violet	phos paper	X934	sheets

Value. Process		Colour	Phosphor	Cat. No.	Source
5p.	litho	lt violet	phos paper	X1003	sheets
5p.	litho	claret	phos paper	X1004/a	sheets
5p.	photo	claret	1 centre band	X867	50p. booklets (FB35/36, 43/6, 48, 50)
5p.	photo	dull red-brown	phos paper	X935	sheets, 17p. m/v coil (X933l), 18p. m/v coil (X933m), 19p m/v coil (X933n)
5½p.	photo	violet	2 bands	X868	sheets
5½p.	photo	violet	1 centre band	X869	sheets
6p.	photo	lt emerald	2 bands	X870/Eg	(a) with P.V.A. gum—sheets, 10p. m/v coil (X841q), 10p. booklets (FA1/3) (b) with gum arabic—sheets
6p.	photo	yellow-olive	phos paper	X936	sheets
6½p.	photo	greenish blue	2 bands	X871	sheets
6½p.	photo	greenish blue	1 centre band	X872	sheets, horizontal and vertical coils, 65p. booklet (FC1)
6½p.	photo	greenish blue	1 side band	X873/Ea	(a) band at right—50p. booklet (FB1A). (b) band at left—50p. booklet (FB1B)
7p.	photo	purple-brown	2 bands	X874	sheets
7p.	photo	purple-brown	1 centre band	X875	sheets, horizontal and vertical coils, 10p. m/v coil (X843l), 10p. booklets (FA4/9), 70p. booklets (FD1/7), £1.60 Christmas booklet (FX1)
7p.	photo	purple-brown	1 side band	X876/Ea	(a) band at right—50p. booklets (FB2A/8A) (b) band at left—50p. booklets (FB2B/8B)
7p.	photo	brownish red	phos paper	X937	sheets
7½p.	photo	pale chestnut	2 bands	X877	sheets
8p.	photo	rosine	2 bands	X878	sheets
8p.	photo	rosine	1 centre band	X879	sheets, vertical coils, 10p. m/v coil (X845m), 10p. booklets (FA10/11), 80p. booklet (FE1), £1.80 Christmas booklet (FX2)
8p.	photo	rosine	1 side band	X880/Ea	(a) band at right—50p. booklets (FB9A/10A) (b) band at left—50p. booklets (FB9B/10B)
8½p	photo	lt yellowish green	2 bands	X881	sheets, horizontal and vertical coils, 50p. booklet (FB1), 85p. booklet (FF1)
8½p.	photo	yellowish green	phos paper	X938	sheets
9p.	photo	yellow-orange and black	2 bands	X882	sheets
9p.	photo	dp violet	2 bands	X883	sheets, horizontal and vertical coils, 50p. booklets (FB2/8), 90p. booklets (FG1/8), £1.60 Christmas booklet (FX1)
9½p	photo	purple	2 bands	X884	sheets
10p.	recess	cerise	phos paper	829	sheets
10p.	photo	orange-brown and chestnut	2 bands	X885	sheets
10p.	photo	orange-brown	2 bands	X886	Type I. sheets, 50p. booklets (FB9/10), £1.80 Christmas booklet (FX2)
10p.	photo	orange-brown	2 bands	X886b	Type II. £4 Christian Heritage booklet (DX5)
10p.	photo	orange-brown	"all-over"	X887	Type I. sheets, vertical coils, £1 booklet (FH1)
10p.	photo	orange-brown	phos paper	X939	Type I. sheets
10p.	photo	orange-brown	1 centre band	X888	Type I. sheets, vertical coils, £1 booklets (FH2/4), £2.20 Christmas booklet (FX3), £3 Wedgwood booklet (DX2)
10p.	photo	orange-brown	1 side band	X889/Ea	Type I. (a) band at right—50p. booklets (FB11A/13A) (b) band at left—50p. booklets (FB11B/13B), £3 Wedgwood booklet (DX2)
10p.	photo	dull orange	phos paper	X940	sheets
10½p.	photo	yellow	2 bands	X890	sheets
10½p.	photo	dp dull blue	2 bands	X891	sheets
11p.	photo	brown-red	2 bands	X892	sheets
11p.	photo	brown-red	phos paper	X941	sheets
11½p	photo	ochre-brown	phos paper	X942	sheets
11½p	photo	drab	1 centre band	X893	sheets, vertical coils, £1.15 booklets (FI1/4), £2.55 Christmas booklet (FX4)
11½p.	photo	drab	1 side band	X894/Ea	(a) band at right—50p. booklets (FB14A/18A), £1.30 booklets (FL1/2) (b) band at left—50p. booklets FB14B/18B), £1.30 booklets (FL1/2)
12p.	photo	yellowish green	phos paper	X943	sheets, vertical coils, £1.20 booklets (FJ1/3)
12p.	photo	yellowish green	2 bands	X895	50p. booklets (FB11/13), £2.20 Christmas booklet (FX3), £3 Wedgwood booklet (DX2)
12p.	photo	brt emerald	1 centre band	X896	sheets, horizontal and vertical coils, 50p. booklet (FB34), £1.20 booklets (FJ4/6), £5 British Rail booklet (DX7)
12p.	photo	brt emerald	1 side band	X897/ Ea	(a) band at right—£1.50 booklets (FP1/2), £5 British Rail booklet (DX7) (b) band at left—£1.50 booklets (FP1/2), £5 British Rail booklet (DX7)
12p.	photo	brt emerald	1 centre band Underprint T.4	X896Eu	sheets
12½p.	process	lt emerald	1 centre band	X898	sheets, vertical coils, 50p. booklets (FB24/6), £1.25 booklets (FK1/8), £4 SG booklet (DX3)
12½p.	photo	lt emerald	1 centre band Underprint T.1	X898Eu	£2.80 Christmas booklet (FX5)
12½p.	photo	lt emerald	1 centre band Underprint T.2	X898Ev	£2.50 Christmas booklet (FX6)
12½p.	photo	lt emerald	1 side band	X899/Ea	(a) band at right—50p. booklets (FB19A/23A), £1.43 booklets (FN1/6), £1.46 booklets (FO1/3), £4 SG booklet (DX3), £4 Royal Mint booklet (DX4) (b) band at left—50p. booklets (FB19B/23B), £1.43 booklets (FN1/6), £1.46 booklets (FO1/3), £4 SG booklet (DX3), £4 Royal Mint booklet (DX4)
13p.	photo	olive-grey	phos paper	X944	sheets
13p.	photo	pale chestnut	1 centre band	X900	sheets, horizontal and vertical coils, 50p. booklets (FB27/30, 35/6, 43/6, 48, 50), 52p. booklet (GA1), £1.30 booklets (FL3/14, GI1), £5 Times booklet (DX6), £5 P & O booklet (DX8)
13p.	photo	pale chestnut	1 centre band Underprint T.2	X900Eu	£1.30 Christmas booklet (FX9)
13p.	photo	pale chestnut	1 side band	X901/Ea	(a) band at right—50p. booklets (FB37/42, 47, 49), £1.54 booklets (FQ1/4), £4 Christian Heritage booklet (DX5), £5 Times booklet (DX6), £5 P & O booklet (DX8) (b) band at left—£1 booklets (FH6/13), £1.54 booklets (FQ1/4), £4 Christian Heritage booklet (DX5), £5 Times booklet (DX6)
13p.	litho	pale chestnut	1 centre band	X1005	£5 Financial Times booklet (DX9)

Value. Process		Colour	Phosphor	Cat. No.	Source
13p.	litho	pale chestnut	1 side band	X1006/Ea	£5 Financial Times booklet (DX9)
13½p.	photo	purple-brown	phos paper	X945	sheets
14p.	photo	grey-blue	phos paper	X946	sheets, vertical coils, £1.40 booklets (FM1/4)
14p.	photo	grey-blue	2 bands	X902	50p. booklets (FB14/16), £1.30 booklets (FL1/2), £2.55 Christmas booklet (FX4)
14p.	photo	dp blue	1 centre band	X903	sheets, horizontal and vertical coils, 56p. booklets (GB1/4), £1.40 booklets (FM5/6, GK1, 3)
14p.	photo	dp blue	1 band at right	X904	50p. booklets (FB51/4), £1 booklets (FH14/15 and 17)
14p.	litho	dp blue	1 centre band	X1007	£1.40 booklets (GK2, 4)
14p.	litho	dp blue	1 band at right	X1051*	£1 booklet (FH16)
15p.	photo	ultramarine	phos paper	X947	sheets
15p.	photo	brt blue	1 centre band	X905	sheets, horizontal and vertical coils
15p.	photo	brt blue	1 side band	X906/Ea	(a) band at left—50p. booklet (FB55)
					(b) band at right—£5 London Life booklet (DX11)
15½p.	photo	pale violet	phos paper	X948	sheets, vertical coils, £1.55 booklets (FR1/6)
15½p.	photo	pale violet	2 bands	X907	£1.43 booklets (FN1/6), £4 SG booklet (DX3)
15½p.	photo	pale violet	2 bands Underprint T.1	X907Eu	£2.80 Christmas booklet (FX5)
16p.	photo	olive-drab	phos paper	X949	sheets, vertical coils, £1.60 booklets (FS1, 3/4), £4 Royal Mint booklet (DX4)
16p.	photo	olive-drab	phos paper Underprint T.3	X949Eu	£1.60 booklet (FS2)
16p.	photo	olive-drab	2 bands	X908	£1.46 booklets (FO1/3)
16½p.	photo	pale chestnut	phos paper	X950	sheets
17p.	photo	lt emerald	phos paper	X951	sheets
17p.	photo	grey-blue	phos paper	X952	sheets, vertical coils, £1 booklet (FH5), £1.70 booklets (FT1, 3 & 5/7), £4 Christian Heritage booklet (DX5), £5 Times booklet (DX6), £5 British Rail booklet (DX7)
17p.	photo	grey-blue	phos paper Underprint T.3	X952Eu	£1.70 booklet (FT2)
17p.	photo	grey-blue	2 bands	X909	50p. booklet (FB33), £1.50 booklets (FP1/3), £1.54 booklets (FQ1/4), £4 Christian Heritage booklet (DX5), £5 Times booklet (DX6), £5 British Rail booklet (DX7)
17p.	photo	grey-blue	2 bands Underprint T.4	X909Eu	50p. booklets (FB31/3)
17p.	photo	dp blue	1 centre band	X910	sheets, vertical coils
17p.	photo	dp blue	1 side band	X911/Ea	(a) band at right—50p. booklet (FB57/8), £1 booklet (FH21/2)
					(b) band at left—50p. booklet (FB57/8)
17p.	litho	dp blue	1 centre band	X1008	£6 Alias Agatha Christie booklet (DX12)
17½p	photo	pale chestnut	phos paper	X953	sheets
18p.	photo	dp violet	phos paper	X954	sheets
18p.	photo	dp olive-grey	phos paper	X955	sheets, vertical coils, 72p. booklet (GC1), £1.80 booklets (FU1/8, GO1), £5 P & O booklet (DX8)
18p.	photo	dp olive-grey	2 bands	X912	50p. booklets (FB37/42, 47, 49), £1 booklet (FH6/13), £5 P & O booklet (DX8)
18p.	litho	dp olive-grey	phos paper	X1009	£5 Financial Times booklet (DX9)
18p.	litho	dp olive-grey	2 bands	X1010	£5 Financial Times booklet (DX9)
18p.	photo	brt green	1 centre band	X913	sheets, vertical coils
18p.	litho	brt green	1 centre band	X1011	£6 Tolkien booklet (DX14)
18p.	litho	brt green	1 side band	X1012/Ea	(a) band at right—£6 Tolkien booklet (DX14).
					(b) band at left—£6 (£5.64) Beatrix Potter booklet (DX15)).
19p.	photo	brt orange-red	phos paper	X956	sheets, vertical coils, 76p. booklets (GD1/4), £1.90 booklets (FV1/2, GP1, 3)
19p.	photo	brt orange-red	2 bands	X914	50p. booklets (FB51/4), £1 booklets (FH14/15, 17)
19p.	litho	brt orange-red	phos paper	X1013	£1.90 booklets (GP2, 4)
19p.	litho	brt orange-red	2 bands	X1052*	£1 booklet (FH16)
19½p	photo	olive-grey	phos paper	X957	sheets
20p.	recess	olive-green	none	830	sheets
20p.	photo	dull purple	2 bands	X915	sheets
20p.	photo	dull purple	phos paper	X958	sheets
20p.	litho	dull purple	2 bands	X998	sheets
20p.	litho	dull purple	phos paper	X999	sheets J.W. ptg.
				X1014	sheets Questa ptg.
20p.	photo	turquoise-green	phos paper	X959	sheets
20p.	photo	brownish black	phos paper	X960	sheets, horizontal and vertical coils, £1 booklet (FH18)
20p.	photo	brownish black	2 bands	X916	50p. booklet (FB55), £5 London Life booklet (DX11)
20½p.	photo	ultramarine	phos paper	X961	sheets
22p.	photo	blue	phos paper	X962	sheets
22p.	photo	yellow-green	phos paper	X963	sheets
22p.	litho	yellow-green	2 bands	X1015	£5 Financial Times booklet (DX9)
22p.	photo	brt orange-red	2 bands	X917*	£1 booklet (FH21/2)
22p.	photo	brt orange-red	phos paper	X964	sheets, vertical coils
22p.	litho	brt orange-red	phos paper	X1016	£6 Alias Agatha Christie booklet (DX12)
23p.	photo	brown-red	phos paper	X965	sheets
23p.	photo	brt green	phos paper	X966	sheets
24p.	photo	violet	phos paper	X967	sheets
24p.	photo	Indian red	phos paper	X968	sheets
24p.	photo	chestnut	phos paper	X969	sheets, vertical coils, 50p. booklets (FB59/66), £1 booklets (FH23/7)
24p.	litho	chestnut	phos paper	X1017	£6 Tolkien booklet (DX14) (Questa ptg)
				X1053*	£1 booklet (FH28/30) Walsall ptg
24p.	litho	chestnut	2 bands	X1018	£6 Tolkien booklet (DX14)
25p.	photo	purple	phos paper	X970	sheets
25p.	photo	rose-red	2 bands	X917a	horizontal coils
26p.	photo	rosine	phos paper	X971	Type I. sheets
26p.	photo	rosine	2 bands	X918	Type I. £5 P & O booklet (DX8)
26p.	photo	rosine	phos paper	X971b	Type II. £1.04 booklet (GE1)
26p.	photo	drab	phos paper	X972	sheets

Value.	Process	Colour	Phosphor	Cat. No.	Source
27p.	photo	chestnut	phos paper	X973	sheets, £1.08 booklets (GF1/2)
27p.	photo	violet	phos paper	X974	sheets
28p.	photo	dp violet	phos paper	X975	sheets
28p.	photo	ochre	phos paper	X976	sheets
28p.	photo	dp bluish grey	phos paper	X977	sheets
29p.	photo	ochre-brown	phos paper	X978	sheets
29p.	photo	dp mauve	phos paper	X979	sheets
29p.	litho	dp mauve	2 bands	X1054*	£1.16 booklet (GG1)
29p.	litho	dp mauve	phos paper	X1055*	£1.16 booklet (GG2)
30p.	photo	dp olive-grey	phos paper	X980	sheets
31p.	photo	purple	phos paper	X981	sheets
31p.	photo	purple	2 bands	X919	£5 British Rail booklet (DX7)
31p.	photo	ultramarine	phos paper	X982	sheets
31p.	litho	ultramarine	phos paper	X1056*	£1.24 booklet (GH1)
32p.	photo	greenish blue	phos paper	X983	sheets
33p.	photo	lt emerald	phos paper	X984	sheets, vertical coils
33p.	litho	lt emerald	phos paper	X1019	£6 Alias Agatha Christie booklet (DX12)
33p.	litho	lt emerald	phos paper	X1057*	£1.32 booklet (GJ1)
33p.	litho	lt emerald	2 bands	X1020	£6 Wales booklet (DX13), £6 (£5.64) Beatrix Potter booklet (DX15)
34p.	photo	ochre-brown	phos paper	X985	sheets
34p.	photo	ochre-brown	2 bands	X920	£5 Times booklet (DX6)
34p.	litho	bistre-brown	2 bands	X1021	£5 Financial Times booklet (DX9)
34p.	photo	dp bluish grey	phos paper	X986	sheets
34p.	photo	dp mauve	phos paper	X987	sheets
35p.	photo	sepia	phos paper	X988	sheets
35p.	photo	yellow	phos paper	X989	sheets
37p.	photo	rosine	phos paper	X990	sheets
39p.	photo	brt mauve	phos paper	X991	sheets, vertical coils
39p.	litho	brt mauve	phos paper	X1058*	78p. booklet (GD4a), £1.56 booklet (GM1)
39p.	litho	brt mauve	2 bands	X1022	£6 Tolkien booklet (DX14), £6 (£5.64) Beatrix Potter booklet (DX15)
50p.	recess	dp ultramarine	none or phos paper	831/Ea	sheets
50p.	photo	ochre-brown	2 bands	X921	sheets
50p.	photo	ochre-brown	none	X992	sheets
50p.	photo	ochre	2 bands	X922	£5 London Life (DX11)
50p.	photo	ochre	none or phos paper	X994	sheets
75p.	litho	black	none	X1023/a	sheets
75p.	litho	brownish grey and black	none	X1024	sheets
75p.	photo	grey-black	none	X993	sheets
£1	recess	bluish black	none	831b	sheets
£1	photo	brt yellow-green and blackish olive	none	1026	sheets
£1.30	photo	drab and dp greenish blue	none	1026b	sheets
£1.33	photo	pale mauve and grey-black	none	1026c	sheets
£1.41	photo	drab and dp greenish blue	none	1026d	sheets
£1.50	photo	pale mauve and grey-black	none	1026e	sheets
£1.60	photo	pale drab and dp greenish blue	none	1026f	sheets
£2	photo	lt emerald and purple-brown	none	1027	sheets
£5	photo	salmon and chalky blue	none	1028	sheets

For 1st and 2nd class no value indicated (NVI) stamps, see Nos. 1445/52, 1511/16 and 1664/71.
For table covering Machin stamps with elliptical perforations see after Nos. Y1667, etc, in 1993.

DECIMAL MACHIN MULTI-VALUE COIL INDEX

The following is a simplified checklist of horizontal multi-value coils, to be used in conjunction with the main listing as details of stamps listed there are not repeated.

Strip Value	Date	Contents	Cat No.
5p.	15.2.71	½p. × 2, 1p. × 2, 2p.	X841n
10p.	3.12.75	½p. × 2, 1p., 2p., 6p.	X841q
10p.	14.12.77	½p. × 2, 1p. × 2, 7p.	X843l
10p.	16.1.80	1p. × 2, 8p. plus 2 labels	X845m
11½p.	6.81	2½p., 3p. × 3	X929l
12½p.	30.12.81	½p., 4p. × 3	X924l
13p.	14.8.84	1p., 4p. × 3	X925l
14p.	5.9.88	2p., 4p. × 3	X928l
15p.	10.10.89	3p., 4p. × 3	X930cl
17p.	27.11.90	4p. × 3, 5p.	X933l
18p.	1.10.91	4p. × 2, 5p. × 2	X933m
19p.	31.1.95	4p., 5p. × 3	X933n

Abbreviations used in the diagrams: 2B = 2 bands, CB = centre band, LB = left band and RB = right band. The shaded squares represent printed labels.
Panes completed by unprinted white labels are outside the scope of this catalogue.

Unless otherwise stated the panes were printed in photogravure. Some panes exist in photogravure and lithography and these are separately identified and listed. **Imperforate or straight edges.** These are described under the appropriate illustration and listed as complete panes.

2	2
½	½

X8411
(2 bands)

2	½
2	½

X8411a
(2 bands)

½	½	½
½	½	½

X841m
(2 bands)

2½ RB	½ 2B	2½ LB	2½ CB
2½ RB	½ 2B	2½ LB	2½ CB
2½ RB	½ 2B	2½ LB	2½ CB

X841o
£1 Wedgwood

½ 2B	2½ LB
½ 2B	2½ LB
½ 2B	½ LB

X841p
£1 Wedgwood

½ 2B	½ 2B
½ 2B	½ 2B

X841r
(2 bands)

½ 2B	½ 2B
1 2B	8½ 2B
1 2B	8½ 2B
6½ RB	8½ 2B
6½ RB	8½ 2B

X841s

½ 2B	½ 2B
8½ 2B	1 2B
8½ 2B	1 2B
8½ 2B	6½ LB
8½ 2B	6½ LB

X841sa

11½ RB	½ 2B
11½ RB	1 2B
11½ RB	14 2B

X841t

½ 2B	11½ LB
1 2B	11½ LB
14 2B	11½ LB

X841ta

½ 2B	3 2B
12½ RB	3 2B
12½ RB	3 2B
12½ RB	3 2B

X841u

3 2B	½ 2B
3 2B	12½ LB
3 2B	12½ LB
3 2B	12½ LB

X841ua

½	
½	1
7	1

X843m
(centre band)

1 2B	1 2B
7 RB	9 2B
7 RB	9 2B
7 RB	9 2B

X844n

1 2B	1 2B
9 2B	7 LB
9 2B	7 LB
9 2B	7 LB

X844na

½	½
1½	1½

X844l
(2 bands)

1½	1
1½	1

X844m
(2 bands)

	1
8	1

X845l

1	1
3½ 12½	
3½ 12½	
3½ 12½	

X845n
(centre band)

1	1
1	13
4	13
4	13

X845p
(centre band)

1	1
12	12
12	12

X845q
(centre band)

1	13
5	13
5	13

X845s/sa
(centre band)
X845sa imperf
at left and right

1	13
LB	RB
18 2B	18 2B

X847l

13 RB	18 2B	18 2B
1 RB	18 2B	26 2B
13 RB	18 2B	18 2B

X847m
£5 P & O

	2 2B
2 2B	10 2B
8 RB	10 2B
8 RB	10 2B

X849l

2 2B	
10 2B	2 2B
10 2B	8 LB
10 2B	8 LB

X849la

	2 RB
2 2B	2 2B
10 RB	12 2B
10 RB	12 2B

X849m

2 2B	
2 2B	2 2B
12 2B	10 LB
12 2B	10 LB

X849ma

12 2B	10 LB	10 CB
12 2B	2 2B	10 CB
12 2B	12 2B	10 CB

X849n
£3 Wedgwood

2	2
2	2
2	2

X849o (2 bands)
£3 Wedgwood

12½ RB	12½ LB	12½ CB
12½ RB	3 2B	12½ LB
12½ RB	2 2B	12½ LB

X849p
£4 Stanley Gibbons

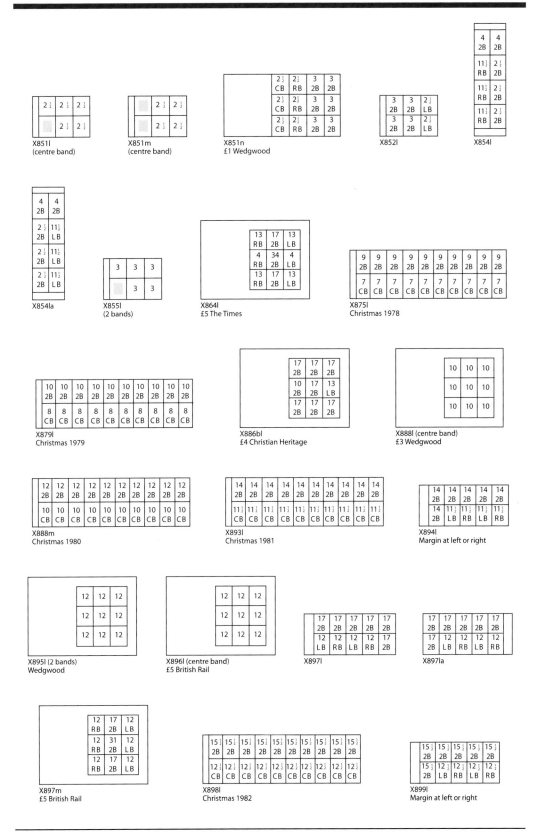

X851l (centre band)

X851m (centre band)

X851n £1 Wedgwood

X852l

X854l

X854la

X855l (2 bands)

X864l £5 The Times

X875l Christmas 1978

X879l Christmas 1979

X886bl £4 Christian Heritage

X888l (centre band) £3 Wedgwood

X888m Christmas 1980

X893l Christmas 1981

X894l Margin at left or right

X895l (2 bands) Wedgwood

X896l (centre band) £5 British Rail

X897l

X897la

X897m £5 British Rail

X898l Christmas 1982

X899l Margin at left or right

12½	12½
ND	LD
12½	12½
RB	LB
12½	12½
RB	LB

X899m
£4 Stanley Gibbons
£4 Royal Mint

16	16	16	16	16
2B	2B	2B	2B	2B
12½	12½	12½	12½	16
LB	RB	LB	RB	2B

X899n

16	16	16	16	16
2B	2B	2B	2B	2B
16	12½	12½	12½	12½
2B	LB	RB	LB	RB

X899na

13	13	13
13	13	13
13	13	13

X900l (centre band)
£5 The Times
£5 P & O

13	13
13	13
13	13

(½)

X900m, (photo), X1005l (litho)
(centre band)
£5 P & O (X900m)
£5 Financial times (X 1005l)

13	13
13	13

X900n (centre band)
52p. Barcode booklet

13	13	13	13	13
13	13	13	13	13

X900o (centre band)
£1.30 Barcode Booklet

17	17	17	17	17
2B	2B	2B	2B	2B
13	13	13	13	17
LB	RB	LB	RB	2B

X901l

17	17	17	17	17
2B	2B	2B	2B	2B
17	13	13	13	13
2B	LB	RB	LB	RB

X901la

13	13
RB	LB
13	13
RB	LB
13	13
RB	LB

X901m
£4 Christian Heritage

13	18
LB	2B
18	18
2B	2B
18	18
2B	2B

X901n/na
901na imperf
at left and right

14	14
14	14

X903l (centre band)
56p. Barcode Booklet

14	14	14	14	14
14	14	14	14	14

X903m
(centre band)
£1.40 Barcode Booklet

14	14
14	14

X903n, X903q
(centre band)
56p. Barcode Booklet
X903n imperf at top
and bottom
X903q imperf 3 sides

14	14	14	14	14
14	14	14	14	14

X903p (centre band)
£1.40 Barcode Booklet
Imperf at top and bottom

	19
	2B
14	19
RB	2B

X904l

14	19
RB	2B
14	19
RB	2B
19	19
2B	2B

X904m (photo)
X1051l (litho)
Imperf at left
and right

	15
	LB
20	17
2B	LB

X906l

2ND	50	1ST
RB	2B	2B
15		20
RB		2B
15	29	20
RB	2B	2B

X906m
£5 London Life
The stamps in the bottom row are
Penny Black Anniversary definitives
(Nos 1468Ea,1470 and 1472)

15½	15½
15½	15½
15½	15½

X907l
(2 bands)
£4 Stanley Gibbons

15½	15½	15½
15½	15½	15½
15½	15½	15½

X907m
(2 bands)
£4 Stanley Gibbons

	17
17	17

X909l (2 bands)
and underprint
X909Ela (as
X909l but with-
out underprint)

	17
	LB
17	17
RB	LB

X911l

	22
	2B
17	22
RB	2B
17	22
RB	2B

X911m
Imperf at left
and right

1	1
24	24

X925m
(phosphorised
paper)

2	2
24	24
24	24

X927l (photo)
X1050l (litho)
(phosphorised
paper) Imperf
at left and right

16	16	16
3½	3	3½
16	16	16

X930b
(phosphorised paper)
£4 Royal mint

X949l
(phosphorised paper)
£4 Royal Mint

X952l
(phosphorised paper)
£4 Christian Heritage
£5 The Times £5 British Rail
X1008l (centre band)
£6 Agatha Christie

X952m
(phosphorised paper)
£5 The Times
£5 British Rail

X955l (photo), X1009l (litho)
(phosphorised paper)
£5 P & O (X955l)
£5 Financial Times (X1009l)

X955m
(phosphorised paper)
72p. Barcode Booklet

X955n
(phosphorised paper)
£1.80 Barcode Booklet

X956l
(phosphorised paper)
76p. Barcode Booklet

X956m
(phosphorised paper)
£1.90 Barcode Booklet

X956n, X956q
(phosphorised paper)
76p. Barcode Booklet
X956n imperf at top
and bottom
X956q imperf on
three sides

X956o
(phosphorised paper)
£1.90 Barcode Booklet Imperf
at top and bottom

X960l
(phosphorised
paper)
Imperf at left
and right

X971bl
(phosphorised paper)
£1.04 Barcode Booklet

X973l
(phosphorised paper)
£1.08 Barcode Booklet

X973m
(phosphorised
paper)
£1.08 Barcode
Booklet
Imperf at top and
bottom

13 RB	22 2B	13 LB
13 RB	34 2B	13 LB
13 RB	18 2B	13 LB

X1006l (litho)
£5 Financial Times

18	18
18	18
18	18

X1009m (litho)
(phosphorised paper)
£5 Financial Times
X1011l (litho) (centre band)
£6 Tolkien

18 RB	39 2B	24 2B
1ST 2B		2ND RB
18 RB	39 2B	24 2B

X1012l (litho)
£6 Tolkien

33 2B	18 LB	39 2B
2ND LB		2ND LB
33 2B	18 LB	39 2B

X1012m (litho)
£6 (£5.64) Beatrix Potter

22	22	22
22	22	22
22	22	22

X1016l (litho)
(phosphorised paper)
£6 Agatha Christie

22	33	22
22		22
22	33	22

X1016m (litho)
(phosphorised paper)
£6 Agatha Christie

24	24
24	24
24	24

X1017l (litho)
(phosphorised paper)
£6 Tolkien

29	29
29	29

X1054l (litho), X1055l (litho)
(X1054l 2 bands)
(X1055l phosphorised paper)
£1.16 Barcode Booklet
Imperf on three sides

31	31
31	31

X1056l (litho)
(phosphorised paper)
£1.24 Barcode Booklet
Imperf top and bottom

33	33
33	33

X1057l
(phosphorised paper)
£1.32 Barcode Booklet
Imperf top and bottom

39	39
39	39

X1058l
(phosphorised paper)
£1.56 Barcode Booklet
Imperf top and bottom

N.V.I. stamps, PVA gum, "standard" perforations

913		**914**

1989 (22 Aug)–**1993**. *Booklet Stamps.*

(a) Photo Harrison. P 15×14.

1445	913	(2nd)	brt blue (1 centre band)	1·00	1·00
		a.	Booklet pane. No. 1445×10 with horizontal edges of pane imperf	11·00	
		b.	Booklet pane. No. 1445×4 with three edges of pane imperf (28.11.89)	22·00	
1446		(2nd)	brt blue (1 band at right) (20.3.90)	3·00	3·25
1447	914	(1st)	brownish black (phosphorised paper)	1·75	1·00
		a.	Booklet pane. No. 1447×10 with horizontal edges of pane imperf	15·00	
		b.	Booklet pane. No. 1447×4 with three edges of pane imperf (5.12.89)	35·00	
1448		(1st)	brownish black (2 phosphor bands) (20.3.90)	3·25	3·00
First Day Cover (Nos. 1445, 1447)					5·00

(b) Litho Walsall. P 14.

1449	913	(2nd)	brt blue (1 centre band)	1·00	90
		a.	Imperf between (vert pair)		
		b.	Booklet pane. No. 1449×4 with three edges of pane imperf	7·00	
		c.	Booklet pane. No. 1449×4 with horiz edges of pane imperf (6.8.91)	3·50	
		d.	Booklet pane. No. 1449×10 with horiz edges of pane imperf (6.8.91)	7·50	
1450	914	(1st)	blackish brown (2 phosphor bands)	2·50	2·40
		a.	Booklet pane. No. 1450×4 with three edges of pane imperf	8·50	
		Ey.	Phosphor omitted	£600	

(c) Litho Questa. P 15×14.

1451	913	(2nd)	brt blue (1 centre band) (19.9.89)	1·00	1·00
		Ey.	Phosphor omitted	£150	
1451*a*		(2nd)	brt blue (1 band at right) (25.2.92)	3·00	3·00
		aEb.	Band at left (10.8.93)	2·00	2·00
		al.	Booklet pane. Nos. 1451aEb and 1514a, each×3, with margins all round (10.8.93)	10·00	
1452	914	(1st)	brownish black (phosphorised paper) (19.9.89)	2·50	2·50

Nos. 1445, 1447 and 1449/52 were initially sold at 14p. (2nd) and 19p. (1st), but these prices were later increased to reflect new postage rates.

Nos. 1446 and 1448 come from the *se-tenant* pane in the London Life £5 Booklet. This pane is listed under No. X906m in the Decimal Machin section.

No. 1451a comes from the *se-tenant* panes in the Wales and Tolkien £6 booklet. These panes are listed under Nos. X1012l and W49a (Wales Regionals). No. 1451aEb comes from the £6 (£5.64) Beatrix Potter booklet.

Nos. 1445, 1447 and 1449/50 do not exist perforated on all four sides, but come with either one or two adjacent sides imperforate.

No. 1450Ey comes from a pane in which one stamp was without phosphor bands due to a dry print.

For illustrations showing the differences between photogravure and lithography see above Type **367**.

For similar designs, but in changed colours, see Nos. 1511/16, for those with elliptical perforations, Nos. 1664/71, and for self-adhesive versions Nos. 2039/40 and 2295.

1990 (7 Aug)–*92. Booklet stamps. As T* **913/14**, *but colours changed.*

(a) Photo Harrison. P 15×14.

1511	913	(2nd)	deep blue (1 centre band)	1·50	1·50
		a.	Booklet pane. No. 1511×10 with horiz edges of pane imperf	12·00	
1512	914	(1st)	brt orange-red (phosphorised paper)	1·50	1·50
		a.	Booklet pane. No. 1512×10 with horiz edges of pane imperf	10·00	

(b) Litho Questa. P 15×14.

1513	913	(2nd)	deep blue (1 centre band)	2·50	2·50
1514	914	(1st)	brt orange-red (phosphorised paper)	1·00	1·00
1514*a*		(1st)	brt orange-red (2 bands) (25.2.92)	2·25	2·25
		aEy.	Phosphor omitted	£750	

(c) Litho Walsall. P 14.

1515	913	(2nd)	deep blue (1 centre band)	1·00	1·00
		a.	Booklet pane. No. 1515×4 with horiz edges of pane imperf	3·75	
		b.	Booklet pane. No. 1515×10 with horiz edges of pane imperf	8·50	
1516	914	(1st)	brt orange-red (phosphorised paper)	1·25	1·25
		a.	Booklet pane. No. 1516×4 with horiz edges of pane imperf	4·00	
		b.	Booklet pane. No. 1516×10 with horiz edges of pane imperf	8·00	
		c.	Perf 13	2·75	3·00
		ca.	Booklet pane. No. 1516c×4 with horiz edges of pane imperf	11·00	
First Day Cover (Nos. 1515/16)					5·00

Nos. 1511/14 and 1515/16 were initially sold at 15p. (2nd) and 20p. (1st), but these prices were later increased to reflect new postage rates.

No. 1514a comes from the *se-tenant* panes in the £6 Wales, £6 Tolkien and £5.64 Beatrix Potter booklets. These panes are listed under Nos. X1012l, 1451al and W49a (Wales Regionals). No. 1514a exists with phosphor omitted (*Price* £700 *unused*).

No. 1516c was caused by the use of an incorrect perforation comb.

Nos. 1511/12 and 1515/16 do not exist with perforations on all four sides, but come with either the top or the bottom edge imperforate.

For similar stamps with elliptical perforations see Nos. 1664/71.

FLUORESCENT PHOSPHOR BANDS. Following the introduction of new automatic sorting machinery in 1991 it was found necessary to substantially increase the signal emitted by the phosphor bands. This was achieved by adding a fluorescent element to the phosphor which appears yellow under U.V. light. This combination was first used on an experimental sheet printing of the 18p., No. X913, produced by Enschedé in 1991. All values with phosphor bands from the elliptical perforations issue, including the No Value Indicated design, originally showed this yellow fluor.

From mid-1995 printings of current sheet and booklet stamps began to appear with the colour of the fluorescent element changed to blue. As such differences in fluor colour can only be identified by use of a U.V. lamp they are outside the scope of this catalogue, but full details will be found in the *Great Britain Specialised Catalogue Volume 4*.

The first commemorative/special issue to show the change to blue fluor was the Centenary of Rugby League set, Nos. 1891/5.

COMPUTER-ENGRAVED CYLINDERS. In 1991 Enschedé introduced a new method of preparing photogravure cylinders for Great Britain stamps. This new method utilised computer-engraving instead of the traditional acid-etching and produced cylinders without the minor flaws which had long been a feature of the photogravure process. Such cylinders were first used on Great Britain stamps for the printing of the 18p. released on 19 November 1991 (see No. X913).

Harrison and Sons continued to use the acid-etching method until mid-1996 after which most Machin values, including N.V.I.'s, were produced from computer-engraved cylinders using a very similar process to that of Enschedé. Some values exist in versions from both cylinder production methods and can often be identified by minor differences. Such stamps are, however, outside the scope of this listing, but full details can be found in the current edition of the *Great Britain Specialised Catalogue Volume 4*.

For commemorative stamps the first Harrison issue to use computer-engraved cylinders was the Centenary of Cinema set (Nos. 1920/4).

When Walsall introduced photogravure printing in 1997 their cylinders were produced using a similar computer-engraved process.

N.V.I. stamps, PVA gum, elliptical perforations

1093a

1993 (6 Apr)–**2008**. *As T* **913/14**, *and* **1093a**. P 14 (No. 1665) or 15 × 14 (others) (both with one elliptical hole in each vertical side).

(a) *Photo*
  Harrison – No. 1666
  Questa Nos. 1664a, 1667a
  Walsall – No. 1665
  Harrison/De La Rue, Questa or Walsall – No. 1667
  Harrison/De La Rue, Enschedé, Questa or Walsall – Nos. 1664, 1668, 1669

1664	913	(2nd)	brt blue (1 centre band) (7.9.93)	1·00	1·00
		a.	Perf 14 (1.12.98)	1·10	1·10
		b.	Imperf (pair)	£1250	
		l.	Booklet pane. Nos. 1664 and 1667 × 3 plus 4 labels ("postcode" on top right label) (27.4.00)	4·50	
		la.	As No. 1664l, but inscr "postcodes" on top right label (17.4.01)	5·50	

	m. Booklet pane. Nos. 1664 × 2 and 1667 × 6 (27.4.00)	6·50		
	n. Booklet pane. Nos. 1664 and 1669, each × 4, with central label and margins all round (6.2.02)	6·00		
	o. Booklet pane. Nos. 1664 and 1668, each × 4, with central label and margins all round (2.6.03)	5·00		
	p. Booklet pane. Nos. 1664 × 4, Y1703 × 2 and Y1709 × 2, with central label and margins all round (24.2.05)	9·25		
1665	(2nd) bright blue (1 band at right) (13.10.98)	1·10	1·10	
	Ec. Band at left	1·00	1·00	
	l. Booklet pane. Nos. 1665 × 3 and N181b, S91a and W80a with margins all round	7·50		
1666 **914**	(1st) brt orange-red (phosphorised paper)	1·50	1·25	
1667	(1st) brt orange-red (2 phosphor bands) (4.4.95)	1·10	1·10	
	Ey. Phosphor omitted	£200		
	a. Perf 14 (1.12.98)	1·50	1·50	
	l. Booklet pane. No. 1667 × 8 with centre label and margins all round (16.2.99)	9·00		
	m. Booklet pane. No. 1667 × 4 plus commemorative label at right (12.5.99)	4·50		
1668	(1st) gold (2 phosphor bands) (21.4.97)...	1·00	1·00	
	a. Imperf (pair)	£150		
	l. Booklet pane. Nos. 1668 and Y1686, each × 4, and centre label with margins all round (23.9.97)	9·00		
	m. Booklet pane. Nos. 1668/9, each × 4, with centre label and margins all round (24.9.02)	12·00		
	o. Booklet pane. Nos. 1668 and Y1698, each × 4, with centre label and margins all round (16.3.04)	8·50		
	p. Booklet pane. Nos. 1668 × 4, Y1709 × 2 and Y1717 × 2, with centre label and margins all round (25.5.04)	8·00		
	q. Booklet pane. Nos. 1668 × 4, Y1719 × 2 and Y1723 × 2, with centre label and margins all round (18.10.05)......	6·50		
	r. Booklet pane. Nos. 1668 × 4, Y1695 × 2 and Y1705 × 2, with centre label and margins all round (23.2.06)	6·50		
1669 **1093a**	(E) deep blue (2 phosphor bands) (19.1.99)	1·25	1·25	

(b) Litho Questa or Walsall (1670), Enschedé, Questa or Walsall (1671) or De La Rue or Walsall (1672).

1670 **913**	(2nd) brt blue (1 centre band)	90	90	
	Ey. Phosphor omitted	£150		
	l. Booklet pane. Nos. 1670 and 1672, each × 4, with central label and margins all round (18.9.08)	5·75		
1671 **914**	(1st) brt orange-red (2 phosphor bands)	1·00	1·00	
	Ey. Phosphor omitted	£190		
	l. Booklet pane. No. 1671 × 4 plus commemorative label at left (27.7.94)	8·50		
	la. Ditto, but with commemorative label at right (16.5.95)	6·00		
	lEy. Phosphor omitted	£1500		
	m. Pane. No. 1671 with margins all round (roul 8 across top corners of pane) (Boots logo on margin) (17.8.94)	2·50		
	mEy. Phosphor omitted	£750		
	ma. Without Boots logo above stamp (11.9.95)	1·25		
	mb. Ditto, but roul 10 across top corners of pane (20.2.97)	1·40		
	n. Booklet pane. No. 1671 × 9 with margins all round (16.2.99)	9·00		
1672	(1st) gold (2 phosphor bands) (8.1.08)	1·50	1·50	
	a. Booklet pane. No. 1672 × 8 with centre label and margins all round (8.1.08)	10·00		

For details of sheets, booklets, etc containing these stamps see Decimal Machin Index following the "Y" numbers.

Nos. 1664/71 were issued in booklet panes showing perforations on all four edges.

On 6 September 1993 Nos. 1670/71 printed in lithography by Questa were made available in sheets from post offices in Birmingham, Coventry, Falkirk and Milton Keynes. These sheet stamps became available nationally on 5 October 1993. On 29 April 1997 No. 1664 printed in photogravure by Walsall became available in sheets. On the same date Nos. 1664 and 1667 were issued in coils printed by Harrison. Sheets of No. 1667 were printed by Walsall from 18 November 1997.

No. 1665 exists with the phosphor band at the left or right of the stamp from separate panes of the £6.16 Speed stamp booklet No. DX21. For pane containing No. 1665bEc see No. Y1676al.

No. 1668 was originally printed by Harrisons in booklets and Walsall in sheets and booklets for The Queen's Golden Wedding and issued on 21 April 1997. It was printed in coils by Enschedé (5.10.02), when gold became the accepted colour for 1st class definitives, and later in sheets and coils by De La Rue.

Booklet pane No. 1668m was issued on 24 September 2002 in the £6·83 "Across the Universe" booklet, No. DX29. It was issued again with a different central label on 25 February 2003 in the £6·99 "Microcosmos" booklet, No. DX30.

No. 1669 was intended for the basic European air mail rate, initially 30p., and was at first only available from Barcode booklet No. HF1, printed by Walsall. It appeared in sheets printed by De La Rue on 5 October 1999.

No. 1671m, printed by Questa, was provided by the Royal Mail for inclusion in single pre-packed greetings cards. The pane shows large margins at top and sides with lines of roulette gauging 8 stretching from the bottom corners to the mid point of the top edge. Examples included with greetings cards show the top two corners of the pane folded over. Unfolded examples were available from the British Philatelic Bureau and from other Post Office philatelic outlets. The scheme was originally limited to Boots and their logo appeared on the pane margin. Other card retailers subsequently participated and later supplies omitted the logo.

A further printing by Enschedé in 1997 showed the roulettes gauging 10 (No. 1671mb). Blank pieces of gummed paper have been found showing the perforation and rouletting of No. 1671mb, but no printing.

In mid-1994 a number of postal forgeries of the 2nd bright blue printed in lithography were detected after having been rejected by the sorting equipment. These show the Queen's head in bright greenish blue, have a fluorescent, rather than a phosphor, band and show matt, colourless gum on the reverse. These forgeries come from booklets of ten which also have forged covers.

No. 1672 was only issued in £7·40 or £7·15 stamp booklets, Nos. DX41/2. For illustration of differences between lithography and gravure see below Types **367** and **367a**.

For self-adhesive stamps in these colours see Nos. 2039/40 and 2295/6.

COMMEMORATIVE BOOKLET PANES. Booklets of four 1st Class stamps with *se-tenant* commemorative label were issued for the following anniversaries or events:

300th Anniversary of the Bank of England (No. 1671l)
Birth Centenary of R. J. Mitchell (No. 1671la)
70th Birthday of Queen Elizabeth II (No. 1671la)
"Hong Kong '97" International Stamp Exhibition (No. 1671la)
Commonwealth Heads of Government Meeting, Edinburgh (No. 1671la)
50th Birthday of Prince of Wales (No. 1671la)
50th Anniversary of Berlin Airlift (No. 1667m)
Rugby World Cup (No. 1667m)

First Day Covers

21.4.97	1st (No. 1668), 26p. (Y1686) (Type G) (Philatelic Bureau or Windsor)	3·50
23.9.97	B.B.C. label pane 1st × 4, 26p × 4 (No. 1668l), (Philatelic Bureau or London W1)	15·00
19.1.99	E (No. 1669) (Type G) (Philatelic Bureau or Windsor)	3·50
16.2.99	"Profile on Print" label pane 1st × 8 (No. 1671n) (see Nos. 2077/9) (Philatelic Bureau or London SW1)	5·50
6.2.02	"A Gracious Accession" label pane 2nd × 4 and E × 4 (No. 1664n) (see Nos. 2253/7) (Tallents House or Windsor)	5·00
24.9.02	"Across the Universe" label pane 1st × 4, E × 4 (No. 1668m) (Tallents House or Star, Glenrothes)	5·00
25.2.03	"Microcosmos" label pane 1st × 4, E × 4 (No. 1668n) (Tallents House or Cambridge)	5·00
2.6.03	"A Perfect Coronation" label pane 2nd × 4, 1st × 4 (No. 1664o) (Tallents House or London SW1)	4·00
16.3.04	"Letters by Night: A Tribute to the Travelling Post Office" label pane 1st × 4, 37p × 4 (No. 1668o) (Tallents House or London NW10)	11·00
25.5.04	"The Glory of the Garden" label pane 1st × 4, 42p × 2, 47p × 2 (No. 1668p) (Tallents House or Wisley, Woking	11·00
24.2.05	The Brontë Sisters label pane 2nd × 4, 39p. × 2, 42p. × 2 (No. 1664p) (Tallents House or Haworth, Keighley) ...	5·00
18.10.05	Bicentenary of the Battle of Trafalgar label pane 1st × 4, 50p. × 2 and 68p. × 2 (No. 1668q) (Tallents House and Portsmouth	8·50
23.2.06	Birth Bicentenary of Isambard Kingdom Brunel label pane 1st × 4, 35p. × 2 and 40p. × 2 (No. 1668r) (Tallents House or Bristol)	7·00
18.1.08	James Bond label pane 1st × 8 (No. 1762a) (Tallents House or London SE1)	7·50
18.9.08	'Pilot to Plane'. RAF Uniforms label pane 2nd×4 and 1st×4 (No.1670l) (Tallents House or Hendon, London NW9)	8·00

Denominated stamps, PVA gum, elliptical perforations

II Normal figures of face value

III Open '4' and open lower curve of '5'

1993 (27 Apr)–**2011**. As Nos. X841, etc, but P 15 × 14 (with one elliptical hole in each vertical side).

(a) Photo

Enschedé: – 20p. (Y1679), 29p., 35p. (Y1692), 36p., 38p. (Y1700), 41p. (Y1706), 43p. (Y1710)

Harrison: – 20p. (Y1681), 25p. (Y1683), 26p. (Y1686), 35p. (Y1693), 41p. (Y1707), 43p. (Y1711)

Walsall: – 10p. (Y1676a), 19p. (Y1678), 38p. (Y1701a), 43p. (Y1711a).

Enschedé or Harrison/De La Rue: – 4p., 5p., 6p., 10p. (Y1676), 25p. (Y1684), 31p., 39p. (Y1702), £1 (Y1725)

Enschedé, Harrison/De La Rue or Questa: – 1p., 2p.

Enschedé, Harrison/De La Rue or Walsall: – 30p., 37p. (Y1697), 42p., 50p. (Y1719), 63p.

Harrison/De La Rue or Questa: – 19p. (Y1677), 20p. (Y1680), 26p. (Y1685)

De La Rue or Walsall: – 38p. (Y1701), 39p. (Y1703), 40p. (Y1704), 64p., 65p., 68p.

De La Rue: – 7p., 8p., 9p., 12p., 14p., 15p., 16p., 17p., 20p. (Y1682), 22p., 33p., 34p., 35p. (Y1694), 37p. (Y1698/9), 41p. (Y1708), 43p. (Y1712), 44p., 45p., 48p., 49p., 50p., (Y1719b), 56p., 60p., 62p., 67p., 72p., 78p., 81p., 88p., 90p., 97p., £1 (Y1725b), £1.46, £1.50, £2, £3, £5

Enschedé or De La Rue: – 35p. (Y1695), 40p. (Y1705), 46p., 47p., 54p.

Y1667	**367**	1p. crimson (2 bands) (8.6.93)	25	25
		l. Booklet pane. Nos. Y1667 × 2, Y1680 and Y1685 × 3 plus 2 labels (1.12.98)	20·00	
		m. Booklet pane. Nos. Y1667/8, Y1677 and Y1685 × 3 plus 2 labels (26.4.99)	6·50	
		n. Booklet pane. Nos. Y1667 × 4, Y1677 × 3 and Y1685 with central label and margins all round (21.9.99)	4·50	
		o. Booklet pane. Nos. Y1667 ×2, Y1716 × 4 and Y1719c × 2 with central label and margins all round (20.9.07)	6·00	
Y1668		2p. dp green (2 bands) (11.4.95)	25	25
		a. Imperf (pair)	£2300	
		b. Booklet pane. Nos. Y1668 × 4 and Nos. Y1716 and Y1717a, each × 2 with centre label and margins all round (5.6.07)	4·25	
Y1669		4p. new blue (2 bands) (14.12.93)	25	25
		a. Imperf	£1700	
Y1670		5p. dull red-brown (Type II) (2 bands) (8.6.93)	25	25
		a. Booklet pane. Nos. Y1670 and 2651, each ×4, with centre label and margins all round (1.3.07)	3·50	
Y1671		6p. yellow-olive (2 bands)	25	30
Y1672		7p. grey (2 bands) (20.4.99)	2·50	2·50
		a. Imperf (pair)	£175	
Y1673		7p. bright magenta (2 bands) (1.4.04)	75	75
		a. Imperf (pair)	£225	
Y1674		8p. yellow (2 bands) (25.4.00)	35	35
Y1675		9p. yellow-orange (2 bands) (5.4.05)	15	20
Y1676		10p. dull orange (2 bands) (8.6.93)	35	35
		aa. Imperf pair	£1000	
		a. Perf 14 (13.10.98)	2·00	2·00
		al. Booklet pane. Nos. Y1676a × 2, 1665Ec and Y1711a, each × 3, with centre label and margins all round	12·00	
Y1676b		12p. greenish blue (2 bands) (1.8.06)	20	25
Y1676c		14p. rose red (2 bands) (1.8.06)	20	25
Y1676d		15p. bright magenta (2 bands) (1.4.08)	35	35
Y1676e		16p. pale cerise (2 bands) (27.3.07)	35	35
Y1676f		17p. brown-olive (2 bands) (31.3.09)	50	50
Y1677		19p. bistre (1 centre band) (26.10.93)	75	75
		a. Imperf (pair)	£500	
		l. Booklet pane. Nos. Y1677 and Y1685 × 7 (26.4.99)	13·00	
		Ey. Phosphor omitted	£125	
Y1678		19p. bistre (1 band at right) (p 14) (15.2.00)	2·00	2·00

		l. Booklet pane. Nos. Y1678 × 4 and Y1701a × 2 with margins all round	22·00	
Y1679		20p. turquoise-green (2 bands) (14.12.93)	90	90
Y1680		20p. brt green (1 centre band) (23.6.98)	70	70
		a. Imperf (horiz pair)	£325	
		l. Booklet pane. Nos. Y1680 and Y1685 × 7 (1.12.98)	22·00	
Y1681		20p. brt green (1 band at right) (23.9.97)	1·50	1·50
		l. Booklet pane. Nos. Y1681 and Y1685, each × 3 with margins all round	6·50	
Y1682		20p. brt green (2 bands) (20.4.99)	75	75
		a. Imperf (pair)	£400	
Y1682b		22p. drab (2 bands) (31.3.09)	50	50
Y1683		25p. rose-red (phosphorised paper) (26.10.93)	1·10	1·10
		a. Imperf (pair)	£900	
		l. Booklet pane. No. Y1683 × 2 plus 2 labels (1.11.93)	2·25	
Y1684		25p. rose-red (2 bands) (20.12.94)	1·10	1·10
		l. Booklet pane. No. Y1684 × 2 plus 2 labels (6.6.95)	3·50	
Y1685		26p. red-brown (2 bands) (25.6.96)	1·10	1·10
		a. Imperf	£600	
Y1686		26p. gold (2 bands) (21.4.97)	1·10	1·10
		ba. Imperf (horiz pair)	£2500	
Y1687		29p. grey (2 bands) (26.10.93)	1·25	1·25
Y1688		30p. dp olive-grey (2 bands) (27.7.93)	1·10	1·10
		a. Imperf (pair)	£1300	
Y1689		31p. dp mauve (2 bands) (25.6.96)	1·20	1·20
Y1690		33p. grey-green (2 bands) (25.4.00)	1·50	1·50
Y1691		34p. yellow-olive (2 bands) (6.5.03)	4·00	3·00
Y1692		35p. yellow (2 bands) (17.8.93)	1·50	1·50
Y1693		35p. yellow (phosphorised paper) (1.11.93)	12·00	12·00
Y1694		35p. sepia (2 bands) (1.4.04)	1·10	1·10
		a. Imperf (pair)	£325	
Y1695		35p. yellow-olive (5.4.05) (1 centre band)	50	55
Y1696		36p. brt ultramarine (2 bands) (26.10.93)	1·50	1·50
Y1697		37p. brt mauve (2 bands) (25.6.96)	1·40	1·40
Y1698		37p. grey-black (2 bands) (4.7.02)	1·40	1·40
Y1699		37p. brown-olive (1 centre band) (28.3.06)	90	90
Y1700		38p. rosine (2 bands) (26.10.93)	1·50	1·50
		a. Imperf (pair)	£350	
Y1701		38p. ultramarine (2 bands) (20.4.99)	2·00	2·00
		a. Perf 14 (15.2.00)	7·50	7·50
Y1702		39p. brt magenta (2 bands) (25.6.96)	1·50	1·50
		a. Imperf (pair)	£1500	
Y1703		39p. grey (2 bands) (1.4.04)	1·20	1·20
		a. Imperf (pair)	£325	
Y1704		40p. dp azure (2 bands) (25.4.00)	1·40	1·40
Y1705		40p. turquoise-blue (2 bands) (1.4.04)	1·30	1·30
		a. Imperf (pair)	£850	
Y1706		41p. grey-brown (2 bands) (26.10.93)	1·75	1·75
Y1707		41p. drab (phosphorised paper) (1.11.93)	12·00	12·00
Y1708		41p. rosine (2 bands) (25.4.00)	1·40	1·40
Y1709		42p. dp olive-grey (2 bands) (4.7.02)	1·40	1·40
Y1710		43p. dp olive-brown (2 bands) (25.6.96)	1·75	1·75
Y1711		43p. sepia (2 bands) (8.7.96)	2·50	2·50
		a. Perf 14 (13.10.98)	2·50	2·50
Y1712		43p. emerald (2 bands) (1.4.04)	1·40	1·40
		a. Imperf (pair)	£300	
Y1713		44p. grey-brown (2 bands) (20.4.99)	5·00	5·00
Y1714		44p. deep bright blue (2 bands) (28.3.06)	1·00	1·00
Y1715		45p. brt mauve (2 bands) (25.4.00)	1·50	1·50
Y1716		46p. yellow (2 bands) (5.4.05)	1·00	1·00
Y1717		47p. turquoise-green (2 bands) (4.7.02)	1·75	1·75
Y1717a		48p. bright mauve (2 bands) (27.3.07)	1·00	1·00
Y1718		49p. red-brown (2 bands) (28.3.06)	1·00	1·00
Y1719		50p. ochre (2 bands) (14.12.93)	1·75	1·75
		a. Imperf (pair)	£500	
Y1719b		50p. grey (2 bands) (27.3.07)	1·00	1·00
Y1719c		54p. red-brown (Type II) (2 bands) (27.3.07)	1·10	1·10
Y1719d		60p. light emerald (2 bands) (30.3.10)	1·40	1·40
Y1719e		62p. rosine (2 bands) (31.3.09)	1·40	1·40
Y1719f		62p. rosine (2 bands) (31.3.09)	1·40	1·40
Y1720		63p. lt emerald (2 bands) (25.6.96)	2·00	2·00
Y1721		64p. turquoise-green (2 bands) (20.4.99)	2·25	2·25
Y1722		65p. greenish blue (2 bands) (25.4.00)	2·10	2·10
Y1722a		67p. bright mauve (2 bands) (30.3.10)	1·50	1·50
Y1723		68p. grey-brown (2 bands) (4.7.02)	2·10	2·10
Y1724		72p. rosine (2 bands) (28.3.06)	1·50	1·50
Y1724a		78p. emerald (2 bands) (27.3.07)	1·50	1·50
Y1724b		81p. turquoise-green (2 bands) (1.4.08)	1·50	1·50
Y1724c		88p. bright magenta (2 bands) (30.3.10)	2·00	2·00

Y1724d	90p. ultramarine (2 bands) (31.3.09)	2·00	2·00
Y1724e	97p. bluish violet (2 bands) (30.3.10)	2·25	2·25
Y1725	£1 bluish violet (2 bands) (22.8.95)	3·25	3·00
	a. Imperf (horiz pair)	£1500	
Y1725b	£1 magenta (2 bands) (5.6.07)	2·00	2·00
	ba. Booklet pane. No. Y1725b × 2 with		
	centre label and margins all round	4·50	
Y1725c	£1.46 greenish blue (2 bands) (30.3.10) ...	3·25	3·25
Y1726	£1.50 brown-red (2 bands) (1.7.03)	4·00	4·00
Y1727	£2 deep blue-green (2 bands) (1.7.03)	5·50	5·50
	a. Missing "£" in value (R. 18/1, Cyl D1		
	no dot)	£175	
Y1728	£3 deep mauve (2 bands) (1.7.03)	8·00	8·00
Y1729	£5 azure (2 bands) (1.7.03)	14·00	14·00

(b) Litho Cartor (1p. (Y1743n), 5p. (Y1743t), 10p. (Y1749a), 16p., 17p., 20p., (Y1751m), 22p., 50p., 54p., 60p. (Y1758a), 62p., 67p., 90p., 97p. De La Rue or Cartor (5p. (Y1743s)), Questa, De La Rue or Cartor (10p. (Y1749)), Questa or Wasall (25p., 35p., 41p.), Walsall (37p., 60p. (Y1758), 63p.), De La Rue (48p.), Questa (others).

Y1743 **367**	1p. lake (2 bands) (8.7.96)	40	40
	Ey. Phosphor omitted	£500	
	l. Booklet pane. Nos. Y1743 × 2,		
	Y1751 and Y1753 × 3 plus 2 labels	5·00	
	lEy. Booklet pane. Phosphor omitted ..	£1200	
Y1743n	1p. reddish purple (2 bands) (17.9.09) ...	1·75	1·75
	na. Booklet pane. Nos. Y1743n×2,		
	Y1749n×4 and Y1760×2 with		
	central label and margins all		
	round	8·00	
Y1743s	5p. chocolate (2 bands) (12.2.09)	2·25	2·25
	sa. Booklet pane. Nos. 1672, Y1743s,		
	Y1749 and Y1757f, each ×2 with		
	central label	8·00	
	saEy. Phosphor omitted		
	sb. Red-brown (13.5.10)	1·00	1·00
	sba. Booklet pane. Nos. Y1743sb ×4,		
	Y1749 ×2 and Y1758a ×2, with		
	central label and margins all		
	round	3·50	
	sc. Lake-brown (22.3.11)	80	80
	sca. Booklet pane. Nos. Y1743sc ×3,		
	Y1749 ×3, Y1759f and Y1761,		
	with central label and margins all		
	round	5·00	
Y1743t	5p. red-brown (2 bands) (Type III)		
	(7.1.10)	2·25	2·25
	ta. Booklet pane. Nos. Y1743t×2,		
	Y1749a×5 and Y1751n×2 with		
	margins all round	5·00	
Y1748	6p. yellow-olive (2 bands) (26.7.94)	12·00	13·00
	l. Booklet pane. Nos. Y1748, Y1750		
	and Y1752 × 4 with margins all		
	round	15·00	
	la. 6p. value misplaced	£2500	
Y1749	10p. dull orange (2 bands) (25.4.95)......	5·00	5·00
	a. Pale orange (7.1.10)	1·00	1·00
	l. Booklet pane. Nos. Y1749, Y1750/		
	Ea, Y1752 × 2, Y1754/5, Y1757Ea		
	and centre label with margins all		
	round	18·00	
Y1749m	16p. pale cerise (2 bands) (13.1.09)	1·95	1·95
	ma. Booklet pane. Nos. Y1749m and		
	1757g, each ×4, with central label	12·00	
Y1749n	17p. bistre (2 bands) (18.8.09)	1·00	1·00
	na. Booklet pane. Nos. Y1749n×4,		
	Y1751×2 and Y1758e×2 with		
	central label and margins all		
	round	6·50	
Y1750	19p. bistre (1 band at left) (26.7.94)......	1·90	1·75
	Ea. Band at right (25.4.95)	2·50	2·50
	l. Booklet pane. Nos. Y1750/Ea,		
	each × 3 with margins all round		
	(25.4.95)	14·00	
Y1751	20p. brt yellow-green (1 centre band)		
	(8.7.96)	2·25	2·25
	Ey. Phosphor omitted	£125	
	l. Booklet pane. Nos. Y1751 and		
	Y1753 × 7	8·00	
	lEy. Booklet pane. Phosphor omitted ..	£200	
Y1751m	20p. light green (2 bands) (7.1.10)	2·50	2·50
	ma. Booklet pane. Nos. Y1751m×4,		
	Y1757j×2 and Y1758e×2 with		
	central label and margins all		
	round	8·00	
Y1751n	22p. olive-brown (2 bands) (18.8.09)	2·50	2·50
	na. Booklet pane. Nos. Y1751n and		
	Y1757j, each×4 with central label		
	and margins all round (25.2.10)	8·00	
Y1752	25p. red (2 bands) (1.11.93)	1·10	1·10
	l. Booklet pane. Nos. Y1752, NI72,		
	S84 and W73, each × 2, with		
	centre label and margins all		
	round (14.5.96)	7·50	

Y1753	26p. chestnut (2 bands) (8.7.96)..............	1·00	1·00
	Ey. Phosphor omitted	10·00	
Y1754	30p. olive-grey (2 bands) (25.4.95)..........	4·25	4·25
Y1755	35p. yellow (2 bands) (1.11.93)	1·60	1·60
Y1756	37p. brt mauve (2 bands) (8.7.96)	3·50	3·50
Y1757	41p. drab (2 bands) (1.11.93)	1·75	1·75
	Ea. Grey-brown (25.4.95)	3·50	3·50
	Ey. Phosphor omitted	£750	
Y1757f	48p. bright mauve (2 bands) (12.2.09).....	2·75	2·75
Y1757g	50p. grey (2 bands) (13.1.09)	2·50	2·50
Y1757j	54p. chestnut (2 bands) (Type III)		
	(7.1.10)	1·50	1·50
Y1758	60p. dull blue-grey (2 bands) (9.8.94)....	2·50	2·50
Y1758a	60p. emerald (2 bands) (13.5.10)	1·40	1·40
Y1758e	62p. rosine (2 bands) (18.8.09)	1·75	1·75
Y1758f	67p. bright mauve (2 bands) (22.3.11).....	2·50	2·50
Y1759	63p. lt emerald (2 bands) (8.7.96)	3·50	3·50
	Ey. Phosphor omitted	£500	
Y1760	90p. bright blue (2 bands) (17.9.09)	4·00	4·00
Y1761	97p. bluish violet (2 bands) (22.3.11)	3·50	3·50

(c) Eng C. Slania. Recess Enschedé (until Mar 2000) or De La Rue (from 11 Apr 2000)

Y1800 **367**	£1.50 red (9.3.99)	4·50	2·00
Y1801	£2 dull blue (9.3.99)	6·00	2·25
Y1802	£3 dull violet (9.3.99)	9·00	3·00
Y1803	£5 brown (9.3.99)	15·50	5·00
	a. Imperf (pair)	£3000	

P.H.Q. Card (No. Y1725).. 3·00 15·00
P.H.Q. Cards (Nos. 1664, 1668, Y1667/8, Y1670, Y1675/6, Y1676d/e, Y1682, Y1717a, Y1719b, Y1719d, Y1724b, Y1725b, Y1726/9, 2357a/9, 2652/3 .... 7·00

No. Y1684 exists with the phosphor bands omitted, but can only be identified by the use of a u.v. lamp (Price £24 unused).

Nos. Y1725/9 are printed in Iriodin ink which gives a shiny effect to the solid part of the background behind the Queen's head.

No. Y1748la shows the 6p. value printed 22 mm to the left so that its position on the booklet pane is completely blank except for the phosphor bands. Other more minor misplacements exist.

The De La Rue printings of the high values, Nos. Y1800/3 cannot easily be identified from the original Enschedé issue as single stamps.

For self-adhesive versions of the 42p. and 68p. see Nos. 2297/8.

First Day Covers

26.10.93	19p., 25p., 29p., 36p., 38p., 41p. (Y1677, Y1683, Y1687, Y1696, Y1700, Y1706)	6·00
9.8.94	60p. (Y1758)	4·00
25.4.95	National Trust se-tenant pane 10p., 19p., 25p., 30p., 35p., 41p. (Y1749l)	5·00
22.8.95	£1 (Y1725)	3·50
14.5.96	European Football Championship se-tenant pane 25p. × 8 (Y1752l)	7·50
25.6.96	20p., 26p., 31p., 37p., 39p., 43p., 63p. (Y1680, Y1685, Y1689, Y1697, Y1702, Y1710, Y1720)	8·00
13.10.98	Speed se-tenant pane 10p., 2nd, 43p. (Y1676al)	6·50
9.3.99	£1·50, £2, £3, £5 (Y1800/3) (Type G) (Philatelic Bureau or Windsor)	27·00
20.4.99	7p., 38p., 44p., 64p. (Y1672, Y1701, Y1713, Y1721) (Type G) (Philatelic Bureau or Windsor)	5·00
21.9.99	World Changers se-tenant pane 1p.,19p., 26p. (Y1667n) (Philatelic Bureau or Downe, Orpington)	4·00
25.4.00	8p., 33p., 40p., 41p., 45p., 65p. (Y1674, Y1690, Y1704, Y1708, Y1715, Y1722) (Type G) (Philatelic Bureau or Windsor)	5·00
4.7.02	37p., 42p., 47p., 68p. (Y1698, Y1709, Y1716, Y1723) (Type K) (Tallents House or Windsor)	4·00
6.5.03	34p., (Y1691) (Type K) (Tallents House or Windsor)	1·20
1.7.03	£1·50, £2, £3, £5 (Nos. Y1726/9) (Type K) (Tallents House or Windsor)	21·00
1.4.04	7p., 35p., 39p., 40p., 43p. Worldwide postcard (Y1673, Y1694, Y1703, Y1705, Y1712, 2357a) (Type K) (Tallents House or Windsor)	9·00
5.4.05	9p., 35p., 46p. (Nos. Y1675, Y1695, Y1716) (Type K) (Tallents House or Windsor)	2·20
28.3.06	37p., 44p., 49p., 72p. (Y1699, Y1714, Y1718, Y1724) (Type K) (Tallents House or Windsor)	4·25
1.3.07	World of Invention label pane 5p., 1st (Y1670a) (Tallents House or Menai Bridge, Gwynedd)	5·00
27.3.07	16p., 48p., 50p., 54p., 78p. (Y1676e, Y1717a, Y1719b/c, Y1724a) (Type K) (Tallents House or Windsor)	6·00
5.6.07	Machin Anniversary se-tenant pane 2p., 46p., 48p. (Y1668b) (Tallents House, Windsor or Stoke-on-Trent)	5·00
20.9.07	Army Uniforms se-tenant pane 1p., 46p., 54p. (Y1667o) (Tallents House or Boot, Holmrook, Cumbria)	7·00
1.4.08	15p., 56p., 81p. (Y1676d, Y1719d, Y1724b) (Type K) (Tallents House or Windsor)	4·50
13.1.09	British Design Classics se-tenant pane 16p., 50p. (Y1749ma) (Tallents House or Longbridge, Birmingham)	7·00
12.2.09	Charles Darwin se-tenant pane 5p., 10p., 1st, 48p. (Y1743ma) (Tallents House or Shrewsbury)	5·00
31.3.09	17p., 22p., 62p., 90p. (Y1676f, Y1682k, Y1719f, Y1724d) (Type K) (Tallents House or Windsor)	6·00

18.8.09	"Treasures of the Arctive" se-tenant pane 17p., 22p., 62p., (Y1749na) (Tallents House or Wakefield, W. Yorkshire)	7·00
17.9.09	Royal Navy Uniforms se-tenant pane 1p., 17p., 90p. (Y1743na) (Tallents House or Portsmouth)	7·00
7.1.10	Classic Album Covers se-tenant pane 20p., 54p., 52p. (Y1751ma) (Tallents House or Oldfield, Keighley)	7·25
25.2.10	Royal Society se-tenant pane 22p., 54p. (Y1751na) (Tallents House or London SW1)	7·00
30.3.10	60p., 67p., 88p., 97p., £1.46, Europe up to 20 grams, Worldwide up to 20 grams (Y1719e, Y1722a, Y1724c, Y1724e, Y1725c, 2357b, 2358a (Type K) (Tallents House or Windwor)	14·00
13.5.10	"Britain Alone" se-tenant pane 5p., 10p., 60p., (Y1743sb) (Tallents House or Dover, Kent)	5·50
22.3.11	WWF se-tenant pane 5p., 10p., 67p., 97p. (Y1743c) (Tallents House or Godalming, Surrey)	7·50

For first day covers for Nos. Y1676b/c see under Nos. 2650/7.

Special First Day of Issue Postmarks

Post Office Presentation Packs

26.10.93	P.O. Pack No. 30. 19p. (1 centre band), 25p. (phos paper), 29p., 36p., 38p. rosine, 41p. grey-brown (Nos. Y1677, Y1683, Y1687, Y1696, Y1700, Y1706)	7·00
21.11.95	P.O. Pack No. 34. 1p. (photo), 2p., 4p., 5p., 6p. (photo), 10p. (photo), 19p. (1 centre band), 20p. turquoise-green, 25p. (photo) (2 bands), 29p., 30p. (photo), 35p. (photo) (2 bands), 36p., 38p. rosine, 41p. grey-brown, 50p., 60p., £1 (Nos. Y1667/71, Y1676/7, Y1679, Y1684, Y1687/8, Y1692, Y1696, Y1700, Y1706, Y1719, Y1758, Y1725)	30·00
25.6.96	P.O. Pack No. 35. 20p. brt green (1 centre band), 26p. (photo), 31p., 37p. (photo), 39p., 43p. deep olive brown, 63p. (photo) (Nos. Y1680, Y1685, Y1689, Y1697, Y1702, Y1710, Y1720)	9·50
21.4.97	P.O. Pack No. 38. 1st, 26p. gold (Nos. 1668, Y1686)	7·50
20.10.98	P.O. Pack No. 41. 2nd brt blue (1 centre band), 1st orange-red (2 phosphor bands), 1p., 2p., 4p., 5p., 6p., 10p., 20p. brt green (1 centre band), 26p., 30p., 31p., 37p., 39p., 43p. sepia, 50p., 63p., £1 (Nos. 1664, 1667, Y1667/71, Y1676, Y1680, Y1685, Y1688/9, Y1697, Y1702, Y1711, Y1719/20, Y1725)	16·00
9.3.99	P.O. Pack No. 43 or 43a. £1·50, £2, £3, £5 (Nos. Y1800/3)	55·00
20.4.99	P.O. Pack No. 44. 7p., 19p., 38p. ultramarine, 44p., 64p. (Nos. Y1672, Y1677, Y1701, Y1713, Y1721)	11·00
25.4.00	P.O. Pack No. 49. 8p., 33p., 40p., 41p. rosine, 45p., 65p. (Nos. Y1674, Y1690, Y1704, Y1708, Y1715, Y1722)	10·00
12.3.02	P.O. Pack No. 57. 2nd, 1st, E, 1p., 2p., 4p., 5p., 8p., 10p., 20p., 33p., 40p., 41p., 45p., 50p., 65p., £1 (Nos. 1664, 1667, 1669, Y1667/70, Y1674, Y1676, Y1682, Y1690, Y1704, Y1708, Y1715, Y1719, Y1722, Y1725)	16·00
4.7.02	P.O. Pack No. 58. 37p., 42p., 47p., 68p. (Nos. Y1698, Y1709, Y1717, Y1723)	7·50
1.7.03	P.O. Pack No. 62. £1·50, £2, £3, £5 (Nos. Y1726/9)	23·00
1.4.04	P.O. Pack No. 67. 1st gold (DLR ptg), 7p., 35p., 39p., 40p., 43p. Worldwide postcard (Nos. 1668, Y1673, Y1694, Y1703, Y1705, Y1712, 2357a)	6·00
6.9.05	P.O. Pack No. 71. 1p., 2p., 5p., 9p., 10p., 20p., 35p., 40p., 42p., 46p., 47p., 50p., 68p., £1., 2nd, 1st, Worldwide postcard, Europe, Worldwide (Nos. Y1667/8, Y1670, Y1675/6, Y1682, Y1695, Y1705, Y1709, Y1716/17, Y1719, Y1723, Y1725, 2039, 2295, 2357a/9)	11·50
28.3.06	P.O. Pack No. 72. 37p., 44p., 49p., 72p. (Nos. Y1699, Y1714, Y1718, Y1724)	3·50
27.3.07	P.O. Pack No. 75. 16p., 48p., 50p., 54p., 78p. (Nos. Y1676e, Y1717a, Y1719b, Y1719c, Y1724a)	6·75
5.6.07	P.O. Pack No. 77. 2nd, 1st, 1p., 2p., 5p., 10p., 14p., 16p., 20p., 46p., 48p., 50p., 54p., 78p., £1, Worldwide postcard, Europe up to 40 grams, Worldwide up to 40 grams, 2nd Large, 1st Large (Nos. 1664, 1666, Y1667/70, Y1670, Y1676, Y1676c/d, Y1682, Y1716, Y1717a, Y1719b/c, Y1724a, Y1725b, 2357a/9, 2652/3)	20·00
1.4.08	P.O. Pack. No. 78. 15p., 56p., 81p. (Nos. Y1676d, Y1719d, Y1724b)	4·00
31.3.09	P.O. Pack No. 84 17p., 22p., 62p., 90p. (Nos. Y1676f, Y1682b, Y1719e, Y1724c)	5·25
30.3.10	P.O. Pack No. 86. 60p. 67p., 88p., 97p., £1.46, Europe up to 20 grams, Worldwide up to 20 grams, 1st Recorded Signed For, 1st Large Recorded Signed For (Nos. Y1719e, Y1722a, Y1724c, Y1724e, Y1725c, 2357b, 2358a, U2940/1)	20·00
8.5.10	P.O. Pack No. 88. 2nd, 1st, 1p., 2p., 5p., 9p., 10p., 20p., 50p., 60p., 67p., 88p., 97p., £1, £1.46, Worldwide postcard, Europe up to 20 grams Worldwide up to 20 grams, Europe up to 40 grams, worldwide up to 40 grams, 2nd Large, 1st Large, 1st Recorded Signed For, 1st Large Recorded Signed For (Nos. 1664, 1668, Y1667, Y1668, Y1670, Y1675, Y1676, Y1682, Y1719b, Y1719e, Y1722a, Y1724c, Y1724e, Y1725b, Y1725c, 2357a/9, 2652/3 and U2940/1)	35·00

In 2002 a 'master' presentation pack entitled 'Royal Mail Definitive Stamps Collection' was released, containing packs 43a, 53, 54, 55, 56 and 57 (Price £120).

Decimal Machin Index
(stamps with elliptical perforations, including (N.V.Is)

Value	Process	Colour	Phosphor	Cat. No.	Source
2nd	litho Questa or Walsall	brt blue	1 centre band	1670	sheets (Questa), booklets of 4 (Walsall – HA6, Walsall HA9/11), booklets of 10 (Questa – HC11, HC13, HC16, HC18, HC20, Walsall – HC12), $7.15 "Pilot to Plane" booklet (Walsall - DX42)
2nd	photo Harrison/De La Rue), Enschedé, Questa or Walsall	brt blue	1 centre band	1664	sheets (Walsall, De La Rue), horizontal coil (Harrison/De La Rue), vertical coils (Harrison/De La Rue or Enschedé) booklets of 4 (Harrison – HA7/8, Walsall – HA12), booklets of 10 (Harrison/De La Rue – HC14/15, HC17, HC19, HC21), £1 booklet (Questa – FH44/a), £2 booklet (Questa – FW12), £7.29 "A Gracious Accession" booklet (Enschedé – DX28), £7.46 "A Perfect Coronation" booklet (Walsall – DX31), £7.43 The Brontë Sisters booklet (Walsall – DX34)
2nd	photo Walsall (p 14)	brt blue	1 band at right	1665	£6.16 British Land Speed Record Holders booklet (DX21)
2nd	photo Walsall (p 14)	brt blue	1 band at left	1665Ec	£6.16 British Land Speed Record Holders booklet (DX21)
2nd	photo Questa (p 14)	brt blue	1 centre band	1664a	booklets of 10 (HC22)
1st	litho Enschedé, Questa or Walsall	brt orange-red	2 bands	1671	sheets (Questa), greetings card panes Questa – Y1671m/ ma, Enschedé – Y1671hb), booklets of 4 (Walsall – HB6, HB8/13, HB15/16, Questa – HB7), booklets of 10 Walsall – HD10, HD12/19, HD22/3, HD25, HD28, HD34, HD36/8, HD40, Questa – HD11, HD21, HD26, HD50), £7.54 "Profile on Print" booklet (Questa – DX22)
1st	photo Harrison	brt orange-red	phos paper	1666	booklets of 4 (HB5), booklets of 10 (HD9, HD20)
1st	photo Harrison/ De La Rue, Questa or Walsall	brt orange-red	2 bands	1667	sheets (Walsall), horizontal and vertical coils (Harrison, De La Rue), booklets of 4 (Walsall – HB14, HB17/18), booklets of 8 with 2 Millennium commems (Walsall – HBA1/2), booklets of 10 (Harrison/De La Rue – HD24, HD27, HD29/33, HD35, HD39, HD45/9, Walsall – HD44), £1 booklet (Questa – FH44/a), £2 booklet (Questa – FW12), £7.54 "Profile on Print" booklet (De La Rue – DX22)
1st	photo Questa (p 14)	brt orange-red	2 bands	1667a	booklets of 10 (HD51)
1st	photo De La Rue, Enschedé, Harrison, Questa or Walsall	gold	2 bands	1668	sheets (Walsall, De La Rue), vertical coils (Enschedé, De La Rue), booklets of 10 (Harrison – HD41, HD43, Walsall – HD42), £6.15 B.B.C. booklet (Harrison – DX19), £6.83 "Across the Universe" booklet (Questa – DX29, £6.99 "Microcosmos" booklet (Enschedé – DX30), £7.46 "A Perfect Coronation" booklet (Walsall – DX31), £7.44 "Letters by Night" booklet (De La Rue – DX32), £7.23 "The Glory of the Garden" booklet (Enschedé – DX33), £7.26 Trafalgar booklet (Walsall – DX35), £7.40 Brunel booklet (Enschedé – DX36)
1st	litho De La Rue or Walsall	gold	2 bands	1672	£7.40 Ian Fleming's James Bond booklet (De La Rue – DX41), £7.15 "Pilot to Plane" booklet (Walsall - DX42)
E	photo De La Rue, Enschedé, Questa or Walsall	deep blue	2 bands	1669	sheets (De La Rue), booklets of 4 (Walsall – HF1), £7.29 "A Gracious Accession" booklet (Enschedé – DX28), £6.83 "Across the Universe" booklet (Questa – DX29), £6.99 "Microcosmos" booklet (Enschedé – DX30)
1p.	photo De La Rue, Enschedé, Harrison or Questa	crimson	2 bands	Y1667	sheets, £1 booklets (Questa – FH42/3), £6.91 World Changers booklet (Questa – DX23) , £7.66 British Army Uniforms booklet (Enschedé – DX40)
1p.	litho Questa	lake	2 bands	Y1743	£1 booklet (FH41)
1p.	litho Cartor	reddish purple	2 bands	Y1743n	£7.93 Royal Navy Uniforms booklet (DX47)
2p.	photo De La Rue, Enschedé, Harrison or Questa	dp green	2 bands	Y1668	sheets, £1 booklet (Questa – FH43), £7.66 "The Machin" booklet (De La Rue – DX39)
4p.	photo De La Rue, Enschedé or Harrison	new blue	2 bands	Y1669	sheets
4p.	photo De La Rue	new blue	phos paper	MS2146	Jeffery Matthews Colour Palette miniature sheet
5p.	photo De La Rue, Enschedé or Harrison	dull red-brown	2 bands	Y1670	sheets , £7.49 World of Invention booklet (De La Rue – DX38)
5p.	photo De La Rue	dull red-brown	phos paper	MS2146	Jeffery Matthews Colour Palette miniature sheet
5p.	litho De La Rue	chocolate	2 bands	Y1743s	£7.75 Charles Darwin booklet (DX45)
5p.	litho Cartor	red-brown	2 bands	Y1743sb	£9.76 Great Britain Alone booklet (DX51)
5p.	litho Cartor	lake-brown	2 bands	Y1743sc	£9.05 WWF booklet (DX52)
5p.	litho Cartor	red-brown	2 bands	Y1743t	Type III. £8.06 Classic Album Covers booklet (DX48)
6p.	photo Enschedé or Harrison	yellow-olive	2 bands	Y1671	sheets
6p.	litho Questa	yellow-olive	2 bands	Y1748	£6.04 Northern Ireland booklet (DX16)
6p.	photo De La Rue	yellow-olive	phos paper	MS2146	Jeffery Matthews Colour Palette miniature sheet
7p.	photo De La Rue	grey	2 bands	Y1672	sheets
7p.	photo De La Rue	bright magenta	2 bands	Y1673	sheets
8p.	photo De La Rue	yellow	2 bands	Y1674	sheets
9p.	photo De La Rue	yellow-orange	2 bands	Y1675	sheets

Value	Process	Colour	Phosphor	Cat. No.	Source
10p.	photo De La Rue, Enschedé or Harrison	dull orange	2 bands	Y1676	sheets
10p.	litho Questa, De La Rue or Cartor	dull orange	2 bands	Y1749	£6 National Trust booklet (Questa - DX17), £7.75 Charles Darwin booklet (De La Rue - DX45), £9.76 "Britain Alone" booklet (Cartor - DX51), £9.05 WWF booklet (Cartor - DX52)
10p.	litho Cartor	pale orange	2 bands	Y1749a	£8.06 Classic Album Covers booklet (DX48)
10p.	photo Walsall (p 14)	dull orange	2 bands	Y1676a	£6.16 British Land Speed Record Holders booklet (DX21)
10p.	photo De La Rue	dull orange	phos paper	MS2146	Jeffery Matthews Colour Palette miniature sheet
12p.	photo De La Rue	greenish blue	2 bands	Y1676b	sheets
14p.	photo De La Rue	rose-red	2 bands	Y1676c	sheets
15p.	photo De La Rue	bright magenta	2 bands	Y1676d	sheets
16p.	photo De La Rue	pale cerise	2 bands	Y1676e	sheets
16p.	litho Cartor	pale cerise	2 bands	Y1749m	£7.75 British Design Classics booklet (DX44)
17p.	photo De La Rue	brown-olive	2 bands	Y1676f	sheets
17p.	litho Cartor	bistre	2 bands	Y1749n	£8.18 "Treasures of the Archive" booklet (DX46) and £7.93 Royal Navy Uniforms booklet (DX47)
19p.	photo Harrison or Questa	bistre	1 centre band	Y1677	sheets, vertical coils, £1 booklet (Questa – FH43), £2 booklet (Questa – FW11), £6.99 World Changers booklet (Questa – DX23)
19p.	litho Questa	bistre	1 band at left	Y1750	£6.04 Northern Ireland booklet (DX16), £6 National Trust booklet (DX17)
19p.	litho Questa	bistre	1 band at right	Y1750Ea	£6 National Trust booklet (DX17)
19p.	photo Walsall (p 14)	bistre	1 band at right	Y1678	£7.50 "Special by Design" booklet (DX24)
20p.	photo Enschedé	turquoise-green	2 bands	Y1679	sheets
20p.	photo Harrison or Questa	brt green	1 centre band	Y1680	sheets, £1 booklet (Questa – FH42), £2 booklet (Questa – FW10)
20p.	litho Questa	brt yellow-green	1 centre band	Y1751	£1 booklet (FH41), £2 booklet (FW9)
20p.	photo Harrison	brt green	1 band at right	Y1681	£6.15 B.B.C. booklet (DX19)
20p.	photo De La Rue	brt green	2 bands	Y1682	sheets
20p.	litho Cartor	light green	2 bands	Y1751m	£8.06 Classic Album Covers booklet (DX48)
22p.	photo De La Rue	drab	2 bands	Y1682b	sheets
22p.	litho Cartor	olive-brown	2 bands	Y1751n	£8.18 "Treasures of the Archive" booklet (DX46), £8.06 Classic Album Covers booklet (DX48) and £7.72 Royal Society booklet (DX49)
25p.	photo Harrison	rose-red	phos paper	Y1683	sheets, vertical coils, 50p booklets (FB67/73), £1 booklets (FH33/7), £2 booklets (FW1/5)
25p.	litho Walsall or Questa	red	2 bands	Y1752	£1 booklets (Walsall – FH31/2), (Questa – FH40), £2 booklet (Questa – FW8), £6.04 Northern Ireland booklet (Questa – DX16), £6 National Trust booklet (Questa – DX17), £6.84 European Football Championship (Questa – DX18)
25p.	photo Harrison or Enschedé	rose-red	2 bands	Y1684	sheets (Harrison or Enschedé), vertical coils (Harrison), 50p booklets (Harrison – FB74/5), £1 booklets (Harrison – FH38/9)), £2 booklets (Harrison – FW6/7)
26p.	photo Harrison or Questa	red-brown	2 bands	Y1685	sheets, £1 booklets (Questa – FH42/3), £2 booklets (Questa – FW10/11), £6.15 B.B.C. booklet (Harrison – DX19), £6.99 World Changers booklet (Questa – DX23)
26p.	litho Questa	chestnut	2 bands	Y1753	£1 booklet (FH41), £2 booklet (FW9)
26p.	photo Harrison	gold	2 bands	Y1686	sheets, £6.15 B B.C. booklet (Harrison – DX19)
29p.	photo Enschedé	grey	2 bands	Y1687	sheets
30p.	photo Enschedé, Harrison or Walsall	dp olive-grey	2 bands	Y1688	sheets, £1.20 booklets (Walsall – GGAI/2)
30p.	litho Questa	olive-grey	2 bands	Y1754	£6 National Trust booklet (DX17)
31p.	photo Enschedé or Harrison	dp mauve	2 bands	Y1689	sheets
31p.	photo De La Rue	dp mauve	phos paper	MS2146	Jeffery Matthews Colour Palette miniature sheet
33p.	photo De La Rue	grey-green	2 bands	Y1690	sheets
34p.	photo De La Rue	yellow-olive	2 bands	Y1691	sheets
35p.	photo Enschedé	yellow	2 bands	Y1692	sheets
35p.	photo Harrison	yellow	phos paper	Y1693	vertical coils
35p.	litho Walsall or Questa	yellow	2 bands	Y1755	£1.40 booklets (Walsall – GK5/7), £6 National Trust booklet (Questa – DX17)
35p.	photo De La Rue	sepia	2 bands	Y1694	sheets
35p.	photo Enschedé or De La Rue	yellow-olive	1 centre band	Y1695	sheets, £7.40 Brunel booklet (Enschedé – DX36)
36p.	photo Enschedé	brt ultramarine	2 bands	Y1696	sheets
37p.	photo Enschedé, Harrison or Walsall	brt mauve	2 bands	Y1697	sheets (Enschedé or Harrison), vertical coils (Harrison), £1.48 booklets (Walsall – GL3/4)
37p.	litho Walsall	brt mauve	2 bands	Y1756	£1.48 booklets (GL1/2)
37p.	photo De La Rue	grey-black	2 bands	Y1698	sheets, £7.44 "Letters by Night" booklet (De La Rue – DX32)
37p.	photo De La Rue	brown-olive	1 centre band	Y1699	sheets
38p.	photo Enschedé	rosine	2 bands	Y1700	sheets
38p.	photo De La Rue or Walsall	ultramarine	2 bands	Y1701	sheets (D.L.R.), £1.52 booklet (Walsall – GLAI)
38p.	photo Walsall (p 14)	ultramarine	2 bands	Y1701a	£7.50 "Special by Design" booklet (DX24)
39p.	photo Enschedé or Harrison	brt magenta	2 bands	Y1702	sheets
39p.	photo De La Rue	brt magenta	phos paper	MS2146	Jeffery Matthews Colour Palette miniature sheet
39p.	photo De La Rue or Walsall	grey	2 bands	Y1703	sheets (De La Rue), £7.43 The Brontë Sisters booklet (Walsall – DX34)
40p.	photo De La Rue or Walsall	deep azure	2 bands	Y1704	sheets (D.L.R.), £1.60 booklet (Walsall – GMA1)

Value	Process	Colour	Phosphor	Cat. No.	Source
40p.	photo De La Rue or Enschede	turquoise-blue	2 bands	Y1705	sheets (D.L.R.), £7.40 Brunel booklet (Enschedé – DX36)
41p.	photo Enschede	grey-brown	2 bands	Y1706	sheets
41p.	photo Harrison	drab	phos paper	Y1707	vertical coils
41p.	photo De La Rue	rosine	2 bands	Y1708	sheets
41p.	litho Walsall	drab	2 bands	Y1757	£1.64 booklets (GN1/3)
41p.	litho Questa	grey-brown	2 bands	Y1757Ea	£6 National Trust booklet (DX17)
42p.	photo De La Rue, Enschedé or Walsall	dp olive-grey	2 bands	Y1709	sheets (De La Rue), £7.23 "The Glory of the Garden" booklet (Enschedé – DX33), £7.43 The Brontë Sisters booklet (Walsall – DX34)
43p.	photo Enschedé	dp olive-brown	2 bands	Y1710	sheets
43p.	photo Harrison	sepia	2 bands	Y1711	sheets, vertical coils
43p.	photo Walsall (p 14)	sepia	2 bands	Y1711a	£6.16 British Land Speed Record Holders booklet (DX21)
43p.	photo De La Rue	emerald	2 bands	Y1712	sheets
44p.	photo De La Rue	grey-brown	2 bands	Y1713	sheets
44p.	photo De La Rue	bright blue	2 bands	Y1714	sheets
45p.	photo De La Rue	brt mauve	2 bands	Y1715	sheets
46p.	photo De La Rue or Enschedé	yellow	2 bands	Y1716	sheets (De La Rue), £7.66 "The Machin" booklet (De La Rue – DX39), £7.66 British Army Uniforms booklet (Enschedé – DX40)
47p.	photo De La Rue or Enschedé	turquoise-green	2 bands	Y1717	sheets (De La Rue), £7.23 "The Glory of the Garden" booklet (Enschedé – DX33)
48p.	photo De La Rue	bright mauve	2 bands	Y1717a	sheets, £7.66 "The Machin" booklet (DX39)
48p.	litho De La Rue	bright mauve	2 bands	Y1757f	£7.75 Charles Darwin booklet (DX45)
49p.	photo De La Rue	red-brown	2 bands	Y1718	sheets
50p.	photo Enschedé, Harrison or Walsall	ochre	2 bands	Y1719	sheets (Enschedé or Harrison), £7.26 Trafalgar booklet (Walsall– DX35), £7.44 Victoria Cross booklet (Enschedé – DX37)
50p.	photo De La Rue	grey	2 bands	Y1719b	sheets
50p.	litho Cartor	grey	2 bands	Y1757g	£7.68 British Design Classics Booklet (DX44)
54p.	photo De La Rue or Enschedé	red-brown	2 bands	Y1719c	sheets (D.L.R.), £7.66 British Army Uniforms booklet (Enschedé – DX40)
54p.	litho Cartor	chestnut	2 bands	Y1757	Type III. £8.06 Classic Album Covers booklet (DX48) and £7.72 Royal Society booklet (DX49)
56p.	photo De La Rue	yellow-olive	2 bands	Y1719d	sheets
60p.	litho Walsall	dull blue-grey	2 bands	Y1758	£2.40 booklets (GQ1/4)
60p.	photo De La Rue	light emerald	2 bands	Y1719e	sheets
60p.	litho Cartor	emerald	2 bands	Y1758a	"Britain Alone" booklet (DX51)
62p.	photo De La Rue	rosine	2 bands	Y1719e	sheets
62p.	litho Cartor	rosine	2 bands	Y1758e	£8.18 "Treasures of the Archive" booklet (DX46) and £8.06 Classic Album Covers booklet (DX48)
63p.	photo Enschedé, Harrison or Walsall	lt emerald	2 bands	Y1720	sheets (Enschedé or Harrison), vertical coils (Harrison) £2.52 booklets (Walsall – GR3/4)
63p.	litho Walsall	lt emerald	2 bands	Y1759	£2.52 booklets (GR1/2)
64p.	photo De La Rue or Walsall	turquoise-green	2 bands	Y1721	sheets (D.L.R.), £2.56 booklet (Walsall – GS1)
64p.	photo De La Rue or Walsall	turquoise-green	phos paper	**MS**2146	Jeffery Matthews Colour Palette miniature sheet
65p.	photo De La Rue or Walsall	greenish blue	2 bands	Y1722	sheets (D.L.R.), £2.60 booklet (Walsall – GT1)
67p.	photo De La Rue	bright mauve	2 bands	Y1722a	sheets
67p.	litho Cartor	bright mauve	2 bands	Y1759f	£9.05 WWF booklet (DX52)
68p.	photo De La Rue or Walsall	grey-brown	2 bands	Y1723	sheets (D.L.R.), £7.26 Trafalgar booklet (Walsall – DX35)
72p.	photo De La Rue	rosine	2 bands	Y1724	sheets
78p.	photo De La Rue	emerald	2 bands	Y1724a	sheets
81p.	photo De La Rue	turquoise-green	2 bands	Y1724b	sheets
88p.	photo De La Rue	bright magenta	2 bands	Y1724c	sheets
90p.	photo De La Rue	ultramarine	2 bands	Y1724c	sheets
90p.	litho Cartor	bright blue	2 bands	Y1760	£7.93 Royal Navy Uniforms booklet (DX47)
97p.	photo De La Rue	violet	2 bands	Y1724e	sheets
97p.	litho Cartor	bluish violet	2 bands	Y1761	£9.05 WWF booklet (DX52)
£1	photo Enschedé or Harrison	bluish violet	2 bands	Y1725	sheets
£1	photo De La Rue	magenta	2 bands	Y1725b	sheets, £7.66 "The Machin" booklet (DX39)
£1	photo De La Rue	bluish violet	phos paper	**MS**2146	Jeffery Matthews Colour Palette miniature sheet
£1.46	photo De La Rue	greenish blue	2 bands	Y1725c	sheets
£1.50	recess	red	—	Y1800	sheets (Enschedé then D.L.R.)
£1.50	photo De La Rue	brown-red	2 bands	Y1726	sheets
£2	recess	dull blue	—	Y1801	sheets (Enschedé then D.L.R.)
£2	photo De La Rue	deep blue-green	2 bands	Y1727	sheets
£3	recess	dull violet	—	Y1802	sheets (Enschedé then D.L.R.)
£3	photo De La Rue	deep mauve	2 bands	Y1728	sheets
£5	recess	brown	—	Y1803	sheets (Enschedé then D.L.R.)
£5	photo De La Rue	azure	2 bands	Y1729	sheets

Note. Harrison and Sons became De La Rue Security Print on 8 September 1997.

SELF-ADHESIVE MACHIN INDEX

Value	Format	Process	Colour	Phosphor	Cat. No.	Source
2nd	horizontal	photo	bright blue	1 centre band	1976	coils
2nd	vertical	photo	bright blue	1 centre band	2039	rolls, sheets, booklets
1st	horizontal	litho	orange-red	2 bands	1789	booklets
1st	horizontal	photo	brt orge-red	2 bands	1977	coils
1st	vertical	photo	brt orge-red	2 bands	2040	coils, sheets, booklets
1st	vertical	photo	gold	2 bands	2295	booklets, sheets
E	vertical	photo	deep blue	2 bands	2296	booklets
42p.	vertical	photo	dp olive-grey	2 bands	2297	booklets
68p.	vertical	photo	grey-brown	2 bands	2298	booklets

N.V.I. stamps, self-adhesive gum, elliptical perforations

1116

(Des J. Matthews. Litho Walsall)

1993 (19 Oct). *Self-adhesive. Two phosphor bands.* Die-cut P 14×15 (with one elliptical hole on each vertical side).

1789	**1116**	(1st) orange-red	1·25	1·40
		Ey. Phosphor omitted	£200	
First Day Cover (No. 1789)				4·50
Presentation Pack (booklet of 20) (P.O. Pack No. 29)			25·00	
PHQ Card (D6)			4·00	8·00

No. 1789 was initially sold at 24p. which was increased to 25p. from November 1993.

It was only issued in booklets containing 20 stamps, each surrounded by die-cut perforations.

For similar 2nd and 1st designs printed in photogravure by Enschedé see Nos. 1976/7.

Special First Day of Issue Postmarks

British Philatelic Bureau, Edinburgh	5·00
Newcastle upon Tyne	5·00

1301 **1302**

(Des J. Matthews. Photo Enschedé)

1997 (18 Mar). *Self-adhesive. One centre phosphor band (2nd) or two phosphor bands (1st).* P 14×15 die-cut (with one elliptical hole in each vertical side).

1976	**1301**	(2nd) bright blue	2·75	2·50
1977	**1302**	(1st) bright orange-red	2·75	2·75
Set of 2			5·00	4·75
First Day Cover				5·50
Presentation Pack (P.O. Pack No. 37)			7·00	

Nos. 1976/7, which were sold at 20p. and 26p., were in rolls of 100 with the stamps separate on the backing paper.

Special First Day of Issue Postmarks

British Philatelic Bureau, Edinburgh	5·50
Glasgow	5·50

(Photo Enschedé, Questa or Walsall)

1998 (6 Apr)–**2001**. *Self-adhesive. Designs as T* **913/14**. *One centre phosphor band (2nd), or two phosphor bands (1st).* P 15×14 die-cut (with one elliptical hole on each vertical side).

2039		(2nd) bright blue	1·00	1·00
		a. Imperf (pair, 6mm. gap) (1998)	£225	
		ab. Imperf (pair, 4mm. gap) (2000)	75·00	
		b. Perf 14½×14 die-cut (22.6.98)	£150	
2040		(1st) bright orange-red	1·50	1·50
		a. Imperf (pair, 6mm. gap) (1998)	£225	
		ab. Imperf (pair, 4mm. gap) (2000)	75·00	
		b. Perf 14½×14 die-cut (22.6.98)	£150	
		Ey. Phosphor omitted	£125	
		l. Booklet pane. No. 2040×6 plus commemorative label at left (29.1.01)	14·00	

Nos. 2039/40, initially sold for 20p. and 26p., were in rolls of 200 printed by Enschedé with the surplus self-adhesive paper removed.

2nd and 1st self-adhesive stamps as Nos. 2039/40 were issued in sheets, printed in photogravure by Walsall Security Printers, on 22 June 1998. These are similar to the previous coil printings, but the sheets retain the surplus self-adhesive paper around each stamp. Stamps from these sheets have square perforation tips instead of the rounded versions to be found on the coils.

2039a/40a come from business sheets printed by Walsall and show a 6mm. space between the stamps. 2039ab/40ab come from business sheets printed by Walsall and Questa respectively and have a 4mm space between stamps. 4mm. pairs also exist from booklets, but are much scarcer from this source.

Nos. 2039b and 2040b come from initial stocks of these Walsall sheet printings sent to the Philatelic Bureau and supplied to collectors requiring single stamps.

They can be indentified by the pointed perforation tips in the corners of the stamp, as illustrated below.

Nos. 2039/40   Nos. 2039b/40b

A further printing in sheets appeared on 4 September 2000 printed by Walsall (2nd) or Questa (1st). These sheets were slightly re-designed to provide a block of 4, rather than a strip, in the top panel. Individual stamps cannot be identified as coming from these new sheets as they have rounded perforation tips similar to those on the original coil printings.

The sheets of 100 were re-issued on 9 May 2002 printed by Enschedé in the same format as used in September 2000. The individual stamps are similar to the Enschedé coil printings of April 1998. A further printing of No. 2039 in sheets of 100 appeared on 4 July 2002 by Enschedé. On this printing the top panel reverted to a strip of 4 with the typography on the label matching that of contemporary stamp booklets.

No. 2039 was issued on 18 March 2003 in stripped matrix sheets of 100, printed by Walsall.

The sheets of 100 were again issued but without the strapline "The Real Network" on 15 June 2004. The stamps in stripped matrix sheets of 100 had rounded perforations and were printed by Walsall.

Both values appeared in stamp booklets from 29 January 2001. No. 2040l comes from self-adhesive booklet No. MB2. The label commemorates the death centenary of Queen Victoria.

See also Nos. 2295/8.

"Millennium" Machins

1437 Queen Elizabeth II

(Des A. Machin, adapted R. Scholey. Photo De La Rue, Questa or Walsall (No. 2124), Walsall (Nos. 2124bl, 2124dl), Questa or Walsall (No. 2124d))

2000 (6 Jan–Aug). *New Millennium. Two phosphor bands.* P 15×14 (with one elliptical hole on each vertical side).

2124	**1437**	(1st) olive-brown	1·00	1·00
		a. Imperf (pair)	£800	
		bl. Booklet pane. No. 2124×4 plus commemorative label at right (21.3.00)	6·00	
		bm. Booklet pane. No. 2124×9 with margins all round (4 Aug)	9·00	
		cEy. Phosphor omitted	£500	
		d. Perf 14	1·00	1·00
		dEa. Phosphor omitted	10·00	
		dl. Booklet pane. No. 2124d×8 with central label and margins all round (15.2.00)	8·00	
First Day Cover (No. 2124) (Philatelic Bureau) (Type G, see Introduction)				3·00
First Day Cover (No. 2124) (Windsor) (Type G)				3·00
First Day Cover (No. 2124bm) (Philatelic Bureau)				6·00
First Day Cover (No. 2124bm) (London SW1)				6·00
First Day Cover (No. 2124dl) (Philatelic Bureau)				6·00
First Day Cover (No. 2124dl) (London SW5)				6·00
Presentation Pack (P.O. Pack No. 48)			9·00	
PHQ Card (23 May) (D16)			5·00	16·00

No. 2124d comes from stamp booklets printed by Questa. Similar booklets produced by Walsall have the same perforation as the sheet stamps. The labels on booklet pane No. 2124bl show either Postman Pat, publicising "The Stamp Show 2000", or the National Botanic Garden of Wales.

Special First Day of Issue Postmarks (for use on No. 2124dl only)

1459

(Des J. Matthews. Photo De La Rue)

2000 (22 May). *Stamp Show 2000 International Stamp Exhibition, London. Jeffery Matthews Colour Palette. Sheet, 124×70 mm. Phosphorised paper.* P 15×14 (with one elliptical hole in each vertical side).

MS2146 **1459** 4p. new blue; 5p. dull red-brown; 6p. yellow-olive; 10p. dull orange; 31p. deep mauve; 39p. bright magenta; 64p. turquoise-green; £1 bluish violet	30·00	30·00
First Day Cover (Philatelic Bureau)		30·00
First Day Cover (Earls Court, London SW5)		28·00
Exhibition Card (wallet, sold at £4.99, containing one mint sheet and one cancelled on postcard)		75·00

The £1 value is printed in Iriodin ink which gives a shiny effect to the solid part of the background behind the Queen's head.

Special First Day of Issue Postmarks

1459a

(Des Delaney Design Consultants. Photo De La Rue)

2000 (23 May). *Stamp Show 2000 International Stamp Exhibition, London. "Her Majesty's Stamps". Sheet 121×89 mm. Phosphorised paper.* P 15×14 (with one elliptical hole in each vertical side of stamps as T **1437**).

MS2147 **1459a** (1st) olive-brown (Type **1437**)×4; £1 slate-green (as Type **163**)	21·00	21·00
First Day Cover (Philatelic Bureau)		22·00
First Day Cover (City of Westminster, London SW1)		24·00
Presentation Pack (P.O. Pack No. M03)	£100	
PHQ Cards (set of 2) (PSM03)	16·00	34·00

The £1 value is an adaptation of the 1953 Coronation 1s.3d. stamp originally designed by Edmund Dulac. It is shown on one of the PHQ cards with the other depicting the complete miniature sheet.

Special First Day of Issue Postmarks

N.V.I. and denominated stamps, self-adhesive gum, elliptical perforations

(Photo Questa, Walsall, Enschedé or De La Rue (1st)), Walsall (others))

2002 (5 June–4 July). *Self-adhesive. Two phosphor bands.* P 15×14 die-cut (with one elliptical hole in each vertical side).

2295	**914**	(1st) gold	1·00	1·00
		a. Imperf (pair)	£1000	
		Ey. Phosphor omitted	£150	
2296	**1093a**	(E) deep blue (4 July)	2·00	2·00
2297	**367a**	42p. deep olive-grey (4 July)	3·00	3·00
2298		68p. grey-brown (4 July)	4·00	4·00
Set of 4			9·00	9·00
PHQ Card (No. 2295) (Walsall) (27.3.03)			60	3·50

No. 2295, sold for 27p., was initially only available in booklets of 6 or 12, printed by Questa or Walsall, with the surplus self-adhesive paper around each stamp removed. Later booklets were also printed by De La Rue. Nos. 2296/8 were only issued in separate booklets, each containing six stamps with the surplus self-adhesive paper around each stamp removed.

A further printing of No. 2295 in sheets of 100 appeared on 4 July 2002 produced by Enschedé and on 18 March 2003 in stripped matrix sheets of 100 printed by Walsall. The top panel shows a strip of four with the typography of the label matching that of booklet Type ME 2.

A postal forgery of No. 2295 exists, produced in booklets of 12 with a varnish band printed across the centre of the stamps to mimic phosphor bands. A similar forgery is known with the wavy 'perforations', gauge 10.

Overseas Booklet Stamps

1655

(Des Sedley Place. Photo Walsall)

2003 (27 Mar)–**10**. *Overseas Booklet Stamps. Self-adhesive. Two phosphor bands.* P 15×14 die-cut with one elliptical hole in each vertical side.

2357a		(Worldwide postcard) grey-black, rosine and ultramarine (1.4.04)	1·50	1·50
2357b		(Europe up to 20 grams) deep blue-green, new blue and rosine (30.3.10)	1·25	1·25
2358	**1655**	(Europe up to 40 grams) new blue and rosine	1·90	1·90
2358a		(Worldwide up to 20 grams) deep mauve, new blue and roseine (30.3.10)	2·00	2·00
2359		(Worldwide up to 40 grams) rosine and new blue	3·25	3·25
Set of 5			7·00	7·00
First Day Cover (Nos. 2358/9) (Tallents House) (Type K, see Introduction)				5·25
First Day Cover (Nos. 2358/9) (Windsor) (Type K)				5·25
Presentation Pack (Nos. 2358/9) (P.O. Pack No. 60)			6·00	
PHQ Card (No. 2358) (D23)			45	3·50

No. 2357a was intended to pay postcard rate to foreign destinations (43p.).

Nos. 2357b and 2358a were intended to pay postage on mail up to 20 grams to either Europe (initially 56p., increasing to 60p. from 6 April 2010) or to foreign destinations outside Europe (90p., 97p. from 6 April 2010).

They were only available in separate booklets of four (Nos. MI2 and MJ3) initially sold at £2.24 and £3.60, increasing to £2.40 and £3.88 from 6 April 2010, with the surplus self-adhesive paper around each stamp removed.

Nos. 2358/9 were intended to pay postage on mail up to 40 grams to either Europe (52p.) or to foreign destinations outside Europe (£1.12).

Operationally they were only available in separate booklets of 4 (Nos. MI1, MJ1 and MJA1), initially sold at £1.72, £2.08 and £4.48, with the surplus self-adhesive paper around each stamp removed.

No. 2357a was available from philatelic outlets as a single stamp or in P.O. Pack No. 67 together with six definitive stamps. These single stamps had white backing paper.

For listings of first day covers (together with definitives issued on the same day) and presentation packs for Nos. 2357a/b and 2358a see after No. Y1803.

Single examples of Nos. 2358/9 were available from philatelic outlets as sets of two or in P.O. Pack No. 60. These stamps had coloured backing paper showing parts of the booklet covers.

"Pricing in Proportion"

| 1915 | 1916 |

(Des J. Matthews)

2006 (1st Aug)-**2007**. *"Pricing in Proportion"*. P 15×14 (with one elliptical hole in each vertical side).

(a) Ordinary gum. Photo De La Rue or Enschedé (No. 2651a).

*(i) As T **1915**.*

2650	(2nd) bright blue (1 centre band)........................	70	40
	a. Booklet pane. Nos. 2650/1, and Nos. 2652/3 each × 2, with centre label and margins all round (5.6.07)............................	5·25	
2651	(1st) gold (2 bands)...	90	50
	a. Booklet pane. Nos. 2651 and Y1719, each ×4, with centre label and margins all round (21 Sept)............................	7·50	

*(ii) As T **1916**.*

| 2652 | (2nd Large) bright blue (2 bands) .... | 1·10 | 60 |
| 2653 | (1st Large) gold (2 bands)................................. | 1·50 | 70 |

(b) Self-adhesive. Photo Walsall.

*(i) As T **1915**.*

2654	(2nd) bright blue (one centre band) (12 Sept) .	70	40
	a. Imperf (pair)	£250	
2655	(1st) gold (2 bands) (12 Sept)...........................	90	50
	Ey. Phosphor omitted..................................	£200	

*(ii) As T **1916**.*

| 2656 | (2nd Large) bright blue (2 bands) (15 Aug) .... | 1·10 | 60 |
| 2657 | (1st Large) gold (2 bands) (15 Aug)................... | 1·40 | 70 |

First Day Cover (Nos. Y1676b/c, 2650/3) (Type K, see Introduction)... 5·00
First Day Cover (Nos. Y1676b/c, 2650/3) (Windsor) (Type K) 6·00
First Day Cover (Victoria Cross label pane 1st×4, 50p.×4 (No. 2651a) (Tallents House or Cuffley, Potters Bar, Herts) 8·50
Presentation Pack (Nos. Y1676b/c, 2650/3) (P.O. Pack No. 74)... 4·75

No. 2650 was issued in sheets (1 August) and coils of 500 (15 August).

Nos. 2654/5 were available in separate booklets of six (No. RC1, sold at £1.92) or twelve (Nos. RD1 and RE1, sold at £2.76 or £3.84 respectively) and in business sheets of 100.

Nos. 2656/7 were initially only available in separate booklets of four (Nos. RA1 and RB1), sold at £1.48 and £1.76.

All these booklets had the surplus self-adhesive paper around each stamp removed.

Nos. 2656/7 were issued in sheets of 50, printed by Walsall, on 27 March 2007.

A postal forgery similar to No. 2651 exists with wavy 'perforations' (gauge 10).

Security Machins

> Please note that the "U" numbers in this section are temporary and subject to change.

On 17 February 2009 a new form of Machin definitive appeared, incorporating additional security features to combat the re-use of uncancelled stamps.

The stamps no longer included a water-soluble layer of gum between the paper and the self-adhesive to prevent them being 'soaked off' envelope paper; in addition, four U-shaped slits were die-cut into the stamps to prevent them being peeled off paper and, to make forgery more difficult, an overall iridescent multiple 'ROYAL MAIL' overprint was incorporated into the design.

Exceptionally, in May 2010 2nd and 1st class stamps were issued in rolls with iridescent overprint but printed on paper with ordinary gum and without U-shaped slits. These are listed as U3001/2.

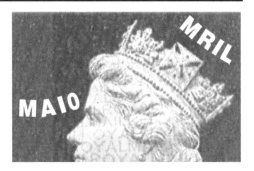

Source Codes: In March 2009 stamps were issued with "codes" incorporated into the iridescent overprint which allowed the source to be identified. The codes may be seen in the words "ROYAL MAIL" in the top right of the stamp, thus "MBIL" signifies that the stamp has come from a Business sheet and "FOYAL" shows that it has come from a booklet pane of Four. In later issues some of these codes appear in other positions.

The codes are:
MAIL (i.e. no code letter) – from counter sheets
MBIL – from Business sheets
MCIL – from 'Custom' booklets, which include special stamps
FOYAL – from booklets of Four
MPIL – from Prestige booklets
MRIL – from Rolls
MSIL – from booklets of Six
MTIL – from booklets of Twelve

Date Codes: From 2010 a year code was added to the iridescent overprint. Initially it appeared in the upper left of the stamp, "MA10" for 2010 and "M11L" for 2011, as shown, but subsequently they appeared in other positions. Stamps are listed without or with date codes, and the different dates known are given in footnotes. Note that year dates given within the listings are years of issue, not code dates.

U-Shaped slits: The first issue featured U-shaped die-cut slits without a break in the middle of each "U", but subsequent issues have incorporated a break to prevent the stamps tearing while being removed from the backing paper on which they were issued. As some of the breaks are difficult to see, we no longer list these as separate varieties but their existence is noted. Note that the stamps previously listed as U2931/4 are now U2947, U2949, U2954 and U2956, respectively, listed according to their source codes rather than by type of U-slit.

A 1st gold stamp with U-slits but without iridescent overprint was supplied only to bulk mailing houses.

2009 (17 Feb)--**2011**. Self-adhesive. Designs as T **367**. Two phosphor bands. U-shaped slits. Iridescent overprint. Die-cut perf 14½×14 (with one elliptical hole in each vertical side).

(a) No source code, no date code, gravure De La Rue

U2911	50p. grey..	1·10	1·10
U2912	£1 magenta..	2·25	2·25
U2913	£1.50 brown-red......................................	3·25	3·25
U2914	£2 deep blue green..................................	4·25	4·25
U2915	£3 deep mauve..	6·25	6·25
U2916	£5 azure...	10·50	10·50
U2911/6 and U2941/4 Set of 10...........................		29·00	29·00

(b) With source and date codes, gravure Walsall

| U2917 | 50p. grey "MPIL" (8.5.10)........................... | 1·75 | 1·75 |
| | a. Booklet pane Nos. U2917×2, U2962×2 and U2966×4, with central label and margins all round.......................... | 7·50 | |

(c) No source code, with date, gravure De La Rue

U2918	68p. deep turquoise-green (29.3.11)	1·60	1·60
U2919	76p. bright rose (29.3.11)..............................	1·75	1·75
U2920	£1.10 yellow-olive (29.3.11)..........................	2·50	2·50
U2921	£1.65 grey-olive (29.3.11).............................	3·75	3·75
U2918/21 Set of 4...		8·50	8·50

No. U2917 was only issued in £11.15 booklets, No DX50.

Nos. U2911/16 are without breaks in the U-shaped slits, No. U2917 exists with breaks in all U-shaped slits or with breaks in the lower "U"s only and Nos. U2918/21 are all "with breaks".

2009 (17 Feb)–**2011**. Self-adhesive. Designs as T **913/14** or T **1916**. One centre band (U2941, U2945/7, U2957 and U2961/3) two bands (others). U-shaped slits. Iridescent overprint. Die-cut perf 14½×14 (with one elliptical hole in each vertical side).

(a) No source code, no date code, gravure De La Rue

U2941	(2nd) bright blue	1·60	1·00
U2942	(1st) gold	1·75	1·25
U2943	(2nd Large) bright blue	2·00	1·50
U2944	(1st Large) gold.......................................	2·50	2·00

*(b) With source code, without date code, gravure De La Rue
("B" and "R" codes) or Walsall (others)*

U2945	(2nd) bright blue ("MBIL") (31.3.09)	1·90	1·90
U2946	(2nd) bright blue ("MRIL") (7.09)	3·25	3·25
U2947	(2nd) bright blue ("MTIL") (31.3.09)	1·40	1·40
U2948	(1st) gold ("MBIL") (31.3.09)	2·10	2·10
U2949	(1st) gold ("MCIL") (10.3.09)	1·50	1·50
U2950	(1st) gold ("MRIL") (7.09)	3·25	3·50
U2951	(1st) gold ("MSIL") (31.3.09)	1·50	1·50
U2952	(1st) gold ("MTIL") (31.3.09)	1·50	1·40
U2953	(2nd Large) ("MBIL") (31.3.09)	2·50	2·75
U2954	(2nd Large) ("FOYAL") (31.3.09)	2·00	2·25
U2955	(1st Large) ("MBIL") (31.3.09)	2·75	3·00
U2956	(1st Large) ("FOYAL") (31.3.09)	2·25	2·00

(c) No source code, with date code, gravure De La Rue

U2957	(2nd) bright blue (7.10)	80	60
U2958	(1st) gold (5.10)	90	80
U2959	(2nd Large) bright blue (1.11)	1·10	90
U2960	(1st Large) gold (6.10)	1·40	1·10

*(d) With source code and date, gravure De La Rue ("B" codes)
or Walsall (others)*

U2961	(2nd) bright blue ("MBIL") (3.10)	1·50	1·50
U2962	(2nd) bright blue ("MPIL") (8.5.10)	1·25	1·25
U2963	(2nd) bright blue ("MTIL") (2.10)	1·10	1·10
U2964	(1st) gold ("MBIL") (6.10)	1·60	1·60
U2965	(1st) gold ("MCIL") (25.2.10)	1·25	1·25
U2966	(1st) gold ("MPIL") (8.5.10)	1·40	1·40
U2967	(1st) gold ("MSIL") (30.3.10)	1·25	1·25
U2968	(1st) gold ("MTIL") (2.10)	1·25	1·25
U2969	(2nd Large) bright blue ("MBIL") (3.11)	1·50	1·50
U2970	(2nd Large) bright blue ("FOYAL") (5.10)	1·25	1·25
U2971	(1st Large) gold ("MBIL") (6.10)	2·00	2·00
U2972	(1st Large) gold ("FOYAL") (5.10)	1·60	1·60

Nos. U2962 and U2966 exist with breaks in all U-shaped slits or with breaks in the lower slits only. U2953 and U2955 are without breaks. U2945 and U2948 exist with and without breaks. The others are with breaks only.

No. U2957/60 and U2965 exist with date codes "MA10" and "M11L". At the time of going to press U2961/4 and U2966/72 have only been seen with "MA10".

No. U2941 originally sold for 27p, U2942 for 36p, U2943 for 42p and U2944 for 52p.

2132a

2132b

2132c

2132d

(Gravure De La Rue)

2009 (17 Nov)–**10**. Self-adhesive. Designs as T **2132a/d**. Two phosphor bands. U-shaped slits. Iridescent overprint. Die-cut perf 14 (U2982) 14½×14 (others) (with one elliptical hole in each vertical side).

U2981	(Recorded Signed for 1st) bright orange-red and lemon	2·25	2·25
U2982	(Recorded Signed for 1st Large) bright orange-red and lemon	2·75	2·75
U2983	(Special delivery up to 100g) blue and silver (26.10.10)	10·00	10·00
U2984	(Special delivery up to 500g) (26.10.10)	11·00	11·00
U2981/4	*Set of 4*	24·00	24·00

Nos. U2981/2 have neither source nor date codes. U2983/4 have no source code but have date codes ("MA10"). All have breaks in the U-shaped slits.

No. U2981 originally sold for £1.14, U2982 for £1.36, U2983 for £5.05 and U2984 for £5.50.

(Gravure De La Rue)

2011 (8 Mar). Self-adhesive. Designs as T **367**. Two phosphor bands. U-shaped slits. Die-cut perf 14½×14 (with one elliptical hole in each vertical side).

U2991	1p. crimson	10	10
U2992	2p. deep green	10	10
U2993	5p. dull red-brown	10	10
U2994	10p. dull orange	25	25
U2995	20p. bright green	50	50
U2991/5	*Set of 5*	1·00	1·00

Nos. U2991/5 have breaks in the U-shaped slits.

(Gravure De La Rue)

2010 (13 May). Ordinary gum. Designs as T **913/14**. One centre phosphor band (2nd) or two bands (1st). Iridescent overprint. Perf 14½×14 (with one elliptical hole in each vertical side).

U3001	(2nd) bright blue	1·00	1·00
U3002	(1st) gold	1·25	1·25

Nos. U3001/2 have source code "MRIL" and year code "MA10".

First Day Covers

17.2.09	Nos. U2911/12 and U2941/4 (Type K, see introduction)		9·00
	Nos. U2911/12 and U2941/4 (Windsor, Type K)		9·00
	Nos. U2913/16 (Type K)		30·00
	Nos. U2913/16 (Windsor)		30·00
17.11.09	Nos. U2981/2 (Type K)		6·75
	Nos. U2981/2 (Windsor)		6·75
8.5.10	No. U2917a (Tallents House or London N1)		10·00
26.10.10	Nos. U2983/4 (Type K)		25·00
	Nos. U2983/4 (Windsor)		25·00
8.3.11	Nos. U2991/5 (Type K)		13·00
	Nos. U2991/5 (Windsor)		13·00
29.3.11	Nos. U2918/21 (Type K)		10·50
	Nos. U2918/21 (Windsor)		10·50

Presentation Packs

Nos. U2911/2 and U2941/4 (P.O. Pack No. 82)		8·00
Nos. U2913/6 (P.O. Pack No. 83)		30·00
Nos. U2918/21 and U2991/5 (P.O. Pack No. 90)		12·00
Nos. U2983/4 (P.O. Pack No. 89)		22·00

For presentation pack containing Nos. U2981/2 see after No. Y1803.

London 2010 Exhibition Miniature Sheet

EXHIBITION SOUVENIR

2268

(Litho Cartor)

2010 (8 May). London 2010 Festival of Stamps. Jeffery Matthews Colour Palette. Sheet 104×95 mm containing stamps as T **367** with a label. Two phosphor bands. P 15×14 (with one elliptical hole on each vertical side).

MS3073	**2268** 1p. reddish purple; 2p. deep grey-green; 5p. reddish-brown; 9p. bright orange; 10p. orange; 20p. light green; 60p. emerald; 67p. bright mauve; 88p. bright magenta; 97p. bluish violet; £1.46 turquoise-blue	11·50	11·50

ROYAL MAIL POST & GO STAMPS

Following trials of a number of self-service machines capable of dispensing postage labels, Royal Mail began installing "Post and Go" machines in larger post offices in October 2000. In addition to postage labels, the machines, manufactured by Wincor Nixdorf, dispense stamps with a pre-printed background and an inkjet printed indicator of the service required, together with a four-part code.

The first machines were sited at the Galleries post office in Bristol and came into use on 8 October 2008. They dispensed five different labels, dependent on the service; the code at the foot of the stamp referring to the branch in which the machine is sited, the machine number within the branch, and the session and transaction numbers.

On 17 September 2010 the first pictorial Post and Go stamps were released, depicting six different British Birds, although the Machin design (T FT1) remained current. As the larger pictorial element in the new stamps required that the service indicator be reduced in size and repositioned to the left as shown in T FT2, this form indicator also exists on the Machin Post and Go stamps.

FT **1**

(Gravure Walsall, inkjet printed service indicator)

2008 (8 Oct). *Type FT* **1**. *Self-adhesive. Olive-brown background. Two phosphor bands.* P 14½.

FS1	"1st Class Up to 100g"	4·50	4·50
	a. smaller service indicator	1·75	1·90
FS2	"1st Large Up to 100g"	5·25	5·25
	a. smaller service indicator	2·25	2·40
FS3	"Europe Up to 20g"	5·25	5·25
	a. smaller service indicator	2·25	2·40
FS4	"Worldwide Up to 10g"	6·50	6·50
	a. smaller service indicator	2·25	2·40
FS5	"Worldwide Up to 20g"	9·00	9·00
	a. smaller service indicator	2·75	3·00
FS1/5 *Set of 5*		27·50	27·50
FS1a/5a *Set of 5*		10·00	10·00
Special Pack (Nos. FS1/5) (31.3.09)		32·50	

The special pack contains separate stamps. These are reproductions of the first "Post and Go" stamps printed at the Galleries Post Offices, Bristol. They differ from machine printed stamps in having the service indicator and branch code printed in gravure.

It is possible to obtain *se-tenant* strips of mixed values from "Post and Go" machines but we do not list these.

FT **2** Blue Tit

(Des Robert Gilmor and Kate Stephens. Gravure Walsall, inkjet printed service indicator).

2010 (17 Sept). Birds of Britain (1st series). Multicoloured. Self-adhesive. Two phosphor bands. P 14½.

FS6	(1st Class up to 100g)	3·00	3·25
FS7	(1st Large up to 100g)	3·50	3·75
FS8	(Europe up to 20g)	3·50	3·75
FS9	(Worldwide up to 10g)	3·50	3·75
FS10	(Worldwide up to 20g)	4·00	4·25
First Day Cover (No. FS6 in 6 designs)			8·50
Special Pack (No. FS6 in 6 designs)		5·50	

Nos. FS6/10 were each available in six different designs: Type FT **2**, goldfinch, wood pigeon, robin, house sparrow and starling.

Nos. FS6/10 were available from Post and Go terminals, initially in 30 post offices.

Stamps from the special pack and first day cover sold by Tallents House differ from machine printed stamps in having the service indicator and branch code printed in gravure.

(Des Robert Gilmor and Kate Stephens. Gravure Walsall, inkjet printed service indicator)

2011 (24 Jan). Birds of Britain (2nd series). Multicoloured. Self-adhesive. Two phosphor bands. P 14.

FS11	(1st class up to 100g)	1·75	1·90
FS12	(1st Large up to 100g)	2·25	2·40
FS13	(Europe up to 20g)	2·25	2·40
FS14	(Worldwide up to 10g)	2·25	2·40
FS15	(Worldwide up to 20g)	2·75	3·00
First Day Cover (No. FS11 in 6 designs)			8·50

Special Pack (No. FS11 in 6 designs)	5·50

Nos. FS11/15 were each available in 6 different designs: blackbird, two magpies, long-tailed tit, chaffinch, collared dove and goldfinch.

Stamps from the special pack and first day cover sold by Tallents House differ from machine printed stamps in having the service indicator and branch code printed in gravure.

ROYAL MAIL POSTAGE LABELS

These imperforate labels were issued as an experiment by the Post Office. Special microprocessor controlled machines were installed at post offices in Cambridge, London, Shirley (Southampton) and Windsor to provide an after-hours sales service to the public. The machines printed and dispensed the labels according to the coins inserted and the buttons operated by the customer. Values were initially available in ½p. steps to 16p. and in addition, the labels were sold at philatelic counters in two packs containing either 3 values (3½, 12½, 16p.) or 32 values (½p. to 16p.).

From 28 August 1984 the machines were adjusted to provide values up to 17p. After 31 December 1984 labels including ½p. values were withdrawn. The machines were taken out of service on 30 April 1985.

Machine postage-paid impression in red on phosphorised paper with grey-green background design. No watermark. Imperforate.

1984 (1 May–28 Aug).

Set of 32 (½p. to 16p.)	15·00	22·00
Set of 3 (3½p., 12½p., 16p.)	2·50	3·00
Set of 3 on First Day Cover (1.5.84)		6·50
Set of 2 (16½p., 17p.) (28.8.84)	4·00	3·00

REGIONAL ISSUES
CHANNEL ISLANDS
GENERAL ISSUE

C **1** Gathering Vraic   C **2** Islanders gathering Vraic

Broken Wheel (R. 20/5)

(Des J. R. R. Stobie (1d.) or from drawing by E. Blampied (2½d.).
Photo Harrison)

1948 (10 May). *Third Anniv of Liberation.* W *127 of Great Britain.* P 15×14.

C1	C **1**	1d. scarlet	25	30
C2	C **2**	2½d. ultramarine	25	30
		a. Broken wheel	50·00	
First Day Cover				35·00

PRINTERS (£.s.d. stamps of all regions):—Photo Harrison & Sons. Portrait by Dorothy Wilding Ltd.

DATES OF ISSUE. Conflicting dates of issue have been announced for some of the regional issues, partly explained by the stamps being released on different dates by the Philatelic Bureau in Edinburgh or the Philatelic Counter in London and in the regions. We have adopted the practice of giving the earliest known dates, since once released the stamps could have been used anywhere in the U.K.

I. ENGLAND

EN **1** Three Lions   EN **2** Crowned
Lion with Shield
of St. George

EN **3** Oak Tree   EN **4** Tudor Rose

(Des Sedley Place, from sculptures by D. Dathan. Photo Questa
(No. EN1b) or De La Rue (others))

2001 (23 Apr)–**02**. *One centre phosphor band (2nd) or two phosphor bands (others).* P 15×14 (with one elliptical hole in each vertical side).

EN1	EN **1**	(2nd) slate-green and silver	1·00	1·00
		a. Imperf (pair)		
		b. Booklet pane. Nos. EN1/2, each×4, and No. S95, with margins all round (24.9.02)	8·50	
EN2	EN **2**	(1st) lake-brown and silver	1·00	1·00
		a. Imperf pair	£300	
EN3	EN **3**	(E) olive-green and silver	1·75	1·75
EN4	EN **4**	65p. deep reddish lilac and silver	3·00	3·00
EN5		68p. deep reddish lilac and silver (4.7.02)	3·00	3·00
Presentation Pack (Nos. EN1/4) (*P.O. Pack No. 54*)			7·50	
PHQ Cards (Nos. EN1/4) (*set of 4*) (D20)			8·00	14·00

Nos. EN1/3 were initially sold at 19p., 27p. and 36p., the latter representing the basic European airmail rate.

First Day Covers

23.4.01	2nd, 1st, E, 65p. (EN1/4) Philatelic Bureau (Type G, see Introduction).		3·25
	Windsor		1·75
4.7.02	68p. (EN5) Tallents House (Type K, see Introduction).		3·50
	London (as Windsor)		2·00

Special First Day of Issue Postmark

Combined Presentation Packs for England, Northern Ireland, Scotland and Wales

4.7.02	P.O. Pack No. 59. 68p. from England, Northern Ireland, Scotland and Wales (*Nos.* EN5, NI93, S99, W88)	9·00
11.5.04	P.O. Pack No. 68. 40p. from England, Northern Ireland, Scotland and Wales (*Nos.* EN9, NI97, S112, W101)	8·00
5.4.05	P.O. Pack No. 70. 42p. from England, Northern Ireland, Scotland and Wales (*Nos.* EN10, NI98, S113, W102)	8·00
28.3.06	P.O. Pack No. 73. 44p. and 72p. from England, Northern Ireland, Scotland and Wales (*Nos.* EN11, EN15, NI99, NI101, S114, S118, W103, W107)	10·00
27.3.07	P.O. Pack No. 76. 48p. and 78p. from England, Northern Ireland, Scotland and Wales (*Nos.* EN12, EN16, NI104, NI106, S115, S119, W104, and W108)	12·50
1.4.08	P.O. Pack. No. 79. 50p. and 81p. from England, Northern Ireland, Scotland and Wales (*Nos.* EN13, EN17, NI105, S116, S120, W105, W109)	11·50
29.9.08	P.O. Pack No. 81. 2nd, 1st, 50p. and 81p. from England, Northern Ireland, Scotland and Wales (*Nos.* EN6/7, EN13, EN17, NI102/3, NI105, NI107, S109/10, S116, S120, W98/9, W105, W109)	16·00
31.3.09	P.O. Pack No. 85. 56p. and 90p. from England, Northern Ireland, Scotland and Wales (*Nos.* EN13*a*, EN17*a*, NI105*a*, NI107*a*, S116*a*, S120*a*, W105*a*, W109*a*)	13·50
30.3.10	P.O. Pack No. 87. 60p. and 97p. from England, Northern Ireland, Scotland and Wales (*Nos.* EN13*b*, EN17*b*, NI105*b*, NI107*b*, S116*b*, S120*b*, W105*b*, W109*b*)	20·00
29.3.11	P.O. Pack No. 91. 68p. and £1.10 from England, Northern Ireland, Scotland and Wales (*Nos.* EN18*b*/*c*, NI100*a*, NI101*a*, S131*a*/*b*, W120*a*/*b*)	18·00

2003 (14 Oct)–**11**. *As Nos*. EN1/3 *and* EN5*, and new values, but with white borders. One centre phosphor band (2nd) or two phosphor bands (others).* P 15×14 (with one elliptical hole in each vertical side).

(a) (Photo Walsall (No. EN6a) or De La Rue (others))

EN6	EN **1**	(2nd) slate-green and silver	75	60
		a. Booklet pane. Nos. EN6 and EN9, each×2, with central label and margins all round (24.2.05)	1·80	
		b. Imperf (pair)	£175	
EN7	EN **2**	(1st) lake-brown and silver	90	75
		a. Imperf (pair)	£225	
EN8	EN **3**	(E) olive-green and silver	2·00	2·00
EN9		40p. olive-green and silver (11.5.04)	1·50	1·50
EN10		42p. olive-green and silver (5.4.05)	1·25	1·25
EN11		44p. olive-green and silver (28.3.06)	1·50	1·50
EN12		48p. olive-green and silver (27.3.07)	1·25	1·25
EN13		50p. olive-green and silver (1.4.08)	90	85
EN13*a*		56p. olive-green and silver (31.3.09)	1·25	1·25
EN13*b*		60p. olive-green and silver (31.3.10)	1·40	1·40
EN14	EN **4**	68p. deep reddish lilac and silver	2·50	2·50
EN15		72p. deep reddish lilac and silver (28.3.06)	2·50	2·50
EN16		78p. deep reddish lilac and silver (27.3.07)	2·50	2·50
EN17		81p. deep reddish lilac and silver (1.4.08)	2·00	2·00
EN17*a*		90p. deep reddish lilac and silver (31.3.09)	2·00	2·00
EN17*b*		97p. deep reddish lilac and silver (31.3.10)	2·25	2·25

(b) Litho Enschedé (1st) or Cartor (others)

EN18	EN **2**	(1st) lake-brown and silver (20.9.07)	7·00	7·00
		a. Booklet pane. Nos. EN18, NI95 S131 and W120 with four labels and margins all round	20·00	
EN18*b*	EN **3**	68p. greenish yellow, bright magenta, new blue and black (29.3.11)	1·50	1·50
EN18*c*	EN **4**	£1.10 greenish yellow, bright magenta, new blue and black (29.3.11)	2·50	2·50
Presentation Pack (Nos. EN6/8, EN14) (*P.O. Pack No. 63*)			6·00	
PHQ Cards (Nos. EN6/8, EN14) (*set of 4*) (D24)			2·00	12·00

No. EN6a comes from booklet No. DX34.

Stamps as Nos. EN16 and EN18 but printed in lithography were only issued within **MS**2796 (EN16) or **MS**2886 (EN18).

No. EN18 comes from £7.66 stamp booklets, No. DX40.

A design as No. EN18 but self-adhesive was issued on 23 April 2007 in sheets of 20, each stamp accompanied by a *se-tenant* label showing an English scene (LS38). These sheets were printed in lithography by Cartor, perforated 15×14 without the elliptical holes, and sold at £7·35 each. They were also available with personalised photographs on the labels at £14·95 from the Royal Mail in Edinburgh.

Stamps as Nos. EN18, NI95, S131 and W120 but self-adhesive were issued on 29 September 2008 in sheets of 20 containing five of each design with *se-tenant* labels (LS49). These sheets were printed in lithography by Cartor and perforated 15×14 with one elliptical hole on each vertical side.

First Day Covers

14.10.03	2nd, 1st, E, 68p. (EN6/8, EN14) Tallents House (Type K, see Introduction)	3·25
	London (as Windsor)	3·50
11.5.04	40p. (EN9) Tallents House (Type K)	2·75
	London (as Windsor)	2·75
5.4.05	42p. (EN10) Tallents House (Type K)	1·40
	London (as Windsor)	1·40
28.3.06	44p., 72p., (EN11, EN15) Tallents House (Type K)	2·75
	London (as Windsor)	2·75
27.3.07	48p., 78p., (EN12, EN16) Tallents House (Type K)	4·00
	London (as Windsor)	4·00
1.4.08	50p., 81p., (EN13, EN17) Tallents House (Type K)	4·00
	London (as Windsor)	4·00
31.3.09	56p., 90p. (EN13*a*, EN17*a*) Tallents House (Type K)	4·75
	London (as Windsor)	4·75
30.3.10	60p., 97p. (EN13*b*, EN17*b*) Tallents House (Type K)	4·00
	London (as Windsor)	4·00
29.3.11	68p., £1.10 (EN18*b/c*) Tallents House (Type K)	6·00
	London (as Windsor)	6·00

EN **5** (Illustration reduced. Actual size 123×70 mm)

(Des Peter Crowther, Clare Melinsky and Silk Pearce. Photo De La Rue)

2007 (23 Apr). *Celebrating England. Sheet 123×70 mm. Two phosphor bands.* P 15×14 (with one elliptical hole in each vertical side) (1st) or 15×14½ (78p.).

MSEN19	(1st) No. EN7; (1st) St. George's flag; 78p. St. George; 78p. Houses of Parliament, London	9·00	9·00
First Day Cover (Tallents House)			9·00
First Day Cover (St. Georges, Telford)			9·00
Presentation Pack (P.O. Pack No. M15)		10·00	
PHQ Cards (set of 5) (CGB2)		4·00	15·00

The five PHQ cards show the four individual stamps and the complete miniature sheet.

Stamps as the 1st class St. George's flag stamp within **MS**EN19 but self-adhesive were issued on 23 April 2009 in sheets of 20 with *se-tenant* labels showing English Castles, No. LS59. These sheets were printed in lithography by Cartor and sold for £8·35 each.

Special First Day of Issue Postmarks

II. NORTHERN IRELAND

N **1**　　N **2**　　N **3**

(Des W. Hollywood (3d., 4d., 5d.), L. Pilton (6d., 9d.), T. Collins (1s.3d., 1s.6d.))

1958–67. W 179. P 15×14.

NI1	N **1**	3d. deep lilac (18.8.58)	15	10
		p. One centre phosphor band (9.6.67)	15	15
NI2		4d. ultramarine (7.2.66)	15	15
		p. Two phosphor bands (10.67)	15	15
NI3	N **2**	6d. deep claret (29.9.58)	30	30
NI4		9d. bronze-green (2 phosphor bands) (1.3.67)	30	70
NI5	N **3**	1s.3d. green (29.9.58)	30	70
NI6		1s.6d. grey-blue (2 phosphor bands) (1.3.67)	30	70
		E*y*. Phosphor omitted	£200	

First Day Covers

18.8.58	3d. (NI1)	30·00
29.9.58	6d., 1s.3d. (NI3, NI5)	35·00
7.2.66	4d. (NI2)	7·00
1.3.67	9d., 1s.6d. (NI4, NI6)	4·00

For Nos. NI1, NI3 and NI5 in Presentation Pack, see below Wales No. W6.

1968–69. *No watermark. Chalk-surfaced paper. One centre phosphor band (Nos. NI8/9) or two phosphor bands (others). Gum arabic (No. NI7) or PVA gum (others).* P 15×14.

NI7	N **1**	4d. dp brt blue (27.6.68)	15	15
		E*v*. PVA gum* (23.10.68)	13·00	
NI8		4d. olive-sepia (4.9.68)	15	15
		E*y*. Phosphor omitted		
NI9		4d. brt vermilion (26.2.69)	20	20
		E*y*. Phosphor omitted	4·50	
NI10		5d. royal blue (4.9.68)	20	20
		E*y*. Phosphor omitted	25·00	
NI11	N **3**	1s.6d. grey-blue (20.5.69)	2·25	2·50
		E*y*. Phosphor omitted	£500	

4.9.68	*First Day Cover* (NI8, NI10)	3·00
	Presentation Pack (containing Nos. NI1p, NI4/6, NI8/10) (9.12.70)	3·50

*No. NI7E*v* was never issued in Northern Ireland. After No. NI7 (gum arabic) had been withdrawn from Northern Ireland but whilst still on sale at the philatelic counters elsewhere, about fifty sheets with PVA gum were sold over the London Philatelic counter on 23 October, 1968, and some were also on sale at the British Philatelic Exhibition Post Office. There was no Post Office first day cover for No. NI9.

N **4**

I　　　　　　　　II

Redrawn design of Type N 4 (litho ptgs.)

Two Types of Crown

Type I:–Crown with all pearls individually drawn.

Type II:–Crown with clear outlines, large pearls and strong white line below them. First 3 pearls at left are joined, except on Nos. NI39 and NI49.

The following stamps printed in lithography show a screened background behind and to the left of the emblem: 11½p., 12½p., 14p. (No. NI38), 15½p., 16p., 18p. (No. NI45), 19½p., 22p. (No. NI53) and 28p. (No. NI62). The 13p. and 17p. (No. NI43) also showed screened backgrounds in Type I, but changed to solid backgrounds for Type II. The 31p. had a solid background in Type I, but changed to a screened background for Type II. All other values printed in lithography have solid backgrounds.

(Des J. Matthews after plaster cast by Arnold Machin)

1971 (7 July)–**93**. *Decimal Currency. Chalk-surfaced paper. Type N* **4**.

(a) Photo Harrison. With phosphor bands. P 15×14.

NI12		2½p. brt magenta (1 centre band)	70	60
NI13		3p. ultramarine (2 bands)	30	30
		E*y*. Phosphor omitted	50·00	
NI14		3p. ultramarine (1 centre band) (23.1.74)	20	15

NI15	3½p. olive-grey (2 bands) (23.1.74)		20	25
NI16	3½p. olive-grey (1 centre band) (6.11.74)		20	25
NI17	4½p. grey-blue (2 bands) (6.11.74)		30	25
NI18	5p. reddish violet (2 bands)		1·00	1·00
NI19	5½p. violet (2 bands) (23.1.74)		20	20
	Ey. Phosphor omitted		£250	
NI20	5½p. violet (1 centre band) (21.5.75)		20	25
NI21	6½p. greenish blue (1 centre band) (14.1.76)		20	20
NI22	7p. purple-brown (1 centre band) (18.1.78)		35	25
NI23	7½p. chestnut (2 bands)		1·75	1·75
	Ey. Phosphor omitted		£100	
NI24	8p. rosine (2 bands) (23.1.74)		35	35
	Ey. Phosphor omitted		75·00	
NI25	8½p. yellowish-green (2 bands) (14.1.76)		35	40
NI26	9p. dp violet (2 bands) (18.1.78)		40	40
	Ey. Phosphor omitted		25·00	
NI27	10p. orange-brown (2 bands) (20.10.76)		40	50
NI28	10p. orange-brown (1 centre band) (23.7.80)		50	50
NI29	10½p. steel-blue (2 bands) (18.1.78)		40	50
NI30	11p. scarlet (2 bands) (20.10.76)		50	50
	Ey. Phosphor omitted		5·00	

(b) Photo Harrison. On phosphorised paper. P 15×14.

NI31	12p. yellowish green (23.7.80)		50	50
NI32	13½p. purple-brown (23.7.80)		60	70
NI33	15p. ultramarine (23.7.80)		60	70

(c) Litho Questa (Type II, unless otherwise stated). P 14 (11½p., 12½p., 14p. (No. NI38), 15½p., 16p., 18p. (No. NI45), 19½p., 20½p., 22p. (No. NI53), 26p. (No. NI60), 28p. (No. NI62)) or 15×14 (others).

NI34	11½p. drab (Type I) (1 side band)		85	85
NI35	12p. brt emerald (1 side band) (7.1.86)		90	90
NI36	12½p. lt emerald (Type I) (24.2.82)		60	60
	a. Perf 15×14 (28.2.84)		5·25	5·25
NI37	13p. pale chestnut (Type I) (1 side band) (23.10.84)		80	50
	Ea. Type II (28.11.86)		1·50	1·00
	Ey. Phosphor omitted (Type I)		£375	
NI38	14p. grey-blue (Type I) (phosphorised paper) (8.4.81)		75	75
NI39	14p. dp blue (1 centre band) (8.11.88)		75	60
NI40	15p. brt blue (1 centre band) (28.11.89)		90	60
NI41	15½p. pale violet (Type I) (phosphorised paper) (24.2.82)		80	80
NI42	16p. drab (Type I) (phosphorised paper) (27.4.83)		1·00	1·00
	a. Perf 15×14 (28.2.84)		8·25	8·50
NI43	17p. grey-blue (Type I) (phosphorised paper) (23.10.84)		90	95
	Ea. Type II (9.9.86)		£175	£120
NI44	17p. dp blue (1 centre band) (4.12.90)		1·00	80
NI45	18p. dp violet (Type I) (phosphorised paper) (8.4.81)		1·00	1·00
NI46	18p. dp olive-grey (phosphorised paper) (6.1.87)		1·00	90
NI47	18p. brt green (1 centre band) (3.12.91)		1·00	95
	a. Perf 14 (31.12.92*)		5·00	5·00
NI48	18p. brt green (1 side band) (10.8.93)		2·25	2·25
	l. Booklet pane. Nos. NI48, NI59, S61, S71, W49Eb and W60 with margins all round		14·00	
NI49	19p. brt orange-red (phosphorised paper) (8.11.88)		1·00	1·00
NI50	19½p. olive-grey (Type I) (phosphorised paper) (24.2.82)		1·50	1·75
NI51	20p. brownish black (phosphorised paper) (28.11.89)		1·00	80
NI52	20½p. ultramarine (Type I) (phosphorised paper) (27.4.83)		4·50	4·25
NI53	22p. blue (Type I) (phosphorised paper) (8.4.81)		1·10	1·10
NI54	22p. yellow-green (Type I) (phosphorised paper) (23.10.84)		1·10	1·10
NI55	22p. brt orange-red (phosphorised paper) (4.12.90)		1·25	90
NI56	23p. brt green (phosphorised paper) (8.11.88)		1·25	1·10
NI57	24p. Indian red (phosphorised paper) (28.11.89)		1·25	1·25
NI58	24p. chestnut (phosphorised paper) (3.12.91)		1·10	90
NI59	24p. chestnut (2 bands) (10.8.93)		2·25	2·50
NI60	26p. rosine (Type I) (phosphorised paper) (24.2.82)		1·25	1·25
	a. Perf 15×14 (Type II) (27.1.87)		3·00	3·25
NI61	26p. drab (phosphorised paper) (4.12.90)		1·75	1·75
NI62	28p. dp violet-blue (Type I) (phosphorised paper) (27.4.83)		1·50	1·50
	a. Perf 15×14 (Type II) (27.1.87)		1·25	1·25
NI63	28p. dp bluish grey (phosphorised paper) (3.12.91)		1·50	1·50
NI64	31p. brt purple (Type I) (phosphorised paper) (23.10.84)		1·75	2·00
	Ea. Type II (14.4.87)		1·90	1·75
NI65	32p. greenish blue (phosphorised paper) (8.11.88)		1·75	1·75

NI66	34p. dp bluish grey (phosphorised paper) (28.11.89)		1·75	1·75
NI67	37p. rosine (phosphorised paper) (4.12.90)		2·00	2·50
NI68	39p. brt mauve (phosphorised paper) (3.12.91)		2·00	2·25

*Earliest known date of use.

No. NI47a was caused by the use of a reserve perforating machine for some printings in the second half of 1992.

Nos. NI48 and NI59 only come from booklets.

From 1972 printings were made on fluorescent white paper and from 1973 most printings had dextrin added to the PVA gum (see notes after 1971 Decimal Machin issue).

First Day Covers

7.7.71	2½p., 3p., 5p., 7½p. (NI12/13, NI18, NI23)	3·50
23.1.74	3p., 3½p., 5½p., 8p. (NI14/15, NI19, NI24)	2·40
6.11.74	4½p. (NI17)	1·50
14.1.76	6½p., 8½p. (NI21, NI25)	1·50
20.10.76	10p., 11p. (NI27, NI30)	1·75
18.1.78	7p., 9p., 10½p. (NI22, NI26, NI29)	1·75
23.7.80	12p., 13½p., 15p. (NI31/3)	3·00
8.4.81	11½p., 14p., 18p., 22p. (NI34, NI38, NI45, NI53)	2·50
24.2.82	12½p., 15½p., 19½p., 26p. (NI36, NI41, NI50, NI60)	4·00
27.4.83	16p., 20½p., 28p. (NI42, NI52, NI62)	4·00
23.10.84	13p., 17p., 22p., 31p. (NI37, NI43, NI54, NI64)	4·75
7.1.86	12p. (NI35)	2·00
6.1.87	18p. (NI46)	2·00
8.11.88	14p., 19p., 23p., 32p. (NI39, NI49, NI56, NI65)	4·25
28.11.89	15p., 20p., 24p., 34p. (NI40, NI51, NI57, NI66)	5·00
4.12.90	17p., 22p., 26p., 37p. (NI44, NI55, NI61, NI67)	5·00
3.12.91	18p., 24p., 28p., 39p. (NI47, NI58, NI63, NI68)	5·50

Presentation Packs

7.7.71	P.O. Pack No. 29. 2½p., 3p. (2 bands) 5p., 7½p. (Nos. NI12/13, NI18, NI23)	3·50
29.5.74	P.O. Pack No. 61. 3p. (1 centre band), 3½p. (2 bands) or (1 centre band), 5½p. (2 bands) or (1 centre band), 8p. (Nos. NI14, NI15 or NI16, NI19 or NI20, NI24). The 4½p. (No. NI17) was added later	2·25
20.10.76	P.O. Pack No. 84. 6½p., 8½p., 10p. (2 bands), 11p. (Nos. NI21, NI25, NI27, NI30)	2·00
28.10.81	P.O. Pack No. 129d. 7p., 9p., 10½p., 12p. (photo), 13½p., 15p. (photo), 11½p., 14p. grey-blue, 18p. dp violet, 22p. blue (Nos. NI22, NI26, NI31/4, NI38, NI45, NI53)	9·00
3.8.83	P.O. Pack No. 4. 10p. (1 centre band), 12½p., 16p., 20½p., 26p. rosine, 28p. dp violet-blue (Nos. NI28, NI36, NI42, NI52, NI60, NI62)	18·00
23.10.84	P.O. Pack No. 8. 10p. (1 centre band), 13p., 16p., 17p. grey-blue, 22p. yellow-green, 26p. rosine, 28p. dp violet-blue, 31p. (Nos. NI28, NI37, NI42a, NI43, NI54, NI60, NI62, NI64)	18·00
3.3.87	P.O. Pack No. 12. 12p. (litho), 13p., 17p. grey-blue, 18p. dp olive-grey, 22p. yellow-green, 26p. rosine, 28p. dp violet-blue, 31p. (Nos. NI35, NI37, NI43, NI46, NI54, NI60a, NI62a, NI64)	20·00

Presentation Packs for Northern Ireland, Scotland and Wales

8.11.88	P.O. Pack No. 17. 14p. dp blue, 19p., 23p., 32p. (Nos. NI39, NI49, NI56, NI65), 14p. (1 centre band), 19p. (phosphorised paper), 23p. (phosphorised paper), 32p. (Nos. S54, S62, S67, S77), 14p. dp blue, 19p., 23p., 32p. (Nos. W40, W50, W57, W66)	17·00
28.11.89	P.O. Pack No. 20. 15p. (litho), 20p., 24p. Indian red, 34p. (Nos. NI40, NI51, NI57, NI66), 15p. (litho), 20p., 24p. Indian red, 34p. (Nos. S56, S64, S69, S78), 15p. (litho), 20p., 24p. Indian red, 34p. (Nos. W41, W52, W58, W67)	16·00
4.12.90	P.O. Pack No. 23. 17p. dp blue, 22p. brt orange-red, 26p. drab, 37p., (Nos. NI44, NI55, NI61, NI67), 17p. dp blue, 22p. brt orange-red, 26p. drab, 37p (Nos. S58, S66, S73, S79), 17p. dp blue, 22p. brt orange-red, 26p. drab, 37p. (Nos. W45, W56, W62, W68)	16·00
3.12.91	P.O. Pack No. 26. 18p. brt green, 24p. chestnut, 28p. dp bluish grey, 39p. (Nos. NI47, NI58, NI63, NI68), 18p. brt green, 24p. chestnut, 28p. dp bluish grey, 39p. (Nos. S60, S70, S75, S80), 18p. brt green, 24p. chestnut, 28p. dp bluish grey, 39p. (Nos. W48, W59, W64, W69)	16·00

(Des J. Matthews after plaster cast by Arnold Machin)

1993 (7 Dec)–**2000**. Chalk-surfaced paper.

(a) Litho Questa. P 15×14 (with one elliptical hole in each vertical side).

NI69	N 4	19p. bistre (1 centre band)	90	80
NI70		19p. bistre (1 band at left) (26.7.94)	1·25	1·75
		Ey. Phosphor omitted	£950	
		a. Booklet pane. Nos. NI70×2, NI72×4, NI74, NI76 and centre label with margins all round	8·00	
		b. Booklet pane. Nos. NI70, NI72, NI74 and NI76 with margins all round	6·00	

bEy. Booklet pane. Phosphor omitted ....
Ec. Band at right (25.4.95) .... 2·50   2·50
d. Booklet pane. Nos. NI70Ec, NI72,
502, 504, W71 and W73 with
margins all round (25.4.95) .... 10·00
da. Part perf pane* ....

NI71		20p. brt green (1 centre band) (23.7.96).	1·50	1·50
NI72		25p. red (2 bands)	75	75
		Ey. Phosphor omitted.............................	£950	
NI73		26p. red-brown (2 bands) (23.7.96)	1·75	1·75
NI74		30p. dp olive-grey (2 bands)	1·25	1·25
		Ey. Phosphor omitted.............................	£950	
NI75		37p. brt mauve (2 bands) (23.7.96)..........	2·75	3·00
NI76		41p. grey-brown (2 bands)	1·50	1·75
		Ey. Phosphor omitted.............................	£950	
NI77		63p. lt emerald (2 bands) (23.7.96)	5·00	5·00

(b) Photo Walsall (19p., 20p., 26p. (No. NI81b), 38p., 40p., 63p., 64p., 65p.),
Harrison or Walsall (26p. (No. NI81), 37p.). P. 14 (No. NI80) or 15×14
(others) (both with one elliptical hole in each vertical side).

NI78	N **4**	19p. bistre (1 centre band) (8.6.99)	3·00	3·00
NI79		20p. brt green (1 centre band) (1.7.97)....	1·95	80
NI80		20p. brt green (1 side band at right) (13.10.98).......................................	3·00	3·00
		al. Booklet pane. Nos. NI80, S90a, W79a and Y1711a×3 with margins all round	10·00	
NI81		26p. chestnut (2 bands) (1.7.97)..............	1·25	1·00
		al. Booklet pane. Nos. NI81/2, S91/2 and W80/1 with margins all round (23.9.97)..	6·00	
		b. Perf 14 (13.10.98).............................	3·00	3·00
NI82		37p. brt mauve (2 bands) (1.7.97)	2·25	2·25
NI83		38p. ultramarine (2 bands) (8.6.99).........	8·00	8·00
NI84		40p. dp azure (2 bands) (25.4.00)............	2·50	2·50
NI85		63p. lt emerald (2 bands) (1.7.97)............	5·00	5·00
NI86		64p. turquoise-green (2 bands) (8.6.99)..	9·00	9·00
NI87		65p. greenish blue (2 bands) (25.4.00)	3·25	3·25

*No. NI70da, which comes from the 1995 National Trust £6 booklet,
shows the top two values in the pane of 6 (Nos. S82, S84) completely
imperforate and the two Wales values below partly imperforate.

Nos. NI70, NI80 and NI81b only come from booklets.

The listed booklet panes come from the following Sponsored Booklets:
NI70a/b   –Booklet DX16
NI70d   –Booklet DX17
NI80al   –Booklet DX21
NI81al   –Booklet DX19

First Day Covers

7.12.93	19p., 25p., 30p., 41p. (NI69, NI72, NI74, NI76)................	6·00
26.7.94	Northern Ireland se-tenant pane 19p., 25p., 30p., 41p. (NI70a)...	8·00
23.7.96	20p., 26p., 37p., 63p. (NI71, NI73, NI75, NI77)...............	8·75
8.6.99	38p., 64p. (NI83, NI86)..	4·00
25.4.00	1st, 40p., 65p. (NI84, NI87, NI88b)...........................	7·00

Presentation Packs

8.6.99	P.O. Pack No. 47. 19p., 26p., 38p., 64p. (Nos. NI78, NI81, NI83, NI86)	17·00
25.4.00	P.O. Pack No. 52. 1st, 40p., 65p. (Nos. NI88b, NI84, NI87)..	18·00

Presentation Packs for Northern Ireland, Scotland and Wales

7.12.93	P.O. Pack No. 31. 19p., 25p., 30p., 41p., each×3 (Nos. NI69, NI72, NI74, NI76, S81, S84, S86, S88, W70, W73, W75, W77)...	16·00
23.7.96	P.O. Pack No. 36. 20p., 26p., 37p., 63p., each×3 (Nos. NI71, NI73, NI75, NI77, S83, S85, S87, S89, W72, W74, W76, W78)..	26·00
20.10.98	P.O. Pack No. 42. 20p. (1 centre band), 26p., 37p., 63p., each×3 (Nos. NI79, NI81/2, NI85, S90/3, W79/82)	26·00

N **5**

(Des J. Matthews. Photo Walsall)

2000 (15 Feb). Type N **4** redrawn with "1st" face value as Type N **5**. Two
phosphor bands. P. 14 (with one elliptical hole in each vertical
side).

NI88	N **5**	(1st) bright orange-red	3·00	3·00
		al. Booklet pane. Nos. NI88, S108 and W97, each×3 with margins all round	13·00	
		b. Perf 15×14 (25 Apr)	12·00	12·00

First Day Cover (se-tenant pane No. NI88al) (Philatelic
Bureau).. 13·00

First Day Cover (se-tenant pane No. NI88al) (London
SW5) .... 13·00
No. NI88 was issued in £7.50 stamp booklets (No. DX24) and No. NI88b
in sheets.

N **6** Basalt Columns,   N **7** Aerial View
Giant's Causeway   of Patchwork Fields

N **8** Linen Pattern   N **9** Vase Pattern
from Belleek

(Des Rodney Miller Associates. Litho Walsall or Enschedé (1st, 2nd), De
La Rue or Walsall (E), Walsall (65p.), De La Rue (68p.))

2001 (6 Mar)–**03**. One centre phosphor band (2nd) or two phosphor
bands (others). P. 15×14 (with one elliptical hole in each vertical
side).

NI89	N **6**	(2nd) black, new blue, bright magenta and greenish yellow	75	75
		a. Booklet pane. No. NI89x5 and No. NI90x4 with margins all round (25.2.03)	7·00	
		Ey. Phosphor omitted...........................	£600	
NI90	N **7**	(1st) black, new blue and greenish yellow	1·20	1·20
		Ey. Phosphor omitted...........................	35·00	
NI91	N **8**	(E) black, new blue and pale orange	1·50	1·50
NI92	N **9**	65p. black, bright magenta and greenish yellow	3·00	3·00
NI93		68p. black, bright magenta and greenish yellow (4.7.02)	3·25	3·25
Presentation Pack (Nos. NI89/92) (P.O. Pack No. 53)..........	7·00		
PHQ Cards (Nos. NI89/92) (set of 4) (D19)	8·00	14·00	

Nos. NI89, NI90 and NI91 were initially sold at 19p., 27p. and 36p.,
the latter representing the basic European airmail rate. A new printing
of No. NI91, produced by De La Rue instead of Walsall, was issued on
15 October 2002. Stamps from this printing do not differ from those
produced by Walsall. Booklet pane No. NI89a was printed by Enschedé.
For combined presentation pack for all four Regions, see under England.

First Day Covers

6.3.01	2nd, 1st, E, 65p. (NI89/92)	
	Philatelic Bureau	4·50
	Belfast	5·00
4.7.02	68p. (NI93)	
	Tallents House (Type K, see Introduction)	2·50
	Belfast	3·00

Special First Day of Issue Postmarks

2003 (14 Oct)–**11**. As Nos. NI89/91 and NI93, and new values, but with
white borders. One centre phosphor band (2nd) or two phosphor
bands (others). P. 15×14 (with one elliptical hole in each vertical
side).

(a) (Litho Walsall (NI98), De La Rue or Enschedé (NI95),
Cartor (NI100a, NI101a) or De La Rue (others))

NI94	N **6**	(2nd) black, new blue, bright magenta and greenish yellow	1·00	1·00
NI95	N **7**	(1st) black, new blue and greenish yellow	1·00	1·00
		a. black omitted....................................		
NI96	N **8**	(E) black and new blue	2·50	2·50
NI97		40p. black and new blue (11.5.04)	1·75	1·75
NI98		42p. black, new blue and orange yellow (5.4.05)..	1·75	1·75
		a. Black, new blue and greenish-yellow (26.7.05)..................................	2·00	2·00

NI99		44p. black, new blue and greenish yellow (28.3.06)	1·00	1·00
NI100	N **9**	68p. black, bright magenta* and greenish yellow	2·75	2·75
NI100*a*	N **8**	68p. greenish yellow, bright magenta, new blue and black (29.3.11)	1·50	1·50
NI101		72p. black, greyish black, bright magenta and greenish yellow (28.3.06)	2·50	2·50
NI101*a*	N **9**	£1.10 greenish yellow, bright magenta, new blue and black (29.3.11)	2·50	2·50

(b) Photo De La Rue

NI102	N **6**	(2nd) bright magenta, greenish yellow, new blue and black (20.9.07)	70	60
NI103	N **7**	(1st) greenish yellow, new blue and black (20.9.07)	90	75
NI104	N **8**	48p. olive-grey and black (27.3.07)	1·20	1·20
NI105		50p. olive-grey and black (1.4.08)	1·20	1·20
NI105*a*		56p. olive-grey and black (31.3.09)	1·25	1·25
NI105*b*		60p. olive-grey and black (30.3.10)	1·40	1·40
NI106	N **9**	78p. bright magenta, greenish yellow and black (27.3.07)	2·00	2·00
NI107		81p. bright magenta, greenish yellow and black (1.4.08)	2·00	2·00
NI107*a*		90p. bright magenta, greenish yellow and black (31.3.09)	2·00	2·00
NI107*b*		97p. bright magenta, greenish yellow and black (30.3.10)	2·25	2·25
Presentation Pack (Nos. NI94/6, NI100) (P.O. Pack No. 66)			7·00	
PHQ Cards (Nos. NI94/6, NI100) (set of 4) (D27)			2·00	10·00

No. NI95 was printed in sheets by De La Rue and was also issued in £7·66 booklets, No. DX40, printed by Enschedé.

NI95*a* originates from an example of booklet pane NI112b with a progressive dry print of black.

No. NI98 (Walsall printing) appears bluish grey and No. NI98a (De La Rue printing) appears olive-grey.

Nos. NI102/3 went on philatelic sale on 20 September 2007. They went on sale in Northern Ireland post offices as supplies of Nos. NI94/95 were used up.

*The bright magenta used on the 68p. is fluorescent.

A stamp as No. NI101 but printed in photogravure was only issued within **MS**2685.

Stamps as Nos. NI106/7 but printed in lithography were only issued within **MS**2796 (NI106) or **MS**2886 (NI107).

A design as No. NI95 but self-adhesive was issued on 11 March 2008 in sheets of 20, each stamp accompanied by a *se-tenant* label showing a Northern Ireland scene (LS46). These sheets, perforated 15×14 without the elliptical holes, were printed in lithography by Cartor and sold at £7·35 each. They were also available with personalised photographs on the labels at £14·95 from the Royal Mail in Edinburgh.

Stamps as EN18, NI95, S131 and W120 but self-adhesive were issued on 29 September 2008 in sheets of 20 containing five of each design with *se-tenant* labels (LS49).

Stamps as NI95 but self-adhesive were issued again on 17 March 2009 in sheets of 20 with *se-tenant* labels showing Northern Ireland Castles, No. S58. These sheets were printed in lithography by Cartor and originally sold at £7·74 each (£8·35 from 6 April 2009).

Nos. NI108/9 are left for possible additions to the above definitive stamps.

First Day Covers

14.10.03	2nd, 1st, E, 68p. (NI94/6, NI100)		
	Tallents House (Type K, see Introduction)		3·25
	Belfast		3·25
11.5.04	40p. (NI97)		
	Tallents House (Type K)		2·75
	Belfast		2·75
5.4.05	42p. (NI98)		
	Tallents House (Type K)		1·40
	Belfast		1·40
28.3.06	44p., 72p. (NI99, NI101)		
	Tallents House (Type K)		2·75
	Belfast		2·75
27.3.07	48p., 78p. (NI104, NI106) Tallents House (Type K)		4·00
	Belfast		4·00
1.4.08	50p., 81p. (NI105, NI107) Tallents House (Type K)		4·00
	Belfast		4·00
31.3.09	56p., 90p. (NI105*a*, NI107*a*) Tallents House (Type K)		4·75
	Belfast		4·75
30.3.10	60p., 97p. (NI105*b*, NI107*b*) Tallents House (Type K)		4·00
	Belfast		4·00
29.3.11	68p., £1.10 (NI100*a*, NI101*a*) Tallents House (Type K)		6·00
	Belfast		6·00

LOOKING FOR THAT ELUSIVE STAMP?

Send your wants lists to our specialist stamp departments at:

399 Strand, London, WC2R 0LX, UK

N **10** (Illustration reduced. Actual size 123×70 mm)

(Des Clare Melinsky and Silk Pearce. Litho De La Rue)

2008 (11 Mar). *Celebrating Northern Ireland. Sheet 123×70 mm. Two phosphor bands.* P 15×14½ (with one elliptical hole in each vertical side) (1st) or 15×14½ (78p).

MSNI110 (1st) Carrickfergus Castle; (1st) Giant's Causeway; 78p. St. Patrick; 78p. Queen's Bridge and 'Angel of Thanksgiving' sculpture, Belfast	6·00	6·00
First Day Cover (Tallents House)		6·00
First Day Cover (Downpatrick, Co. Down)		6·00
Presentation Pack (P.O. Pack No. 410)	8·00	
PHQ Cards (set of 5) (CGB3)	4·00	17·00

The five PHQ cards depict the complete miniature sheet and the four stamps within it.

Special First Day of Issue Postmarks

N **11** (Illustration reduced. Actual size 124×70 mm)

(Des Sedley Place. Photogravure De La Rue)

2008 (29 Sept). *50th Anniv of the Country Definitives. Sheet 124×70 mm, containing designs as Nos. NI1, NI3, NI5, S1, S3, S5, W1, W3 and W5 (regional definitives of 1958) but inscribed 1st and printed on pale cream. Two phosphor bands.* P 15×14 (with one elliptical hole in each vertical side).

MSNI111 N **11** (1st)×9 As No. W1; As No. S1; As No. W5; As No. S5; As No. NI1; As No. W3; As No. S3; As No. NI3; As No. NI5	8·25	8·25
First Day Cover (Tallents House)		10·00
First Day Cover (Gloucester)		10·00
Presentation Pack	12·00	
PHQ Cards (set of 10) (D29)	6·00	18·00

The ten PHQ cards show the nine individual stamps and the complete sheet.

Special First Day of Issue Postmarks

(Litho De La Rue)

2008 (29 Sept). *50th Anniv of the Country Definitives (2nd issue). As Nos. NI1, NI3 and NI5 (definitives of 1958) but inscribed 1st. Two phosphor bands.* P 15×14½ (with one elliptical hole in each vertical side).

NI112	N **1**	(1st) deep lilac	2·50	2·50
		a. Booklet pane. Nos. NI112/14, S134/6 and W122/4	14·00	
		b. Booklet pane. Nos. NI112/14 and NI95×3	6·00	
NI113	N **3**	(1st) green	2·50	2·50
NI114	N **2**	(1st) deep claret	2·50	2·50

Nos. NI112/14 come from £9.72 booklets, No. DX43.

First Day Cover (No. NI112a) (Tallents House) ..... 10·00
First Day Cover (No. NI112a) (Gloucester) ..... 10·00

III. SCOTLAND

S **1**   S **2**   S **3**

(Des. G. Huntly (3d., 4d., 5d.), J. Fleming (6d., 9d.),
A. Imrie (1s.3d., 1s.6d.))

1958–67. W 179. P 15×14.

S1	S **1**	3d. dp lilac (18.8.58)	15	15
		p. Two phosphor bands (29.1.63)	13·00	2·75
		pa. One phosphor band at right (30.4.65)	20	25
		pb. Band at left	20	25
		pc. Horiz pair. Nos. S1pa/pb	40	1·00
		pd. One centre phosphor band (9.11.67)	15	15
S2		4d. ultramarine (7.2.66)	15	15
		p. Two phosphor bands	15	15
S3	S **2**	6d. dp claret (29.9.58)	20	15
		p. Two phosphor bands (29.1.63)	20	20
S4		9d. bronze-green (2 phosphor bands) (1.3.67)	35	40
S5	S **3**	1s.3d. green (29.9.58)	40	40
		p. Two phosphor bands (29.1.63)	40	40
S6		1s.6d. grey-blue (2 phosphor bands) (1.3.67)	45	50

First Day Covers

18.8.58	3d. (S1)	17.00
29.9.58	6d., 1s.3d. (S3, S5)	25.00
7.2.66	4d. (S2)	7.00
1.3.67	9d., 1s.6d. (S4, S6)	6.00

The one phosphor band on No. S1pa was produced by printing broad phosphor bands across alternate vertical perforations. Individual stamps show the band at right or left (same prices either way).

For Nos. S1, S3 and S5 in Presentation Pack, see below Wales No. W6.

1967–70. *No watermark. Chalk-surfaced paper. One centre phosphor band (S7, S9/10) or two phosphor bands (others). Gum arabic (Nos. S7, S8) or PVA gum (others).* P 15×14.

S7	S **1**	3d. dp lilac (16.5.68)	10	15
		Ey. Phosphor omitted	7·00	
		Ev. PVA gum	10	
		Eya. Phosphor omitted (No. S7Ev)	4·00	
S8		4d. dp brt blue (28.11.67)	10	15
		Ey. Phosphor omitted	10·00	
		Ev. PVA gum (25.7.68)	10	
S9		4d. olive-sepia (4.9.68)	10	10
		Ey. Phosphor omitted	3·00	
S10		4d. brt vermilion (26.2.69)	10	10
		Ey. Phosphor omitted	2·50	
S11		5d. royal blue (4.9.68)	20	10
		Ey. Phosphor omitted	55·00	
S12	S **2**	9d. bronze-green (28.9.70)	6·00	6·00
		Ey. Phosphor omitted	£250	
S13	S **3**	1s.6d. grey-blue (12.12.68)	1·75	1·50
		Ey. Phosphor omitted	£125	

There was no Post Office first day cover for No. S10.

4.9.68	First Day Cover (S9, S11)	3·00
	Presentation Pack (containing Nos. S3, S5p, S7, S9/13) (9.12.70)	8·00

S **4**

I   II

Redrawn design of Type S 4 (litho ptgs.)

The introduction of the redrawn lion took place in 1983 when Waddington's had the contract and therefore the 13, 17, 22 and 31p. exist in both types and perforated 14. The Questa printings, perforated 15×14, are all Type II.

The Types of Lion.

Type I:–The eye and jaw appear larger and there is no line across the bridge of the nose.

Type II:–The tongue is thick at the point of entry to the mouth and the eye is linked to the background by a solid line.

The following stamps printed in lithography show a screened background behind and to the left of the emblem: 12½p., 15½p., 16p., 19½p., 28p. (Nos. S50 and S74) and 31p. (Nos. S51 and S76). The 13p. and 17p. (No. S43) also showed screened backgrounds for both Type I and II of the John Waddington printings, but changed to solid backgrounds for the Questa Type II. All other values printed in lithography have solid backgrounds.

(Des J. Matthews after plaster cast by Arnold Machin)

1971 (7 July)–**93.** *Decimal Currency. Chalk-surfaced paper. Type S **4**.*

(a) Photo Harrison. With phosphor bands. P 15×14.

S14		2½p. brt magenta (1 centre band)	25	20
		Ey. Phosphor omitted	8·00	
		Eg. Gum arabic (22.9.72)	30	
		Egy. Phosphor omitted	20·00	
S15		3p. ultramarine (2 bands)	35	15
		Ey. Phosphor omitted	15·00	
		Eg. Gum arabic (14.12.72)	30	
		Ega. Imperf (pair)	£700	
		Egy. Phosphor omitted	50·00	
S16		3p. ultramarine (1 centre band) (23.1.74)	15	15
S17		3½p. olive-grey (2 bands) (23.1.74)	20	25
		Ey. Phosphor omitted	50·00	
S18		3½p. olive-grey (1 centre band) (6.11.74)	20	25
S19		4½p. grey-blue (2 bands) (6.11.74)	30	25
S20		5p. reddish violet (2 bands)	1·00	1·25
S21		5½p. violet (2 bands) (23.1.74)	20	20
S22		5½p. violet (1 centre band) (21.5.75)	20	25
		a. Imperf (pair)	£600	
S23		6½p. greenish blue (1 centre band) (14.1.76)	20	20
S24		7p. purple-brown (1 centre band) (18.1.78)	30	30
S25		7½p. chestnut (2 bands)	1·25	1·25
		Ey. Phosphor omitted	5·00	
S26		8p. rosine (2 bands) (23.1.74)	45	40
S27		8½p. yellow-green (2 bands) (14.1.76)	40	40
S28		9p. deep violet (2 bands) (18.1.78)	40	40
S29		10p. orange-brown (2 bands) (20.10.76)	45	50
S30		10p. orange-brown (1 centre band) (23.7.80)	40	50
S31		10½p. steel-blue (2 bands) (18.1.78)	45	50
S32		11p. scarlet (2 bands) (20.10.76)	50	50
		Ey. Phosphor omitted	2·00	

(b) Photo Harrison. On phosphorised paper. P 15×14.

S33		12p. yellowish green (23.7.80)	50	50
S34		13½p. purple-brown (23.7.80)	70	80
S35		15p. ultramarine (23.7.80)	60	70

(c) Litho J.W. (Type I unless otherwise stated). One side phosphor band (11½p., 12p., 12½p., 13p.) or phosphorised paper (others). P 14.

S36		11½p. drab (8.4.81)	80	80
		Ey. Phosphor omitted	£1000	
S37		12p. brt emerald (Type II) (7.1.86)	2·00	2·00
S38		12½p. lt emerald (24.2.82)	60	70
S39		13p. pale chestnut (Type I) (23.10.84)	85	75
		Ey. Phosphor omitted	£1000	
		Ea. Type II (1.85)	8·00	8·00
		Eay. Phosphor omitted	£1000	
S40		14p. grey-blue (8.4.81)	75	75
S41		15½p. pale violet (24.2.82)	80	80
S42		16p. drab (Type II) (27.4.83)	80	85
S43		17p. grey-blue (Type I) (23.10.84)	1·50	1·50
		Ea. Type II (1.85)	1·75	1·75
S44		18p. dp violet (8.4.81)	80	80
S45		19½p. olive-grey (24.2.82)	1·75	1·75
S46		20½p. ultramarine (Type II) (27.4.83)	3·50	3·50
S47		22p. blue (8.4.81)	1·00	1·00
S48		22p. yellow-green (Type I) (23.10.84)	4·25	4·25
		Ea. Type II (1.86)	50·00	30·00

S49	26p. rosine (24.2.82)	1·25	1·25
S50	28p. dp violet-blue (Type II) (27.4.83)	1·25	1·25
S51	31p. brt purple (Type I) (23.10.84)	2·50	2·50
	Ea. Type II (11.85*)	£150	£150

(d) Litho Questa (Type II) P 15×14

S52	12p. brt emerald (1 side band) (29.4.86)........	2·00	2·25
S53	13p. pale chestnut (1 side band) (4.11.86)	70	75
S54	14p. dp blue (1 centre band) (8.11.88)	60	70
	I. Booklet pane. No. S54×6 with margins		
	all round (21.3.89)	3·50	
S55	14p. dp blue (1 side band) (21.3.89)	80	90
	I. Booklet pane. No. S55×5, S63×2, S68		
	and centre label with margins all round .	18·00	
	Ia. Error. Booklet pane imperf.	£2300	
S56	15p. brt blue (1 centre band) (28.11.89)	70	70
	a. Imperf (three sides) (block of four)	£275	
S57	17p. grey-blue (phosphorised paper)		
	(29.4.86)	4·00	4·00
S58	17p. dp blue (1 centre band) (4.12.90)	1·00	1·10
S59	18p. dp olive-grey (phosphorised paper)		
	(6.1.87)	1·10	85
S60	18p. brt green (1 centre band) (3.12.91)	1·25	90
	a. Perf 14 (26.9.92*)	1·00	1·00
	aEy. Phosphor omitted	£1250	
S61	18p. brt green (1 side band) (10.8.93)	2·75	3·00
S62	19p. brt orange-red (phosphorised paper)		
	(8.11.88)	70	70
	I. Booklet pane. No. S62×9 with margins		
	all round (21.3.89)	5·50	
	m. Booklet pane. No. S62×6 with margins		
	all round (21.3.89)	4·50	
S63	19p. brt orange-red (2 bands) (21.3.89)	2·25	2·00
S64	20p. brownish black (phosphorised paper)		
	(28.11.89)	95	95
S65	22p. yellow-green (phosphorised paper)		
	(27.1.87)	1·25	1·50
S66	22p. brt orange-red (phosphorised paper)		
	(4.12.90)	1·25	90
S67	23p. brt green (phosphorised paper) (8.11.88)	1·25	1·10
S68	23p. brt green (2 bands) (21.3.89)	14·00	14·00
S69	24p. Indian red (phosphorised paper)		
	(28.11.89)	1·25	1·25
S70	24p. chestnut (phosphorised paper) (3.12.91)	1·40	1·25
	a. Perf 14 (10.92*)	6·00	6·00
S71	24p. chestnut (2 bands) (10.8.93)	2·75	3·00
S72	26p. rosine (phosphorised paper) (27.1.87)......	3·75	4·00
S73	26p. drab (phosphorised paper) (4.12.90)........	1·25	1·25
S74	28p. dp violet-blue (phosphorised paper)		
	(27.1.87)	1·25	1·25
S75	28p. dp bluish grey (phosphorised paper)		
	(3.12.91)	1·25	1·50
	a. Perf 14 (18.2.93*)	8·00	8·00
S76	31p. brt purple (phosphorised paper)		
	(29.4.86)	2·25	2·25
S77	32p. greenish blue (phosphorised paper)		
	(8.11.88)	1·75	2·00
S78	34p. dp bluish grey (phosphorised paper)		
	(28.11.89)	1·75	1·75
S79	37p. rosine (phosphorised paper) (4.12.90).....	2·00	2·25
S80	39p. brt mauve (phosphorised paper) (3.12.91)	2·00	2·25
	a. Perf 14 (11.92)	7·00	7·00

*Earliest known date of use.

Nos. S55, S61, S63, S68 and S71 only come from booklets.
The listed booklet panes come from the following Sponsored Booklets:

S54I	–Booklet DX10
S55I	–Booklet DX10
S62I/m	–Booklet DX10

No. S56a occured in the second vertical row of two sheets. It is best collected as a block of four including the left-hand vertical pair imperforate on three sides.

Nos. S60a, S70a, S75a and S80a were caused by the use of a reserve perforating machine for some printings in the second half of 1992.

From 1972 printings were on fluorescent white paper. From 1973 most printings had dextrin added to the PVA gum (see notes after the 1971 Decimal Machin issue).

First Day Covers

7.7.71	2½p., 3p., 5p., 7½p. (S14/15, S20, S25)		3·00
23.1.74	3p., 3½p., 5½p., 8p. (S16/17, S21, S26)		2·50
6.11.74	4½p. (S19)		1·50
14.1.76	6½p., 8½p. (S23, S27)		1·50
20.10.76	10p., 11p. (S29, S32)		1·50
18.1.78	7p., 9p., 10½p. (S24, S28, S31)		1·75
23.7.80	12p., 13½p., 15p. (S33/5)		2·75
8.4.81	11½p., 14p., 18p., 22p. (S36, S40, S44, S47)		2·50
24.2.82	12½p., 15½p., 19½p., 26p. (S38, S41, S45, S49)		3·50
27.4.83	16p., 20½p., 28p. (S42, S46, S50)		4·00
23.10.84	13p., 17p., 22p., 31p. (S39, S48, S43, S51)		4·00
7.1.86	12p. (S37)		2·00
6.1.87	18p. (S59)		1·80
8.11.88	14p., 19p., 23p., 32p. (S54, S62, S67, S77)		4·25

21.3.89	Scots Connection *se-tenant* pane 14p., 19p., 23p. (S55I)	14·00
28.11.89	15p., 20p., 24p., 34p. (S56, S64, S69, S78)	5·00
4.12.90	17p., 22p., 26p., 37p. (S58, S66, S73, S79)	5·00
3.12.91	18p., 24p., 28p., 39p. (S60, S70, S75, S80)	5·50

Presentation Packs

7.7.71	P.O. Pack No. 27. 2½p., 3p. (*2 bands*), 5p., 7½p. (*Nos. S14/15, S20, S25*).	3·50
29.5.74	P.O. Pack No. 62. 3p. (*1 centre band*), 3½p. (*2 bands*) or (1 centre band), 5½p. (*2 bands*) or (1 centre band), 8p. (*Nos. S16, S17 or S18, S21 or S22, S26*). The 4½p. (*No. S19*) was added later	2·50
20.10.76	P.O. Pack No. 85. 6½p., 8½p., 10p. (*2 bands*), 11p. (*Nos. S23, S27, S29, S32*).	2·00
28.10.81	P.O. Pack No. 129b. 7p., 9p., 10½p., 12p. (*photo*), 13½p., 15p. (*photo*), 11½p., 14p. dp violet, 18p. dp violet, 22p. blue (*Nos. S24, S28, S31, S33/6, S40, S44, S47*) ...	9·00
3.8.83	P.O. Pack No. 2. 10p. (*1 centre band*), 12½p., 16p., 20½p., 26p. (J.W.), 28p. (J.W.) (*Nos. S30, S38, S42, S46, S49/50*)	18·00
23.10.84	P.O. Pack No. 6. 10p. (*1 centre band*), 13p. (J.W.), 16p., 17p. (J.W.), 22p. yellow-green, 26p. (J.W.), 28p. (J.W.), 31p. (J.W.), (*Nos. S30, S39, S42/3, S48/51*)	17·00
3.3.87	P.O. Pack No. 10. 12p. (litho), 13p. (Questa), 17p. grey-blue (Questa), 18p. dp olive-grey, 22p. yellow-green, 26p. rosine (Questa), 28p. dp violet-blue (Questa), 31p. (Questa) (*Nos. S52/3, S57, S59, S65, S72, S74, S76*)......	20·00

Presentation Packs containing stamps of Northern Ireland, Scotland and Wales are listed after those for Northern Ireland.

1977–78 EXPERIMENTAL MACHINE PACKETS. These are small cartons containing loose stamps for sale in vending machines. The experiment was confined to the Scottish Postal Board area, where six vending machines were installed, the first becoming operational in Dundee about February 1977.

The cartons carry labels inscribed "ROYAL MAIL STAMPS", their total face value (30p. or 60p.) and their contents.

At first the 30p. packet contained two 6½p. and two 8½p. Scottish Regional stamps and the 60p. packet had four of each. The stamps could be in pairs or blocks, but also in strips or singles.

With the change in postal rates on 13 June 1977 these packets were withdrawn on 11 June and on 13 June the contents were changed, giving three 7p. and one 9p. for the 30p. packet and double this for the 60p. packet. However, this time ordinary British Machin stamps were used. Moreover the Edinburgh machine, situated in an automatic sorting area, was supplied with 7p. stamps with two phosphor bands instead of the new centre band 7p. stamps, despite instructions having been given to withdraw the two band stamps. However, the demand for these packets was too great to be filled and by 27 June the machine was closed down. It was brought back into use on 16 August 1977, supplying 7p. stamps with the centre band.

The 6½p. and 8½p. Scottish Regional packets were put on sale at the Edinburgh Philatelic Bureau in June 1977 and withdrawn in April 1978. The packets with the 7p. and 9p. Machin stamps were put on sale at the Bureau in June 1977 and withdrawn in December 1978.

Such machine packets are outside the scope of this catalogue.

(Des J. Matthews after plaster cast by Arnold Machin)

1993 (7 Dec)–**98**. *Chalk-surfaced paper.*

(a) Litho Questa. P 15×14 (with one elliptical hole in each vertical side).

S81	**S 4**	19p. bistre (1 centre band)...........................	80	70
S82		19p. bistre (1 band at right) (25.4.95).......	3·00	3·25
S83		20p. brt green (1 centre band) (23.7.96).	1·50	1·50
S84		25p. red (2 bands)	1·10	1·00
S85		26p. red-brown (2 bands) (23.7.96)	1·75	2·00
S86		30p. dp olive-grey (2 bands)	1·25	1·25
S87		37p. brt mauve (2 bands) (23.7.96)	2·75	3·00
S88		41p. grey-brown (2 bands)	1·75	2·00
		Ey. Phosphor omitted	£300	
S89		63p. lt emerald (2 bands) (23.7.96)	4·00	4·25

(b) Photo Walsall (20p., 26p. (No. S91a), 63p.), Harrison or Walsall (26p. (No. S91), 37p.). P 14 (No. S90a) or 15×14 (others) (both with one elliptical hole in each vertical side).

S90	**S 4**	20p. brt green (1 centre band) (1.7.97)....	1·00	90
S90a		20p. brt green (1 side band at right) (13.10.98)..	3·50	3·50
S91		26p. chestnut (2 bands) (1.7.97).............	1·20	1·20
		a. Perf 14 (13.10.98)	3·50	3·50
S92		37p. brt mauve (2 bands) (1.7.97)...........	1·50	1·50
S93		63p. lt emerald (2 bands) (1.7.97)...........	4·00	4·00

Nos. S82, S90a and S91a only come from booklets. The Harrison printings of Nos. S91/2 come from booklet pane No. NI81al.

First Day Covers

7.12.93	19p., 25p., 30p., 41p. (S81, S84, S86, S88)......................		6·00
23.7.96	20p. 26p., 37p., 63p. (S83, S85, S87, S89)......................		8·75

For Presentation Pack containing stamps of Northern Ireland, Scotland and Wales see after No. NI87 of Northern Ireland.

S **5** Scottish Flag

S **6** Scottish Lion

S **7** Thistle

S **8** Tartan

S **9**

(Des A. Morris (2nd), F. Pottinger and T. Chalk (1st, E). Adapted Tayburn. Photo Questa (Nos. S94a, S95a), De La Rue (No. S99), De La Rue or Walsall (Nos. S94/5), Walsall (others))

1999 (8 June)–**2002**. *One centre phosphor band (2nd) or two phosphor bands (others). P 15×14 (with one elliptical hole in each vertical side).*

S94	S **5**	(2nd) new blue, blue and silver...............	75	75
		a. Booklet pane. Nos. S94×6 and S98×2 with centre label and margins all round (4.8.00)..................	7·00	
S95	S **6**	(1st) greenish yellow, dp rose-red, rose-red and silver............	1·00	1·00
		a. Booklet pane. Nos. S95/6, each×4, with centre label and margins all round (22.10.01)............	7·75	
S96	S **7**	(E) brt lilac, dp lilac and silver..............	2·00	2·00
S97	S **8**	64p. greenish yellow, brt magenta, new blue, grey-black and silver........	9·00	9·00
S98		65p. greenish yellow, brt magenta, new blue, grey-black and silver (25.4.00)	3·00	3·25
S99		68p. greenish yellow, bright magenta, new blue, grey-black and silver (4.7.02)...........	3·25	3·25

Presentation Pack (P.O. Pack No. 45) (2nd, 1st, E, 64p.)
(Nos. S94/7).................. 14·00

Presentation Pack (P.O. Pack No. 50) (65p.) (No. S98)........ 11·00

Presentation Pack (P.O. Pack No. 55) (2nd, 1st, E, 65p.)
(Nos. S94/6, S98)........... 15·00

PHQ Cards (set of 4) (Nos. S94/7) (D12).............. 8·00 14·00

Nos. S94, S95 and S96 were initially sold at 19p., 26p. and 30p., the latter representing the basic European airmail rate.

New printings of Nos. S94/5, produced by De La Rue instead of Walsall were introduced on 5 June 2002. Stamps from this printing do not differ from those produced by Walsall.

No. S94a comes from booklet No. DX25.

No. S95a comes from booklet No. DX27.

For combined presentation pack for all four Regions, see under England.

First Day Covers

8.6.99	2nd, 1st, E, 64p. (S94/7) Philatelic Bureau......................	6·00	
	Edinburgh........................	6·50	
25.4.00	65p. (S98) Philatelic Bureau..............	3·00	
	Edinburgh................	3·50	
4.8.00	Queen Elizabeth the Queen Mother *se-tenant* pane 2nd, 65p. (S94a) Philatelic Bureau (as for Nos. 2160/1)	4·75	
	London SW1 (*as for Nos.* 2160/1)................	4·75	
22.10.01	Unseen and Unheard *se-tenant* pane (1st), E, (S95a) Philatelic Bureau (as for **MS**2206)........	7·00	
	Rosyth, Dunfermline (as for **MS**2206).........	7·00	
4.7.02	68p. (S99) Tallents House (Type K) (*see Introduction*)	1·75	
	Edinburgh................	1·75	

Special First Day of Issue Postmarks
(for use on Nos. S94, S95/8)

(Des J. Matthews. Photo Walsall)

2000 (15 Feb). *Type S **4** redrawn with "1st" face value as Type S **9**. Two phosphor bands. P 14 (with one elliptical hole in each vertical side).*

S108	S **9**	(1st) bright orange-red	3·00	3·25

No. S108 was only issued in £7·50 stamp booklets (No. DX24).

2003 (14 Oct)–**11**. *As Nos. S94/6 and S99, and new values, but with white borders. One centre phosphor band (2nd) or two phosphor bands (others). P 15×14 (with one elliptical hole in each vertical side).*

(a) Photo Walsall or De La Rue (42p.) or De La Rue (others)

S109	S **5**	(2nd) new blue, blue and silver..................	70	60
		a. Booklet pane. Nos. S109 and EN14, each×3, with margins all round (16.3.04)	8·50	
		b. Booklet pane. Nos. S109 and W103, each ×3, with margins all round (1.3.07)................	3·00	
S110	S **6**	(1st) rose-red, greenish yellow, deep rose-red and silver...............	90	85
S111	S **7**	(E) bright lilac, deep lilac and silver........	2·50	2·50
S112		40p. bright lilac, deep lilac and silver (11.5.04)...............	1·75	1·75
S113		42p. bright lilac, deep lilac and silver (5.4.05)................	1·75	1·75
S114		44p. bright lilac, deep lilac and silver (28.3.06)...............	1·50	1·50
S115		48p. bright lilac, deep lilac and silver (27.3.07)...............	90	90
S116		50p. bright lilac, deep lilac and silver (1.4.08)................	80	75
S116a		56p. bright lilac, deep lilac and silver (31.3.09)...............	1·25	1·25
S116b		60p. bright lilac, deep lilac and silver (30.3.10)...............	1·40	1·40
S117	S **8**	68p. bright magenta, greenish yellow, new blue, grey-black and silver........	2·00	2·00
S118		72p. bright magenta, greenish yellow, new blue, grey-black and silver (28.3.06)...............	1·75	1·75
S119		78p. bright magenta, greenish yellow, new blue, grey-black and silver (27.3.07)...............	1·50	1·50
S120		81p. bright magenta, greenish yellow, new blue, grey-black and silver (1.4.08)................	1·40	1·30
S120a		90p. bright magenta, greenish yellow, new blue, grey-black and silver (31.3.09)...............	2·00	2·00
S120b		97p. bright magenta, greenish yellow, new blue, grey-black and silver (30.3.10)	2·25	2·25

(b) Litho Enschedé (1st) or Cartor (others)

S131	S **6**	(1st) rose-red, greenish yellow, deep rose-red and silver (20.9.07)	7·50	7·50
S131a	S **7**	68p. greenish yellow, bright magenta, new blue and black (29.3.11)	1·50	1·50
S131b	S **8**	£1.10 greenish yellow, bright magenta, new blue and black (29.3.11)	2·50	2·50

Presentation Pack (Nos. S109/11, S117) (P.O. Pack No. 64) 7·00

PHQ Cards (Nos. S109/11, S117) (set of 4) (D25)................ 2·00 10·00

No. S109a comes from booklet No. DX32.

The Walsall printing of No. S113 was issued on 5 April 2005, and the De La Rue printing on 24 May 2005.

Stamps as No. S119/20 but printed in lithography were only issued within **MS**2796 (S119) or **MS**2886 (S120).

No. S131 was only issued in £7·66 stamp booklets, No. DX40.

A design as No. S131 but self-adhesive was issued on 30 November 2007 in sheets of 20, each stamp accompanied by a *se-tenant* label showing a Scottish scene (LS44). These sheets were printed in lithography by Cartor, perforated 15×14 without the elliptical holes, and sold at £7·35. They were also available with personalised photographs on the labels at £14·95 from the Royal Mail in Edinburgh.

Stamps as Nos. EN18, NI95, S131 and W120 but self-adhesive were issued on 29 September 2008 in sheets of 20 containing five of each design with *se-tenant* labels (LS49).

Nos. S121/30 are left for possible additions to the above definitive series.

First Day Covers

14.10.03	2nd, 1st, E, 68p. (S109/11, S117) Tallents House (Type K, see Introduction)	3·25	
	Edinburgh................	3·25	

11.5.04	40p. (S112) Tallents House (Type K)		2·75
	Edinburgh		2·75
5.4.05	42p. (S113) Tallents House (Type K)		1·40
	Edinburgh		1·40
28.3.06	44p., 72p. (S114, S118) Tallents House (Type K)		2·75
	Edinburgh		2·75
27.3.07	48p., 78p. (S115, S119) Tallents House (Type K)		4·00
1.4.08	50p., 81p. (S116, S120) Tallents House (Type K)		4·00
31.3.09	56p., 90p. (S116a, S120a) Tallents House (Type K)		4·75
	Edinburgh		4·75
30.3.10	60p., 97. (S116b, S120b) Tallents House (Type K)		4·00
	Edinburgh		4·00
29.3.11	68p., £1.10 (S131a/b) Tallents House (Type K)		6·00
	Edinburgh		6·00

(Des H. Brown. Photo De La Rue)

2004 (5 Oct). *Opening of New Scottish Parliament Building, Edinburgh. Sheet 123×70 mm. Printed in photogravure by De La Rue. One centre phosphor band (2nd) or two phosphor bands (others). P 15×14 (with one elliptical hole in each vertical side).*

MSS132 Nos. S109, S110×2 and S112×2		6·00	6·00
First Day Cover (Tallents House)			8·00
First Day Cover (Edinburgh)			7·25

Special First Day of Issue Postmarks

S **10** (Illustration reduced. Actual size 124×71 mm)

(Des P. Crowther, Clare Melinsky and Silk Pearce. Photo De La Rue)

2006 (30 Nov). *Celebrating Scotland. Sheet 124×71 mm. Two phosphor bands. P 15×14 (with one elliptical hole in each vertical side) (1st) or 14½×14 (72p).*

MSS133 (1st) As No. S110; (1st) Scottish Flag; 72p. St. Andrew; 72p. Edinburgh Castle		6·00	6·00
First Day Cover (Tallents House)			6·50
First Day Cover (St Andrews, Fife)			6·50
Presentation Pack (P.O. Pack No. M14)		8·00	
PHQ Cards (set of 5) (CGB1)		4·00	17·00

The five PHQ cards depict the complete miniature sheet and the four stamps within it.

Stamps as the 1st class Scottish flag stamp within **MS**S133 but self-adhesive were issued on 30 November 2009 in sheets of 20 with *se-tenant* labels showing Scottish Castles, No. LS68. These sheets were printed in lithography by Cartor and sold for £8·35 each.

Special First Day of Issue Postmarks

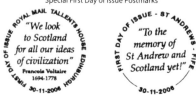

(Litho De La Rue)

2008 (29 Sept). *50th Anniv. of the Country Definitives. As Nos. S1, S3 and S5 (definitives of 1958) but inscribed 1st. Two phosphor bands. P 15×14½ (with one elliptical hole in each vertical side).*

S134	S **1**	(1st) deep lilac	2·50	2·50
		a. Booklet pane. Nos. S134/6 and S131×3	6·00	
S135	S **3**	(1st) green	2·50	2·50
S136	S **2**	(1st) deep claret	2·50	2·50

Nos. S134/6 come from £9.72 booklets, No. DX43.

S **11** (Illustration reduced. Actual size 145×74 mm)

(Des Tayburn. Photo Enschedé)

2009 (22 Jan). *250th Birth Anniv of Robert Burns (Scottish poet). Sheet 145×74 mm. One centre phosphor band (2nd) or two phosphor bands (others). P 14½ (size 34×34 mm) or 15×14 (with one elliptical hole in each vert side) (others).*

MSS137 (2nd) No. S109; (1st) "A Man for a' that" and Burns ploughing (detail) (James Sargent Storer) (34×34 mm); (1st) No. S110; (1st) Portrait of Burns (Alexander Nasmyth) (34×34 mm); 50p. No. S116; 81p. S120.		8·00	8·00
First Day Cover (Tallents House)			8·50
First Day Cover (Alloway, Ayr)			8·50
Presentation Pack		12·00	
PHQ Cards (set of 3) (319)		3·50	12·00

The three PHQ cards show the two 34×34 mm Robert Burns stamps and the complete miniature sheet.

Special First Day of Issue Postmarks

IV. WALES

From the inception of the Regional stamps, the Welsh versions were tendered to members of the public at all Post Offices within the former County of Monmouthshire but the national alternatives were available on request. By August 1961 the policy of "dual stocking" of definitive stamps was only maintained at Abergavenny, Chepstow, Newport and Pontypool. Offices with a Monmouthshire postal address but situated outside the County, namely Beachley, Brockweir, Redbrook, Sedbury, Tutshill, Welsh Newton and Woodcroft, were not supplied with the Welsh Regional stamps. With the re-formation of Counties, Monmouthshire became known as Gwent and was also declared to be part of Wales. From 1 July 1974, therefore, except for the offices mentioned above, only Welsh Regional stamps were available at the offices under the jurisdiction of Newport, Gwent.

W **1**   W **2**   W **3**

(Des R. Stone)

1958–67. W **179**. P 15×14.

W1	W **1**	3d. dp lilac (18.8.58)	15	15
		p. One centre phosphor band (16.5.67)	20	15
W2		4d. ultramarine (7.2.66)	20	15
		p. Two phosphor bands (10.67)	20	15
W3	W **2**	6d. dp claret (29.9.58)	35	30
W4		9d. bronze-green (2 phosphor bands) (1.3.67)	40	35
		Ey. Phosphor omitted	£350	

W5	**W 3** 1s.3d. green (29.9.58)		40	40
W6	1s.6d. grey-blue (2 phosphor bands) (1.3.67)		40	40
	Fy. Phosphor omitted		50·00	

First Day Covers

18.8.58	3d. (W1)		12·00
29.9.58	6d., 1s.3d. (W3, W5)		25·00
7.2.66	4d. (W2)		7·00
1.3.67	9d., 1s.6d. (W4, W6)		4·00
	Presentation Pack*		£100

*This was issued in 1960 and comprises Guernsey No. 7, Jersey No. 10, Isle of Man No. 2, Northern Ireland Nos. NI1, NI3 and NI5, Scotland Nos. S1, S3 and S5 and Wales Nos. W1, W3 and W5 together with a 6-page printed leaflet describing the stamps. There exist two forms: (a) inscribed "7s.3d." for sale in the U.K.; and (b) inscribed "$1.20" for sale in the U.S.A.

1967–69. No wmk. Chalk-surfaced paper. One centre phosphor band (W7, W9/10) or two phosphor bands (others). Gum arabic (3d.) or PVA gum (others). P 15×14.

W7	**W 1** 3d. dp lilac (6.12.67)		10	15
	Ey. Phosphor omitted		60·00	
W8	4d. ultramarine (21.6.68)		10	15
W9	4d. olive-sepia (4.9.68)		15	15
W10	4d. brt vermilion (26.2.69)		15	15
	Ey. Phosphor omitted		2·00	
W11	5d. royal blue (4.9.68)		15	15
	Ey. Phosphor omitted		3·00	
W12	**W 3** 1s.6d. grey-blue (1.8.69)		3·50	3·50

There was no Post Office first day cover for No. **W10**.

4.9.68	First Day Cover (W9, W11)		3·00
	Presentation Pack (containing Nos. W4, W6/7, W9/11) (9.12.70)		4·00

W **4** With "p"

I   II

Redrawn design of Type W 4 (litho ptgs.)

Two Types of Dragon

Type I:-The eye is complete with white dot in the centre. Wing-tips, tail and tongue are thin.

Type II:-The eye is joined to the nose by a solid line. Tail, wing-tips, claws and tongue are wider than in Type I.

The following stamps printed in lithography show a screened background behind and to the left of the emblem: 11½p., 12½p., 14p. (No. W39), 15½p., 16p., 18p. (No. W46), 19½p., 22p. (No. W54) and 28p. (No. W63). The 13p. and 17p. (No. W44) also show screened backgrounds in Type I, but changed to solid backgrounds for Type II. All other values printed in lithography have solid backgrounds.

(Des J. Matthews after plaster cast by Arnold Machin)

1971 (7 July)–93. Decimal Currency. Chalk-surfaced paper. Type W **4**.

(a) Photo Harrison. With phosphor bands. P 15×14.

W13	2½p. brt magenta (1 centre band)		20	20
	Ey. Phosphor omitted		7·50	
	Eg. Gum arabic (22.9.72)		20	
	Ega. Imperf (pair)		£750	
W14	3p. ultramarine (2 bands)		25	20
	Ey. Phosphor omitted		30·00	
	Eg. Gum arabic (6.6.73)		25	
	Eya. Phosphor omitted (No. W14Eg)		12·00	
W15	3p. ultramarine (1 centre band) (23.1.74)		25	25
W16	3½p. olive-grey (2 bands) (23.1.74)		20	30
W17	3½p. olive-grey (1 centre band) (6.11.74)		20	30
W18	4½p. grey-blue (2 bands) (6.11.74)		30	30
W19	5p. reddish violet (2 bands)		1·25	1·25
	Fy. Phosphor omitted		20·00	
W20	5½p. violet (2 bands) (23.1.74)		25	30
	Ey. Phosphor omitted		£180	
W21	5½p. violet (1 centre band) (21.5.75)		25	30

	a. Imperf (pair)		£675	
W22	6½p. greenish blue (1 centre band) (14.1.76)		20	20
W23	7p. purple-brown (1 centre band) (18.1.78)		25	25
W24	7½p. chestnut (2 bands)		1·75	1·75
	Ey. Phosphor omitted		95·00	
W25	8p. rosine (2 bands) (23.1.74)		30	35
	Ey. Phosphor omitted		£800	
W26	8½p. yellow-green (2 bands) (14.1.76)		30	35
W27	9p. dp violet (2 bands) (18.1.78)		40	40
W28	10p. orange-brown (2 bands) (20.10.76)		40	40
W29	10p. orange-brown (1 centre band) (23.7.80)		40	40
W30	10½p. steel-blue (2 bands) (18.1.78)		45	45
W31	11p. scarlet (2 bands) (20.10.76)		45	45

(b) Photo Harrison. On phosphorised paper. P 15×14.

W32	12p. yellowish green (23.7.80)		50	50
W33	13½p. purple-brown (23.7.80)		60	70
W34	15p. ultramarine (23.7.80)		60	70

(c) Litho Questa (Type II unless otherwise stated). P 14 (11½p., 12½p., 14p. (No. W39), 15½p., 16p., 18p. (No. W46), 19½p., 20½p., 22p. (No. W54), 26p. (No. W61), 28p. (No W63)) or 15×14 (others).

W35	11½p. drab (Type I) (1 side band) (8.4.81)		90	80
W36	12p. brt emerald (1 side band) (7.1.86)		2·00	2·00
W37	12½p. lt emerald (Type I) (1 side band) (24.2.82)		70	70
	a. Perf 15×14 (Type I) (10.1.84)		4·75	4·25
W38	13p. pale chestnut (Type I) (1 side band) (23.10.84)		60	60
	Ea. Type II (1.87)		1·90	1·75
W39	14p. grey-blue (Type I) (phosphorised paper) (8.4.81)		70	70
W40	14p. dp blue (1 centre band) (8.11.88)		75	75
W41	15p. brt blue (1 centre band) (28.11.89)		80	75
	Ey. Phosphor omitted		£125	
W42	15½p. pale violet (Type I) (phosphorised paper) (24.2.82)		75	75
W43	16p. drab (Type I) (phosphorised paper) (27.4.83)		1·75	1·75
	a. Perf 15×14 (Type I) (10.1.84)		1·75	1·75
W44	17p. grey-blue (Type I) (phosphorised paper) (23.10.84)		70	80
	Ea. Type II (18.8.86)		55·00	45·00
W45	17p. dp blue (1 centre band) (4.12.90)		90	80
	Ey. Phosphor omitted		18·00	
W46	18p. dp violet (Type I) (8.4.81)		1·00	95
W47	18p. dp olive-grey (phosphorised paper) (6.1.87)		95	90
W48	18p. brt green (1 centre band) (3.12.91)		75	75
	Ey. Phosphor omitted		£200	
	a. Booklet pane. No. W48×6 with margins all round (25.2.92)		3·25	
	aEy. Phosphor omitted			
	b. Perf 14 (12.1.93*)		7·50	7·50
W49	18p. brt green (1 side band at right) (25.2.92)		2·00	2·00
	a. Booklet pane. No. X1020×2, 1451a, 1514a, W49×2, W60×2 and centre label with margins all round		11·00	
	aEy. Phosphor omitted		£200	
	Eb. Band at left (10.8.93)		2·00	2·00
W50	19p. brt orange-red (phosphorised paper) (8.11.88)		1·00	80
W51	19½p. olive-grey (Type I) (phosphorised paper) (24.2.82)		1·75	2·00
W52	20p. brownish black (phosphorised paper) (28.11.89)		90	90
W53	20½p. ultramarine (Type I) (phosphorised paper) (27.4.83)		3·75	3·75
W54	22p. blue (Type I) (phosphorised paper) (8.4.81)		1·10	1·10
W55	22p. yellow-green (Type I) (phosphorised paper) (23.10.84)		95	1·10
W56	22p. brt orange-red (phosphorised paper) (4.12.90)		1·00	1·10
W57	23p. brt green (phosphorised paper) (8.11.88)		1·00	1·10
W58	24p. Indian red (phosphorised paper) (28.11.89)		1·25	1·25
W59	24p. chestnut (phosphorised paper) (3.12.91)		75	75
	a. Booklet pane. No. W59x6 with margins all round (25.2.92)		5·00	
	b. Perf 14 (14.9.92*)		7·50	7·50
W60	24p. chestnut (2 bands) (25.2.92)		1·25	1·50
W61	26p. rosine (Type I) (phosphorised paper) (14.1.81)		1·10	1·10
	a. Perf 15×14 (Type II) (27.1.87)		5·75	6·00
W62	26p. drab (phosphorised paper) (4.12.90)		1·75	1·75
W63	28p. dp violet-blue (Type I) (phosphorised paper) (27.4.83)		1·50	1·50
	a. Perf 15×14 (Type II) (27.1.87)		1·50	1·50
W64	28p. dp bluish grey (phosphorised paper) (3.12.91)		1·50	1·50
W65	31p. brt purple (Type I) (phosphorised paper) (23.10.84)		1·75	1·75
W66	32p. greenish blue (phosphorised paper) (8.11.88)		1·75	1·75

W67	34p. dp bluish grey (phosphorised paper)		
	(28.11.89)...	1·75	1·75
W68	37p. rosine (phosphorised paper) (4.12.90)........	2·25	2·25
W69	39p. brt mauve (phosphorised paper) (3.12.91)	2·25	2·25

*Earliest known date of use.

Nos. W48b and W59b were caused by the use of a reserve perforating machine for some printings in the second half of 1992.

Nos. W49, W49Eb and W60 only come from booklets.

The listed booklet panes come from the following Sponsored Booklets:

W48a	– Booklet DX13
W49a	– Booklet DX13
W59a	– Booklet DX13

No. W60 exists with the phosphor omitted, but cannot be identified without the use of u.v. light (*Price* £375 *unused*).

From 1972 printings were on fluorescent white paper. From 1973 most printings had dextrin added to the PVA gum (see notes after 1971 Decimal Machin issue).

First Day Covers

7.7.71	2½p., 3p., 5p., 7½p., (W13/14, W19, W24)	3·00
23.1.74	3p., 3½p., 5½p., 8p. (W15/16, W20, W25)	2·50
6.11.74	4½p. (W18)	1·50
14.1.76	6½p., 8½p. (W22, W26)	1·50
20.10.76	10p., 11p. (W28, W31)	1·50
18.1.78	7p., 9p., 10½p. (W23, W27, W30)	1·75
23.7.80	12p., 13½p., 15p. (W32/4)	3·00
8.4.81	11½p., 14p., 18p., 22p. (W35, W39, W46, W54).............	2·50
24.2.82	12½p., 15½p., 19½p., 26p. (W37, W42, W51, W61)	3·50
27.4.83	16p., 20½p., 28p. (W43, W53, W63)	3·50
23.10.84	13p., 17p., 22p., 31p. (W38, W44, W55, W65)	4·25
7.1.86	12p. (W36)...	2·00
6.1.87	18p. (W47)..	2·00
8.11.88	14p., 19p., 23p., 32p. (W40, W50, W57, W66)	4·50
28.11.89	15p., 20p., 24p., 34p. (W41, W52, W58, W67)	5·00
4.12.90	17p., 22p., 26p., 37p (W45, W56, W62, W68)	5·00
3.12.91	18p., 24p., 28p., 39p. (W48, W59, W64, W69)	5·50
25.2.92	Cymru-Wales *se-tenant* pane 18p. (*2nd*), 24p. (1st), 33p. (W49a)	10·00

Presentation Packs

7.7.71	P.O. Pack No. 28. 2½p., 3p. (2 *bands*), 5p., 7½p. (*Nos.* W13/14, W19, W24)	3·50
29.5.74	P.O. Pack No. 63. 3p. (1 *centre band*), 3½p. (2 *bands*) or (1 *centre band*), 5½p. (2 *bands*) or (1 *centre band*), 8p. (*Nos.* W15, W16 or W17, W20 or W21, W25). The 4½p. (No. W18) was added later	2·50
20.10.76	P.O. Pack No. 86. 6½p., 8½p., 10p. (2 *bands*), 11p. (*Nos.* W22, W26, W28, W31)	2·00
28.10.81	P.O. Pack No. 129c. 7p., 9p., 10½p., 12p. (*photo*), 13½p., 15p. (photo), 11½p., 14p. grey-blue, 18p. dp violet, 22p. blue (*Nos.* W23, W27, W30, W32/5, W39, W46, W54)	9·00
3.8.83	P.O. Pack No. 3. 10p. (1 *centre band*), 12½p., 16p., 20½p., 26p. rosine, 28p. dp violet-blue (*Nos.* W29, W37, W43, W53, W63)	20·00
23.10.84	P.O. Pack No. 7. 10p. (1 *centre band*), 13p., 16p., 17p. grey-blue, 22p. yellow-green, 26p. rosine, 28p. dp violet-blue, 31p. (*Nos.* W29, W38, W43a, W44, W55, W61, W63, W65)	17·00
3.3.87	P.O. Pack No. 11. 12p. (litho), 13p., 17p. grey-blue, 18p. dp olive-grey, 22p. yellow-green, 26p. rosine, 28p. dp violet-blue, 31p. (*Nos.* W36, W38, W44, W47, W55, W61a, W63a, W65)	20·00

Presentation Packs containing stamps of Northern Ireland, Scotland and Wales are listed after those for Northern Ireland.

(Des J. Matthews after plaster cast by Arnold Machin. Litho Questa)

1993 (7 Dec)–**96**. *Chalk-surfaced paper.* P 15×14 (with one elliptical hole in each vertical side).

W70	W **4**	19p. bistre (1 centre band)...............................	80	70
W71		19p. bistre (1 band at right) (25.4.95).......	3·75	4·00
W72		20p. brt green (1 centre band) (23.7.96)...	1·75	2·00
W73		25p. red (2 bands)	1·25	1·00
W74		26p. red-brown (2 bands) (23.7.96)	2·00	2·25
W75		30p. dp olive-grey (2 bands)	1·25	1·25
W76		37p. brt mauve (2 bands) (23.7.96)	2·75	3·00
W77		41p. grey-brown (2 bands)	2·00	2·00
W78		63p. lt emerald (2 bands) (23.7.96)	4·50	4·75

No. W71 only comes from booklets.

First Day Covers

7.12.93	19p., 25p., 30p., 41p. (W70, W73, W75, W77)	6·00
23.7.96	20p., 26p., 37p., 63p. (W72, W74, W76, W78)	7·00

For Presentation Packs containing stamps of Northern Ireland, Scotland and Wales see after No. NI85 of Northern Ireland.

W **5** Without "p"

(Photo Walsall (20p., 26p. (No. W80a), 63p.), Harrison or Walsall (26p. (No. W80), 37p.))

1997 (1 July)–**98**. *Chalk-surfaced paper.* P 14 (No. W79a) or 15×14 (others) (both with one elliptical hole in each vertical side).

W79	W **5**	20p. brt green (1 centre band)	80	80
W79*a*		20p. brt green (1 side band at right) (13.10.98)	3·00	3·00
W80		26p. chestnut (2 bands)	1·00	1·00
		a. Perf 14 (13.10.98)	3·00	3·00
W81		37p. brt mauve (2 bands)	2·75	2·75
W82		63p. lt emerald (2 bands)............................	5·00	5·00

Nos. W79a and W80a were only issued in booklets.

The Harrison printings of Nos. W80/1 come from booklet pane No. NI81al.

First Day Cover

1.7.97	20p., 26p., 37p., 63p. (W79, W80/2)............................	6·00
	Presentation Pack 1.7.97 P.O. Pack No. 39. 20p., 26p., 37p., 63p. (*Nos.* W79, W80/2)	17·00

W **6** Leek

W **7** Welsh Dragon

W **8** Daffodil

W **9** Prince of Wales Feathers

(Des D. Petersen (2nd), T. & G. Petersen (1st), I. Rees (E), R. Evans (64p., 65p.). Adapted Tutssels. Photo De La Rue or Walsall (2nd, 1st), De La Rue (68p.), Walsall (others))

1999 (8 June)–**2002**. *One phosphor band (2nd) or two phosphor bands (others).* P 14 (No. W83a) or 15×14 (others) (both with one elliptical hole in each vertical side).

W83	W **6**	(2nd) orange-brown, yellow-orange and black (1 centre band)	60	50
W83*a*		(2nd) orange-brown, yellow-orange and black (1 band at right) (p 14) (18.9.00)	4·00	4·00
		al. Booklet pane. No. 2124d and W83a, each×4, with centre label and margins all round....................	15·00	
W84	W **7**	(1st) blue-green, greenish yellow, silver and black...	1·00	1·00
W85	W **8**	(E) greenish blue, dp greenish blue and grey-black..	1·75	1·75
W86	W **9**	64p. violet, gold, silver and black	9·00	9·00
W87		65p. violet, gold, silver and black (25.4.00)	3·25	3·25
W88		68p. violet, gold, silver and black (4.7.02)	3·25	3·25
Presentation Pack (*P.O. Pack No.* 46) (2nd, 1st, E, 64p.) (*Nos.* W83, W84/6)			14·00	
Presentation Pack (*P.O. Pack No.* 51) (65p.) (*No.* W87)......			12·00	
Presentation Pack (*P.O. Pack No.* 56) (2nd, 1st, E, 65p.) (*Nos.* W83, W84/5, W87)..			18·00	
PHQ Cards (*set of* 4) (*Nos.* W83, W84/6) (D13)			8·00	14·00

Nos. W83, W84 and W85 were initially sold at 19p., 26p. and 30p., the latter representing the basic European airmail rate.

New printings of Nos. W83 and W84, produced by De La Rue instead of Walsall, were issued on 28 May 2003 and 4 March 2003. Stamps from these printings do not differ from those produced by Walsall.

No. W83a comes from the £7 Treasury of Trees booklet (No.DX26).

For combined presentation pack for all four Regions, see under England.

First Day Covers

8.6.99	2nd (*centre band*), 1st, E, 64p. (W83, W84/6)		
	Philatelic Bureau		6·00
	Cardiff		6·50
25.4.00	65p. (W87) Philatelic Bureau		3·00
	Cardiff		3·50

18.9.00   Treasury of Trees *se-tenant* pane 1st (*Millennium*), 2nd
          (2124d, W83*a*)
          Philatelic Bureau .... 5·00
          Llangernyw Abergele .... 5·00
4.7.02   68p. (W88) Tallents House (Type K) (*see Introduction*)   1·75
          Cardiff .... 1·75

Special First Day of Issue Postmarks

W **10**

(Des J. Matthews. Photo Walsall)

2000 (15 Feb). Type W **4** redrawn with "1af/st" face value as Type W **10**.
   Two phosphor bands. P 14 (with one elliptical hole in each
   vertical side).

W97   W **10**   (1st) bright orange-red .... 3·00   2·75
   No. W97 was only issued in £7·50 stamp booklets (No. DX24).

2003 (14 Oct)–**11**. As Nos. W83, W84/5 and W88, and new values,
   but with white borders. One centre phosphor band (2nd) or two
   phosphor bands (others). P 15×14 (with one elliptical hole in each
   vertical side).

   (a) (Photo Walsall or De La Rue (42p.) or De La Rue (others))

W98   W **6**   (2nd) orange-brown, deep orange-
                 brown and black 80   75
W99   W **7**   (1st) blue-green, greenish yellow, silver
                 and black 80   75
W100   W **8**   (E) greenish blue, deep greenish blue
                 and grey-black .... 2·50   2·50
W101   40p. greenish blue, deep greenish blue
                 and grey-black (11.5.04) .... 1·50   1·50
W102   42p. greenish blue, deep greenish blue
                 and grey-black (5.4.05) .... 1·50   1·50
W103   44p. greenish blue, deep greenish blue
                 and grey-black (28.3.06) .... 1·50   1·50
W104   48p. greenish blue, deep greenish blue
                 and grey-black (27.3.07) 90   90
W105   50p. greenish blue, deep greenish blue
                 and grey-black (1.4.08) .... 1·00   1·00
W105*a*   56p. greenish blue, deep greenish blue
                 and grey-black (31.3.09) .... 1·25   1·25
W105*b*   60p. greenish blue, deep greenish blue
                 and grey-black (30.3.10) .... 1·40   1·40
W106   W **9**   68p. violet, gold, silver and black .... 2·00   2·00
W107   72p. violet, gold, silver and black
                 (28.3.06) .... 2·00   2·00
W108   78p. violet, gold, silver and black
                 (27.3.07) .... 1·40   1·30
W109   81p. violet, gold, silver and black
                 (1.4.08) .... 1·75   1·75
W109*a*   90p. violet, gold, silver and black
                 (31.3.09) .... 2·00   2·00
W109*b*   97p. violet, gold, silver and black
                 (30.3.10) .... 2·25   2·25

   (b) Litho Enschedé (1st) or Cartor (others)

W120   W **7**   (1st) blue-green, greenish yellow, silver
                 and black (20.9.07) .... 4·25   4·25
W120*a* W **8** 68p. greenish yellow, bright magenta,
                 new blue and black (29.3.11) .... 1·50   1·50
W120*b* W **9** £1.10 greenish yellow, bright magenta,
                 new blue and black (29.3.11) .... 2·50   2·50

Presentation Pack (Nos. W98/100, W106). (P.O. Pack No. 65)   7·00
PHQ Cards (Nos. W98/100, W106) (set of 4) (D26) .... 2·00   6·00
   The Walsall printing of No. W102 was issued on 5 April 2005 and the
De La Rue on 24 May 2005.
   Stamps as Nos. W108/9 but printed in lithography were only issued
within **MS**2796 (W108) or **MS**2886 (W109).
   No. W120 was only issued in £7·66 stamp booklets, No. DX40 and
MSW125.
   A design as No. W120 but self-adhesive was issued on 1 March 2007
in sheets of 20, each stamp accompanied by a *se-tenant* label showing a
Welsh scene (LS37). These sheets were printed in lithography by Cartor,
perforated 15×14 without the elliptical holes, and sold at £6.55 each.
They were also available with personalised photographs on the labels
at £14·95 from Royal Mail in Edinburgh.
   Stamps as Nos. EN18, NI95, S131 and W120 but self-adhesive were
issued on 29 September 2008 in sheets of 20 containing five of each
design with *se-tenant* labels (LS49).
   Nos. W110/19 are left for possible additions to the above definitive
series.

First Day Covers

14.10.03   2nd, 1st, E, 68p. (W98/100, W106) Tallents House (Type
           K) (*see Introduction*)............................... 3·25
           Cardiff .... 3·25
11.5.04   40p. (W101) Tallents House (Type K) .... 2·75
           Cardiff .... 2·75
5.4.05   42p. (W102) Tallents House (Type K) .... 1·40
           Cardiff .... 1·40
28.3.06   44p., 72p. (W103, W107) Tallents House (Type K)....... 2·75
           Cardiff .... 2·75
27.3.07   48p., 78p. (W104, W108) Tallents House (Type K)....... 3·50
           Cardiff .... 3·50
1.4.08   50p., 81p. (W105, W109) Tallents House (Type K)....... 4·00
           Cardiff .... 4·00
31.3.09   56p., 90p. (W105*a*, W109*a*) Tallents House (Type K).. 4·75
           Cardiff .... 4·75
30.3.10   60p., 97p. (W105*b*, W109*b*) Tallents House (Type K).. 4·00
           Cardiff .... 4·00
29.3.11   68p., £1.10 (W120*a/b*) Tallents House (Type K)........ 6·00
           Cardiff .... 6·00

(Des Silk Pearce. Photo De La Rue)

2006 (1 Mar). *Opening of New Welsh Assembly Building, Cardiff. Sheet*
   123×70 mm. One centre phosphor band (2nd) or two phosphor
   bands (others). P 15×14 (with one elliptical hole in each vertical
   side).

MSW121 Nos. W98, W99×2 and W106×2 .... 5·00   5·00
First Day Cover (Tallents House) .... 6·00
First Day Cover (Cardiff) .... 6·00

(Litho De La Rue)

2008 (29 Sept). 50th Anniv of the Country Definitives. As Nos. W1,
   W3 and W5 (definitives of 1958) but inscribed 1st. Two phosphor
   bands. P 15×14½ (with one elliptical hole in each vertical side).

W122   W **1**   (1st) deep lilac .... 2·50   2·50
                 a. Booklet pane. Nos. W122/4 and
                    W120×3 .... 6·00
W123   W **3**   (1st) green .... 2·50   2·50
W124   W **2**   (1st) deep claret .... 2·50   2·50
   Nos. W122/4 come from £9.72 booklets, No. DX43.

DATHLU CYMRU · CELEBRATING WALES

W **11** (Illustration reduced. Actual size 123×70 mm)

(Des Clare Melinsky and Silk Pearce. Litho De La Rue)

2009 (26 Feb). *Celebrating Wales. Sheet 123×70 mm. Two phosphor*
   bands. P 15×14 (with one elliptical hole in each vertical side (1st)
   or 14½×14 (81p.).

MSW125 (1st) Red dragon; (1st) No. W120; 81p.
   St. David; 81p. National Assembly for Wales, Cardiff... 6·00   6·00
First Day Cover (Tallents House)................................. 7·00
First Day Cover (St. Davids) .... 7·00
Presentation Pack .... 8·00
PHQ Cards (set of 5) (CGB4) .... 4·00   17·00
   The five PHQ cards show the four individual stamps and the complete
miniature sheet.

Stamps as the 1st class Red dragon stamp from **MS**W125 but self-adhesive were issued on 1 March 2010 in sheets of 20 with se-tenant labels showing Welsh Castles, No. LS71. These sheets were printed in lithography by Cartor and sold for £8·35 each.

Miniature sheet collection containing Nos. **MS**EN19, **MS**N110, **MS**S133 and **MS**W125 in a folder was available from 6 March 2009, sold at £31·95.

Special First Day of Issue Postmarks

V. GUERNSEY
War Occupation Issues

BISECTS. On 24 December 1940 authority was given, by Post Office notice, that prepayment of penny postage could be effected by using half a British 2d. stamp, diagonally bisected. Such stamps were first used on 27 December 1940.

The 2d. stamps generally available were those of the Postal Centenary issue, 1940 (S.G. 482) and the first colour of the King George VI issue (S.G. 465). These are listed under Nos. 482a and 465b. A number of the 2d. King George V, 1912–22, and of the King George V photogravure stamp (S.G. 442) which were in the hands of philatelists, were also bisected and used.

1

1a Loops (half actual size)

(Des E. W. Vaudin. Typo Guernsey Press Co Ltd)

1941–44. Rouletted.

(a) White paper. No wmk.

1	1	½d. light green (7.4.41)	6·00	3·50
		a. Emerald-green (6.41)	6·00	2·00
		b. Bluish green (11.41)	32·00	13·00
		c. Brt green (2.42)	22·00	10·00
		d. Dull green (9.42)	4·00	2·00
		e. Olive-green (2.43)	45·00	25·00
		f. Pale yellowish green (7.43 and later) (shades)	4·00	3·00
		g. Imperf (pair)	£225	
		h. Imperf between (horiz pair)	£750	
		i. Imperf between (vert pair)	£875	
2		1d. scarlet (18.2.41)	3·25	2·00
		a. Pale vermilion (7.43)	5·00	2·00
		b. Carmine (1943)	3·50	2·00
		c. Imperf (pair)	£175	90·00
		d. Imperf between (horiz pair)	£750	
		da. Imperf vert (centre stamp of horiz strip of 3)	£875	
		e. Imperf between (vert pair)	£875	
		f. Printed double (scarlet shade)	£110	
3		2½d. ultramarine (12.4.44)	13·00	12·00
		a. Pale ultramarine (7.44)	10·00	7·00
		b. Imperf (pair)	£550	
		c. Imperf between (horiz pair)	£1100	
Set of 3			15·00	14·00

First Day Covers

18.2.41	1d.		15·00
7.4.41	½d.		10·00
12.4.44	2½d.		20·00

*(b) Bluish French bank-note paper. W **1a** (sideways).*

4	1	½d. bright green (11.3.42)	30·00	22·00
5		1d. scarlet (9.4.42)	16·00	22·00

First Day Covers

11.3.42	½d.		£300
9.4.42	1d.		£100

The dates given for the shades of Nos. 1/3 are the months in which they were printed as indicated on the printer's imprints. Others are issue dates.

2   3

(Des E. A. Piprell. Portrait by Dorothy Wilding Ltd.
Photo Harrison & Sons)

1958 (18 Aug)–**67.** W **179** of Great Britain. P 15×14.

6	2	2½d. rose-red (8.6.64)	35	40
7	3	3d. dp lilac	30	30
		p. One centre phosphor band (24.5.67)	15	20
8		4d. ultramarine (7.2.66)	25	30
		p. Two phosphor bands (24.10.67)	15	20
Set of 3 (cheapest)			70	80

First Day Covers

18.8.58	3d.		20·00
8.6.64	2½d.		30·00
7.2.66	4d.		8·00

For No. 7 in Presentation Pack, see Regional Issues below Wales No. W6.

1968–69. No wmk. Chalk-surfaced paper. PVA gum*. One centre phosphor band (Nos. 10/11) or two phosphor bands (others). P 15×14.

9	3	4d. pale ultramarine (16.4.68)	10	20
		Ey. Phosphor omitted	45·00	
10		4d. olive-sepia (4.9.68)	10	15
		Ey. Phosphor omitted	45·00	
11		4d. brt vermilion (26.2.69)	20	25
12		5d. royal blue (4.9.68)	20	30
Set of 4			50	1·00

First Day Cover

4.9.68	4d., 5d	3·00

No. 9 was not issued in Guernsey until 22 April.
*PVA Gum. See note after No. 722 of Great Britain.

VI. ISLE OF MAN

Although specifically issued for use in the Isle of Man, these issues were also valid for use throughout Great Britain.

DATES OF ISSUE. The note at the beginning of Northern Ireland also applies here.

Nos. 8/11 and current stamps of Great Britain were withdrawn from sale on the island from 5 July 1973 when the independent postal administration was established but remained valid for use there for a time. They also remained on sale at the Philatelic Sales counters in the United Kingdom until 4 July 1974.

1   2

(Des J. Nicholson. Portrait by Dorothy Wilding Ltd. Photo Harrison)

1958 (18 Aug)–**68.** W **179.** P 15×14.

1	1	2½d. carmine-red (8.6.64)	50	1·25
2	2	3d. dp lilac	50	20
		a. Chalk-surfaced paper (17.5.63)	12·00	12·00
		p. One centre phosphor band (27.6.68)	20	50
3		4d. ultramarine (7.2.66)	1·50	1·50
		p. Two phosphor bands (5.7.67)	20	30
Set of 3 (cheapest)			80	1·60

First Day Covers

18.8.58	3d		32·00
8.6.64	2½d.		45·00
7.2.66	4d		15·00

No. 2a was released in London sometime after 17 May 1963, this being the date of issue in Douglas.

For No. 2 in Presentation Pack, see Regional Issues below Wales No. W6.

1968–69. *No wmk. Chalk-surfaced paper. PVA gum. One centre phosphor band (Nos. 5/6) or two phosphor bands (others)*. P 15×14.

4	**2**	4d. blue (24.6.68)	25	30
5		4d. olive-sepia (4.9.68)	25	30
		Ey. Phosphor omitted	22·00	
6		4d. brt vermilion (26.2.69)	45	75
7		5d. royal blue (4.9.68)	45	75
		Ey. Phosphor omitted	£175	
Set of 4			1·25	2·00

First Day Cover

4.9.68	4d., 5d.	4·00

3

(Des J. Matthews. Portrait after plaster cast by Arnold Machin. Photo Harrison)

1971 (7 July). *Decimal Currency. Chalk-surfaced paper. One centre phosphor band (2½p.) or two phosphor bands (others)*. P 15×14.

8	**3**	2½p. brt magenta	20	15
		Ey. Phosphor omitted	£1500	
9		3p. ultramarine	20	15
10		5p. reddish violet	80	80
		Ey. Phosphor omitted	£275	
11		7½p. chestnut	90	90
Set of 4			1·80	1·80
Presentation Pack			3·25	

First Day Cover

7.7.71	2½p., 3p., 5p., 7½p.	3·00

All values exist with PVA gum on ordinary cream paper and the 2½p. and 3p. also on fluorescent white paper.

VII. JERSEY

War Occupation Issues

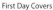

5

(Des Major N. V. L. Rybot. Typo Evening Post, Jersey)

1941–43. *White paper (thin to thick)*. No wmk. P 11.

1	**5**	½d. brt green (29.1.42)	8·00	6·00
		a. Imperf between (vert pair)	£850	
		b. Imperf between (horiz pair)	£750	
		c. Imperf (pair)	£275	
		d. On greyish paper (1.43)	12·00	12·00
2		1d. scarlet (1.4.41)	8·00	5·00
		a. Imperf between (vert pair)	£850	
		b. Imperf between (horiz pair)	£750	
		c. Imperf (pair)	£300	
		d. On chalk-surfaced paper	55·00	48·00
		e. On greyish paper (1.43)	14·00	14·00

First Day Covers

1.4.41	1d.	7·00
29.1.42	½d.	7·00

6 Old Jersey Farm   **7** Portelet Bay

8 Corbière Lighthouse   **9** Elizabeth Castle

10 Mont Orgueil Castle   **11** Gathering Vraic (seaweed)

(Des E. Blampied. Eng H. Cortot. Typo French Govt Ptg Works, Paris)

1943–44. *No wmk*. P 13½.

3	**6**	½d. green (1 June)	12·00	12·00
		a. Rough, grey paper (6.10.43)	15·00	14·00
4	**7**	1d. scarlet (1 June)	3·00	50
		a. On newsprint (28.2.44)	3·50	75
5	**8**	1½d. brown (8 June)	8·00	5·75
6	**9**	2d. orange-yellow (8 June)	7·50	2·00
7	**10**	2½d. blue (29 June)	3·00	1·00
		a. On newsprint (25.2.44)	1·00	1·75
		ba. Thin paper*	£225	
8	**11**	3d. violet (29 June)	3·00	2·75
Set of 6			30·00	21·00
First Day Covers (3)				30·00
Set of 6 Gutter Pairs			60·00	

*On No. 7ba the design shows clearly through the back of the stamp.

12   **13**

(Des. E. Blampied (T **8**), W. Gardner (T **9**). Portrait by Dorothy Wilding Ltd. Photo Harrison & Sons)

1958 (18 Aug)–*67*. W *179* of Great Britain. P 15×14.

9	**12**	2½d. carmine-red (8.6.64)	30	45
		a. Imperf three sides (pair)	£3000	
10	**13**	3d. dp lilac	30	25
		p. One centre phosphor band (9.6.67)	15	15
11		4d. ultramarine (7.2.66)	25	30
		p. Two phosphor bands (5.9.67)	15	25
Set of 3 (cheapest)			50	75

First Day Covers

18.8.58	3d	20·00
8.6.64	2½d	30·00
7.2.66	4d	10·00

For No. 10 in Presentation Pack, see Regional Issues below Wales No. W6.

1968–69. *No wmk. Chalk-surfaced paper. PVA gum*. *One centre phosphor band (4d. values) or two phosphor bands (5d.)*. P 15×14.

12	**9**	4d. olive-sepia (4.9.68)	15	25
		Ey. Phosphor omitted	£1000	
13		4d. brt vermilion (26.2.69)	15	25
14		5d. royal blue (4.9.68)	15	50
Set of 3			40	1·10

First Day Cover

4.9.68	4d., 5d.	3·00

*PVA Gum. See note after No. 722 of Great Britain.

POSTAGE DUE STAMPS

PERFORATIONS. All postage due stamps to No. D101 are perf 14×15.

WATERMARK. The watermark always appears sideways and this is the "normal" listed in this Catalogue for Nos. D1/D68. Varieties occur as follows. The point of identification is which way the top of the crown points, but (where they occur) the disposition of the letters needs to be noted also. The meaning of the terms is given below: (1) as described and illustrated in the Catalogue, i.e. as read through the front of the stamp, and (2) what is seen during watermark detection when the stamp is face down and the back is under examination.

Watermark	Crown pointing	Letters reading
	(1) As described	
Sideways	left	upwards
Sideways-inverted	right	downwards
Sideways and reversed	left	downwards, back to front
Sideways-inverted and reversed	right	upwards, back to front

Watermark	Crown pointing	Letters reading

(2) As detected (stamp face down)

Sideways	right	upwards, back to front
Sideways-inverted	left	downwards, back to front
Sideways and reversed	right	downwards
Sideways-inverted and reversed	left	upward

D **1**   D **2**

(Des G. Eve. Typo Somerset House (early trial printings of ½d., 1d., 2d. and 5d.; all printings of 1s.) or Harrison (later printings of all values except 1s.))

1914 (20 Apr)–**22**. W **100** (*Simple Cypher*) (*sideways*).

			Unmtd mint	Mtd mint	Used
D1	D **1**	½d. emerald	1·50	50	25
		Wi. Watermark sideways-inverted	2·00	1·00	1·00
		Wj. Watermark sideways and reversed	30·00	18·00	20·00
		Wk. Watermark sideways-inverted and reversed			20·00
		s. Optd "SPECIMEN"		45·00	
D2		1d. carmine	1·50	50	25
		a. *Pale carmine*	1·50	75	50
		Wi. Watermark sideways-inverted	2·00	1·00	1·00
		Wj. Watermark sideways and reversed			20·00
		Wk. Watermark sideways-inverted and reversed	30·00	18·00	20·00
		s. Optd "SPECIMEN"		45·00	
D3		1½d. chestnut (1922)	£150	48·00	20·00
		Wi. Watermark sideways-inverted	£190	70·00	20·00
		s. Optd "SPECIMEN"		75·00	
D4		2d. agate	1·50	50	25
		Wi. Watermark sideways-inverted	3·00	2·00	2·00
		Wj. Watermark sideways-inverted and reversed	25·00	15·00	18·00
		s. Optd "SPECIMEN"		40·00	
D5		3d. violet (1918)	28·00	5·00	75
		a. *Bluish violet*	28·00	6·00	2·75
		Wi. Watermark sideways-inverted	40·00	15·00	10·00
		Wj. Watermark sideways-inverted and reversed			
		s. Optd "SPECIMEN"		45·00	
D6		4d. dull grey-green (12.20)	£300	£150	50·00
		Wi. Watermark sideways-inverted	£150	40·00	5·00
		s. Optd "SPECIMEN"		45·00	
D7		5d. brownish cinnamon	23·00	7·00	3·50
		Wi. Watermark sideways-inverted	40·00	16·00	16·00
		s. Optd "SPECIMEN"		45·00	
D8		1s. brt blue (1915)	£150	40·00	5·00
		a. *Dp brt blue*	£150	40·00	5·00
		Wi. Watermark sideways-inverted	£150	40·00	40·00
		Wj. Watermark sideways-inverted and reversed			
		s. Optd "SPECIMEN"		45·00	
Set of 8			£450	£120	32·00

Stamps from the above issue are known bisected and used for half their face value at the following sorting offices:

1d. Barrhead (1922), Bristol (1918), Cowes (1923), Elgin (1921), Kidlington (1922, 1923), Kilburn, London NW (1923), Malvern (1915), Palmers Green, London N (1922), Plaistow, London E (1916), River, Dover (1922), Rock Ferry, Birkenhead (1915, 1918), St. Ouens, Jersey (1924), Salford, Manchester (1914), South Tottenham, London N (1921), Warminster (1922), Wavertree, Liverpool (1921), Whitchurch (1922), Winton, Bournemouth (1921), Wood Green, London N (1921)

2d. Anerley, London SE (1921), Bethnal Green, London E (1918), Christchurch (1921), Didcot (1919), Ealing, London W (1921), Hythe, Southampton (1923), Kirkwall (1922), Ledbury (1921), Malvern (1921, 1923), Sheffield (1921), Shipley (1922), Streatham, London SW (1921), Victoria Docks & North Woolwich (1921), West Kensington, London W (1921, 1922)

3d. Malvern (trisected and used for 1d.) (1921), Warminster (1922)

(Typo Waterlow)

1924. As 1914–22, but on thick chalk-surfaced paper.

D9	D **1**	1d. carmine	10·00	6·00	6·00
		Wi. Watermark sideways-inverted			

(Typo Waterlow and (from 1934) Harrison)

1924–31. W **111** (*Block Cypher*) *sideways*.

D10	D **1**	½d. emerald (6.25)	2·50	1·25	75
		Wi. Watermark sideways-inverted	6·00	3·00	1·50
		s. Optd "SPECIMEN"		45·00	
D11		1d. carmine (4.25)	2·50	60	25
		Wi. Watermark sideways-inverted	—	—	30·00
		s. Optd "SPECIMEN"		55·00	
D12		1½d. chestnut (10.24)	£160	47·00	22·00
		Wi. Watermark sideways-inverted	—	—	75·00
		s. Optd "SPECIMEN"		55·00	
D13		2d. agate (7.24)	9·00	1·00	25
		Wi. Watermark sideways-inverted	—	—	30·00
		s. Optd "SPECIMEN"		45·00	
D14		3d. dull violet (10.24)	15·00	1·50	25
		a. Printed on gummed side	£150	£125	†
		b. Experimental paper W **111a**	£110	60·00	50·00
		Wi. Watermark sideways-inverted	50·00	20·00	40·00
		s. Optd "SPECIMEN"		55·00	
D15		4d. dull grey-green (10.24)	70·00	15·00	4·25
		Wi. Watermark sideways-inverted	£100	40·00	40·00
		s. Optd "SPECIMEN"		55·00	
D16		5d. brownish cinnamon (1.31)	£175	65·00	45·00
D17		1s. dp blue (9.24)	60·00	8·50	50
		Wi. Watermark sideways-inverted			
		s. Optd "SPECIMEN"		55·00	
D18	D **2**	2s.6d. purple/*yellow* (5.24)	£275	85·00	1·75
		Wi. Watermark sideways-inverted	£750	—	40·00
		s. Optd "SPECIMEN"		55·00	
Set of 9			£725	£200	60·00

Stamps from the above issue are known bisected and used for half their face value at the following sorting offices:

1d. Ashton under Lyne (1932), Hastings (1930), Penryn, Cornwall (1928), Shenfield (1926), Wimbledon, London SW (1925)

2d. Perranwell Station (1932)

1936–37. W **125** (*E 8 R*) *sideways*.

D19	D **1**	½d. emerald (6.37)	15·00	10·50
D20		1d. carmine (5.37)	2·00	1·75
D21		2d. agate (5.37)	15·00	12·00
D22		3d. dull violet (3.37)	2·00	2·00
		s. Optd "SPECIMEN"		
D23		4d. dull grey-green (12.36)	65·00	34·00
		s. Optd "SPECIMEN"		
D24		5d. brownish cinnamon (11.36)	90·00	30·00
		a. *Yellow-brown* (1937)	40·00	28·00
		s. Optd "SPECIMEN"		
D25		1s. dp blue (12.36)	25·00	8·50
		s. Optd "SPECIMEN"		
D26	D **2**	2s.6d. purple/*yellow* (5.37)	£350	12·00
Set of 8			£500	90·00

The 1d. of the above issue is known bisected and used for half its face value at the following sorting office:

1d. Solihull (1937)

1937–38. W **127** (*G VI R*) *sideways*.

D27	D **1**	½d. emerald (5.38)	13·00	3·75
D28		1d. carmine (5.38)	3·00	50
		Wi. Watermark sideways-inverted	£150	
D29		2d. agate (5.38)	2·75	30
		Wi. Watermark sideways-inverted	£150	
D30		3d. violet (12.37)	10·50	30
		Wi. Watermark sideways-inverted	£150	
D31		4d. dull grey-green (9.37)	£110	10·00
		Wi. Watermark sideways-inverted	£300	
D32		5d. yellow-brown (11.38)	16·50	75
		Wi. Watermark sideways-inverted	£150	
D33		1s. dp blue (10.37)	78·00	75
		Wi. Watermark sideways-inverted	£150	
D34	D **2**	2s.6d. purple/*yellow* (9.38)	85·00	1·25
Set of 8			£260	18·00

The 2d. from the above issue is known bisected and used for half its face value at the following sorting offices:

2d. Boreham Wood (1951), Camberley (1951), Harpenden (1951, 1954), St. Albans (1951)

DATES OF ISSUE. The dates for Nos. D35/68 are those on which stamps were first issued by the Supplies Department to postmasters.

1951–52. *Colours changed and new value (1½d.).* W **127** (G VI R) sideways.

D35	D **1**	½d. yellow-orange (18.9.51)	3·50	3·50
		a. Bright orange (5.54)	40·00	
D36		1d. violet-blue (6.6.51)	1·50	75
		Wi. Watermark sideways-inverted		
D37		1½d. green (11.2.52)	2·00	2·00
		Wi. Watermark sideways-inverted	£120	£120
D38		4d. blue (14.8.51)	50·00	22·00
		Wi. Watermark sideways inverted	†	£1000
D39		1s. ochre (6.12.51)	28·00	5·25
		Wi. Watermark sideways-inverted		
Set of 5			75·00	28·00

The 1d. of the above issue is known bisected and used for half its face value at the following sorting offices:
1d. Camberley (1954), Capel, Dorking (1952)

1954–55. W **153** *(Mult Tudor Crown and E 2 R) sideways.*

D40	D **1**	½d. bright orange (8.6.55)	7·00	5·25
		Wi. Watermark sideways-inverted	75·00	
D41		2d. agate (28.7.55)	26·00	23·00
		Wi. Watermark sideways-inverted		
D42		3d. violet (4.5.55)	75·00	60·00
D43		4d. blue (14.7.55)	26·00	32·00
		a. Imperf (pair)	£250	
D44		5d. yellow-brown (19.5.55)	20·00	20·00
D45	D **2**	2s.6d. purple/*yellow* (11.54)	£275	5·75
		Wi. Watermark sideways-inverted		
Set of 6			£250	£120

1955–57. W **165** *(Mult St. Edward's Crown and E 2 R) sideways.*

D46	D **1**	½d. bright orange (16.7.56)	2·75	3·25
		Wi. Watermark sideways-inverted	50·00	
D47		1d. violet-blue (7.6.56)	5·00	1·50
D48		1½d. green (13.2.56)	8·50	7·00
		Wi. Watermark sideways-inverted	50·00	
D49		2d. agate (22.5.56)	45·00	3·50
D50		3d. violet (5.3.56)	6·00	1·50
		Wi. Watermark sideways-inverted	75·00	
D51		4d. blue (24.4.56)	25·00	6·00
		Wi. Watermark sideways-inverted	£100	
D52		5d. brown-ochre (23.3.56)	26·00	20·00
D53		1s. ochre (22.11.55)	65·00	2·25
		Wi. Watermark sideways-inverted		
D54	D **2**	2s.6d. purple/yellow (28.6.57)	£200	8·25
		Wi. Watermark sideways-inverted		
D55		5s. scarlet/yellow (25.11.55)	£150	32·00
Set of 10			£425	65·00

Stamps from the above issue are known bisected and used for half their face value at the following sorting offices:
1d. Beswick, Manchester (1958), Huddersfield (1956), London SE (1957)
2d. Eynsham, Oxford (1956), Garelochhead, Helensburgh (1956), Harpenden (1956), Hull (1956), Kingston on Thames (1956), Leicester Square, London WC (1956), London WC (1956)
3d. London SE (1957) 4d. Poplar, London E (1958)

1959–63. W **179** *(Mult St. Edward's Crown) sideways.*

D56	D **1**	½d. bright orange (18.10.61)	15	1·25
		Wi. Watermark sideways-inverted	2·00	
D57		1d. violet-blue (9.5.60)	15	50
		Wi. Watermark sideways-inverted	75·00	
D58		1½d. green (5.10.60)	2·50	2·50
D59		2d. agate (14.9.59)	1·10	50
		Wi. Watermark sideways-inverted	£125	
D60		3d. violet (24.3.59)	30	30
		Wi. Watermark sideways-inverted	50·00	
D61		4d. blue (17.12.59)	30	30
		Wi. Watermark sideways-inverted	£200	
D62		5d. yellow-brown (6.11.61)	45	60
		Wi. Watermark sideways-inverted	5·00	6·00
D63		6d. purple (29.3.62)	50	30
		Wi. Watermark sideways-inverted	£200	
D64		1s. ochre (11.4.60)	90	30
		Wi. Watermark sideways-inverted	30·00	
D65	D **2**	2s.6d. purple/*yellow* (11.5.61)	3·00	50
		Wi. Watermark sideways-inverted	15·00	2·00
D66		5s. scarlet/*yellow* (8.5.61)	8·25	1·00
		Wi. Watermark sideways-inverted	25·00	3·00
D67		10s. blue/*yellow* (2.9.63)	11·50	5·75
		Wi. Watermark sideways-inverted	40·00	20·00
D68		£1 black/*yellow* (2.9.63)	45·00	8·25
Set of 13			70·00	20·00

Whiter paper. The note after No. 586 also applies to Postage Due stamps.

Stamps from the above issue are known bisected and used for half their face value at the following sorting offices:
1d. Chieveley, Newbury (1962, 1963), Henlan, Llandyssil (1961), Mayfield (1962), St. Albans (1964)
2d. Doncaster (?)

1968–69. *Typo. No wmk. Chalk-surfaced paper.*

D69	D **1**	2d. agate (11.4.68)	75	1·00
		Ev. PVA gum (26.11.68)	75	
D70		3d. violet (9.9.68)	1·00	1·00
D71		4d. blue (6.5.68)	1·00	1·00
		Ev. PVA gum	£2000	
D72		5d. orange-brown (3.1.69)	8·00	11·00
D73		6d. purple (9.9.68)	2·25	1·75
D74		1s. ochre (19.11.68)	4·00	2·50
Set of 6			17·00	20·00

The 2d. and 4d. exist with gum arabic and PVA gum; the remainder with PVA gum only.
Stamps from the above issue are known bisected and used for half their face value at the following sorting offices:
4d. Northampton (1970)
6d. Kilburn, London NW (1968)

1968–69. *Photo. No wmk. Chalk-surfaced paper. PVA gum.*

D75	D **1**	4d. blue (12.6.69)	7·00	6·75
D76		8d. red (3.10.68)	50	1·00

Nos. D75/6 are smaller, 21½x17½ mm.

D **3** D **4**

(Des J. Matthews. Photo Harrison)

1970 (17 June)**–75.** *Decimal Currency. Chalk-surfaced paper.*

D77	D **3**	½p. turquoise-blue (15.2.71)	15	2·50
D78		1p. dp reddish purple (15.2.71)	15	15
D79		2p. myrtle-green (15.2.71)	20	15
D80		3p. ultramarine (15.2.71)	20	15
D81		4p. yellow-brown (15.2.71)	25	15
D82		5p. violet (15.2.71)	25	15
D83		7p. red-brown (21.8.74)	35	1·00
D84	D **4**	10p. carmine	30	30
D85		11p. slate-green (18.6.75)	50	1·00
D86		20p. olive-brown	60	25
D87		50p. ultramarine	2·00	1·25
D88		£1 black	4·00	1·00
D89		£5 orange-yellow and black (2.4.73)	36·00	1·50
Set of 13			40·00	7·75

Presentation Pack (P.O. Pack No. 36) (Nos. D77/82, D84, D86/8 (3.11.71) | | | 20·00 |
Presentation Pack (P.O. Pack No. 93) (Nos. D77/88) (30.3.77) | | | 10·00 |

Later printings were on fluorescent white paper, some with dextrin added to the PVA gum (see notes after X1058).
The 2p. from the above issue is known bisected and used for half its face value at the following sorting office:
2p. Exeter (1977)

D **5** D **6**

(Des Sedley Place Design Ltd. Photo Harrison)

1982 (9 June). *Chalk-surfaced paper.*

D90	D **5**	1p. lake	10	30
D91		2p. brt blue	30	30
D92		3p. dp mauve	15	30
D93		4p. dp blue	15	25
D94		5p. sepia	20	25
D95	D **6**	10p. lt brown	30	40
D96		20p. olive-green	50	60
D97		25p. dp greenish blue	80	90
D98		50p. grey-black	1·75	1·75
D99		£1 red	3·25	1·25
D100		£2 turquoise-blue	7·00	4·25
D101		£5 dull orange	14·00	2·25
Set of 12			24·00	10·00
Set of 12 Gutter Pairs			10·00	
Presentation Pack			48·00	

D **7**

(Des Sedley Place Design Ltd. Litho Questa)

1994 (15 Feb). P 15×14 (with one elliptical hole in each vertical side).

D102	D **7**	1p. red, yellow & black	10	75
D103		2p. magenta, purple & black	10	75
D104		5p. yellow, red-brown & black	15	50
D105		10p. yellow, emerald & black	30	75
D106		20p. blue-green, violet & black	75	1·50
D107		25p. cerise, rosine & black	1·50	2·00
D108		£1 violet, magenta & black	7·00	10·00
D109		£1.20 greenish blue, blue-green & black..	8·00	12·00
D110		£5 greenish black, blue-green & black	30·00	20·00
Set of 9			45·00	45·00
First Day Cover				22·00
Presentation Pack			60·00	

Special First Day of Issue Postmark

London EC3 ....22·00

Following changes in the method of collecting money due on unpaid or underpaid mail the use of postage due stamps was restricted from April 1995 to mail addressed to business customers and to Customs/V.A.T. charges levied by the Royal Mail on behalf of the Customs and Excise. The use of postage due stamps ceased on 28 January 2000.

POSTAL FISCAL STAMPS

PRICES. Prices in the used column are for stamps with genuine postal cancellations dated from the time when they were authorised for use as postage stamps. Beware of stamps with fiscal cancellations removed and fraudulent postmarks applied.

VALIDITY. The 1d. surface-printed stamps were authorised for postal use from 1 June 1881 and at the same time the 1d. postage issue, No. 166, was declared valid for fiscal purposes. The 3d. and 6d. values together with the embossed issues were declared valid for postal purposes by another Act effective from 1 January 1883.

SURFACE-PRINTED ISSUES
(Typo Thomas De La Rue & Co.)

F **1** Rectangular Buckle · · · · · · · · · · F **2**

F **3** Octagonal Buckle · · · · · · · · · · F **4**

F **5** Double-lined Anchor · · · · · · F **6** Single-lined Anchor

1853–57. P 15½×15.

(a) Wmk F **5** *(inverted) (1853–55)*.

			Un	*Used	Used on cover
F1	F **1**	1d. lt blue (10.10.53)	40·00	55·00	£190
		Wi. Watermark upright	£150		
		Wj. Watermark reversed*	£150		
F2	F **2**	1d. ochre (10.53)	£110	£130	£500
		a. *Tête-bêche* (in block of four)	£18000		
		Wi. Watermark upright			
F3	F **3**	1d. pale turquoise-blue (12.53)	30·00	50·00	£275
F4		1d. lt blue/*blue* (12.53)	75·00	80·00	£450
		Wi. Watermark upright	£130	£225	
F5	F **4**	1d. reddish lilac/*blue glazed paper* (25.3.55)	£110	£130	£375
		Wi. Watermark upright	£160	£250	

*Watermark reversed: with the stamp upright and viewed from the front the cable finishes to the right of the base of the anchor shaft.

Only one example is known of No. F2a outside the National Postal Museum and the Royal Collection.

(b) Wmk F **6** *(1856–57)*.

F6	F **4**	1d. reddish lilac (*shades*)	10·00	8·50	£150
		Wi. Watermark inverted	£130		
		Wj. Watermark reversed	£150		
		s. Optd "SPECIMEN" (2)	£140		
F7		1d. reddish lilac/*bluish* (*shades*) (1857)	10·00	8·50	£150
		Wj. Watermark reversed	£150		

(F **7**)

1860 (3 Apr). *No.* F7 *optd with Type* F **7**, *in red*.

F8	F **4**	1d. dull reddish lilac/*blue*	£750	£600	£1200
		Wj. Wmk reversed			

BLUE PAPER. In the following issues we no longer distinguish between bluish and white paper. There is a range of papers from white or greyish to bluish.

F **8** · · · · · · · · · · · · · · · · F **9**

F **10**

1860–67. *Bluish to white paper.* P 15½×15.

(a) Wmk F **6** *(1860)*.

F9	F **8**	1d. reddish lilac (May)	12·00	12·00	£150
		Wi. Watermark inverted	£110		
		s. Optd "SPECIMEN" (2)	£150		
F10	F **9**	3d. reddish lilac (June)	£375	£275	£450
		s. Optd "SPECIMEN" (2)	£200		
F11	F **10**	6d. reddish lilac (Oct)	£180	£175	£375
		Wi. Watermark inverted	£225	£180	
		Wj. Watermark reversed	£225	£180	
		s. Optd "SPECIMEN" (2)	£180		

(b) W **40**. *(Anchor 16 mm high) (1864)*.

F12	F **8**	1d. pale reddish lilac (Nov)	10·00	12·00	£150
		Wi. Watermark inverted			
F13	F **9**	3d. pale reddish lilac	£225	£170	£450
		s. Optd "SPECIMEN" (9)	£175		
F14	F **10**	6d. pale reddish lilac	£200	£170	£375
		Wi. Watermark inverted	£300		

(c) W **40** *(Anchor 18 mm high) (1867).*

F15	F **8**	1d. reddish lilac............	20·00	20·00	£225
F16	F **9**	3d. reddish lilac............	£100	£100	£375
		s. Optd "SPECIMEN" (9, 10)..	£160		
F17	F **10**	6d. reddish lilac............	90·00	80·00	£250
		s. Optd "SPECIMEN" (9, 10)..	£160		

For stamps perf 14, see Nos. F24/7.

F **11**

F **12**

Four Dies of Type F 12

Round "O" (Dies 1 to 3)

Oval "O" (Die 4)

Small corner ornaments (Dies 1 and 2)

Medium corner ornaments (Die 3)

Large corner ornaments (Die 4)

Four lines of shading In left-hand ribbon (Die 1)

Two lines of shading in left-hand ribbon (Die 2)

Three lines of shading In left-hand ribbon (Die 3)

Heavy shading in both ribbons (Die 4)

Band of crown shaded (Dies 1 and 2)

Band of crown unshaded (Die 3)

Band of crown unshaded at front only (Die 4)

Die 1: Round "O" in "ONE"
Small corner ornaments
Four lines of shading in left-hand ribbon
Band of crown shaded

Die 2: Round "O" in "ONE"
Small corner ornaments
Two lines of shading in left-hand ribbon
Band of crown shaded

Die 3: Round "O" in "ONE"
Medium corner ornaments
Three lines of shading in left-hand ribbon
Band of crown unshaded

Die 3: Oval "O" in "ONE"
Large corner ornaments
Heavy shading in both ribbons
Band of crown unshaded at front only

1867–81. *White to bluish paper.* P 14.

(a) W **47** (Small Anchor).

F18	F **11**	1d. purple (1.9.67)	18·00	20·00	£120
		Wi. Watermark inverted	£110		
F19	F **12**	1d. purple (Die I) (6.68)	6·00	7·50	£120
		Wi. Watermark inverted	75·00		
F20		1d. purple (Die 2) (6.76)	22·00	18·00	£250
		s. Optd "SPECIMEN" (9)	90·00		
F21		1d. purple (Die 3) (3.77)	12·00	15·00	£175
		s. Optd "SPECIMEN" (9)	75·00		
F22		1d. purple (Die 4) (7.78)	7·00	8·00	£100

(b) W **48** (Orb).

F23	F **12**	1d. purple (Die 4) (1.81)	7·00	4·00	90·00
		Wi. Watermark inverted	£110		

1881. *White to bluish paper.* P 14.

(a) W **40** (Anchor 18 mm high) (Jan).

F24	F **9**	3d. reddish lilac	£700	£425	£800
F25	F **10**	6d. reddish lilac	£325	£180	£375

(b) W **40** (Anchor 20 mm high) (May).

F26		3d. reddish lilac	£525	£350	£575
		s. Optd "SPECIMEN" (9)	£275		

F27		6d. reddish lilac	£300	£170	£375
		s. Optd "SPECIMEN" (9)	£250		

ISSUES EMBOSSED IN COLOUR
(Made at Somerset House)

The embossed stamps were struck from dies not appropriated to any special purpose on paper which had the words "INLAND REVENUE" previously printed, and thus became available for payment of any duties for which no special stamps had been provided.

The die letters are included in the embossed designs and holes were drilled for the insertion of plugs showing figures indicating dates of striking.

F **13**   F **14**

(F **15**)

1860 (3 Apr)–**71**. *Types F* **13/14** *and similar types embossed on bluish paper. No wmk. Imperf.*

F28	2d. pink (Die A) (1.1.71)	£650	
	s. Optd "SPECIMEN" (2, 9)	£170	
F29	3d. pink (Die C)	£170	
	a. Tête-bêche (vert pair)	£1400	
F30	3d. pink (Die D)	£650	
F31	6d. pink (Die T)		
F32	6d. pink (Die U)	£350	
	a. Tête-bêche (vert pair)		
F33	9d. pink (Die C) (1.1.71)	£825	
	s. Optd "SPECIMEN" (2, 9)	£170	
F34	1s. pink (Die E) (28.6.61)	£650	
	a. Tête-bêche (vert pair)		
F35	1s. pink (Die F) (28.6.61)	£250	
	a. Tête-bêche (vert pair)	£950	
	s. Optd "SPECIMEN" (2, 9)	£170	
F36	2s. pink (Die K) (6.8.61)	£650	
F37	2s.6d. pink (Die N) (28.6.61)		
F38	2s.6d. pink (Die O) (28.6.61)	£350	
	s. Optd "SPECIMEN" (2, 9)	£170	

1871 (Aug). *As last but perf 12½.*

F39	2d. pink (Die A)	£425	
	a. Tête-bêche (vert pair)		
	s. Optd "SPECIMEN" (9)	£100	
F42	9d. pink (Die C)	£950	
	s. Optd "SPECIMEN" (9)	£170	
F43	1s. pink (Die E)	£650	
F44	1s. pink (Die F)	£575	
	s. Optd "SPECIMEN" (9)	£160	
F45	2s.6d. pink (Die O)	£300	
	s. Optd "SPECIMEN" (9)	£160	

1874 (Nov). *Type F* **15** *embossed on white paper. Underprint, in green.* W **47** (Small Anchor). P 12½.

F48	1s. pink (Die F)	£650	

1875 (Nov)–**80**. *Types F* **13/15** *and similar but colour changed and underprint as F* **15**. *On white or bluish paper.* P 12½.

F50	2d. vermilion (Die A) (1880)	£500	
	s. Optd "SPECIMEN" (9)	£170	
F51	9d. vermilion (Die C) (1876)	£650	
	s. Optd "SPECIMEN" (9, 10)	£170	
F52	1s. vermilion (Die E)	£425	
	s. Optd "SPECIMEN" (9, 10)	£170	
F53	1s. vermilion (Die F)	£950	
F54	2s.6d. vermilion (Die O) (1878)	£425	
	s. Optd "SPECIMEN" (9)	£170	

1882 (Oct). *As last but* W **48** *(Orbs).*

F55	2d. vermilion (Die A)	†	
	s. Optd "SPECIMEN" (9)	£190	
F56	9d. vermilion (Die C)	†	
	s. Optd "SPECIMEN" (9)	£190	
F57	1s. vermilion (Die E)	†	
	s. Optd "SPECIMEN" (9)	£190	
F58	2s.6d. vermilion (Die O)	£825	£650
	s. Optd "SPECIMEN" (9)	£190	

Although specimen overprints of Nos. F55/7 are known they were never issued.

The sale of Inland Revenue stamps up to the 2s. value ceased from 30 December 1882 and stocks were called in and destroyed. The 2s.6d. value remained on sale until 2 July 1883 when it was replaced by the 2s.6d. "Postage & Revenue" stamps. Inland Revenue stamps still in the hands of the public continued to be accepted for revenue and postal purposes.

POST OFFICE STAMP BOOKLETS

The following listing covers all booklets sold by post offices from 1904.

All major variations of contents and cover are included, but minor changes to the covers and differences on the interleaves have been ignored.

From 1913 each booklet carried an edition number, linked to an internal Post Office system of identification which divided the various booklets into series. In 1943 these edition numbers were replaced by edition dates. No attempt has been made to list separate edition numbers for booklets prior to 1943, although notes giving their extent are provided for each booklet. Edition dates from August 1943 are listed separately and exist for all £.s.d. and most Decimal Stitched booklets (except for the 1s. booklets, the 2s. booklets (N1/3), the 5s. "Philympia" booklets (No. HP34), the £1 "Stamps for Cooks" booklet (No. ZP1) and the Decimal Sponsored booklets). They are those found printed upon the booklets, either on the outer back cover or on the white leaves.

ERRORS OF MAKE-UP of booklets exist but we do not list them here. More detailed listings can be found in the 2nd, 3rd and 4th volumes of the *Great Britain Specialised Catalogue*.

ILLUSTRATIONS. The illustrations of the covers are ¾ size except where otherwise stated. Those in Queen Elizabeth II Decimal Sections C to H are ⅔ size, except where otherwise stated.

> **PRICES** quoted are for complete booklets containing stamps with "average" perforations (i.e. full perforations on two edges of the pane only). Booklets containing panes with complete perforations are worth more.

KING EDWARD VII

2s. Booklets

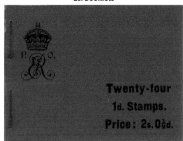

BA **1**

1904 (Mar). *Red cover printed in black as Type* BA **1**. *Pages of six stamps:* 24 × 1d. *Wmk Imperial Crown (No. 219).*
BA1 .... £450

BA **2**

1906 (June). *Red cover printed in black as Type* BA **2**. *As before but make-up changed to include* 12 × 1d. *and* 23 × ½d. *and label showing one green cross (Nos. 217 and 219).*
BA2 .... £2000

1907 (Aug). *Red cover printed in black as Type* BA **2**. *Make-up changed to include* 18 × 1d. *and* 11 × ½d. *and label showing one green cross (Nos. 217 and 219).*
BA3 .... £2600

1908 (Aug). *As before, but interleaves used for post office adverts printed in red.*
BA4 .... £2800

1909 (Aug). *As before, but interleaves used for trade advert printed in green.*
BA5 .... £2400

BA **6**

1911 (June). *Red cover printed in black as Type* BA **2** *but showing a larger Post Office cypher on cover. As before, but containing stamps by Harrison & Sons (Nos. 267 and 272).*
BA6 .... £2400

KING GEORGE V

2s. Booklets

BB **1**

1911 (Aug). *Red cover printed in black as Type* BA **2** *showing King George V cypher. Pages of six stamps:* 18 × 1d. *and* 12 × ½d. *Wmk Crown (Nos. 325, 329) Die 1B.*
BB1 .... £1400

BB **2**

1912 (April). *As before, but red cover printed in black as Type* BB **2**.
BB2 .... £1650

1912 (Sept). *As before, but wmk Simple Cypher (Nos. 334, 336) Die 1B.*
BB3 .... £1200

BB **5**

1912 (Nov). *As before, but red cover printed in black as Type BB* **5** *but without edition number.*
BB4 .... £1400

1913 (Jan). *As before, but red cover printed in black as Type BB* **5**.
BB5   Edition numbers 8 or 9... £1200

1913 (April). *As before, but 1912–22 wmk Simple Cypher (Nos. 351, 357).*
BB6   Edition numbers 10 to 35... £1200

1915 (Nov). *As before, except lower panel of front cover which was changed to show "New rates of postage".*
BB7   Edition numbers 36 to 42... £1300

1916 (May). *As before, but interleave adverts printed in black instead of green.*
BB8   Edition numbers 43 to 45... £1400

1916 (July). *As before, but orange cover printed in black as Type BB* **5**.
BB9   Edition numbers 46 to 64... £1200

BB **10**

1917 (Sept). *As before, but orange cover printed in black as Type BB* **10**.
BB10   Edition numbers 65 to 81... £1200

BB **11**

1924 (Feb). *Blue cover printed in black as Type BB* **11**. *Pages of six stamps: 10×1½d. (first completed by two perforated labels), 6×1d. and 6×½d. 1912–22 wmk Simple Cypher (Nos. 351, 357, 362).*
BB11   Edition numbers 1 or 2... £2250

1924 (Mar). *As before, but 1924–26 wmk Block Cypher (Nos. 418/20).*
BB12   Edition numbers 3 to 102 & 108 to 254..................... £875

BB **13**

1929 (May). *Postal Union Congress issue. Cover of special design as Type BB* **13** *printed in blue on buff as before but containing stamps of the P.U.C. issue (Nos. 434/6).*
BB13   Edition numbers 103 to 107... £500

1934 (Feb). *Blue cover printed in black as Type BB* **11**, *but containing stamps with Block Cypher wmk printed by Harrison & Sons (Nos. 418/20).*
BB14   Edition numbers 255 to 287.. £950

1935 (Jan). *As before, but containing stamps of the photogravure issue (intermediate format) with the se-tenant advertisements printed in brown (Nos. 439/41).*
BB15   Edition numbers 288 to 297.. £2500

BB **16**

1935 (May). *Silver Jubilee issue. Larger size cover printed in blue on buff as Type BB* **16** *and containing pages of four stamps with no se-tenant advertisements: 12×1½d., 4×1d. and 4×½d. (Nos. 453/5).*
BB16   Edition numbers 298 to 304.. 90·00

1935 (July). *As No. BB* **15**, *but containing stamps of the photogravure (small format) issue with se-tenant advertisements printed in black (Nos. 439/41).*
BB17   Edition numbers 305 to 353.. £575

3s. Booklets

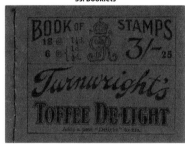

BB **19**

1918 (Oct). *Orange cover printed in black as Type BB* **19**. *Pages of six stamps: 12×1½d., 12×1d. and 12×½d. 1912–22 wmk Simple Cypher (Nos. 351, 357, 362).*
BB18   Edition numbers 1 to 11... £1650

1919 (July). *As before, but make-up altered to contain 18×1½d., 6×1d. and 6×½d.*
BB19   Edition numbers 12 to 26... £1650

BB **20**

1921 (April). *Experimental booklet bound in blue covers as Type BB* **20**, *containing pages of six stamps: 18×2d. (Die I) (No. 368).*
BB20   Edition numbers 35 and part 37.................................. £2000

1921 (Dec). *As before, but containing 2d. (Die II) (No. 370).*
BB21   Edition numbers 12, 13 and part 37............................ £2000

BB **22**

1922 (May). *Scarlet cover printed in black as Type BB* **22**. *Pages of six stamps: 18 × 1½d., 6 × 1d. and 6 × ½d. (Nos. 351, 357, 362).*
BB22　Edition numbers 19, 20, 22, 23 and 25 to 54 .... £2000

BB **23**

1922 (June). *Experimental booklet as Edition numbers 12 and 13 bound in blue covers as Type BB* **22**, *containing pages of six stamps: 24 × 1½d. (No. 362).*
BB23　Edition numbers 21 or 24 .... £2000

1924 (Feb). *Scarlet cover printed in black as Type BB* **22**, *but containing stamps with Block Cypher wmk, printed by Waterlow & Sons (Nos. 418/20).*
BB24　Edition numbers 55 to 167 & 173 to 273 .... £525

1929 (May). *Postal Union Congress issue. Cover of special design as Type BB* **13** *printed in red on buff as before but containing stamps of the P.U.C. issue (Nos. 434/6).*
BB25　Edition numbers 168 to 172 .... £450

1934 (Mar). *Scarlet cover printed in black as Type BB* **22**, *but containing stamps with the Block Cypher wmk printed by Harrison & Sons (Nos. 418/20).*
BB26　Edition numbers 274 to 288 .... £625

1935 (Jan). *As No. BB* **29**, *but containing stamps of the photogravure issue (intermediate format).*
BB27　Edition numbers 289 to 293 .... £1850

1935 (May). *Silver Jubilee issue. Larger size cover printed in red on buff as Type BB* **16** *and containing pages of four stamps: 20 × 1½d., 4 × 1d. and 4 × ½d. (Nos. 453/5).*
BB28　Edition numbers 294 to 297 .... 90·00

1935 (July). *As No. BB* **26**, *but containing stamps of the photogravure issue (small format) (Nos. 439/41).*
BB29　Edition numbers 298 to 319 .... £525

3s.6d. Booklets

BB **30**

1920 (July). *Orange cover printed in black as Type BB* **30**, *containing pages of six stamps: 18 × 2d. and 6 × 1d. (Nos. 357, 368).*
BB30　Edition numbers 27 to 32 .... £2000

BB **31**

1921 (Jan). *Orange-red cover printed in black as Type BB* **31**, *as before but make-up changed to include stamps of 1912–22 issue with the Simple Cypher wmk: 12 × 2d. (Die I), 6 × 1½d., 6 × 1d. and 6 × ½d. (Nos. 351, 357, 362, 368).*
BB31　Edition numbers 33, 34, 36 & 38 .... £2000

1921 (July). *As BB* **31** *including stamps of the 1912-22 issue with Simple Cypher wmk: 12 × 2d. (Die I or II), 6 × 1½d., 6 × 1d. and 6 × ½d. (Nos. 351, 357, 362, 368 or 370).*
BB32　Edition numbers 1 to 11, 14 to 18 .... £2000

5s. Booklets

BB **33**

1931 (Aug). *Green cover printed in black as Type BB* **33**. *Pages of six stamps: 34 × 1½d., 6 × 1d. and 6 × ½d. The first 1½d. pane completed by two se-tenant advertisements. Printed by Waterlow & Sons on paper with Block Cypher wmk (Nos. 418/20).*
BB33　Edition number 1 .... £5500

1932 (June). *As before, but buff cover printed in black.*
BB34　Edition numbers 2 to 6 .... £4500

1934 (July). *As before, but containing stamps with Block Cypher wmk printed by Harrison & Sons (Nos. 418/20).*
BB35　Edition numbers 7 or 8 .... £2000

1935 (Feb). *As before, but containing stamps of the photogravure issue (intermediate format) with se-tenant advertisements printed in brown (Nos. 439/41).*
BB36　Edition number 9 .... £5500

1935 (July). *As before, but containing stamps of the photogravure issue (small format) with se-tenant advertisements printed in black (Nos. 439/41).*
BB37　Edition numbers 10 to 15 .... £600

KING EDWARD VIII

6d. Booklet

1936. *Buff unglazed cover without inscription containing 4 × 1½d. stamps, in panes of two (No. 459).*
BC1　Edition numbers 354 to 385 .... 65·00

2s. Booklet

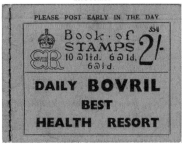

BC **2**

1936 (Oct). *Blue cover printed in black as Type BC* **2**, *containing pages of six stamps: 10×1½d., 6×1d. & 6×½d. (Nos. 457/9).*
BC2   Edition numbers 354 to 385 .... £140

3s. Booklet

1936 (Nov). *As No. BB* **29**, *except for the K.E.VIII cypher on the cover but without "P" and "O" on either side of the crown, and containing Nos. 457/9.*
BC3   Edition numbers 320 to 332 .... £110

5s. Booklet

1937 (Mar). *As No. BB* **37**, *but with the K.E.VIII cypher on the cover and containing Nos. 457/9.*
BC4   Edition numbers 16 or 17 .... £275

KING GEORGE VI

6d. Booklets

1938 (Jan). *As No. BC* **1**, *but containing stamps in the original dark colours. Buff cover without inscription (No. 464).*
BD1   .... 65·00

1938 (Feb). *As before, but pink unprinted cover and make-up changed to contain 2 × 1½d., 2 × 1d. and 2 × ½d. in the original dark colours (Nos. 462/4).*
BD2   .... £300

1940 (June). *Pale green unprinted cover and make-up changed to include two panes of four stamps with wmk sideways. Stamps in original dark colours with binding margin either at the top or bottom of the pane: 4 × 1d., 4 × ½d. (Nos. 462a/3a).*
BD3   .... £150

1s. Booklets with Panes of 2

1947 (Dec). *Cream cover, unglazed and without inscription containing panes of two stamps in pale shades, all with wmk normal. Panes of two stamps: 4 × ½d., 4 × 1d. and 4 × 1½d. (Nos. 485/7).*
BD4   .... 28·00

1951 (May). *As before, but containing stamps in changed colours (Nos. 503/5).*
BD5   .... 28·00

1s. Booklets with Panes of 4

1948. *Cream cover as before, but make-up changed to contain 4 × 1½d., 4 × 1d. and 4 × ½d. in panes of four of the pale shades with wmk normal (Nos. 485/7).*
BD6   .... £8500

1951 (May). *As before, but stamps in new colours all wmk normal, margins at either top or at the bottom. (Nos. 503/5).*
BD7   .... 35·00

BD **8**

1952 (Dec). *Cream cover printed in black as Type BD* **8**. *Make-up as before but with wmk either upright or inverted and margins only at the top (Nos. 503/5).*
BD8   .... 25·00

BD **10**

1954. *As before but cover showing GPO emblem with St. Edward's crown and oval frame as Type BD* **10** *(Nos. 503/5).*
BD10   .... 35·00

2s. Booklets

BD **11**

1937 (Aug). *Blue cover printed in black as Type BB* **11**, *but with K.G.VI cypher on the cover and containing stamps in the original dark colours. Panes of six stamps: 10 × 1½d., 6 × 1d. and 6 × ½d. The first 1½d. pane completed by two se-tenant advertisements. (Nos. 462/4).*
BD11   Edition numbers 386 to 412 .... £950

BD **12**

1938 (Mar). *Blue cover printed in black as Type BD* **12** *(Nos. 462/4).*
BD12   Edition numbers 413 to 508 .... £950

2s.6d. Booklets

BD **13**

1940 (June). *Scarlet cover printed in black as Type* BD **13**, *containing panes of six stamps in original dark colours: 6 × 2½d., 6 × 2d. and 6 × ½d. (Nos. 462, 465/6).*
BD13   Edition numbers 1 to 8 (part).. £1500

1940 (Sept). *As before, but blue cover printed in black as Type* BD **13**.
BD14   Edition numbers 8 (part) to 13 .... £1500

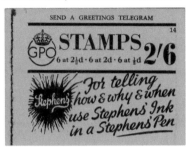

BD **15**

1940 (Oct). *As before, but with green cover printed in black as Type* BD **15** *(Nos. 462, 465/6).*
BD15   Edition numbers 14 to 94 .... £850

1942 (Mar). *As before, but containing stamps in pale shades (Nos. 485, 488/9).*
BD16   Edition numbers 95 to 146 (Part)................................ £850

1942 (October). *Composition as before, but with unglazed green covers.*
BD17   Edition numbers 146 (Part) to 214 .... £850

Type **A** Circular GPO Cypher

1943 (Aug). *As before, but green cover printed in black as Type* **A**, *with different contents details (Nos. 485, 488/9).*
BD18   Edition dates August 1943 to February 1951 .... 95·00

(1) AUG 1943 .... £110	(34) JUNE 1946 .... £140
(2) OCT 1943 .... £140	(35) JULY 1946 .... £140
(3) NOV 1943 .... £170	(36) AUG 1946 .... £140
(4) DEC 1943 .... £150	(37) SEPT 1946 .... £140
(5) JAN 1944 .... £150	(38) OCT 1946 .... £300
(6) FEB 1944 .... £150	(39) NOV 1946 .... £140
(7) MAR 1944 .... £150	(40) DEC 1946 .... £140
(8) APR 1944 .... £150	(41) JAN 1947 .... £140
(9) MAY 1944 .... £150	(42) FEB 1947 .... £140
(10) JUNE 1944 .... £150	(43) MAR 1947 .... £140
(11) JULY 1944 .... £150	(44) APR 1947 .... £140
(12) AUG 1944 .... £150	(45) MAY 1947 .... £140
(13) SEPT 1944 .... £150	(46) JUNE 1947 .... £140
(14) OCT 1944 .... £150	(47) JULY 1947 .... £140
(15) NOV 1944 .... £150	(48) AUG 1947 .... £140
(16) DEC 1944 .... £150	(49) SEPT 1947 .... £140
(17) JAN 1945 .... £150	(50) OCT 1947 .... £140
(18) FEB 1945 .... £150	(51) NOV 1947 .... £140
(19) MAR 1945 .... £150	(52) DEC 1947 .... £140
(20) APR 1945 .... £150	(53) JAN 1948 .... £160
(21) MAY 1945 .... £150	(54) FEB 1948 .... £140
(22) JUNE 1945 .... £150	(55) MAR 1948 .... £140
(23) JULY 1945 .... £150	(56) APR 1948 .... £140
(24) AUG 1945 .... £150	(57) MAY 1948 .... £140
(25) SEPT 1945 .... £150	(58) JUNE 1948 .... £140
(26) OCT 1945 .... £150	(59) JULY 1948 .... £140
(27) NOV 1945 .... £150	(60) AUG 1948 .... £140
(28) DEC 1945 .... £150	(61) OCT 1948 .... £100
(29) JAN 1946 .... £140	(62) NOV 1948 .... £100
(30) FEB 1946 .... £140	(63) DEC 1948 .... £100
(31) MAR 1946 .... £140	(64) JAN 1949 .... £100
(32) APR 1946 .... £140	(65) FEB 1949 .... £120
(33) MAY 1946 .... £140	(66) MAR 1949 .... £120

(67) APR 1949 .... £120	(78) APR 1950 .... £120
(68) MAY 1949 .... £120	(79) MAY 1950 .... £120
(69) JUNE 1949 .... £120	(80) JUNE 1950 .... £120
(70) JULY 1949 .... £120	(81) JULY 1950 .... 95·00
(71) AUG 1949 .... £120	(82) AUG 1950 .... 95·00
(72) OCT 1949 .... £120	(83) SEPT 1950 .... 95·00
(73) NOV 1949 .... £120	(84) OCT 1950 .... 95·00
(74) DEC 1949 .... £120	(85) NOV 1950 .... 95·00
(75) JAN 1950 .... £120	(86) DEC 1950 .... 95·00
(76) FEB 1950 .... £120	(87) JAN 1951 .... 95·00
(77) MAR 1950 .... £120	(88) FEB 1951 .... 95·00

1951 (May). *As before, but containing stamps in the new colours (Nos. 503, 506/7).*
BD19   Edition dates May 1951 to February 1952........................... 55·00

(1) MAY 1951 .... 55·00	(6) OCT 1951 .... 55·00
(2) JUNE 1951 .... 65·00	(7) NOV 1951 .... 55·00
(3) JULY 1951 .... 65·00	(8) DEC 1951 .... 55·00
(4) AUG 1951 .... 55·00	(9) JAN 1952 .... 55·00
(5) SEPT 1951 .... 65·00	(10) FEB 1952 .... 55·00

1952 (March). *As before, but make-up changed to contain: 6 × 2½d., 6 × 1½d., 3 × 1d. and 6 × ½d. The 1d. pane was completed by three perforated labels in the lower row inscribed "MINIMUM INLAND PRINTED PAPER RATE 1½d." (Nos. 503/5, 507).*
BD20   Edition dates March 1952 to May 1953 .... 48·00

(1) MAR 1952 .... 48·00	(9) NOV 1952 .... 48·00
(2) APR 1952 .... 55·00	(10) DEC 1952 .... 48·00
(3) MAY 1952 .... 48·00	(11) JAN 1953 .... 48·00
(4) JUNE 1952 .... 55·00	(12) FEB 1953 .... 48·00
(5) JULY 1952 .... 55·00	(13) MAR 1953 .... 48·00
(6) AUG 1952 .... 48·00	(14) APR 1953 .... 48·00
(7) SEPT 1952 .... 48·00	(15) MAY 1953 .... 55·00
(8) OCT 1952 .... 48·00	

3s. Booklets

BD **21**

1937 (Aug). *Scarlet cover printed black as Type* BD **21**, *containing pages of six stamps: 18 × 1½d., 6 × 1d. & 6 × ½d. in the original dark colours (Nos. 462/4).*
BD21   Edition numbers 333 to 343 .... £1700

BD **22**

1938 (April). *As before, but scarlet cover printed in black as Type* BD **22** *(Nos. 462/4).*
BD22   Edition numbers 344 to 377 .... £1700

5s. Booklets

1937 (Aug). *Buff cover printed in black as Type* BB **33**, *containing stamps of the new reign in the original dark colours. Pages of six stamps: 34 × 1½d., 6 × 1d. and 6 × ½d. The first 1½d. pane completed by two se-tenant advertisements. (Nos. 462/4).*
BD23   Edition numbers 18 to 20 .... £1900

BD **24**

1938 (May). *As before, but with redesigned front cover showing GPO emblem as Type BD* **24** *instead of royal cypher.*
BD24   Edition numbers 21 to 29 .... £1900

1940 (July). *As before, but make-up changed to contain:* 18×2½d., 6×2d. *and* 6×½d. *in the original dark colours (Nos. 462, 465/6).*
BD25   Edition numbers 1 to 16 (part) £1900

1942 (Mar). *As before, but containing stamps in pale shades (Nos. 485, 488/9).*
BD26   Edition numbers 16 (part) to 36 .... £1900

1943 (Sept). *As before, but buff cover printed in black as Type* A *(see No.* BD **18**, 2s.6d.) *(Nos. 485, 488/9).*
BD28   Edition dates September 1943 to December 1950 .... £130

(1) SEPT 1943 .... £150	(26) JUNE 1947 .... £170
(2) OCT 1943 .... £220	(27) AUG 1947 .... £170
(3) NOV 1943 .... £170	(28) OCT 1947 .... £170
(4) DEC 1943 .... £220	(29) DEC 1947 .... £170
(5) FEB 1944 .... £170	(30) FEB 1948 .... £170
(6) MAR 1944 .... £170	(31) APR 1948 .... £170
(7) AUG 1944 .... £170	(32) JUNE 1948 .... £170
(8) OCT 1944 .... £170	(33) JULY 1948 .... £170
(9) NOV 1944 .... £170	(34) AUG 1948 .... £170
(10) JAN 1945 .... £170	(35) OCT 1948 .... £170
(11) FEB 1945 .... £180	(36) DEC 1948 .... £180
(12) APR 1945 .... £180	(37) FEB 1949 .... £180
(13) JUNE 1945 .... £180	(38) APR 1949 .... £180
(14) AUG 1945 .... £180	(39) JUNE 1949 .... £170
(15) OCT 1945 .... £180	(40) AUG 1949 .... £170
(16) DEC 1945 .... £180	(41) SEPT 1949 .... £170
(17) JAN 1946 .... £180	(42) OCT 1949 .... £170
(18) MAR 1946 .... £170	(43) DEC 1949 .... £170
(19) MAY 1946 .... £170	(44) FEB 1950 .... £130
(20) JUNE 1946 .... £170	(45) APR 1950 .... £130
(21) AUG 1946 .... £170	(46) JUNE 1950 .... £130
(22) OCT 1946 .... £170	(47) AUG 1950 .... £130
(23) DEC 1946 .... £170	(48) OCT 1950 .... £130
(24) FEB 1947 .... £170	(49) DEC 1950 .... £130
(25) APR 1947 .... £170	

BD **29**

1944 (Apr). *As before, but buff cover printed in black as Type* BD **29** *(Nos. 485, 488/9).*
BD29   Edition dates April or June 1944 .... £2750

(1) APR 1944 .... £2750   (2) JUNE 1944 .... £2750

1951 (May). *As before, but buff cover changed back to Type* A *(see No.* BD **18**, 2s.6d.) *and containing stamps in the new colours (Nos. 503, 506/7).*
BD30   Edition dates May 1951 to January 1952 .... 65·00

(1) MAY 1951 .... 65·00   (4) NOV 1951 .... 65·00
(2) JULY 1951 .... 65·00   (5) JAN 1952 .... 65·00
(3) SEPT 1951 .... 65·00

1952 (Mar). *As before, make-up changed to contain:* 18×2½d., 6×1½d., 3×1d. *and* 6×½d.. *The 1d. pane was completed by three perforated labels in the lower row inscribed* "MINIMUM INLAND PRINTED PAPER RATE 1¼d." *(Nos. 503/5, 507).*
BD31   Edition dates March to November 1952 .... 55·00

(1) MAR 1952 .... 55·00   (4) SEPT 1952 .... 55·00
(2) MAY 1952 .... 55·00   (5) NOV 1952 .... 55·00
(3) JULY 1952 .... 55·00

1953 (Jan). *As before, but make-up changed again to include the 2d. value and containing:* 12×2½d., 6×2d., 6×1½d., 6×1d. *and* 6×½d. *(Nos. 503/7).*
BD32   Edition dates January or March 1953 .... 65·00

(1) JAN 1953 .... 65·00   (2) MAR 1953 .... 65·00

QUEEN ELIZABETH II
I. £.s.d. Booklets, 1953–70.

TYPES OF BOOKLET COVER WITH GPO CYPHER

Type **A** Circular GPO Cypher
(See illustration above No. BD18)

Type **B** Oval Type GPO Cypher

Type **C** New GPO Cypher (small)

Type **D** New GPO Cypher (large)

1s. Booklets

1953 (2 Sept)–**59**. *I. White unprinted cover. Pages of two stamps:* 4×1½d., 4×1d., 4×½d. *For use in experimental "D" machines.*

A. Wmk Tudor Crown (Nos. 515/17) EE
E1   No date .... 9·25

B. Wmk St. Edward's Crown (Nos. 540/2)
E2   No date (11.57) .... 50·00

II. White printed cover as Type **B**. *Pages of four stamps:* 4×1½d., 4×1d., 4×½d. *For use in "E" machines.*

A. Wmk Tudor Crown (Nos. 515/17)
K1   No date (22.7.54) .... 8·00

B. Wmk St. Edward's Crown (Nos. 540/2)
K2   No date (5.7.56) .... 8·00

	C. Wmk Crowns (Nos. 570/2)	
K3	No date (13.8.59)..	8·00

2s. Booklets

1959 (22 Apr)–**65.** *Pages of stamps:* 4×3d., 4×1½d., 4×1d., 4×½d.

I. Salmon cover as Type **B***. Wmk. St. Edward's Crown (Nos.540/2 and 545).*

N1	No date..	9·00

II. Salmon cover as Type **C***. Wmk Crowns (Nos. 570/2 and 575).*

N2	No date (2.11.60)..	10·50

III. Lemon cover as Type **C***. Wmk Crowns (Nos. 570/2 and 575).*

N3	No date (2.61)...	10·50

IV. Lemon cover as Type **C***. Wmk Crowns (sideways) (Nos. 570a, 571a, 572b, 575a) or phosphor (Nos. 610a, 611a, 612a, 615b).*

N4	APR 1961...	38·00
	p. With phosphor bands	80·00
N5	SEPT 1961	60·00
N6	JAN 1962	55·00
N7	APR 1962...	65·00
N8	JULY 1962	60·00
	p. With phosphor bands	£110
N9	NOV 1962..	80·00
	p. With phosphor bands	£120
N10	JAN 1963	60·00
	p. With phosphor bands	£160
N11	MAR 1963..	60·00
N12	JUNE 1963	60·00
	p. With phosphor bands	95·00
N13	AUG 1963	60·00
	p. With phosphor bands	95·00
N14	OCT 1963	60·00
	p. With phosphor bands	£160
N15	FEB 1964	60·00
	p. With phosphor bands	95·00
N16	JUNE 1964	60·00
	p. With phosphor bands	£130
N17	AUG 1964	80·00
	p. With phosphor bands	£130
N18	OCT 1964	60·00
	p. With phosphor bands	85·00
N19	DEC 1964..	70·00
	p. With phosphor bands	85·00
N20	APR 1965...	60·00
	p. With phosphor bands	80·00

1965 (16 Aug)–**67.** *New Composition. Pages of four stamps: 4×4d. and pane of 2×1d. and 3×3d. arranged se-tenant horiz. Orange-yellow cover as Type* **C** *printed in black. Wmk Crowns (sideways) (Nos. 571a, 575a and 576ab) or phosphor (Nos. 611a, 615d or 615dEa (one side phosphor band) and 616ab).*

N21	JULY 1965	5·00
	p. With phosphor bands	18·00
N22	OCT 1965	5·25
	p. With phosphor bands	18·00
N23	JAN 1966	8·50
	p. With phosphor bands	26·00
N24	APR 1966...	8·00
	p. With phosphor bands	12·00
N25	JULY 1966	6·00
	p. With phosphor bands	70·00
N26	OCT 1966	8·00
	p. With phosphor bands	16·00
N27	JAN 1967	9·00
	p. With phosphor bands	8·00
N28p	APR 1967. With phosphor bands	10·00
N29p	JULY 1967. With phosphor bands	6·75
N30p	OCT 1967. With phosphor bands........................	6·75

In the *se-tenant* pane the 3d. appears at left or right to facilitate the application of phosphor bands.

The following illustration shows how the *se-tenant* stamps with one phosphor band on 3d. were printed and the arrows indicate where the guillotine fell. The result gives 1d. stamps with two bands and the 3d. stamps with one band either at left or right.

| 3d. | 1d. | 1d. | 3d. | 3d. | 1d. | 1d. | 3d. |

1967 (Nov)–**68.** *Composition and cover as Nos. N21/30. Wmk Crowns (sideways) (Nos. 611a, 615b (two phosphor bands) and 616ab).*

N31p	JAN 1968	4·00
N32p	MAR 1968	4·50

2s. Booklets with Machin type stamps

1968 (6 Apr–Aug). *Orange-yellow cover as Type* **C***. Pages of four stamps: 4×4d. and pane of 2×1d. and 2×3d. arranged se-tenant horiz. PVA gum (Nos. 724, 730, 731Ev).*

NP27	MAY 1968	1·60
NP28	JULY 1968	1·40
NP29	AUG 1968	5·25

1968 (16 Sept)–**70.** *Grey cover as Type* **C***. New Composition. 4d. stamps only comprising page of 4×4d. with two phosphor bands (No. 731Ev) and page of 2×4d. with one centre phosphor band (No. 732) se-tenant with two printed labels.*

NP30	SEPT 1968	1·10
NP31	JAN 1969	£275

Same composition but all six 4d. stamps have one centre phosphor band (No. 732).

NP31a	SEPT 1968	£650
NP32	NOV 1968..	1·10
NP33	JAN 1969	1·10

Same composition but change to 4d. bright vermilion with one centre phosphor band (No. 733).

NP34	MAR 1969..	1·60
NP35	MAY 1969	1·90
NP36	JULY 1969	2·50
NP37	SEPT 1969	1·90
NP38	NOV 1969..	1·90
NP39	JAN 1970	2·75
NP40	MAR 1970..	2·75
NP41	MAY 1970	2·75
NP42	JULY 1970	2·75
NP43	AUG 1970	2·75
NP44	OCT 1970	2·75
NP45	DEC 1970..	2·75

2s. Booklets for Holiday Resorts

1963 (15 July)–**64.** *I. Lemon cover as Type* **C** *printed in red. New composition. Pages of four stamps: two of 4×2½d. and one of 3×½d. and 1×2½d. arranged se-tenant. Chalky paper. Wmk Crowns (Nos. 570k and 574k).*

NR1	No date, black stitching	5·00
	a. White stitching (3.9.63)	5·50

II. Lemon cover as Type **C** *printed in red. Composition changed again. Pages of four stamps 2×½d. and 2×2½d. arranged sideways, vertically se-tenant. Wmk Crowns (sideways) (No. 570n×4).*

NR2	1964 (1.7.64)..	2·25

2s. Booklet for Christmas Cards

1965 (6 Dec). *Orange-yellow cover as Type* **C** *printed in red. Two panes of 4×3d. arranged sideways. Wmk Crowns (sideways) (No. 575a).*

NX1	1965..	1·00

2s.6d. Booklets

Green cover. Pages of six stamps: 6×2½d., 6×1½d., 3×1d. (page completed by three perforated labels), 6×½d..

LABELS. The wording printed on the labels differs as follows:

"PPR" = "MINIMUM INLAND PRINTED PAPER RATE 1½d.."
Two types exist:

    A. Printed in photogravure, 17 mm high.
    B. Typographed, 15 mm high.

"Shorthand" = "SHORTHAND IN 1 WEEK" (covering all three labels).
"Post Early" = "PLEASE POST EARLY IN THE DAY".
"PAP" = "PACK YOUR PARCELS SECURELY" (1st label)
    "ADDRESS YOUR LETTERS CORRECTLY" (2nd label),
    "AND POST EARLY IN THE DAY" (3rd label).

1953–54. *Composite booklets containing stamps of King George VI and Queen Elizabeth II.*

A. K.G.VI ½d. and 1d. (Nos. 503/4) and Q.E.II 1½d. and 2½d. (Nos. 517 and 519b). Cover as Type **A***. No interleaving pages.*

F1	MAY 1953 (PPR 17 mm)	32·00
F2	JUNE 1953 (PPR 17 mm)	35·00
F3	JULY 1953 (PPR 17 mm)	42·00
F4	AUG 1953 (PPR 17 mm)	38·00

B. Same composition but with addition of two interleaving pages, one at each end. Cover as Type **A***.*

F5	SEPT 1953 (PPR 17 mm)	£200
F6	SEPT 1953 (PPR 15 mm)	£140

C. Same composition and with interleaving pages but with cover as Type **B***.*

F7	OCT 1953 (PPR 17 mm)	55·00
F8	OCT 1953 (PPR 15 mm)	£120
F9	NOV 1953 (PPR 17 mm)	60·00
F10	NOV 1953 (PPR 15 mm)	£200
F11	DEC 1953 (PPR 17 mm)	60·00
F12	JAN 1954 (Shorthand)	90·00
F13	FEB 1954 (Shorthand)	95·00

D. New composition: K.G.VI 1d. (No. 504) and Q.E.II ½d., 1½d. and 2½d. (Nos. 515, 517 and 519b).

F14	MAR 1954 (PPR 17 mm)	£550
F14a	MAR 1954 (Shorthand)	

1954–57. *Booklets containing only Queen Elizabeth II stamps. All covers as Type* **B**.

A. *Wmk Tudor Crown (Nos. 515/17 and 519b).*

F15	MAR 1954 (PPR 15 mm)	£325
F16	APR 1954 (Post Early)	50·00
F17	MAY 1954 (Post Early)	50·00
F18	JUNE 1954 (Post Early)	50·00
F19	JULY 1954 (Post Early)	50·00
F20	AUG 1954 (Post Early)	55·00
F21	SEPT 1954 (Post Early)	50·00
F22	OCT 1954 (Post Early)	50·00
F23	NOV 1954 (Post Early)	50·00
F24	DEC 1954 (Post Early)	50·00

B. *Same composition but with interleaving pages between each pane of stamps.*

F25	JAN 1955 (Post Early)	60·00
F26	JAN 1955 (PAP)	£140
F27	FEB 1955 (PAP)	55·00
F28	MAR 1955 (PAP)	55·00
F29	APR 1955 (PAP)	55·00
F30	MAY 1955 (PAP)	55·00
F31	JUNE 1955 (PAP)	55·00
F32	JULY 1955 (PAP)	55·00
F33	AUG 1955 (PAP)	55·00

C. *Mixed watermarks. Wmk Tudor Crown (Nos. 515/17 and 519b) and wmk St. Edward's Crown (Nos. 540/2 and 544b) in various combinations.*

F34	SEPT 1955 (PAP)	From 60·00

2s.6d. booklets dated AUGUST, OCTOBER, NOVEMBER and DECEMBER 1955, JANUARY, MAY and JUNE 1956 exist both as listed and with the two watermarks mixed. There are so many different combinations that we do not list them separately, but when in stock selections can be submitted. The SEPTEMBER 1955 booklet (No. F34) only exists in composite form.

D. *Wmk St. Edward's Crown (Nos. 540/2 and 544b).*

F35	OCT 1955 (PAP)	40·00
F36	NOV 1955 (PAP)	40·00
F37	DEC 1955 (PAP)	40·00
F38	JAN 1956 (PAP)	40·00
F39	FEB 1956 (PAP)	40·00
F40	MAR 1956 (PAP)	40·00
F41	APR 1956 (PAP)	50·00
F42	MAY 1956 (PAP)	40·00
F43	JUNE 1956 (PAP)	45·00
F44	JULY 1956 (PAP)	40·00
F45	AUG 1956 (PAP)	30·00
F46	SEPT 1956 (PAP)	48·00
F47	OCT 1956 (PAP)	40·00
F48	NOV 1956 (PAP)	40·00
F49	DEC 1956 (PAP)	40·00
F50	JAN 1957 (PAP)	40·00
F51	FEB 1957 (PAP)	30·00
F52	MAR 1957 (PAP)	40·00

E. *Same wmk but new composition. Pages of six stamps: 6 × 2½d. (No. 544b), 6 × 2d. (No. 543b) and 6 × ½d. (No. 540).*

F53	APR 1957	40·00
F54	MAY 1957	35·00
F55	JUNE 1957	35·00
F56	JULY 1957	35·00
F57	AUG 1957	35·00
F58	SEPT 1957	35·00
F59	OCT 1957	35·00
F60	NOV 1957	28·00
F61	DEC 1957	48·00

3s. Booklets

1958–65. *Pages of six stamps: 6 × 3d., 6 × 1½d., 6 × 1d., 6 × ½d. I. Red cover as Type* **B**.

A. *Wmk St. Edward's Crown (Nos. 540/2 and 545).*

M1	JAN 1958	28·00
M2	FEB 1958	28·00
M3	MAR 1958	28·00
M4	APR 1958	28·00
M5	MAY 1958	28·00
M6	JUNE 1958	28·00
M7	JULY 1958	28·00
M8	AUG 1958	32·00
M9	NOV 1958	32·00

The 3s. booklets dated NOVEMBER 1958, DECEMBER 1958 and JANUARY 1959 exist both as listed and with mixed St. Edward's Crown and Crowns wmks.

B. *Wmk Crowns (Nos. 570/2 and 575) or graphite lines (Nos. 587/9 and 592).*

M10	DEC 1958	38·00
M11	JAN 1959	35·00
M12	FEB 1959	35·00
M13	AUG 1959	38·00
	g. With graphite lines	£275
M14	SEPT 1959	38·00
	g. With graphite lines	£350

II. *Brick-red cover as Type* **C**. *Wmk Crowns (Nos. 570/2 and 575), graphite lines (Nos. 587/9 and 592) or phosphor (Nos. 610/12 and 615).*

M15	OCT 1959	38·00
	g. With graphite lines	£350
M16	NOV 1959	38·00
M17	DEC 1959	38·00
M18	JAN 1960	38·00
M19	FEB 1960	38·00
	g. With graphite lines	£325
M20	MAR 1960	38·00
	g. With graphite lines	£400
M21	APR 1960	38·00
	g. With graphite lines	£325
M22	MAY 1960	38·00
M23	JUNE 1960	38·00
M24	JULY 1960	38·00
M25	AUG 1960	38·00
	p. With phosphor bands	75·00
M26	SEPT 1960	38·00
M27	OCT 1960	38·00
M28	NOV 1960	38·00
	p. With phosphor bands	80·00

III. *Brick-red cover as Type* **D**. *Wmk Crowns (Nos. 570/2 and 575) or phosphor (Nos. 610/12 and 615).*

M29	DEC 1960	40·00
	p. With phosphor bands	85·00
M30	JAN 1961	38·00
M31	FEB 1961	38·00
M32	MAR 1961	32·00
M33	APR 1961	38·00
	p. With phosphor bands	75·00
M34	MAY 1961	38·00
M35	JUNE 1961	38·00
M36	JULY 1961	38·00
	p. With phosphor bands	75·00
M37	AUG 1961	38·00
	p. With phosphor bands	70·00
M38	SEPT 1961	38·00
	p. With phosphor bands	85·00
M39	OCT 1961	38·00
	p. With phosphor bands	80·00
M40	NOV 1961	38·00
M41	DEC 1961	38·00
M42	JAN 1962	38·00
M43	FEB 1962	38·00
	p. With phosphor bands	80·00
M44	MAR 1962	38·00
	p. With phosphor bands	80·00
M45	APR 1962	38·00
	p. With phosphor bands	80·00
M46	MAY 1962	38·00
	p. With phosphor bands	80·00
M47	JUNE 1962	38·00
	p. With phosphor bands	80·00
M48	JULY 1962	32·00
M49	AUG 1962	35·00
	p. With phosphor bands	80·00
M50	SEPT 1962	38·00
	p. With phosphor bands	80·00
M51	OCT 1962	40·00
	p. With phosphor bands	80·00
M52	NOV 1962	38·00
	p. With phosphor bands	80·00
M53	DEC 1962	38·00
	p. With phosphor bands	80·00
M54	JAN 1963	38·00
M55	FEB 1963	35·00
	p. With phosphor bands	80·00
M56	MAR 1963	38·00
	p. With phosphor bands	80·00
M57	APR 1963	38·00
	p. With phosphor bands	80·00
M58	MAY 1963	38·00
	p. With phosphor bands	£275
M59	JUNE 1963	38·00
	p. With phosphor bands	55·00
M60	JULY 1963	38·00
	p. With phosphor bands	80·00
M61	AUG 1963	38·00
	p. With phosphor bands	80·00
M62	SEPT 1963	38·00
M63	OCT 1963	38·00
M64	NOV 1963	32·00
	p. With phosphor bands	80·00
M65	DEC 1963	45·00
	p. With phosphor bands	£180
M66	JAN 1964	45·00
	p. With phosphor bands	60·00
M67	MAR 1964	42·00
	p. With phosphor bands	80·00
M68	MAY 1964	42·00

	p. With phosphor bands	£110
M69	JULY 1964	38·00
	p. With phosphor bands	80·00
M70	SEPT 1964	45·00
	p. With phosphor bands	80·00
M71	NOV 1964	45·00
	p. With phosphor bands	60·00
M72	JAN 1965	45·00
	p. With phosphor bands	60·00
M73	MAR 1965	30·00
	p. With phosphor bands	60·00
M74	MAY 1965	30·00
	p. With phosphor bands	60·00

3s.9d. Booklets

1953–57. *Red cover as Type* **B**. *Pages of six stamps:* 18 × 2½d.

A. Wmk Tudor Crown (No. 519b)

G1	NOV 1953	40·00
G2	JAN 1954	40·00
G3	MAR 1954	40·00
G4	DEC 1954	40·00
G5	FEB 1955	40·00
G6	APR 1955	40·00
G7	JUNE 1955	40·00
G8	AUG 1955	40·00
G9	OCT 1955	40·00
G10	DEC 1955	40·00

3s.9d. booklets dated OCTOBER and DECEMBER 1955 exist both as listed and with the two wkms mixed.

B. Wmk St. Edward's Crown (No. 544b). Same composition but with interleaving pages between each pane of stamps.

G12	FEB 1956	30·00
G13	APR 1956	30·00
G14	JUNE 1956	30·00
G15	AUG 1956	30·00
G16	OCT 1956	30·00
G17	DEC 1956	30·00
G18	FEB 1957	30·00
G19	APR 1957	30·00
G20	JUNE 1957	17·00
G21	AUG 1957	40·00

4s.6d. Booklets

1957–65. *Pages of six stamps:* 18 × 3d. I. *Purple cover as Type* **B**.

A. Wmk St. Edward's Crown (No. 545).

L1	OCT 1957	30·00
L2	DEC 1957	30·00
L3	FEB 1958	35·00
L4	APR 1958	30·00
L5	JUNE 1958	32·00
L6	OCT 1958	30·00
L7	DEC 1958	30·00

B. Wmk Crowns (No. 575).

L8	DEC 1958	£100

II. *Purple cover as Type* **C**. *Wmk Crowns (No. 575) or graphite lines (No. 592)*

L9	FEB 1959	30·00
L10	JUNE 1959	30·00
L11	AUG 1959	30·00
	g. With graphite lines	45·00
L12	OCT 1959	45·00
L13	DEC 1959	35·00

III. *Violet cover as Type* **C**. *Wmk Crowns (No. 575), graphite lines (No. 592) or phosphor (No. 615).*

L14	FEB 1959	45·00
L15	APR 1959	35·00
	g. With graphite lines	30·00
L16	JUNE 1959	35·00
	g. With graphite lines	30·00
L17	DEC 1959	35·00
L18	FEB 1960	35·00
	g. With graphite lines	35·00
L19	APR 1960	35·00
	g. With graphite lines	35·00
L20	JUNE 1960	35·00
L21	AUG 1960	35·00
	p. With phosphor bands	60·00
L22	OCT 1960	35·00

IV. *Violet cover as Type* **D**. *Wmk Crowns (No. 575) or phosphor (No. 615).*

L23	DEC 1960	60·00
L24	FEB 1961	60·00
	p. With phosphor bands	48·00
L25	APR 1961	42·00
	p. With phosphor bands	45·00
L26	JUNE 1961	42·00
L27	AUG 1961	42·00

	p. With phosphor bands	55·00
L28	OCT 1961	40·00
	p. With phosphor bands	55·00
L29	DEC 1961	40·00
L30	FEB 1962	55·00
	p. With phosphor bands	40·00
L31	APR 1962	55·00
	p. With phosphor bands	55·00
L32	JUNE 1962	55·00
	p. With phosphor bands	75·00
L33	AUG 1962	40·00
	p. With phosphor bands	80·00
L34	OCT 1962	40·00
	p. With phosphor bands	£225
L35	DEC 1962	40·00
	p. With phosphor bands	55·00
L36	FEB 1963	40·00
	p. With phosphor bands	55·00
L37	APR 1963	40·00
	p. With phosphor bands	55·00
L38	JUNE 1963	40·00
	p. With phosphor bands	48·00
L39	AUG 1963	40·00
	p. With phosphor bands	60·00
L40	OCT 1963	40·00
	p. With phosphor bands	60·00
L41	NOV 1963	40·00
	p. With phosphor bands	60·00
L42	DEC 1963	40·00
	p. With phosphor bands	£225
L43	JAN 1964	85·00
L44	FEB 1964	40·00
	p. With phosphor bands	48·00
L45	MAR 1964	80·00
	p. With phosphor bands	£130
L46	APR 1964	80·00
	p. With phosphor bands	55·00
L47	MAY 1964	40·00
	p. With phosphor bands	55·00
L48	JUNE 1964	40·00
	p. With phosphor bands	55·00
L49	JULY 1964	40·00
	p. With phosphor bands	55·00
L50	AUG 1964	45·00
	p. With phosphor bands	40·00
L51	SEPT 1964	55·00
	p. With phosphor bands	45·00
L52	OCT 1964	40·00
	p. With phosphor bands	55·00
L53	NOV 1964	40·00
	p. With phosphor bands	55·00
L54	DEC 1964	40·00
	p. With phosphor bands	55·00
L55	JAN 1965	32·00
	p. With phosphor bands	55·00
L56	FEB 1965	32·00
	p. With phosphor bands	55·00
L57	MAR 1965	35·00
	p. With phosphor bands	£400
L58	APR 1965	30·00

1965 (26 July)–**67**. *New composition. Pages of six stamps:* 12 × 4d., 6 × 1d. *Slate-blue cover as Type* **D**. *Wmk Crowns (Nos. 571 and 576a) or phosphor (Nos. 611 and 616a).*

L59	JULY 1965	30·00
	p. With phosphor bands	32·00
L60	SEPT 1965	30·00
	p. With phosphor bands	32·00
L61	NOV 1965	30·00
	p. With phosphor bands	32·00
L62	JAN 1966	30·00
	p. With phosphor bands	29·00
L63	MAR 1966	30·00
	p. With phosphor bands	30·00
L64	JAN 1967	24·00
	p. With phosphor bands	23·00
L65	MAR 1967	40·00
	p. With phosphor bands	18·00
L66p	MAY 1967. With phosphor bands	12·00
L67p	JULY 1967. With phosphor bands	18·00
L68p	SEPT 1967. With phosphor bands	18·00
L69p	NOV 1967. With phosphor bands	12·00
L70p	JAN 1968. With phosphor bands	12·00
L71p	MAR 1968. With phosphor bands	10·00

4s.6d. Booklets with Machin type stamps

1968–70. *Slate-blue cover as Type* **D**. *Pages of six stamps:* 12 × 4d., 6 × 1d. *PVA gum (Nos. 724, 731Ev).*

LP45	MAY 1968	7·25

LP **46** Ships Series with GPO Cypher

(Des S. Rose)

Blue cover as Type LP **46**. *Ships Series. Composition as last.*

LP46	JULY 1968 (*Cutty Sark*)	1·80

Same composition but changed to 4d. with one centre phosphor band (No. 732).

LP47	SEPT 1968 (*Golden Hind*)	2·40
LP48	NOV 1968 (*Discovery*)	2·40

Same composition but changed to 4d. bright vermilion with one centre phosphor band (No. 733).

LP49	JAN 1969 (*Queen Elizabeth 2*)	4·00
LP50	MAR 1969 (*Sirius*)	3·50
LP51	MAY 1969 (*Sirius*)	3·00
LP52	JULY 1969 (*Dreadnought*)	3·50
LP53	SEPT 1969 (*Dreadnought*)	6·00
LP54	NOV 1969 (*Mauretania*)	4·25
LP55	JAN 1970 (*Mauretania*)	6·00
LP56	MAR 1970 (*Victory*)	4·75
LP57	MAY 1970 (*Victory*)	12·00

LP **58** Ships Series with Post Office Corporation Crown Symbol

(Des S. Rose)

As last but cover changed to Type LP **58**.

LP58	AUG 1970 (*Sovereign of the Seas*)	4·50
LP59	OCT 1970 (*Sovereign of the Seas*)	12·00

5s. Booklets

1953–57. *Buff cover. Pages of six stamps.* 12×2½d., 6×2d., 6×1½d., 6×1d., 6×½d.

I. Composite booklets containing stamps of King George VI and Queen Elizabeth II.

A. *K.G.VI* ½d., 1d. *and* 2d. (*Nos.* 503/4 *and* 506) *and Q.E.II* 1½d. *and* 2½d. (*Nos.* 517 *and* 519b). *Cover as Type A. No interleaving pages.*

H1	MAY 1953	48·00
H2	JULY 1953	50·00

B. *Same composition but with addition of two interleaving pages, one at each end. Cover as Type* **A**.

H3	SEPT 1953	50·00

C. *Same composition and with interleaving pages but cover as Type* **B**.

H4	NOV 1953	48·00
H5	JAN 1954	48·00

D. *New composition: K.G.VI* 1d. *and* 2d. (*Nos.* 504 *and* 506) *and Q.E.II* ½d., 1½d. *and* 2½d. (*Nos.* 515, 517 *and* 519b).

H6	MAR 1954	£400

E. *New composition: K.G.VI* 2d. (*No.* 506) *and Q.E.II* ½d. 1d., 1½d. *and* 2½d.. (*Nos.* 515/17 *and* 519b).

H7	MAR 1954	£225

II. Booklets containing only Queen Elizabeth II stamps. Buff cover as Type **B**. *Two interleaving pages as before.*

A. *Wmk Tudor Crown* (*Nos.* 515/18 *and* 519b).

H8	MAR 1954	£170
H9	MAY 1954	85·00
H10	JULY 1954	95·00
H11	SEPT 1954	50·00
H12	NOV 1954	85·00

ZB. *Same composition but with interleaving pages between each pane of stamps.*

H13	JAN 1955	85·00
H14	MAR 1955	75·00
H15	MAY 1955	75·00
H16	JULY 1955	75·00

C. *Wmk St. Edward's Crown* (*Nos.* 540/3 *and* 544b).

H17	SEPT 1955	40·00
H18	NOV 1955	42·00
H19	JAN 1956	55·00
H20	MAR 1956	55·00
H21	MAY 1956	48·00
H22	JULY 1956	48·00
H23	SEPT 1956	48·00
H24	NOV 1956	48·00
H25	JAN 1957	50·00

5s. booklets dated SEPTEMBER and NOVEMBER 1955 and JANUARY 1956 exist both as listed and with the two watermarks mixed. There are so many different combinations that we do not list them separately, but when in stock selections can be submitted.

D. *Same watermark. Introduction of 2d. light red-brown* (*No.* 543b) *in place of No.* 543.

H26	JAN 1957	48·00
H27	MAR 1957	60·00
H28	MAY 1957	50·00
H29	JULY 1957	42·00
H30	SEPT 1957	42·00
H31	NOV 1957	42·00

1958–65. E. *New composition. Pages of six stamps:* 12×3d. (*No.* 545), 6×2½d. (*No.* 544b), 6×1d. (*No.* 541), 6×½d. (*No.* 540). *Wmk St. Edward's Crown.*

H32	JAN 1958	42·00
H33	MAR 1958	42·00
H34	MAY 1958	42·00
H35	JULY 1958 (11.58)	30·00
H36	NOV 1958	30·00

5s. booklets dated JULY 1958, NOVEMBER 1958 and JANUARY 1959 exist with mixed watermarks.

F. *Blue cover as Type* **C**. *Wmk Crowns* (*Nos.* 570/1, 574/5), *graphite lines* (*Nos.* 587/8 *and* 591/2) *or phosphor* (*Nos.* 610/11, 614 *and* 615).

H37	JAN 1959	35·00
H38	MAR 1959	42·00
H39	JULY 1959	42·00
	g. With graphite lines	£150
H40	SEPT 1959	42·00
H41	NOV 1959	42·00
H42	JAN 1960	42·00
H43	MAR 1960	42·00
	g. With graphite lines	£170
H44	MAY 1960	50·00
H45	JULY 1960	50·00
H46	SEPT 1960	60·00
	g. With graphite lines	£170
	p. With phosphor bands	£120
H47	NOV 1960	55·00

G. *As last but blue cover as Type* **D**. *Same composition.*

I. *Phosphor has two bands on* 2½d. (*No.* 614).

H48	JAN 1961	60·00
H49	MAR 1961	60·00
	p. With phosphor bands	£150
H50	MAY 1961	60·00
H51	JULY 1961	60·00
	p. With phosphor bands	£200
H52	SEPT 1961	60·00
	p. With phosphor bands	£200
H53	NOV 1961	60·00
H54	JAN 1962	60·00
	p. With phosphor bands	£200

II. *As last but phosphor has one band on* 2½d. (*No.* 614a).

H55	MAR 1962	60·00
	p. With phosphor bands	£200
H56	MAY 1962	60·00
	p. With phosphor bands	£180
H57	JULY 1962	60·00
	p. With phosphor bands	£180
H58	SEPT 1962	60·00
	p. With phosphor bands	£200
H59	NOV 1962	60·00
	p. With phosphor bands	£200
H60	JAN 1963	60·00
	p. With phosphor bands	£500
H61	MAR 1963	60·00
	p. With phosphor bands	£200
H62	MAY 1963	60·00
	p. With phosphor bands	£200
H63	JULY 1963	60·00
	p. With phosphor bands	£200
H64	SEPT 1963	60·00
	p. With phosphor bands	£225

H65	NOV 1963	60·00
	p. With phosphor bands........................	£200
H66	JAN 1964	60·00
	p. With phosphor bands........................	£120
H67	MAR 1964	60·00
	p. With phosphor bands........................	£120
H68	MAY 1964	60·00
	p. With phosphor bands........................	£200
H69	JULY 1964	60·00
	p. With phosphor bands........................	£180
H70	SEPT 1964	60·00
	p. With phosphor bands........................	£180
H71	NOV 1964	55·00
	p. With phosphor bands........................	£120
H72	JAN 1965	60·00
	p. With phosphor bands........................	£120
H73	MAR 1965	50·00
	p. With phosphor bands........................	£180
H74	MAY 1965	45·00
	p. With phosphor bands........................	£120

5s. Booklets with Machin type stamps

HP **26** English Homes Series with GPO Cypher

(Des S. Rose)

1968 (27 Nov)–**70**. *Cinnamon cover as Type* HP **26** (*English Homes Series*). *Pages of six stamps:* 12×5d. (*No.* 735).

HP26	DEC 1968 (Ightham Mote)	3·00
HP27	FEB 1969 (Little Moreton Hall)	3·00
HP28	APR 1969 (Long Melford Hall)	3·00
HP29	JUNE 1969 (Long Melford Hall)	3·00
HP30	AUG 1969 (Long Melford Hall)	4·75

HP **31** English Homes Series with Post Office Corporation Crown Symbol

(Des S. Rose)

As last but cover changed to Type HP **31**.

HP31	OCT 1969 (Mompesson House)	3·00
HP32	DEC 1969 (Mompesson House)	3·50
HP33	FEB 1970 (Cumberland Terrace)	3·00

HP **34**

(Des P. Gauld)

As last but cover changed to Type HP **34** (*special edition to advertise Philympia International Philatelic Exhibition, London, September 1970*).

HP34	(no date) (3.3.70)	3·00

As last but cover changed to Type HP **31**.

HP35	JUNE 1970 (The Vineyard, Saffron Walden)	3·50
HP36	AUG 1970 (The Vineyard, Saffron Walden)	4·75
HP37	OCT 1970 (Mereworth Castle)	4·50
HP38	DEC 1970 (Mereworth Castle)	4·75

6s. Booklets

1965 (21 June)–**67**. *Claret cover as Type* **D**. *Wmk Crowns* (*No.* 576a) *or phosphor* (*No.* 616a). *Pages of six stamps:* 18×4d.

Q1	JUNE 1965	40·00
	p. With phosphor bands	40·00
Q2	JULY 1965	40·00
	p. With phosphor bands	40·00
Q3	AUG 1965	45·00
	p. With phosphor bands	48·00
Q4	SEPT 1965	40·00
	p. With phosphor bands	45·00
Q5	OCT 1965	40·00
	p. With phosphor bands	45·00
Q6	NOV 1965	40·00
	p. With phosphor bands	45·00
Q7	DEC 1965	40·00
	p. With phosphor bands	45·00
Q8	JAN 1966	42·00
	p. With phosphor bands	45·00
Q9	FEB 1966	42·00
	p. With phosphor bands	45·00
Q10	MAR 1966	42·00
	p. With phosphor bands	45·00
Q11	APR 1966	42·00
	p. With phosphor bands	£120
Q12	MAY 1966	40·00
	p. With phosphor bands	55·00
Q13	JUNE 1966	40·00
	p. With phosphor bands	45·00
Q14	JULY 1966	45·00
	p. With phosphor bands	65·00
Q15	AUG 1966	45·00
	p. With phosphor bands	£180
Q16	SEPT 1966	40·00
	p. With phosphor bands	40·00
Q17	OCT 1966	45·00
	p. With phosphor bands	£120
Q18	NOV 1966	48·00
	p. With phosphor bands	40·00
Q19	DEC 1966	40·00
	p. With phosphor bands	45·00
Q20	JAN 1967	55·00
	p. With phosphor bands	55·00
Q21	FEB 1967	55·00
	p. With phosphor bands	40·00
Q22	MAR 1967	45·00
	p. With phosphor bands	40·00
Q23	APR 1967	40·00
	p. With phosphor bands	40·00
Q24p	MAY 1967. With phosphor bands	40·00
Q25p	JUNE 1967. With phosphor bands	40·00
Q26p	JULY 1967. With phosphor bands	45·00
Q27p	AUG 1967. With phosphor bands	55·00

6s. Booklets with Machin type stamps

1967–70. *Claret cover as Type* **D**. *Pages of six stamps:* 18×4d. *Two phosphor bands. Gum arabic* (*No.* 731).

QP28	SEPT 1967	55·00
QP29	OCT 1967	55·00
QP30	NOV 1967	55·00
QP31	DEC 1967	55·00
QP32	JAN 1968	50·00
QP33	FEB 1968 (No. 731*Ea*)	50·00
QP34	MAR 1968 (No. 731*Ea*)	50·00
QP35	APR 1968 (No. 731*Ea*)	42·00
QP36	MAY 1968 (No. 731*Ea*)	21·00

Change to PVA gum (*No.* 731*Ev*).

QP37	MAY 1968	£500

NEW INFORMATION

The editor is always interested to correspond with people who have new information that will improve or correct this catalogue

QP **38** Birds Series with GPO Cypher

(Des S. Rose)

Orange-red cover as Type QP **38** (Birds Series). Same composition. Two phosphor bands. PVA gum (No. 731Ev).

QP38	JUNE 1968 (Kingfisher) (4.6.68)	2·50
QP39	JULY 1968 (Kingfisher)	13·00
QP40	AUG 1968 (Peregrine Falcon)	2·00

Change to one centre phosphor band (No. 732).

QP41	SEPT 1968 (Peregrine Falcon) (16.9.68)	2·10
QP42	OCT 1968 (Pied Woodpecker)	2·10
QP43	NOV 1968 (Pied Woodpecker)	2·25
QP44	DEC 1968 (Great Crested Grebe)	2·25
QP45	JAN 1969 (Barn Owl)	3·50

Change to 4d. bright vermilion with one centre phosphor band (No. 733).

QP46	FEB 1969 (Barn Owl) (20.2.69)	4·25
QP47	MAR 1969 (Jay)	3·50
QP48	MAY 1969 (Jay)	4·25
QP49	JULY 1969 (Puffin)	3·50
QP50	SEPT 1969 (Puffin)	6·00

QP **51** Birds Series with Post Office Corporation Crown Symbol

(Des S. Rose)

As last but cover changed to Type QP **51**.

QP51	NOV 1969 (Cormorant)	4·25
QP52	JAN 1970 (Cormorant)	5·00
QP53	APR 1970 (Wren)	4·25
QP54	AUG 1970 (Golden Eagle)	4·25
QP55	OCT 1970 (Golden Eagle)	4·25

10s. Booklets

1961 (10 Apr–Oct). Green cover as Type **D**. Pages of six stamps: 30×3d., 6×2d., 6×1½d., 6×1d., 6×½d.. Wmk Crowns (Nos. 570/3 and 575).

X1	No date	£150
X2	OCT 1961	£190

1962–64. New Composition. Pages of six stamps: 30×3d., 6×2½d., 6×1½d., 6×1d. (Nos. 571/2 and 574/5).

X3	APR 1962	£140
X4	AUG 1962	£180
X5	MAR 1963	£180
X6	JULY 1963	£180
X7	DEC 1963	£180
X8	JULY 1964	£140
X9	DEC 1964	£350

1965 (23 Aug)–**66**. Ochre cover as Type **D**. Pages of six stamps: 24×4d., 6×3d., 6×1d. Wmk Crowns (Nos. 571, 575, 576a).

X10	AUG 1965	38·00
X11	DEC 1965	55·00
X12	FEB 1966	55·00
X13	AUG 1966	38·00
X14	NOV 1966	38·00

1967–68. Ochre cover as Type **D**. Pages of six phosphor stamps: 24×4d., 6×3d., 6×1d. Wmk Crowns (Nos. 611, 615c (one side phosphor band), 616a).

X15p	FEB 1967	10·00

Composition as No. X15p. Wmk Crowns (Nos. 611, 615e (one centre phosphor band), 616a).

X16p	AUG 1967	7·25
X17p	FEB 1968	9·00

10s. Booklets with Machin type stamps

XP **4** Explorers Series with GPO Cypher

(Des S. Rose)

1968 (25 Mar–Aug). Bright purple cover as Type XP **4** (Explorers Series). Pages of six stamps: 24×4d., 6×3d., 6×1d. PVA gum (Nos. 724, 729Ev, 731Ev).

XP4	MAY 1968 (Livingstone)	6·00
XP5	AUG 1968 (Livingstone)	6·00

1968 (16 Sept)–**70**. Yellow-green covers as Type XP **4** (Explorers Series). New composition. Pages of six stamps: 12×5d. (with two phosphor bands), 12×4d. (with one centre phosphor band) and pane comprising 4×1d. se-tenant with vert pair of 4d. (each with one centre phosphor band). PVA gum (Nos. 725, 732 and 735).

XP6	SEPT 1968 (Scott)	4·75

Change to 4d. bright vermilion (one centre band) but se-tenant pane comprises 1d. with two phosphor bands and 4d. with one left side phosphor band (Nos. 724 and 733/4).

XP7	FEB 1969 (Mary Kingsley) (6.1.69)	3·50
XP8	MAY 1969 (Mary Kingsley)	4·75
XP9	AUG 1969 (Shackleton)	4·75
XP10	NOV 1969 (Shackleton)	7·25

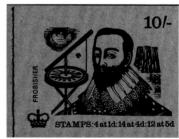

XP **11** Explorers Series with Post Office Corporation Crown Symbol

(Des S. Rose)

As last but cover changed to Type XP **11**.

XP11	FEB 1970 (Frobisher)	7·25
XP12	NOV 1970 (Captain Cook)	7·25

£1 Booklet with Machin type stamps

ZP **1**

1969 (1 Dec). *"Stamps for Cooks". Type ZP* **1** *(150×72 mm) with full colour pictorial cover showing "Baked, Stuffed Haddock". Contains 12 recipes on interleaving pages and on se-tenant labels attached to booklet panes. PVA gum. Stapled.*

ZP1 £1 containing panes of fifteen stamps (5×3): 15×5d. (No. 735), 30×4d. (No. 733) and pane comprising 6×4d. (three each of Nos. 734 and 734Eb) *se-tenant* with 6×1d. (No. 724) and 3×5d. (No. 735) £400

ZP1a As last but booklet is sewn with thread instead of being stapled .... 13·00

<h3 style="text-align:center">II. Decimal Booklets, 1971 onwards.</h3>

A. Stitched Booklets.

The 25p., 30p., 35p., 45p. and 50p. booklets have pictorial covers (except for the 35p. and 45p.) without the design inscription. This was no longer necessary as the designs and background information were given on the inside of the front cover. Each series was numbered.

10p. Booklets

DN **46** British Pillar Box Series

(Des R. Maddox)

1971 (15 Feb–1 June). *British Pillar Box Series. Orange yellow cover as Type DN* **46**. *Pages of four stamps: 2×2p. se-tenant vertically with 2×½p. and 2×1p. se-tenant vertically with 2×1½p. (Nos. X841l and X844l).*

DN46 FEB 1971 (No. 1 1855 type) .... 2·50
DN47 APR 1971 (No. 1 1855 type) (19.3.71) .... 2·00
DN48 JUNE 1971 (No. 2 1856 type) (1.6.71) .... 2·50
  In No. DN47 the pillar box is slightly reduced in size.

1971 (14 July)–**74**. *British Pillar Box Series continued. Orange-yellow cover as Type DN* **46**. *Contents unchanged but panes are se-tenant horizontally (Nos. X841la and X844m).*

DN49 AUG 1971 (No. 2 1856 type) (14.7.71) .... 3·00
DN50 OCT 1971 (No. 3 1857–9 type) (27/8/71) .... 3·00
DN51 DEC 1971 (No. 3 1857–9 type) (6.10.71) .... 4·00
DN52 FEB 1972 (No. 4 1866–79 type) (8.12.71) .... 4·00
DN53 APR 1972 (No. 4 1866–79 type) (24.2.72) .... 2·75
DN54 JUNE 1972 (No. 5 1899 type) (12.4.72) .... 2·50
DN55 AUG 1972 (No. 5 1899 type) (8.6.72) .... 3·00
DN56 OCT 1972 (No. 6 1968 type) (2.8.72) .... 3·00
DN57 DEC 1972 (No. 6 1968 type) (30.10.72) .... 3·00
DN58 FEB 1973 (No. 7 1936 type) (5.1.73) .... 3·00
DN59 APR 1973 (No. 7 1936 type) (2.4.73) .... 5·00
DN60 JUNE 1973 (No. 8 1952 type) (18.4.73) .... 3·00
DN61 AUG 1973 (No. 8 1952 type) (4.7.73) .... 16·00
DN62 OCT 1973 (No. 9 1973 type) (16.8.73) .... 3·50
DN63 DEC 1973 (No. 9 1973 type) (12.11.73) .... 2·50
DN64 FEB 1974 (No. 9 1973 type) (17.12.73) .... 3·25
DN65 APR 1974 (No. 10 1974 type) (22.2.74) .... 2·50
DN66 JUNE 1974 (No. 10 1974 type) (23.4.74) .... 2·25

DN **67** Postal Uniforms Series

(Des C. Abbott)

1974 (23 July)–**76**. *Postal Uniforms Series. Orange-yellow cover as Type DN* **67**. *Contents unchanged.*

DN67 AUG 1974 (No. 1 1793 type) .... 1·80
DN68 OCT 1974 (No. 1 1793 type) (27.8.74) .... 1·80
DN69 DEC 1974 (No. 2 1837 type) (25.10.74) .... 1·80
DN70 FEB 1975 (No. 2 1837 type) (12.12.74) .... 1·80
DN71 APR 1975 (No. 3 1855 type) (26.3.75) .... 1·60
DN72 JUNE 1975 (No. 3 1855 type) (21.5.75) .... 1·75
DN73 AUG 1975 (No. 3 1855 type) (27.6.75) .... 1·75
DN74 OCT 1975 (No. 3 1855 type) (3.10.75) 90
DN75 JAN 1976 (No. 3 1855 type) (16.3.76) 90

25p. Booklets

DH **39** Veteran Transport Series

(Des D. Gentleman)

1971 (15 Feb). *Veteran Transport Series. Dull purple cover as Type DH* **39**. *Pages of six stamps: 5×2½p. with one printed label, 4×2½p. with two printed labels, 5×½p. with one printed label (Nos. X841m and X851l/m).*

DH39 FEB 1971 (No. 1 Knife-board omnibus) .... 3·50

DH **40**

1971 (19 Mar). *Issued to publicise the National Postal Museum Exhibition of 80 Years of British Stamp Booklets. Dull purple cover as Type DH* **40**.

DH40 APR 1971.. 5·00

1971 (11 June)–**73**. *Dull purple cover as Type DH* **39**. *Veteran Transport Series continued.*

DH41 JUNE 1971 (No. 2 B-type omnibus) .... 5·00
DH42 AUG 1971 (No. 2 B-type omnibus) (17.9.71) .... 11·50
DH43 OCT 1971 (No. 3 Showman's Engine) (22.11.71) .... 11·50
DH44 FEB 1972 (No. 4 Mail Van) (23.12.71) .... 7·25
DH45 APR 1972 (No. 4 Mail Van) (13.3.72) .... 8·75
DH46 JUNE 1972 (No. 5 Motor Wagonette) (24.4.72) .... 6·00
DH47 AUG 1972 (No. 5 Motor Wagonette) (14.6.72) .... 11·50
DH48 OCT 1972 (No. 6 Taxi Cab) (17.7.72) .... 9·00
DH49 DEC 1972 (No. 6 Taxi Cab) (19.10.72) .... 11·50
DH50 DEC 1972 "Issues S" (No. 6 Taxi Cab) (6.11.72) . ... 7·25
DH51 FEB 1973 (No. 7 Electric Tramcar) (26.2.73) .... 9·00
  Nos. DH42/51 contain panes showing the perforations omitted between the label and the binding margin.

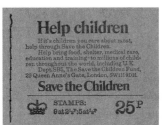

DH **52**

1973 (7 June). *Dull mauve cover as Type DH* **52**.
DH52   JUNE 1973 .... 9·00
   No. DH52 contains panes showing the perforations omitted between the label and the binding margin.

30p. Booklets

DQ **56** British Birds Series

(Des H. Titcombe)

1971 (15 Feb). *British Birds Series. Bright purple cover as Type DQ* **56**. *Pages of six stamps:* 2 panes of 5×3p. with one printed label (No. X855l).
DQ56   FEB 1971 (No. 1 Curlew) .... 4·50

1971 (19 Mar). *Bright purple cover as Type DH* **40**.
DQ57   APR 1971 .... 6·00

1971 (26 May)–73. *Bright purple cover as Type DQ* **56**. *British Birds Series continued.*
DQ58   JUNE 1971 (No. 2 Lapwing) .... 6·00
DQ59   AUG 1971 (No. 2 Lapwing) (23.7.71) .... 6·00
DQ60   OCT 1971 (No. 3 Robin) (1.10.71) .... 6·00
DQ61   DEC 1971 (No. 3 Robin) (10.11.71) .... 7·25
DQ62   FEB 1972 (No. 4 Pied Wagtail) (21.12.71) ...... 6·00
DQ63   APR 1972 (No. 4 Pied Wagtail) (9.2.72) .... 6·00
DQ64   JUNE 1972 (No. 5 Kestrel) (12.4.72) .... 6·00
DQ65   AUG 1972 (No. 5 Kestrel) (8.6.72) .... 6·25
DQ66   OCT 1972 (No. 6 Black Grouse) (31.7.72) .... 6·75
DQ67   DEC 1972 (No. 6 Black Grouse) (30.10.72) ..... 6·75
DQ68   DEC 1972 "Issue S" (No. 6 Black Grouse) (6.12.72) ... 6·75
DQ69   FEB 1973 (No. 7 Skylark) (29.1.73) .... 6·25
DQ70   APR 1973 (No. 7 Skylark) (2.4.73) .... 5·75
DQ71   JUNE 1973 (No. 8 Oyster-catcher) (8.5.73) ..... 6·25
DQ72   AUG 1973 (No. 8 Oyster-catcher) (7.6.73) ...... 9·50
DQ72a   As DQ72 but buff cover (10.8.73)* .... 7·00
   Nos. DQ59/72a contain panes showing the perforations omitted between the label and the binding margin.*No. DQ 72a was printed with a buff cover because of a shortage of the original purple-coloured card.

1974 (30 Jan). *Red cover similar to Type DH* **52**. *Make-up as before but containing panes of* 5×3p. (1 centre band) (No. X856) with blank label.
DQ73   SPRING 1974 .... 5·00

1974 (2 June). *Red cover similar to Type DT* **9**. *Make-up as before.*
DQ74   JUNE 1974 .... 5·00

35p. Booklets

DP **1** British Coins Series

(Des P Gauld)

1973 (12 Dec)–74. *British Coins Series. Blue cover as Type DP* **1**. *Pages of six stamps:* 2 pages of 5×3½p. with one blank label (No. X858Eb).
DP1   AUTUMN 1973 (No. 1 Cuthred's Penny) .... 3·50
DP2   APR 1974 (No. 1 Cuthred's Penny) (10.4.74) ...... 6·50
DP3   JUNE 1974 (No. 2 Silver Groat) (4.7.74) .... 4·00

1974 (23 Oct). *Blue cover as Type DT* **9**. *Make-up as before but with No. X859.*
DP4   SEPT 1974 .... 4·00

45p. Booklets

1974 (9 Oct–26 Nov). *British Coins Series continued. Yellow-brown cover as Type DP* **1**. *Pages of six stamps:* 2 pages of 5×4½p. (No. X 865) with one blank label.
DS1   SEPT 1974 (No. 3 Elizabeth Gold Crown) .... 6·00
DS2   DEC 1974 (No. 3 Elizabeth Gold Crown) (1.11.74) ... 6·00
DS2a   As DS2 but orange-brown cover (26.11.74)* ..... 14·50
   *No. DS2a was printed with an orange-brown cover because of a shortage of the original yellow-brown card.

50p. Booklets

DT **1**

(Des Rosalie Southall)

1971 (15 Feb)–72. *British Flowers Series. Turquoise-green cover as Type DT* **1**. *Pages of six stamps:* 6×3p., 4×3p. se-tenant horizontally with 2×2½p. (side band), 5×2½p. (centre band) with one printed label and 5×½p. with one printed label (Nos. X841m, X851l, X852l and X855×6).
DT1   FEB 1971 (No. 1 Large Bindweed) .... 9·00
DT2   MAY 1971 (No. 2 Primrose) (24.3.71) .... 10·00
DT3   AUG 1971 (No. 3 Honeysuckle) (28.6.71) .... 10·00
DT4   NOV 1971 (No. 4 Hop) (17.9.71) .... 11·00
DT5   FEB 1972 (No. 5 Common Violet) (23.12.71)* ... 11·00
DT6   MAY 1972 (No. 6 Lords-and-Ladies) (13.3.72) ... 11·00
DT7   AUG 1972 (No. 7 Wood Anemone) (31.5.72) .... 11·00
DT8   NOV 1972 (No. 8 Deadly Nightshade) (15.9.72) ... 9·00
   Nos. DT4/8 contain panes showing the perforations omitted between the label and the binding margin.
   *Although generally released on 24 December, this booklet was put on sale at the London E.C.1 Philatelic Counter and also at one other Philatelic Counter on 23 December.

DT **9**

1973 (19 Jan–June). *Turquoise-green cover as Type DT* **9**.
DT9   FEB 1973 .... 9·00
DT10   APR 1973 (26.2.73) .... 12·00
DT11   MAY 1973 (2.4.73) .... 11·50
DT12   AUG 1973 (14.6.73) .... 17·00

1973 (14 Nov)–74. *Moss-green cover similar to Type DT* **9**. *Pages of six stamps:* 2 pages of 5×3½p. with one blank label (No. X858Eb) and 1 page of 5×3p. (centre band) and one blank label (No. X856).
DT13   AUTUMN 1973 .... 8·00
DT14   MAR 1974 (18.2.74) .... 6·00

85p. Booklet

1974 (13 Nov). *Purple cover similar to Type DT* **9**.
DW1   Containing 3 pages of 5×4½p. (No. X865) with one blank label and 1 page of 5×3½p. (No. X859) with one blank label .... 9·00

Sponsored Booklets

DX **1**

(Des J. Wallis)

1972 (24 May). *"The Story of Wedgwood". Full colour pictorial cover, Type DX* **1** *(150×72 mm). Containing information and illustrations on interleaving panes and on se-tenant label attached to booklet panes.*
DX1   £1 containing Nos. X841o/p, X851n and 855n booklet
        panes .... 75·00
   Price quoted for No. DX1 is for examples showing the ½p. 1 side band, No. X842, (in pane No. X841p) with full perforations. Examples of the booklet with this ½p. value showing trimmed perforations are priced at £25.

ILLUSTRATIONS. Sponsored booklet covers from No. DX2 are illustrated at one-third linear size *unless otherwise stated.*

DX **2**

(Des J. Wallis)

1980 (16 Apr). *"The Story of Wedgwood". Multicoloured cover, Type DX* **2** *(163×97 mm) showing painting "Josiah Wedgwood and his Family" by George Stubbs. Booklet contains text and illustrations on the labels attached to panes and on interleaving pages.*
DX2   £3 containing booklet panes Nos. X849n, X849o, X888l
        and X895l .... 8·00
   No. DX2 is inscribed "January 1980".

DX **3**

(Des B. Dedman)

1982 (19 May). *"Story of Stanley Gibbons". Multicoloured cover, Type DX* **3** *(163×97 mm) showing early envelope design on front and stamp album with text on back. Booklet contains text and illustrations on labels attached to panes and on interleaving pages.*
DX3   £4 containing booklet panes Nos. X849p, X899m and
        X907l/m .... 11·00
   No. DX3 is inscribed "February 1982".

DX **4**

(Des B. West)

1983 (14 Sept). *"Story of the Royal Mint". Multicoloured cover, Type DX* **4** *(163×97 mm) showing current coins, die and tools. Booklet contains text and illustrations on labels attached to panes and on interleaving pages.*
DX4   £4 containing booklet panes Nos. X899m×2, X930b and
        X949l .... 11·00

DX **5**

(Des P. Miles)

1984 (4 Sept). *"The Story of our Christian Heritage". Multicoloured cover, Type DX* **5** *(163×97 mm) showing mosaic of Christ from Hinton St. Mary Roman villa. Booklet contains text and illustrations on labels attached to panes and on interleaving pages.*
DX5   £4 containing booklet panes Nos. X886bl, X901m×2 and
        X952l .... 30·00

DX **6**

(Des D. Driver)

1985 (8 Jan). *"Story of The Times" (newspaper). Multicoloured cover, Type DX* **6** *(163×95 mm) showing "Waiting for The Times" (painting by Haydon). Booklet contains text and illustrations on labels attached to panes and on interleaving pages.*
DX6   £5 containing booklet panes Nos. X864l, X900l, X952l and
        X952m .... 20·00

DX **7**

(Des Trickett and Webb Ltd)

1986 (18 Mar). *"The Story of British Rail". Multicoloured cover, Type DX* **7** *(162×95 mm) showing diesel locomotive. Booklet contains text and illustrations on labels attached to panes and on interleaving pages.*
DX7   £5 containing booklet panes Nos. X896l, X897m, X952l
        and X952m .... 30·00

DX **8**

(Des Aitken Blakeley Designers)

1987 (3 Mar). *"The Story of P & O". Multicoloured cover, Type DX* **8** *(162×95 mm) showing the "William Fawcett". Booklet contains text and illustrations on labels attached to panes and on interleaving pages.*

DX8   £5 containing booklet panes Nos. X847m, X900l, X900m
and X955l .... 25·00

DX **9**

(Des The Partners)

1988 (9 Feb). *"The Story of the Financial Times" (newspaper). Multicoloured cover, Type DX* **9** *(162×97 mm). Booklet contains text and illustrations on labels attached to the panes and on interleaving pages.*

DX9   £5 containing booklet panes Nos. X1005l, X1006l, X1009l
and X1009m .... 40·00

DX **10**

(Des Tayburn)

1989 (21 Mar). *"The Scots Connection". Multicoloured cover, Type DX* **10** *(162×97 mm). Booklet contains text and illustrations on labels attached to the panes and on interleaving pages.*

DX10   £5 containing booklet panes Nos. S54l, S55l, S62l and
S62m .... 22·00

DX **11**

(Des D. Driver)

1990 (20 Mar). *"London Life". Multicoloured cover, Type DX* **11** *(162×97 mm). Booklet contains text and illustrations on labels attached to the panes and on interleaving pages.*

DX11   £5 containing booklet panes Nos. X906m, 1469n×2 and
1493a .... 28·00

DX **12**

(Des Trickett and Webb Ltd)

1991 (19 Mar). *"Alias Agatha Christie". Multicoloured cover, Type DX* **12** *(162×97 mm). Booklet contains text and illustrations on labels attached to the panes and on interleaving pages.*

DX12   £6 containing booklet panes Nos. X1008l×2, X1016l and
X1016m .... 20·00

DX **13**

(Des G. Evernden and J. Gibbs)

1992 (25 Feb). *"Cymru–Wales". Multicoloured cover, Type DX* **13** *(162×97 mm). Booklet contains text and illustrations on labels attached to the panes and on interleaving pages.*

DX13   £6 Containing booklet panes Nos. 1591a, W48a, W49a
and W59a .... 20·00

DX **14**

(Des The Partners)

1992 (27 Oct). *Birth Centenary of J. R. R. Tolkien (author). Multicoloured cover, Type DX* **14** *(162×97 mm). Booklet contains text and illustrations on labels attached to the panes and on interleaving pages.*

DX14   £6 containing booklet panes Nos. X1011l, X1012l and
X1017l×2 .... 20·00

DX **15**

(Des The Partners)

1993 (10 Aug). *"The Story of Beatrix Potter". Multicoloured cover, Type DX* **15** *(162×97 mm). Booklet contains text and illustrations on labels attached to the panes and on interleaving pages.*

DX15   £5.64, containing booklet panes Nos. X1012m, 1451al,
1649a and NI48l .... 20·00

Although inscribed "£6.00" No. DX 15 was sold at the face value of its contents, £5.64.

DX **16**

(Des Carroll, Dempsey and Thirkell Ltd)

1994 (26 July). *"Northern Ireland". Multicoloured cover, Type* DX **16** *(162×97 mm). Booklet contains text and illustrations on labels attached to the panes and on interleaving pages.*

DX16 £6.04, containing booklet panes Nos. Y1748l, 1812a and NI70a/b, together with a 35p. postal stationery air card . 25·00

DX **17**

(Des The Partners)

1995 (25 Apr). *Centenary of the National Trust. Multicoloured cover, Type* DX **17** *(162×97 mm). Booklet contains text and illustrations on labels attached to the panes and on interleaving pages.*

DX17 £6 containing booklet panes Nos. Y1749l, Y1750l, 1869a and NI70d .... 25·00

DX **18**

(Des Why Not Associates)

1996 (14 May). *European Football Championship. Multicoloured cover, Type* DX **18** *(162×97 mm). Booklet contains text and illustrations on labels attached to the panes and on interleaving pages.*

DX18 £6.48, containing booklet panes Nos. Y1752l, 1925a, 1926a and 1927a .... 20·00

DX **19**

(Des H. Brown)

1997 (23 Sept). *75th Anniv of the B.B.C. Multicoloured cover, Type* DX **19** *(162×97 mm). Booklet contains text and illustrations on labels attached to the panes and on interleaving pages.*

DX19 £6.15, containing booklet panes Nos. Y1681l, 1940ab, 1668l and NI81al .... 20·00

DX **20**

(Des Dew Gibbons Design Group)

1998 (10 Mar). *The Wildings Definitives. Black and gold cover, Type* DX **20** *(162×96 mm). Booklet contains text and illustrations on labels attached to the panes and on interleaving pages.*

DX20 £7.49, containing booklet panes Nos. 2031b/c and 2032a/b. .... 26·00
Folder containing DX20, DX22, DX24 *and* **MS**2147 cancelled on presentation card... £150

DX **21**

(Des Roundel Design Group)

1998 (13 Oct). *"Breaking Barriers". British Speed Record Holders. Multicoloured cover, Type* DX **21** *(161×96 mm). Booklet contains text and illustrations on labels attached to the panes and on interleaving pages.*

DX21 £6.16, containing booklet panes Nos. 1665l, Y1676al, 2059ac and NI80al .... 35·00

(Des Dew Gibbons Design Group)

1999 (16 Feb). *"Profile on Print". Multicoloured cover as Type* DX **20** *(162×96 mm). Booklet contains text and illustrations on labels attached to the panes and on interleaving pages.*

DX22 £7.54, containing booklet panes Nos. 1667l, 1671n and 2077l/9l .... 40·00

DX **23**

(Des Silk Pearce)

1999 (21 Sept). *"World Changers". Multicoloured cover as Type* DX **23** *(163×96 mm). Booklet contains text and illustrations on labels attached to the panes and on interleaving pages.*

DX23 £6.99, containing booklet panes Nos. Y1667n, 2072ab, 2080a, 2103ba and 2104ab .... 35·00

(Des Dew Gibbons Design Group)

2000 (15 Feb). *"Special by Design". Multicoloured cover as Type* DX **20** *(162×96 mm). Booklet contains text and illustrations on labels attached to the panes and on interleaving pages.*

DX24 £7.50, containing booklet panes Nos. Y1678l, 2124dl, 2133l and NI88al .... 45·00

DX **25**

(Des J. Gibbs)

2000 (4 Aug). *Queen Elizabeth the Queen Mother's 100th Birthday. Brownish grey and grey cover as Type* DX **25** *(162×96 mm). Booklet contains text and illustrations on labels attached to the panes and on interleaving pages.*

DX25 £7.03, containing booklet panes Nos. 2124bm, 2160a, **MS**2161a and S94a .... 31·00

DX **26**

(Des Roundel Design Group)

2000 (18 Sept). *A Treasury of Trees. Slate-green and bright green cover as Type DX* **26** *(162×95 mm). Booklet contains text and illustrations on panes and interleaving pages.*
DX26   £7 containing booklet panes Nos. 2155a, 2156a, 2158a,
2159a and W83al .... 40·00

DX **27**

(Des D. Davis)

2001 (22 Oct). *"Unseen and Unheard". Centenary of Royal Navy Submarine Service. Black, greenish yellow, new blue and red cover as Type DX* **27** *(162×97 mm). Booklet contains text and illustrations on labels attached to the panes and on interleaving pages.*
DX27   £6.76, containing booklet panes Nos. 2202ab, 2203ab,
MS2206a and S95a .... 40·00

DX **28**

(Des GBH)

2002 (6 Feb). *"A Gracious Accession". Golden Jubilee of Queen Elizabeth II. Multicoloured cover as Type DX* **28** *(161×96 mm). Booklet contains text and illustrations on labels attached to the panes and interleaving pages.*
DX28   £7.29, containing booklet panes Nos. 1664n, 2253b/4b
and 2258b .... 45·00

DX **29**

(Des CDT Design)

2002 (24 Sept). *"Across the Universe". Multicoloured cover as Type DX* **29** *(164×95 mm). Booklet contains text and illustrations on labels attached to the panes and interleaving pages. Stitched.*
DX29   £6.83, containing booklet panes Nos. 1668m, 2126ac,
MS2315a and EN1b .... 34·00

DX **30**

(Des CDT Design)

2003 (25 Feb). *"Microcosmos". 50th Anniv of Discovery of DNA. Multicoloured cover as Type DX* **30** *(164×95 mm). Booklet contains text and illustrations on labels attached to the panes and interleaving pages. Stitched.*
DX30   £6.99, containing booklet panes Nos. 1668m, 2343a,
2345a and NI89a .... 30·00

DX **31**

(Des GBH)

2003 (2 June). *"A Perfect Coronation". 50th Anniv of Coronation. Multicoloured cover as Type DX* **31** *(161×96 mm). Booklet contains text and illustrations on labels attached to the panes and on interleaving pages.*
DX31   £7.46, containing booklet panes Nos. 1664o, 2368b/9b
and 2378a .... 70·00

DX **32**

(Des Kate Stephens)

2004 (16 Mar). *"Letters by Night A Tribute to the Travelling Post Office". Multicoloured cover as Type DX* **32** *(164×95 mm). Booklet contains text and illustrations on labels attached to the panes and interleaving pages. Stitched.*
DX32   £7.44, containing booklet panes Nos. 1668o, 2392a,
2418a and S109a .... 26·00

DX **33**

(Des John and Orna Designs)

2004 (25 May). *"The Glory of the Garden". Bicentenary of the Royal Horticultural Society. Multicoloured cover as Type* DX **33** *(162×96 mm). Booklet contains text and illustrations on labels attached to the panes and interleaving pages. Stitched.*

DX33 £7.23, containing booklet panes Nos. 1668p, 2456a, 2457a and 2463a .... 40·00

DX **34**

(Des Morgan Radcliffe)

2005 (24 Feb). *The Brontë Sisters. 150th Death Anniv of Charlotte Brontë. Multicoloured cover as Type* DX **34** *(162×96 mm). Booklet contains text and illustrations on panes and interleaving pages. Stitched.*

DX34 £7.43, containing booklet panes Nos. 1664p, EN6a, 2518a and 2520a .... 28·00

DX **35** White Ensign

(Des Webb & Webb)

2005 (18 Oct). *Bicentenary of the Battle of Trafalgar. Black, scarlet and ultramarine cover as Type* DX **35** *(162×96 mm). Booklet contains text and illustrations on labels attached to the panes and interleaving pages. Stitched.*

DX35 £7.26 containing booklet panes Nos. 1668q, 2574b/5b and 2581a .... 24·00

DX **36** Plaque showing Clifton Suspension Bridge

(Des Hat-trick Design)

2006 (23 Feb). *Birth Bicentenary of Isambard Kingdom Brunel. Grey and grey-black cover as Type* DX **36** *(162×96 mm). Booklet contains text and illustrations on panes and interleaving pages. Stitched.*

DX36 £7.40 containing booklet panes Nos. 1668r, 2607a/8a and 2610a .... 26·00

DX **37**

(Des Atelier Works)

2006 (21 Sept). *150th Anniv of the Victoria Cross. Blackish-brown and gold cover as Type* DX **37** *(162×96 mm). Booklet contains text and illustrations on panes and interleaving pages. Stitched.*

DX37 £7.44 containing booklet panes Nos. 2651a, 2659b, 2660b and 2666a .... 35·00

DX **38**

(Des R. Warren-Fisher)

2007 (1 Mar). *World of Invention. Black, olive-grey and grey cover as Type* DX **38** *(162×95 mm). Booklet contains text and illustrations on panes and interleaving pages. Stitched.*

DX38 £7.49 containing booklet panes Nos. S109b, Y1670a and 2721a/b .... 24·00

DX **39**

(Des R. Warren-Fisher)

2007 (5 June). *"The Machin The Making of a Masterpiece". Multicoloured cover as Type* DX **39** *(165×96 mm). Booklet contains text and illustrations on panes and interleaving pages. Stitched.*

DX39 £7.66 containing booklet panes Nos. Y1668b, Y1725ba, 2650a and 2741a .... 24·00

DX **40** Soldiers of 1854

(Des Atelier Works)

2007 (20 Sept). *British Army Uniforms. Multicoloured cover as Type* DX **40** *(164×96 mm). Booklet contains text and illustrations on panes and interleaving pages. Stitched.*
DX40 £7.66 containing booklet panes Nos. Y1667o, 2774b, 2777b and EN18a.. 26·00

DX **41** Typewriter and Casino Royale

(Des GBH)

2008 (8 Jan). *Ian Fleming's James Bond. Multicoloured cover as Type* DX **41** *(164×96 mm). Booklet contains text and illustrations on panes and interleaving pages. Stitched.*
DX41 £7.40 containing booklet panes Nos. 1672a, 2797a/8a and 2805a.. 22·00

DX **42** RAF Badge

(Des Silk Pearce)

2008 (18 Sept). *"Pilot to Plane". RAF Uniforms. Black on light blue cover as Type* DX **42** *(162×96 mm). Booklet contains text and illustrations on panes and interleaving pages. Stitched.*
DX42 £7.15 containing booklet panes Nos. 1670l, 2862b, 2865b and 2868a.. 20·00

DX **43** Symbols of Northern Ireland, Scotland and Wales

(Des Sedley Place)

2008 (29 Sept). *50th Anniv of the Country Definitives. Multicoloured cover as Type* DX **43** *(162×96 mm). Booklet contains text and illustrations on panes and interleaving pages. Stitched.*
DX43 £9.72 containing booklet panes Nos. NI112a/b, S134a and W122a.. 28·00

DX **44** Graphic Drawings of Spitfire, Anglepoise Lamp and Routemaster Bus

(Des HGV)

2009 (13 Jan). *British Design Classics. Multicoloured cover as Type* DX **44** *(162×96 mm). Booklet contains text and illustrations on panes and interleaving pages. Stitched.*
DX44 £7.68 containing booklet panes Nos. Y1749ma, 2887b, 2888a and 2891a.. 38·00

DX **45** Charles Darwin

(Des Howard Brown)

2009 (12 Feb). *Birth Bicentenary of Charles Darwin. Multicoloured cover as Type* DX **45** *(162×96 mm). Booklet contains text and illustrations on panes and interleaving pages. Stitched.*
DX45 £7.75 containing booklet panes Nos. Y1743sa, **MS**2904a, 2905a and 2906a .... 40·00

DX **46** Proof Sheet of Penny Black Stamps

(Des Silk Pearce)

2009 (18 Aug). *'Treasures of the Archive'. Clear cover showing illustrated pane as Type* DX **46** *(162×96 mm). Booklet contains text and illustrations on panes and interleaving pages. Stitched.*
DX46 £8.18 containing booklet panes Nos. Y1749na, 2950a, 2955a and 2957a .... 18·00

DX **47** Officers, Marines and Seamen on Deck

(Des Webb and Webb Design Ltd)

2009 (17 Sept). *Royal Navy Uniforms. Multicoloured cover as Type* DX **47** *(163×96 mm). Booklet contains text and illustrations on panes and interleaving pages. Stitched.*
DX47 £7.93 containing booklet panes Nos. Y1743na, 2964b, 2967b and 2970a.. 20·00

DX **48** Vinyl Disc

(Des True North)

2010 (7 Jan). *Classic Album Covers. Black and pale blue cover as Type* DX **48** (162×96 mm). *Booklet contains text and illustrations on panes and interleaving pages. Stitched.*
DX48 £8.06 containing booklet panes Nos. Y1743ta, Y1751ma,
3009a and 3015a .... 30·00

DX **49** Diagram and Signatures

(Des Russell Warren-Fisher)

2010 (25 Feb). 350th *Anniv of the Royal Society. Multicoloured cover as Type* DX **49** (162×96 mm). *Booklet contains text and illustrations on panes and interleaving pages. Stitched.*
DX49 £7.72 containing booklet panes Nos. Y1751na, 3026b,
3027a and 3029a .... 20·00

DX **50**

(Des Silk Pearce)

2010 (8 May). Centenary of Accession of King George V. Deep carmine and cream cover, 162×97 mm, as Type DX**50**. Booklet contains text and illustrations on panes and interleaving pages. Stitched.
DX50 £11.15 containing booklet panes Nos. U2917a,
3066a/7a and 3070a... 25·00

DX **51**

(Des Why Not Associates)

2010 (13 May). 'Britain Alone'. Grey, black and stone cover, 163×96 mm, as Type DX **51**. Booklet contains text and illustrations on panes and interleaving pages. Stitched.
DX51 £9.76 containing booklet panes Nos. Y1743sb, 3074a,
3076a and 3082a .... 22·00

DX **52** Wildlife

(Des Russell Warren-Fisher)

2011 (22 Mar). 50th Anniv of the WWF. Multicoloured cover, 162×96 mm, as Type DX **52**. Booklet contains text and illustrations on panes and interleaving pages. Stitched.
DX52 £9.05 containing booklet panes Nos. Y1743sc, 3162b,
3164b and **MS**3172a... 21·00

B. Folded Booklets.

NOTE: All panes are attached to the covers by the selvedge. Inscribed dates are those shown with the printer's imprint.

Illustrations for 10p., 50p., £1 and £2 booklets are 3/4 size; others are 2/3 size.

10p. Booklets

FA **1**

1976 (10 Mar)–**77.** *Cover as Type* FA **1** *printed in dull rose on very pale lavender. Containing booklet pane No.* X841r.
FA1   NOV 1975 .... 1·10
FA2   MAR 1976 (9.6.76)... 1·20
FA3   JUNE 1977 (13.6.77) 80

FA **4**

(Des N. Battershill)

1978 (8 Feb)–**79.** *Farm Buildings Series. Bistre-brown and turquoise-blue covers as Type* FA **4,** *containing booklet pane No.* X843m.
FA4   Design No. 1, Oast Houses 70
FA5   Design No. 2, Buildings in Ulster (3.5.78) 80
FA6   Design No. 3, Buildings in Yorkshire (9.8.78) 70
FA7   Design No. 4, Buildings in Wales (25.10.78) 70
FA8   Design No. 5, Buildings in Scotland (10.1.79) 70
FA9   Design No. 6, Buildings in Sussex (4.4.79) 70
    Nos. FA4/5 are inscribed "January 1978", FA6 "July 1978", FA7 "October 1978", FA8 "December 1978" and FA9 "March 1979".

FA **10**

(Des Hamper and Purssell)

1979 (17 Oct)–**80.** *London 1980 International Stamp Exhibition. Red and blue cover as Type ΓA **10** showing Post Office exhibition stand and containing No. X045l.*
FA10 Inscr "August 1979"... 60
FA11 Inscr "January 1980" (12.1.80) 70

50p. Booklets

All booklets were sold at the cover price of 50p. although some contain stamps to a greater value.

FB **1**

1977 (26 Jan). *Cover as Type FB **1** printed in maroon and paleblue.*
FB1A Containing booklet pane X841s.............................. 3·00
FB1B Containing booklet pane X841sa........................... 3·00

1977 (13 June). *Cover as Type FB **1**. Printed in chestnut and stone.*
FB2A Containing booklet pane X844n .... 5·00
FB2B Containing booklet pane X844na.......................... 3·00

FB **3**

(Des J. Ireland)

1978 (8 Feb)–**79.** *Commercial Vehicles Series. Olive-yellow and grey covers as Type FB **3**. A. Containing booklet pane No. X844n. B. Containing booklet pane No. X844na.*

		A	B
FB3	Design No. 1, Clement Talbot van	5·00	3·25
FB4	Design No. 2, Austin taxi (3.5.78)	5·00	3·00
FB5	Design No. 3, Morris Royal Mail van (9.8.78)	5·00	3·00
FB6	Design No. 4, Guy Electric dustcart (25.10.78)	7·50	3·25
FB7	Design No. 5, Albion van (10.1.79)	8·00	7·50
FB8	Design No. 6, Leyland fire engine (4.4.79)	5·50	3·50

Nos. FB3/4 are inscribed "January 1978", FB5 "July 1978", FB6 "October 1978", FB7 "December 1978" and FB8 "March 1979".

1979 (28 Aug). *Contents changed. A. Containing booklet pane No. X849l. B. Containing booklet pane No. X849la.*

		A	B
FB9	Design No. 6, Leyland fire engine	3·00	3·00

FB **10**

(Des B. Smith)

1979 (3 Oct)–**81.** *Veteran Cars Series. Orange-red and reddish lilac covers as Type FB **10**. A. Containing booklet pane No. X849l. B. Containing booklet pane No. X849la.*

		A	B
FB10	Design No. 1, 1907 Rolls-Royce Silver Ghost	3·00	3·00

No. FB10 is inscribed "August 1979".

Contents changed. A. Containing booklet pane No. X849m. B. Containing booklet pane No. X849ma.

		A	B
FB11	Design No. 2, 1908 Grand Prix Austin (4.2.80)	2·75	2·75
FB12	Design No. 3, 1903–5 Vauxhall (25.6.80)	2·75	2·75

				A	B
FB13	Design No. 4, 1897–1900 Daimler (24.9.80)			2·50	2·50

No. FB11 is inscribed "January 1980", No. FB 12 "May 1980" and No. FB 13 "July 1980".

Contents changed. A. Containing No. X841t. B. Containing No. X841ta.

		A	B
FB14	Design No. 5, 1896 Lanchester (26.1.81)	2·50	3·00
FB15	Design No. 6, 1913 Bull-nose Morris (18.3.81)	3·00	3·00

Nos. FB14/15 are inscribed "January 1981".

FB **16**

(Des R. Downer)

1981 (6 May)–**82.** *Follies Series. Brown and orange-brown covers as Type FB **16**. A. Containing No. X841t. B. Containing No. X841ta.*

		A	B
FB16	Design No. 1, Mugdock Castle, Stirlingshire	2·50	2·50

No. FB16 is inscribed "January 1981".

Contents changed. A. Containing No. X854l. B. Containing No. X854la.

		A	B
FB17	Design No. 1, Mugdock Castle, Stirlingshire (26.8.81)	8·00	14·00
FB18	Design No. 2, Mow Cop Castle, Cheshire–Staffs border (30.9.81)	8·00	10·00

Nos. FB17/18 are inscribed "January 1981".

Contents changed. A. Containing No. X841u. B. Containing No. X841ua.

		A	B
FB19	Design No. 3, Paxton's Tower, Llanarthney, Dyfed (1.2.82)	3·00	3·00
FB20	Design No. 4, Temple of the Winds, Mount Stewart, Northern Ireland (6.5.82)	3·00	3·00
FB21	Design No. 5, Temple of the Sun, Stourhead, Wilts (11.8.82)	3·00	3·00
FB22	Design No. 6, Water Garden, Cliveden, Bucks (6.10.82)	3·00	3·00

Nos. FB19/22 are inscribed "February 1982".

FB **23**

(Des H. Titcombe)

1983 (16 Feb–26 Oct). *Rare Farm Animals Series. Bright green and black covers as Type FB **23**. A. Containing booklet pane No. X841u. B. Containing booklet pane No. X841ua.*

		A	B
FB23	Design No. 1, Bagot Goat	3·50	3·50

Contents changed. Containing No. X845n.
FB24	Design No. 2, Gloucester Old Spot Pig (5.4.83)	7·00	
	b. Corrected rate..	20·00	
FB25	Design No. 3, Toulouse Goose (27.7.83)	7·50	
FB26	Design No. 4, Orkney Sheep (26.10.83)	7·50	

No. FB23 is inscribed "February 1982" and Nos. FB24/6 "April 1983". The corrected rate reads, "36p. for 200g" instead of "37p. for 200g".

FB **27**

(Des P. Morter)

1984 (3 Sept)–**85.** *Orchids Series. Yellow-green and lilac covers as Type* FB **27.** *Containing booklet pane No. X845p.*
FB27 Design No. 1, *Dendrobium nobile* and *Miltonia* hybrid .... 4·00
FB28 Design No. 2, *Cypripedium calceolus* and *Ophrys apifera* (15.1.85) .... 4·00
FB29 Design No. 3, *Bifrenaria* and Vanda tricolor (23.4.85) .... 4·00
FB30 Design No. 4, *Cymbidium* and *Arpophyllum* (23.7.85) .... 4·00
   Nos. FB27/30 are inscribed "September 1984".

Type FB **31**

(Des M. Thierens Design)

1985 (4 Nov). *Cover as Type FB* **31** *printed in black and bright scarlet. Containing booklet pane No. X909l.*
FB31 Pillar box design .... 5·00
   No. FB 31 is inscribed "November 1985".

FB **32**

(Des P. Morter)

1986 (20 May–12 Aug). *Pond Life Series. Dull blue and emerald covers as Type FB* **32.** *Containing booklet pane No. X909l.*
FB32 Design No. 1, Emperor Dragonfly, Fourspotted Libellula and Yellow Flag .... 3·00
FB33 Design No. 2. Common Frog, Fennel-leaved Pondweed and Long-stalked Pondweed (29.7.86) .... 4·00
   a. Containing booklet pane No. X909Ela(12.8.86) .... 3·75
   Nos. FB32/33a are inscribed "November 1985".

FB **34**

(Des N. Battershill)

1986 (29 July). *Roman Britain Series. Brown-ochre and Indian red cover as Type FB* **34.** *Containing booklet pane No. X845q.*
FB34 Design No. 1, Hadrian's Wall .... 12·00
   No. FB34 is inscribed "November 1985".

1986 (20 Oct)–**87.** *Pond Life Series continued. Dull blue and emerald covers as Type FB* **32.** *Containing booklet pane No. X845s.*
FB35 Design No. 3, Moorhen and Little Grebe .... 6·00
FB36 Design No. 4, Giant Pond and Great Ramshorn Snails (27.1.87) .... 6·00
   No. FB36 is inscribed "October 1986".

1986 (20 Oct)–**87.** *Roman Britain Series continued. Brown ochre and Indian red covers as Type FB* **34.** *Containing booklet pane No. X847l.*
FB37 Design No. 2, Roman Theatre of Verulamium, St. Albans 4·00
FB38 Design No. 3, Portchester Castle, Hampshire (27.1.87) ..... 4·00
   No. FB38 is inscribed "October 1986".

FB **39**

(Des Patricia Howes)

1987 (14 Apr)–**88.** *Bicentenary of Marylebone Cricket Club Series. Brown and dull ultramarine covers as Type FB* **39.** *Containing booklet pane No. X847l.*
FB39 Design No. 1, Father Time weather vane .... 3·00
FB40 Design No. 2, Ashes urn and embroidered velvet bag (14.7.87) .... 3·00
FB41 Design No. 3, Lord's Pavilion and wrought iron decoration on roof (29.9.87) .... 3·00
FB42 Design No. 4, England team badge and new stand at Lord's (26.1.88) .... 3·00
   Nos. FB39/42 are inscribed "October 1986".

FB **43**

(Des G. Evernden)

1987 (14 Apr)–**88.** *Botanical Gardens Series. Covers as Type FB* **43.** *Containing booklet panes No. X845s (FB43/4) or X845sa (FB45/6).*
FB43 Design No. 1 (cover in ultramarine and rosered), Rhododendron "Elizabeth", Bodnant .... 6·00
FB44 Design No. 2 (cover in deep ultramarine and cobalt), Gentiana sino-ornata, Edinburgh (14.7.87) .... 6·00
FB45 Design No. 3 (cover in dull ultramarine and orange-yellow), Lilium auratum and "Mount Stuart" (incorrect inscr) .... 4·00
   a. With corrected spelling "Mount Stewart" (30.10.87) ..... 4·00
FB46 Design No. 4 (cover in dull ultramarine and yellow-orange), Strelitzia reginae, Kew (26.1.88).............................. 4·00
   Nos. FB43/6 are inscribed "October 1986".
   The panes from Nos. FB45/6 have imperforate vertical sides.

FB **47**

1988 (12 Apr–5 July). *London Zoo. Children's Drawings Series. Covers as Type FB* **47.**
FB47 Pigs design (cover in black and rose) containing booklet pane No. X847l .... 4·00
FB48 Birds design (cover in black and yellow) containing booklet pane No. X845sa .... 4·00
FB49 Elephants design (cover in black and grey) containing booklet pane No. X847l (5.7.88) .... 4·00
   Nos. FB47/9 are inscribed "October 1986". The pane from No. FB48 has imperforate vertical sides.

FB **50**

(Des P. Morter)

1988 (5 July). *Marine Life Series. Blue and orange-brown cover as Type FB 50. Containing booklet pane No. X845sa.*

FB50 Design No. 1, Parasitic Anemone on Common Whelk
Shell and Umbrella Jellyfish .... 4·00

No. FB50 is inscribed "October 1986" and has the vertical sides of the pane imperforate.

FB **51**

(Des Lynda Gray)

1988 (5 Sept)–**89.** *Gilbert and Sullivan Operas Series. Black and red covers as Type FB* **51**. *Containing booklet pane No. X904l.*

FB51	Design No. 1, *The Yeomen of the Guard*	9·00
FB52	Design No. 2, *The Pirates of Penzance* (24.1.89)	9·00
FB53	Design No. 3, *The Mikado* (25.4.89)	9·00

1989 (18 July). *Marine Life Series continued. Blue and orange brown cover as Type FB No. 50. Containing booklet pane No. X904l.*

FB54 Design No. 2, Common Hermit Crab, Bladder Wrack and
Laver Spire Shell .... 9·00

For Design No. 3, see £1 Booklet No. FH17.

FB **55**

(Des P. Hutton)

1989 (2 Oct)–**90.** *Aircraft Series. Turquoise-green and light brown covers as Type FB* **55.** *Containing booklet pane No. X906l.*

FB55 Design No. 1, HP42, Armstrong Whitworth Atalanta and
de Havilland Dragon Rapide .... 14·00

No. FB55 was incorrectly inscribed "Atlanta".

As before, but containing Penny Black Anniversary booklet pane No. 1468l.

FB56 Design No. 2, Vickers Viscount 806 and de Havilland
Comet 4 (30.1.90) .... 12·00

1990 (4 Sept)–**91.** *Aircraft Series continued. Turquoise-green and light brown covers as Type FB* **55.** *Containing booklet pane No. X911l.*

FB57	Design No. 3, BAC 1-11 and VC10	8·00
FB58	Design No. 4, BAe ATP, BAe 146 and Aérospatiale–BAC Concorde (25.6.91)	8·00

FB **59**

(Des A. Drummond)

1991 (10 Sept)–**92.** *Archaeology Series. Covers as Type FB* **59.** *Containing booklet pane No. X925m.*

FB59	Design No. 1 (cover in bright blue and lakebrown), Sir Arthur Evans at Knossos, Crete	3·00
	a. Corrected rate (10.91)	3·50
FB60	Design No. 2 (cover in bright blue and yellow), Howard Carter in the Tomb of Tutankhamun (21.1.92)	3·00
FB61	Design No. 3 (cover in bright blue and yellow), Sir Austen Layard at Assyrian site (28.4.92)	2·40
FB62	Design No. 4 (cover in new blue and yellow), Sir Flinders Petrie surveying the Pyramids and temples of Giza (28.7.92)	3·00

On the inside front cover of No. FB59 the inland letter rates are shown as 1st class 24, 35, 43, 51p. and 2nd class 18, 28, 33, 39p. These were corrected on No. FB59a to read: 1st class 24, 36, 45, 54p. and 2nd class 18, 28, 34, 41p.

FB **63**

(Des J. Matthews)

1992 (22 Sept). *1000th Anniv of Appointment of Sheriffs. Dull blue and scarlet cover as Type FB* **63**. *Containing booklet pane No. X925m.*

FB63 Design showing Crest, with Helm and Mantling, and
Badge of The Shrievalty Association .... 2·75

FB **64**

(Des M. Newton)

1993 (9 Feb–6 July). *Postal History Series. Covers as Type FB* **64**. *Containing booklet pane No. X925m.*

FB64	Design No. 1 (cover in grey-green and greyblack), Airmail postmarks	2·50
FB65	Design No. 2 (cover in dull orange and black), Ship mail postmarks (6.4.93)	2·50
FB66	Design No. 3 (cover in blue and grey-black), Registered mail postmarks (6.7.93)	2·50

1993 (1 Nov). *Postal History Series continued. Rose-red and grey-black cover as Type FB* **64** *containing booklet pane No. Y1683l.*

FB67 Design No. 4, "Paid" postmarks .... 2·50

FB **68**

(Des A. Davidson)

1994 (25 Jan–6 Sept). *Coaching Inns Series. Covers as Type FB* **68**. *Containing booklet pane No. Y1683l.*

FB68	Design No. 1 (cover in myrtle-green and pale myrtle-green), "Swan with Two Necks"	2·50
FB69	Design No. 2 (cover in sepia and buff), "Bull and Mouth" (26.4.94)	2·50
FB70	Design No. 3 (cover in reddish brown and cinnamon), "Golden Cross" (6.6.94)	2·50
FB71	Design No. 4 (cover in black and slate-blue), "Pheasant Inn", Wiltshire (6.9.94)	2·50

FB **72**

(Des D. Davis)

1995 (7 Feb–4 Apr). *Sea Charts Series. Rosine and black covers as Type* FB **72**, *containing booklet pane No.* Y1683l.

FB72	Design No. 1, John o' Groats, 1800	2·50
FB73	Design No. 2, Land's End, 1808 (4.4.95)	2·50

1995 (6 June–4 Sept). *Sea Charts Series continued. Rosine and black covers as Type* FB **72**, *containing booklet pane No.* Y1684l.

FB74	Design No. 3, St. David's Head, 1812	3·50
FB75	Design No. 4, Giant's Causeway, 1828 (4.9.95)	3·50

65p. Booklet

1976 (14 July). *Cover as Type* FB **1**, *but larger* (90×49 mm). *Printed in turquoise-blue and pale buff.* A. *Selvedge at left.* B. *Selvedge at right.*

		A	B
FC1	Containing ten 6½p. (No. X872)	18·00	10·00

No. FC1 is inscribed "March 1976".

70p. Booklets

1977 (13 June). *Cover as Type* FB **1**, *but larger* (90×49 mm). *Printed in purple-brown and dull rose.* A. *Selvedge at left.* B. *Selvedge at right.*

		A	B
FD1	Containing ten 7p. (No. X875)	8·00	8·00

FD **2**

(Des E. Stemp)

1978 (8 Feb)–**79**. *Country Crafts Series. Grey-green and red brown covers as Type* FD **2** (90×49 mm). *Containing ten 7p.* (No. X875). A. *Selvedge at left.* B. *Selvedge at right.*

		A	B
FD2	Design No. 1, Horse-shoeing	60·00	5·00
FD3	Design No. 2, Thatching (3.5.78)	£250	5·00
FD4	Design No. 3, Dry-stone-walling (9.8.78)	£250	5·00
FD5	Design No. 4, Wheel-making (25.10.78)	10·00	8·00
FD6	Design No. 5, Wattle fence-making (10.1.79)	22·00	8·00

Nos. FD2/3 are inscribed "January 1978", FD4 "July 1978", FD5 "October 1978" and FD6 "December 1978".

FD **7**

(Des F. Wegner)

1979 (5 Feb). *Official opening of Derby Mechanised Letter Office. Pale yellow-green and lilac cover as Type* FD **7** (90×49 mm). *Containing ten 7p.* (No. X875). A. *Selvedge at left.* B.*Selvedge at right.*

		A	B
FD7	Kedleston Hall	9·00	9·00

No. FD7 is inscribed "December 1978".
On sale only in the Derby Head Post Office area to promote postcode publicity and also at the Philatelic Bureau and philatelic sales counters.

1979 (4 Apr). *Country Crafts Series continued. Grey-green and red-brown covers as Type* FD **2** (90×49 mm). A. *Selvedge at left.* B. *Selvedge at right.*

		A	B
FD8	Design No. 6, Basket-making	10·00	5·00

No. FD8 is inscribed "March 1979".

80p. Booklet

FE **1**

(Des P. Hutton)

1979 (3 Oct). *Military Aircraft Series. Blue and grey cover as Type* FE **1** (90×49 mm). *Containing ten 8p.* (No. X879) *attached by the selvedge.* A. *Selvedge at left.* B. *Selvedge at right.*

		A	B
FE1	Design No. 1, BE2B, 1914, & Vickers Gun Bus, 1915	4·00	4·00

No. FE1 is inscribed "August 1979".

85p. Booklet

1976 (14 July). *Cover as Type* FB **1** *but larger* (90×49 mm). *Printed in light yellow-olive and brownish grey.* A. *Selvedge at left.* B. *Selvedge at right.*

		A	B
FF1	Containing ten 8½p. (No. X881)	10·00	14·00

No. FF1 is inscribed "March 1976".

90p. Booklets

1977 (13 June). *Cover as Type* FB **1**, *but larger* (90×49 mm). *Printed in deep grey-blue and cobalt.* A. *Selvedge at left.* B. *Selvedge at right.*

		A	B
FG1	Containing ten 9p. (No. X883)	6·00	10·00

FG **2**

(Des R. Maddox)

1978 (8 Feb)—**79**. *British Canals Series. Yellow-olive and new blue covers as Type* FG **2** (90×49 mm). *Containing ten 9p.* (No. X883). A. *Selvedge at left.* B. *Selvedge at right.*

		A	B
FG2	Design No. 1, Grand Union	30·00	8·00
FG3	Design No. 2, Llangollen (3.5.78)	6·00	£550
FG4	Design No. 3, Kennet & Avon (9.8.78)	18·00	14·00
FG5	Design No. 4, Caledonian (25.10.78)	8·00	8·00
FG6	Design No. 5, Regents (10.1.79)	20·00	12·00

Nos. FG2/3 are inscribed "January 1978", FG4 "July 1978", FG5 "October 1978" and FG6 "December 1978".

(Des F. Wegner)

1979 (5 Feb). *Official Opening of Derby Mechanised Letter Office. Violet-blue and rose cover as Type* FD **7** (90×49 mm). *Containing ten 9p.* (No. X883). A. *Selvedge at left.* B. *Selvedge at right.*

		A	B
FG7	Tramway Museum, Crich	12·00	12·00

No. FG7 is inscribed "December 1978".
On sale only in the Derby Head Post Office area to promote postcode publicity and also at the Philatelic Bureau and philatelic sales counters.

1979 (4 Apr). *British Canals Series continued. Yellow-olive and new blue cover as Type* FG **2**. A. *Selvedge at left.* B. *Selvedge at right.*

		A	B
FG8	Design No. 6, Leeds & Liverpool	6·00	6·00

No. FG8 is inscribed "March 1979".

£1 Booklets

All booklets were sold at the cover price of £1 although some contain stamps to a greater value.

FH **1**

(Des N. Battershill)

1979 (3 Oct). *Industrial Archaeology Series. Red and green cover as Type* FH **1** (90×49 mm). *Containing ten 10p. (No. X887). A. Selvedge at left. B. Selvedge at right.*

	A	B
FH1 Design No. 1, Ironbridge, Telford, Salop	4·50	4·50

No. FH1 is inscribed "August 1979".

1980 (4 Feb—24 Sept). *Military Aircraft Series continued. Blue and grey covers as Type* FE **1** (90×49 mm). *Containing ten 10p. (No. X888). A. Selvedge at left. B. Selvedge at right.*

	A	B
FH2 Design No. 2, Sopwith Camel & Vickers Vimy	4·50	4·50
FH3 Design No. 3, Hawker Hart* & Handley Page Heyford (25.6.80)	6·00	6·00
FH4 Design No. 4, Hurricane & Wellington (24.9.80)	4·50	4·50

No FH2 is inscribed "January 1980", No. FH3 "May 1980" and No. FH4 "July 1980".

*On the booklet cover the aircraft is wrongly identified as a Hawker Fury.

FH **5**

(Des M. Newton and S. Paine)

1986 (29 July)–**87**. *Musical Instruments Series. Scarlet and black covers as Type* FH **5**. *Containing six 17p. (X952).*

FH5 Design No. 1, Violin	5·00

No. FH5 is inscribed "November 1985".
Contents changed. Containing No. X901n.

FH6 Design No. 2, French horn (20.10.86)	5·00
FH7 Design No. 3, Bass clarinet (27.1.87)	5·00

No. FH7 is inscribed "October 1986".

FH **8**

(Des A. Davidson)

1987 (14 Apr)–**88**. *Sherlock Holmes Series. Bright scarlet and grey-black covers as Type* FH **8**. *Containing booklet pane No. X901n (FH8/9) or* X901na (FH10/11).

FH8 Design No. 1, *A Study in Scarlet*	5·50
FH9 Design No. 2, *The Hound of the Baskervilles* (14.7.87)	5·50
FH10 Design No. 3, *The Adventure of the Speckled Band* (29.9.87)	5·50
FH11 Design No. 4, *The Final Problem* (26.1.88)	5·50

Nos. FH8/11 are inscribed "October 1986".
The panes from Nos. FH10/11 have imperforate vertical sides.

1988 (12 Apr). *London Zoo. Children's Drawings Series. Cover as Type* FB **47** *in black and brown. Containing booklet pane No. X901na.*

FH12 Bears design	5·50

No. FH12 is inscribed "October 1986" and has the vertical sides of the pane imperforate.

FH **13**

(Des Liz Moyes)

1988 (5 July)–**89**. *Charles Dickens Series. Orange-red and maroon covers as Type* FH **13**.

FH13 Designs No. 1, *Oliver Twist*, containing booklet pane No. X901na	6·50
FH14 Design No. 2, *Nicholas Nickleby*, containing booklet pane No. X904m (5.9.88)	6·50
FH15 Design No. 3, *David Copperfield*, containing booklet pane No. X904m (24.1.89)	6·50
FH16 Design No. 4, *Great Expectations*, containing booklet pane No. X1051l (25.4.89)	14·00

No. FH13 is inscribed "October 1986" and No. FH16 "September 1988", Nos. FH13/16 have the vertical sides of the pane imperforate.

1989 (18 July). *Marine Life Series continued. Cover as Type* FB **50** *in turquoise-green and scarlet. Containing booklet pane No. X904m.*

FH17 Design No. 3, Edible Sea Urchin, Common Starfish and Common Shore Crab	6·00

No. FH17 has the vertical edges of the pane imperforate.

FH **18**

(Des J. Sancha)

1989 (2 Oct)–**90**. *Mills Series. Grey-black and grey-green matt card cover as Type* FH **18**.

FH18 Design No. 1, Wicken Fen, Ely containing booklet pane No. X960l	7·50

As Type FH18 *but glossy card cover containing Penny Black Anniversary booklet pane No. 1476l printed in litho by Walsall.*

FH19 Design No. 1 (cover in bottle-green and pale green), Wicken Fen, Ely (30.1.90)	16·00

No. FH19 was an experimental printing to test a new cover material. This appears glossy when compared with Nos. FH18 and FH20.

As Type FH18 *but changed to matt card cover containing Penny Black Anniversary booklet pane No. 1469l printed in photo by Harrison.*

FH20 Design No. 2 (cover in grey-black and bright green), Click Mill, Dounby, Orkney (30.1.90)	9·00

1990 (4 Sept)–**91**. *Mills Series continued. Covers as Type* FH **18**. *Containing booklet pane No. X911m.*

FH21 Design No. 3 (cover printed in light blue and buff) Jack and Jill Mills, Clayton, Sussex	5·00
FH22 Design No. 4 (cover printed in dull blue and bright yellow-green). Howell Mill, Llanddeusant, Anglesey (25.6.91)	5·00

Nos. FH18/22 have the vertical edges of the pane imperforate.

FH **23**

(Des J. Gibbs)

1991 (10 Sept)–**92.** *150th Anniv of Punch Magazine. Magenta and grey-black covers as Type* FH **23** *containing booklet pane No.* X927l.

FH23	Design No. 1, Illustrations by Richard Doyle and Hoffnung	3·50
	a. Corrected rate (10.91)	3·50
FH24	Design No. 2, Illustrations by Sir John Tenniel and Eric Burgin (21.1.92)	3·50
FH25	Design No. 3, Illustrations by Sir John Tenniel and Anton (28.4.92)	3·50
FH26	Design No. 4, Illustrations by Sir John Tenniel and Hewison (28.7.92)	3·50

Nos. FH23/6 have the vertical edges of the pane imperforate. No. FH23a has corrected letter rates as No. FB59a.

(Des J. Matthews)

1992 (22 Sept). *1000th Anniv of Appointment of Sheriffs. Scarlet and dull blue cover as Type* FB **63** *containing booklet pane No.* X927l.

FH27	Design as Type FB63 but elements in reverse order	3·50

No. FH27 has the vertical edges of the pane imperforate.

FH **28**

(Des J. Lawrence)

1993 (9 Feb–6 July). *Educational Institutions Series. Covers as Type* FH **28** *containing booklet pane No.* X1050l *printed in litho by Walsall.*

FH28	Design No. 1 (cover in lake-brown and light blue), University of Wales	7·25
FH29	Design No. 2 (cover in deep dull green and lemon), St. Hilda's College, Oxford (6.4.93)	7·25
FH30	Design No. 3 (cover in purple-brown and flesh), Marlborough College, Wiltshire (6.7.93)	7·25

1993 (1 Nov). *Educational Institutions Series continued. Deep bluish green and lilac cover as Type* FH **28** *containing four 25p. (No.* Y1752) *printed in litho by Walsall.*

FH31	Design No. 4, Free Church of Scotland College, Edinburgh	7·00

FH **32**

(Des H. Brockway)

1994 (25 Jan). *20th-century Prime Ministers Series. Brown and pale brown cover as Type* FH **32** *containing four 25p. (No.* Y1752) *printed in litho by Walsall.*

FH32	Design No. 1, Herbert Asquith	3·00

(Des H. Brockway)

1994 (26 Apr–6 Sept). *20th-century Prime Ministers Series continued. Covers as Type* FH **32**. *Containing four 25p. (No.* Y1683) *printed in photo by Harrison.*

FH33	Design No. 2 (cover in sepia and buff) David Lloyd-George	3·00
FH34	Design No. 3 (cover in greenish blue and pale blue), Winston Churchill (6.6.94)	3·00
FH35	Design No. 4 (cover in black and yellow-olive), Clement Attlee (6.9.94)	3·00

FH **36**

(Des L. Thomas)

1995 (7 Feb–4 Apr). *50th Anniv of End of Second World War. Covers as Type* FH **36** *containing four 25p. (No.* Y1683) *printed in photo by Harrison.*

FH36	Design No. 1 (cover in brown-olive and brownish black), Violette Szabo (S.O.E. agent)	3·00
FH37	Design No. 2 (cover in red-brown and black), Dame Vera Lynn (entertainer) (4.4.95)	3·00

1995 (16 May–4 Sept). *50th Anniv of End of Second World War Series continued. Covers as Type* FH **36** *containing four 25p. (No.* Y1684) *printed in photo by Harrison.*

FH38	Design No. 3 (cover in black and steel-blue), R. J. Mitchell (designer of Spitfire)	3·00
FH39	Design No. 4 (cover in grey-green and black), Archibald Mcindoe (plastic surgeon) (4.9.95)	3·50

FH **40**

1996 (16 Jan). *Multicoloured laminated cover as Type* FH **40**. *Stamps printed in litho by Questa.*

FH40	Containing four 25p. stamps (No. Y1752)	7·00

For an initial test period No. FH40 was only available from machines at twelve post offices, five in London and seven in Scotland, in addition to philatelic outlets. Stocks were distributed nationally from May 1996.

1996 (8 July)–**97.** *Multicoloured laminated cover as Type* FH **40**. *Stamps printed in litho by Questa.*

FH41	Containing booklet pane of 1p.×2, 20p., 26p.×3 and 2 labels (No. Y1743l)	6·00
	a. Corrected rate (4.2.97)	5·50

No. FH41 was reissued on 4 February 1997 showing the 200g second class rate on the inside cover altered from 47p. to 45p. A further printing issued 5 May 1998 was without the overseas postage rate table.

1998 (1 Dec). *Multicoloured laminated cover as Type* FH **40**. *Stamps printed in photo by Questa.*

FH42	Containing booklet pane of 1p.×2, 20p., 26p.×3 and 2 labels (No. Y1667l)	30·00

1999 (26 Apr). *Multicoloured laminated cover as Type* FH **40**. *Stamps printed in photo by Questa.*

FH43	Containing booklet pane of 1p., 2p., 19p., 26p.×3 and 2 labels (No. Y1667m)	6·50

2000 (27 Apr)–**01.** *Multicoloured laminated cover as Type* FH **40**. *Stamps printed in photo by Questa.*

FH44	Containing booklet pane of 2nd, 1st×3 and 4 labels (No. 1664l)	8·00
	a. Containing booklet pane No. 1664la (17.4.01)	7·50

£1.15 Booklets

1981 (26 Jan–18 Mar). *Military Aircraft Series continued. Blue and grey covers as Type* FE **1** (90×49 *mm). Containing ten 11½p. (No.* X893). A. *Selvedge at left.* B. *Selvedge at right.*

		A	B
FI1	Design No. 5, Spitfire & Lancaster	5·00	5·00
FI2	Design No. 6, Lightning & Vulcan (18.3.81)	5·00	5·00

Nos. FI1/2 are inscribed "January 1981".

FI **3**

(Des R. Maddox)

1981 (6 May–30 Sept). *Museums Series. Blue and turquoise green covers as Type* FI **3** (90×49 mm). *Containing ten* 11½p. (No. X893). A. *Selvedge at left.* B. *Selvedge at right.*

		A	B
FI3	Design No. 1, Natural History Museum (British Museum), London	5·00	5·00
FI4	Design No. 2, National Museum of Antiquities of Scotland (30.9.81)	5·00	5·00

Nos. FI3/4 are inscribed "January 1981".

£1.20 Booklets

1980 (4 Feb–24 Sept). *Industrial Archaeology Series continued. Red and green covers as Type* FH **1** (90×49 mm). *Containing ten* 12p. (No. X943). A. *Selvedge at left.* B. *Selvedge at right.*

		A	B
FJ1	Design No. 2, Beetle Mill, Ireland	5·00	5·00
FJ2	Design No. 3, Tin Mines, Cornwall (25.6.80)	5·00	6·50
FJ3	Design No. 4, Bottle Kilns, Gladstone, Stoke-on-Trent (24.9.80)	5·00	5·00

No. FJ1 is inscribed "January 1980", No. FJ2 "May 1980" and No. FJ3 "July 1980".

1986 (14 Jan). *Pillar box "Write Now" cover as Type* FB **31** (90×49 mm), printed in yellow-green and pale red. *Containing ten* 12p. (No. X896). A. *Selvedge at left.* B. *Selvedge at right.*

		A	B
FJ4	"Write Now" (Pillar box design) (no imprint date)	8·00	8·00

FJ **5**

(Des R. Maddox)

1986 (29 Apr). *National Gallery cover as Type* FJ **5** (90×49mm), printed in magenta and blue-green. *Containing ten* 12p. (No. X896). A. *Selvedge at left.* B. *Selvedge at right.*

		A	B
FJ5	National Gallery design	7·50	7·50

No. FJ5 is inscribed "November 1985".

FJ **6**

(Des Trickett and Webb Ltd)

1986 (29 July). *Handwriting cover as Type* FJ **6** (90×49 mm), printed in bright orange and bright blue. *Containing ten* 12p. (No. X896). A. *Selvedge at left.* B. *Selvedge at right.*

		A	B
FJ6	"Maybe"	7·50	7·50

No. FJ6 is inscribed "November 1985".

£1.25 Booklets

1982 (1 Feb–6 Oct). *Museums Series continued. Blue and turquoise-green covers as Type* FJ **3** (90×49 mm). *Containing ten* 12½p. (No. X898). A. *Selvedge at left.* B. *Selvedge at right.*

		A	B
FK1	Design No. 3, Ashmolean Museum, Oxford	5·50	5·50
FK2	Design No. 4, National Museum of Wales, Cardiff (6.5.02)	5·50	5·50
FK3	Design No. 5, Ulster Museum, Belfast (11.8.82)	5·50	5·50
FK4	Design No. 6, Castle Museum, York (6.10.82)	5·50	5·50

Nos. FK1/4 are inscribed "February 1982".

FK **5**

(Des S. Paine)

1983 (16 Feb–26 Oct). *Railway Engines Series. Red and blue-green covers as Type* FK **5** (90×49 mm). *Containing ten* 12½p. (No. X898). A. *Selvedge at left.* B. *Selvedge at right.*

		A	B
FK5	Design No. 1, GWR *Isambard Kingdom Brunel*	8·00	8·00
FK6	Design No. 2, LMS Class 4P Passenger Tank Engine (5.4.83)	8·50	8·50
	a. Corrected rate	£110	£150
FK7	Design No. 3, LNER *Mallard* (27.7.83)	8·00	8·00
FK8	Design No. 4, SR/BR *Clan Line* (26.10.83)	8·00	8·00

No. FK5 is inscribed "February 1982" and Nos. FK6/8 "April 1983". The corrected rate reads "36p. for 200g" instead of "37p. for 200g".

£1.30 Booklets

FL **1**

(Des J. Gibbs)

1981 (6 May–30 Sept). *Postal History Series. Covers as Type* FL **1** (90×49 mm). *Containing No.* X894l. A. *Selvedge at left.* B. *Selvedge at right.*

		A	B
FL1	Design No. 1, Penny Black (red & black cover)	7·00	5·50
FL2	Design No. 2, The Downey Head, 1911 (red and green cover) (20.9.81)	9·50	30·00

No. FL1 is inscribed "April 1981" and No. FL2 "September 1981".

FL **3**

(Des J. Thirsk)

1984 (3 Sept)–**85**. *Trams Series. Yellow-orange and purple covers as Type* FL **3** (90×49 mm). *Containing ten* 13p. (No. X900). A. *Selvedge at left.* B. *Selvedge at right.*

		A	B
FL3	Design No. 1, Swansea/Mumbles Railway Car No. 3	5·50	5·50
FL4	Design No. 2, Glasgow Car No. 927 and Car No. 1194 (15.1.85)	6·25	6·25
FL5	Design No. 3, Car No. 717, Blackpool (23.4.85)	6·25	6·25
FL6	Design No. 4, Car No. 120 and "D" Class Car, London (23.7.85)	5·50	5·50

Nos. FL3/6 are inscribed "September 1984".

FL **7**

(Des Anne Morrow)

1986 (20 Oct). *Books for Children. Cover as Type* FL **7** *(90×49 mm)* *printed in rose-red and lemon. Containing ten 13p. (No. X900). A. Selvedge at left. B. Selvedge at right.*

		A	B
FL7	Teddy bears design	5·50	5·50

FL **8**

(Des Trickett and Webb Ltd)

1987 (27 Jan). *"Keep in Touch" cover as Type* FL **8** *(90×49 mm), printed in light green and bright blue. Containing ten 13p. (No. X900). A. Selvedge at left. B. Selvedge at right.*

		A	B
FL8	Handclasp and envelope design	5·50	5·50

No. FL8 is inscribed "October 1986".

FL **9**

(Des Hannah Firmin)

1987 (14 Apr). *"Ideas for your Garden". Cover as Type* FL **9** *(90×49 mm) printed in bistre and orange-brown. Containing ten 13p. stamps (No. X900). A. Selvedge at left. B. Selvedge at right.*

		A	B
FL9	Conservatory design	5·50	5·50

No. FL9 is inscribed "October 1986".

FL **10**

(Des Trickett and Webb Ltd)

1987 (4 July). *"Brighter Writer". Cover as Type* FL **10** *(90×49 mm) printed in orange and bright reddish violet. Containing ten 13p. stamps (No. X900)* A *Selvedge at left.* B. *Selvedge at right.*

		A	B
FL10	Flower design	5·50	5·50

No. FL10 is inscribed "October 1986".

FL **11**

(Des E. Stemp)

1987 (29 Sept). *"Jolly Postman". Cover as Type* FL **11** *(90×49 mm) printed in pale blue and deep blue. Containing ten 13p. stamps (No. X900). A. Selvedge at left. B. Selvedge at right.*

		A	B
FL11	Boy drawing design	5·75	5·75

No. FL11 is inscribed "October 1986".

FL **12**

(Des E. Hughes)

1988 (26 Jan). *Bicentenary of Linnean Society. Cover as Type* FL **12** *(90×49 mm) printed in blue and claret. Containing ten 13p. stamps (No. X900). A. Selvedge at left. B. Selvedge at right.*

		A	B
FL12	Mermaid, fish and insect (from "Hortus Sanibatis", 1497)	6·75	6·75

No. FL12 is inscribed "October 1986".

FL **13**

1988 (12 Apr). *Recipe Cards. Cover as Type* FL **13** *(90×49 mm) printed in brown and green. Containing ten 13p. stamps (No. X900). A. Selvedge at left. B. Selvedge at right.*

		A	B
FL13	Vegetables design	5·50	5·50

No. FL13 is inscribed "October 1986".

FL **14**

(Des Trickett and Webb Ltd)

1988 (5 July). *"Children's Parties".* Cover as Type FL **14** (90×49 *mm*) *printed in blue-green and bright purple. Containing ten 13p. stamps* (No. X900). A. *Selvedge at left.* B. *Selvedge at right.*

		A	B
FL14	Balloons and streamers design	5·50	5·50

No. FL14 is inscribed "October 1986".

£1.40 Booklets

1981 (26 Jan–18 Mar). *Industrial Archaeology Series continued. Red and green covers as Type FH* **1** (90×49 *mm*). *Containing ten 14p.* (No. X946). A. *Selvedge at left.* B. *Selvedge at right.*

		A	B
FM1	Design No. 5, Preston Mill, Scotland	5·50	5·50
FM2	Design No. 6, Talyllyn Railway, Tywyn (18.3.81)	5·50	5·50

Nos. FM1/2 are inscribed "January 1981".

FM **3**

(Des E. Stemp)

1981 (6 May–30 Sept). *19th-century Women's Costume Series. Claret and blue covers as Type FM* **3** (90×49 *mm*). *Containing ten 14p.* (No. X946). A. *Selvedge at left.* B. *Selvedge at right.*

		A	B
FM3	Design No. 1, Costume, 1800–15	5·50	5·50
FM4	Design No. 2, Costume, 1815–30 (30.9.81)	5·50	5·50

Nos. FM3/4 are inscribed "January 1981".

FM **5**

(Des A. Drummond)

1988 (5 Sept). *"Pocket Planner". Cover as Type FM* **5** (90×49 *mm*) *printed in grey-black and yellow. Containing ten 11p. stamps* (No. X903). A. *Selvedge at left.* B. *Selvedge at right.*

		A	B
FM5	"Legal Charge" design	5·50	5·50

FM **6**

(Des Debbie Cook)

1989 (24 Jan). *150th Anniv of Fox Talbot's Report on the Photographic Process to Royal Society. Cover as Type FM* **6** (90×49 *mm*) *printed in reddish orange and black. Containing ten 14p. stamps* (No. X903). A. *Selvedge at left.* B. *Selvedge at right.*

		A	B
FM6	Photographs and darkroom equipment	5·75	5·75

No. FM6 is inscribed "September 1988".

£1.43 Booklets

1982 (1 Feb–6 May). *Postal History Series continued. Covers as Type FL* **1** (90×49 *mm*). *Containing No. X899l.* A. *Selvedge at left.* B. *Selvedge at right.*

		A	B
FN1	Design No. 3, James Chalmers (postal reformer) (orange and turquoise-blue cover)	6·00	6·00
FN2	Design No. 4, Edmund Dulac (stamp designer) (brown and red cover) (6.5.82)	6·00	6·00

FN **3**

(Des J. Gardner)

1982 (12 July). *"Holiday Postcard Stamp Book". Purple and turquoise-blue cover as Type FN* **3** (90×49 *mm*). *Containing No. X899l.* A. *Selvedge at left.* B. *Selvedge at right.*

		A	B
FN3	Golden Hinde on front, postcard voucher on back	6·00	6·00

1982 (21 July)–**83**. *Postal History Series continued. Covers as Type FL* **1** (90×49 *mm*). *Containing No. X899l.* A. *Selvedge at left.* B. *Selvedge at right.*

		A	B
FN4	Design No. 5, "Forces Postal Service" (grey and violet cover)	6·00	6·00
FN5	Design No. 6, The £5 Orange (orange and black cover) (6.10.82)	6·00	6·00
FN6	Design No. 7, Postmark History (bright scarlet and deep dull blue cover) (16.2.83)	6·00	6·00

No. FN1 is inscribed "February 1982". FN2/3 "May 1982", FN4 "July 1982", FN5 "October 1982", FN6 "November 1982".

For booklet No. FS2 with cover price of £1.45, see £1.60 booklets.

£1.46 Booklets

1983 (5 Apr–26 Oct). *Postal History Series continued. Covers as Type FL* **1** (90×49 *mm*). A. *Containing No. X899n.* B. *Containing No. X900n.*

		A	B
FO1	Design No. 8, Seahorse High Values (blue and green cover)	11·00	11·00
	a. Corrected rate	85·00	28·00
FO2	Design No. 9, Parcel Post Centenary (turquoise-blue and carmine cover) (27.7.83)	9·50	9·50
FO3	Design No. 10, Silver Jubilee of Regional Stamps (dull green & reddish violet cover) (26.10.83)	9·50	9·50

No. FO1 is inscribed "March 1983", No. FO2 "May 1983" and No. FO3 "June 1983".

The corrected rate reads "36p. for 200g" instead of "37p. for 200g".

£1.50 Booklets

1986 (14 Jan). *Pillar box "Write Now" cover as Type* FB **31** *(90×49 mm), printed in ultramarine and red. A. Containing No.* X897l. B. *Containing No.* X897la.

		A	B
FP1	"Write Now" (Pillar box design)	7·00	7·00

No. FP1 shows no imprint date.

1986 (29 Apr). *National Gallery cover as Type* FJ **5** *(90×49 mm), printed in violet and vermilion. A. Containing No.* X897l. B. *Containing No.* X897la.

		A	B
FP2	National Gallery design	7·00	7·00

No. FP2 is inscribed "November 1985".

1986 (29 July). *Handwriting cover as Type* FJ **6** *(90×49 mm), printed in blue-green and bright blue. A. Containing No.* X897l. B. *Containing No.* X897la.

		A	B
FP3	"No"	7·00	7·00

No. FP3 is inscribed "November 1985".

£1.54 Booklets

1984 (3 Sept)–**85**. *Postal History Series continued. Covers as Type* FL **1** *(90×49 mm). A. Containing No.* X901l. B. *Containing No.* X901la.

		A	B
FQ1	Design No. 11, Old and new Postage Dues (reddish purple and pale blue cover)	6·00	6·00
FQ2	Design No. 12, Queen Victoria embossed stamps (yellow-green and blue-cover) (15.1.85)	6·00	6·00
FQ3	Design No. 13, Queen Victoria surface printed stamps (blue-green and carmine cover) (23.4.85)	6·00	6·00
FQ4	Design No. 14, 17th-century mounted and foot messengers (deep brown & orange-red cover) (23.7.85)	6·00	6·00

No. FQ1 is inscribed "July 1984" and Nos. FQ2/4 are inscribed "September 1984".

£1.55 Booklets

1982 (1 Feb–6 Oct). *19th-century Women's Costume Series continued. Claret and blue covers as Type* FM **3** *(90×49 mm). Containing ten* 15½p. *(No.* X948). A. *Selvedge at left.* B. *Selvedge at right.*

		A	B
FR1	Design No. 3, Costume, 1830–50	5·75	5·75
FR2	Design No. 4, Costume, 1850–60 (6.5.82)	5·75	5·75
FR3	Design No. 5, Costume, 1860–80 (11.8.82)	5·75	5·75
FR4	Design No. 6, Costume, 1880–1900 (6.10.82)	5·75	5·75

Nos. FR1/4 are inscribed "February 1982".

£1.60 Booklets

FS **1**

(Des Carol Walklin)

1983 (5 Apr). *"Birthday Box" Design. Magenta and red-orange cover as Type* FS **1** *(90×49 mm). Depicting birthday cake and associated items.* A. *Selvedge at left.* B. *Selvedge at right.*

		A	B
FS1	Containing ten 16p. stamps (No. X949) (no imprint date)	7·00	7·00
	a. Rates altered and "February 1983" imprint date	95·00	£150

The converted rate reads "36p. for 200g." instead of 37p. for 200g.".

FS **2**

(Des R. Maddox)

1983 (10 Aug). *British Countryside Series. Special Discount Booklet (sold at £1.45). Greenish blue and ultramarine cover as Type* FS **2** *(90×49 mm). Containing ten* 16p. *stamps (No.* X949Eu). A. *Selvedge at left.* B. *Selvedge at right.*

		A	B
FS2	Design No. 1, Lyme Regis, Dorset	9·00	9·00

Stamps from No. FS2 show a double-lined "D" printed in blue on the reverse over the gum.

No. FS2 is inscribed "April 1983".

1983 (21 Sept). *British Countryside Series continued. Dull green on violet cover as Type* FS **2** *(90×49 mm). Containing ten* 16p. *stamps (No.* X949). A. *Selvedge at left.* B. *Selvedge at right.*

		A	B
FS3	Design No. 2, Arlington Row, Bibury, Gloucestershire	6·00	6·00

No. FS3 is inscribed "April 1983".

FS **4**

(Des M. Newton)

1984 (14 Feb). *"Write it" Design. Vermilion and ultramarine cover as Type* FS **4** *(90×49 mm). Containing ten* 16p. *stamps (No.* X949). A. *Selvedge at left.* B. *Selvedge at right.*

		A	B
FS4	Fountain pen	7·00	7·00

No. FS4 is inscribed "April 1983".

£1.70 Booklets

FT **1**

1984 (3 Sept). *Social Letter Writing Series. Rose and deep claret cover as Type* FT **1** *(90×49 mm). Containing ten* 17p. *(No.* X952). A. *Selvedge at left.* B. *Selvedge at right.*

		A	B
FT1	Design No. 1, "Love Letters"	7·00	7·00

No. FT1 is inscribed "September 1984".

1985 (5 Mar). *Social Letter Writing Series continued. Special Discount Booklet (sold at £1.55). Turquoise-blue and deep claret cover as Type* FT **1** *(90×49 mm). Containing ten* 17p. *(No.* X952Eu). A. *Selvedge at left.* B. *Selvedge at right.*

		A	B
FT2	Design No. 2, "Letters abroad"	7·00	7·00

Stamps from No. FT2 show a double-lined "D" printed in blue on the reverse over the gum.

No. FT2 is inscribed "September 1984".

1985 (9 Apr). *Social Letter Writing Series continued. Bright blue and deep claret cover as Type* FT **1** *(90×49 mm). Containing ten* 17p. *(No.* X952). A. *Selvedge at left.* B. *Selvedge at right.*

		A	B
FT3	Design No. 3, "Fan letters"	6·50	6·50

No. FT3 is inscribed "September 1984".

£1.53

Royal Mail
Stamps

Ten at 17p

Free
Stamp

10 for the
price of 9

FT **4**

(Des B. Smith)

1985 (30 July). *350 Years of Royal Mail Public Postal Service. Special Discount Booklet (sold at £1.53). Cover Type FT* **4** *(90 × 60 mm), printed in rosine and bright blue. Containing ten 17p. (No. 1290Eu) with selvedge at top.*

FT4   Datapost Service design .... 7·00
   The stamps from this booklet show double-lined letters "D" printed on the reverse over the gum.
   No. FT4 is inscribed "September 1984".

1985 (8 Oct)–**86**. *Social Letter Writing Series continued. Black and bright scarlet cover as Type FT* **1** *(90 × 49 mm). Containing ten 17p. (No. X952). A. Selvedge at left. B. Selvedge at right.*

		A	B
FT5	Design No. 4, "Write Now" (Pillar box)	6·50	6·50
	a. Revised rates (2nd class (60g) 12p.) (1.86)	25·00	15·00

1986 (29 Apr). *National Gallery cover as Type FJ* **5** *(90 × 49 mm), printed in blue-green and blue. Containing ten 17p. (No. X952). A. Selvedge at left. B. Selvedge at right.*

		A	B
FT6	National Gallery design	7·00	7·00

No. FT6 is inscribed "November 1985".

1986 (29 July). *Handwriting cover as Type FJ* **6** *(90 × 49 mm) printed in red and bright blue. Containing ten 17p. (No. X952). A. Selvedge at left. B. Selvedge at right.*

		A	B
FT7	"Yes"	7·00	7·00

No. FT7 is inscribed "November 1985".

£1.80 Booklets

1986 (20 Oct). *Books for Children. New blue and orange-brown cover as Type FL* **7**. *Containing ten 18p. (No. X955). A. Selvedge at left. B. Selvedge at right.*

		A	B
FU1	Rabbits design	7·00	7·00

1987 (27 Jan). *"Keep in Touch" cover as Type FL* **8** *printed in magenta and bright blue. Containing ten 18p. (No. X955). A. Selvedge at left. B. Selvedge at right.*

		A	B
FU2	Handclasp and envelope design	7·00	7·00

No. FU2 is inscribed "October 1986".

1987 (14 Apr). *"Ideas for your Garden". Claret and brown-olive cover as Type FL* **9** *(90 × 49 mm). Containing ten 18p. stamps (No. X955). A. Selvedge at left. B. Selvedge at right.*

		A	B
FU3	Garden path design	7·00	7·00

No. FU3 is inscribed "October 1986".

1987 (14 July). *"Brighter Writer". Turquoise-green and reddish orange cover as Type FL* **10** *(90 × 49 mm). Containing ten 18p. stamps (No. X955). A. Selvedge at left. B. Selvedge at right.*

		A	B
FU4	Berries and leaves design	7·00	7·00

No. FU4 is inscribed "October 1986".

1987 (29 Sept). *"Jolly Postman". Cover as Type FL* **11** *(90 × 49 mm) printed in deep blue and claret. Containing ten 18p. stamps (No. X955). A. Selvedge at left. B. Selvedge at right.*

		A	B
FU5	Girl drawing design	7·00	7·00

No. FU5 is inscribed "October 1986".

1988 (26 Jan). *Bicentenary of Linnean Society. Cover as Type FL* **12** *(90 × 49 mm) printed in dull yellow-green and dull claret. Containing ten 18p. stamps (No. X955). A. Selvedge at left. B. Selvedge at right.*

		A	B
FU6	Wolf and birds (from "Hortus Sanitatis", 1497)	7·00	7·00
	a. Inside cover text for FL12	11·00	11·00

No. FU6 is inscribed "October 1986".
The inside cover text for FU6a has the special offer of the £1.30 booklet, No. FL12 (four 13p. stamps).

1988 (12 Apr). *Recipe Cards. Cover as Type FL* **13** *(90 × 49 mm) printed in claret and Indian red. Containing ten 18p. stamps (No. X955). A. Selvedge at left. B. Selvedge at right.*

		A	B
FU7	Fruits, pudding and jam design	7·00	7·00

No. FU7 is inscribed "October 1986".

1988 (5 July). *"Children's Parties". Cover as Type FL* **14** *(90 × 49 mm) printed in violet and rosine. Containing ten 18p. stamps (No. X955). A. Selvedge at left. B. Selvedge at right.*

		A	B
FU8	Balloons and party hats design	7·00	7·00

No. FU8 is inscribed "October 1986".

£1.90 Booklets

1988 (5 Sept). *"Pocket Planner". Cover as Type FM* **5** *(90 × 49 mm) printed in yellow-green and magenta. Containing ten 19p. stamps (No. X956). A. Selvedge at left. B. Selvedge at right.*

		A	B
FV1	"Marriage Act" design	8·75	8·75

1989 (24 Jan). *150th Anniv of Fox Talbot's Report on the Photographic Process to Royal Society. Cover as Type FM* **6** *(90 × 49 mm) printed in emerald and black. Containing ten 19p. stamps (No. X956). A. Selvedge at left. B. Selvedge at right.*

		A	B
FV2	Fox Talbot with camera and Lacock Abbey............	8·75	8·75

No. FV2 is inscribed "September 1988".

£2 Booklets

£2

Royal Mail
Stamps

Eight at 25p

FW **1**

(Des Debbie Cook)

1993 (1 Nov)–**94**. *Postal Vehicles Series. Covers as Type FW* **1**. *Containing eight 25p. (No. Y1683).*

FW1	Design No. 1 (cover in dull vermilion and deep blue), Motorised cycle-carrier	6·50
FW2	Design No. 2 (cover in green and deep violet-blue), Experimental motor-mail van (26.4.94)	6·50
FW3	Design No. 3 (cover in red and black), Experimental electric mail van, 1932 (6.9.94)	6·50

£2

Royal Mail
Stamps

Eight at 25p

LONDON TO
BRIGHTON

FW **3**

(Des The Four Hundred)

1995 (7 Feb–4 Apr). *Birth Bicentenary of Sir Rowland Hill. Covers as Type FW* **3**. *Containing eight 25p. (No. Y1683).*

FW4	Design No. 1 (cover in purple and new blue), Rowland Hill as director of London and Brighton Railway Company	6·50
FW5	Design No. 2 (cover in deep mauve and greenish blue), Rowland Hill and Hazlewood School (1.1.95)	6·50

1995 (6 June–4 Sept). *Birth Bicentenary of Sir Rowland Hill Series continued. Covers as Type FW* **3**. *Containing eight 25p. (No. Y1684).*

FW6	Design No. 3 (cover in deep blue-green and dull orange), Rowland Hill as Secretary to the Post Office...........	7·00
FW7	Design No. 4 (cover in red-brown and orange), Uniform Penny Postage petition and Mulready envelope (4.9.95).	7·00

1996 (16 Jan). *Multicoloured laminated cover as Type FH* **40**. *Stamps printed in litho by Questa.*

FW8	Containing eight 25p. stamps (No. Y1752)	7·50

For an initial test period No. FW 8 was only available from machines at twelve post offices, five in London and seven in Scotland, in addition to philatelic outlets. Stocks were distributed nationally from May 1996.

1996 (8 July)–**97**. *Multicoloured laminated cover as Type* FH **40**. *Stamps printed in litho by Questa.*
FW9　Containing booklet pane of 20p. and 26p.×7 (No. Y1751l)　8·00
　　a. Corrected rate (4.2.97)..　8·00
　　No. FW9 was reissued on 4 February 1997 showing the 200g second class rate on the inside cover altered from 47p. to 45p. A further printing issued 5 May 1998 was without the overseas postage rate table.

1998 (1 Dec). *Multicoloured laminated cover as Type* FH **40**. *Stamps printed in photo by Questa.*
FW10　Containing booklet pane of 20p. and 26p.×7 (No. Y1680l)　35·00

1999 (26 Apr). *Multicoloured laminated cover as Type* FH **40**. *Stamps printed in photo by Questa.*
FW11　Containing booklet pane of 19p. and 26p.×7 (No. Y1677l)　13·00

2000 (27 Apr). *Multicoloured laminated cover as Type* FH **40**. *Stamps printed in photo by Questa.*
FW12　Containing booklet pane of 2nd×2 and 1st×6 (No. 1664m)　8·00

Christmas Booklets

FX **1**

(Des J. Matthews)

1978 (15 Nov). *"Christmas Greetings". Cover Type* FX **1** *(90×49 mm). Printed in rose-red and sage-green.*
FX1　£1.60, containing booklet pane No. X875l...........................　5·00
　　No. FX1 is inscribed "August 1978".

FX **2**

(Des P. Sharland)

1979 (14 Nov). *"Christmas Greetings". Red and green cover as Type* FX **2** *(90×49 mm), showing Christmas cracker.*
FX2　£1.80, containing booklet pane No. X879l...........................　6·00
　　No. FX2 is inscribed "October 1979".

FX **3**

(Des E. Fraser)

1980 (12 Nov). *Christmas. Red and blue cover as Type* FX **3** *(90×49 mm), showing Nativity scene.*
FX3　£2.20, containing booklet pane No. X888m.....................　6·50
　　No. FX3 is inscribed "September 1980".

FX **4**

(Des W. Sanderson)

1981 (11 Nov). *Christmas. Red and blue cover as Type* FX **4**, *(90×49 mm), showing skating scene.*
FX4　£2.55, containing booklet pane No. X893l...........................　8·50
　　No. FX4 is inscribed "January 1981".

FX **5**

(Des A. Davidson)

1982 (10 Nov). *Christmas. Red and green cover as Type* FX **5** *(90×49 mm), showing Christmas Mummers.*
FX5　£2.50, containing booklet pane No. X898l...........................　10·00
　　No. FX5 is inscribed "February 1982" and was sold at a discount of 30p. off the face value of the stamps.
　　Each stamp in the pane has a blue star printed on the reverse over the gum.

FX **6**

(Des Barbara Brown)

1983 (9 Nov). *Christmas. Brown-lilac and yellow cover as Type* FX **6** *(90×49 mm), showing pantomime scenes.*
FX6　£2.20, containing twenty 12½p. (No. X898Ev)....................　8·50
　　No. FX6 is inscribed "April 1983" and was sold at a discount of 30p. off the face value of the stamps.
　　Each stamp in the pane has a double-lined blue star printed on the reverse over the gum.

FX **7**

(Des Yvonne Gilbert)

1984 (20 Nov). *Christmas. Light brown and red-orange cover as Type* FX **7** *(90×60 mm), showing Nativity scene.*
FX7　£2.30, containing twenty 13p. (No. 1267Eu)....................　10·00

No. FX7 is inscribed "September 1984" and was sold at a discount of 30p. off the face value of the stamps.

The stamps from this booklet show double-lined blue stars printed on the reverse over the gum.

FX **8**

(Des A. George)

1985 (19 Nov). *Christmas. Bright blue and rose cover as Type* FX **8** *(90×60 mm), showing The Pantomime.*

FX8   £2.40, containing twenty 12p. (No. 1303Eu).......................... 9·00

The stamps from this booklet show double-lined blue stars printed on the reverse over the gum.

FX **9**

(Des Lynda Gray)

1986 (2 Dec). *Christmas. Red and dull blue-green cover as Type* FX **9** *(90×49 mm), showing Shetland Yule cakes.* A. *Selvedge at left.* B. *Selvedge at right.*

	A	B
FX9 £1.20, containing ten 13p. (No. X900Eu)	9·00	16·00

No. FX9 is inscribed "October 1986" and was sold at a discount of 10p. off the face value of the stamps.

Each stamp in the pane has a blue star printed on the reverse over the gum.

For 1990 and later Christmas stamps, see Barcode Booklets Section G.

£1.90 Greetings Booklet

FY **1**

(Des L. Moberly)

1989 (31 Jan). *Greetings Stamps. Multicoloured cover as Type* FY **1** *(89×60 mm). Containing booklet pane No. 1423a, including twelve special greetings labels in a block (3×4) at right, attached by the selvedge.*

FY1   Greetings design .... 48·00

No. FY1 is inscribed "September 1988".

The cover of No. FY **1** shows an overall pattern of elements taken from the stamp designs. Due to the method of production the position of these elements varies from cover to cover.

For Greetings stamps in Barcode booklets, see Barcode Booklets Section F.

BARCODE BOOKLETS

These booklets are listed in 11 sections.

SECTION C.   G numbers containing Machin stamps with face values

SECTION D.   H numbers containing Machin NVI stamps

BARCODE BOOKLETS

SECTION E.	J numbers containing Machin Penny Black Anniversary stamps
SECTION F.	KX numbers containing Greetings stamps
SECTION G.	LX numbers containing Christmas stamps
SECTION H.	M numbers containing self-adhesive NVI definitive stamps
SECTION I.	N numbers containing self-adhesive definitive stamps with face values
SECTION J.	PM numbers containing both special and definitive self-adhesive NVI stamps
SECTION K.	Q numbers containing NVI "Smilers" stamps in definitive size
SECTION L.	R numbers containing stamps with value indicator at upper left
SECTION M.	SA numbers containing NVI "Smilers" stamps and definitive stamps.

These are produced for sale in both post offices and commercial outlets.

NOTE: All panes are attached to the covers by the selvedge. Barcode booklet covers are illustrated at two-thirds linear size *unless otherwise stated.*

C. Barcode Booklets containing Machin stamps with values shown as Type 367.

COVERS. These are all printed in scarlet, lemon and black with the barcode on the reverse. Type GA1 has a clear "window" to view the contents. Type GB3 is shorter and has a stamp illustration printed on the cover to replace the "window". These illustrations show an oblique white line across the bottom right-hand corner of the "stamp". Unless otherwise stated all covers were printed by Harrison.

From early 1997 the printer of each booklet is identified by a small capital letter below the barcode on the outside back cover.

52p. Booklet

GA **1**

1987 (4 Aug). *Laminated cover Type* GA **1** *(75×60 mm).*

GA1   Containing booklet pane No. X900n .... 4·00

No. GA1 is inscribed "20 October 1986".

56p. Booklets

1988 (23 Aug). *Laminated cover as Type* GA **1** *(75×56 mm).*

GB1   Containing booklet pane No. X903l .... 6·00

1988 (11 Oct). *Laminated cover as Type* GA **1** *(75×56 mm) printed by Walsall.*

GB2   Containing booklet pane No. X903l .... 10·00

GB **3** Large Crown

1988 (11 Oct). *Laminated cover as Type GB* **3** (75×48 mm) *with stamp printed on the cover in deep blue.*
GB3   Containing booklet pane No. X903n .... 8·00
  No. GB3 is inscribed "5 September 1988" and has the horizontal edges of the pane imperforate.

1989 (24 Jan). *Laminated cover as Type GB* **3** (75×48 mm) *with stamp printed on the cover in deep blue by Walsall.*
GB4   Containing booklet pane No. X903q .... 40·00
  No. GB4 is inscribed "5 September 1988" and has the three edges of the pane imperforate.

72p. Booklet

1987 (4 Aug). *Laminated cover as Type GA* **1** (75×60 mm).
GC1   Containing booklet pane No. X955m .... 4·00
  No. GC1 is inscribed "20 October 1986".

76p. Booklets

1988 (23 Aug). *Laminated cover as Type GA* **1** (75×56 mm).
GD1   Containing booklet pane No. X956l .... 8·00

1988 (11 Oct). *Laminated cover as Type GA* **1** (75×56 mm) *printed by Walsall.*
GD2   Containing booklet pane No. X956l .... 8·00

1988 (11 Oct). *Laminated cover as Type GB* **3** (75×48 mm) *with stamp printed on the cover in bright orange-red.*
GD3   Containing booklet pane No. X956n .... 9·50
  No. GD3 is inscribed "5 September 1988" and has the horizontal edges of the pane imperforate.

1989 (24 Jan). *Laminated cover as Type GB* **3** (75×48 mm) *with stamp printed on the cover in bright orange-red by Walsall.*
GD4   Containing booklet pane No. X956q .... 40·00
  No. GD4 is inscribed "5 September 1988" and has the three edges of the pane imperforate.

78p. Booklet

GD **4a** (As Type GM **1** but without "4")

1992 (28 July). *Multicoloured laminated cover as Type GD* **4a** (75×49 mm) *with stamp printed on the cover in bright mauve by Walsall.*
GD4a   Containing two 39p. stamps (No. X1058) (pane No. X1058l with right-hand vert pair removed) and pane of 4 air mail labels .... 4·00
  Stamps in No. GD4a have top or bottom edge imperforate. Booklet No. GD4a was produced in connection with a Kellogg's Bran Flakes promotion.

£1.04 Booklet

1987 (4 Aug). *Laminated cover as Type GA* **1** (75×60 mm).
GE1   Containing booklet pane No. X971bl .... 20·00
  No. GE1 is inscribed "20 October 1986".

£1.08 Booklets

1988 (23 Aug). *Laminated cover as Type GA* **1** (75×56 mm).
GF1   Containing booklet pane No. X973l .... 14·00

1988 (11 Oct). *Laminated cover as Type GB* **3** (75×48 mm) *with stamp printed on the cover in chestnut.*
GF2   Containing booklet pane No. X973m .... 35·00
  No. GF2 is inscribed "5 September 1988" and has the horizontal edges of the pane imperforate.

£1.16 Booklets

GG **1** Redrawn Crown

1989 (2 Oct). *Laminated cover as Type GG* **1** (75×48 mm) *with stamp printed on the cover in deep mauve by Walsall.*
GG1   Containing booklet pane No. X1054l .... 18·00
  No. GG1 has three edges of the pane imperforate.

1990 (17 Apr). *Laminated cover as Type GG* **1** (75×48 mm) *with stamp printed on the cover in deep mauve by Walsall.*
GG2   Containing booklet pane No. X1055l .... 20·00
  No. GG2 has three edges of the pane imperforate.

£1.20 Booklets

GGA **1** ("BY AIR MAIL *par avion*" at bottom left)

1998 (5 May). *Multicoloured laminated cover as Type GGA* **1** (75×50 mm) *with stamps printed on cover in olive-grey by Walsall. Inscr "For items up to 20g" on yellow tab at right.*
GGA1   Containing four 30p. (photo) (No. Y1688) and a pane of 4 air mail labels .... 4·25

GGA **2** "Create a card Design"

1998 (3 Aug). *Multicoloured laminated cover as Type GGA* **2** (75×50 mm) *printed by Walsall. Inscr "See inside for offer details" on yellow tab at right.*
GGA2   Containing four 30p. (photo) (No. Y1688) and a pane of 4 air mail labels .... 4·25
  This booklet was not placed on philatelic sale until 7 September 1998.

£1.24 Booklet

GH **1** Crown on White

1990 (17 Sept). *Multicoloured laminated cover as Type GH* **1** (75×49 mm) *with stamp printed on the cover in ultramarine by Walsall.*
GH1   Containing booklet pane No. X1056I ....   7·50
No. GH1 has the horizontal edges of the pane imperforate.

£1.30 Booklet

1987 (4 Aug). *Laminated cover as Type GA* **1** (98×60 mm).
GI1   Containing booklet pane No. X900o ....   6·00
No. GI1 is inscribed "20 October 1986".

£1.32 Booklet

GJ **1**

1991 (16 Sept)–**92.** *Multicoloured laminated cover as Type GJ* **1** (75×49 mm) *with stamp printed on the cover in light emerald by Walsall. Inscr "For letters up to 10g" on yellow strip at right.*
GJ1   Containing booklet pane No. X1057I and a pane of 4 air mail labels ....   6·50
    a. Inscr "For Worldwide Postcards" on yellow strip (8.9.92)   12·00
Nos. GJ1/a have the horizontal edges of the pane imperforate.

£1.40 Booklets

1988 (23 Aug). *Laminated cover as Type GA* **1** (97×56 mm).
GK1   Containing booklet pane No. X903m ....   16·00

1988 (11 Oct). *Laminated cover as Type GA* **1** (97×56 mm) *printed by Questa.*
GK2   Containing ten 14p. (No. X1007) ....   18·00

1988 (11 Oct). *Laminated cover as Type GB* **3** (75×48 mm) *with stamp printed on the cover in deep blue.*
GK3   Containing booklet pane No. X903p ....   10·00
No. GK3 is inscribed "5 September 1988" and has horizontal edges of the pane imperforate.

1988 (11 Oct). *Laminated cover as Type GB* **3** (75×48 mm) *with stamp printed on the cover in deep blue by Questa.*
GK4   Containing ten 14p. (No. X1007) ....   18·00

1993 (1 Nov). *Laminated cover as Type GJ* **1** (76×50 mm) *with stamp printed on the cover in yellow by Walsall.*
GK5   Containing four 35p. (No. Y1755) and a pane of 4 air mail labels ....   6·25

GK **6**

Type GK6 (without diagonal white line across corners of stamps)

1995 (16 May). *Multicoloured laminated cover as Type GK* **6** (75×48 mm) *with stamps printed on the cover in yellow by Walsall.*
GK6   Containing four 35p. (No. Y1755) and a pane of 4 air mail labels ....   6·25

1996 (19 Mar). *Multicoloured laminated cover as Type GK* **6** (75×48 mm) *without "International" and showing Olympic symbols on the back. Stamps printed on the cover in yellow by Walsall.*
GK7   Containing four 35p. (No. Y1755) and a pane of 4 air mail labels ....   6·50

£1.48 Booklets

GL **1** ("Worldwide Postcard Stamps" ranged left without diagonal white lines across corner of stamps)

1996 (8 July). *Multicoloured laminated cover as Type GL* **1** (75×48 mm) *showing Olympic symbols on the back. Stamps printed on the cover in bright mauve by Walsall. Inscribed "For Worldwide Postcards" on yellow tab at right.*
GL1   Containing four 37p. (No. Y1756) and a pane of 4 air mail labels ....   10·00

1997 (4 Feb). *Multicoloured laminated cover as Type GL* **1** (75×48 mm) *without Olympic symbols on the back. Stamps printed on the cover in bright mauve by Walsall. Inscribed "For Worldwide Postcards" on yellow tab at right.*
GL2   Containing four 37p. (No. Y1756) and a pane of 4 air mail labels ....   10·00

GL **3**

1997 (26 Aug)–**98.** *Multicoloured laminated cover as Type GL* **3** (75×48 mm) *printed by Walsall. Inscribed "For Worldwide Postcards" on yellow tab at right.*
GL3   Containing four 37p. (photo) (No. Y1697) and a pane of 4 new design air mail labels ....   6·00
    a. Showing validity notice on inside backcover (5.5.98)....   6·00
No. GL3 has the postage rate table on the inside back cover.

1998 (3 Aug). *Multicoloured laminated cover as Type GGA* **2** ("Create a card" design) (75×50 mm) *printed by Walsall.*
GL4   Containing four 37p. (photo) (No. Y1697) and a pane of 4 air mail labels ....   5·00
This booklet was not placed on philatelic sale until 7 September 1998.

£1.52 Booklet

1999 (26 Apr). *Multicoloured laminated cover as Type GGA* **1** (76×50 mm) *with stamps printed on cover in ultramarine by Walsall. Inscr "For Worldwide Postcards" on yellow tab at right.*
GLA1   Containing four 38p. (photo) (No. Y1701) and a pane of 4 air mail labels ....   6·00

£1.56 Booklet

GM **1**

1991 (16 Sept). *Multicoloured laminated cover as Type GM* **1** (75×49 mm) *with stamp printed on the cover in bright mauve by Walsall.*
GM1   Containing booklet pane No. X1058I and a pane of 4 air mail labels ....   11·00
No. GM1 has the horizontal edges of the pane imperforate.

£1.60 Booklet

2000 (27 Apr). *Multicoloured laminated cover as Type GGA* **1** (76×50 *mm) with stamps printed on cover in deep azure by Walsall. Inscr "For Worldwide Postcards" on yellow tab at right.*
GMA1 Containing four 40p. (photo) (No. Y1704) and a pane of 4 air mail labels .... 7·50

£1.64 Worldwide Air Mail Stamps Booklets

1993 (1 Nov). *Laminated cover as Type GM* **1** (76×50 *mm) with stamp printed on the cover in drab by Walsall.*
GN1 Containing four 41p. (No. Y1757) and a pane of 4 air mail labels .... 6·00

1995 (16 May). *Multicoloured laminated cover as Type GK* **6** (75×48 *mm) with stamps printed on the cover in drab by Walsall.*
GN2 Containing four 41p. (No. Y1757) and a pane of 4 air mail labels .... 6·00

1996 (19 Mar). *Multicoloured laminated cover as Type GK* **6** (75×48 *mm) without "International" and showing Olympic symbols on the back. Stamps printed on the cover in drab by Walsall.*
GN3 Containing four 41p. (No. Y1757) and a pane of 4 air mail labels .... 7·00

£1.80 Booklet

1987 (4 Aug). *Laminated cover as Type GA* **1** (98×60 *mm).*
GO1 Containing booklet pane No. X955n .... 9·00
No. GO1 is inscribed "20 October 1986".

£1.90 Booklets

1988 (23 Aug). *Laminated cover as Type GA* **1** (97×56 *mm).*
GP1 Containing booklet pane No. X956m .... 12·00

1988 (11 Oct). *Laminated cover as Type GA* **1** (97×56 *mm) printed by Questa.*
GP2 Containing ten 19p. (No. X1013) .... 24·00

1988 (11 Oct). *Laminated cover as Type GB* **3** (75×48 *mm) with stamp printed on the cover in bright orange-red.*
GP3 Containing booklet pane No. X956o .... 12·00
No. GP 3 is inscribed "5 September 1988" and has the horizontal edges of the pane imperforate.

1988 (11 Oct). *Laminated cover as Type GB* **3** (75×48 *mm) with stamp printed on the cover in bright orange-red by Questa.*
GP4 Containing ten 19p. (No. X1013) .... 24·00

£2.40 Booklets

1994 (9 Aug). *Laminated cover as Type GM* **1** (75×49 *mm) with stamp printed on the cover in dull blue-grey by Walsall.*
GQ1 Containing four 60p. (No. Y1758) and a pane of 4 air mail labels .... 8·00

GQ **2**

1994 (4 Oct). *Laminated cover as Type GQ* **2** (75×49 *mm) with stamp printed on the cover in dull blue-grey by Walsall.*
GQ2 Containing four 60p. (No. Y1758) and a pane of 4 air mail plus 4 "Seasons Greetings" labels .... 8·00

1995 (16 May). *Laminated cover as Type GK* **6** (75×48 *mm) with stamps printed on the cover in dull blue-grey by Walsall.*
GQ3 Containing four 60p. (No. Y1758) and a pane of 4 air mail labels .... 8·00

1996 (19 Mar). *Multicoloured laminated cover as Type GK* **6** (75×48 *mm) without "International" and showing Olympic symbols on the back. Stamps printed on the cover in dull grey blue by Walsall.*
GQ4 Containing four 60p. (No. Y1758) and a pane of 4 air mail labels .... 8·00

£2.52 Booklets

1996 (8 July). *Multicoloured laminated cover as Type GL* **1** (75×48 *mm) but inscr "Worldwide Airmail Stamps" and showing Olympic symbols on the back. Stamps printed on the cover in light emerald by Walsall. Inscribed "For items up to 20g" on yellow tab at right.*
GR1 Containing four 63p. (No. Y1759) and a pane of 4 air mail labels .... 15·00

1997 (4 Feb). *Multicoloured laminated cover as Type GL* **1** (75×48 *mm) without Olympic symbols on the back. Stamps printed on the cover in light emerald by Walsall. Inscribed "For items up to 20g" on yellow tab at right.*
GR2 Containing four 63p. (No. Y1759) and a pane of 4 air mail labels .... 15·00

1997 (26 Aug). *Multicoloured laminated cover as Type GL* **1** (75×48 *mm). Stamps printed on the cover in light emerald by Walsall. Inscribed "For items up to 20g" on yellow tab at right.*
GR3 Containing four 63p. (photo) (No. Y1720) and a pane of 4 air mail labels .... 9·00

1998 (5 May). *Multicoloured laminated cover as Type GGA* **1** (75×50 *mm). Stamps printed on the cover in light emerald by Walsall. Inscr "For items up to 20g" on yellow tab at right.*
GR4 Containing four 63p. (photo) (No. Y1720) and a pane of 4 new design air mail labels .... 9·00

£2.56 Booklets

1999 (26 Apr). *Multicoloured laminated cover as Type GGA* **1** (75×50 *mm). Stamps printed on cover in turquoise-green by Walsall. Inscr "For items up to 20g" on yellow tab at right.*
GS1 Containing four 64p. (photo) (No. Y1721) and a pane of 4 air mail labels .... 9·00

£2.60 Booklet

2000 (27 Apr). *Multicoloured laminated cover as Type GGA* **1** (76×50 *mm) with stamps printed on cover in greenish blue by Walsall. Inscr "For items up to 20g" on yellow tab at right.*
GT1 Containing four 65p. (photo) (No. Y1722) and a pane of 4 air mail labels .... 10·00

D. Barcode Booklets containing No Value Indicated stamps with barcodes on the back cover.

Panes of four 2nd Class stamps.

HA **1** Redrawn Crown (small)

1989 (22 Aug). *Laminated cover as Type HA* **1** (75×48 *mm) with stamp printed on the cover in bright blue by Walsall.*
HA1 Containing booklet pane No. 1449b .... 6·00
No. HA1 has three edges of the pane imperforate.
No. HA1 was initially sold at 56p., which was increased to 60p. from 2.10.89.

1989 (28 Nov). *Laminated cover as Type HA* **1** (75×48 *mm) with stamp printed on the cover in bright blue by Walsall containing stamps printed in photo by Harrison.*
HA2 Containing booklet pane No. 1445b .... 30·00
No. HA2 has three edges of the pane imperforate and was sold at 60p.

HA **3** Crown on white

1990 (7 Aug). *Multicoloured laminated cover as Type HA* **3** (75×48 *mm) with stamp printed on the cover in deep blue by Walsall.*
HA3 Containing booklet pane No. 1515a .... 4·00
No. HA3 has the horizontal edges of the pane imperforate.
No. HA3 was initially sold at 60p., which was increased to 68p. from 17.9.90 and to 72p. from 16.9.91.

1991 (6 Aug). *Multicoloured laminated cover as Type HA **3** (75 × 48 mm) with stamp printed on the cover in bright blue by Walsall.*
HA4   Containing booklet pane No. 1449c................................   4·00
No. HA4 has the horizontal edges of the pane imperforate.
No. HA4 was initially sold at 68p., which was increased to 72p. from 16.9.91.
No. HA4 exists with the barcode printed in either black or blue.

HA **5** Olympic Symbols

1992 (21 Jan). *Multicoloured laminated cover as Type HA **5** (75 × 48 mm) with stamp printed on the cover in bright blue by Walsall.*
HA5   Containing booklet pane No. 1449c................................   6·00
No. HA5 has the horizontal edges of the pane imperforate and was sold at 72p.

PERFORATIONS. Booklets from No. HA6 show perforations on all edges of the pane.

1993 (6 Apr). *Multicoloured laminated cover as Type HA **3** (75 × 48 mm) with stamp printed on the cover in bright blue by Walsall.*
HA6   Containing four 2nd Class stamps (No. 1670) ....   4·00
No. HA6 was initially sold at 72p., which was increased to 76p. from 1.11.93.
No. HA6 was re-issued on 6 December 1994 showing the inscriptions on the inside of the cover re-arranged.

1993 (7 Sept). *Multicoloured laminated cover as Type HA **3** (75 × 48 mm) with stamp printed on the cover in bright blue by Harrison.*
HA7   Containing four 2nd Class stamps (No. 1664) ....   4·00
No. HA7 was initially sold at 72p., which was increased to 76p. from 1.11.93.

Type HA **8** ("Second Class Stamps" centred) (with diagonal white line across corners of stamps)

1995 (10 Jan). *Multicoloured laminated cover as Type HA **8** (75 × 48 mm) with stamps printed on the cover in bright blue by Harrison.*
HA8   Containing four 2nd Class stamps (No. 1664) ....   4·00
No. HA8 was initially sold at 76p., which was increased to 80p. from 8.7.96.

1995 (12 Dec). *Multicoloured laminated cover as Type HA **8** (75 × 48 mm) with stamps printed on the cover in bright blue by Walsall, but without "Pull Open" inscription on yellow tab.*
HA9   Containing four 2nd Class stamps (No. 1670) ....   4·00
No. HA9 was initially sold at 76p, which was increased to 80p. from 8.7.96.

1996 (6 Feb). *Multicoloured laminated cover as Type HA **8** (75 × 48 mm) but without "Pull Open" inscription on yellow tab and showing Olympic symbols on the back. Stamps printed on the cover in bright blue by Walsall.*
HA10 Containing four 2nd Class stamps (No. 1670)....................   4·00
No. HA10 was initially sold at 76p., which was increased to 80p. from 8.7.96.

NOTE: From No. HA11 onwards, the printer of each booklet is identified by a small capital letter below the barcode on the outside back cover.

HA **11** ("Second Class Stamps" ranged left) (without diagonal white line across corners of stamps)

1997 (4 Feb). *Multicoloured laminated cover as Type HA **11** (75 × 48 mm). Stamps printed on the cover in bright blue by Walsall.*
HA11 Containing four 2nd Class stamps (No. 1670) ....   4·00
No. HA11 was sold at 80p.

1997 (26 Aug). *Multicoloured laminated cover as Type HA **11** (75 × 48 mm). Stamps printed on the cover in bright blue by Walsall.*
HA12 Containing four 2nd Class stamps (photo) (No. 1664).......   4·00
No. HA12 was initially sold at 80p. It was re-issued on 5 May 1998 showing the positions of the imprint and the post code notice transposed, and again on 14 March 2000 with changed telephone number and added website address. The booklet was sold at 76p. from 26.4.99.

Panes of four 1st Class stamps

1989 (22 Aug). *Laminated cover as Type HA **1** (75 × 48 mm) with stamp printed on the cover in brownish black by Walsall.*
HB1   Containing booklet pane No. 1450a ....   8·50
No. HB1 has three edges of the pane imperforate.
No. HB1 was initially sold at 76p., which was increased to 80p. from 2.10.89.

1989 (5 Dec). *Laminated cover as Type HA **1** (75 × 48 mm) with stamp printed on the cover in brownish black by Walsall containing stamps printed in photo by Harrison.*
HB2   Containing booklet pane No. 1447b ....   40·00
No. HB2 has three edges of the pane imperforate and was sold at 80p.

1990 (7 Aug). *Multicoloured laminated cover as Type HA **3** (75 × 48 mm) with stamp printed on the cover in bright orange-red by Walsall.*
HB3   Containing booklet pane No. 1516a ....   4·00
        a. Containing pane No. 1516ca ....   12·00
No. HB3 has the horizontal edges of the pane imperforate.
No. HB3 was initially sold at 80p., which was increased to 88p. from 17.9.90 and to 96p. from 16.9.91.

1992 (21 Jan). *Multicoloured laminated cover as Type HA **5** (75 × 48 mm) with stamp printed on the cover in bright orange-red by Walsall.*
HB4   Containing booklet pane No. 1516a ....   4·00
No. HB4 has the horizontal edges of the pane imperforate and was initially sold at 96p., which was increased to £1 from 1.11.93.

PERFORATIONS. Booklets from No. HB5 show perforations on all edges of the pane.

1993 (6 Apr). *Multicoloured laminated cover as Type HA **3** (75 × 48 mm) with stamp printed on the cover in bright orange-red by Harrison.*
HB5   Containing four 1st Class stamps (No. 1666) ....   6·00
No. HB5 was initially sold at 96p., which was increased to £1 from 1.11.93.

1993 (17 Aug). *Multicoloured laminated cover as Type HA **3** (76 × 50 mm) with stamp printed on the cover in bright orange-red by Walsall.*
HB6   Containing four 1st Class stamps (No. 1671)........................   4·00
No. HB6 was initially sold at 96p., which was increased to £1 from 1.11.93.

1994 (27 July). *Multicoloured laminated cover as Type HA **3** (76 × 50 mm) with stamp printed on the cover in bright orange-red by Questa.*
HB7   Containing booklet pane No. 1671l which includes a label commemorating the 300th anniv of the Bank of England ....   9·50
No. HB7 was sold at £1.

1995 (10 Jan). *Multicoloured laminated cover as Type HA **8** (75 × 48 mm) with stamps printed on the cover in bright orange-red by Walsall.*
HB8   Containing four 1st Class stamps (No. 1671) ....   4·00
No. HB8 was initially sold at £1, which was increased to £1.04 from 8.7.96.

1995 (16 May). *Multicoloured laminated cover as Type HA **8** (75×48 mm) with stamps printed on the cover in bright orange-red by Walsall.*

HB9　Containing booklet pane No. 1671la which includes a label commemorating the birth centenary of R. J. Mitchell (designer of Spitfire) .... 6·50

No. HB9 was sold at £1.

1996 (6 Feb–Aug). *Multicoloured laminated cover as Type HA **8** (75×48 mm) showing Olympic symbols on the back. Stamps printed on the cover in bright orange-red by Walsall.*

HB10　Containing four 1st Class stamps (No. 1671) .... 6·00

　　　a. Without diagonal white line across corners of stamps (Aug) £120

No. HB10 was initially sold at £1, which was increased to £1.04 from 8.7.96.

1996 (16 Apr). *Multicoloured laminated cover as Type HA **11** (75×48 mm) with stamps printed on the cover in bright orange-red by Walsall. Inscribed "Commemorative Label Inside" on yellow tab at right.*

HB11　Containing booklet pane No. 1671la (includes label commemorating the 70th birthday of Queen Elizabeth II) 7·00

No. HB11 was initially sold at £1, which was increased to £1.04 from 8.7.96.

NOTE: From No. HB12 onwards, the printer of each booklet (with the exception of No. HB19) is identified by a small capital letter below the barcode on the outside back cover.

1997 (4 Feb). *Multicoloured laminated cover as Type HA **11** (75×48 mm). Stamps printed on the cover in bright orange-red by Walsall.*

HB12　Containing four 1st Class stamps (No. 1671) .... 4·00

No. HB12 was sold at £1.04.

1997 (12 Feb). *Multicoloured laminated cover as Type HA **11** (75×48 mm). Stamps printed on the cover in bright orange-red by Walsall. Inscribed "Special Label Inside" on yellow tab at right.*

HB13　Containing booklet pane No. 1671la (includes label commemorating Hong Kong '97 international stamp exhibition) .... 6·50

No. HB13 was initially sold at £1.04.

1997 (26 Aug). *Multicoloured laminated cover as Type HA **11** (75×48 mm). Stamps printed on the cover in bright orange-red by Walsall.*

HB14　Containing four 1st Class stamps (photo) (No. 1667) .... 4·00

No. HB14 was sold at £1.04. It was re-issued on 5 May 1998 showing the positions of the imprint and the post code notice transposed, on 16 March 1999 with "Please note that the First Class rate is no longer valid to Europe" added to inside back cover and again on 14 March 2000 with changed telephone number and added website address.

1997 (21 Oct). *Multicoloured laminated cover as Type HA **11** (75×48 mm). Stamps printed on the cover in bright orange-red by Walsall. Inscribed "Commemorative Label Inside" on yellow tab at right.*

HB15　Containing booklet pane No. 1671la (litho) (includes label commemorating Commonwealth Heads of Government Meeting, Edinburgh) .... 12·00

No. HB15 was sold at £1.04.

1998 (14 Nov). *Multicoloured laminated cover as Type HA **11** (75×48 mm). Stamps printed on the cover in bright orange-red by Walsall. Inscribed "Commemorative Label Inside" on yellow tab at right.*

HB16　Containing booklet pane No. 1671la (litho) (includes label commemorating 50th birthday of the Prince of Wales) .... 8·00

No. HB16 was sold at £1.04.

1999 (12 May). *Multicoloured laminated cover as Type HA **11** (75×48 mm). Stamps printed on the cover in bright orange-red by Walsall. Inscribed "Commemorative Label Inside" on yellow tab at right.*

HB17　Containing booklet pane No. 1667m (photo) (includes label commemorating 50th anniv of Berlin Airlift) .... 8·50

No. HB17 was sold for £1.04.

1999 (1 Oct). *Multicoloured laminated cover as Type HA **11** (76×50 mm). Stamps printed on the cover in bright orange-red by Walsall. Inscribed "Commemorative Label Inside" on yellow tab at right.*

HB18　Containing booklet pane No. 1667m (photo) (includes label commemorating Rugby World Cup) .... 6·00

No. HB18 was sold at £1.04.

2000 (21 Mar). *Multicoloured laminated cover as Type HA **11** (75×48 mm). Stamps printed on the cover in olive-brown by Walsall with Postman Pat. Inscribed "Postman Pat Label Inside" on yellow tab at right.*

HB19　Containing booklet pane No. 2124bl (photo) (includes label commemorating "Stamp Show 2000", Earls Court).. 6·00

No. HB19 was initially sold at £1.04, which was increased to £1.08 from 27.4.2000.

2000 (4 Apr). *Opening of National Botanic Garden of Wales. Multicoloured laminated cover as Type HA **11** (75×48 mm). Stamps printed on the cover in olive-brown by Walsall. Inscribed "Botanic Garden Label Inside" on yellow tab at right.*

HB20　Containing booklet pane No. 2124bl .... 6·00

No. HB20 was initially sold at £1.04, which was increased to £1.08 from 27.4.2000.

Panes of eight 1st Class stamps plus pane of 2 Millennium commemoratives

HBA **1**

1999 (12 May). *Multicoloured laminated cover as Type HBA **1** (76×50 mm) showing Millennium and Machin stamps printed by Walsall.*

HBA1　Containing booklet pane No. 2085a and eight 1st Class stamps (photo) (No. 1667) .... 12·00

No. HBA1 was sold at £2.60.

1999 (21 Sept). *Multicoloured laminated cover as Type HBA **1** (76×50 mm) showing Millennium and Machin stamps printed by Walsall.*

HBA2　Containing booklet pane No. 2108a and eight 1st Class stamps (photo) (No. 1667)... 12·00

No. HBA2 was sold at £2.60.

2000 (26 May). *Multicoloured laminated cover as Type HBA **1** (76×50 mm) showing Millennium and Machin stamps printed by Walsall.*

HBA3　Containing booklet pane No. 2126ab and eight 1st Class stamps (photo) (No. 2124).. 14·00

No. HBA3 was sold at £2.70.

2000 (5 Sept). *Multicoloured laminated cover as Type HBA **1** (76×50 mm) showing Millennium and Machin stamps printed by Walsall.*

HBA4　Containing booklet pane No. 2153a and eight 1st Class stamps (photo) (No. 2124) .... 14·00

No. HBA4 was sold at £2.70.

Panes of ten 2nd Class stamps

1989 (22 Aug–2 Oct). *Laminated cover as Type HA **1** (75×48 mm) with stamp printed on the cover in bright blue by Harrison.*

HC1　Containing booklet pane No. 1445a .... 12·00

　　　a. Inside cover with new rates (2 Oct) .... 13·00

Nos. HC1/a have the horizontal edges of the pane imperforate.

No. HC1 was initially sold at £1.40, which was increased to £1.50 from 2.10.89. No. HC1a was sold at £1.50.

1989 (19 Sept). *Laminated cover as Type HA **1** (75×48 mm) with stamp printed on the cover in bright blue by Questa.*

HC2　Containing ten 2nd Class stamps (No. 1451) .... 10·00

No. HC2 has perforations on all edges of the pane and was initially sold at £1.40, which was increased to £1.50 from 2.10.89.

1990 (7 Aug). *Multicoloured laminated cover as Type HA **3** (75×48 mm) with stamp printed on the cover in deep blue by Harrison.*

HC3　Containing booklet pane No. 1511a .... 12·00

No. HC3 has the horizontal edges of the pane imperforate.

No. HC3 was initially sold at £1.50, which was increased to £1.70 from 17.9.90.

1990 (7 Aug). *Multicoloured laminated cover as Type HA **3** (75×48 mm) with stamp printed on the cover in deep blue by Questa.*

HC4　Containing ten 2nd Class stamps (No. 1513) .... 15·00

No. HC4 has perforations on all edges of the pane and was initially sold at £1.50, which was increased to £1.70 from 17.9.90.

1990 (7 Aug). *Multicoloured laminated cover as Type HA **3** (75×48 mm) with stamp printed on the cover in deep blue by Walsall.*

HC5　Containing booklet pane No. 1515b .... 8·50

No. HC5 has the horizontal edges of the pane imperforate.

No. HC5 was initially sold at £1.50, which was increased to £1.70 from 17.9.90, and to £1.80 from 16.9.91.

1991 (6 Aug). *Multicoloured laminated cover as Type HA **3** (75×48 mm) with stamp printed on the cover in bright blue by Questa.*

HC6　Containing ten 2nd Class stamps (No. 1451) .... 8·00

No. HC6 has perforations on all edges of the pane and was initially sold at £1.70, which was increased to £1.80 from 16.9.91.

1991 (6 Aug). *Multicoloured laminated cover as Type HA **3** (75×48 mm) with stamp printed on the cover in bright blue by Walsall.*

HC7　Containing booklet pane No. 1449d .... 8·00

No. HC7 has the horizontal edges of the pane imperforate.

No. HC7 was initially sold at £1.70, which was increased to £1.80 from 16.9.91.

1992 (21 Jan). *Multicoloured laminated cover as Type* HA **5** (75×48 mm) with stamp printed on the cover in bright blue by Walsall.

HC8 Containing booklet pane No. 1449d .... 8·00

No. HC8 has the horizontal edges of the pane imperforate and was initially sold at £1.80, which was increased to £1.84 from 1.11.93.

1992 (31 Mar). *Multicoloured laminated cover as Type* HA **5** (75×48 mm) with stamp printed on the cover in bright blue by Questa.

HC9 Containing ten 2nd Class stamps (No. 1451) .... 10·00

No. HC9 has perforations on all edges of the pane and was sold at £1.80.

1992 (22 Sept). *Multicoloured laminated cover as Type* HA **3** (75×48 mm) with stamp printed on the cover in bright blue by Harrison.

HC10 Containing booklet pane No. 1445a .... 9·00

No. HC10 has the horizontal edges of the pane imperforate and was sold at £1.80.

PERFORATIONS. Booklets from No. HC11 show perforations on all edges of the pane.

1993 (6 Apr). *Multicoloured laminated cover as Type* HA **3** (75×48 mm) with stamp printed on the cover in bright blue by Questa.

HC11 Containing ten 2nd Class stamps (No. 1670) .... 8·50

No. HC11 was initially sold at £1.80, which was increased to £1.90 from 1.11.93.

No. HC11 was re-issued on 17 August 1993 showing changes to the text on the inside of the cover and again on 6 September 1994 showing further changes.

1993 (1 Nov). *Multicoloured laminated cover as Type* HA **3** (75×48 mm) with stamp printed on the cover in bright blue by Walsall.

HC12 Containing ten 2nd Class stamps (No. 1670) .... 10·00

No. HC 12 was sold at £1.90.

1995 (10 Jan). *Multicoloured laminated cover as Type* HA **8** (75×48 mm) with stamps printed on the cover in bright blue by Questa.

HC13 Containing ten 2nd Class stamps (No. 1670) .... 10·00

No. HC13 was initially sold at £1.90, which was increased to £2 from 8.7.96.

1995 (12 Dec). *Multicoloured laminated cover as Type* HA **8** (75×48 mm) with stamps printed on cover in bright blue by Harrison.

HC14 Containing ten 2nd Class stamps (No. 1664) .... 8·50

No. HC14 was initially sold at £1.90, which was increased to £2 from 8.7.96.

1996 (6 Feb). *Multicoloured laminated cover as Type* HA **8** (75×48 mm) showing Olympic symbols on the back. Stamps printed on the cover in bright blue by Harrison.

HC15 Containing ten 2nd Class stamps (No. 1664)........................ 8·50

No. HC15 was initially sold at £1.90, which was increased to £2 from 8.7.96.

1996 (6 Feb). *Multicoloured laminated cover as Type* HA **8** (75×48 mm) showing Olympic symbols on the back. Stamps printed on the cover in bright blue by Questa.

HC16 Containing ten 2nd Class stamps (No. 1670) .... 10·00

No. HC16 was initially sold at £1.90, which was increased to £2 from 8.7.96.

NOTE: From No. HC17 onwards, the printer of each booklet is identified by a small capital letter below the barcode on the outside back cover.

1996 (6 Aug). *Multicoloured laminated cover as Type* HA **8** (75×48 mm) but with diagonal white lines across corners of stamps, showing Olympic symbols on the back. Stamps printed on the cover in bright blue by Harrison.

HC17 Containing ten 2nd Class stamps (No. 1664) .... 8·50

No. HC17 was sold at £2.

1996 (6 Aug). *Multicoloured laminated cover as Type* HA **11** (75×48 mm) showing Olympic symbols on the back. Stamps printed on the cover in bright blue by Questa.

HC18 Containing ten 2nd Class stamps (No. 1670) .... 10·00

No. HC18 was sold at £2.

1997 (4 Feb). *Multicoloured laminated cover as Type* HA **11** (75×48 mm). Stamps printed on the cover in bright blue by Harrison.

HC19 Containing ten 2nd Class stamps (No. 1664)........................ 8·50

No. HC19 was sold at £2.

1997 (4 Feb). *Multicoloured laminated cover as Type* HA **11** (75×48 mm). Stamps printed on the cover in bright blue by Questa.

HC20 Containing ten 2nd Class stamps (No. 1670) .... 8·50

No. HC20 was initially sold at £2. It was re-issued on 5 May 1998 showing the positions of the imprint and the post code notice transposed. The booklet was sold at £1.90 from 26.4.99.

1998 (5 May). *Multicoloured laminated cover as Type* HA **11** (75×48 mm) Stamps printed on the cover in bright blue by De La Rue.

HC21 Containing ten 2nd Class stamps (No. 1664) .... 8·50

No. HC21 was initially sold at £2, which was decreased to £1.90 from 26.4.99.

1998 (1 Dec). *Multicoloured laminated cover as Type* HA **11** (75×48 mm). Stamps printed on the cover in bright blue by Questa.

HC22 Containing ten 2nd Class stamps (No. 1664a) (photo) ...... 10·00

No. HC22 was initially sold at £2, which was decreased to £1.90 from 26.4.99. It was re-issued on 14 March 2000 with changed telephone number and added website address.

Panes of ten 1st Class stamps

1989 (22 Aug–2 Oct). *Laminated cover as Type* HA **1** (75×48 mm) with stamp printed on the cover in brownish black by Harrison.

HD1 Containing booklet pane No. 1447a .... 15·00
 a. Inside cover with new rates (2 Oct) .... 14·00

Nos. HD1/a have the horizontal edges of the pane imperforate.

No. HD1 was initially sold at £1.90, which was increased to £2 from 2.10.89. No. HD1a was sold at £2.

1989 (19 Sept). *Laminated cover as Type* HA **1** (75×48 mm) with stamp printed on the cover in brownish black by Questa.

HD2 Containing ten 1st Class stamps (No. 1452) .... 20·00

No. HD2 has perforations on all edges of the pane and was initially sold at £1.90, which was increased to £2 from 2.10.89.

1990 (7 Aug). *Multicoloured laminated cover as Type* HA **3** (75×48 mm) with stamp printed on the cover in bright orange-red by Harrison.

HD3 Containing booklet pane No. 1512a .... 12·00

No. HD3 has the horizontal edges of the pane imperforate. No. HD3 was initially sold at £2, which was increased to £2.20 from 17.9.90 and to £2.40 from 16.9.91.

1990 (7 Aug). *Multicoloured laminated cover as Type* HA **3** (75×48 mm) with stamp printed on the cover in bright orange-red by Questa.

HD4 Containing ten 1st Class stamps (No. 1514) .... 12·00

No. HD4 has perforations on all edges of the pane and was initially sold at £2, which was increased to £2.20 from 17.9.90 and to £2.40 from 16.9.91.

1990 (7 Aug). *Multicoloured laminated cover as Type* HA **3** (75×48 mm) with stamp printed on the cover in bright orange-red by Walsall.

HD5 Containing booklet pane No. 1516b .... 12·00

No. HD5 has the horizontal edges of the pane imperforate and was intially sold at £2, which was increased to £2.20 from 17.9.90 and to £2.40 from 16.9.91.

1992 (21 Jan). *Multicoloured laminated cover as Type* HA **5** (75×48 mm) with stamp printed on the cover in bright orange-red by Harrison.

HD6 Containing booklet pane No. 1512a .... 12·00

No. HD6 has the horizontal edges of the pane imperforate and was sold at £2.40.

1992 (21 Jan). *Multicoloured laminated cover as Type* HA **5** (75×48 mm) with stamp printed on the cover in bright orange-red by Walsall.

HD7 Containing booklet pane No. 1516b........................ 12·00

No. HD7 has the horizontal edges of the pane imperforate and was sold at £2.40.

1993 (9 Feb). *Multicoloured laminated cover as Type* HA **3** (77×44 mm) with advertisement for Greetings Booklet on reverse showing Rupert Bear as in Type KX **5**. Stamp printed on the cover in bright orange-red by Walsall.

HD8 Containing booklet pane No. 1516b .... 12·00

No. HD8 has the horizontal edges of the pane imperforate and was sold at £2.40.

PERFORATIONS. Booklets from No. HD9 show perforations on all edges of the pane.

1993 (6 Apr). *Multicoloured laminated cover as Type* HA **3** (75×48 mm) with stamp printed on the cover in bright orange-red by Harrison.

HD9 Containing ten 1st Class stamps (No. 1666) .... 12·00

No. HD9 was initially sold at £2.40, which was increased to £2.50 from 1.11.93.

No. HD9 was re-issued on 17 August 1993 showing changes to the text on the inside of the covers.

1993 (6 Apr). *Multicoloured laminated cover as Type* HA **3** (75×48 mm) with stamp printed on the cover in bright orange-red by Walsall.

HD10 Containing ten 1st Class stamps (No. 1671) .... 12·00

No. HD10 was initially sold at £2.40, which was increased to £2.50 from 1.11.93.

No. HD10 was re-issued on 17 August 1993 showing changes to the text on the inside of the covers.

1993 (1 Nov). *Laminated cover as Type* HA **3** (75×50 mm) with stamp printed on the cover in bright orange-red by Questa.

HD11 Containing ten 1st Class stamps (No. 1671) .... 12·00

No. HD11 was sold at £2.50.

No. HD11 was re-issued on 4 October 1994 showing changes to the text on the inside of the cover.

1993 (1 Nov). *Laminated cover as Type* HA **3** (75×50 mm) with advertisement for Greetings Booklet on reverse showing Rupert Bear as in Type KX **5**. Stamp printed on the cover in bright orange-red by Walsall.

HD12 Containing ten 1st Class stamps (No. 1671) .... 12·00

1994 (22 Feb). *Multicoloured laminated cover as Type HA* **3** *(75×48 mm) with stamp printed on the cover in bright orange-red by Walsall. Inscribed "FREE POSTCARDS" on yellow tab at right.*
HD13 Containing ten 1st Class stamps (No. 1671) and additional
      page giving details of Greetings Stamps postcard offer ..   12·00
  No. HD13 was sold at £2.50.

1994 (1 July). *Multicoloured laminated covers as Type HA* **3** *(76×50 mm) with advertisement for Greetings Booklet on reverse showing Rupert Bear as in Type KX* **5**. *Stamp printed on the cover in bright orange-red by Walsall. Inscribed "OPEN NOW Chance to win a kite" on yellow tab at right.*
HD14 Containing ten 1st Class stamps (No. 1671) with "Better
      luck next time." etc on inside back cover .... 12·00
HD15 Containing ten 1st Class stamps (No. 1671) with "You've
      Won!" etc on inside back cover .... 12·00
  Nos. HD14/15 sold at £2.50 each and were initially only available from branches of W.H. Smith and Son. They were issued in connection with a competition in which the prizes were Paddington Bear kites. The booklets were not available from Royal Mail philatelic outlets until 4 October 1994.

HD **16**

1994 (20 Sept). *Multicoloured laminated covers as Type HD* **16** *(76×50 mm) printed by Walsall. Inscribed "ORDER YOURS INSIDE" on yellow tab at right.*
HD16 Containing ten 1st Class stamps (No. 1671) with "DO
      NOT OPEN UNTIL....."on front cover .... 12·00
HD17 Containing ten 1st Class stamps (No. 1671) with "KEEP IN
      TOUCH" on front cover .... 12·00
HD18 Containing ten 1st Class stamps (No. 1671) with "HAPPY
      BIRTHDAY" on front cover .... 12·00
HD19 Containing ten 1st Class stamps (No. 1671) with "What's
      Happenin'?" on front cover .... 12·00
  Nos. HD16/19 were sold at £2.50 each.

1995 (10 Jan). *Multicoloured laminated cover as Type HA* **8** *(75×48 mm) with stamps printed on the cover in bright orange-red by Harrison.*
HD20 Containing ten 1st Class stamps (No. 1666) .... 14·00

1995 (10 Jan). *Multicoloured laminated cover as Type HA* **8** *(75×48 mm) with stamps printed on the cover in bright orange-red by Questa.*
HD21 Containing ten 1st Class stamps (No. 1671) .... 12·00

1995 (10 Jan). *Multicoloured laminated cover as Type HA* **8** *(75×48 mm) with stamps printed on the cover in bright orange-red by Walsall.*
HD22 Containing ten 1st Class stamps (No. 1671) .... 12·00
  Nos. HD20/2 were initially sold at £2.50 each, which was increased to £2.60 from 8.7.96.

HD **23**

1995 (14 Feb). *Multicoloured laminated cover as Type HD* **23** *(76×50 mm) showing card, Thorntons chocolates and box, printed by Walsall. Inscribed "DETAILS INSIDE" on yellow tab at right.*
HD23 Containing ten 1st Class stamps (No. 1671) .... 12·00
  No. HD23 was sold at £2.50.

1995 (4 Apr). *Multicoloured laminated cover as Type HA* **8** *(76×48 mm) with stamps printed on cover in bright orange-red by Harrison.*
HD24 Containing ten 1st Class stamps (No. 1667) .... 12·00
  No. HD24 was sold at £2.50.

1995 (24 Apr). *Multicoloured laminated cover as Type HA* **8** *(75×48 mm) with stamps printed on cover in bright orange-red by Walsall. Inscribed "W H Smith Special Offer" on yellow tab at right.*
HD25 Containing ten 1st Class stamps (No. 1671) .... 12·00
  No. HD25 was sold at £2.50 and was initially only available from W. H. Smith branches and offered 50p. off the purchase of own brand stationery. The booklet was not placed on philatelic sale until 3 October 1995. Its price was increased to £2.60 on 8.7.96.

1995 (26 June). *Multicoloured laminated cover as Type HA* **8** *(76×48 mm) with stamps printed on cover in bright orange red by Questa. Inscribed "Sainsbury's Promotion" on yellow tab at right.*
HD26 Containing ten 1st Class stamps (No. 1671) .... 12·00
  No. HD26 was sold at £2.50 and was initially only available from Sainsbury's branches and offered the chance to win a year's free shopping. The booklet was not placed on philatelic sale until 5 September 1995. Its price was increased to £2.60 on 8.7.96

1995 (4 Sept). *Multicoloured laminated cover as Type HD* **23** *(76×48 mm) showing ceramic figures of Benjy Bear and Harry Hedgehog, printed by Harrison.*
HD27 Containing ten 1st Class stamps (No. 1667) .... 12·00
  No. HD27 was initially sold at £2.50, which was increased to £2.60 from 8.7.96.

1996 (6 Feb). *Multicoloured laminated cover as Type HA* **8** *(76×48 mm) showing Olympic symbols on the back. Stamps printed on the cover in bright orange-red by Walsall.*
HD28 Containing ten 1st Class stamps (No. 1671) .... 12·00
  No. HD28 was initially sold at £2.50, which was increased to £2.60 from 8.7.96.

1996 (19 Feb). *Multicoloured laminated cover as Type HD* **23** *(76×48 mm) showing Walt Disney World, printed by Harrison.*
HD29 Containing ten 1st Class stamps (No. 1667) .... 12·00
  No. HD 29 was initially sold at £2.50, which was increased to £2.60 from 8.7.96.

1996 (19 Mar). *Multicoloured laminated cover as Type HA* **8** *(76×48 mm) showing Olympic symbols on the back, printed by Harrison.*
HD30 Containing ten 1st Class stamps (No. 1667) .... 12·00
  No. HD30 was initially sold at £2.50, which was increased to £2.60 from 8.7.96.

HD **31**

1996 (13 May). *Multicoloured laminated covers as Type HD* **31** *(76×48 mm) showing woman lighting Olympic torch, printed by Harrison, with each booklet showing a scratchcard on the reverse based on different Olympic events.*
HD31 Containing ten 1st Class stamps (No. 1667) (Shot Put)...... 11·00
HD32 Containing ten 1st Class stamps (No. 1667) (Hurdles)....... 11·00
HD33 Containing ten 1st Class stamps (No. 1667) (Archery)....... 11·00
  Nos. HD31/3 were initially each sold at £2.50, which was increased to £2.60 from 8.7.96.

NOTE: From No. HD34 onwards, the printer of each booklet is identified by a small capital letter below the barcode on the outside back cover.

1996 (15 July). *Multicoloured laminated cover as Type HA* **11** *(76×48 mm) showing Olympic symbols on the back. Stamps printed on the cover in bright orange-red by Walsall. Inscribed "WHSmith Offer Inside" on yellow tab at right.*
HD34 Containing ten 1st Class stamps (No. 1671) .... 11·00
  No. HD34 was sold at £2.60 and was initially only available from branches of W. H. Smith and Sons. It was issued in connection with a special offer of AA/OS Leisure Guides. The booklets were not available from Royal Mail philatelic outlets until 17 September 1996.

1996 (6 Aug). *Multicoloured laminated cover as Type HA* **11** *(76×48 mm), but with diagonal white line across corners of stamps and showing Olympic symbols on the back. Stamps printed on the cover in bright orange-red by Harrison.*
HD35 Containing ten 1st Class stamps (No. 1667) .... 12·00
  No. HD35 was sold at £2.60.

1996 (6 Aug). *Multicoloured laminated cover as Type HA* **11** *(76×48 mm) showing Olympic symbols on the back. Stamps printed on the cover in bright orange-red by Walsall.*
HD36 Containing ten 1st Class stamps (No. 1671) .... 11·00
  No. HD36 was sold at £2.60.

1996 (9 Sept). *Multicoloured laminated cover as Type HD **31** (76×48 mm) showing iced cakes on front and back, printed by Walsall. Inscribed "OPEN FOR DETAILS" on yellow tab at right.*
HD37 Containing ten 1st Class stamps (No. 1671) .... 11·00
   No. HD37 was sold at £2.60.

1996 (7 Oct). *Multicoloured laminated cover as Type HA **11** (76×48 mm) showing Olympic symbols on the back. Stamps printed on cover in bright orange-red by Walsall. Inscribed "Offer Inside" on yellow tab at right.*
HD38 Containing ten 1st Class stamps (No. 1671) .... 11·00
   No. HD38 was sold at £2.60 and was initially only available from ASDA stores and offered £1 off greetings cards. The booklet was not placed on philatelic sale until 13 January 1997.

1997 (4 Feb). *Multicoloured laminated cover as Type HA **11** (76×48 mm). Stamps printed on the cover in bright orange-red by Harrison.*
HD 39 Containing ten 1st Class stamps (No. 1667) .... 11·00
   No. HD39 was sold at £2.60.

1997 (4 Feb). *Multicoloured laminated cover as Type HA **11** (76×48 mm). Stamps printed on the cover in bright orange-red by Walsall.*
HD40 Containing ten 1st Class stamps (No. 1671) .... 11·00
   No. HD40 was sold at £2.60.

1997 (21 Apr). *Royal Golden Wedding. Multicoloured laminated cover as Type HA **11** (76×48 mm). Stamps printed on the cover in gold by Harrison.*
HD41 Containing ten 1st Class stamps (No. 1668) .... 11·00
   No. HD41 was sold at £2.60.

1997 (21 Apr). *Royal Golden Wedding. Multicoloured laminated cover as Type HA **11** (76×48 mm). Stamps printed on the cover in gold by Walsall.*
HD42 Containing ten 1st Class stamps (No. 1668) .... 12·00
   No. HD42 was sold at £2.60.

1997 (15 Sept). *Multicoloured laminated cover as Type HD **31** (76×48 mm) showing a tropical beach scene printed by Harrison. Inscr "FIRST CLASS TRAVEL" on front, and "OPEN FOR DETAILS" on yellow tab at right.*
HD43 Containing ten 1st Class stamps (No. 1668) .... 11·00
   No. HD43 was sold at £2.60.

1997 (8 Nov). *Multicoloured laminated cover as Type HA **11** (76×48 mm). Stamps printed on the cover in bright orange-red by Walsall.*
HD44 Containing ten 1st Class stamps (photo) (No. 1667) .... 11·00
   No. HD44 was sold at £2.60. It was re-issued on 5 May 1998 showing the positions of the imprint, which was now vertical, and the post code notice transposed and again on 16 March 1999 with "Please note that the First Class rate is no longer valid to Europe" added to inside back cover.

HD **45**

1998 (2 Feb). *Multicoloured laminated cover as Type HD **45** (76×48 mm) showing Disney illustration printed by De la Rue, with a scratch card on the reverse. Inscr "See reverse for Scratch and Win" on yellow tab at right.*
HD45 Containing ten 1st Class stamps (photo) (No. 1667) .... 11·00
   No. HD45 was sold at £2.60.

HD **46**

1998 (27 Apr). *Multicoloured laminated cover as Type HD **46** (76×48 mm) showing Peugeot 106 printed by De La Rue. Inscr "WIN A PEUGEOT 106" on yellow tab at right.*
HD46 Containing ten 1st Class stamps (photo) (No. 1667) .... 11·00
   No. HD46 was sold at £2.60. This booklet was not placed on philatelic sale until 23 June 1998.

1998 (5 May). *Multicoloured laminated cover as Type HA **11** (76×48 mm). Stamps printed on the cover in bright orange-red by De La Rue.*
HD47 Containing ten 1st Class stamps (photo) (No. 1667) .... 7·75
   No. HD47 was initially sold at £2.60, which was increased to £2.70 from 27.4.2000.

1998 (1 July). *Multicoloured laminated cover as Type HD **46** (76×48 mm) showing JVC Camcorder printed by De La Rue. Inscr "WIN A JVC CAMCORDER" on yellow tab at right.*
HD48 Containing ten 1st Class stamps (photo) (No. 1667) .... 11·00
   No. HD48 was sold at £2.60. This booklet was not placed on philatelic sale until 27 August 1998.

1998 (3 Aug). *Multicoloured laminated cover as Type GGA **2** (76×48 mm) inscr ("Create a card design"), printed by De La Rue.*
HD49 Containing ten 1st Class stamps (photo) (No. 1667) .... 11·00
   No. HD49 was sold at £2.60. This booklet was not placed on philatelic sale until 7 September 1998.

1998 (7 Sept). *Multicoloured laminated cover as Type HA **11** (75×49 mm), with stamps printed on the cover in bright orange-red by Questa.*
HD50 Containing ten 1st Class stamps (litho) (No. 1671) .... 11·00
   No. HD50 was sold at £2·60.

1998 (1 Dec). *Multicoloured laminated cover as Type HA **11** (75×48 mm). Stamps printed on the cover in bright orange-red by Questa.*
HD51 Containing ten 1st Class stamps (photo) (No. 1667a) .... 16·00
   No. HD51 was sold at £2.60. It was re-issued on 16 March 1999 with "Please note that the First Class rate is no longer valid to Europe" added to inside back cover.

2000 (6 Jan). *Multicoloured laminated cover as Type HA **11** (75×48 mm). Millennium definitives printed on the cover in olive-brown by Questa.*
HD52 Containing ten 1st Class stamps (photo) (No. 2124d) .... 11·00
   No. HD52 was sold at £2.60, which was increased to £2.70 from 27 April 2000. It was re-issued on 14 March 2000 with a changed telephone number on the inside back cover.

2000 (6 Jan). *Multicoloured laminated cover as Type HA **11** (75×48 mm). Millennium definitives printed on the cover in olive-brown by Walsall.*
HD53 Containing ten 1st Class stamps (photo) (No. 2124) .... 11·00
   No. HD53 was initially sold at £2.60, which was increased to £2.70 from 27 April 2000. It was re-issued on 14 March 2000 with a changed telephone number on the inside back cover.

Panes of four European Air Mail stamps

HF **1**

1999 (19 Jan). *Multicoloured laminated cover as Type HF **1** (75×50 mm). Stamps printed on the cover in deep blue by Walsall. Inscr "For items up to 20g" on yellow tab at right.*
HF1   Containing four European Air Mail stamps (No. 1669) and pane of four air mail labels .... 6·00
   No. HF1 was initially sold at £1.20 which was increased to £1.36 from 25.10.99 and £1.44 from 27.4.2000.
   It was re-issued on 27 April 2000 showing an amended Customer Services telephone number on the inside back cover.

E. Barcode Booklets containing Penny Black Anniversary stamps with barcodes on back cover.

60p. Booklet

JA **1**

1990 (30 Jan). *Laminated cover as Type JA* **1** *(75×48 mm) showing Penny Black Anniversary stamp in bright blue. Containing booklet pane No. 1475l, printed in litho by Walsall.*
JA1   Containing booklet pane No. 1475l .... 7·00
No. JA1 has three edges of the pane imperforate.

80p. Booklets

1990 (30 Jan). *Laminated cover as Type JA* **1** *(75×48 mm) showing Penny Black Anniversary stamp in brownish black and cream. Containing booklet pane No. 1476m, printed in litho by Walsall.*
JB1   Containing booklet pane No. 1476m .... 8·00
No. JB1 has three edges of the pane imperforate.

1990 (17 Apr). *Laminated cover as Type JA* **1** *(75×48 mm) showing Penny Black Anniversary stamp printed on the cover in brownish black by Walsall. Containing stamps printed in photo by Harrison.*
JB2   Containing booklet pane No. 1469r .... 8·00
No. JB2 has three edges of the pane imperforate.

£1.50 Booklets

1990 (30 Jan). *Laminated cover as Type JA* **1** *(75×48 mm) showing Penny Black Anniversary stamp in bright blue. Containing booklet pane No. 1467l printed in photo by Harrison.*
JC1   Containing booklet pane No. 1467l .... 10·00
No. JC1 has the horizontal edges of the pane imperforate.

1990 (17 Apr). *Laminated cover as Type JA* **1** *(75×48 mm) showing Penny Black Anniversary stamp printed on the cover in bright blue, printed in litho by Questa.*
JC2   Containing ten 15p. (No. 1477) .... 20·00

1990 (12 June). *Laminated cover as Type JA* **1** *(75×48 mm) showing Penny Black Anniversary stamp in bright blue. Containing booklet pane No. 1475m, printed in litho by Walsall.*
JC3   Containing booklet pane No. 1475m .... 12·00
No. JC3 has three edges of the pane imperforate.

£2 Booklets

1990 (30 Jan). *Laminated cover as Type JA* **1** *(75×48 mm) showing Penny Black Anniversary stamp in brownish black and cream. Containing booklet pane. No. 1469m, printed in photo by Harrison.*
JD1   Containing booklet pane No. 1469m .... 11·00
No. JD1 has the horizontal edges of the pane imperforate.

1990 (17 Apr). *Laminated cover as Type JA* **1** *(75×48 mm) showing Penny Black Anniversary stamp printed on the cover in brownish black, printed in litho by Questa.*
JD2   Containing ten 20p. (No. 1478) .... 22·00

1990 (12 June). *Laminated cover as Type JA* **1** *(75×48 mm) showing Penny Black Anniversary stamp in brownish black and cream. Containing booklet pane No. 1476n, printed in litho by Walsall.*
JD3   Containing booklet pane No. 1476n .... 18·00
No. JD3 has three edges of the pane imperforate.

F. Barcode Booklets containing Greetings stamps with barcodes on the back cover.

£2 Greetings Booklet

KX **1** (*Illustration reduced. Actual size 135×85 mm*)

(Des Michael Peters and Partners)

1990 (6 Feb). *Greetings Stamps. Cover printed in scarlet, lemon and black as Type* KX **1** *(135×85 mm). Containing booklet pane No. 1483a, and a separate sheet of 12 greetings labels.*
KX1   "Smile" design cut-out showing stamps inside .... 26·00

Greetings Booklets containing No Value Indicated stamps

KX **2**

(Des T. Meeuwissen)

1991 (5 Feb). *Greetings Stamps. Multicoloured laminated cover as Type* KX **2** *(95×69 mm). Containing booklet pane No. 1536a, including twelve special greetings labels in a block (3×4) at right, attached by the selvedge.*
KX2   "Good Luck" charms design .... 15·00
No. KX2 was initially sold at £2.20, which was increased to £2.40 from 16.9.91.

KX **3**

(Des Michael Peters and Partners)

1991 (26 Mar). *Greetings Stamps. Multicoloured laminated cover as Type* KX **3** *(95×69 mm). Containing booklet pane No. 1550a, including twelve special greetings labels in a block (3×4) at right, attached by the selvedge.*
KX3   Laughing pillar box design .... 12·00
      a. Amended text to inside back cover (3.3.92) .... 14·00

No. KX3 was initially sold at £2.20, which was increased to £2.40 from 16.9.91 and to £2.50 from 1.11.93.

The note on the inside back cover of No. KX3 is headed "Greetings Stamps". In No. KX3a there is no heading but details of the validity of the stamps to European destinations have been added.

KX **4**

(Des Trickett and Webb)

1992 (28 Jan). *Greetings Stamps. Multicoloured laminated cover as Type KX* **4** *(95×69 mm). Containing booklet pane No. 1592a, including twelve special greetings labels in a block (3×4) at right, attached by selvedge.*

KX4   Pressed Flowers design .... 13·00

No. KX4 was initially sold at £2.40, which was increased to £2.50 from 1.11.93 and to £2.60 from 8.7.96.

KX **5**

(Des Newell and Sorrell)

1993 (2 Feb). *Greetings Stamps. Multicoloured laminated cover as Type KX* **5** *(96×60 mm). Containing booklet pane No. 1644a and pane of twenty special greetings labels in a block (5×4), both panes attached by a common gutter margin.*

KX5   Children's Characters design .... 12·00

No. KX5 was initially sold at £2.40, which was increased to £2.50 from 1.11.93.

No. KX5 was re-issued on 15 June 1993 with "Thompson" corrected to "Thomson" (bottom line at left) and on 17 August 1993 with "Sorell" corrected to "Sorell".

KX **6**

(Des Newell and Sorrell)

1994 (1 Feb). *Greetings Stamps. Multicoloured cover as Type KX* **6** *(96×60 mm). Containing booklet pane No. 1800a and pane of twenty special greetings labels in a block (5×4), both panes attached by a common gutter margin.*

KX6   Children's Characters design .... 14·00

No. KX6 was initially sold at £2.50, which was increased to £2.60 from 8.7.96.

KX **7**

(Des Newell and Sorrell)

1995 (21 Mar)–**96**. *Greetings Stamps. Multicoloured cover as Type KX* **7** *(96×60 mm). Containing booklet pane No. 1858a and pane of twenty special greetings labels in a block (5×4), both panes attached by a common gutter margin. Inscr "Pull Open" on yellow strip at right.*

KX7   Clown design .... 12·00
      a. No inscr on yellow strip (5.2.96) .... 14·00

Nos. KX7/a were initially sold at £2.50, which was increased to £2.60 from 8.7.96.

KX **8**

(Des M. Wolff)

1996 (26 Feb–11 Nov). *Greetings Stamps. Multicoloured cover as Type KX* **8** *(96×60 mm). Containing booklet pane No. 1905a and pane of twenty special greetings labels in a block (5×4), both panes attached by a common gutter margin.*

KX8   "MORE! LOVE" design .... 12·00
      a. Containing pane No. 1905pa (11 Nov) .... 42·00

No. KX8 was initially sold at £2.50, which was increased to £2.60 from 8.7.96.

No. KX8a shows a redesigned inside front cover which omits references to 1996 dates.

KX **9**

(Des Tutssels)

1997 (6 Jan). *Greetings Stamps. 19th-century Flower Paintings. Multicoloured cover as Type KX* **9** *(96×61 mm). Containing booklet pane No. 1955a and pane of twenty special greetings labels in a block (5×4), both panes attached by a common gutter margin.*

KX9   Gentiana acaulis design .... 12·00

No. KX9 was sold at £2.60. It was re-issued on 16 March 1999 with "Please note that the First Class rate is no longer valid to Europe" added to inside front cover.

1997 (3 Feb). *Greetings Stamps. 19th-century Flower Paintings. Multicoloured cover as Type KX **9** (96×61 mm) but with box inscribed "WIN A BEAUTIFUL BOUQUET INSTANTLY?" printed in yellow on red over the flower on the front and with a scratch card on the inside back cover. Inscribed "Open now – See if you've won" on yellow tab at right. Containing booklet pane No. 1955a and pane of twenty special greetings labels in a block (5×4), both panes attached by a common gutter margin.*

KX10 *Gentiana acaulis* design .... 12·00
    No. KX10 was sold at £2.60.

KX **11**

(Des Tutssels)

1998 (5 Jan). *Greetings Stamps. 19th-century Flower Paintings. Multicoloured cover as Type KX **11** (96×61 mm). Inscribed "See reverse for special offer" on yellow tab at right. Containing booklet pane No. 1955a and pane of twenty special greetings labels in a block (5×4), both attached by a common gutter margin.*

KX11 Chocolate design .... 14·00
    No. KX11 was sold at £2.60.

1998 (3 Aug). *Greetings Stamps. 19th-century Flower Paintings. Multicoloured cover as Type GGA **2** (88×61 mm) printed by Walsall. Containing booklet pane No. 1955a and pane of twenty special greetings labels in a block (5×4), both attached by a common gutter margin.*

KX12 "Create a card" design .... 12·00
    No. KX12 was sold at £2.60. This booklet was not placed on philatelic sale until 7 September 1998.

G. Barcode Booklets containing Christmas stamps with barcode on the back.

LX **1**

(Des A. Davidson)

1990 (13 Nov). *Christmas. Multicoloured laminated cover as Type LX **1** (96×60 mm). Containing booklet pane No. 1526b, attached by the selvedge.*

LX1 £3.40, Snowman design .... 11·00

1991 (12 Nov). *Multicoloured laminated cover as Type LX **1**, but 95×70 mm. Containing booklet pane No. 1582b attached by the selvedge.*

LX2 £3.60, Holly design .... 11·00

LX **3**

(Des Karen Murray)

1992 (10 Nov). *Multicoloured laminated cover as Type LX **3** (95×70 mm). Containing booklet pane No. 1634a attached by the selvedge.*

LX3 £3.60, Santa Claus and Reindeer design .... 11·00

1993 (9 Nov). *Multicoloured laminated covers as Type LX **3**, but 95×60 mm, each showing Santa Claus and Reindeer. Panes attached by selvedge.*

LX4 £2.50, containing ten 25p. stamps (No. 1791) .... 9·00
LX5 £3.80, containing twenty 19p. stamps (No. 1790) .... 12·00
    No. LX4 was only available from Post Offices in the Central T.V. area and from philatelic outlets.

LX **6**

(Des Yvonne Gilbert)

1994 (1 Nov). *Multicoloured laminated covers as Type LX **6** (95×60 mm), showing different Nativity Play props. Panes attached by selvedge.*

LX6 £2.50, containing ten 25p. stamps (No. 1844) .... 7·00
LX7 £3.80, containing twenty 19p. stamps (No. 1843) .... 11·00

LX **8**

(Des K. Lilly)

1995 (30 Oct). *Multicoloured laminated covers as Type LX **8** (95×60 mm), showing Robins as depicted on the contents. Panes attached by selvedge.*

LX8 £2.40, containing four 60p. stamps (No. 1900) plus 4 air mail labels .... 7·50
LX9 £2.50, containing ten 25p. stamps (No. 1897) .... 7·50
LX10 £3.80, containing twenty 19p. stamps (No. 1896) .... 12·00

LX **11**

1996 (28 Oct). *Multicoloured laminated covers as Type LX **11** (95×60 mm), showing scenes from the Nativity as depicted on the contents. Panes attached by selvedge.*
LX11   Containing ten 1st Class stamps (No. 1951) ....   12·00
LX12   Containing twenty 2nd Class stamps (No. 1950) ....   14·00
    No. LX11 was sold at £2.60 and No. LX12 at £4.

LX **13**

1997 (27 Oct). *Multicoloured laminated covers as Type LX **13** (95×60 mm), showing Father Christmas and crackers as depicted on the contents. Panes attached by selvedge.*
LX13   Containing ten 1st Class stamps (No. 2007) ....   11·00
LX14   Containing twenty 2nd Class stamps (No. 2006) ....   14·00
    No. LX13 was sold at £2.60 and No. LX14 at £4.

LX **15**

1998 (2 Nov). *Multicoloured red laminated covers as Type LX **15** (95×60 mm), showing angels as depicted on the contents. Panes attached by selvedge.*
LX15   £2.60 booklet containing ten 26p. stamps (No. 2065) ......   8·00
LX16   £4 booklet containing twenty 20p. stamps (No. 2064) .....   12·00

LX **17**

1999 (2 Nov). *Multicoloured laminated covers as Type LX **17** (95×70 mm), showing designs as depicted on the contents. Panes attached by selvedge.*
LX17   £2.60 booklet containing ten 26p. stamps (No. 2116) ....   8·50
LX18   £3.90 booklet containing twenty 19p. stamps (No. 2115)   12·00

LX **19**

2000 (7 Nov). *Multicoloured laminated covers as Type LX **19** (96×70 mm), showing designs as depicted on the contents. Inscribed "Season's Greetings" on yellow tab at right. Panes attached by selvedge.*
LX19   £2.70, containing ten 1st Class stamps (No. 2171) ....   11·00
LX20   £3.80, containing twenty 2nd Class stamps (No. 2170) ....   14·00

2001 (6 Nov). *Self-adhesive booklet containing Nos. 2238a and 2239a, each with a multicoloured header label showing barcode and Royal Mail emblem and further label at foot with telephone numbers, folded to form booklets 119×81 mm.*
LX21   £3.24, booklet containing twelve 1st Class stamps
       (No. 2239a)..   14·00
LX22   £4.56, booklet containing twenty-four 2nd Class stamps
       (No. 2238a)..   18·00
    Nos. LX21/2 show the surplus self-adhesive paper around each stamp retained.

2002 (5 Nov). *Self-adhesive booklet containing Nos. 2321a and 2322a, each with a multicoloured header label showing barcode and Royal Mail emblem and further label at foot with telephone numbers, folded to form booklets 105×72 mm.*
LX23   £3.24, booklet containing twelve 1st Class stamps
       (No. 2322a)..   14·00
LX24   £4.56, booklet containing twenty-four 2nd Class stamps
       (No. 2321a)..   18·00
    No. LX23 was sealed into a cellophane packet which also contained a Lord of the Rings game card.
    Nos. LX23/4 show the surplus self-adhesive paper around each stamp retained.

2003 (4 Nov). *Self-adhesive booklet containing Nos. 2410a and 2411a, each with a multicoloured header label showing barcode and Royal Mail emblem and further label at foot with telephone numbers, folded to form booklets 106×71 mm.*
LX25   £3.36, booklet containing twelve 1st Class stamps
       (No. 2411a)..   14·00
LX26   £4.80, booklet containing twenty-four 2nd Class stamps
       (No. 2410a)..   18·00
    Nos. LX25/6 have the surplus self-adhesive paper around each stamp removed.

2004 (2 Nov). *Self-adhesive booklet containing Nos. 2495a and 2496a, each with a multicoloured header label showing barcode and Royal Mail emblem and further label at foot with contact information, folded to form booklets 105×71 mm.*

LX27 £3.36 booklet containing twelve 1st Class stamps
(No. 2496a).. 14·00
LX28 £5.04 booklet containing twenty-four 2nd Class stamps
(No. 2495a).. 20·00
Nos. LX27/8 have the surplus self-adhesive paper around each stamp removed.

2005 (1 Nov). *Self-adhesive booklet containing Nos. 2582a and 2583a, each with a multicoloured header label showing barcode and Royal Mail emblem and further label at foot with contact information, folded to form booklets 106×71 mm.*

LX29 £3.60 booklet containing twelve 1st Class stamps
(No. 2583a).. 14·00
LX30 £5.04 booklet containing twenty-four 2nd Class stamps
(No. 2582a).. 18·00
Nos. LX29/30 have the surplus self-adhesive paper around each stamp removed.

LX **31**

2006 (7 Nov). *Covers as Type* LX **31** *(75×57 mm). Self-adhesive.*
LX31 £2.76 booklet containing twelve 2nd Class stamps
(No. 2678a) (Type LX **31**)...................................... 10·00
LX32 £3.84 booklet containing twelve 1st Class stamps
(No. 2679a) (red cover inscr "12×1st")..................... 14·00
Nos. LX31/2 have the surplus self-adhesive paper around each stamp removed.

2007 (6 Nov). *Covers as Type* LX **31** *(75×57 mm). Self-adhesive.*
LX33 £2.88 booklet containing twelve 2nd Class stamps
(No. 2789a) (Type LX **31**)...................................... 10·00
LX34 £4.08 booklet containing twelve 1st Class stamps
(No. 2790a) (red cover inscr '12×1st') .... 14·00
Nos. LX33/4 have the surplus self-adhesive paper around each stamp removed.

2008 (4 Nov). *Covers as Type* LX **31** *(75×57 mm). Self-adhesive.*
LX35 £3.24 booklet containing twelve 2nd Class stamps
(No. 2876a) (Type LX **31**)...................................... 10·00
a. "Oh YES it is!" along right-hand edge of pane.................. 10·00
LX36 £4.32 booklet containing twelve 1st Class stamps
(No. 2877a) (red cover inscr "12×1st")..................... 14·00
a. "It's behind you!" along right-hand edge of pane .... 14·00
Nos. LX35/6 have the surplus self-adhesive paper around each stamp removed.
No. LX35 is inscr "Oh NO it isn't!" and No. LX36 "Abracadabra!", both along the right-hand edges of the booklet panes.

2009 (3 Nov). *Christmas. Covers as Type* LX **31** *(75×57 mm). Self-adhesive.*
LX37 £3.60 booklet containing twelve 2nd class stamps
(No. 2991a) (Type LX 31).. 10·00
LX38 £4.68 booklet containing twelve 1st class stamps
(No. 2992a) (red cover inscr '12×1st') .... 14·00
Nos. LX37/8 have the surplus self-adhesive paper around each stamp removed.

LX **32** Wallace and Gromit posting Christmas Cards

2010 (2 Nov). *Christmas. Multicoloured covers as Type* LX **32** *(74×58 mm). Self-adhesive.*
LX39 £3.84 booklet containing twelve 2nd class stamps
(No. 3128a) (Type LX**32**)...................................... 8·50
LX40 £4.92 booklet containing twelve 1st class stamps
(No. 3129a) (cover as Type LX **32** but red background)... 11·00
Nos. LX39/40 have the surplus self-adhesive paper around each stamp removed.

H. Self-adhesive Barcode Booklets containing No Value Indicated stamps.

NOTE. All booklets in this section show the surplus self-adhesive paper around each stamp retained, unless otherwise stated.

Containing six 2nd class stamps.

MA **1**

2001 (29 Jan). *Multicoloured laminated cover as Type* MA **1** *(74×56 mm). Stamps printed on the cover in bright blue by Walsall.*
MA1 Containing six 2nd Class self-adhesive stamps (No. 2039) . 6·00
No. MA1 was sold at £1.14. It was re-issued on 1 August 2001 showing "Cod Post" added to the "Ffôn Testun" inscription on the back cover.
No. MA1 exists imperforate.

Containing six 1st Class stamps

2001 (29 Jan). *Multicoloured laminated cover as Type* MA **1** *(74×56 mm). Stamps printed on the cover in bright orange-red by Walsall.*
MB1 Containing six 1st Class self-adhesive stamps (No. 2040) 7·00
No. MB1 was sold at £1.62. It was re-issued on 1 August 2001 showing "Cod Post" added to the "Ffôn Testun" inscription on the back cover.

MB **2**

2001 (29 Jan). *Multicoloured laminated cover as Type* MB **2** *(74×56 mm). Stamps printed on the cover in bright orange-red with portrait of Queen Victoria by Walsall.*

MB2   Containing No. 2040l (includes label commemorating
            death centenary of Queen Victoria)... 20·00
No. MB2 was sold at £1.62.

MB **3**

2002 (5 June). *Gold laminated cover as Type* MB **3** *(74×56 mm) by Questa.*

MB3   Containing six 1st Class self-adhesive stamps (No. 2295)   6·00
No. MB3 was sold at £1.62. It shows the surplus self-adhesive paper around each stamp removed and a single notch at top right.

2002 (5 June) – **2008**. *Gold laminated cover as Type* MB **3** *(74×56 mm) by Walsall.*

MB4   Containing six 1st Class self-adhesive stamps (No. 2295)   6·00
            a. Inside cover with Smilers advertisement (27.1.05) ....   6·00
            b. Back cover with added text about new pricing
            structure (25.4.06) ....   6·00
            c. Inside cover with "To find the correct postcodes for
            your mail" notice (5.6.07) ....   6·00
            d. Inside cover with commemorative inscription for
            Machin Anniversary (5.6.07) ....   6·00
            e. Inside cover with Harry Potter stamps advertisement
            (28.8.07) ....   6·00
            f. Inside cover with postcode text in English and Welsh
            (20.9.07) ....   6·00
            g. Inside cover with *Carry On* stamps advertisemant
            (10.6.08) ....   6·00
No. MB4 was sold at £1.62. It shows the surplus self-adhesive paper around each stamp removed and a single notch at top right.

No. MB4 was re-issued on 27 January 2005 (MB4a) with a Smilers advertisement (showing No. 2262 and photograph of baby) on the inside front cover. It was re-issued again on 26 July 2005 with a different Smilers advertisement (showing No. 2261 and photograph of bride).

No. MB4a was available from Tallents House from 27 January 2005, and from general post offices from 22 March 2005.

No. MB4b does not have Smilers advertisement.

The added text on the back cover of No. MB4b reads "Valid for items up to 60g before 21 August 2006. Under new pricing structure from 21 August 2006 – valid for postal items up to: 240 mm Long; 165 mm Wide; 5 mm Thick; 100g Weight."

The text on the back cover of Nos. MB4c/g reads "Valid for items up to: 240 mm Long 165 mm Wide 5 mm Thick 100g Weight".

No. MB4d has Arnold Machin's signature along the right hand edge of the booklet pane.

No. MB4g has characters from *Carry On* films illustrated along the right -hand edge of the booklet pane.

2002 (4 July). *Multicoloured laminated cover as Type* MA **1** *(74×56 mm) with stamps printed on the cover in bright orange-red by Questa.*

MB5   Containing six 1st Class self-adhesive stamps (No. 2010)   6·00
No. MB5 was sold at £1.62.

MB **6** ("The Real Network" added below logo)

2003 (27 Mar). *Gold cover with multicoloured emblem as Type* MB **6** *(74×56 mm) by Walsall.*

MB6   Containing six 1st Class self-adhesive stamps (No. 2295)   8·00
No. MB6 was initially sold at £1.62. It shows the surplus self-adhesive paper around each stamp removed and has a single notch at top right. No. MB6 exists imperforate.

MB **7** (Supporting London 2012)

2004 (15 June). *London's bid to host Olympic Games, 2012. Gold cover with multicoloured emblem as Type* MB **7** *(74×56 mm) by Walsall.*

MB7   Containing six 1st Class self-adhesive stamps (No. 2295)   10·00
No. MB7 was sold at £1.62. It has the surplus self-adhesive paper around each stamp removed and a single notch at top right.

Containing six 1st Class stamps

2009 (31 Mar)–**10**. *Gold cover with multicoloured emblem as Type* MB **3** *(74×57 mm) by Walsall.*

MB8   Containing six 1st Class self-adhesive stamps
            (No. U2951) ....   8·00
            b. Inside cover with inscription and emblem for London
            2010 Festival of Stamps (30.3.10) ....   5·25
No. MB8 was originally sold at £2.16. It has the surplus self-adhesive paper around each stamp removed and a single small notch at top right. The e-mail address on the inside front cover reads 'www.royalmail.com/ Postcodes4free'.

No. MB8 was re-issued on 26 January 2010 with a lower case p in this email address 'www.royalmail.com/postcodes4free'.

No. MB8 was re-issued again on 19 August 2010 with the printer's name omitted from the back cover.

No. MB8b has 'LONDON 2010 FESTIVAL OF STAMPS' along the right hand edge of the booklet pane.

Containing ten 2nd Class stamps

2001 (29 Jan). *Multicoloured laminated cover as Type* MA **1** *(74×56 mm). Stamps printed on the cover in bright blue by Questa.*

MC1   Containing ten 2nd Class self-adhesive stamps (No. 2039)   8·00
No. MC1 was sold at £1.90 and was intended for use in stamp machines.

Containing ten 1st Class stamps

2001 (29 Jan). *Multicoloured laminated cover as Type* MA **1** *(74×56 mm). Stamps printed on the cover in bright orange-red by Questa.*

MD1   Containing ten 1st Class self-adhesive stamps (No. 2040)   12·00
No. MD1 was sold at £2.70 and was intended for use in stamp machines.

Containing 12 2nd Class stamps

2001 (29 Jan). *Multicoloured laminated cover as Type MA **1** (74×56 mm). Stamps printed on the cover in bright blue by Questa.*
ME1   Containing twelve 2nd Class self-adhesive stamps
    (No. 2039) .... 10·00
    No. MF1 was sold at £2.28. It was re-issued on 1 August 2001 showing "Cod Post" added to the "Ffôn Testun" inscription on the back cover.

ME **2**

2002 (4 July). *Multicoloured laminated cover as Type ME **2** (74×57 mm) printed by Questa with the surplus self-adhesive paper around each stamp removed.*
ME2   Containing twelve 2nd Class self-adhesive stamps
    (No. 2039) .... 10·00
    No. ME2 was sold at £2.28. It shows the surplus self-adhesive paper around each stamp removed and two notches at top right.

ME **3** ("The Real Network" added below logo)

2003 (27 Mar). *Blue cover with multicoloured emblem as Type ME **3** (74×57 mm) by Walsall.*
ME3   Containing twelve 2nd Class self-adhesive stamps
    (No. 2039) .... 10·00
    No. ME3 was initially sold for £2.28. It shows the surplus self-adhesive paper around each stamp removed and has two notches at top right.

2004 (15 June). *Blue cover with multicoloured emblem as Type ME **2** (74×56 mm) by Walsall.*
ME4   Containing twelve 2nd Class self-adhesive stamps
    (No. 2039) .... 12·00
    a. Back cover with added text about new pricing
    structure (25.4.06) .... 12·00
    b. Back cover with text about validity (5.6.07) .... 12·00
    No. ME4 was sold for £2.52. It has the surplus self-adhesive paper around each stamp removed and has two notches at top right.
    The back cover of No. ME4a has added text as No. MB4b.
    The back cover of No. ME4b has text as No. MB4c/d.

Containing 12 2nd Class stamps

2009 (31 Mar). *Blue cover with multicoloured emblem as Type ME **2** (74×57 mm) by Walsall.*
ME5   Containing twelve 2nd Class self-adhesive stamps
    (No. U2947) .... 9·00
    No. ME5 was originally sold at £3.24. It has the surplus self-adhesive paper around each stamp removed and has two small notches at top right.
    No. ME5 was re-issued on 19 August 2010 with the printer's name omitted from the back cover.

Containing 12 1st Class stamps

2001 (29 Jan). *Multicoloured laminated covers as Type MA **1** (74×56 mm). Stamps printed on the covers in bright orange-red by Questa (No. MF1) or Walsall (No, MF2).*
MF1   Containing twelve 1st Class self-adhesive stamps
    (No. 2040) (Questa) .... 14·00
MF2   Containing twelve 1st Class self-adhesive stamps
    (No. 2040) (Walsall) .... 14·00
    Nos. MF1/2 were each sold at £3.24. They were re-issued on 1 August 2001 showing "Cod Post" added to the "Ffôn Testun" inscription on the back covers.

2002 (5 June)–**2007**. *Gold laminated cover as Type MB **3** (74×56 mm) by Walsall.*
MF3   Containing twelve 1st Class self-adhesive stamps
    (No. 2295) .... 14·00
    a. Back cover with added text about new pricing
    structure (25.4.06) .... 14·00
    b. Back cover with text about validity (5.6.07) .... 14·00
    No. MF3 was sold at £3.24. It shows the surplus self-adhesive paper around each stamp removed and a single notch at the top right hand edge to facilitate identification by the blind.
    The back cover of No. MF3a has added text as No. MB4b.
    The back cover of No. MF3b has text as No. MB4c/d.

2003 (27 Mar). *Gold cover with multicoloured emblem as Type ME **3** (74×57 mm) by Walsall.*
MF4   Containing twelve 1st Class self-adhesive stamps
    (No. 2295) .... 14·00
    No. MF4 was initially sold for £3.24. It shows the surplus self-adhesive paper around each stamp removed and has a single notch at top right.

Containing 12 1st Class stamps

2009 (31 Mar). *Gold cover with multicoloured emblem as Type MB **3** (74×57 mm) by Walsall.*
MF5   Containing twelve 1st Class self-adhesive stamps
    (No. U2952) .... 12·00
    No. MF5 was originally sold for £4.32. It has the surplus self-adhesive paper around each stamp removed and has a single small notch at top right.
    It has a 'Walsall Security Printers Limited, UK' inscription along the left-hand edge of the back cover.
    No. MF5 was re-issued on 15 December 2009 without this inscription.

Containing 20 1st Class stamps

MG **1**

1993 (19 Oct). *Multicoloured cover as Type MG **1** (91×77 mm).*
MG1   Containing booklet pane No. 1789a .... 20·00
    No. MG1 was initially sold at £4.80 which was increased to £5 from 1.11.93.

Containing six E stamps

2002 (4 July). *Multicoloured laminated cover as Type ME **2** (74×57 mm) printed by Walsall with the surplus self-adhesive paper around each stamp removed.*
MH1   Containing six E stamps (No. 2296) and six Air Mail
    labels.. 16·00
    No. MH1 was sold at £2.22. It shows the surplus self-adhesive paper around each stamp removed.

2003 (28 May). *Multicoloured cover as Type MB **6** (74×57 mm with "The Real Network" added below logo) printed by Walsall with the surplus self-adhesive paper around each stamp removed.*
MH2   Containing six E stamps (No. 2296) and six Air Mail
    labels.. 16·00
    No. MH2 was sold at £2.28.

Containing four Europe stamps

All booklets in this section show the surplus self-adhesive paper around each stamp removed.

MI **1** ("The Real Network" below logo)

2003 (27 Mar). *Ultramarine cover with multicoloured emblem as Type MI* **1** *(74×57 mm) by Walsall.*
MI1   Containing four Europe self-adhesive stamps (No. 2358)
and four Air Mail labels.. 12·00
No. MI1 was sold at £2.08.

MI **2**

2004 (15 June). *Ultramarine cover with multicoloured emblem as Type MI* **2** *(74×57 mm) by Walsall.*
MI2   Containing four Europe self-adhesive stamps (No. 2358)
and four Air Mail labels.. 10·00
No. MI2 was sold at £2.28.

2010 (30 Mar). *Deep green cover with multicoloured emblem as Type MI* **2** *(74×57 mm) by Walsall.*
MI3   Containing four Europe self-adhesive stamps
(No. 2358a) and four air mail labels .... 5·00

Containing four Worldwide stamps

All booklets in this section show the surplus self-adhesive paper around each stamp removed.

2003 (27 Mar). *Red cover with multicoloured emblem as Type MI* **1** *(74×57 mm) by Walsall.*
MJ1   Containing four Worldwide self-adhesive stamps
(No. 2359) and four Air Mail labels .... 16·00
No. MJ1 was sold at £4·48.

2004 (15 June). *Red cover with multicoloured emblem as Type MI* **2** *(74×57 mm) by Walsall.*
MJ2   Containing four Worldwide self-adhesive stamps
(No. 2359) and four Air Mail labels .... 18·00
No. MJ2 was sold at £4.48.

2010 (30 Mar). *Deep mauve cover with multicoloured emblem as Type MI* **2** *(74×57 mm) by Walsall.*
MJ3   Containing four Worldwide self-adhesive stamps
(No. 2359a) and four air mail labels .... 8·00

Containing four Worldwide postcard stamps

All booklets in this section have the surplus self-adhesive paper around each stamp removed.

2004 (1 Apr). *Grey-black cover with multicoloured emblem as Type MI* **2** *(74×57 mm) by Walsall.*
MJA1   Containing four Worldwide postcard self-adhesive
stamps (No. 2357a) and four Air Mail labels .... 6·00
No. MJA1 was sold for £1.72.

I. Self-adhesive. Barcode Booklets containing stamps with face values.

NOTE. All booklets in this section show the surplus self-adhesive paper around each stamp removed.

£2.52 Booklets

2002 (4 July). *Multicoloured laminated cover as Type ME* **2** *(74×57 mm) printed by Walsall with the surplus self-adhesive paper around each stamp removed.*
NA1   Containing six 42p. stamps (No. 2297) and six Air Mail
labels.. 35·00

2003 (28 May). *Multicoloured cover as Type MB* **6** *(74×57 mm with "The Real Network" added below logo) printed by Walsall.*
NA2   Containing six 42p. stamps (No. 2297) and six Air Mail
labels.. 30·00

£4.08 Booklets

2002 (4 July). *Multicoloured laminated cover as Type ME* **2** *(74×57 mm) printed by Walsall with the surplus self-adhesive paper around each stamp removed.*
NB1   Containing six 68p. stamps (No. 2298) and six Air Mail
labels.. 38·00

2003 (28 May). *Multicoloured cover as Type MB* **6** *(74×57 mm with "The Real Network" added below logo) printed by Walsall.*
NB2   Containing six 68p. stamps (No. 2298) and six Air Mail
labels.. 38·00

J. Self-adhesive Barcode Booklets containing No Value Indicated Special or Occasions issues, with Definitive stamps.

NOTE. All booklets in this section show the surplus self-adhesive paper around each stamp retained, unless otherwise stated.

PM **1**

2001 (13 Feb). *Cats and Dogs. Multicoloured cover as Type PM* **1** *(84×64 mm). Printed by Walsall.*
PM1   (£3.24) booklet containing twelve 1st stamps (No.
2187b).. 40·00

PM **2**

2001 (17 Apr). *Centenary of Royal Navy Submarine Service. Multicoloured cover as Type PM* **2** *(75×57 mm). Printed by Questa.*
PM2   (£1.62) booklet containing No. 2207a.................... £110

2001 (4 Sept). *Punch and Judy Show Puppets. Multicoloured cover as Type PM* **2** *(74×57 mm). Printed by Questa.*
PM3   (£1.62) booklet containing No. 2230a...................................... 25·00

2001 (22 Oct). *Flags and Ensigns. Multicoloured cover as Type* PM **2** *(74×57 mm). Printed by Questa.*
PM4   (£1.62) booklet containing No. 2208a...................................... 25·00

2002 (2 May). *50th Anniv of Passenger Jet Aviation. Airliners. Multicoloured cover as Type PM* **2** *(74×57 mm). Printed by Questa.*
PM5   (£1.62) booklet containing No. 2290a...................................... 12·00

2002 (21 May). *World Cup Football Championship, Japan and Korea. Multicoloured cover as Type PM* **2** *(74×57 mm). Printed by Walsall.*
PM6   (£1.62) booklet containing No. 2293a...................................... 12·00

PM **7**

2002 (10 Sept). *Bridges of London. Gold cover with multicoloured emblem and stamp illustration as Type PM* **7** *(74×57 mm). Printed by Questa.*
PM7   (£1.62) booklet containing No. 2314a...................................... 12·00
No. PM7 shows the surplus self-adhesive paper around each stamp removed and a single notch at top right.

2003 (4 Mar). *"Occasions" Greetings Stamps. Gold cover with multicoloured emblem and stamp illustration as Type PM* **7** *(74×57 mm). Printed by Questa.*
PM8   (£1.62) booklet containing No. 2264ab.................................... 14·00
No. PM8 shows the surplus self-adhesive paper around each stamp removed and a single notch at top right.

PM **9** ("The Real Network" added below logo)

2003 (29 Apr). *Extreme Endeavours. Gold cover with multicoloured emblem and stamp illustration as Type PM* **9** *(74×57 mm). Printed by De La Rue.*
PM9   (£1.62) booklet containing No. 2366a...................................... 14·00
No. PM9 shows the surplus self-adhesive paper around each stamp removed and has a single notch at top right.

2003 (15 July). *A British Journey: Scotland. Gold cover with multicoloured emblem and stamp illustration as Type PM* **9** *(74×57 mm). Printed by De La Rue.*
PM10   (£1.68) booklet containing No. 2391a...................................... 14·00
No. PM10 shows the surplus self-adhesive paper around each stamp removed and has a single notch at top right.

2003 (18 Sept). *Classic Transport Toys. Gold cover with multicoloured emblem and stamp illustration as Type PM* **7** *(74×57 mm). Printed by De La Rue.*
PM11   (£1.68) booklet containing No. 2403a...................................... 14·00
No. PM11 shows the surplus self-adhesive paper around each stamp removed and has a single notch at top right.

2004 (16 Mar). *A British Journey: Northern Ireland. Gold cover with multicoloured emblem and stamp illustration as Type PM* **7** *(74×57 mm). Printed by De La Rue.*
PM12   (£1.68) booklet containing No. 2445a...................................... 14·00
No. PM12 shows the surplus self-adhesive paper around each stamp removed and has a single notch at top right.

2004 (13 Apr). *Ocean Liners. Gold cover with multicoloured emblem and stamp illustration as Type PM* **7** *(74×57 mm). Printed by De La Rue.*
PM13   (£1.68) booklet containing No. 2455a...................................... 14·00
No. PM13 has the self-adhesive paper around each stamp removed and has a single notch at top right.

2004 (15 June). *A British Journey: Wales. Gold cover with multicoloured emblem and stamp illustration as Type PM* **7** *(74×57 mm). Printed by De La Rue.*
PM14   (£1.68) booklet containing No. 2472a...................................... 15·00
No. PM14 has the self-adhesive paper around each stamp removed and has a single notch at top right.

PM **15**

2008 (13 May). *Beside the Seaside. Red cover with multicoloured emblem (74×57 mm) as Type PM* **15***. Printed by Walsall.*
PM15   (£2.16) booklet containing No. 2848a...................................... 10·00
No. PM15 has the self-adhesive paper removed from around the 1st class gold stamps only and has a single notch at top right.

2009 (10 Mar). *Design Classics. Red cover with multicoloured emblem as Type PM* **15** *(74×57 mm). Printed by Walsall.*
PM16   (£2.16) booklet containing pane No. 2911a .... 10·00
No. PM16 has the self-adhesive paper removed from around the 1st class gold stamps (No. U2949) only and has a single notch at top right.

2009 (21 Apr). *Design Classics. Red cover with multicoloured emblem as Type PM* **15** *(74×57 mm). Printed by Walsall.*
PM17   (£2.34) booklet containing pane No. 2913a .... 10·00
No. PM17 has the self-adhesive paper removed from around the 1st class gold stamps (No. U2949) only and has a single notch at top right.

2009 (21 May). *50th Anniv of NAFAS (National Association of Flower Arrangement Societies). Red cover with multicoloured emblem as Type PM* **15** *(74×57 mm). Printed by Walsall.*
PM18   (£2.34) booklet containing No. 2942a...................................... 12·00
No. PM18 has the self-adhesive paper removed from around the 1st class gold stamps only and has a single notch at top right.

2009 (18 Aug). *Design Classics. Red cover with multicoloured emblem as Type PM* **15** *(74×57 mm). Printed by Walsall.*
PM19   (£2.34) booklet containing pane No. 2914a .... 5·25
No. PM19 has the self-adhesive paper removed from around the 1st class gold stamps (No. U2949) only and has a single notch at top right.

2009 (17 Sept). *Design Classics. Red cover with multicoloured emblem as Type PM* **15** *(74×57 mm). Printed by Walsall.*
PM20   (£2.34) booklet containing pane No. 2915a .... 5·25
No. PM20 has the self-adhesive paper removed from around the 1st class gold stamps (No. U2949) only and has a single notch at top right.

2010 (7 Jan). *Olympic and Paralympic Games, London (2012). Red cover with multicoloured emblem as Type PM* **15** *(74×57 mm). Printed by Walsall.*
PM21   (£2.34) booklet containing pane No. 3020a .... 5·50
No. PM21 has the self-adhesive paper removed from around the 1st class gold stamps (No. U2949) only and has a single notch at top right.

2010 (25 Feb). *Olympic and Paralympic Games, London (2012). Red cover with multicoloured emblem as Type* PM **15** *(74×57 mm). Printed by Walsall.*
PM22   (£2.34) booklet containing pane No. 3022a .... 5·50
No. PM22 has the self-adhesive paper removed from around the 1st class gold stamps (No. U2965) only and has a single notch at top right.

2010 (15 June). *Mammals. Red cover with multicoloured emblem as Type PM* **15** *(74×57 mm). Printed by Walsall.*
PM23   (£2.46) booklet containing pane No. 3095a .... 5·50
No. PM23 has the self-adhesive paper removed from around the 1st class gold stamps (No. U2965) only and has a single notch at top right.

2010 (27 July). Olympic and Paralympic Games, London (2012). Red cover with multicoloured emblem as Type PM **15** (74×57 mm). Printed by Walsall.

PM24 (£2.46) booklet containing pane No. 310/a .... 5·50

No. PM24 has the self-adhesive paper removed from around the 1st class gold stamps (No. U2965) only and has a single notch at top right.

2010 (15 Sept). British Design Classics. Red cover with multicoloured emblem as Type PM **15** (74×57 mm). Printed by Walsall.

PM25 (£2.46) booklet containing pane No. 2915b.......................... 5·50

No. PM25 has the self-adhesive paper removed from around the 1st class gold stamps (No. U2965) only and has a single notch at top right.

2010 (12 Oct). Olympic and Paralympic Games, London (2012). Red cover with multicoloured emblem as Type PM 15 (74×57 mm). Printed by Walsall.

PM26 (£2.46) booklet containing pane No. 3108ab........................ 5·50

No. PM26 has the self-adhesive paper removed from around the 1st class gold stamps (No. U2965) only and has a single notch at top right.

2011 (11 Jan). 'F.A.B. The Genius of Gerry Anderson'. Red cover with multicoloured emblem as Type PM **15** (74×57 mm). Printed by Walsall.

PM27 (£2.46) booklet containing pane No. 3143a .... 5·50

No.PM27 has the self-adhesive paper removed from around the 1st class gold stamps (No. U2965) only and has a single notch at top right.

2011 (24 Feb). 50th Anniv of the British Heart Foundation. Red cover with multicoloured emblems as Type PM **15** (74×57 mm). Printed by Walsall.

PM28 (£2.46) booklet containing pane No. 3153a .... 5·50

No. PM28 has the self-adhesive paper removed from around the 1st class gold stamps (No. U2965) only and has a single notch at top right.

K. Self-adhesive Barcode Booklets containing No Value Indicated "Smilers" stamps in definitive size.

Containing six "Smilers" stamps

NOTE. Nos. QA1–4 have the self-adhesive paper around each stamp removed and have a single notch at top right.

QA **1**

2005 (4 Oct). Gold cover with multicoloured emblem as Type QA **1** (74×56 mm) by Walsall.

QA1 (£1.80) booklet containing No. 2567a...................... 15·00

QA **2**

2006 (17 July). Gold cover with multicoloured emblem as Type QA **2** (74×56 mm) by Walsall.

QA2 (£1.92) booklet containing No. 2567a .... 18·00

2006 (17 Oct). Gold cover with multicoloured emblem as Type QA **1** (74×56 mm) by Walsall.

QA3 (£1.92) containing No. 2672a .... 12·00

2008 (28 Feb). Gold cover with multicoloured emblem as Type QA **2** (74×56 mm) by Walsall.

QA4 (£2.04) booklet containing No. 2819a..................................... 10·00

L. Self-adhesive Barcode Booklets containing stamps with value indicator at upper left.

Containing four 2nd Class Large stamps

RA **1**

2006 (15 Aug). Blue cover with multicoloured emblem as Type RA **1** (74×57 mm) by Walsall.

RA1 Containing four 2nd Class Large self-adhesive stamps (No. 2656) .... 8·00

No. RA1 was sold at £1.48. It has the surplus self-adhesive paper around each stamp removed and two notches at top right for identification by the blind.

2009 (31 Mar). Blue cover with multicoloured emblem as Type RA **1** (74×57 mm) by Walsall.

RA2 Containing four 2nd Class Large self-adhesive stamps (No. U2943) .... 5·00

No. RA2 was originally sold for £1.68. It has the surplus self-adhesive paper around each stamp removed and two large notches at top right. No. RA2 was re-issued on 22 March 2011 with the printer's name omitted from the book cover.

Containing four 1st Class Large stamps

RB **1**

2006 (15 Aug). Gold cover with multicoloured emblem as Type RB **1** (74×57 mm) by Walsall.

RB1 Containing four 1st Class Large self-adhesive stamps (No. 2657) .... 8·00

No. RB1 was sold at £1.76. It has the surplus self-adhesive paper around each stamp removed and a single notch at top right.

2009 (31 Mar). Gold cover with multicoloured emblem as Type RB **1** (74×57 mm) by Walsall.

RB2 Containing four 1st Class Large self-adhesive stamps (No. U2944) .... 6·00

No. RB2 was originally sold for £2.08. It has the surplus self-adhesive paper around each stamp removed and a large notch at top right. No. RB2 was re-issued on 22 March 2011 with the printer's name omitted from the back cover.

Containing six 1st class stamps

2006 (12 Sept)–**2007**. Gold cover with multicoloured emblem as Type MB **3** (74×57 mm) by Walsall.

RC1 Containing six 1st Class self-adhesive stamps (No. 2655) .. 10·00

a. Inside cover with "don't just send a stamp" advertisement (2.10.06) .... 11·00

b. Inside cover with "To find the correct postcodes for your mail" notice (1.2.07) .... 10·00

No. RC1 was sold at £1.92. It has the surplus self-adhesive paper around each stamp removed and a notch at top right.

Containing 12 2nd class stamps

2006 (12 Sept). *Blue cover with multicoloured emblem as Type* ME **2** *(74×57 mm) by Walsall.*
RD1   Containing twelve 2nd Class self-adhesive stamps
         (No. 2654) .... 10·00
         No. RD1 was sold at £2.76. It has the surplus self-adhesive paper around each stamp removed and two notches at top right.

Containing 12 1st class stamps

2006 (12 Sept). *Gold cover with multicoloured emblem as Type* MB **3** *(74×57 mm) by Walsall.*
RE1   Containing twelve 1st Class self-adhesive stamps (No. 2655)   14·00
         No. RE1 was sold at £3.84. It has the surplus self-adhesive paper around each stamp removed and a notch at top right.

M. Self-adhesive Barcode Booklets containing No Value Indicated "Smilers" stamps in definitive size, with Definitive stamps.

NOTE. Nos. SA1 and SA2 have the surplus self-adhesive paper around each stamp removed and a notch at top right.

2007 (16 Jan). *Gold cover with multicoloured emblem as Type* MB **3** *(74×57 mm) by Walsall.*
SA1   (£1.92) booklet containing No. 2693a .... 30·00

2008 (15 Jan). *Gold cover with multicoloured emblem as Type* MB **3** *(74×57 mm) by Walsall.*
SA2   (£2.04) booklet containing No. 2693b .... 20·00

POST OFFICE LABEL SHEETS

At the Stamp Show 2000 International Stamp Exhibition visitors could purchase sheets of 10 × 1st class stamps in the "Smiles" designs (as Nos. 1550/9), each stamp having a *se-tenant* label on which the exhibition visitor's picture was printed, the photographs being taken in a booth at the exhibition.

For those unable to visit the exhibition, the same sheet could be purchased from the Philatelic Bureau and from Post Office philatelic outlets with a "Stamp Show 2000" label in place of the photograph.

For Christmas 2000, sheets of 20 × 19p stamps in the "Robin in Pillar Box" design (as No. 1896) or 10 × 1st class "Father Christmas with Cracker" design (as No. 2007) were available through the Philatelic Bureau, with *se-tenant* labels as part of a "customised" service, purchasers supplying their own photographs for reproduction on the *se-tenant* label.

This service has continued under the name "Smilers", after the initial set of stamp designs employed, and was also made available at photo-booths at selected post offices. Corporate label panes, allowing commercial and charitable organisations to have their logo or message reproduced on the *se-tenant* labels were made available through the Bureau from 2000.

Label sheets have continued to be offered with a standard greeting or message. These "Generic Smilers" have been available from the Philatelic Bureau or from philatelic outlets.

As "personalised", "corporate" and "generic" label sheets could only be purchased at a premium over the face value of the stamps within them, they are not given full listing in this catalogue; neither are individual stamps (with or without their *se-tenant* label), some of which are identifiable as having come from Label Sheets, due to perforation, phosphor or printing differences.

The list which follows comprises the "generic" sheets only. Differences between the stamp in the Label Sheets and those of the standard issues are given under the respective listings in this catalogue.

An asterisk (*) in the listing indicates a difference in process, phosphor or perforation from the original design.

LS **1**

2000 (22 May). *The Stamp Show 2000. Type* LS **1**. *Photo Questa. Original selling price £2.95.* P 15×14.
LS1   10×(1st) "Smiles" stamps, as Nos. 1550/9 and attached
         labels... 45·00

LS **2**

LS **3**

2000 (3 Oct)–**01**. *Christmas. Types* LS **2** *and* LS **3**. *Photo Questa. Original selling price £3.99 (LS* **2/2a**) *and £2.95 (LS* **3/a**). P 15×14.
LS2   20×19p. "Robin in Pillar Box" stamps, as No. 1896
         and attached labels (Imprint "Post Office 2000").........   £200
         a. Imprint "Consignia 2001" (9.10.01)....................................   £700
LS3   10×(1st) "Father Christmas with Cracker" stamps, as
         No. 2007 and attached labels (Imprint "Post Office
         2000")...   £200
         a. Imprint "Consignia 2001" (9.10.01)....................................   £700

LS **4**

2001 (5 June). *"Occasions". Type* LS **4**. *Litho* Questa. Original selling price £5.95.* P 14×14½.
LS4   20×(1st) "Occasions" stamps as Nos. 2182/6 in four
         vertical columns of five with attached labels.....................   £200

2001 (3 July). *"Smiles". As Type* LS **1** *but with greetings shown in attached labels. Litho* Questa. Original selling price £2.95.* P 14½×14*.
LS5   10×(1st) "Smiles" stamps, as Nos. 1550/9 and attached
         labels...   £220

LS **6**

2001 (18 Dec). *"Greetings Cartoons". Type* LS **6**. *Litho Questa. Original selling price £2.95. Two phosphor bands.* P 14½×14 *(without* elliptical holes).*
LS6   10×(1st) Greetings Cartoons, as Nos. 1905p/14p and
         attached labels... 55·00

LS **7**

2002 (23 Apr). *"Occasions" Stamps. Type* LS **7**. *Litho Questa. Original selling price* £5.95. P 14*.
LS7 20×(1st) "Occasions" stamps as Nos. 2260/4 in four
vertical columns of five with attached labels .... 95·00

LS **8**

2002 (21 May). *Football World Cup. Type* LS **8**. *Litho* Questa. *Original selling price* £5.95. P 14½×14.
LS8 20×(1st) as bottom right quarter of flag stamp in
MS2292 and attached labels .... 40·00

LS **9**

2002 (1 Oct). *"Smiles". Type* LS **9**. *Litho* Questa. *Original selling price* £5.95. P 15×14.
LS9 10×(1st) "Teddy Bear" and 10 × (1st) Dennis the Menace,
as Nos. 1550/1, each with attached labels .... 40·00

LS **10**

2002 (1 Oct). *Christmas. Type* LS **10**. *Litho* Questa. *Original selling price* £5.95. P 14½×14*.
LS10 20×(1st) "Father Christmas with Cracker", as No. 2007,
with attached greetings labels .... 42·00

LS **11**

2003 (21 Jan). *Flower Paintings. Type* LS **11**. *Litho Questa. Original selling price* £5.95. P 14½×14 (*without* elliptical holes).
LS11 20×(1st) Flowers Greetings Stamps, as Nos. 1955/64
(two of each design) with floral labels attached .... 48·00

LS **12**

2003 (4 Feb). *"Occasions". Type* LS **12**. *Litho Questa. Original selling price* £5.95. P 14½×14.
LS12 20×(1st) "Tick box" Occasions stamps, as Nos. 2337/42
(four of Nos. 2338 and 2340 and 3 each of the others)
with attached labels .... 35·00
a. "Multiple Choice" in green.
"Multiple Choice" at top left of sheet is generally in red. LS12a is
believed to have come from trial sheets which were put on sale in
error.

LS **13**

2003 (29 July). *Crossword Cartoons. Type* LS **13**. *Litho Questa. Original selling price* £6.15. *Two phosphor bands.* P 14½×14 (*without* elliptical holes).
LS13 20×(1st) Cartoons as Nos. 1905p/14p with "Crossword"
labels attached .... 30·00

LS **14**

2003 (30 Sept). *Christmas. "Winter Robins". Type* LS **14**. *Litho* De La Rue. *Original selling price* £6.15. P 14½.
LS14 20×(1st) Winter Robins, self-adhesive, as No. 2239 with
labels alongside .... 30·00

LS **15**

LS **16**

2003 (4 Nov). *Christmas. Types LS* **15** *and LS* **16**. *Litho* De La Rue. Original selling prices £4.20 (2nd) and £6.15 (1st). P 14½×14.*
LS15   20×(2nd) Ice Sculptures, self-adhesive, as No. 2410 with labels showing ice sculptures of polar fauna alongside ...   38·00
LS16   20×(1st) Ice Sculptures, self-adhesive, as No. 2411 with labels showing photographs of polar fauna alongside.....   38·00

LS **17**

2004 (30 Jan). *Hong Kong Stamp Expo. Litho Walsall. Original selling price £6.15.*
LS17   20×(1st) "Hello" greetings stamps, as No. 2262 with labels alongside ....   25·00

LS **18**

2004 (3 Feb). *Occasions "Entertaining Envelopes". Type LS* **18**. *Litho De La Rue. Original selling price £6.15. P 14½×14.*
LS18   20×(1st) "Entertaining Envelopes" greetings stamps, as Nos. 2424/8 (four of each design) with attached labels....   25·00

LS **19**

2004 (25 May). *Royal Horticultural Society. Type LS* **19**. *Litho* Walsall. Original selling price £6.15. P 14½.*
LS19   20×(1st) Dahlia, as No. 2457 with attached labels...............   26·00

LS **20**

2004 (27 July). *"Rule Britannia". Type LS* **20**. *Litho* Walsall. Original selling price £6.15. P 14½.*
LS20   20×(1st) Union Flag, as Type **1517** with attached labels .   28·00

LS **21**

2004 (2 Nov). *Christmas. Type LS* **21**. *Litho* De La Rue. Original selling price £5.40. P 14½×14.*
LS21   10×(2nd) and 10×(1st) "Father Christmas", self-adhesive, as Nos. 2495/6 with attached labels...   25·00

LS **22**

2005 (11 Jan). *Farm Animals. Type LS* **22**. *Litho* Walsall. Original selling price £6.15. P 14½.*
LS22   20×(1st) Farm Animals, as Nos. 2502/11 with attached labels..   35·00

LS **23**

2005 (15 Mar). *Centenary of the Magic Circle. Type LS* **23**. *Litho* Walsall. Original selling price £6.15. P 14½×14.*
LS23   20×(1st) Spinning Coin, as No. 2525 with attached
labels .... 32·00

LS **24**

2005 (21 Apr). *Pacific Explorer 2005 World Stamp Expo. Type LS* **24**. *Litho Walsall. Original selling price £6.55. P 14*.*
LS24   20×(1st) "Hello" greetings stamps, as No. 2262 with
attached labels .... 25·00

LS **25**

2005 (21 June). *The White Ensign. Type LS* **25**. *Litho* Cartor. Original selling price £6.55. P 14½.*
LS25   20×(1st) White Ensign stamps, as Type **1516** with
attached labels .... 25·00

LS **26**

2005 (15 Sept). *Classic ITV. Type LS* **26**. *Litho Walsall. Original selling price £6.55. P 14½×14.*
LS26   20×(1st) Emmerdale stamps, as No. 2562 with attached
labels .... 24·00

LS **27**

2005 (1 Nov). *Christmas. "Christmas Robins". Type LS* **27**. *Litho* Cartor. Original selling price £5.60. P 14½.*
LS27   10×(2nd) and 10×(1st) Robins, self-adhesive, as
Nos. 2238/9 with attached labels .... 20·00

LS **28**

2006 (10 Jan). *A Bear called Paddington. Type LS* **28**. *Litho Cartor. Original selling price £6.55. P 14½.*
LS28   20×(1st) Paddington Bear, self-adhesive*, as No. 2592
with attached labels .... 25·00

LS **29**

2006 (7 Mar). *Fun Fruit and Veg. Type LS* **29**. *Litho Cartor. Original selling price £6.55. P 14½×14.*
LS29   20×(1st) Fruit and Vegetables stamps, self-adhesive as
Nos. 2348/g57 with attached labels .... 32·00

LS **30**

2006 (25 May). *Washington 2006 International Stamp Exhibition. Type LS* **30**. *Litho Cartor. Original selling price £6.95. P 14*.*
LS30   20×(1st) "Hello" greetings stamps, as No. 2262 with
attached labels .... 26·00

LS **31**

2006 (6 June). *World Cup Football Championship, Germany. World Cup Winners. Type* LS **31**. *Litho Cartor. Original selling price* £6.95. P 14½.
LS31   20×(1st) England footballer (1966) stamps, as No. 2628
             with attached labels .... 32·00

LS **32**

2006 (4 July). *"For Life's Special Moments". Type* LS **32**. *Litho* Cartor. Original selling price* £6.95. P 15×14.
LS32   20×(1st) "Smilers" stamps self-adhesive as Nos. 2567/72
             (four of Nos. 2568/9 and 3 each of the others) with
             attached labels .... 24·00

LS **33**

2006 (17 Oct). *"Extra Special Moments". Type* LS **33**. *Litho* Cartor. Original selling price* £6.95. P 15×14.
LS33   20×(1st) "Smilers" stamps self-adhesive as Nos. 2672/7
             (four of Nos. 2672 and 2677, 3 each of the others) with
             attached labels .... 24·00

LS **34**

2006 (7 Nov). Christmas. *Type* LS **34**. *Litho* Cartor. Original selling price* £6. P 15×14.
LS34   10×(2nd) and 10×(1st) Christmas self-adhesive as Nos.
             2678/9 with attached labels .... 25·00

LS **35**

2006 (9 Nov). *"We Will Remember Them". Type* LS **35**. *Litho* Cartor. Original selling price* £6.95. P 14½.
LS35   20×(1st) Poppies on barbed wire stems stamps as Type
             1941 with attached labels .... 24·00

LS **36**

2006 (14 Nov). *Belgica* 2006 *International Stamp Exhibition, Brussels. Type* LS **36**. *Litho Cartor. Original selling price* £6.95. P 14*.
LS36   20×(1st) "Hello" greetings stamps, No. 2262 with
             attached labels .... 24·00

LS **37**

2007 (1 Mar). *"Glorious Wales". Type* LS **37**. *Litho Cartor. Original selling price* £6.95. P 15×14 (*without* elliptical holes*).
LS37   20×(1st) Wales stamps, self-adhesive*, as No. W120 with
             attached labels .... 24·00

LS **38**

2007 (23 Apr). *"Glorious England". Type* LS **38**. *Litho Cartor. Original selling price* £7.35. P 15×14 (*without* elliptical holes*).
LS38   20×(1st) England stamps, self-adhesive* as No. EN18
             with attached labels .... 24·00
         On labels from the original printing "Isle of Wight" was incorrectly
spelled "Isle of White". These were recalled before issue but some were
released in error.

LS **39**

2007 (17 May). *"Memories of Wembley Stadium". Type* LS **39**. *Litho* Cartor. Original selling price £7.35.* P 14½×14.

LS39   20×(1st) stamps as No. 2291 but without "WORLD CUP 2002" inscription with attached labels .... 24·00

LS **40**

2007 (5 June). *40th Anniv of the First Machin Definitives. Type* LS **40**. *Litho Cartor. Original selling price £7.35. Phosphor frame*.* P 14½.

LS40   20×(1st) stamps as Type **1984** with attached labels .... 24·00

LS **41**

2007 (17 July). *Harry Potter. Type* LS **41**. *Litho Walsall. Original selling price £7.35.* P 15×14.

LS41   20×(1st) stamps as within **MS**2757 but self-adhesive*, four of each design with attached labels................................. 24·00

LS **42**

2007 (6 Nov). *Christmas. Type* LS **42**. *Litho* Cartor. Original selling price £8.30.* P 15×14.

LS42   8×(2nd), 8×(1st) and 4×78p. Christmas self-adhesive as Nos. 2789/90 and 2793 with attached labels .... 24·00

LS **43**

2007 (8 Nov). *"Letters from the Front". Type* LS **43**. *Litho Cartor. Original selling price £7.35.* P 14½.

LS43   20×(1st) Soldiers in poppy flower stamps as Type **2038** with attached labels .... 24·00

LS **44**

2007 (30 Nov). *"Glorious Scotland". Type* LS **44**. *Litho Cartor. Original selling price £7.35.* P 15×14 (*without* elliptical holes*).

LS44   20×(1st) Scotland stamps, self-adhesive*, as No. S131 with attached labels .... 24·00

LS **45**

2008 (15 Jan). *"I wrote to say?". Type* LS **45**. *Litho* Cartor. Original selling price £7.35.* P 15×14 (*with one elliptical hole in each vert side**).

LS45   20×(1st) "Smilers" stamps self-adhesive as Nos. 2568/70 (eight of No. 2569, 6 each of Nos. 2568 and 2570) with attached circular labels .... 30·00

LS **46**

2008 (11 Mar). *"Glorious Northern Ireland". Type* LS **46**. *Litho Cartor. Original selling price £7.35.* P 15×14 (*without* elliptical holes*).

LS46   20×(1st) Northern Ireland stamps, self-adhesive*, as No. NI95 with attached labels .... 20·00

LS **47**

2008 (17 July). *Air Displays.* Type LS **47**. *Litho Cartor. Original selling price £7.75.* P 14½×14.
LS47   20 ×(1st) Red Arrows stamps as No. 2855 with attached
labels... 20·00

LS **48**

2008 (5 Aug). *Beijing 2008 Olympic Expo.* Type LS **48**. *Litho Cartor. Original selling price £7.75.* P 14*.
LS48   20 (1st) "Hello" greetings stamps No. 2262 with attached
labels... 22·00

LS **49**

2008 (29 Sept). *"Glorious United Kingdom".* Type LS **49**. *Litho Cartor. Original selling price £7.75.* P 15×14 (with one elliptical hole in each vertical side).
LS49   4 ×1st England, 4×1st Northern Ireland, 4×1st Scotland
and 4×1st Wales stamps, self-adhesive*, as Nos. EN18,
NI95, S131 and W120 with attached labels............................ 22·00

LS **50**

LS **51**

LS **52**

LS **53**

2008 (28 Oct). *"Smilers for Kids"* (1st series). Type LS **50** *and similar designs. Litho Cartor. Original selling price £7.95.* P 15×14 (with one elliptical hole on each vertical side).
LS50   (1st) ×20 New Baby stamps as No. 2672* with attached
circular Peter Rabbit labels.................................. 20·00
LS51   (1st) ×20 Sunflower stamps No. 2820 with attached
circular Almond Blossom fairy labels.................... 20·00
LS52   (1st) ×20 Balloons stamps No. 2822 with attached
circular Mr. Men labels....................................... 20·00
LS53   (1st) ×20 Balloons stamps No. 2822 with attached
circular Noddy labels.. 20·00
No. LS50 contains stamps as No. 2672 but perforated with one elliptical hole on each vertical side.
Sheets as Nos. LS50/3 but containing ten stamps and ten labels were sold in packs at £7.95 per pack.

LS **54**

2008 (4 Nov). *Christmas.* Type LS **54**. *Litho* Cartor. Original selling price £8.85.* P 15×14.
LS54   8 ×(2nd), 8×(1st) and 4×81p. Christmas self-adhesive as
Nos. 2876/7 and 2881 with attached labels.......................... 20·00

LS **55**

2008 (6 Nov). *"We Will Remember".* Type LS **55**. *Litho Cartor. Original selling price £7.75.* P 14½.
LS55   20 ×(1st) Soldier's face in poppy flower stamps as
No. 2885 with attached labels .... 20·00

LS **56**

2009 (13 Jan). *Design Classics. Type LS* **56**. *Litho Cartor. Original selling price £7.75. P 14×14½.*
LS56   20×(1st) Mini stamps as No. 2889 with attached labels..   20·00

LS **57**

2009 (2 Mar). *40th Anniv of the First Flight of Concorde. Type LS* **57**. *Litho Cartor. Original selling price £7.75. P 14×14½*.*
LS57   20×(1st) Concorde stamps as No. 2891...............................   20·00

LS **58**

2009 (17 Mar). *Castles of Northern Ireland. Type LS* **58**. *Litho Cartor. Original selling price £7.74. P 15×14 (with one elliptical hole in each vertical side).*
LS58   20×(1st) Northern Ireland stamps, self-adhesive*, as
              No. NI95 with attached labels ....   20·00

LS **59**

2009 (23 Apr). *Castles of England. Type LS* **59**. *Litho Cartor. Original selling price £8.35. P 15×14 (with one elliptical hole in each vertical side).*
LS59   20×(1st) As St. George's flag stamp from **MS**EN19 but
              self-adhesive* with attached labels......................   20·00

LS **60**

LS **61**

LS **62**

LS **63**

2009 (30 Apr). *"Smilers for Kids" (2nd series). Type LS* **60/3**. *Litho Cartor. Original selling price £8.50. P 15×14 (with one elliptical hole in each vertical side).*
LS60   20×(1st) "Hello" stamps as No. 2819 with attached
              circular Jeremy Fisher labels..................................   20·00
LS61   20×(1st) Sunflower stamps as No. 2820 with attached
              circular Wild Cherry fairy labels.............................   20·00
LS62   20×(1st) Balloons stamps as No. 2822 with attached
              circular LIttle Miss Sunshine labels ....   20·00
LS63   20×(1st) Balloons stamps as No. 2822 with attached
              circular Big Ears labels ....   20·00
    Sheets as Nos. LS60/3 but containing ten stamps and ten labels were sold in packs at £7.95 per pack.

LS **64**

2009 (3 Aug). *Thaipex 09 International Stamp Exhibition, Bangkok. Type* LS **64**. *Litho Cartor. Original selling price* £8.35. P 14*.
LS64   20×(1st) "Hello" greetings stamps as No. 2262 with
                attached labels .... 20·00

LS **65**

2009 (18 Aug). *Post Boxes. Type* LS **65**. *Litho Cartor. Original selling price* £8.35. P 14.
LS65   20×(1st) Letter box stamps as Type **2165** with attached
                labels .... 20·00

LS **66**

2009 (21 Oct). *Italia 2009 International Stamp Exhibition, Rome. Type* LS **66**. *Litho Cartor. Original selling price* £8.35. P 14*.
LS66   20×(1st) "Hello" greetings stamps as No. 2262 with
                attached labels .... 20·00

LS **67**

2009 (3 Nov). *Christmas. Type* LS **67**. *Litho Cartor. Original selling price* £9. P 14½×14 (with one elliptical hole in each vertical side).
LS67   8×(2nd), 8×(1st), 2×56p. and 2×90p. Christmas self-
                adhesive as Nos. 2991/2 and 2995/6 .... 22·00

LS **68**

2009 (30 Nov). *Castles of Scotland. Type* LS **68**. *Litho Cartor. Original selling price* £8.35. P 15×14 (with one elliptical hole in each vertical side).
LS68   20×(1st) As Scottish flag stamp from **MS**S133 but self-
                adhesive with attached labels .... 20·00

LS **69**

2009 (4 Dec). *MonacoPhil 2009 International Stamp Exhibition, Monaco. Type* LS **69**. *Litho Cartor. Original selling price* £8.35. P 14*.
LS69   20×(1st) "Hello" greetings stamps as No. 2262 with
                attached labels .... 20·00

LS **70**

2010 (26 Jan). *"For all occasions". Type* LS **70**. *Litho Cartor. Original selling price* £9.70. P 14½×14 (with one elliptical hole in each vertical side).
LS70   16×(1st), 2×(Europe up to 20 grams) and 2×(Worldwide
                up to 20 grams) stamps as within **MS**3024 but self-
                adhesive* two of each design with attached labels .... 22·00

LS **71**

2010 (1 Mar). *Castles of Wales. Type* LS **71**. *Litho Cartor. Original selling price* £8.35. P 15×14 (with one elliptical hole in each vertical side).
LS71   20×(1st) As Red Dragon stamp from **MS**W125 but self-
                adhesive* with attached labels .... 20·00

LS **72**

2010 (8 May). *London 2010 Festival of Stamps. Type* LS **72**. *Litho Cartor. Original selling price* £8.50. Die-cut perf 15×14 (with one elliptical hole in each vertical side).
LS72   20×(1st) "Hello" greetings stamps as No. 2819 with
                attached labels .... 19·00

LS **73**

2010 (8 May). 'Keep Smiling 10 Years of Smilers'. Type LS **73**. Litho Cartor. Original selling price £10. Die-cut perf 15×14 (with one elliptical hole in each vertical side).

LS73   3× No. 2821 (1st) Union Jack, one each of
Nos. 2572 (1st) Robin in pillar box, 2674 (1st)
THANK YOU, 2693 (1st) LOVE, 2822 (1st)
Balloons, 2823 (1st) Fireworks and also 4×(1st)
Birthday cake, 4×(1st) Birthday present,
2×(Europe up to 20 grams) and 2×(Worldwide
up to 20 grams) stamps as within **MS**3024 but
self-adhesive* with attached labels...................... 22·00

LS **74**

2010 (15 Sept). 70th Anniv of the Battle of Britain. Type LS **74**. Litho Cartor. Original selling price £8.50. P 14×14½*.

LS74   20×(1st) Spitfire stamps as No. 2887 with attached
labels... 19·00

LS **75**

2010 (2 Nov). Christmas. Type LS **75**. Litho Cartor. Original selling price £9.30. P 14½×14 (with one elliptical hole in each vertical side).

LS75   8×(2nd), 8×(1st), 2×60p. and 2×97p. Christmas self-
adhesive as Nos. 3128/34 .... 21·00

LS **76**

2011 (12 Feb). Indipex International Stamp Exhibition, New Delhi. Type LS **76**. Litho Cartor. Original selling price £8.50. P 15×14 (with one elliptical hole in each vertical side).

LS76   20×(1st) Union Jack self-adhesive stamps as No. 2821
with attached labels.................................... 19·00

ROYAL MAIL "COMMEMORATIVE SHEETS"

The following Royal Mail commemorative sheets were sold at a significant premium over the face value of the stamps:

1.4.2008	100 Years of the Territorial Army 10×1st Union Jack stamps with labels
24.7.2008	The London 1908 Olympic Games 10×1st Union Jack stamps with labels
14.11.2008	60th Birthday of Prince Charles 10×1st Wales self-adhesive stamps with labels
21.7.2009	40th anniv of Moon Landing 10×1st Union Jack stamps with labels
18.9.2009	Big Ben 10×1st Union Jack stamps with labels
7.10.2009	800th Anniv of the University of Cambridge 10×1st Fireworks stamps (as Type **1993**) with labels
22.10.2009	Olympic and Paralympic Games 10×1st as Types **2192/2201** with labels
18.5.2010	Halley's Comet10×1st Union Jack stamps with labels
8.7.2010	Grand Prix 10×1st Union Jack stamps with labels
27.7.2010	Olympic and Paralympic Games (II) 10×1st as Types **2290/9** with labels
10.8.2010	10th Anniv of the London Eye 10×1st Union Jack stamps with labels
28.10.2010	Rememberance: The National Memorial Arboretum 10×1st Poppies on Barbed Wire Stem stamps (as Type **2112**)
30.3.2011	50th Anniv of the E Type Jaguar 10×1st Union Jack stamps with labels

STANLEY GIBBONS

Est 1856

Dear Catalogue User,

As a collector and Stanley Gibbons catalogue user for many years myself, I am only too aware of the need to provide you with the information you seek in an accurate, timely and easily accessible manner. Naturally, I have my own views on where changes could be made, but one thing I learned long ago is that we all have different opinions and requirements.

I would therefore be most grateful if you would complete the form overleaf and return it to me. Please contact Lorraine Holcombe (lholcombe@stanleygibbons.co.uk) if you would like to be emailed the questionnaire.

Very many thanks for your help.

Yours sincerely,

Hugh Jefferies,
Editor.

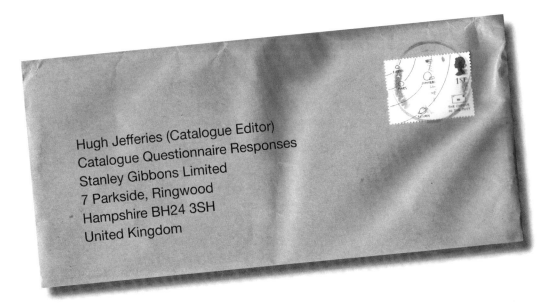

Hugh Jefferies (Catalogue Editor)
Catalogue Questionnaire Responses
Stanley Gibbons Limited
7 Parkside, Ringwood
Hampshire BH24 3SH
United Kingdom

Questionnaire

2011 Great Britain Concise Stamp Catalogue

1. **Level of detail**
    Do you feel that the level of detail in this catalogue is:
    a. too specialised   O
    b. about right   O
    c. inadequate   O

2. **Frequency of issue**
    How often would you purchase a new edition of this catalogue?
    a. Annually   O
    b. Every two years   O
    c. Every three to five years O
    d. Less frequently   O

3. **Design and Quality**
    How would you describe the layout and appearance of this catalogue?
    a. Excellent   O
    b. Good   O
    c. Adequate   O
    d. Poor   O

4. How important to you are the prices given in the catalogue:
    a. Important   O
    b. Quite important   O
    c. Of little interest   O
    d. Of no interest   O

5. Would you be interested in an online version of this catalogue?
    a. Yes   O
    b. No   O

6. Do you like the 'layflat binding'?
    a. Yes   O
    b. No   O

7. What changes would you suggest to improve the catalogue? E.g. Which other features would you like to see included?

    ....
    ....
    ....
    ....

8. Which of the SG Great Britain Specialised catalogues do you buy?

    ....
    ....
    ....
    ....

9. Would you like us to let you know when the next edition of this catalogue is due to be published?
    a. Yes   O
    b. No   O

    If so please give your contact details below.

    Name: ....
    Address:..
    ....
    ....
    ....
    Email: ....
    Telephone:..

10. Which other Stanley Gibbons Catalogues are you interested in?
    a. ....
    b. ....
    c. ....

Many thanks for your comments.

Please complete and return it to: Hugh Jefferies (Catalogue Editor)
Stanley Gibbons Limited, 7 Parkside, Ringwood, Hampshire BH24 3SH, United Kingdom
or email: lholcombe@stanleygibbons.co.uk to request a soft copy